A GUIDE TO STATISTICAL TECHNIQUES

Problem Objectives

DATA TYPES	Describe a Population	Compare Two Populations	Compare Two or More Populations	Analyze Relationship between Two Variables	Analyze Relationship among Two or More Variables
Interval	Histogram **Section 3-1** Line chart **Section 3-2** Mean, median, and mode **Section 4-1** Range, variance, and standard deviation **Section 4-2** Percentiles and quartiles **Section 4-3** t-test and estimator of a mean **Section 12-1** Chi-squared test and estimator of a variance **Section 12-2**	Equal-variances t-test and estimator of the difference between two means: independent samples **Section 13-1** Unequal-variances t-test and estimator of the difference between two means: independent samples **Section 13-1** t-test and estimator of mean difference **Section 13-3** F-test and estimator of ratio of two variances **Section 13-4** Wilcoxon rank sum test **Section 19-1** Wilcoxon signed rank sum test **Section 19-2**	One-way analysis of variance **Section 14-1** LSD multiple comparison method **Section 14-2** Tukey's multiple comparison method **Section 14-2** Two-way analysis of variance **Section 14-4** Two-factor analysis of variance **Section 14-5** Kruskal–Wallis test **Section 19-3** Friedman test **Section 19-3**	Scatter diagram **Section 3-3** Covariance **Section 4-4** Coefficient of correlation **Section 4-4** Coefficient of determination **Section 4-4** Least squares line **Section 4-4** Simple linear regression and correlation **Chapter 16** Spearman rank correlation **Section 19-4**	Multiple regression **Chapters 17 & 18**
Nominal	Frequency distribution **Section 2-2** Bar chart **Section 2-2** Pie chart **Section 2-2** z-test and estimator of a proportion **Section 12-3** Chi-squared goodness-of-fit test **Section 15-1**	z-test and estimator of the difference between two proportions **Section 13-5** Chi-squared test of a contingency table **Section 15-2**	Chi-squared test of a contingency table **Section 15-2**	Chi-squared test of a contingency table **Section 15-2**	Not covered
Ordinal	Median **Section 4-1** Percentiles and quartiles **Section 4-3**	Wilcoxon rank sum test **Section 19-1** Sign test **Section 19-2**	Kruskal–Wallis test **Section 19-3** Friedman test **Section 19-3**	Spearman rank correlation **Section 19-4**	Not covered

GENERAL SOCIAL SURVEY AND SURVEY OF CONSUMER FINANCES EXERCISES

APPLICATION SECTIONS

APPLICATION SUBSECTION

APPLICATION BOXES

Accounting

Economics

Finance

Human Resource Management

Marketing

Operations Management

Index of Computer Output and Instructions

Cengage Technology Edition combines a full ebook or digital solutions
package with each print edition. Use this new hybrid edition for maximum
flexibility and benefits.

CENGAGE
TECHNOLOGY
EDITION

FOR USE IN ASIA ONLY

11th edition

Statistics for Management and Economics

Gerald Keller

Australia • Brazil • Mexico • Singapore • United Kingdom • United States

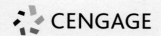

Statistics for Management and Economics, Eleventh Edition
Gerald Keller

Senior Regional Director:
Janet Lim

Senior Product Manager:
Charles Ho

Senior Editorial Manager:
Lian Siew Han

Senior Development Editor:
Tanmayee Bhatwadekar

Development Editors:
Kenneth Chow
Ng Wei Yi
Elaine Chew
Willie Ong

Senior Regional Manager,
Production and Rights:
Pauline Lim

Production Executive:
Rachael Tan

Creative Manager:
Melvin Chong

Senior Graphic Designer:
Benson Tan

Cover Image:
© ktsimage/iStock/Thinkstock

For product information and technology assistance, contact us at
Cengage Learning Asia Customer Support, 65-6410-1200

For permission to use material from this text or product,
submit all requests online at **cengageasia.com/permissions**
Further permissions questions can be emailed to
asia.permissionrequest@cengage.com

ISBN: 978-981-4792-39-4

Cengage Learning Asia Pte Ltd
151 Lorong Chuan #02-08
New Tech Park (Lobby H)
Singapore 556741

Cengage Learning is a leading provider of customized learning solutions with office locations around the globe, including Singapore, the United Kingdom, Australia, Mexico, Brazil, and Japan. Locate your local office at **cengage.com/global**

Cengage Learning products are represented in Canada by Nelson Education, Ltd.

To learn more about Cengage Learning Solutions, visit **cengageasia.com**

Printed in Singapore
Print Number: 01   Print Year: 2017

BRIEF CONTENTS

Access these chapters from your ebook.

𝒆 Access these chapters from your ebook.

CONTENTS

Access these chapters from your ebook.

Access these chapters from your ebook.

Access this chapter from your ebook.

PREFACE

Businesses are increasingly using statistical techniques to convert data into information. For students preparing for the business world, it is not enough merely to focus on mastering a diverse set of statistical techniques and calculations. A course and its attendant textbook must provide a complete picture of statistical concepts and their applications to the real world. ***Statistics for Management and Economics*** is designed to demonstrate that statistical methods are vital tools for today's managers and economists.

Fulfilling this objective requires the several features that I have built into this book. First, I have included data-driven examples, exercises, and cases that demonstrate statistical applications that are and can be used by marketing managers, financial analysts, accountants, economists, operations managers, and others. Many are accompanied by large and genuine data sets. Second, I reinforce the applied nature of the discipline by teaching students how to choose the correct statistical technique. Third, I teach students the concepts that are essential to interpret the statistical results.

Why I Wrote This Book

Business is complex and requires effective management to succeed. Managing complexity requires many skills. There are more competitors, more places to sell products, and more places to locate workers. As a consequence, effective decision-making is more crucial than ever before. On the other hand, managers have more access to larger and more detailed data that are potential sources of information. However, to achieve this potential requires that managers know how to convert data into information. This knowledge extends well beyond the arithmetic of calculating statistics. Unfortunately, this is what most textbooks offer—a series of unconnected techniques illustrated mostly with manual calculations. This continues a pattern that goes back many years. What is required now is a complete approach to applying statistical techniques.

When I started teaching statistics in 1971, books demonstrated how to calculate statistics and, in some cases, how various formulas were derived. One reason for doing so was the belief that by doing calculations by hand, students would be able to understand the techniques and concepts. When the first edition of this book was published in 1988, an important goal was to teach students to identify the correct technique. Through the next 10 editions, I refined my approach to emphasize interpretation and decision-making equally. I now divide the solution of statistical problems into three stages and include them in every appropriate example: (1) *identify* the technique, (2) *compute* the statistics, and (3) *interpret* the results. The compute stage can be completed in any or all of three ways: manually (with the aid of a calculator), using Excel, and using XLSTAT. For those courses that wish to use the computer extensively, manual calculations can be played down or omitted completely. Conversely, those that wish to emphasize manual calculations may easily do so, and the computer solutions can be selectively introduced or skipped entirely. This approach is designed to provide maximum flexibility, and it leaves to the instructor the decision of if and when to introduce the computer.

I believe that my approach offers several advantages:

- An emphasis on identification and interpretation provides students with practical skills that they can apply to real problems they will face regardless of whether a course uses manual or computer calculations.

- Students learn that statistics is a method of converting data into information. With 1136 data files and corresponding problems that ask students to interpret statistical results, students are given ample opportunities to practice data analysis and decision-making.

- The optional use of the computer allows for larger and more realistic exercises and examples.

Placing calculations in the context of a larger problem allows instructors to focus on more important aspects of the decision problem. For example, more attention needs to be devoted to interpret statistical results. Proper interpretation of statistical results requires an understanding of the probability and statistical concepts that underlie the techniques and an understanding of the context of the problems. An essential aspect of my approach is teaching students the concepts. I do so by providing Excel worksheets that allow students to perform "what-if" analyses. Students can easily see the effect of changing the components of a statistical technique, such as the effect of increasing the sample size.

Efforts to teach statistics as a valuable and necessary tool in business and economics are made more difficult by the positioning of the statistics course in most curricula. The required statistics course in most undergraduate programs appears in the first or second year. In many graduate programs, the statistics course is offered in the first semester of a three-semester program and the first year of a two-year program. Accounting, economics, finance, human resource management, marketing, and operations management are usually taught after the statistics course. Consequently, most students will not be able to understand the general context of the statistical application. This deficiency is addressed in this book by "Applications in …" sections, subsections, and boxes. Illustrations of statistical applications in businesses that students are unfamiliar with are preceded by an explanation of the background material.

- For example, to illustrate graphical techniques, we use an example that compares the histograms of the returns on two different investments. To explain what financial analysts look for in the histograms requires an understanding that risk is measured by the amount of variation in the returns. The example is preceded by an "Applications in Finance" box that discusses how return on investment is computed and used.

- Later when I present the normal distribution, I feature another "Applications in Finance" box to show why the standard deviation of the returns measures the risk of that investment.

- Forty-two application boxes are scattered throughout the book.

Some applications are so large that I devote an entire section or subsection to the topic. For example, in the chapter that introduces the confidence interval estimator of a proportion, I also present market segmentation. In that section, I show how the confidence interval estimate of a population proportion can yield estimates of the sizes of market segments. In other chapters, I illustrate various statistical techniques by showing how marketing managers can apply these techniques to determine the differences that exist between market segments. There are five such sections and one subsection in this book.

The "Applications in ..." segments provide great motivation to the student who asks, "How will I ever use this technique?"

New in This Edition

The data from the last eight General Social Surveys and the last four Surveys of Consumer Finances have been included, which produced 528 new exercises. Students will have the opportunity to convert real data into information. Instructors can use these data sets to create hundreds of additional examples and exercises.

Many of the examples, exercises, and cases using real data in the 10th edition have been updated. These include the data on wins, payrolls, and attendance in baseball, basketball, football, and hockey; returns on stocks listed on the New York Stock Exchange, NASDAQ, and Toronto Stock Exchange; and global warming.

I've created many new examples and exercises. Here are the numbers for the 11th edition: 142 solved examples, 2460 exercises, 32 cases, 1136 data sets, 31 appendixes containing 37 solved examples, 98 exercises, and 25 data sets, for a grand total of 179 worked examples, 2558 exercises, 32 cases, and 1161 data sets.

Data Driven: The Big Picture

Solving statistical problems begins with a problem and data. The ability to select the right method by problem objective and data type is **a valuable tool for business**. Because business decisions are driven by data, students will leave this course equipped with the tools they need to make effective, informed decisions in all areas of the business world.

tzf/Shutterstock.com

Identify the Correct Technique

Examples introduce the first crucial step in this three-step (*identify–compute–interpret*) approach. Every example's solution begins by examining the data type and problem objective and then identifying the right technique to solve the problem.

EXAMPLE 13.1*

DATA
Xm13-01

Direct and Broker-Purchased Mutual Funds

Millions of investors buy mutual funds (see page 178 for a description of mutual funds), choosing from thousands of possibilities. Some funds can be purchased directly from banks or other financial institutions whereas others must be purchased through brokers, who charge a fee for this service. This raises the question, Can investors do better by buying mutual funds directly than by purchasing mutual funds through brokers? To help answer this question, a group of researchers randomly sampled the annual returns from mutual funds that can be acquired directly and mutual funds that are bought through brokers and recorded the net annual returns, which are the returns on investment after deducting all relevant fees. These are listed next.

Direct					Broker				
9.33	4.68	4.23	14.69	10.29	3.24	3.71	16.4	4.36	9.43
6.94	3.09	10.28	−2.97	4.39	−6.76	13.15	6.39	−11.07	8.31
16.17	7.26	7.1	10.37	−2.06	12.8	11.05	−1.9	9.24	−3.99
16.97	2.05	−3.09	−0.63	7.66	11.1	−3.12	9.49	−2.67	−4.44
5.94	13.07	5.6	−0.15	10.83	2.73	8.94	6.7	8.97	8.63
12.61	0.59	5.27	0.27	14.48	−0.13	2.74	0.19	1.87	7.06
3.33	13.57	8.09	4.59	4.8	18.22	4.07	12.39	−1.53	1.57
16.13	0.35	15.05	6.38	13.12	−0.8	5.6	6.54	5.23	−8.44
11.2	2.69	13.21	−0.24	−6.54	−5.75	−0.85	10.92	6.87	−5.72
1.14	18.45	1.72	10.32	−1.06	2.59	−0.28	−2.15	−1.69	6.95

Can we conclude at the 5% significance level that directly purchased mutual funds outperform mutual funds bought through brokers?

SOLUTION:

IDENTIFY

To answer the question, we need to compare the population of returns from direct and the returns from broker-bought mutual funds. The data are obviously interval (we've recorded real numbers). This problem objective–data type combination tells us that the parameter to be tested is the difference between two means, $\mu_1 - \mu_2$. The hypothesis

*Source: D. Bergstresser, J. Chalmers, and P. Tufano, "Assessing the Costs and Benefits of Brokers in the Mutual Fund Industry."

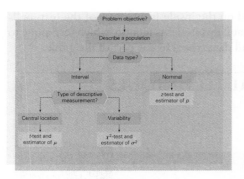

Appendixes 13, 14, 15, 16, 17, and **19** reinforce this problem-solving approach and allow students to hone their skills.

Flowcharts, found within the appendixes, help students develop the logical process for choosing the correct technique, reinforce the learning process, and provide easy review material for students.

APPENDIX 14 / REVIEW OF CHAPTERS 12 TO 14

The number of techniques introduced in Chapters 12 to 14 is up to 20. As we did in Appendix 13, we provide a table of the techniques with formulas and required conditions, a flowchart to help you identify the correct technique, and 25 exercises to give you practice in how to choose the appropriate method. The table and the flowchart have been amended to include the three analysis of variance techniques introduced in this chapter and the three multiple comparison methods.

TABLE **A14.1** **Summary of Statistical Techniques in Chapters 12 to 14**

t-test of μ

Estimator of μ (including estimator of $N\mu$)

χ^2 test of σ^2

Estimator of σ^2

z-test of p

Estimator of p (including estimator of Np)

Equal-variances t-test of $\mu_1 - \mu_2$

Equal-variances estimator of $\mu_1 - \mu_2$

Unequal-variances t-test of $\mu_1 - \mu_2$

Unequal-variances estimator of $\mu_1 - \mu_2$

t-test of μ_D

Estimator of μ_D

F-test of σ_1^2/σ_2^2

Estimator of σ_1^2/σ_2^2

z-test of $p_1 - p_2$ (Case 1)

z-test of $p_1 - p_2$ (Case 2)

Estimator of $p_1 - p_2$

One-way analysis of variance (including multiple comparisons)

Two-way (randomized blocks) analysis of variance

Two-factor analysis of variance

Factors that Identify the t-Test and Estimator of μ_D

1. **Problem objective:** Compare two populations
2. **Data type:** Interval
3. **Descriptive measurement:** Central location
4. **Experimental design:** Matched pairs

Factors That Identify ... boxes are found in each chapter after a technique or concept has been introduced. These boxes allow students to see a technique's essential requirements and give them a way to easily review their understanding. These essential requirements are revisited in the review chapters, where they are coupled with other concepts illustrated in flowcharts.

A Guide to Statistical Techniques, found on the inside front cover of the text, pulls everything together into one useful table that helps students identify which technique to perform based on the problem objective and data type. Here is part of the guide.

A GUIDE TO STATISTICAL TECHNIQUES

Problem Objectives

DATA TYPES		Describe a Population	Compare Two Populations	Compare Two or More Populations
	Interval	Histogram Section 3-1 Line chart Section 3-2 Mean, median, and mode Section 4-1 Range, variance, and standard deviation Section 4-2 Percentiles and quartiles Section 4-3 t-test and estimator of a mean Section 12-1 Chi-squared test and estimator of a variance Section 12-2	Equal-variances t-test and estimator of the difference between two means: independent samples Section 13-1 Unequal-variances t-test and estimator of the difference between two means: independent samples Section 13-1 t-test and estimator of mean difference Section 13-3 F-test and estimator of ratio of two variances Section 13-4 Wilcoxon rank sum test Section 19-1 Wilcoxon signed rank sum test Section 19-2	One-way analysis of variance Section 14-1 LSD multiple comparison method Section 14-2 Tukey's multiple comparison method Section 14-2 Two-way analysis of variance Section 14-4 Two-factor analysis of variance Section 14-5 Kruskal-Wallis test Section 19-3 Friedman test Section 19-3
	Nominal	Frequency distribution Section 2-2 Bar chart Section 2-2 Pie chart Section 2-2 z-test and estimator of a proportion Section 12-3 Chi-squared goodness-of-fit test Section 15-1	z-test and estimator of the difference between two proportions Section 13-5 Chi-squared test of a contingency table Section 15-2	Chi-squared test of a contingency table Section 15-2
	Ordinal	Median Section 4-1 Percentiles and quartiles Section 4-3	Wilcoxon rank sum test Section 19-1 Sign test Section 19-2	Kruskal-Wallis test Section 19-3 Friedman test Section 19-3

More Data Sets

A total of 1136 data sets available to be downloaded provide ample practice. These data sets contain real data, including stock market returns, climate change temperature anomalies and atmospheric carbon dioxide, baseball, basketball, football and hockey team payrolls, wins, and attendance.

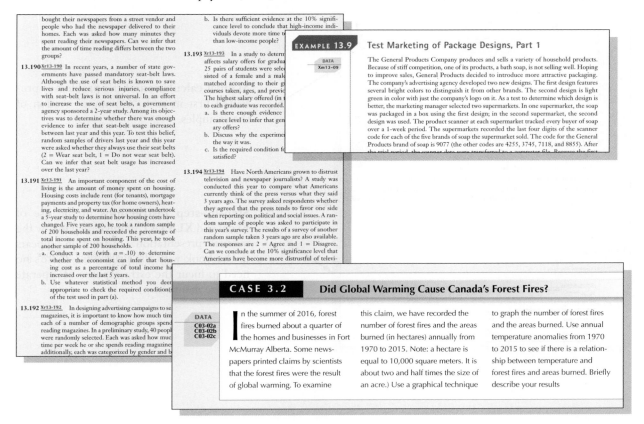

bought their newspapers from a street vendor and people who had the newspaper delivered to their homes. Each was asked how many minutes they spent reading their newspapers. Can we infer that the amount of time reading differs between the two groups?

13.190 Xr13-190 In recent years, a number of state governments have passed mandatory seat-belt laws. Although the use of seat belts is known to save lives and reduce serious injuries, compliance with seat-belt laws is not universal. In an effort to increase the use of seat belts, a government agency sponsored a 2-year study. Among its objectives was to determine whether there was enough evidence to infer that seat-belt usage increased between last year and this year. To test this belief, random samples of drivers last year and this year were asked whether they always use their seat belts (2 = Wear seat belt, 1 = Do not wear seat belt). Can we infer that seat belt usage has increased over the last year?

13.191 Xr13-191 An important component of the cost of living is the amount of money spent on housing. Housing costs include rent (for tenants), mortgage payments and property tax (for home owners), heating, electricity, and water. An economist undertook a 5-year study to determine how housing costs have changed. Five years ago, he took a random sample of 200 households and recorded the percentage of total income spent on housing. This year, he took another sample of 200 households.
a. Conduct a test (with $\alpha = .10$) to determine whether the economist can infer that housing cost as a percentage of total income has increased over the last 5 years.
b. Use whatever statistical method you deem appropriate to check the required condition(s) of the test used in part (a).

13.192 Xr13-192 In designing advertising campaigns to sell magazines, it is important to know how much time each of a number of demographic groups spend reading magazines. In a preliminary study, 40 people were randomly selected. Each was asked how much time per week he or she spends reading magazines; additionally, each was categorized by gender and by

b. Is there sufficient evidence at the 10% significance level to conclude that high-income individuals devote more time than low-income people?

13.193 Xr13-193 In a study to determine salary offers for graduate 25 pairs of students were selected sisted of a female and a male matched according to their g courses taken, ages, and previo The highest salary offered (in to each graduate was recorded.
a. Is there enough evidence cance level to infer that gen ary offers?
b. Discuss why the experimen the way it was.
c. Is the required condition f satisfied?

13.194 Xr13-194 Have North Americans grown to distrust television and newspaper journalists? A study was conducted this year to compare what Americans currently think of the press versus what they said 3 years ago. The survey asked respondents whether they agreed that the press tends to favor one side when reporting on political and social issues. A random sample of people was asked to participate in this year's survey. The results of a survey of another random sample taken 3 years ago are also available. The responses are 2 = Agree and 1 = Disagree. Can we conclude at the 10% significance level that Americans have become more distrustful of televi-

---

EXAMPLE 13.9   Test Marketing of Package Designs, Part 1

DATA
Xm13-09

The General Products Company produces and sells a variety of household products. Because of stiff competition, one of its products, a bath soap, is not selling well. Hoping to improve sales, General Products decided to introduce more attractive packaging. The company's advertising agency developed two new designs. The first design features several bright colors to distinguish it from other brands. The second design is light green in color with just the company's logo on it. As a test to determine which design is better, the marketing manager selected two supermarkets. In one supermarket, the soap was packaged in a box using the first design; in the second supermarket, the second design was used. The product scanner at each supermarket tracked every buyer of soap over a 1-week period. The supermarkets recorded the last four digits of the scanner code for each of the five brands of soap the supermarket sold. The code for the General Products brand of soap is 9077 (the other codes are 4255, 3745, 7118, and 8855). After the trial period, the scanner data were transferred to a computer file.

CASE 3.2   Did Global Warming Cause Canada's Forest Fires?

DATA
C03-02a
C03-02b
C03-02c

In the summer of 2016, forest fires burned about a quarter of the homes and businesses in Fort McMurray Alberta. Some newspapers printed claims by scientists that the forest fires were the result of global warming. To examine this claim, we have recorded the number of forest fires and the areas burned (in hectares) annually from 1970 to 2015. Note: a hectare is equal to 10,000 square meters. It is about two and half times the size of an acre.) Use a graphical technique to graph the number of forest fires and the areas burned. Use annual temperature anomalies from 1970 to 2015 to see if there is a relationship between temperature and forest fires and areas burned. Briefly describe your results

---

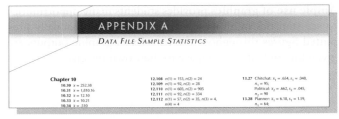

APPENDIX A

Data File Sample Statistics

Chapter 10		
10.30 $x = 252.38$	12.108 $n(1) = 153, n(2) = 24$	13.27 Chitchat: $x_1 = .654, s_1 = .048,$
10.31 $x = 1,810.16$	12.109 $n(1) = 92, n(2) = 28$	$n_1 = 95;$
10.32 $x = 12.10$	12.110 $n(1) = 603, n(2) = 905$	Political: $x_2 = .662, s_2 = .045,$
10.33 $x = 10.21$	12.111 $n(1) = 92, n(2) = 334$	$n_2 = 90$
10.34 $x = .510$	12.112 $n(1) = 57, n(2) = 35, n(3) = 4,$	13.28 Planner: $x_1 = 6.18, s_1 = 1.59,$
	$n(4) = 4$	$n_1 = 64;$

Appendix A provides summary statistics for many of the exercises with large data sets. This feature offers unparalleled flexibility allowing students to solve most exercises by hand or by computer!

Real Data Sets

The data from the last eight General Social Surveys and the last four Surveys of Consumer Finances are included. These feature thousands of observations and dozens of selected variables. Solving more than 500 exercises associated with these surveys encourages students to uncover interesting aspects of the society. For example, students can determine the incomes, education, and working hours of people who are self-employed and compare them to people who work for someone else. They can see the effect of education on income, assets, investments, and net worth. Instructors can use the data to create their own examples and exercises.

Compute the Statistics

Once the correct technique has been identified, examples take students to the next level within the solution by asking them to compute the statistics.

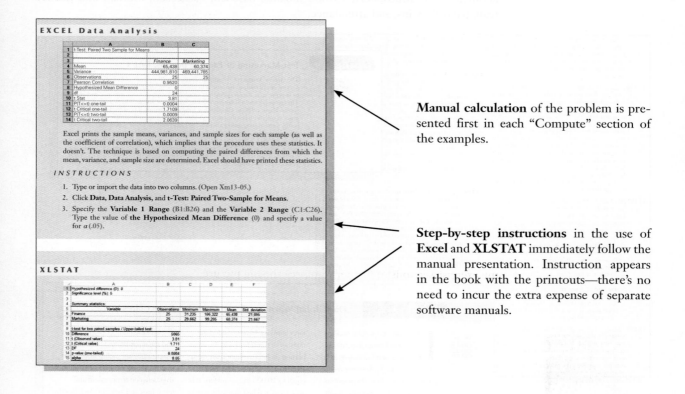

Manual calculation of the problem is presented first in each "Compute" section of the examples.

Step-by-step instructions in the use of Excel and XLSTAT immediately follow the manual presentation. Instruction appears in the book with the printouts—there's no need to incur the extra expense of separate software manuals.

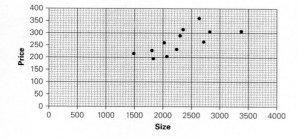

Ample use of graphics provides students many opportunities to see statistics in all its forms. In addition to manually presented figures throughout the text, Excel graphic outputs are given for students to compare to their own results.

Interpret the Results

In the real world, it is not enough to know *how* to generate the statistics. To be truly effective, a business person must also know how to **interpret and articulate** the results. Furthermore, students need a framework to understand and apply statistics **within a realistic setting** by using realistic data in exercises, examples, and case studies.

Examples round out the final component of the identify–compute–interpret approach by asking students to interpret the results in the context of a business-related decision. This final step motivates and shows how statistics is used in everyday business situations.

An Applied Approach

With **Applications in …** sections and boxes, *Statistics for Management and Economics* now includes 42 **applications** (in finance, marketing, operations management, human resources, economics, and accounting) highlighting how statistics is used in those professions. For example, "Applications in Finance: Portfolio Diversification and Asset Allocation" shows how probability is used to help select stocks to minimize risk. Another optional section, "Applications in Marketing: Market Segmentation" demonstrates how to estimate the size of a market segment.

In addition to sections and boxes, **Applications in … exercises** can be found within the exercise sections to further reinforce the big picture.

APPLICATIONS in **OPERATIONS MANAGEMENT**

Quality

A critical aspect of production is quality. The quality of a final product is a function of the quality of the product's components. If the components don't fit, the product will not function as planned and likely cease functioning before its customers expect it to. For example, if a car door is not made to its specifications, it will not fit. As a result, the door will leak both water and air.

Operations managers attempt to maintain and improve the quality of products by ensuring that all components are made so that there is as little variation as possible. As you have already seen, statisticians measure variation by computing the variance. Incidentally, an entire chapter (Chapter 21) is devoted to the topic of quality.

Nielsen Ratings

Statistical techniques play a vital role in helping advertisers determine how many viewers watch the shows that they sponsor. Although several companies sample television viewers to determine what shows they watch, the best known is the A. C. Nielsen firm. The Nielsen ratings are based on a random sample of approximately 5,000 of the 115 million households in the United States with at least one television (in 2013). A meter attached to the televisions in the selected households keeps track of when the televisions are turned on and what channels they are tuned to. The data are sent to the Nielsen's computer every night from which Nielsen computes the rating and sponsors can determine the number of viewers and the potential value of any commercials. Of particular interest to advertisers are 18- to 49-year-olds, who are considered the most likely to buy advertised products. In 2013 there were 126.54 million Americans who were between 18 and 49 years old.

On page 415, we provide a solution to this problem.

Chapter-opening examples and solutions present compelling discussions of how the techniques and concepts introduced in that chapter are applied to real-world problems. These examples are then revisited with a solution as each chapter unfolds, applying the methodologies introduced in the chapter.

Nielsen Ratings: Solution

IDENTIFY

The problem objective is to describe the population of television shows watched by viewers across the country. The data are nominal. The combination of problem objective and data type make the parameter to be estimated the proportion of the entire population of 18- to 49-year-olds that watched *Big Bang Theory* (code = 2). The confidence interval estimator of the proportion is:

$$\hat{p} \pm z_{\alpha/2}\sqrt{\frac{\hat{p}(1 - \hat{p})}{n}}$$

COMPUTE

MANUALLY:

To solve manually, we count the number of 2's in the file. We find this value to be 275. Thus,

$$\hat{p} = \frac{x}{n} = \frac{275}{5,000} = .0550$$

The confidence level is $1 - \alpha = .95$. It follows that $\alpha = .05$, $\alpha/2 = .025$, and $z_{\alpha/2} = z_{.025} = 1.96$. The 95% confidence interval estimate of p is:

$$\hat{p} \pm z_{\alpha/2}\sqrt{\frac{\hat{p}(1 - \hat{p})}{n}} = .0550 \pm 1.96\sqrt{\frac{(.0550)(1 - .0550)}{5,000}} = .0550 \pm .0063$$

LCL = .0487   UCL = .0613

EXCEL Workbook

	A	B	C	D	E
1	z-Estimate of a Proportion				
2					
3	Sample proportion	0.055	Confidence Interval Estimate		
4	Sample size	5000	0.055	±	0.0063
5	Confidence level	0.95	Lower confidence limit		0.0487
6			Upper confidence limit		0.0613

INSTRUCTIONS

1. Type or import the data into one column. (Open Xm12-00.) In any empty cell, calculate the number of "successes" (=COUNTIF A1:A5001, 2). Divide that number by the sample size to obtain sample proportion.

2. Open the **Estimators Workbook** and click the **z-Estimate_Proportion** tab. Type or copy the sample proportion. Type the value of the sample size and the value of α.

XLSTAT

	A	B	C	D	E
1	Proportion: 0.055				
2	Sample size: 5000				
3					
4	95% confidence interval on the proportion (Wald):				
5	0.0487 0.0613				

CASE 12.5   Bias in Roulette Betting

The game of roulette consists of a wheel with 38 colored and numbered slots. The numbers are 1 to 36, 0 and 00. Half of the slots numbered 1 to 36 are red and the other half are black. The two "zeros" are green. The wheel is spun and an iron ball is rolled, which eventually comes to rest in one of the slots. Gamblers can make several different kinds of bets. Most players bet on one or more numbers or on a color (black or red). Here is the layout of the roulette betting table:

```
 0  3  6  9 12 15 18 21 24 27 30 33 36
00  2  5  8 11 14 17 20 23 26 29 32 35
 1  4  7 10 13 16 19 22 25 28 31 34
```

Two statisticians recorded the bets on 904 spins. There were 21,731 bets.

Researchers wanted to use these data to examine *middle bias*, which is the tendency for guessers in multiple-choice exams to select the middle answers. For example, if there are five choices a, b, c, d, and e, guessers will tend to select answer c.

Most players stand on both sides of the betting table so that the middle numbers are 2, 5, 8, 11, 14, 17, 20, 23, 26, 29, 32, and 35.

a. If there is no middle bias, what proportion of the bets

will be on 1 of the 12 middle numbers?

b. Conduct a test at the 5% significance level to determine whether middle bias exists.

c. The middle of the middle are the numbers 17 and 20. If there is no middle bias, what proportion of the bets will be either 17 or 20?

d. Test with a 5% significance level to determine whether middle of the middle bias exists.

Source: Maya Bar-Hillel and Ro'i Zultan, "We Sing the Praise of Good Displays: How Gamblers Bet in Casino Roulette," Chance, Volume 25, No. 2, 2012.

DATA
C12-05

Many of the **examples, exercises, and cases are based on actual studies** performed by statisticians and published in journals, newspapers, and magazines, or presented at conferences. Many data files were recreated to produce the original results.

Chapter summaries briefly review the material and list important terms, symbols, and formulas.

CHAPTER SUMMARY

The inferential methods presented in this chapter address the problem of describing a single population. When the data are interval, the parameters of interest are the population mean μ and the population variance σ^2. The Student t-distribution is used to test and estimate the mean when the population standard deviation is unknown. The chi-squared distribution is used to make inferences about a population variance. When the data are nominal, the parameter

to be tested and estimated is the population proportion p. The sample proportion follows an approximate normal distribution, which produces the test statistic and the interval estimator. We also discussed how to determine the sample size required to estimate a population proportion. We introduced market segmentation and described how statistical techniques presented in this chapter can be used to estimate the size of a segment.

IMPORTANT TERMS:

t-statistic 373
Student t-distribution 373

Robust 379
Chi-squared statistic 389

SYMBOLS:

Symbol	Pronounced	Represents
ν	nu	Degrees of freedom
χ^2	chi squared	Chi-squared statistic
$\hat{p}$	p hat	Sample proportion
$\tilde{p}$	p tilde	Wilson estimator

FORMULAS:

Test statistic for μ

$$t = \frac{\bar{x} - \mu}{s/\sqrt{n}}$$

Confidence interval estimator of μ

$$\bar{x} \pm t_{\alpha/2} \frac{s}{\sqrt{n}}$$

Confidence interval estimator of σ^2

$$LCL = \frac{(n-1)s^2}{\chi^2_{\alpha/2}}$$

$$UCL = \frac{(n-1)s^2}{\chi^2_{1-\alpha/2}}$$

Test statistic for p

Instructor Resources

To access the instructor and student textbook resources, go to **www.cengage.com/login**, log in with your faculty account username and password, and use ISBN 9781337093453 to search for and add instructor resources to your account. Excel data sets for students can be found here as well.

ACKNOWLEDGMENTS

Although there is only one name on the cover of this book, the number of people who made contributions is large. I would like to acknowledge the work of all of them, with particular emphasis on the following: Paul Baum, California State University, Northridge, and John Lawrence, California State University, Fullerton, reviewed the page proofs. Their job was to find errors in presentation, arithmetic, and composition. The following individuals played important roles in the production of this book: Senior Product Manager Aaron Arnsparger, Content Developer Conor Allen, and Senior Content Project Manager Martha Conway. (For all remaining errors, place the blame where it belongs—on me.) Their advice and suggestions made my task considerably easier.

Fernando Rodriguez produced the test bank.

Trent Tucker, Wilfrid Laurier University, and Zvi Goldstein, California State University, Fullerton, each produced a set of PowerPoint slides.

The author extends thanks also to the survey participants and reviewers of the previous editions: Roger Bailey, Vanderbilt University; Paul Baum, California State University–Northridge; Nagraj Balakrishnan, Clemson University; Chen-Huei Chou, College of Charleston; Howard Clayton, Auburn University; Philip Cross, Georgetown University; Barry Cuffe, Wingate University; Ernest Demba, Washington University–St. Louis; Michael Douglas, Millersville University; Neal Duffy, State University of New York–Plattsburgh; John Dutton, North Carolina State University; Ehsan Elahi, University of Massachusetts–Boston; Erick Elder, University of Arkansas; Mohammed El-Saidi, Ferris State University; Grace Esimai, University of Texas–Arlington; Leila Farivar, The Ohio State University; Homi Fatemi, Santa Clara University; Abe Feinberg, California State University–Northridge; Samuel Graves, Boston College; Robert Gould, UCLA; Darren Grant, Sam Houston State University; Shane Griffith, Lee University; Paul Hagstrom, Hamilton College; John Hebert, Virginia Tech; James Hightower, California State University, Fullerton; Bo Honore, Princeton University; Ira Horowitz, University of Florida; Onisforos Iordanou, Hunter College; Torsten Jochem, University of Pittsburgh; Gordon Johnson, California State University–Northridge; Hilke Kayser, Hamilton College; Kenneth Klassen, California State University–Northridge; Roger Kleckner, Bowling Green State University–Firelands; Eylem Koca, Fairleigh Dickinson University; Harry Kypraios, Rollins College; John Lawrence, California State University–Fullerton; Tae H. Lee, University of California–Riverside; Dennis Lin, Pennsylvania State University; Jialu Liu, Allegheny College; Chung-Ping Loh, University of North Florida; Neal Long, Stetson University; Jayashree Mahajan, University of Florida; George Marcoulides, California State University–Fullerton;

Paul Mason, University of North Florida; Walter Mayer, University of Mississippi; John McDonald, Flinders University; Richard McGowan, Boston College; Richard McGrath, Bowling Green State University; Amy Miko, St. Francis College; Janis Miller, Clemson University; Glenn Milligan, Ohio State University; James Moran, Oregon State University; Robert G. Morris, University of Texas–Dallas; Patricia Mullins, University of Wisconsin; Adam Munson, University of Florida; David Murphy, Boston College; Kevin Murphy, Oakland University; Pin Ng, University of Illinois; Des Nicholls, Australian National University; Andrew Paizis, Queens College; David Pentico, Duquesne University; Ira Perelle, Mercy College; Nelson Perera, University of Wollongong; Bruce Pietrykowski, University of Michigan–Dearborn; Amy Puelz, Southern Methodist University; Lawrence Ries, University of Missouri; Colleen Quinn, Seneca College; Tony Quon, University of Ottawa; Madhu Rao, Bowling Green State University; Yaron Raviv, Claremont McKenna College; Jason Reed, Wayne State University; Phil Roth, Clemson University; Deb Rumsey, The Ohio State University; Farhad Saboori, Albright College; Don St. Jean, George Brown College; Hedayeh Samavati, Indiana–Purdue University; Sandy Shroeder, Ohio Northern University; Chris Silvia, University of Kansas; Jineshwar Singh, George Brown College; Natalia Smirnova, Queens College; Eric Sowey, University of New South Wales; Cyrus Stanier, Virginia Tech; Stan Stephenson, Southwest Texas State University; Gordon M. Stringer, University of Colorado–Colorado Springs; Arnold Stromberg, University of Kentucky; Pandu Tadikamalla, University of Pittsburgh; Patrick Thompson, University of Florida; Steve Thorpe, University of Northern Iowa; Sheldon Vernon, Houston Baptist University; John J. Wiorkowski, University of Texas–Dallas; and W. F. Younkin, University of Miami.

iStockphoto.com/leluconcepts

WHAT IS STATISTICS?

INTRODUCTION

Statistics is a way to get information from data. That's it! Most of this textbook is devoted to describing how, when, and why managers and statistics practitioners* conduct statistical procedures. You may ask, "If that's all there is to statistics, why is this book (and most other statistics books) so large?" The answer is that students of applied statistics will be exposed to different kinds of information and data. We demonstrate some of these with a case and two examples that are featured later in this book.

The first may be of particular interest to you.

---

*The term *statistician* is used to describe so many different kinds of occupations that it has ceased to have any meaning. It is used, for example, to describe a person who calculates baseball statistics as well as an individual educated in statistical principles. We will describe the former as a *statistics practitioner* and the

(*continued*)

1

EXAMPLE **3.3**

Business Statistics Marks (See Chapter 3)

A student enrolled in a business program is attending his first class of the required statistics course. The student is somewhat apprehensive because he believes the myth that the course is difficult. To alleviate his anxiety, the student asks the professor about last year's marks. Because this professor is friendly and helpful, like all other statistics professors, he obliges the student and provides a list of the final marks, which are composed of term work plus the final exam. What information can the student obtain from the list?

This is a typical statistics problem. The student has the data (marks) and needs to apply statistical techniques to get the information he requires. This is a function of **descriptive statistics**.

Descriptive Statistics

Descriptive statistics deals with methods of organizing, summarizing, and presenting data in a convenient and informative way. One form of descriptive statistics uses graphical techniques that allow statistics practitioners to present data in ways that make it easy for the reader to extract useful information. In Chapters 2 and 3 we will present a variety of graphical methods.

Another form of descriptive statistics uses numerical techniques to summarize data. One such method that you have already used frequently calculates the average or mean. In the same way that you calculate the average age of the employees of a company, we can compute the mean mark of last year's statistics course. Chapter 4 introduces several numerical statistical measures that describe different features of the data.

The actual technique we use depends on what specific information we would like to extract. In this example, we can see at least three important pieces of information. The first is the "typical" mark. We call this a *measure of central location*. The average is one such measure. In Chapter 4, we will introduce another useful measure of central location, the median. Suppose the student was told that the average mark last year was 67. Is this enough information to reduce his anxiety? The student would likely respond "No" because he would like to know whether most of the marks were close to 67 or were scattered far below and above the average. He needs a *measure of variability*. The simplest such measure is the *range*, which is calculated by subtracting the smallest number from the largest. Suppose the largest mark is 96 and the smallest is 24. Unfortunately, this provides little information since it is based on only two marks. We need other measures—these will be introduced in Chapter 4. Moreover, the student must determine more about the marks. In particular, he needs to know how the marks are distributed between 24 and 96. The best way to do this is to use a graphical technique, the histogram, which will be introduced in Chapter 3.

---

latter as a *statistician*. A statistics practitioner is a person who uses statistical techniques properly. Examples of statistics practitioners include the following:

1. a financial analyst who develops stock portfolios based on historical rates of return;

2. an economist who uses statistical models to help explain and predict variables such as inflation rate, unemployment rate, and changes in the gross domestic product; and

3. a market researcher who surveys consumers and converts the responses into useful information.

Our goal in this book is to convert you into one such capable individual.

The term *statistician* refers to an individual who works with the mathematics of statistics. His or her work involves research that develops techniques and concepts, which in the future may help the statistics practitioner. Statisticians are also statistics practitioners, frequently conducting empirical research and consulting. If you're taking a statistics course, your instructor is probably a statistician.

Case 12.1 Pepsi's Exclusivity Agreement with a University (see Chapter 12) In the last few years, colleges and universities have signed exclusivity agreements with a variety of private companies. These agreements bind the university to sell these companies' products exclusively on the campus. Many of the agreements involve food and beverage firms.

A large university with a total enrollment of about 50,000 students has offered Pepsi-Cola an exclusivity agreement that would give Pepsi exclusive rights to sell its products at all university facilities for the next year with an option for future years. In return, the university would receive 35% of the on-campus revenues and an additional lump sum of $200,000 per year. Pepsi has been given 2 weeks to respond.

The management at Pepsi quickly reviews what it knows. The market for soft drinks is measured in terms of 12-ounce cans. Pepsi currently sells an average of 22,000 cans per week over the 40 weeks of the year that the university operates. The cans sell for an average of one dollar each. The costs, including labor, total 30 cents per can. Pepsi is unsure of its market share but suspects it is considerably less than 50%. A quick analysis reveals that if its current market share were 25%, then, with an exclusivity agreement, Pepsi would sell 88,000 (22,000 is 25% of 88,000) cans per week or 3,520,000 cans per year. The gross revenue would be computed as follows[†]:

Gross revenue $= 3,520,000 \times \$1.00/\text{can} = \$3,520,000$

This figure must be multiplied by 65% because the university would rake in 35% of the gross. Thus,

Gross revenue after deducting 35% university take
$= 65\% \times \$3,520,000 = \$2,288,000$

The total cost of 30 cents per can (or $1,056,000) and the annual payment to the university of $200,000 are subtracted to obtain the net profit:

Net profit $= \$2,288,000 - \$1,056,000 - \$200,000 = \$1,032,000$

Pepsi's current annual profit is

40 weeks $\times$ 22,000 cans/week $\times \$.70 = \$616,000$

If the current market share is 25%, the potential gain from the agreement is

$\$1,032,000 - \$616,000 = \$416,000$

The only problem with this analysis is that Pepsi does not know how many soft drinks are sold weekly at the university. Coke is not likely to supply Pepsi with information about its sales, which together with Pepsi's line of products constitute virtually the entire market.

Pepsi assigned a recent university graduate to survey the university's students to supply the missing information. Accordingly, she organizes a survey that asks 500 students to keep track of the number of soft drinks they purchase in the next 7 days. The responses are stored in a file C12-01 available to be downloaded.

Inferential Statistics

The information we would like to acquire in Case 12.1 is an estimate of annual profits from the exclusivity agreement. The data are the numbers of cans of soft drinks consumed in 7 days by the 500 students in the sample. We can use descriptive techniques to

---

[†]We have created an Excel spreadsheet that does the calculations for this case. See Appendix 1 for instructions on how to download this spreadsheet from Cengage's website plus hundreds of data sets and much more.

learn more about the data. In this case, however, we are not so much interested in what the 500 students are reporting as in knowing the mean number of soft drinks consumed by all 50,000 students on campus. To accomplish this goal we need another branch of statistics: **inferential statistics**.

Inferential statistics is a body of methods used to draw conclusions or inferences about characteristics of populations based on sample data. The population in question in this case is the university's 50,000 students. The characteristic of interest is the soft drink consumption of this population. The cost of interviewing each student in the population would be prohibitive and extremely time consuming. Statistical techniques make such endeavors unnecessary. Instead, we can sample a much smaller number of students (the sample size is 500) and infer from the data the number of soft drinks consumed by all 50,000 students. We can then estimate annual profits for Pepsi.

EXAMPLE 12.5

Exit Polls (See Chapter 12)

When an election for political office takes place, the television networks cancel regular programming to provide election coverage. After the ballots are counted, the results are reported. However, for important offices such as president or senator in large states, the networks actively compete to see which one will be the first to predict a winner. This is done through **exit polls** in which a random sample of voters who exit the polling booth are asked for whom they voted. From the data, the sample proportion of voters supporting the candidates is computed. A statistical technique is applied to determine whether there is enough evidence to infer that the leading candidate will garner enough votes to win. Suppose that the exit poll results from the state of Florida during the year 2000 elections were recorded. Although several candidates were running for president, the exit pollsters recorded only the votes of the two candidates who had any chance of winning: Republican George W. Bush and Democrat Albert Gore. The results (765 people who voted for either Bush or Gore) were stored in file Xm12-05. The network analysts would like to know whether they can conclude that George W. Bush will win the state of Florida.

Example 12.5 describes a common application of statistical inference. The population the television networks wanted to make inferences about is the approximately 5 million Floridians who voted for Bush or Gore for president. The sample consisted of the 765 people randomly selected by the polling company who voted for either of the two main candidates. The characteristic of the population that we would like to know is the proportion of the Florida total electorate that voted for Bush. Specifically, we would like to know whether more than 50% of the electorate voted for Bush (counting only those who voted for either the Republican or Democratic candidate). It must be made clear that we cannot predict the outcome with 100% certainty because we will not ask all 5 million actual voters for whom they voted. This is a fact that statistics practitioners and even students of statistics must understand. A sample that is only a small fraction of the size of the population can lead to correct inferences only a certain percentage of the time. You will find that statistics practitioners can control that fraction and usually set it between 90% and 99%.

Incidentally, on the night of the U.S. election in November 2000, the networks goofed badly. Using exit polls as well as the results of previous elections, all four networks concluded at about 8 P.M. that Al Gore would win Florida. Shortly after 10 P.M., with a large percentage of the actual vote having been counted, the networks reversed course and declared that George W. Bush would win the state. By 2 A.M., another verdict was declared: The result was too close to call. Since then, this experience has likely been used by statistics instructors when teaching how *not* to use statistics.

Notice that, contrary to what you probably believed, data are not necessarily numbers. The marks in Example 3.3 and the number of soft drinks consumed in a week in Case 12.1, of course, are numbers; however, the votes in Example 12.5 are not. In Chapter 2, we will discuss the different types of data you will encounter in statistical applications and how to deal with them.

1-1 / KEY STATISTICAL CONCEPTS

Statistical inference problems involve three key concepts: the population, the sample, and the statistical inference. We now discuss each of these concepts in more detail.

1-1a Population

A **population** is the group of all items of interest to a statistics practitioner. It is frequently very large and may, in fact, be infinitely large. In the language of statistics, *population* does not necessarily refer to a group of people. It may, for example, refer to the population of ball bearings produced at a large plant. In Case 12.1, the population of interest consists of the 50,000 students on campus. In Example 12.5, the population consists of the Floridians who voted for Bush or Gore.

A descriptive measure of a population is called a **parameter**. The parameter of interest in Case 12.1 is the mean number of soft drinks consumed by all the students at the university. The parameter in Example 12.5 is the proportion of the 5 million Florida voters who voted for Bush. In most applications of inferential statistics, the parameter represents the information we need.

1-1b Sample

A **sample** is a set of data drawn from the studied population. A descriptive measure of a sample is called a **statistic**. We use statistics to make inferences about parameters. In Case 12.1, the statistic we would compute is the mean number of soft drinks consumed in the last week by the 500 students in the sample. We would then use the sample mean to infer the value of the population mean, which is the parameter of interest in this problem. In Example 12.5, we compute the proportion of the sample of 765 Floridians who voted for Bush. The sample statistic is then used to make inferences about the population of all 5 million votes—that is, we predict the election results even before the actual count.

1-1c Statistical Inference

Statistical inference is the process of making an estimate, prediction, or decision about a population based on sample data. Because populations are almost always very large, investigating each member of the population would be impractical and expensive. It is far easier and cheaper to take a sample from the population of interest and draw conclusions or make estimates about the population on the basis of information provided by the sample. However, such conclusions and estimates are not always going to be correct. For this reason, we build into the statistical inference a measure of reliability. There are two such measures: the **confidence level** and the **significance level**. The *confidence level* is the proportion of times that an estimating procedure will be correct. For example, in Case 12.1, we will produce an estimate of the average number of soft drinks to be consumed by all 50,000 students that has a confidence level of 95%. In other words, estimates based on this form of statistical inference will be correct 95% of the time. When the purpose of the statistical inference is to draw a conclusion about a population, the *significance level* measures how frequently the conclusion will be wrong. For example, suppose that, as a result of the analysis in Example 12.5, we conclude that more than 50% of the electorate will vote for George W. Bush, and thus he will win the state of Florida. A 5% significance level means that samples that lead us to conclude that Bush wins the election will be wrong 5% of the time.

1-2 / STATISTICAL APPLICATIONS IN BUSINESS

An important function of statistics courses in business and economics programs is to demonstrate that statistical analysis plays an important role in virtually all aspects of business and economics. We intend to do so through examples, exercises, and cases. However, we assume that most students taking their first statistics course have not taken courses in most of the other subjects in management programs. To understand fully how statistics is used in these and other subjects, it is necessary to know something about them. To provide sufficient background to understand the statistical application, we introduce applications in accounting, economics, finance, human resources management, marketing, and operations management. We provide readers with some background of these applications by describing their functions in two ways.

1-2a Application Sections and Subsections

We feature five sections that describe statistical applications in the functional areas of business. In Section 4-5, we discuss an application in finance, the market model, which introduces an important concept in investing. Section 7-3 describes another application in finance that describes a financial analyst's use of probability and statistics to construct portfolios that decrease risk. Section 12-4 is an application in marketing, market segmentation. In Section 14-6, we present an application in operations management, finding and reducing variation. In Section 18-3, we provide an application in human resources, pay equity. A subsection in Section 6-4 presents an application in medical testing (useful in the medical insurance industry).

1-2b Application Boxes

For other topics that require less-detailed description, we provide application boxes with a relatively brief description of the background followed by examples or exercises. These boxes are scattered throughout the book. For example, in Section 4-1, we discuss the geometric mean and why it is used instead of the arithmetic mean to measure variables that are rates of change.

1-3 / LARGE REAL DATA SETS

The author believes that you learn statistics by doing statistics. For their lives after college and university, we expect graduates to have access to large amounts of real data that must be summarized to acquire the information needed to make decisions. We include the data from two sources: the General Social Survey (GSS) and the Survey of Consumer Finances (SCF). We have scattered examples, exercises, and cases for these surveys throughout the book.

1-3a General Social Survey

Since 1972, the GSS has been tracking American attitudes on a wide variety of topics. With the exception of the U.S. Census, the GSS is the most frequently used source of information about American society. The surveys now conducted every second year measure hundreds of variables and thousands of observations. The data for the eight most recent surveys are stored in files GSS2000, GSS2002, GSS2004, GSS2006, GSS2008, GSS2010, GSS2012, and GSS2014. The sample sizes are 2,817, 2,765, 2,812, 4,510, 2,023, 2,044, 1,974, and 2,538, respectively. We have removed the missing data codes representing "No answer," "Don't know," and so on and replaced them with blanks. Be aware that Excel and XLSTAT have different ways of dealing with blanks.

A list of all the variables and their definitions is available as an online appendix.

1-3b Survey of Consumer Finances

The SCF is conducted every 3 years to provide detailed information on the finances of U.S. households. The study is sponsored by the Federal Reserve Board in cooperation with the Department of the Treasury. Since 1992, data have been collected by the National Opinion Research Center (NORC) at the University of Chicago. The data for the four most recent surveys are stored in folders SCF2004, SCF2007, SCF2010, and SCF2013. The sample sizes are 4,519, 4,417, 6,482, and 6,015, respectively. Because the samples are so large and the range of some of the variables so wide, there are problems summarizing and describing the data. To solve the problem, we have created subsamples based on percentiles of the net worth of the households being sampled. Here is a list of the subsamples.

All: Includes all observations

B1: Lowest 1%

Poor (P): 1%–5%

Working poor (WP): 5%–20%

Lower Middle Class (LMC): 20%–40%

Middle Class (MC): 40%–60%

Upper Middle Class (UMC): 60%–80%

Upper Class (UC): 80%–90%

Wealthy (W): 90%–95%

Super Rich (SR): 95%–99%

T1: Top 1%

A complete list of the variables and their definitions is available as an online appendix.

1-4 STATISTICS AND THE COMPUTER

In virtually all applications of statistics, the statistics practitioner must deal with large amounts of data. For example, Case 12.1 (Pepsi-Cola) involves 500 observations. To estimate annual profits, the statistics practitioner would have to perform computations on the data. Although the calculations do not require any great mathematical skill, the sheer amount of arithmetic makes this aspect of the statistical method time consuming and tedious. Fortunately, numerous commercially prepared computer programs are available to perform the arithmetic. We have chosen to use Microsoft Excel in the belief that virtually all university graduates use it now and will in the future.

1-4a Excel

Excel can perform statistical procedures in several ways.

1. **Statistical** (which includes probability) and other functions f_x: We use some of these functions to help create graphical techniques in Chapter 2, calculate statistics in Chapters 3 and 4, and to compute probabilities in Chapters 7 and 8.

2. **Spreadsheets:** We use statistical functions to create spreadsheets that calculate statistical inference methods in Chapters 10–16. These can be downloaded from Cengage's website. Additionally, the spreadsheets can be used to conduct what–if analyses. The rationale for their use is described in subsection 1-4f.

3. **Analysis ToolPak:** This group of procedures comes with every version of Excel. The techniques are accessed by clicking Data and Data Analysis. One of its drawbacks is that it does not offer a complete set of the statistical techniques we introduce in this book.

4. **XLSTAT** is a commercially created add-in that can be loaded onto your computer to enable you to use Excel for almost all statistical procedures introduced in this book. XLSTAT can be downloaded from Cengage's website.

1-4b Data Analysis Plus

We have offered Data Analysis Plus in the last seven editions of this book. Unfortunately, we have encountered problems with some of the combinations of Excel versions and operating systems. As a result it is no longer possible to offer Data Analysis Plus as a universal tool for all Excel users of this book. Appendix 1 lists the combinations that do work. Data Analysis Plus can be downloaded from the author's website. Printouts and instructions are available as appendixes that can be downloaded from the Cengage's website.

1-4c Minitab

Like Data Analysis Plus, Minitab has been used in many editions of this book. Because of decreasing demand, we have decided to discontinue Minitab use. However, printouts and instructions for Minitab 17 are available as online appendixes.

1-4d File names and Notation

A large proportion of the examples, exercises, and cases feature large data sets. These are denoted with the file name next to the exercise number. The data sets associated with examples are denoted as Xm. To illustrate, the data for Example 2.2 are stored in file Xm02-02 in the Chapter 2 folder. The data for exercises and cases are stored in files prefixed by Xr and C, respectively. The prefix GSS designates data for the General Social Surveys. The data for the Surveys of Consumer Finances data are stored in folders SCF2004, SCF2007, SCF2010, and SCF2013.

In many real applications of statistics, additional data are collected. For instance, in Example 12.5, the pollster often records the voter's gender and asks for other information including race, religion, education, and income. Many other data sets are similarly constructed. In later chapters, we will return to these files and require other statistical techniques to extract the needed information. (Files that contain additional data are denoted by an asterisk on the file name.)

1-4e Our Approach

The approach we prefer to take is to minimize the time spent on manual computations and to focus instead on selecting the appropriate method for dealing with a problem and on interpreting the output after the computer has performed the necessary computations. In this way, we hope to demonstrate that statistics can be as interesting and as practical as any other subject in your curriculum.

1-4f Excel Spreadsheets

Books written for statistics courses taken by mathematics or statistics majors are considerably different from this one. It is not surprising that such courses feature mathematical proofs of theorems and derivations of most procedures. When the material is covered in this way, the underlying concepts that support statistical inference are exposed and relatively easy to see. However, this book was created for an applied course in business and economics statistics. Consequently, we do not address directly the mathematical principles of statistics. However, as we pointed out previously, one of the most important functions of statistics practitioners is to properly interpret statistical results, whether produced manually or by computer. And, to correctly interpret statistics, students require an understanding of the principles of statistics.

To help students understand the basic foundation, we offer readers Excel spreadsheets that allow for *what–if* analyses. By changing some of the input value, students can see for themselves how statistics works. (The term is derived from *what* happens to the statistics *if* I change this value?)

CHAPTER SUMMARY

IMPORTANT TERMS:

Descriptive statistics 2	Sample 5
Inferential statistics 4	Statistic 5
Exit polls 4	Statistical inference 5
Population 5	Confidence level 5
Parameter 5	Significance level 5

CHAPTER EXERCISES

1.1 In your own words, define and give an example of each of the following statistical terms.
  a. population
  b. sample
  c. parameter
  d. statistic
  e. statistical inference

1.2 Briefly describe the difference between descriptive statistics and inferential statistics.

1.3 A politician who is running for the office of mayor of a city with 25,000 registered voters commissions a survey. In the survey, 48% of the 200 registered voters interviewed say they plan to vote for her.
  a. What is the population of interest?
  b. What is the sample?
  c. Is the value 48% a parameter or a statistic? Explain.

1.4 A manufacturer of computer chips claims that less than 10% of its products are defective. When 1,000 chips were drawn from a large production, 7.5% were found to be defective.
  a. What is the population of interest?
  b. What is the sample?
  c. What is the parameter?
  d. What is the statistic?
  e. Does the value 10% refer to the parameter or to the statistic?
  f. Is the value 7.5% a parameter or a statistic?
  g. Explain briefly how the statistic can be used to make inferences about the parameter to test the claim.

1.5 Suppose you believe that, in general, graduates who have majored in *your* subject are offered higher salaries upon graduating than are graduates of other programs. Describe a statistical experiment that could help test your belief.

1.6 You are shown a coin that its owner says is fair in the sense that it will produce the same number of heads and tails when flipped a very large number of times.
  a. Describe an experiment to test this claim.
  b. What is the population in your experiment?
  c. What is the sample?
  d. What is the parameter?
  e. What is the statistic?
  f. Describe briefly how statistical inference can be used to test the claim.

1.7 Suppose that in Exercise 1.6 you decide to flip the coin 100 times.
  a. What conclusion would you be likely to draw if you observed 95 heads?
  b. What conclusion would you be likely to draw if you observed 55 heads?
  c. Do you believe that, if you flip a perfectly fair coin 100 times, you will always observe exactly 50 heads? If you answered "no," then what numbers do you think are possible? If you answered "yes," how many heads would you observe if you flipped the coin twice? Try flipping a coin twice and repeating this experiment 10 times and report the results.

1.8 Xr01-08 The owner of a large fleet of taxis is trying to estimate his costs for next year's operations. One major cost is fuel purchase. To estimate fuel purchase, the owner needs to know the total distance his taxis will travel next year, the cost of a gallon of fuel, and the fuel mileage of his taxis. The owner has been provided with the first two figures (distance estimate and cost of a gallon of fuel). However, because of the high cost of gasoline, the owner has recently converted his taxis to operate on propane. He has measured and recorded the propane mileage (in miles per gallon) for 50 taxis.
  a. What is the population of interest?
  b. What is the parameter the owner needs?
  c. What is the sample?
  d. What is the statistic?
  e. Describe briefly how the statistic will produce the kind of information the owner wants.

APPENDIX 1 / Material to Download

Author's Website

Website:www.KellerStatistics.com/KellerStatistics/DataAnalysisPlus
Download Data Analysis Plus from this site. Here are the Excel Versions and Operating Systems that work with Data Analysis Plus. (Some other combinations may work.)

Excel Version	Operating System
2016	Windows
2013	Windows
2007	Windows
2003	Windows
2011 Mac	Mac OS
2004 Mac	Mac OS
2001 Mac	Mac OS

Note that in the 2013 and 2016 versions of Excel, Data Analysis Plus conflicts with Data Analysis. As a result, in order to use Data Analysis Plus, it is necessary to temporarily remove the Analysis ToolPak.

© Steve Cole/Digital Vision/Getty Images

2

GRAPHICAL DESCRIPTIVE TECHNIQUES I

CHAPTER OUTLINE

Do Male and Female Americans Differ in Their Political Party Affiliation?

DATA
GSS2014*

In Chapter 1, we introduced the General Social Survey (GSS), which is conducted every two years with the objective to track the experiences, behaviors, and attitudes of Americans. One question that has been asked in all General Social Surveys is "Generally speaking, do you think of yourself as Republican, Democrat, Independent, or what?" The responses are as follows:

0. Strong Democrat

1. Not Strong Democrat

2. Independent, Near Democrat

Daniel Sofer/Photos.com

On page 38, we will provide our answer.

3. Independent

4. Independent, Near Republican

5. Not Strong Republican

6. Strong Republican

7. Other Party

Respondents are also identified by sex: 1 = Male, and 2 = Female. The data are stored in the file GSS2014. Note that the file contains other variables that are not needed in this example. The variable SEX is stored in column B and PARTYID is stored in Column AE. Some of the data are listed here.

ID	SEX	PARTYID
57062	1	5
57063	2	5
57064	1	6
⋮	⋮	⋮
59597	1	2
59598	1	1
59599	2	4

Determine whether American males and females differ in their political affiliations. See page 38 for our solution.

INTRODUCTION

In Chapter 1, we pointed out that statistics is divided into two basic areas: descriptive statistics and inferential statistics. The purpose of this chapter, together with the next, is to present the principal methods that fall under the heading of descriptive statistics. In this chapter, we introduce graphical and tabular statistical methods that allow managers to summarize data visually to produce useful information that is often used in decision making. Another class of descriptive techniques, numerical methods, is introduced in Chapter 4.

Managers frequently have access to large masses of potentially useful data. But before the data can be used to support a decision, they must be organized and summarized. Consider, for example, the problems faced by managers who have access to the databases created by the use of debit cards. The database consists of the personal information supplied by the customer when he or she applied for the debit card. This information includes age, gender, residence, and the cardholder's income. In addition, each time the card is used the database grows to include a history of the timing, price, and brand of each product purchased. Using the appropriate statistical technique, managers can determine which segments of the market are buying their company's brands. Specialized marketing campaigns, including telemarketing, can be developed. Both descriptive and inferential statistics would likely be employed in the analysis.

Descriptive statistics involves arranging, summarizing, and presenting a set of data in such a way that useful information is produced. Its methods make use of graphical techniques and numerical descriptive measures (such as averages) to summarize and present the data, allowing managers to make decisions based on the information generated. Although descriptive statistical methods are quite straightforward, their importance should not be underestimated. Most management, business, and economics students will encounter numerous opportunities to make valuable use of graphical and numerical descriptive techniques when preparing reports and presentations in the workplace. According to a Wharton Business School study, top managers reach a consensus 25% more quickly when responding to a presentation in which graphics are used.

In Chapter 1, we introduced the distinction between a population and a sample. Recall that a population is the entire set of observations under study, whereas a sample is a subset of a population. The descriptive methods presented in this chapter and in Chapters 3 and 4 apply to both a set of data constituting a population and a set of data constituting a sample.

In both the preface and Chapter 1, we pointed out that a critical part of your education as statistics practitioners includes an understanding of not only *how* to draw graphs and calculate statistics (manually or by computer) but also *when* to use each technique that we cover. The two most important factors that determine the appropriate method to use are (1) the type of data and (2) the information that is needed. Both are discussed next.

2-1 / TYPES OF DATA AND INFORMATION

The objective of statistics is to extract information from data. There are different types of data and information. To help explain this important principle, we need to define some terms.

A **variable** is some characteristic of a population or sample. For example, the mark on a statistics exam is a characteristic of statistics exams that is certainly of interest to readers of this book. Not all students achieve the same mark. The marks will vary from student to student, thus the name *variable*. The price of a stock is another variable. The prices of most stocks vary daily. We usually represent the name of the variable using uppercase letters such as X, Y, and Z.

The **values** of the variable are the possible observations of the variable. The values of statistics exam marks are the integers between 0 and 100 (assuming the exam is marked out of 100). The values of a stock price are real numbers that are usually measured in dollars and cents (sometimes in fractions of a cent). The values range from 0 to hundreds of dollars.

Data* are the observed values of a variable. For example, suppose that we observe the following midterm test marks of 10 students:

| 67 | 74 | 71 | 83 | 93 | 55 | 48 | 82 | 68 | 62 |

These are the data from which we will extract the information we seek. Incidentally, *data* is plural for **datum**. The mark of one student is a datum.

When most people think of data, they think of sets of numbers. However, there are three types of data: interval, nominal, and ordinal.[†]

---

*Unfortunately, the term *data*, like the term *statistician*, has taken on several different meanings. For example, dictionaries define data as facts, information, or statistics. In the language of computers, data may refer to any piece of information such as this textbook or an essay you have written. Such definitions make it difficult for us to present *statistics* as a method of converting data into *information*. In this book, we carefully distinguish among the three terms.

[†]There are actually four types of data, the fourth being *ratio* data. However, for statistical purposes there is no difference between ratio and interval data. Consequently, we combine the two types.

Interval data are real numbers, such as heights, weights, incomes, and distances. We also refer to this type of data as **quantitative** or **numerical**.

The values of **nominal** data are categories. For example, responses to questions about marital status produce nominal data. The values of this variable are single, married, divorced, and widowed. Notice that the values are not numbers but instead are words that describe the categories. We often record nominal data by arbitrarily assigning a number to each category. For example, we could record marital status using the following codes:

single = 1,   married = 2,   divorced = 3,   widowed = 4

However, any other numbering system is valid provided that each category has a different number assigned to it. Here is another coding system that is just as valid as the previous one.

Single = 7,   married = 4,   divorced = 13,   widowed = 1

Nominal data are also called **qualitative** or **categorical**.

The third type of data is ordinal. **Ordinal** data appear to be nominal, but the difference is that the order of their values has meaning. For example, at the completion of most college and university courses, students are asked to evaluate the course. The variables are the ratings of various aspects of the course, including the professor. Suppose that in a particular college the values are

poor,   fair,   good,   very good,   and   excellent

The difference between nominal and ordinal types of data is that the order of the values of the latter indicate a higher rating. Consequently, when assigning codes to the values, we should maintain the order of the values. For example, we can record the students' evaluations as

Poor = 1,   Fair = 2,   Good = 3,   Very good = 4,   Excellent = 5

Because the only constraint that we impose on our choice of codes is that the order must be maintained, we can use any set of codes that are in order. For example, we can also assign the following codes:

Poor = 6,   Fair = 18,   Good = 23,   Very good = 45,   Excellent = 88

As we discuss in Chapter 19, which introduces statistical inference techniques for ordinal data, the use of any code that preserves the order of the data will produce exactly the same result. Thus, it's not the magnitude of the values that is important, it's their order.

Students often have difficulty distinguishing between ordinal and interval data. The critical difference between them is that the intervals or differences between values of interval data are consistent and meaningful (which is why this type of data is called *interval*). For example, the difference between marks of 85 and 80 is the same five-mark difference that exists between 75 and 70—that is, we can calculate the difference and interpret the results.

Because the codes representing ordinal data are arbitrarily assigned except for the order, we cannot calculate and interpret differences. For example, using a 1-2-3-4-5 coding system to represent poor, fair, good, very good, and excellent, we note that the difference between excellent and very good is identical to the difference between good and fair. With a 6-18-23-45-88 coding, the difference between excellent and very good is 43, and the difference between good and fair is 5. Because both coding systems are valid, we cannot use either system to compute and interpret differences.

Here is another example. Suppose that you are given the following list of the most active stocks traded on the NASDAQ in descending order of magnitude:

Order	Most Active Stocks
1	Microsoft
2	Cisco Systems
3	Dell Computer
4	Sun Microsystems
5	JDS Uniphase

Does this information allow you to conclude that the difference between the number of stocks traded in Microsoft and Cisco Systems is the same as the difference in the number of stocks traded between Dell Computer and Sun Microsystems? The answer is "no" because we have information only about the order of the numbers of trades, which are ordinal, and not the numbers of trades themselves, which are interval. In other words, the difference between 1 and 2 is not necessarily the same as the difference between 3 and 4.

2-1a Calculations for Types of Data

Interval Data All calculations are permitted on interval data. We often describe a set of interval data by calculating the average. For example, the average of the 10 marks listed on page 14 is 70.3. As you will discover, there are several other important statistics that we will introduce.

Nominal Data Because the codes of nominal data are completely arbitrary, we cannot perform any calculations on these codes. To understand why, consider a survey that asks people to report their marital status. Suppose that the first 10 people surveyed gave the following responses:

Single, Married, Married, Married, Widowed,
Single, Married, Married, Single, Divorced

Using the codes

Single = 1,   Married = 2,   Divorced = 3,   Widowed = 4

we would record these responses as

1   2   2   2   4   1   2   2   1   3

The average of these numerical codes is 2.0. Does this mean that the average person is married? Now suppose four more persons were interviewed, of whom three are widowed and one is divorced. The data are given here:

1   2   2   2   4   1   2   2   1   3   4   4   4   3

The average of these 14 codes is 2.5. Does this mean that the average person is married—but halfway to getting divorced? The answer to both questions is an emphatic "no." This example illustrates a fundamental truth about nominal data: Calculations based on the codes used to store this type of data are meaningless. All that we are permitted to do with nominal data is count or compute the percentages of the occurrences of each category. Thus, we would describe the 14 observations by counting the number of each marital status category and reporting the frequency as shown in the following table.

Category	Code	Frequency
Single	1	3
Married	2	5
Divorced	3	2
Widowed	4	4

The remainder of this chapter deals with nominal data only. In Chapter 3, we introduce graphical techniques that are used to describe interval data.

Ordinal Data The most important aspect of ordinal data is the order of the values. As a result, the only permissible calculations are those involving a ranking process. For example, we can place all the data in order and select the code that lies in the middle. As we discuss in Chapter 4, this descriptive measurement is called the *median*.

2-1b Hierarchy of Data

The data types can be placed in order of the permissible calculations. At the top of the list, we place the interval data type because virtually *all* computations are allowed. The nominal data type is at the bottom because *no* calculations other than determining frequencies are permitted. (We are permitted to perform calculations using the frequencies of codes, but this differs from performing calculations on the codes themselves.) In between interval and nominal data lies the ordinal data type. Permissible calculations are ones that rank the data.

Higher-level data types may be treated as lower-level ones. For example, in universities and colleges, we convert the marks in a course, which are interval, to letter grades, which are ordinal. Some graduate courses feature only a pass or fail designation. In this case, the interval data are converted to nominal. It is important to point out that when we convert higher-level data as lower-level we lose information. For example, a mark of 89 on an accounting course exam gives far more information about the performance of that student than does a letter grade of B, which might be the letter grade for marks between 80 and 90. As a result, we do not convert data unless it is necessary to do so. We will discuss this later.

It is also important to note that we cannot treat lower-level data types as higher-level types.

The definitions and hierarchy are summarized in the following box.

Types of Data

Interval

   Values are real numbers.

   All calculations are valid.

   Data may be treated as ordinal or nominal.

Ordinal

Values must represent the ranked order of the data.

Calculations based on an ordering process are valid.

Data may be treated as nominal but not as interval.

Nominal

Values are the arbitrary numbers that represent categories.

Only calculations based on the frequencies or percentages of occurrence are valid.

Data may not be treated as ordinal or interval.

2-1c Interval, Ordinal, and Nominal Variables

The variables whose observations constitute our data will be given the same name as the type of data. Thus, for example, interval data are the observations of an interval variable.

2-1d Problem Objectives and Information

In presenting the different types of data, we introduced a critical factor in deciding which statistical procedure to use. A second factor is the type of information we need to produce from our data. We discuss the different types of information in greater detail in Section 11-4 when we introduce *problem objectives*. However, in this part of the book (Chapters 2–5), we will use statistical techniques to describe a set of data, compare two or more sets of data, and describe the relationship between two variables. In Section 2-2, we introduce graphical and tabular techniques employed to describe a set of nominal data. Section 2-3 shows how to describe the relationship between two nominal variables and compare two or more sets of nominal data.

EXERCISES

2.1 Provide two examples each of nominal, ordinal, and interval data.

2.2 For each of the following examples of data, determine the type.
  a. The number of miles joggers run per week
  b. The starting salaries of graduates of MBA programs
  c. The months in which a firm's employees choose to take their vacations
  d. The final letter grades received by students in a statistics course

2.3 For each of the following examples of data, determine the type.
  a. The weekly closing price of the stock of Amazon.com
  b. The month of highest vacancy rate at a La Quinta motel
  c. The size of soft drink (small, medium, or large) ordered by a sample of McDonald's customers
  d. The number of Toyotas imported monthly by the United States over the last 5 years
  e. The marks achieved by the students in a statistics course final exam marked out of 100

2.4 The placement office at a university regularly surveys the graduates 1 year after graduation and asks for the following information. For each, determine the type of data.
   a. What is your occupation?
   b. What is your income?
   c. What degree did you obtain?
   d. What is the amount of your student loan?
   e. How would you rate the quality of instruction? (excellent, very good, good, fair, poor)

2.5 Residents of condominiums were recently surveyed and asked a series of questions. Identify the type of data for each question.
   a. What is your age?
   b. On what floor is your condominium?
   c. Do you own or rent?
   d. How large is your condominium (in square feet)?
   e. Does your condominium have a pool?

2.6 A sample of shoppers at a mall was asked the following questions. Identify the type of data each question would produce.
   a. What is your age?
   b. How much did you spend?
   c. What is your marital status?
   d. Rate the availability of parking: excellent, good, fair, or poor
   e. How many stores did you enter?

2.7 Information about a magazine's readers is of interest to both the publisher and the magazine's advertisers. A survey of readers asked respondents to complete the following:
   a. Age
   b. Gender
   c. Marital status
   d. Number of magazine subscriptions
   e. Annual income
   f. Rate the quality of our magazine: excellent, good, fair, or poor

   For each item identify the resulting data type.

2.8 Baseball fans are regularly asked to offer their opinions about various aspects of the sport. A survey asked the following questions. Identify the type of data.
   a. How many games do you attend annually?
   b. How would you rate the quality of entertainment? (excellent, very good, good, fair, poor)
   c. Do you have season tickets?
   d. How would you rate the quality of the food? (edible, barely edible, horrible)

2.9 A survey of golfers asked the following questions. Identify the type of data each question produces.
   a. How many rounds of golf do you play annually?
   b. Are you a member of a private club?
   c. What brand of clubs do you own?

2.10 At the end of the term, university and college students often complete questionnaires about their courses. Suppose that in one university, students were asked the following.
   a. Rate the course (highly relevant, relevant, irrelevant)
   b. Rate the professor (very effective, effective, not too effective, not at all effective)
   c. What was your midterm grade (A, B, C, D, F)?

   Determine the type of data each question produces.

2.11 A survey of taxpayers who complete their own tax returns were asked the following questions. Determine the type of data each question produces.
   a. Did you use software?
   b. How long did it take you to complete this year's return?
   c. Rate the ease with which you completed this year's return (very easy, quite easy, neither easy or difficult, quite difficult, very difficult)

2.12 A random sample of car owners was asked these questions. Identify the type of data.
   a. Make of car
   b. Age of your car in months
   c. Amount of annual insurance
   d. Number of miles on odometer

2-2 / DESCRIBING A SET OF NOMINAL DATA

As we discussed in Section 2-1, the only allowable calculation on nominal data is to count the frequency or compute the percentage that each value of the variable represents. We can summarize the data in a table, which presents the categories and their counts, called a **frequency distribution**. A **relative frequency distribution** lists the categories and the proportion with which each occurs. We can use graphical techniques to present a picture of the data. There are two graphical methods we can use: the bar chart and the pie chart.

EXAMPLE **2.1**

Work Status in the GSS 2014 Survey

A major problem with the official unemployment rate is that it excludes people who have given up trying to find a job even though they would like to find employment. In an effort to track the numbers of Americans in the various categories of work status the GSS asked "Last week were you working full time, part time, going to school, keeping house, or what?" The responses are as follows:

1. Working full time
2. Working part time
3. Temporarily not working
4. Unemployed, laid off
5. Retired
6. School
7. Keeping house
8. Other

The responses were recorded using the codes 1,2,3,4,5,6,7, and 8, respectively. The first 150 observations are listed here. The name of the variable is WRKSTAT and is stored in Column X. Construct a frequency and relative frequency distribution for these data and graphically summarize the data by producing a bar chart and a pie chart.

1	7	1	7	2	1	2	8	1	1	1	1	7	1	1
1	8	7	1	5	1	1	5	4	5	1	1	5	1	1
4	5	7	3	8	1	8	1	4	8	1	1	2	5	1
2	1	6	1	1	7	1	1	7	2	1	1	5	3	1
5	6	1	1	1	1	1	1	7	4	1	7	1	8	5
1	2	2	1	1	2	1	7	7	3	1	1	5	1	3
9	2	1	1	1	5	1	1	4	3	5	7	5	1	1
1	1	1	1	1	1	1	1	1	1	5	1	1	5	7
8	1	1	2	1	1	1	7	1	1	1	1	1	1	1
1	1	1	1	1	7	1	8	1	4	1	1	5	1	1

SOLUTION:

Scan the data. Have you learned anything about the responses of these 150 Americans? Unless you have special skills you have probably learned little about the numbers. If we had listed all 2,536 observations you would be even less likely to discover anything useful about the data. To extract useful information requires the application of a statistical or graphical technique. To choose the appropriate technique we must first identify the type of data. In this example the data are nominal because the numbers represent categories. The only calculation permitted on nominal data is to count the number of occurrences of each category. Hence, we count the number of 1s, 2s, 3s, 4s, 5s, 6s, 7s, and 8s. The list of the categories and their counts constitute the frequency distribution. The relative frequency distribution is produced by converting the frequencies into proportions. The frequency and the relative frequency distributions are combined in Table 2.1.

There were two individuals who refused to answer resulting in a total of 2,536 observations.

As promised in Chapter 1 (and in the preface) here are the Excel outputs and instructions on how to produce the frequency and the relative frequency distributions and specifically how to get the results shown in Table 2.1.

TABLE **2.1** **Frequency and Relative Frequency Distributions for Example 2.1**

WORK STATUS	CODE	FREQUENCY	RELATIVE FREQUENCY (%)
Working full time	1	1,230	48.5
Working part time	2	273	10.8
Temporarily not working	3	40	1.6
Unemployed, laid off	4	104	4.1
Retired	5	460	18.1
School	6	90	3.5
Keeping house	7	263	10.4
Other	8	76	3.0
Total		2,536	100

EXCEL

INSTRUCTIONS

(Specific commands for this example are highlighted.)

1. Type or import the data into one or more columns. (Open GSS2014)
2. Activate any empty cell and type

$$=COUNTIF \text{ ([Input range], [Criteria])}$$

Input range are the cells containing the data. In this example, the range is X1:X2539. The criteria are the codes you want to count: (1) (2) (3) (4) (5) (6) (7) (8). For example, to count the number of 1s (Working full time), type

$$=COUNTIF \text{ (X1:X2539, 1)}$$

and the frequency will appear in the active cell. Change the criteria to produce the frequency of the remaining seven categories. To produce the printout below we copied the WRKSTAT variable into Column A in a new spreadsheet. We typed the codes 1 to 8 in rows 1 to 8 in Column B and then employed COUNTIF to get the frequencies. Column C calculated the relative frequencies.

	A	B	C
1	**WRKSTAT**	**Count**	**Percent**
2	*1*	*1230*	*48.5%*
3	*2*	*273*	*10.8%*
4	*3*	*40*	*1.6%*
5	*4*	*104*	*4.1%*
6	*5*	*460*	*18.1%*
7	*6*	*90*	*3.5%*
8	*7*	*263*	*10.4%*
9	*8*	*76*	*3.0%*

INTERPRET

Only 48.5% of respondents were working full time, 18.1% were retired, 10.4% were keeping house, 10.8% were working part time, and the remaining 12.2% were in one of the other four categories.

Bar and Pie Charts

The information contained in the data is summarized well in the table. However, graphical techniques generally catch a reader's eye more quickly than does a table of numbers. Two graphical techniques can be used to display the results shown in the table. A bar chart is often used to display frequencies; a pie chart graphically shows relative frequencies. The bar chart is created by drawing a rectangle representing each category. The height of the rectangle represents the frequency. The base is arbitrary. Figure 2.1 depicts the manually drawn bar chart for Example 2.1.

FIGURE **2.1** Bar Chart for Example 2.1

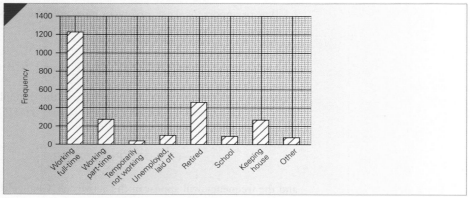

If we wish to emphasize the relative frequencies instead of drawing the bar chart, we draw a pie chart. A pie chart is simply a circle subdivided into slices that represent the categories. It is drawn so that the size of each slice is proportional to the percentage corresponding to that category. For example, because the entire circle is composed of 360 degrees, a category that contains 25% of the observations is represented by a slice of the pie that contains 25% of 360 degrees, which is equal to 90 degrees. The number of degrees for each category in Example 2.1 is shown in Table 2.2.

TABLE **2.2** **Proportion in Each Category in Example 2.1**

WORK STATUS	RELATIVE FREQUENCY (%)	SLICE OF THE PIE (°)
Working full time	48.5	174.6
Working part time	10.8	38.9
Temporarily not working	1.6	5.8
Unemployed, laid off	4.1	14.8
Retired	18.1	65.1
School	3.5	12.6
Keeping house	10.4	37.4
Other	3.0	10.8
Total	100.0	360

EXCEL

Here is Excel version of the bar and pie charts for Example 2.1.

INSTRUCTIONS

1. After creating the frequency distribution, highlight the column of frequencies.
2. For a bar chart, click **Insert**, **Column**, and the first **2-D Column**. You can make changes to the chart. We removed the **Gridlines**, **Legend**, and clicked the **Data Labels** to create the titles.
3. For a pie chart, click **Pie** and **Chart Tools** to edit the graph.

Working with the General Social Survey and the Survey of Consumer Finances

There are hundreds of exercises scattered throughout this book that use the data in the General Social Survey and the Survey of Consumer Finances. Here are some hints on how to work with these data.

1. After you have downloaded all the data sets we recommend that you store them all onto your computer. Make no changes to these files.

2. To work with one or more columns we suggest that you copy the column or columns into a new spreadsheet. For example, in this example we need Column X (WRKSTAT) in the GSS2014 file. Copy the entire column into Column A of another worksheet. Then use the new spreadsheet to conduct any graphical or numerical technique.

3. To take a subset of any column of data use the DATA and SORT commands. Suppose that we are interested in the work status of respondents who have completed a graduate degree (DEGREE: 4 = graduate). Proceed as follows.

    Copy Column T (DEGREE) into Column A of a new worksheet.

    Copy Column X (WRKSTAT) into Column B.

    Highlight both columns.

    Click **DATA** and **SORT**.

    Specify **Sort by** Column A (or use the name of the variable).

    Scroll down Column A until you reach the rows containing 4s.

    Use the data in Column B to conduct your statistical analysis.

2-2a Other Applications of Pie Charts and Bar Charts

Pie and bar charts are used widely in newspapers, magazines, and business and government reports. One reason for this appeal is that they are eye-catching and can attract the reader's interest whereas a table of numbers might not. Perhaps no one understands this better than the newspaper *USA Today*, which typically has a colored graph on the front page and others inside. Pie and bar charts are frequently used to simply present numbers associated with categories. The only reason to use a bar or pie chart in such a situation would be to enhance the reader's ability to grasp the substance of the data. It might, for example, allow the reader to more quickly recognize the relative sizes of the categories, as in the breakdown of a budget. Similarly, treasurers might use pie charts to show the breakdown of a firm's revenues by department, or university students might use pie charts to show the amount of time devoted to daily activities (e.g., eat 10%, sleep 30%, and study statistics 60%).

APPLICATIONS in **ECONOMICS**

Macroeconomics

Macroeconomics is a major branch of economics that deals with the behavior of the economy as a whole. Macroeconomists develop mathematical models that predict variables such as gross domestic product, unemployment rates, and inflation. These are used by governments and corporations to help develop strategies. For example, central banks attempt to control inflation by lowering or raising interest rates. To do this requires that economists determine the effect of a variety of variables, including the supply and demand for energy.

APPLICATIONS in **ECONOMICS**

Energy Economics

One variable that has had a large influence on the economies of virtually every country is energy. The 1973 oil crisis in which the price of oil quadrupled over a short period of time is generally considered to be one of the largest financial shocks to our economy. In fact, economists often refer to two different economies: before the 1973 oil crisis and after. Unfortunately, the world will be facing more shocks to our economy because of energy for two primary reasons. The first is the depletion of nonrenewable sources of energy and the resulting price increases. The second is the possibility that burning fossil fuels and the creation of carbon dioxide may be the cause of global warming. One economist predicted that the cost of global warming will be calculated in trillions of dollars. Statistics can play an important role by determining whether Earth's temperature has been increasing and, if so, whether carbon dioxide is the cause. (See Case 3.1.) In this chapter, you will encounter other examples and exercises that involve the issue of energy.

EXAMPLE 2.2

DATA
Xm02-02

Energy Consumption in the United States in 2015

Table 2.3 lists the total energy consumption of the United States from all sources in 2015 (latest data available at publication). To make it easier to see the details, the table measures the energy in quadrillions of British thermal units (BTUs). Use an appropriate graphical technique to depict these figures.

TABLE **2.3** **Energy Consumption in the United States by Source, 2012**

ENERGY SOURCES	QUADRILLIONS OF BTUs
Nonrenewable Energy Sources	
Petroleum	34.78
Natural gas	26.59
Coal and coal products	17.99
Nuclear	8.33
Renewable Energy Sources	
Biofuels	3.89
Hydroelectric	2.47
Wind	1.73
Waste	0.47
Solar	0.43
Geothermal	0.22
Total	96.90

Source: U.S. Energy Administration.

SOLUTION:

We are interested in describing the proportion of total energy consumption for each source. Thus, the appropriate technique is the pie chart. The next step is to determine the proportions and sizes of the pie slices from which the pie chart is drawn. The following pie chart was created by Excel.

EXCEL

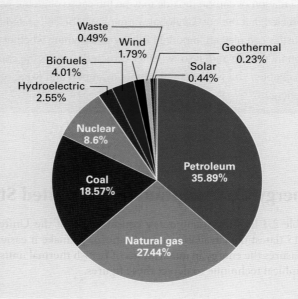

INTERPRET

The United States depends heavily on petroleum, coal, and natural gas. More than 80% of national energy use is based on these sources. The renewable energy sources amount to less than 9%, of which about a third is hydroelectric and probably cannot be expanded much further. Wind and solar barely appear in the chart. See Exercises 2.13 to 2.18 for more information on the subject.

EXAMPLE 2.3

DATA
Xm02-03

Beer Consumption (Top 20 Countries)

Table 2.4 lists the per capita beer consumption for each of the top 20 countries around the world. Graphically present these numbers.

TABLE **2.4** Beer Consumption, Top 20 Countries

COUNTRY	PER CAPITA BEER CONSUMPTION (L/YR)
Australia	109.9
Austria	108.3
Belgium	93.0
Croatia	81.2
Czech Republic	156.9
Denmark	89.9
Estonia	104.0
Finland	85.0
Germany	115.8
Hungary	75.3
Ireland	131.3
Lithuania	89.0
Luxembourg	84.5
Netherlands	79.0
New Zealand	77.0
Romania	90.0
Slovakia	84.1
Spain	83.8
United Kingdom	99.0
United States	81.6

Source: www.beerinfo.com.

SOLUTION:

In this example, we are primarily interested in the numbers. There is no use in presenting proportions here. The following is Excel version of the bar chart.

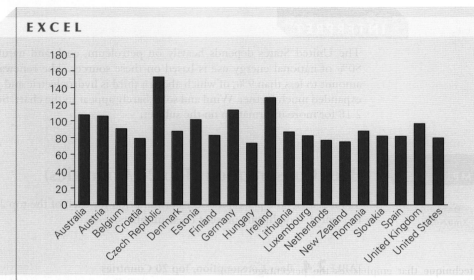

EXCEL

INTERPRET

The Czech Republic, Ireland, and Germany head the list. Both the United States and the United Kingdom rank far lower. Surprised?

2-2b Describing Ordinal Data

There are no specific graphical techniques for ordinal data. Consequently, when we wish to describe a set of ordinal data, we will treat the data as if they were nominal and use the techniques described in this section. The only criterion is that the bars in bar charts should be arranged in ascending (or descending) ordinal values; in pie charts, the wedges are typically arranged clockwise in ascending or descending order.

We complete this section by describing when bar and pie charts are used to summarize and present data.

Factors That Identify When to Use Frequency and Relative Frequency Tables, and Bar and Pie Charts

1. Objective: Describe a single set of data.
2. Data type: Nominal or ordinal

EXERCISES

2.13 <u>Xr02-13</u> When will the world run out of oil? One way to judge is to determine the oil reserves of the countries around the world. The next table displays the known reserves of the top 15 countries. Graphically describe the figures.

Country	Oil Reserves (Barrels)
Brazil	15,310,000,000
Canada	172,500,000,000
China	24,650,000,000
Iran	157,800,000,000

Country	Oil Reserves (Barrels)
Iraq	144,200,000,000
Kazakhstan	30,000,000,000
Kuwait	104,000,000,000
Libya	48,360,000,000
Nigeria	37,070,000,000
Qatar	25,240,000,000
Russia	103,200,000,000
Saudi Arabia	268,300,000,000
United Arab Emirates	97,800,000,000
United States	36,520,000,000
Venezuela	298,400,000,000

Source: CIA World Factbook 2015.

2.14 [Refer to Exercise 2.13.] The total reserves of oil in the world are 1,689,078,618,100 barrels. The total reserves of the top 15 countries listed in Exercise 2.13 are 1,563,350,000,000 barrels. Use a graphical technique that emphasizes the percentage breakdown of the top 15 countries.

2.15 Xr02-15 The following table lists the average oil consumption per day of the top 20 oil-consuming nations. Use a graphical technique to display this information.

Country	Consumption of Oil (Barrels per Day)
Australia	1,082,000
Brazil	3,003,000
Canada	2,413,000
China	10,480,000
France	1,706,000
Germany	2,399,000
India	3,660,000
Indonesia	1,718,000
Iran	1,885,000
Italy	1,235,000
Japan	4,297,000
Mexico	1,966,000
Russia	2,800,000
Saudi Arabia	2,961,000
Singapore	1,240,000
South Korea	2,350,000
Spain	1,209,000
Thailand	1,171,000
United Kingdom	1,505,000
United States	19,030,000

Source: CIA World Factbook 2015.

2.16 Xr02-16 There are 42 gallons in a barrel of oil. The number of products produced and the proportion of the total are listed in the following table. Draw a graph to depict these numbers.

Product	Proportion
Gasoline	51.4
Distillate fuel oil	15.3
Jet fuel	12.6
Still gas	5.4
Marketable coke	5.0
Residual fuel oil	3.3
Liquefied refinery gas	2.8
Asphalt and road oil	1.9
Lubricants	0.9
Other	1.5

Source: California Energy Commission

2.17 Xr02-17 The table below lists the electricity consumption (in Kilowatt-hours) in the top 20 electricity using countries. Graph the numbers to help describe the figures.

Country	Electricity Consumption (Kilowatt-Hours)
Australia	222,600,000,000
Brazil	483,500,000,000
Canada	524,800,000,000
China	5,523,000,000,000
European Union	2,771,000,000,000
France	451,100,000,000
Germany	540,100,000,000
India	864,700,000,000
Italy	303,100,000,000
Japan	921,000,000,000
Korea, South	482,400,000,000
Mexico	234,000,000,000
Russia	1,065,000,000,000
Saudi Arabia	231,600,000,000
South Africa	211,600,000,000
Spain	243,100,000,000
Taiwan	224,300,000,000
Turkey	197,000,000,000
United Kingdom	319,100,000,000
United States	3,832,000,000,000

Source: International Energy Association.

2.18 Xr02-18 The planet may be threatened by global warming/climate change, possibly caused by burning fossil fuels (petroleum, natural gas, and coal) that produced carbon dioxide (CO_2). The following table lists the top 15 producers of CO_2 and the annual amounts (in millions of metric tons) from fossil fuels. Graphically depict these figures.

Country	CO_2 (Millions of Metric Tons)
Australia	417.7
Canada	541.0

(Continued)

Country	CO$_2$ (Millions of Metric Tons)
China	7706.8
Germany	765.6
India	1591.1
Iran	528.6
Italy	407.9
Japan	1098.0
Korea, South	528.1
Mexico	443.6
Russia	1556.7
Saudi Arabia	438.2
South Africa	451.2
United Kingdom	519.9
United States	5424.5

Source: The Statistical Abstract of the United States, 2012, Table 1389.

2.19 <u>Xr02-19</u> The production of steel has often been used as a measure of the economic strength of a country. The next table lists the steel produced in the 20 largest steel-producing nations in 2014. The units are millions of metric tons. Use a graphical technique to display these figures.

Country	Steel Production (Millions of Metric Tons)	Country	Steel Production (Millions of Metric Tons)
Austria	7.9	Poland	8.6
Brazil	33.9	Russia	71.5
Canada	12.7	South Korea	71.5
China	822.7	Spain	14.2
France	16.1	Taiwan	23.1
Germany	42.9	Turkey	34.0
India	86.5	Ukraine	27.2
Iran	16.3	United	
Italy	23.7	Kingdom	12.1
Japan	110.7	United	
Mexico	19.0	States	88.2

Source: World Steel Association, 2014.

2.20 Last year the world generated almost 2.6 trillion pounds of garbage. Here is a breakdown of the amounts of garbage produced by different regions of the world. Use a graphical technique to present these statistics.

Region	Amount of Garbage
Latin America and Caribbean (LAC)	322,065,200,000
Europe and Central Asia (ECA)	184,408,300,000
Middle East and North Africa (MENA)	161,032,600,000
South Asia (SAR)	132,462,300,000
Africa (AFR)	127,267,700,000
East Asia and Pacific (EAP)	535,043,800,000
Organization for Economic Cooperation and Development (OECD)	1,135,020,100,000

2.21 Refer to Exercise 2.20. The table below is breakdown of types and amounts of garbage the world creates. Use an appropriate graphical technique to present these figures.

Type	Amount of Garbage
Organic	1,189,563,400,000
Paper	446,735,600,000
Plastic	267,521,900,000
Glass	132,462,300,000
Metal	106,489,300,000
Other	454,527,500,000

2.22 <u>Xr02-22</u> The following table lists the top 10 countries and the amounts of oil (in thousands of barrels per day) they exported to the United States in 2015.

Country	Oil Imports (Thousands of Barrels per Day)
Angola	124
Brazil	189
Canada	3,169
Colombia	370
Ecuador	225
Iraq	229
Kuwait	206
Mexico	688
Saudi Arabia	1,051
Venezuela	779

Use an appropriate graphical technique to summarize these figures.

2.23 <u>Xr02-23</u> Each year Michigan State University's Collegiate Employment Research Institute (CERI) conducts a broad-based survey that tracks starting salaries. This year CERI collected data from the employment offices at 200 universities, which gathered starting salaries from 3,300 employers. The table below lists the undergraduate degrees with the 25 highest average starting salaries. Use an appropriate graphical technique to display the results.

University Degree	Average Starting Salary ($)
Accounting	44,525
Advertising	36,638
Agricultural Sciences	38,854
Biology	38,806
Chemistry	43,344
Civil Engineering	51,622
Construction	45,591
Economics	41,118
Finance	44,699
Human Resources	42,495
Humanities and Liberal Arts	39,162
Marketing	41,481
Mathematics	47,952
Nursing	43,481
Psychology	36,973
Public Relations	38,568
Social Work	36,639
Supply Chain	45,508

2.24 Xr02-24   The following table lists the annual world production of 21 fruits (in millions of metric tons). Use a graphical technique to present these figures.

Fruit	Annual Production (Millions of Metric Tons)
Apples	80.82
Apricots	4.11
Avocados	4.72
Bananas	106.71
Cherries	2.29
Dates	7.68
Grapefruits	8.45
Grapes	77.18
Kiwi Fruit	3.26
Lemons & Limes	15.19
Mangoes	43.3
Oranges	71.45
Papayas	12.42
Peaches & Nectarines	21.64
Pears	25.2
Persimmons	4.64
Pineapples	24.79
Plantains	37.88
Plums and Sloes	11.53
Strawberries	7.74
Tangerines	28.68

Source: Team Market Report, Matthew Coutts.

2.25 Xr02-25   Governments in both Canada and the United States have considered passing legislation that increases the minimum hourly wage to $15. The current (as of October 2015) minimum hourly wage in each Canadian province and the percentage of employees earning the minimum wage was recorded and listed below. Use a graphical technique to present these figures.

Province	Minimum Wage	Percent Earning Minimum Wage
Alberta	10.20	2.20%
British Columbia	10.45	5.60%
Saskatchewan	10.20	3.30%
Manitoba	10.70	4.90%
Ontario	11.25	11.70%
Quebec	10.55	5.90%
New Brunswick	10.30	7.00%
Nova Scotia	10.60	5.60%
Prince Edward Island	10.50	6.00%
Newfoundland and Labrador	10.50	5.90%

The following exercises require a computer and software.

2.26 Xr02-26   What are the most important characteristics of colleges and universities? This question was asked of a sample of college-bound high school seniors. The responses are as follows:

1. Location
2. Majors
3. Academic reputation
4. Career focus
5. Community
6. Number of students

The results were stored using the codes. Use a graphical technique to summarize and present the data.

2.27 Xr02-27   Where do consumers get information about cars? A sample of recent car buyers was asked to identify the most useful source of information about the cars they purchased. The responses are as follows:

1. Consumer guide
2. Dealership
3. Word of mouth
4. Internet

The responses were stored using the codes. Graphically depict these responses.

Source: Automotive Retailing Today, the Gallup Organization.

2.28 Xr02-28 A survey asked 392 homeowners which area of the home they would most like to renovate. The responses and frequencies are shown next. Use a graphical technique to present these results. Briefly summarize your findings.

Area	Code
Basement	1
Bathroom	2
Bedroom	3
Kitchen	4
Living/dining room	5

2.29 Xr02-29 Subway train riders frequently pass the time by reading a newspaper. New York City has a subway and four newspapers. A sample of 360 subway riders who regularly read a newspaper was asked to identify that newspaper. The responses are as follows:

1. *New York Daily News*
2. *New York Post*
3. *New York Times*
4. *Wall Street Journal*

The responses were recorded using the numerical codes shown.

a. Produce a frequency distribution and a relative frequency distribution.
b. Draw an appropriate graph to summarize the data. What does the graph tell you?

2.30 Xr02-30 Who applies to MBA programs? To help determine the background of the applicants, a sample of 230 applicants to a university's business school was asked to report their undergraduate degree. The degrees were recorded using these codes.

1. BA
2. BBA
3. B.Eng
4. BSc
5. Other

a. Determine the frequency distribution.
b. Draw a bar chart.
c. Draw a pie chart.
d. What do the charts tell you about the sample of MBA applicants?

2.31 Xr02-31 Many business and economics courses require the use of computer, so students often must buy their own computers. A survey asks students to identify which computer brand they have purchased. The responses are as follows:

1. HP
2. Lenovo
3. Dell
4. Other

a. Use a graphical technique that depicts the frequencies.
b. Graphically depict the proportions.
c. What do the charts tell you about the brands of computers used by the students?

2.32 Xr02-32 An increasing number of statistics courses use a computer and software rather than manual calculations. A survey of statistics instructors asked each to report the software his or her course uses. The responses are as follows:

1. Excel
2. Minitab
3. SAS
4. SPSS
5. Other

a. Produce a frequency distribution.
b. Graphically summarize the data so that the proportions are depicted.
c. What do the charts tell you about the software choices?

2.33 Xr02-33* The total light beer sales in the United States is approximately 3 million gallons annually. With this large a market, breweries often need to know more about who is buying their product. The marketing manager of a major brewery wanted to analyze the light beer sales among college and university students who do drink light beer. A random sample of 285 graduating students was asked to report which of the following is their favorite light beer:

1. Bud Light
2. Busch Light
3. Coors Light
4. Michelob Light
5. Miller Lite
6. Natural Light
7. Other brands

The responses were recorded using the codes 1, 2, 3, 4, 5, 6, and 7, respectively. Use a graphical technique to summarize these data. What can you conclude from the chart?

Opinion Surveys: Pew Research Center and the Gallup Organization

There are numerous organizations that conduct surveys for political parties, government agencies, and private corporations. Two of the most famous are the Pew Research Center and the Gallup Organization. Both conduct nonpartisan public opinion surveys, which are published in newspapers and discussed on television newscasts. We will use some of their results throughout this book to create exercises whose data sets will produce the same results as the original study.

In the next seven exercises we specify the date, the population surveyed, the question, and the codes representing the responses.

2.34 Xr02-34*   Pew Research Center

Date: June 2015

Population: Americans who are most likely to vote, donate to campaigns, and participate directly in politics. (They comprise about 20% of all Americans.)

Question: Views of their close friends.

Responses:

1. Many close friends share my views on government and politics.
2. Some of my close friends share my views but many do not.
3. I don't really know what my close friends think.

Use a graphical method to describe the results of the survey.

2.35 Xr02-35*   Gallup Organization

Date: April 2016

Population: American adults

Question: "As I read off some different groups, please tell me if you think they are paying their FAIR share in federal taxes, paying too MUCH or paying too LITTLE? First, how about upper-income people?

Responses:

1. Fair share
2. Too much
3. Too little
4. No opinion

a. Determine the frequency and the relative frequency distributions.
b. Draw a bar chart.
c. Draw a pie chart.
d. Briefly describe your findings.

2.36 Xr02-36   Pew Research Center

Date: December 2015

Population: American adults

Question 1: "Which Social Class does the Republican Party favor?"

Question 2: "Which Social Class does the Democratic Party favor?" (Each question was posed to a different sample.)

Responses:

1. Rich
2. Middle class
3. Poor

a. For each question draw a pie chart.
b. What do the pie charts tell you about Americans' perception of the Republican and Democratic parties?

2.37 Xr02-37   Pew Research Center

Date: November 2015

Population: Married, two-parent households with at least one child under 18

Question: How do working parents share the work load at home?

Responses:

1. Mom: Full time; Dad: Full time
2. Mom: Part time; Dad: Full time
3. Mom: Not employed; Dad: Full time
4. Mom: Full time; Dad: Part time or not employed
5. Mom: Not employed; Dad: Not employed
6. Other

a. Create the frequency and the relative frequency distributions.
b. Draw a pie chart.
c. Draw a bar chart.
d. Describe your results.

Pew Research Center

2.38 Xr02-38* Gallup Organization

Date: May 2016

Population: American adults

Question "Please tell me whether you strongly favor or strongly oppose keeping the Affordable Care Act in place.

Responses:

1. Favor
2. Oppose
3. No opinion

Use a graphical technique to summarize these data. Describe what you discovered.

2.39 Xr02-39* Gallup Organization

Date: May 2016

Population: American adults

Question: "Describe your views on social issues."

Responses:

1. Liberal
2. Moderate
3. Conservative

a. Determine the frequency and the relative frequency distributions.
b. Draw a pie chart and describe the results.

2.40 Xr02-40* Gallup Organization

Date: May 2016

Population: American adults

Question: "Describe your views on economic issues."

Responses:

1. Liberal
2. Moderate
3. Conservative

a. Determine the frequency and the relative frequency distributions.
b. Draw a pie chart and describe the results.

Gallup Organization

2-3 / DESCRIBING THE RELATIONSHIP BETWEEN TWO NOMINAL VARIABLES AND COMPARING TWO OR MORE NOMINAL DATA SETS

In Section 2-2, we presented graphical and tabular techniques used to summarize a set of nominal data. Techniques applied to single sets of data are called **univariate**. There are many situations where we wish to depict the relationship between variables; in such cases, **bivariate** methods are required. A **cross-classification table** (also called a **cross-tabulation table**) is used to describe the relationship between two nominal variables. A variation of the bar chart introduced in Section 2-2 is employed to graphically describe the relationship. The same technique is used to compare two or more sets of nominal data.

2-3a Tabular Method of Describing the Relationship between Two Nominal Variables

To describe the relationship between two nominal variables, we must remember that we are permitted only to determine the frequency of the values. As a first step, we need to produce a cross-classification table that lists the frequency of each combination of the values of the two variables.

EXAMPLE 2.4

DATA
Xm02-04

Newspaper Readership Survey

A major North American city has four competing newspapers: the Globe and Mail (G&M), Post, Star, and Sun. To help design advertising campaigns, the advertising managers of the newspapers need to know which segments of the newspaper market are reading their papers. A survey was conducted to analyze the relationship between newspapers read and occupation. A sample of newspaper readers was asked to report which newspaper they read—Globe and Mail (1), Post (2), Star (3), and Sun (4)—and indicate whether they were blue-collar workers (1), white-collar workers (2), or professionals (3). Some of the data are listed here.

Reader	Occupation	Newspaper
1	2	2
2	1	4
3	2	1
⋮	⋮	⋮
352	3	2
353	1	3
354	2	3

Determine whether the two nominal variables are related.

SOLUTION:

By counting the number of times each of the 12 combinations occurs, we produced the Table 2.5.

TABLE **2.5** Cross-Classification Table of Frequencies for Example 2.4

OCCUPATION	NEWSPAPER				
	G&M	POST	STAR	SUN	TOTAL
Blue collar	27	18	38	37	120
White collar	29	43	21	15	108
Professional	33	51	22	20	126
Total	89	112	81	72	354

If occupation and newspaper are related, there will be differences in the newspapers read among the occupations. An easy way to see this is to convert the frequencies in each row (or column) to relative frequencies in each row (or column). That is, compute the row (or column) totals and divide each frequency by its row (or column) total, as shown in Table 2.6. Totals may not equal 1 because of rounding.

TABLE **2.6** Cross-Classification Table of Row proportions for Example 2.4

OCCUPATION	NEWSPAPER				
	G&M	POST	STAR	SUN	TOTAL
Blue collar	.23	.15	.32	.31	1.00
White collar	.27	.40	.19	.14	1.00
Professional	.26	.40	.17	.16	1.00
Total	.25	.32	.23	.20	1.00

EXCEL

Excel can produce the cross-classification table using several methods. We will use and describe the PivotTable in two ways: (1) to create the cross-classification table featuring the counts and (2) to produce a table showing the row relative frequencies.

	A	B	C	D	E	F
1	Count of Reader	Column Labels ▼				
2	Row Labels ▼		1	2	3	4 Grand Total
3	1		27	18	38	37	120
4	2		29	43	21	15	108
5	3		33	51	22	20	126
6	Grand Total		89	112	81	72	354

	A	B	C	D	E	F
	Count of Reader	Column Labels ▼				
	Row Labels ▼		1	2	3	4 Grand Total
	1		0.23	0.15	0.32	0.31	1.00
	2		0.27	0.40	0.19	0.14	1.00
	3		0.26	0.40	0.17	0.16	1.00
	Grand Total		0.25	0.32	0.23	0.20	1.00

INSTRUCTIONS

The data must be stored in (at least) three columns as we have done in Xm02-04. Put the cursor somewhere in the data range.

1. Click **Insert** and **PivotTable**.
2. Make sure that the **Table/Range** is correct. Click **OK**.
3. In the **PivotTable Fields** Click **Occupation**, right click and choose **Add to Row Labels**.
4. Click **Newspaper**, right click and choose **Add to Column Labels**.
5. Place the cursor in the table and right click **Summarize Values by** and click **Count**.
6. To convert to row percentages, right-click any number, click **Show Values As** and click **% of rows**. We then formatted the data into decimals.

XLSTAT

Another method of creating the cross-classification table is through XLSTAT.

	A	B	C	D	E
1	Contingency table (Occupation / Newspaper):				
2					
3		1	2	3	4
4	1	27	18	38	37
5	2	29	43	21	15
6	3	33	51	22	20

INSTRUCTIONS

1. Click **XLSTAT**.
2. Click **Tests on contingency tables (Chi-square...)**.
3. Click **Qualitative variables**.
4. Specify **Row variable(s)** (B1:B355).
5. Specify **Column variable(s)** (C1:C355).
6. Click **Variable labels** if the first row contains the names of the variables.

INTERPRET

Notice that the relative frequencies in the second and third rows are similar and that there are large differences between row 1 and rows 2 and 3. This tells us that blue-collar workers tend to read different newspapers from both white-collar workers and professionals and that white-collar workers and professionals are quite similar in their newspaper choices.

Graphing the Relationship between Two Nominal Variables

We have chosen to draw three bar charts, one for each occupation depicting the four newspapers. We'll use Excel for this purpose. The manually drawn charts are identical.

EXCEL

There are several ways to graphically display the relationship between two nominal variables. We have chosen two-dimensional bar charts for each of the three occupations. The charts can be created from the output of the PivotTable either with counts or with row proportions (as we have done).

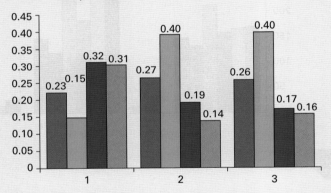

INSTRUCTIONS

From the cross-classification table, click **Insert** and **Column**. You can do the same from any completed cross-classification table.

INTERPRET

If the two variables are unrelated, then the patterns exhibited in the bar charts should be approximately the same. If some relationship exists, then some bar charts will differ from others.

The graphs tell us the same story as did the table. The shapes of the bar charts for occupations 2 and 3 (white collar and professional) are very similar. Both differ considerably from the bar chart for occupation 1 (blue collar).

2-3b Comparing Two or More Sets of Nominal Data

We can interpret the results of the cross-classification table of the bar charts in a different way. In Example 2.4, we can consider the three occupations as defining three different populations. If differences exist between the columns of the frequency distributions (or between the bar charts), then we can conclude that differences exist among the three populations. Alternatively, we can consider the readership of the four newspapers as four different populations. If differences exist among the frequencies or the bar charts, then we conclude that there are differences between the four populations.

Do Male and Female Americans Differ in Their Political Party Affiliation?

Daniel Sofer/ Photos.com

Data
GSS2014*

Using the technique introduced above, we produced the Excel bar chart.

EXCEL

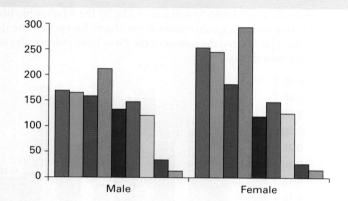

INTERPRET

Because of the way the categories were recorded the bar charts represent the frequencies of (in order from left to right) Strong Democrat, Not Strong Democrat, Independent, Near Democrat, Independent, Independent, Near Republican, Not Strong Republican, Strong Republican, Other Party, and Blank (No answer).

There are some similarities and some differences. For both men and women the most common party affiliation is Independent, followed by Strong Democrat and Not Strong Democrat. Women tend to classify themselves as Democrat more than do men; men tend to be Republican supporters more than do women.

2-3c Data Formats

There are several ways to store the data to be used in this section to produce a table or a bar or pie chart.

1. The data are in two columns. The first column represents the categories of the first nominal variable, and the second column stores the categories for the second. Each row represents one observation of the two variables. The number of observations in each column must be the same. Excel can produce a cross-classification table from these data. (To use Excel's PivotTable, there also must be a third variable representing the observation number.) This is the way the data for Example 2.4 were stored.

2. The data are stored in two or more columns, with each column representing the same variable in a different sample or population. For example, the variable may be the type of undergraduate degree of applicants to an MBA program, and there may be five universities we wish to compare. To produce a cross-classification table, we would have to count the number of observations of each category (undergraduate degree) in each column.

3. The table representing counts in a cross-classification table may have already been created.

We complete this section with the factors that identify the use of the techniques introduced here.

Factors That Identify When to Use a Cross-Classification Table
1. Objective: Describe the relationship between two variables and compare two or more sets of data.
2. Data type: Nominal

EXERCISES

2.41 Xr02-41 Has the educational level of adults changed over the past 15 years? To help answer this question the Bureau of Labor Statistics compiled the following table, which lists the number (1,000) of adults 25 years of age and older who are employed. Use a graphical technique to present these figures. Briefly describe what the chart tells you.

Education	2000	2005	2010	2015
Less than high school	27,854	28,017	25,711	24,582
High school	58,086	60,893	62,456	62,575
Some college	44,445	48,076	53,920	56,031
College graduate	44,845	52,381	59,840	68,945

Source: U.S. Census Bureau.

2.42 Xr02-42 How do governments spend the tax dollars they collect, and has this changed over the past decade? The following table displays state and local government expenditures for public works in years 1995, 2000, 2005, and 2008 in millions of dollars. Use a graphical technique to present these figures. Have the ways state and local governments spend money changed over the decade?

	1995	2000	2005	2008
Highways	77,109	101,336	124,602	153,515
Air transportation	8,397	13,160	17,962	21,264
Port facilities	2,309	3,141	3,896	4,940
Sewerage	23,583	28,052	36,599	46,679
Waste management	14,990	17,208	21,469	23,757
Water supply	28,041	35,789	45,799	55,215
Mass transit	25,719	31,883	44,310	50,944

Source: The Statistical Abstract of the United States, 2012, Table 438.

The following exercises require a computer and software.

2.43 Xr02-43 The average loss from robbery in the United States in 2014 (last year available) was $1,227. Suppose that an insurance analyst wanted to know whether the type of robbery differs in the years 1995, 2000, 2005, 2009, and 2014. A random sample of robbery reports was taken from each of these years and the types recorded using the codes that follow. Determine whether there are differences in the types of robberies over the 19-year span.

1. Street or highway
2. Commercial house
3. Gas station
4. Convenience store
5. Residence
6. Bank
7. Other

Source: Federal Bureau of Investigation

2.44 Xr02-44 The associate dean of a business school was looking for ways to improve the quality of the applicants to its MBA program. In particular she wanted to know whether the undergraduate degree of applicants differed among her school and the three nearby universities with MBA programs. She sampled 100 applicants of her program and an equal number from each of the other universities. She recorded their undergraduate degree (1 = BA, 2 = B.Eng, 3 = BBA, and 4 = Other) as well as the university (codes 1, 2, 3, and 4). Use a tabular technique to determine whether the undergraduate degree and the university each person applied to appear to be related.

2.45 Xr02-45 Is there brand loyalty among car owners in their purchases of gasoline? To help answer the question a random sample of car owners was asked to record the brand of gasoline in their last two purchases (1 = Exxon, 2 = Amoco, 3 = Texaco, and 4 = Other). Use a tabular technique to formulate your answer.

2.46 Xr02-46 The costs of smoking for individuals, companies for whom they work, and society in general is in the many billions of dollars. In an effort to reduce smoking various government and non-government organizations have undertaken information campaigns about the dangers of smoking. Most of these have been directed at young people. This raises the question: Are you more likely to smoke if your parents smoke? To shed light on the issue a sample of 20- to 40-year-old people was asked whether they smoked and whether their parents smoked. The results are stored the following way:

Column 1: 1 = do not smoke, 2 = smoke
Column 2: 1 = neither parent smoked,
2 = father smoked, 3 = mother smoked,
4 = both parents smoked

Use a tabular technique to produce the information you need.

2.47 Xr02-47 In 2009 there were 8,626,000 men and 6,199,000 women who were unemployed at some time during the year. A statistics practitioner wanted to investigate the reason for that unemployment status and whether the reasons differed by gender. A random sample of people 16 years of age and older was drawn. The reasons given for their status are as follows:

1. Lost job
2. Left job
3. Reentrants
4. New entrants

Determine whether there are differences between unemployed men and women in terms of the reasons for unemployment.

Source: U.S. Bureau of Labor Statistics.

2.48 Xr02-48 In 2010, the total number of prescriptions sold in the United States was 3,676,000 (*Source:* National Association of Drug Store Chains). The sales manager of a chain of drug stores wanted to determine whether changes in where the prescriptions were filled had changed. A survey of prescriptions was undertaken in 1995, 2000, 2005, and 2010. The year and type of each prescription were recorded using the codes below. Determine whether there are differences between the years.

1. Traditional chain store
2. Independent drug store
3. Mass merchant
4. Supermarket
5. Mail order

Adapted from the *Statistical Abstract of the United States,* 2012, Table 159.

2.49 Xr02-33* Refer to Exercise 2.33. Also recorded was the gender (1 = male, 2 = female) of the respondents. Use a graphical technique to determine whether the choice of light beers differs between genders.

The following exercises are based on the Pew Research Center and the Gallup Organization exercises.

2.50 Xr02-34* Exercise 2.34 presented the data from a Pew Research Center survey of American adults describing whether their friends share their political views. Also recorded were the political views of the respondents. The responses are as follows:

1. Consistent conservative
2. Mostly conservative
3. Mixed
4. Mostly liberal
5. Consistent liberal

Use a graphical technique to determine whether the responses to the question differs between the five political views.

2.51 <u>Xr02-35*</u> In Exercise 2.35 a Gallup survey asked American adults whether they believed that upper-income people are paying their fair share in federal taxes. Each respondent was also classified as

1. Conservative
2. Moderate
3. Liberal

Present a graphical method to determine whether there are differences between the three political groups in their responses to the issue of higher-income people paying their fair share of federal taxes.

2.52 <u>Xr02-38*</u> In addition to asking American adults whether they support keeping the Affordable Care Act the Gallup poll determined whether the respondents were 1. Democrats or 2. Republicans. Determine whether Democrats and Republicans differ in their support of the Affordable Care Act.

2.53 <u>Xr02-39*</u> Exercise 2.39 featured a Gallup survey of American adults asking whether they are liberal,

moderate or conservative on social issues. In addition, the survey asked respondents whether they considered themselves to be

1. Democrat
2. Independent
3. Republican

Develop a graph that depicts the differences between the three political parties with respect to their responses about social issues.

2.54 <u>Xr02-40*</u> The Gallup poll in Exercise 2.40 asked American adults about their views on economic issues. The survey also asked which political party they supported.

1. Democrat
2. Independent
3. Republican

Use a graphical technique to gauge the differences between the three political parties concerning economic issues.

CHAPTER SUMMARY

Descriptive statistical methods are used to summarize data sets so that we can extract the relevant information. In this chapter, we presented graphical techniques for nominal data.

Bar charts, pie charts, and frequency and relative frequency distributions are employed to summarize single sets of nominal data. Because of the restrictions applied to this type of data, all that we can show is the frequency and proportion of each category.

To describe the relationship between two nominal variables, we produce cross-classification tables and bar charts.

IMPORTANT TERMS:

Variable 14
Values 14
Data 14
Datum 14
Interval 15
Quantitative 15
Numerical 15
Nominal 15
Qualitative 15

Categorical 15
Ordinal 15
Frequency distribution 19
Relative frequency distribution 19
Bar chart 22
Pie chart 22
Univariate 34
Bivariate 33
Cross-classification (cross-tabulation) table 33

COMPUTER OUTPUT AND INSTRUCTIONS:

Graphical Technique	Excel
Bar chart	23
Pie chart	23

CHAPTER EXERCISES

2.55 Xr02-55   As of May 2016 the U.S. government owes $19,190,059,553,782. To whom does the U.S. government owe money? The list is shown below (in $billions). Use a graphical technique to depict these figures.

U.S. Individuals and Institutions	5,699.4
U.S. Social Security Trust Fund	2,897.7
U.S. Federal Reserve	2,648.2
U.S. Civil Service Retirement Fund	863.6
U.S. Military Retirement Fund	556.5
Foreign Nations	6,542.6

2.56 Xr02-56   Refer to Exercise 2.55. Here is a list of the top 10 foreign governments that own the U.S. debt (in order of magnitude). Depict these figures with a graph.

Government	Debt
China, mainland	1,254.8
Japan	1,149.2
Caribbean banking centers (e.g. Bermuda & Cayman Islands)	322.0
Oil exporters (e.g. Saudi Arabia & Iran)	291.4
Brazil	255.0
Ireland	232.9
Switzerland	225.6
United Kingdom	210.6
Hong Kong	197.0
Luxembourg	188.2

2.57 Xr02-57   June 7 is known as Tax Freedom day in Canada. The annual taxes paid by an average Canadian family earning $105,236 is $45,167. The breakdown of these taxes is shown in the table below. Use an appropriate graphical technique to present these figures.

Income taxes	14,732
Payroll/health taxes	10,043
Sales taxes	7,013
Property taxes	4,214
Profit taxes	3,895
Liquor and Tobacco taxes	2,397
Vehicle and fuel taxes	1,225
Other taxes	1,648

2.58 Xr02-58   The Consumer Expenditure Survey measures how consumers allocate their spending. A recent survey asked respondents to specify the amount of their budget spent on food, housing, transportation, healthcare, and insurance and pensions. Also recorded were the composition of the consumer unit. These are summarized in the table below. Use a pie chart to allow a comparison of the three consumer units.

Item	Married Couple No Children	Married Couple with Children	One Parent, At Least 1 Child under 18
Food	11.8	12.9	12.4
Housing	30.5	31.8	36.7
Transportation	17.5	17.3	15.9
Healthcare	10.3	7.3	7.3
Insurance & pensions	11.1	12.5	8.9
Other	18.8	18.2	18.8

2.59 Xr02-59   The primary objective of the Affordable Care Act was to decrease the number of nonelderly without any health insurance. It is estimated that there are still approximately 40 million Americans without health insurance. Researchers asked a sample of them why they are not insured. The responses and the percentages are listed in the table below. Use a graphical method to depict these figures. (Numbers do not add to 100% because of rounding.)

Primary Reason for No Insurance	Percentage
Too expensive	48
Don't need it	6
Opposed to the ECA/prefer to pay penalty	3
Don't know how to get it	3
Immigration status	7
Told they were ineligible	7
Unemployed/work doesn't offer/not eligible at work	12
Don't know/refused	4
Other reasons	12

The following exercises require a computer and software.

2.60 Xr02-60   Refer to Exercise 2.59. The percentage of uninsured in 2013 and 2014 in each of the 50 states plus District of Columbia was recorded. Use a graphical technique to show the decrease in the uninsured rate.

Source: The Henry J. Kaiser Family Foundation

2.61 Xr02-61   The Wilfrid Laurier University bookstore conducts annual surveys of its customers. One question asks respondents to rate the prices of textbooks.

The wording is, "The bookstore's prices of textbooks are reasonable." The responses are as follows:

1. Strongly disagree
2. Disagree
3. Neither agree nor disagree
4. Agree
5. Strongly agree

The responses for a group of 115 students were recorded. Graphically summarize these data and report your findings.

2.62   <u>Xr02-62</u>   A sample of 200 people who had purchased food at the concession stand at Yankee Stadium was asked to rate the quality of the food. The responses are as follows:

1. Poor
2. Fair
3. Good
4. Very good
5. Excellent

Draw a graph that describes the data. What does the graph tell you?

2.63   <u>Xr02-63</u>   There are several ways to teach applied statistics. The most popular approaches are as follows:

1. Emphasize manual calculations.
2. Use a computer combined with manual calculations.
3. Use a computer exclusively with no manual calculations.

A survey of 100 statistics instructors asked each to report his or her approach. Use a graphical method to extract the most useful information about the teaching approaches.

2.64   <u>Xr02-64</u>   The Red Lobster Restaurant chain conducts regular surveys of its customers to monitor the performance of individual restaurants. One of the questions asks customers to rate the overall quality of their last visit. The listed responses are Poor (1), Fair (2), Good (3), Very good (4), and Excellent (5). The survey also asks respondents whether their children accompanied them (1 = yes and 2 = no) to the restaurant. Graphically depict these data and describe your findings.

2.65   <u>Xr02-65*</u>   A survey of the business school graduates undertaken by a university placement office asked, among other questions, in which area each person was employed. The areas of employment are as follows:

1. Accounting
2. Finance
3. General management
4. Marketing/Sales
5. Other

Additional questions were asked and the responses were recorded in the following way.

Column	Variable
A	Identification number
B	Area
C	Gender (1 = female, 2 = male)
D	Job satisfaction (4 = very, 3 = quite, 2 = little, and 1 = none)

The placement office wants to know the following:

a. Do female and male graduates differ in their areas of employment? If so, how?
b. Are area of employment and job satisfaction related?

GENERAL SOCIAL SURVEY EXERCISES

The following exercises are based on the General Social Survey in 2014 featuring the variables listed next.

SEX: 1. Male; 2. Female

RACE: 1. White; 2. Black; 3. Other

MARITAL: 1. Married; 2. Widowed; 3. Divorced; 4. Separated; 5. Never married

DEGREE: 0. Left high school; 1. Graduated high school; 2. Completed junior college; 3. Completed Bachelor's degree; 4. Completed graduate degree

WRKGOVT: 1. Government; 2. Private

WRKSLF: 1. Self-employed; 2. Work for someone else

2.66   <u>GSS2014*</u>   The population of the United States is approximately evenly divided between men and women. Draw a pie chart of the number of male and female respondents. Does it appear that the General Social Survey chose its respondents at random?

2.67 <u>GSS2014*</u>   Graphically describe the racial makeup of the respondents.

2.68 <u>GSS2014*</u>

a. Determine the relative frequency distribution of marital status.
b. Which graphical technique would you use to graphically describe marital status?
c. Use your choice of graph.

2.69 <u>GSS2014*</u>   Graphically describe the respondents' highest completed degree.

2.70 <u>GSS2014*</u>   Are there differences between men and women in terms of the completion of their highest degree? Use a graphical method to answer the question.

2.71 <u>GSS2014*</u>   Use a pie chart to depict the proportion of respondents who worked for the government or worked in the private sector.

2.72 <u>GSS2014*</u>   Are there differences between the three categories of race with respect to working for the government or working in the private sector? Draw a graph to depict the differences.

2.73 <u>GSS2014*</u>   Use a graphical method to determine whether men and women differ with respect to working for themselves or someone else.

SURVEY OF CONSUMER FINANCES EXERCISES

The following exercises are based on the 2013 Survey of Consumer Finances featuring the variables listed next. (The data are in folder SCF2013.)

HHSEX (head of household): 1. Male; 2. Female

EDCL: 1. No high school diploma; 2. High school diploma or GED; 3 Some college; 4. College degree

FAMSTRUCT: 1. Not married or living with partner; 2. Not married or living with partner, no children, head under 55; 3. Not married or living with partner, no children, head 55 or older; 4. Married or living with partner with children; 5. Married or living with partner with no children

HOUSECL: 1. Owns ranch/farm/mobile home/house/condo/coop/etc.; 2. Otherwise

RACE: 1. White, non-Hispanic; 2. Black/African American; 3. Hispanic; 5. Other

2.74 <u>SCF2013:\ALL*</u>   Use a graphical technique to describe the respondents' family structure.

2.75 <u>SCF2013:\ALL*</u>   Are there differences between men and women heads of households in terms of education category (EDCL)? Use a graphical method to answer the question.

2.76 <u>SCF2013:\ALL*</u>   Graphically describe the racial makeup of the respondents.

2.77 <u>SCF2013:\ALL*</u>   Are there differences between the races in terms of family structure? Graphically answer the question.

2.78 <u>SCF2013:\ALL*</u>   Are there differences between the four categories of education in terms of home ownership. Use a graph to answer the question.

wrangler/Shutterstock.com

GRAPHICAL DESCRIPTIVE TECHNIQUES II

CHAPTER OUTLINE

3-1 Graphical Techniques to Describe a Set of Interval Data

3-2 Describing Time-Series Data

3-3 Describing the Relationship between Two Interval Variables

3-4 Art and Science of Graphical Presentations

What Is Happening to the Price of Gasoline?

In the past two decades, the price of gasoline has been on a roller coaster. In 1995, the

DATA
Xm03-00

average retail price of unleaded regular gasoline in the United States was about $1.20. Over the next 13 years, the average price rose to over $4.00. It then fell precipitously to less than $1.80 in early 2016. (One U.S. gallon equals 3.79 liters.) While the lower price is appreciated by all drivers, the rapidly changing price is somewhat bewildering to motorists. When the price was rising we understood there were several reasons. First, oil is a finite resource; the world will eventually run out. In 2016, the world was consuming more than 100 million barrels per day—more than 36 billion barrels per year. The total proven world reserves of oil are 1,689,078,618,100

Comstock Images/Getty Images

On page 70, you will find our answer.

barrels. At today's consumption levels, the proven reserves will be exhausted in 47 years. (It should be noted, however, that in 2009, the proven reserves of oil amounted to 1,349.4 billion barrels and in 2012 the proven reserves were 1,481.5 billion barrels, indicating that new oil discoveries are offsetting increasing usage.) Second, China's and India's industries are rapidly increasing and require ever-increasing amounts of oil. Third, over the last 20 years, hurricanes have threatened the oil rigs in the Gulf of Mexico. In 1995, the price of oil (West Texas intermediate crude) was under $20 per barrel (one barrel equals 42 U.S. gallons). In 2008, the price rose to over $130, and in early 2016 the price fluctuated between $30 and $40. To help understand the gasoline/oil price relationship, we determined the monthly average price of gasoline and the price of a barrel of West Texas intermediate crude for the period 1995 to 2016. Use a graphical technique to describe the relationship. See page 70 for our solution.

INTRODUCTION

Chapter 2 introduced graphical techniques used to summarize and present nominal data. In this chapter, we do the same for interval data. Section 3-1 presents techniques to describe a set of interval data, Section 3-2 introduces time series and the method used to present time-series data, and Section 3-3 describes the technique we use to describe the relationship between two interval variables. We complete this chapter with a discussion of how to properly use graphical methods in Section 3-4.

3-1 / GRAPHICAL TECHNIQUES TO DESCRIBE A SET OF INTERVAL DATA

In this section we introduce the histogram, which is a powerful graphical technique used to summarize a set of interval data. As you will see the histogram is also used to help explain an important aspect of probability (see Chapter 8).

EXAMPLE 3.1

DATA
Xm03-01

Ages of Duplicate Bridge Players

The game of bridge is played all over the world. There are two versions. There is rubber bridge, which is usually played in private and often for money. The second, more popular version is duplicate bridge, which is played in clubs and tournaments around the world. The American Contract Bridge League (ACBL) is the organization that runs duplicate bridge. Anyone who has played in club games will notice that a great majority of players are seniors. The ACBL is concerned about the increasing average age of its members and the relative scarcity of younger players. To help determine whether efforts should be made to encourage younger bridge players to join ACBL, a random sample of 200 ACBL members was drawn, with each reporting his or her age. The results are shown here. What information can be extracted from these data?

73	77	62	35	33	63	68	31	20	93
53	73	94	75	72	66	64	55	60	73
66	68	64	83	62	38	24	25	58	58
82	72	83	26	82	54	68	49	73	27
54	57	24	30	70	75	96	54	52	40
53	30	28	28	32	23	85	69	35	49
78	28	69	61	33	19	64	41	54	54

33	71	62	52	44	65	60	67	50	30
35	30	25	36	30	44	39	28	60	80
40	59	63	37	76	37	32	90	51	62
65	74	81	38	53	25	51	52	56	53
74	28	65	24	60	30	53	49	45	50
55	55	91	22	31	38	16	71	60	36
82	52	26	18	63	27	27	57	46	90
74	75	35	70	69	33	60	82	56	82
76	61	52	71	69	49	61	60	31	60
57	36	83	36	79	42	65	38	72	51
63	37	25	54	65	71	78	76	46	32
65	95	63	48	52	66	45	16	67	22
33	54	99	31	76	42	74	65	27	17

S O L U T I O N :

Little information can be developed just by casually reading through the 200 observa-tions. If you examine the data more carefully, you may discover that the youngest bridge player in this sample is 16 and the oldest is 99. To gain useful information, we need to know how the ages are distributed between 16 and 99. Are there many old players with few young ones? Are the ages somewhat similar or do they vary considerably? To help answer these questions and others like them, we will construct a frequency distribution from which a histogram can be drawn. In the previous chapter, a frequency distribution was created by counting the number of times each category of the nominal variable occurred. We create a frequency distribution for interval data by counting the number of observations that fall into each of a series of intervals, called **classes** that cover the complete range of observations. We discuss how to decide the number of classes and the upper and lower limits of the intervals later. We have chosen nine classes defined in such a way that each observation falls into one and only one class. These classes are defined as follows:

Classes

Ages that are more than 10 and less than or equal to 20

Ages that are more than 20 but less than or equal to 30

Ages that are more than 30 but less than or equal to 40

Ages that are more than 40 but less than or equal to 50

Ages that are more than 50 but less than or equal to 60

Ages that are more than 60 but less than or equal to 70

Ages that are more than 70 but less than or equal to 80

Ages that are more than 80 but less than or equal to 90

Ages that are more than 90 but less than or equal to 100

Notice that the intervals do not overlap, so there is no uncertainty about which inter-val to assign to any observation. Moreover, because the smallest number is 16 and the largest is 99, every observation will be assigned to a class. Finally, the intervals are equally wide. Although this is not essential, it makes the task of reading and inter-preting the graph easier. To create the frequency distribution manually, we count the number of observations that fall into each interval. Table 3.1 presents the frequency distribution.

TABLE **3.1** Frequency Distribution of ACBL Members' Ages

CLASS LIMITS	FREQUENCY
10–20	6
20–30	27
30–40	30
40–50	16
50–60	40
60–70	36
70–80	27
80–90	12
90–100	6
Total	200

Although the frequency distribution provides information about how the numbers are distributed, the information is more easily understood and imparted by drawing a picture or graph. The graph is called a **histogram**. A histogram is created by drawing rectangles whose bases are the intervals and whose heights are the frequencies. Figure 3.1 exhibits the histogram that was drawn by hand.

FIGURE **3.1** Histogram for Example 3.1

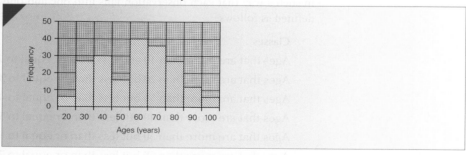

EXCEL Data Analysis

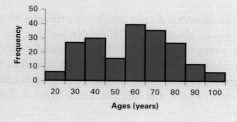

INSTRUCTIONS

1. Type or import the data into one column. (Open Xm03-01) In another column, type the upper limits of the class intervals. Excel calls them bins. (You can put any name in the first row; we typed "Ages.")

2. Click **Data, Data Analysis,** and **Histogram.**

3. Specify the **Input Range** (A1:A201) and the **Bin Range** (B1:B10). Click **Chart Output.** Click **Labels** if the first row contains names.

4. To remove the gaps, place the cursor over one of the rectangles and click the right button of the mouse. Click (with the left button) **Format Data Series . . . .** move the pointer to **Gap Width** and use the slider to change the number from 150 to 0.

Note that except for the first class, Excel counts the number of observations in each class that are greater than the lower limit and less than or equal to the upper limit. Note that the numbers along the horizontal axis represent the upper limits of each class although they appear to be placed in the centers.

XLSTAT

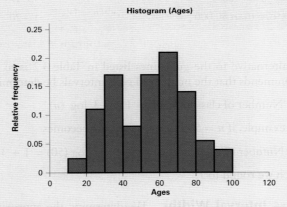

INSTRUCTIONS

1. Type or import the data into one column. (Open Xm03-01.)

2. Click **XLSTAT** and **Describing data** (or **Visualizing data**), and **Histograms.**

3. In the **Data:** dialog box type the input range (A1:A201). Under **Data type** specify **Continuous.**

4. Click the **Options** tab and specify the **Number** of class intervals (9).

5. Click **Charts** and under **Histograms** check **Bars.** Click **OK** and **Continue.**

INTERPRET

The histogram gives us a clear view of the way the ages are distributed. As expected about 40% of the sample are older than 60. About a sixth are in their teens and twenties. There appears to be a good supply of younger players. However, there is an unexpected gap of players in the 40 to 60 range, particularly in the 40 to 50 range. This group may be individuals who are working and have little time for bridge. Most club games start at 7:00 pm and end after 10:00. Perhaps scheduling shorter games may result in attracting working people to become members of the ACBL.

3-1a Determining the Number of Class Intervals

The number of class intervals we select depends entirely on the number of observations in the data set. The more observations we have, the larger the number of class intervals we need to use to draw a useful histogram. Table 3.2 provides guidelines on choosing the number of classes. In Example 3.1, we had 200 observations. The table tells us to use 7, 8, 9, or 10 classes.

TABLE **3.2** Approximate Number of Classes in Histograms

NUMBER OF OBSERVATIONS	NUMBER OF CLASSES
Less than 50	5–7
50–200	7–9
200–500	9–10
500–1,000	10–11
1,000–5,000	11–13
5,000–50,000	13–17
More than 50,000	17–20

An alternative to the guidelines listed in Table 3.2 is to use Sturges's formula, which recommends that the number of class intervals be determined by the following:

Number of class intervals = $1 + 3.3 \log (n)$

For example, if $n = 50$ Sturges's formula becomes

Number of class intervals = $1 + 3.3 \log (50) = 1 + 3.3(1.7) = 6.6$

which we round to 7.

Class Interval Widths   We determine the approximate width of the classes by subtracting the smallest observation from the largest and dividing the difference by the number of classes. Thus,

$$Class\ width = \frac{Largest\ Observation - Smallest\ Observation}{Number\ of\ Classes}$$

In Example 3.1, we calculated

$$Class\ width = \frac{99 - 16}{9} = 9.22$$

We often round the result to some convenient value. We then define our class limits by selecting a lower limit for the first class from which all other limits are determined. The only condition we apply is that the first class interval must contain the smallest observation. In Example 3.1, we rounded the class width to 10 and set the lower limit of the first class to 10. Thus, the first class is defined as "Amounts that are greater than or equal to 10 but less than or equal to 20." Table 3.2 and Sturges's formula are guidelines only. It is more important to choose classes that are easy to interpret. For example, suppose that we have recorded the marks on an exam of the 100 students registered in the course where the highest mark is 94 and the lowest is 48. Table 3.2 suggests that we use 7, 8, or 9 classes, and Sturges's formula computes the approximate number of classes as:

Number of class intervals = 1 + 3.3 log (100) = 1 + 3.3(2) = 7.6

which we round to 8. Thus,

$$Class\ width = \frac{94 - 48}{8} = 5.75$$

which we would round to 6. We could then produce a histogram whose upper limits of the class intervals are 50, 56, 62, . . . , 98. Because of the rounding and the way in which we defined the class limits, the number of classes is 9. However, a histogram that is easier to interpret would be produced using classes whose widths are 5; that is, the upper limits would be 50, 55, 60, . . . , 95. The number of classes in this case would be 10.

Exceptions to the Guidelines   In some situations, the guidelines we have just provided may not yield useful results. One such example occurs when there is a wide range of values with very large numbers of observations in some class intervals. This may result in some empty or nearly empty classes in the middle of the histogram. One solution is to create unequal class intervals. Unfortunately, this produces histograms that are more difficult to interpret. Another solution is to allow the last interval to be "more than the upper limit of the previous interval." To see why and how problems occur, see Exercises 3.30 and 3.31.

3-1b Shapes of Histograms

The purpose of drawing histograms, like that of all other statistical techniques, is to acquire information. Once we have the information, we frequently need to describe what we've learned to others. We describe the shape of histograms on the basis of the following characteristics.

Symmetry   A histogram is said to be **symmetric** if, when we draw a vertical line down the center of the histogram, the two sides are identical in shape and size. Figure 3.2 depicts three symmetric histograms.

FIGURE **3.2** **Three Symmetric Histograms**

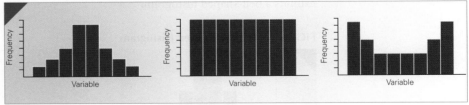

Skewness   A skewed histogram is one with a long tail extending to either the right or the left. The former is called **positively skewed**, and the latter is called **negatively skewed**. Figure 3.3 shows examples of both. Incomes of employees in large firms tend to be positively skewed because there is a large number of relatively low-paid workers and a small number of well-paid executives. The time taken by students to write exams is frequently negatively skewed because few students hand in their exams early; most prefer to reread their papers and hand them in near the end of the scheduled test period.

FIGURE **3.3** Positively and Negatively Skewed Histograms

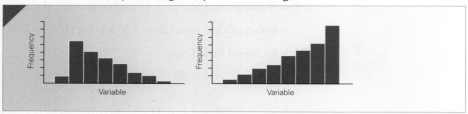

Number of Modal Classes   As we discuss in Chapter 4, a *mode* is the observation that occurs with the greatest frequency. A **modal class** is the class with the largest number of observations. A **unimodal histogram** is one with a single peak. The histogram in Figure 3.4 is unimodal. A **bimodal histogram** is one with two peaks, not necessarily equal in height. Bimodal histograms often indicate that two different distributions are present. (See Example 3.4.) Figure 3.5 depicts bimodal histograms.

FIGURE **3.4** A Unimodal Histogram

FIGURE **3.5** Bimodal Histograms

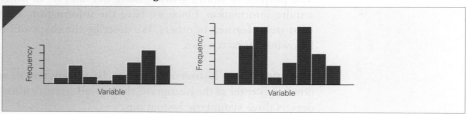

Bell Shape   A special type of symmetric unimodal histogram is one that is bell shaped. In Chapter 8, we will explain why this type of histogram is important. Figure 3.6 exhibits a bell-shaped histogram.

FIGURE **3.6** Bell-Shaped Histogram

Now that we know what to look for, let's examine some examples of histograms and see what we can discover.

APPLICATIONS in **FINANCE**

Stock and Bond Valuation

A basic understanding of how financial assets, such as stocks and bonds, are valued is critical to good financial management. Understanding the basics of valuation is necessary for capital budgeting and capital structure decisions. Moreover, understanding the basics of valuing investments such as stocks and bonds is at the heart of the huge and growing discipline known as *investment management.*

A financial manager must be familiar with the main characteristics of the capital markets where long-term financial assets such as stocks and bonds trade. A well-functioning capital market provides managers with useful information concerning the appropriate prices and rates of return that are required for a variety of financial securities with differing levels of risk. Statistical methods can be used to analyze capital markets and summarize their characteristics, such as the shape of the distribution of stock or bond returns.

APPLICATIONS in **FINANCE**

Return on Investment

The return on an investment is calculated by dividing the gain (or loss) by the value of the investment. For example, a $100 investment that is worth $106 after 1 year has a 6% rate of return. A $100 investment that loses $20 has a −20% rate of return. For many investments, including individual stocks and stock portfolios (combinations of various stocks), the rate of return is a variable. In other words, the investor does not know in advance what the rate of return will be. It could be a positive number, in which case the investor makes money—or negative, and the investor loses money.

Investors are torn between two goals. The first is to maximize the rate of return on investment. The second goal is to reduce risk. If we draw a histogram of the returns for a certain investment, the location of the center of the histogram gives us some information about the return one might expect from that investment. The spread or variation of the histogram provides us with guidance about the risk. If there is little variation, an investor can be quite confident in predicting what his or her rate of return will be. If there is a great deal of variation, the return becomes much less predictable and thus riskier. Minimizing the risk becomes an important goal for investors and financial analysts.

EXAMPLE 3.2

DATA
Xm03-02

Comparing Returns on Two Investments

Suppose that you are facing a decision about where to invest that small fortune that remains after you have deducted the anticipated expenses for the next year from the earnings from your summer job. A friend has suggested two types of investment, and to help make the decision you acquire some rates of return from each type. You would like to know what you can expect by way of the return on your investment, as well as other types of information, such as whether the rates are spread out over a wide range (making the investment risky) or are grouped tightly together (indicating relatively low risk). Do the data indicate that it is possible that you can do extremely well with little likelihood of a large loss? Is it likely that you could lose money (negative rate of return)?

The returns for the two types of investments are listed here. Draw histograms for each set of returns and report on your findings. Which investment would you choose and why?

Returns on Investment A				Returns on Investment B			
30.00	6.93	13.77	−8.55	30.33	−34.75	30.31	24.3
−2.13	−13.24	22.42	−5.29	−30.37	54.19	6.06	−10.01
4.30	−18.95	34.40	−7.04	−5.61	44.00	14.73	35.24
25.00	9.43	49.87	−12.11	29.00	−20.23	36.13	40.7
12.89	1.21	22.92	12.89	−26.01	4.16	1.53	22.18
−20.24	31.76	20.95	63.00	0.46	10.03	17.61	3.24
1.20	11.07	43.71	−19.27	2.07	10.51	1.2	25.1
−2.59	8.47	−12.83	−9.22	29.44	39.04	9.94	−24.24
33.00	36.08	0.52	−17.00	11	24.76	−33.39	−38.47
14.26	−21.95	61.00	17.30	−25.93	15.28	58.67	13.44
−15.83	10.33	−11.96	52.00	8.29	34.21	0.25	68.00
0.63	12.68	1.94		61.00	52.00	5.23	
38.00	13.09	28.45		−20.44	−32.17	66	

SOLUTION:

We draw the histograms of the returns on the two investments.

EXCEL Data Analysis

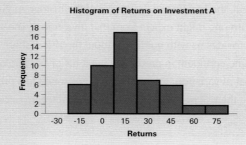

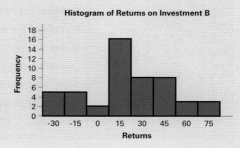

INTERPRET

Comparing the two histograms, we can extract the following information:

1. The center of the histogram of the returns of investment A is slightly lower than that for investment B.

2. The spread of returns for investment A is considerably less than that for investment B.

3. Both histograms are slightly positively skewed.

These findings suggest that investment A is superior. Although the returns for A are slightly less than those for B, the wider spread for B makes it unappealing to most investors. Both investments allow for the possibility of a relatively large return.

The interpretation of the histograms is somewhat subjective. Other viewers may not concur with our conclusion. In such cases, numerical techniques provide the detail and precision lacking in most graphs. We will redo this example in Chapter 4 to illustrate how numerical techniques compare to graphical ones.

EXAMPLE 3.3

DATA
Xm03-03*

Business Statistics Marks

A student enrolled in a business program is attending the first class of the required statistics course. The student is somewhat apprehensive because he believes the myth that the course is difficult. To alleviate his anxiety, the student asks the professor about last year's marks. The professor obliges and provides a list of the final marks, which is composed of term work plus the final exam. Draw a histogram and describe the result, based on the following marks:

65	81	72	59
71	53	85	66
66	70	72	71
79	76	77	68
65	73	64	72
82	73	77	75
80	85	89	74
86	83	87	77
67	80	78	69
64	67	79	60
62	78	59	92
74	68	63	69
67	67	84	69
72	62	74	73
68	83	74	65

SOLUTION:

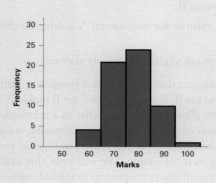

EXCEL Data Analysis

INTERPRET

The histogram is unimodal and approximately symmetric. There are no marks below 50, with the great majority of marks between 60 and 90. The modal class is 70 to 80, and the center of the distribution is approximately 75.

EXAMPLE 3.4

Mathematical Statistics Marks

DATA
Xm03-04*

Suppose the student in Example 3.3 obtained a list of last year's marks in a mathematical statistics course. This course emphasizes derivations and proofs of theorems. Use the accompanying data to draw a histogram and compare it to the one produced in Example 3.3. What does this histogram tell you?

77	67	53	54
74	82	75	44
75	55	76	54
75	73	59	60
67	92	82	50
72	75	82	52
81	75	70	47
76	52	71	46
79	72	75	50
73	78	74	51
59	83	53	44
83	81	49	52
77	73	56	53
74	72	61	56
78	71	61	53

S O L U T I O N :

EXCEL Data Analysis

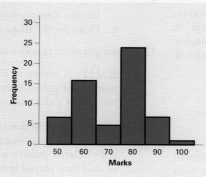

INTERPRET

The histogram is bimodal. The larger modal class is composed of the marks in the 70s. The smaller modal class includes the marks that are in the 50s. There appear to be few marks in the 60s. This histogram suggests that there are two groups of students. Because of the emphasis on mathematics in the course, one may conclude that those who performed poorly in the course are weaker mathematically than those who performed well. The histograms in this example and in Example 3.3 suggest that the courses are quite different from one another and have a completely different distribution of marks.

Here is a summary of this section's technique.

Factors That Identify When to Use a Histogram

1. Objective: Describe a single set of data
2. Data type: Interval

EXERCISES

3.1 How many classes should a histogram contain if the number of observations is 125?

3.2 Determine the number of classes of a histogram for 1500 observations.

3.3 A data set consists of 300 observations that range between 147 and 241.
  a. What is an appropriate number of classes to have in the histogram?
  b. What class intervals would you suggest?

3.4 A statistics practitioner would like to draw a histogram of 40 observations that range from 5.2 to 6.1.
  a. How many class intervals should the histogram use?
  b. Define the upper limits of the classes.

3.5 Xr03-05   An Uber driver kept track of the number of calls he received over a 28-day period. The data are listed here. Create a histogram.

10	10	7	7	3	8	11
8	10	7	7	7	5	4
9	7	8	4	17	13	9
7	12	8	10	4	7	5

3.6 **Xr03-06**   There are a number of minor-league baseball players who never make it to the major leagues. A statistics practitioner kept track of the age at which 32 players realized their dream of playing in the majors would never be fulfilled and retired. Draw a histogram of these data.

23	31	31	30	29	28	32	33
29	27	35	32	41	28	30	35
26	25	32	26	30	32	32	28
30	29	24	25	32	35	27	22

3.7 **Xr03-07**   The 17th hole at the TPC (Tournament Players Club) is an island green that causes even professional players to put their tee shots into the surrounding pond. A statistics practitioner kept track of the number of golf balls put into the pond by amateurs for each of 30 days with the results listed here. Draw a histogram of these data.

81	94	82	79	70	76	70	85	102	91
71	69	95	57	85	85	84	87	67	71
115	102	70	63	81	81	76	99	87	93

3.8 **Xr03-08**   The numbers of weekly sales calls by a sample of 30 telemarketers are listed here. Draw a histogram of these data and describe it.

14	12	9	17	8	3	10	20	19	15
8	21	3	9	18	17	15	17	7	10
6	4	25	5	16	19	5	14	10	8

3.9 **Xr03-09**   The amount of time (in seconds) needed to complete a critical task on an assembly line was measured for a sample of 50 assemblies. These data are listed here. Draw a histogram to describe these data.

30.3	34.5	31.1	30.9	33.7
31.9	33.1	31.1	30.0	32.7
34.4	30.1	34.6	31.6	32.4
32.8	31.0	30.2	30.2	32.8
31.1	30.7	33.1	34.4	31.0
32.2	30.9	32.1	34.2	30.7
30.7	30.7	30.6	30.2	33.4
36.8	30.2	31.5	30.1	35.7
30.5	30.6	30.2	31.4	30.7
30.6	37.9	30.3	34.1	30.4

3.10 **Xr03-10**   A survey of 60 individuals leaving a mall asked how many stores they entered during this visit to the mall. The figures are listed here.

3	2	4	3	3	9
2	4	3	6	2	2
8	7	6	4	5	1
5	2	3	1	1	7
3	4	1	1	4	8

0	2	5	4	4	4
6	2	2	5	3	8
4	3	1	6	9	1
4	4	1	0	4	6
5	5	5	1	4	3

a. Draw a histogram to summarize these data.
b. Describe the shape of the histogram.

The following exercises require a computer and statistical software.

3.11 **Xr03-11**   A survey of 50 baseball fans to report the number of games they attended last year. Draw a histogram and describe its shape.

3.12 **Xr03-12**   To help determine the need for more golf courses, a survey was undertaken. A sample of 75 self-declared golfers was asked how many rounds of golf they played last year. Draw a histogram and describe what it tells you.

3.13 **Xr03-13**   The annual incomes for a sample of 200 first-year accountants were recorded. Draw a histogram and describe its shape.

3.14 **Xr03-14**   Currently Ebay lists over 550,000 U.S. collector coins for sale or auction. An avid collector tracked the number of days it took for 500 coins to be sent to his home. Create a histogram of these figures. What information can you draw from the shape of the histogram?

3.15 **Xr03-15**   The number of customers entering a bank in the first hour of operation for each of the last 200 days was recorded. Draw a histogram and describe its shape.

3.16 **Xr03-16**   Users of previous editions of this book could download an Excel add-in called Data Analysis Plus from our website. We recorded the number of daily downloads during a 78-day period.
a. Draw a histogram.
b. Describe its shape.

3.17 **Xr03-17**   The marks of 320 students on an economics midterm test were recorded. Use a graphical technique to summarize these data. What does the graph tell you?

3.18 **Xr03-18**   The lengths (in inches) of 150 newborn babies were recorded. Use whichever graphical technique you judge suitable to describe these data. What have you learned from the graph?

3.19 **Xr03-19**   The number of copies made by an office copier was recorded for each of the past 75 days. Graph the data using a suitable technique. Describe what the graph tells you.

3.20 **Xr03-20**   Each of a sample of 240 tomatoes grown with a new type of fertilizer was weighed (in ounces) and recorded. Draw a histogram and describe your findings.

3.21 <u>Xr03-21</u>   The volume of water used by each of a sample of 350 households was measured (in gallons) and recorded. Use a suitable graphical statistical method to summarize the data. What does the graph tell you?

3.22 <u>Xr03-22</u>   The number of books shipped out daily by Amazon.com was recorded for 100 days. Draw a histogram and describe your findings.

GENERAL SOCIAL SURVEY EXERCISES

The following exercises are based on the General Social Survey of 2014.

3.23 <u>GSS2014*</u>   Draw a histogram of the ages (AGE) of the respondents. What information do you draw from the histogram?

3.24 <u>GSS2014*</u>   How educated were American adults in 2014? Draw a histogram to help provide a graphical answer (EDUC).

3.25 <u>GSS2014*</u>   How well were Americans doing financially in 2014. Draw a histogram of respondents' incomes (RINCOME). Describe the shape.

3.26 <u>GSS2014*</u>   How much television were American adults watching in 2014 (TVHOURS)? Produce a histogram to help answer the question.

3.27 <u>GSS2014*</u>   Among American adults with children draw a histogram of their ages when their first child was born (AGEKDBRN).

SURVEY OF CONSUMER FINANCES EXERCISES

The following exercises are based on the 2013 Survey of Consumer Finances

3.28 <u>[SCF2013:\ALL*]</u>   Draw a histogram of the ages of the respondents in the 2013 survey. What information can you extract from the histogram?

3.29 <u>[SCF2013:\ALL*]</u>   Create a histogram of the number of children. Despite the fact that the sample size is over 6,000, why should you not have 20 class intervals?

3.30 <u>[SCF2013:\ALL*]</u>   One of the questions asked respondents to report the total value of assets held by the household in 2013 dollars. Note that the range is very large. The minimum is $0 and the maximum is $1,312,587,840.
   a. Draw a histogram using the number of class intervals suggested by Table 3.2; that is, between 13 and 17 class intervals. What problems did you encounter?
   b. Try drawing a histogram with the following class intervals 10,000, 20,000, . . . 200,000 What problem do you encounter?

   c. Draw a histogram with the following class intervals 100,000, 200,000, . . . 2,000,000
   d. Briefly discuss which histogram drawn in (a), (b), and (c) is best.

3.31 <u>[SCF2013:\ALL*]</u>   Respondents were asked to report the total value of certificates of deposit (CDs) in 2013 dollars held by the household.
   a. Try drawing histograms with different numbers of class intervals and different upper limits.
   b. What problem do you encounter in drawing a histogram of CDs?
   c. Suggest ways of solving the problem of drawing histograms when the range is very large.

3-2 / DESCRIBING TIME-SERIES DATA

Besides classifying data by type, we can also classify them according to whether the observations are measured at the same time or whether they represent measurements at successive points in time. The former are called **cross-sectional data** and the latter **time-series data**.

The technique described in Section 3-1 is applied to cross-sectional data. All the data, for Example 3.1, were probably determined within the same day. We can probably say the same thing for Examples 3.2 to 3.4.

To give another example, consider a real estate consultant who feels that the selling price of a house is a function of its size, age, and lot size. To estimate the specific form of the function, she samples, say, 100 homes recently sold and records the price, size, age, and lot size for each home. These data are cross-sectional in that they all are observations at the same point in time. The real estate consultant is also working on a separate project to forecast the monthly housing starts in the northeastern United States over the next year. To do so, she collects the monthly housing starts in this region for each of the past 5 years. These 60 values (housing starts) represent time-series data, because they are observations taken over time.

Note that the original data may be interval or nominal. All of these illustrations deal with interval data. A time series can also list the frequencies and relative frequencies of a nominal variable over a number of time periods. For example, a brand-preference survey asks consumers to identify their favorite brand. These data are nominal. If we repeat the survey once a month for several years, the proportion of consumers who prefer a certain company's product each month would constitute a time series.

3-2a Line Chart

Time-series data are often graphically depicted on a **line chart**, which is a plot of the variable over time. It is created by plotting the value of the variable on the vertical axis and the time periods on the horizontal axis.

The chapter-opening example addresses the issue of the relationship between the price of gasoline and the price of oil. We will introduce the technique we need to answer the question in Section 3-3. In discussing the price of gasoline we noted that the price has fluctuated wildly in the last 20 years. The questions that arise are how expensive was gas at its high point (in 2008) and how cheap it became in 2016.

EXAMPLE 3.5

DATA
Xm03-05

Price of Gasoline

We recorded the monthly average retail price of gasoline (regular unleaded in cents per gallon) since 1976. The first 4 months and the last 4 months are displayed here. Draw a line chart to describe these figures and describe the results.

Year	Month	Price per Gallon (Cents)
1976	1	60.5
1976	2	60.0
1976	3	59.4
1976	4	59.2
2016	1	196.7
2016	2	176.7
2016	3	195.8
2016	4	213.4

SOLUTION:

EXCEL Chart

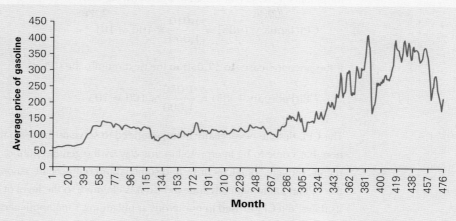

INSTRUCTIONS

1. Type or import the data into one column. (Open Xm03-05.)

2. Highlight the column of data. Click **Insert**, **Line**, and the first **2-D Line**. You can draw two or more line charts (for two or more variables) by highlighting all columns of data you wish to graph.

INTERPRET

The price of gasoline rose from about $.60 to over $1.00 in the late 1970s (months 1 to 49), fluctuated between $.90 and $1.50 until 2000 (months 49 to 313), then rose rapidly to month 396, before dropping sharply.

APPLICATIONS in ECONOMICS

Measuring inflation: Consumer Price Index

Inflation is the increase in the prices for goods and services. In most countries, inflation is measured using the Consumer Price Index (CPI). The CPI works with a basket of some 300 goods and services in the United States (and a similar number in other countries), including such diverse items as food, housing, clothing, transportation, health, and recreation. The basket is defined for the "typical" or "average" middle-income family, and the set of items and their weights are revised periodically (every 10 years in the United States and every 7 years in Canada). Prices for each item in this basket are computed on a monthly basis and the CPI is computed from these prices. Here is how it works. We start by setting a period of time as the base. In the United States, the base is the years 1982–1984. Suppose that the basket of goods and services

(Continued)

cost $1,000 during this period. Thus, the base is $1,000, and the CPI is set at 100. Suppose that in the next month (January 1985) the price increases to $1,010. The CPI for January 1985 is calculated in the following way:

$$CPI(January\ 1985) = \frac{1,010}{1,000} \times 100 = 101$$

If the price increases to $1,050 in the next month, the CPI is

$$CPI(February\ 1985) = \frac{1,050}{1,000} \times 100 = 105$$

The CPI, despite never really being intended to serve as the official measure of inflation, has come to be interpreted in this way by the general public. Pension-plan payments, old-age Social Security, and some labor contracts are automatically linked to the CPI and automatically indexed (so it is claimed) to the level of inflation. Despite its flaws, the CPI is used in numerous applications. One application involves adjusting prices by removing the effect of inflation, making it possible to track the "real" changes in a time series of prices.

In Example 3.5, the figures shown are the actual prices measured in what are called current dollars. To remove the effect of inflation, we divide the monthly prices by the CPI for that month and multiply by 100. These prices are then measured in constant 1982–1984 dollars. This makes it easier to see what has happened to the prices of the goods and services of interest. We created two data sets to help you calculate prices in constant 1982–1984 dollars. File Ch03:\\U.S. CPI Annual and Ch03:\\U.S. CPI Monthly list the values of the CPI where 1982–1984 is set at 100 for annual values and monthly values, respectively.

EXAMPLE 3.6

DATA

Xm03-06

Price of Gasoline in 1982–1984 Constant Dollars

Remove the effect of inflation in Example 3.5 to determine how high gasoline prices were in 2008 and how low they have become.

SOLUTION:

Here are the average monthly prices of gasoline, the CPI, and the adjusted prices for the first four months of 1976 and the first four months of 2016.

Year	Month	Price of Gasoline	CPI	Adjusted Price of Gasoline
1976	1	60.5	55.8	108.4
1976	2	60.0	55.9	107.3
1976	3	59.4	56.0	106.1
1976	4	59.2	56.1	105.5
2016	1	196.7	238.1	82.6
2016	2	176.7	237.7	74.3
2016	3	195.8	237.9	82.3
2016	4	213.4	238.9	89.3

EXCEL Chart

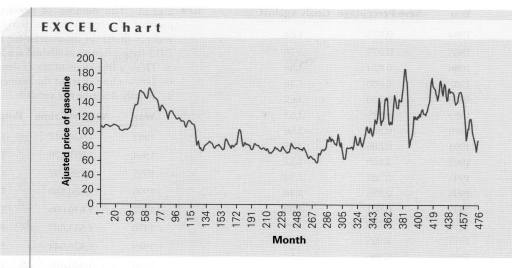

INTERPRET

Using constant 1982–1984 dollars, we can see that the average price of a gallon of gasoline hit its peak in the middle of 2008 (month 385). From there, it dropped rapidly until the 2016. At that point, the adjusted price was lower than the adjusted price in 1976.

Exercises

3.32  How well have Canada and the United States performed at the Winter Olympics? In the table displayed here, we list the total number of medals won by the two countries in each year. Draw a chart to describe both time series.

Year	Canada	United States
1924	1	4
1928	1	6
1932	7	12
1936	1	4
1948	3	9
1952	2	11
1956	3	7
1960	4	10
1964	3	7
1968	3	7
1972	1	8
1976	3	10
1980	2	12
1984	4	8

(Continued)

Year	Canada	United States
1988	5	6
1992	7	11
1994	13	13
1998	15	13
2002	17	34
2006	24	25
2010	26	37
2014	25	28

3.33 Xr03-33 It won't come as a surprise to hockey fans that with each passing season the number of goals scored is decreasing. Many experts blame goalie equipment. The oversized pads and other protection for goalies now makes even relatively small goalies look like 250-pound athletes. To learn more about the problem a statistics practitioner recorded the save percentage (the percentage of shots that a goalie saves) and the goals against average (the average number of goals allowed) for each season between 1984 and 2016. These data are listed here.
a. Draw a line chart of the save percentage
b. Draw a line chart of the goals against average
c. Briefly describe your findings.

Year	Save Percentage	Goals Against
1984	0.873	3.83
1985	0.875	3.78
1986	0.874	3.86
1987	0.880	3.56
1988	0.880	3.62
1989	0.879	3.63
1990	0.881	3.56
1991	0.886	3.35
1992	0.888	3.37
1993	0.885	3.53
1994	0.895	3.14
1995	0.901	2.89
1996	0.898	3.04
1997	0.905	2.80
1998	0.906	2.53
1999	0.908	2.54
2000	0.904	2.64
2001	0.903	2.65
2002	0.908	2.51
2003	0.909	2.56
2004	0.911	2.46
2006	0.901	2.93
2007	0.905	2.77
2008	0.909	2.61
2009	0.908	2.73
2010	0.911	2.66
2011	0.913	2.61
2012	0.914	2.54
2013	0.912	2.54
2014	0.914	2.56
2015	0.915	2.52
2016	0.916	2.48

3.34 Xr03-34 The number of violent crimes and the number of property crimes (burglary, larceny theft, and car theft) (in thousands) for the years 1993 to 2012 (latest figures available) are listed here.
a. Draw a line chart of the violent crimes.
b. Draw a line chart of the property crimes
c. Briefly describe the results.

Year	Violent Crime	Property Crime
1993	1,926,017	12,218,777
1994	1,857,670	12,131,873
1995	1,798,792	12,063,935
1996	1,688,540	11,805,323
1997	1,636,096	11,558,475
1998	1,533,887	10,951,827
1999	1,426,044	10,208,334
2000	1,425,486	10,182,584
2001	1,439,480	10,437,189
2002	1,423,677	10,455,277
2003	1,383,676	10,442,862
2004	1,360,088	10,319,386
2005	1,390,745	10,174,754
2006	1,435,123	10,019,601
2007	1,422,970	9,882,212
2008	1,394,461	9,774,152
2009	1,325,896	9,337,060
2010	1,251,248	9,112,625
2011	1,206,005	9,052,743
2012	1,214,462	8,975,438

Source: U.S. Federal Bureau of Investigation.

APPLICATIONS in ECONOMICS

Per Capita Comparisons

In this section, we introduced the CPI, which allows statisticians, statistics practitioners, and economists to compare prices over different periods of time. When dealing with statistics in different countries or in one country in different years another useful adjustment is per capita statistics, which allows us to make more realistic comparisons. For example, if we're interested in comparing government expenditures this year versus 20 years ago we need to incorporate the size of the population. In the following 11 exercises, you will have an opportunity to see how and why per capita statistics work. To assist you we have created a file listing the total population of the United States from 1935 to 2015. It is stored in Chapter 3 as U.S. Population 1935–2015.

The following exercises require a computer and statistical software.

Exercises 3.35 to 3.45 deal with various parts of the U.S. federal budget. For each exercise, draw the following line charts and briefly describe what the chart tells you about each variable.
a. Original data
b. Per capita data
c. Per capita in constant 1982–1984 dollars

3.35 Xr03-35   The United States spends more money on health care than any other country. To gauge how fast costs are rising we recorded the total health care costs since 1950.

3.36 Xr03-36   The U.S. government provides Medicare to Americans who are 65 years and older. Medicare Part A pays the costs of hospital and nursing care, but not physicians' bills. The file lists Medicare Part A costs since 1966.

3.37 Xr03-37   Medicare Part B pays for a portion of physicians' visits, medical equipment, outpatient procedures, rehabilitative therapy, laboratory tests, X-rays, ambulance service, and blood. Costs were recorded for 1967 to 2015.

3.38 Xr03-38   Medicaid is a program created by the federal government, but administered by the state, to provide payment for medical services for low-income citizens. The costs were recorded from 1962 to 2015.

3.39 Xr03-39   Social Security Disability Insurance a program that pays monthly benefits to individuals who have become disabled before reaching retirement age and aren't able to work. SSDI costs were recorded for the years 1958 to 2015.

3.40 Xr03-40   Social Insurance Old Age Survivor Insurance provides a pension for Americans who are over 60 years of age and whose spouse has died. Costs for 1958 to 2015 were recorded.

3.41 Xr03-41   The defense budget for years 1935 to 2015 were recorded.

3.42 Xr03-42   Total Federal government spending from 1935 to 2015 is stored.

3.43 Xr03-43   Welfare payments for 1965 to 2015 were recorded.

3.44 Xr03-44   Education spending from 1935 to 2015 was recorded.

3.45 Xr03-45   Interest on Federal Debt from 1935 to 2015 was recorded.

3.46   Refer to Exercise 3.34.
a. Calculate the violent crime and property crime rates per 100,000 of population.
b. Draw a line chart of the violent crime rate per 100,000 of population.
c. Draw a line chart of the property crime rate per 100,000 of population.
d. Describe your findings.

3.47 Xr03-47   The average daily U.S. oil consumption and production (thousands of barrels) was recorded for the years 1973 to 2015. Draw a line chart for both sets of figures. Describe what you have learned.

3.48 Xr03-48   The gross domestic product (GDP) is the sum total of the economic output of a country. It is an important measure of the wealth of a country. The GDP of the United States from 1935 to 2015 is stored in the file.
a. Draw a line chart of the GDP.
b. Adjust the GDP for inflation and draw line chart of the adjusted GDP
c. Briefly describe what the charts tell you.

3.49 Xr03-49   The monthly value of U.S. exports to Canada (in $millions) and imports from Canada from 1985 to 2016 was recorded.
a. Draw a line chart of U.S. exports to Canada.
b. Draw a line chart of U.S. imports from Canada.
c. Calculate the trade balance and draw a line chart.
d. What do all the charts reveal?

3.50 Xr03-50   The monthly value of U.S. exports to Japan (in $millions) and imports from Japan from 1985 to 2016 was recorded.
a. Draw a line chart of U.S. exports to Japan.
b. Draw a line chart of U.S. imports from Japan.
c. Calculate the trade balance and draw a line chart.
d. What do all the charts reveal?

3.51 Xr03-51   The monthly value of U.S. exports to China (in $millions) and imports from China from 1985 to 2016 was recorded.
a. Draw a line chart of U.S. exports to China.
b. Draw a line chart of U.S. imports from China.
c. Calculate the trade balance and draw a line chart.
d. What do all the charts reveal?

3.52 Xr03-52   The exchange rate of the Canadian dollar to one U.S. dollar was recorded monthly for the period 1971 to 2016. Draw a graph of these figures and interpret your findings.

3.53 Xr03-53   The exchange rate of the Japanese Yen to one U.S. dollar was recorded monthly for the period 1971 to 2016. Draw a graph of these figures and interpret your findings.

3.54 Xr03-54   The Jones Industrial Average was recorded monthly (close) from 1950 to 2016. Use a graph to describe these numbers.

Source: The Wall Street Journal.

3.55   Refer to Exercise 3.54. Use the U.S. CPI monthly file to measure the Dow Jones Industrial Average in 1982–1984 constant dollars. What have you learned?

3-3 / DESCRIBING THE RELATIONSHIP BETWEEN TWO INTERVAL VARIABLES

Statistics practitioners frequently need to know how two interval variables are related. For example, financial analysts need to understand how the returns of individual stocks are related to the returns of the entire market. Marketing managers need to understand the relationship between sales and advertising. Economists develop statistical techniques to describe the relationship between such variables as unemployment rates and inflation. The technique is called a **scatter diagram**.

To draw a scatter diagram, we need data for two variables. In applications where one variable depends to some degree on the other variable, we label the dependent variable Y and the other, called the *independent variable*, X. For example, an individual's income depends somewhat on the number of years of education. Accordingly, we identify income as the dependent variable and label it Y, and we identify years of education as the independent variable and label it X. In other cases where no dependency is evident, we label the variables arbitrarily.

EXAMPLE 3.7

DATA
Xm03-07

Analyzing the Relationship between Price and Size of House

A real estate agent wanted to know to what extent the selling price of a home is related to its size. To acquire this information, he took a sample of 12 homes that had recently sold, recording the price in thousands of dollars and the size in square feet. These data are listed in the accompanying table. Use a graphical technique to describe the relationship between size and price.

Size (ft²)	Price ($1,000)
2,354	315
1,807	229
2,637	355
2,024	261
2,241	234
1,489	216
3,377	308
2,825	306
2,302	289
2,068	204
2,715	265
1,833	195

SOLUTION:

Using the guideline just stated, we label the price of the house Y (dependent variable) and the size X (independent variable). Figure 3.7 depicts the scatter diagram.

FIGURE **3.7** **Scatter Diagram for Example 3.7**

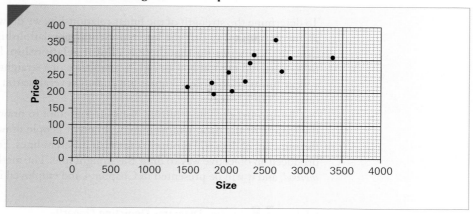

EXCEL Chart

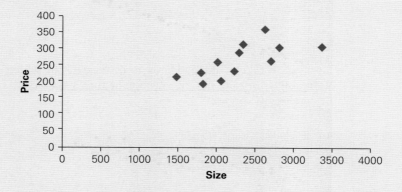

INSTRUCTIONS

1. Type or import the data into two adjacent columns. Store variable X in the first column and variable Y in the next column. (Open Xm03-07.)

2. Click **Insert** and **Scatter**.

INTERPRET

The scatter diagram reveals that, in general, the greater the size of the house, the greater the price. However, there are other variables that determine price. Further analysis may reveal what these other variables are.

3-3a Patterns of Scatter Diagrams

As was the case with histograms, we frequently need to describe verbally how two variables are related. The two most important characteristics are the strength and direction of the linear relationship.

3-3b Linearity

To determine the strength of the linear relationship, we draw a straight line through the points in such a way that the line represents the relationship. If most of the points fall close to the line, we say that there is a **linear relationship**. If most of the points appear to be scattered randomly with only a semblance of a straight line, there is no, or at best, a weak linear relationship. Figure 3.8 depicts several scatter diagrams that exhibit various levels of linearity.

In drawing the line freehand, we would attempt to draw it so that it passes through the middle of the data. Unfortunately, different people drawing a straight line through the same set of data will produce somewhat different lines. Fortunately, statisticians have produced an objective way to draw the straight line. The method is called the *least squares method*, and it will be presented in Chapter 4 and employed in Chapters 16, 17, and 18.

FIGURE **3.8** Scatter Diagrams Depicting Linearity

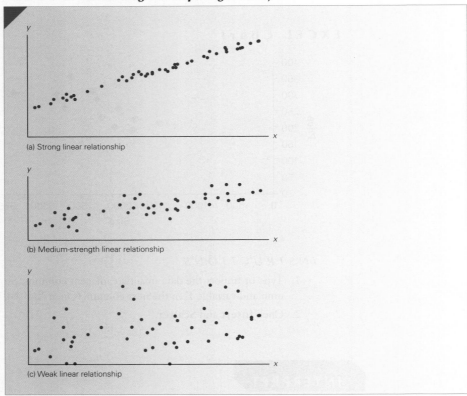

(a) Strong linear relationship

(b) Medium-strength linear relationship

(c) Weak linear relationship

Note that there may well be some other type of relationship, such as a quadratic or exponential one.

3-3c Direction

In general, if one variable increases when the other does, we say that there is a **positive linear relationship**. When the two variables tend to move in opposite directions, we describe the nature of their association as a **negative linear relationship**. (The terms *positive* and *negative* will be explained in Chapter 4.) See Figure 3.9 for examples of scatter diagrams depicting a positive linear relationship, a negative linear relationship, no relationship, and a nonlinear relationship.

3-3d Interpreting a Strong Linear Relationship

In interpreting the results of a scatter diagram it is important to understand that if two variables are linearly related it does not mean that one is causing the other. In fact, we can never conclude that one variable causes another variable. We can express this more eloquently as

Correlation is not causation.

Now that we know what to look for, we can answer the chapter-opening example.

FIGURE **3.9** **Scatter Diagrams Describing Direction**

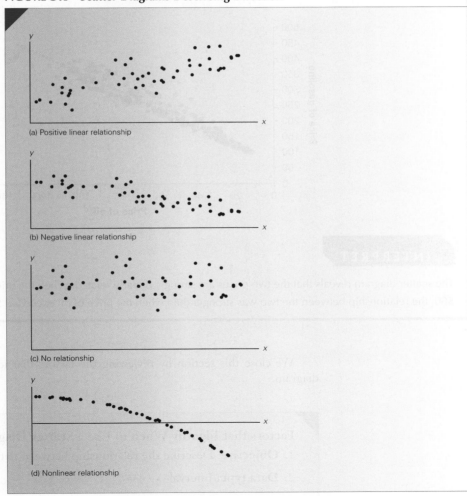

What Is Happening to the Price of Gasoline: Solution

Comstock Images/Getty Images

To understand the fluctuations in the price of gasoline, we need to determine the relationship between the prices of gasoline and crude oil. The appropriate statistical technique is the scatter diagram.

We label the price of gasoline Y (the dependent variable) and the price of oil X (the independent variable).

EXCEL Chart

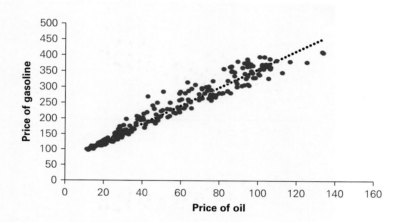

INTERPRET

The scatter diagram reveals that the two prices are strongly linearly related. When the price of oil was below $60, the relationship between the two was stronger than when the price of oil exceeded $60.

We close this section by reviewing the factors that identify the use of a scatter diagram.

Factors that Identify When to Use a Scatter Diagram

1. **Objective**: Describe the relationship between two variables
2. **Data type**: Interval

EXERCISES

3.56 Xr03-56 Black Friday in the United States is the day after Thanksgiving. Many retailers offer door-crasher specials to induce customers to shop at their stores. The number of door-crasher specials is limited. However, the sale price is so low that people who want to buy that item often line up outside the store to wait for it to open. A random sample of Black Friday shoppers was asked how long they waited outside for the store to open (hours) and the amount they expected to save by buying the door-crasher special. Draw a scatter diagram and describe what you have learned from the graph.

Time	3.0	2.5	1.5	5.0	3.0	4.5	7.0	0.5	6.5	6.0
Savings	325	250	275	150	225	350	375	100	400	350

3.57 Xr03-57 Because inflation reduces the purchasing power of the dollar, investors seek investments that will provide higher returns when inflation is higher. It is frequently stated that common stocks provide just such a hedge against inflation. The annual percentage rates of return on common stock and annual inflation rates for a recent 10-year period are listed here.

Year	1	2	3	4	5	6	7	8	9	10
Returns	25	8	6	11	21	−15	12	−1	33	0
Inflation	4.4	4.2	4.1	4.0	5.2	5.0	3.8	2.1	1.7	0.2

Draw a scatter diagram and describe what it tells you about the relationship between returns and inflation.

3.58 Xr03-58 In a university where calculus is a prerequisite for the statistics course, a sample of 15 students was drawn. The marks for calculus and statistics were recorded for each student. The data are as follows:

Calculus	65	58	93	68	74	81	58	85
Statistics	74	72	84	71	68	85	63	73
Calculus	88	75	63	79	80	54	72	
Statistics	79	65	62	71	74	68	73	

a. Draw a scatter diagram of the data.
b. What does the scatter diagram tell you about the relationship between marks in calculus and statistics?

3.59 Xr03-59 The cost of repairing cars involved in collisions is one reason insurance premiums are so high. In an experiment, 10 cars were driven into a wall. The speeds were varied between 2 and 20 mph. The costs of repair were estimated and are listed here. Draw an appropriate graph to analyze the relationship between the two variables. What does the graph tell you?

Speed	2	4	6	8	10	12
Cost	88	124	358	519	699	816

Speed	14	16	18	20
Cost	905	1,521	1,888	2,201

3.60 Xr03-60 It is well known that mathematicians do their best work before the age of 30. But, what happens to them as they grow older? A statistician took a random sample of mathematics professors who were older than 40 and determined their age and the number of top-tier journal publication they produced in the previous 5 years. Draw a scatter diagram and report what it tells you about the research productivity as mathematicians grow older.

Age	48	71	73	41	66	57	50	42	47	59
Publications	12	4	8	22	7	14	16	8	10	13

3.61 Xr03-61 A statistics professor formed the theory that students who handed in quiz and exams early outperformed students who handed in their papers later. To develop data to decide whether her theory is valid, she recorded the amount of time (in minutes) taken by students to submit their midterm tests (time limit 90 minutes) and the subsequent mark for a sample of 12 students.

Time	90	73	86	85	80	87	90	78	84	71	72	88
Mark	68	65	58	94	76	91	62	81	75	83	85	74

Draw a scatter diagram and describe what it tells you about the professor's theory.

The following exercises require the use of a computer.

3.62 Xr03-62 In attempt to determine the factors that affect the amount of energy used, 200 households were analyzed. The number of occupants and the amount of electricity used were measured for each household. Produce a scatter diagram. What does the graph tell you about the relationship between number of people in a household and electrical use?

3.63 Xr03-63 Many downhill skiers eagerly look forward to the winter months and fresh snowfalls.

However, winter also entails cold days. How does the temperature affect skiers' desire? To answer this question, a local ski resort recorded the temperature for 50 randomly selected days and the number of lift tickets they sold. Use a graphical technique to describe the data and interpret your results.

3.64 Xr03-64 One general belief held by observers of the business world is that taller men earn more money than shorter men. In a University of Pittsburgh study, 250 MBA graduates, all about 30 years old, were polled and asked to report their height (in inches) and their annual income (to the nearest $1,000). Draw a scatter diagram and report whether the general belief holds some validity.

3.65 Xr03-65 Do chief executive officers (CEOs) of publicly traded companies earn their compensation? Every year the National Post's Business magazine attempts to answer the question by reporting the CEO's annual compensation ($1,000), the profit (or loss) ($1,000), and the three-year share return (%) for the top 50 Canadian companies.
  a. Draw a scatter diagram of the CEO's annual compensation and the profit of the company.
  b. Draw a scatter diagram of the CEO's annual compensation of the three-year share return.
  c. Based on the scatter diagrams in (a) and (b) report whether the CEO's earn their compensation.

3.66 Xr03-66 Are younger workers less likely to stay with their jobs? To help answer this question, a random sample of workers was selected. All were asked to report their ages and how many months they had been employed with their current employers.
  a. Produce a scatter diagram.
  b. Does your graph produce evidence to indicate that younger workers are less likely to stay with their jobs?

3.67 Xr03-67 A very large contribution to profits for a movie theater is the sales of popcorn, soft drinks, and candy. A movie theater manager speculated that the longer the time between showings of a movie, the greater the sales of concession items. To acquire more information, the manager conducted an experiment. For a month he varied the amount of time between movie showings and calculated the sales.
  a. Draw a scatter diagram of the relationship between sales and time between movie showings.
  b. Is there a positive relationship between the two variables?

3.68 Xr03-68 An analyst employed at a commodities trading firm wanted to explore the relationship between prices of grains and livestock. Theoretically, the prices should move in the same direction because, as the price of livestock increases, more livestock are bred, resulting in a greater demand for grains to feed them. The analyst recorded the monthly grains and livestock subindexes for 1971 to 2008. (Subindexes are based on the prices of several similar commodities. For example, the livestock subindex represents the prices of cattle and hogs.) Draw a scatter diagram of the two subindexes. In general, do the two subindexes move in the same direction?

Source: Bridge Commodity Research Bureau.

3.69 Xr03-69 It is generally believed that higher interest rates result in less employment because companies are more reluctant to borrow to expand their business. To determine whether there is a relationship between bank prime rate and unemployment, an economist collected the monthly prime bank rate and the monthly unemployment rate for the years 1950 to 2012.
  a. Create a scatter diagram of the employment and interest rates.
  b. Is there a negative relationship?

3.70 Xr03-70 Coin collecting is big business around the world. As an illustration, there are more than 500,000 American coins and more than 100,000 Canadian coins for sale/auction on Ebay. Moreover, there are dozens of other coin auctions every month. There are three critical factors that determine the value of a coin. They are rarity, condition, and demand. Condition is now measured on a 70-point scale where 0 is very poor and 70 is perfect. To determine how condition affects price a random sample of auction sales of a 1925 Canadian nickel (a relatively rare coin) was drawn. The auction price ($Canadian), including buyer's premium and the condition were recorded over the past 3 years.
  a. Draw a scatter diagram
  b. What does the graph tell you about condition and price?

3.71 Xr03-71 Does temperature affect the distance that golf balls travel? A Florida golfer decided to try to answer the question. Over the course of a year he measured the distance his drive traveled on a particular flat 400 yard par 4. The temperature (degrees Fahrenheit) was also recorded.

Draw a scatter diagram and describe what it tells you.

GENERAL SOCIAL SURVEY EXERCISES

The following exercises are based on the General Social Survey of 2014.

3.72 GSS2014*   Do educated people tend to marry other educated people? Draw a scatter diagram of EDUC and SPEDUC. What conclusions can you draw from the graph?

3.73 GSS2014*   Do more educated people have children who are also more educated? Answer this question by drawing a scatter diagram of the years of education (EDUC) and the years of education of his or her father (PAEDUC).

3.74 GSS2014*   Refer to Exercise 3.73. Draw a scatter diagram of years of education (EDUC) and years of education of mothers (MAEDUC). What conclusion can you draw?

3.75 GSS2014*   If one half of a married couple works long hours, does the spouse work less? Draw a scatter diagram of HRS and SPHRS to answer the question.

3.76 GSS2014*   Do older people watch more television? Draw a scatter diagram of AGE and TVHOURS. What conclusion can you draw for the chart?

3.77 GSS2014*   Do more educated people watch less television? Draw a scatter diagram of EDUC and TVHOURS. Describe what you have discovered.

3.78 GSS2014*   It seems reasonable to assume that more educated people will wait longer before having children. To determine whether this is reasonable draw a scatter diagram of years of education (EDUC) and the age at which a first child is born (AGEKDBRN). Describe your findings.

Source: Based on General Social Survey of 2014.

SURVEY OF CONSUMER FINANCES EXERCISES

The following exercises are based on the Survey of Consumer Finances 2013.

3.79 [SCF2013 :\MC*]   It seems reasonable to believe that as one grows older one accumulates more money. To see if this is true use a graphical method to determine whether AGE and ASSETS are related. What did you discover?

3.80 [SCF2013:\MC*]   Are younger Americans more educated than older Americans? Answer the question by using a graphical technique to examine the relationship between AGE and EDUC. What does the graph tell you?

3.81 [SCF2013:\MC*]   How long does it take for someone to be deeply in debt? If it takes a long time we would expect AGE and DEBT to be related. Determine if they are by using a graphical technique. What have you learned?

3-4 / ART AND SCIENCE OF GRAPHICAL PRESENTATIONS

In this chapter and in Chapter 2, we introduced a number of graphical techniques. The emphasis was on how to construct each one manually and how to command the computer to draw them. In this section, we discuss how to use graphical techniques effectively. We introduce the concept of **graphical excellence**, which is a term we apply to techniques that are informative and concise and that impart information clearly to their viewers. Additionally, we discuss an equally important concept: graphical integrity and its enemy **graphical deception**.

3-4a Graphical Excellence

Graphical excellence is achieved when the following characteristics apply.

1. **The graph presents large data sets concisely and coherently.** Graphical techniques were created to summarize and describe large data sets. Small data sets are easily summarized with a table. One or two numbers can best be presented in a sentence.

2. **The ideas and concepts the statistics practitioner wants to deliver are clearly understood by the viewer.** The chart is designed to describe what would otherwise be described in words. An excellent chart is one that can replace thousand words and still be clearly comprehended by its readers.

3. **The graph encourages the viewer to compare two or more variables.** Graphs displaying only one variable provide very little information. Graphs are often best used to depict relationships between two or more variables or to explain how and why the observed results occurred.

4. **The display induces the viewer to address the substance of the data and not the form of the graph.** The form of the graph is supposed to help present the substance. If the form replaces the substance, the chart is not performing its function.

5. **There is no distortion of what the data reveal.** You cannot make statistical techniques say whatever you like. A knowledgeable reader will easily see through distortions and deception. We will endeavor to make you a knowledgeable reader by describing graphical deception later in this section.

Edward Tufte, professor of statistics at Yale University, summarized graphical excellence this way:

1. Graphical excellence is the well-designed presentation of interesting data—a matter of substance, of statistics, and of design.

2. Graphical excellence is that which gives the viewer the greatest number of ideas in the shortest time with the least ink in the smallest space.

3. Graphical excellence is nearly always multivariate.

4. Graphical excellence requires telling the truth about the data.

Now let's examine the chart that has been acclaimed the best chart ever drawn.

Figure 3.10 depicts a graph drawn by Charles Joseph Minard, a French civil engineer. It describes an important historical event, Napoleon Bonaparte's invasion of Russia in 1812. The striped band is a time series depicting the size of the army at various places on the map, which is also part of the chart. When Napoleon invaded Russia by crossing the Niemen River on June 21, 1812, there were 422,000 soldiers. By the time the army reached Moscow, the number had dwindled to 100,000. At that point, the army started its retreat. The black band represents the army in retreat. At the bottom of the chart, we see the dates starting with October 1813. Just above the dates, Minard drew another time series, this one showing the temperature. It was bitterly cold during the fall, and many soldiers died of exposure. As you can see, the temperature dipped to −30 on December 6. The chart is effective because it depicts five variables clearly and succinctly.

FIGURE **3.10**   **Chart Depicting Napoleon's Invasion and Retreat from Russia in 1812**

Source: Edward Tufte, *The Visual Display of Quantitative Information* (Cheshire, CT: Graphics Press, 1983), p .41.

3-4b Graphical Deception

The use of graphs and charts is pervasive in newspapers, magazines, business and economic reports, and seminars, in large part because of the increasing availability of computers and software that allow the storage, retrieval, manipulation, and summary of large masses of raw data. It is therefore more important than ever to be able to evaluate critically the information presented by means of graphical techniques. In the final analysis, graphical techniques merely create a visual impression, which is easy to distort. In fact, distortion is so easy and commonplace that in 1992, the Canadian Institute of Chartered Accountants found it necessary to begin setting guidelines for financial graphics, after a study of hundreds of the annual reports of major corporations found that 8% contained at least one misleading graph that covered up bad results. Although the heading for this section mentions deception, it is quite possible for an inexperienced person inadvertently to create distorted impressions with graphs. In any event, you should be aware of possible methods of graphical deception. This section illustrates a few of them.

The first thing to watch for is a graph without a scale on one axis. The line chart of a firm's sales in Figure 3.11 might represent a growth rate of 100% or 1% over the 5 years depicted, depending on the vertical scale. It is best simply to ignore such graphs.

FIGURE **3.11**   **Graph without Scale**

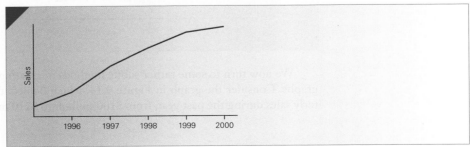

A second trap to avoid is being influenced by a graph's caption. Your impression of the trend in interest rates might be different, depending on whether you read a newspaper carrying caption (a) or caption (b) in Figure 3.12.

FIGURE **3.12** **Graphs with Different Captions**

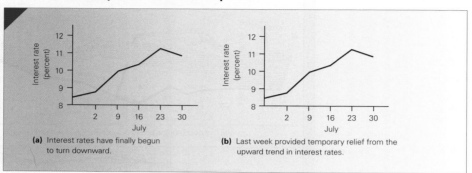

(a) Interest rates have finally begun to turn downward.

(b) Last week provided temporary relief from the upward trend in interest rates.

Perspective is often distorted if only absolute changes in value, rather than percentage changes, are reported. A $1 drop in the price of your $2 stock is relatively more distressing than a $1 drop in the price of your $100 stock. On January 9, 1986, newspapers throughout North America displayed graphs similar to the one shown in Figure 3.13 and reported that the stock market, as measured by the Dow Jones Industrial Average (DJIA), had suffered its worst 1-day loss ever on the previous day. The loss was 39 points, exceeding even the loss of Black Tuesday: October 28, 1929. While the loss was indeed a large one, many news reports failed to mention that the 1986 level of the DJIA was much higher than the 1929 level. A better perspective on the situation could be gained by noticing that the loss on January 8, 1986, represented a 2.5% decline, whereas the decline in 1929 was 12.8%. As a point of interest, we note that the stock market was 12% higher within 2 months of this historic drop and 40% higher 1 year later. The largest one-day percentage drop in the DJIA is 24.4% (December 12, 1914).

FIGURE **3.13** **Graph Showing Drop in the DJIA**

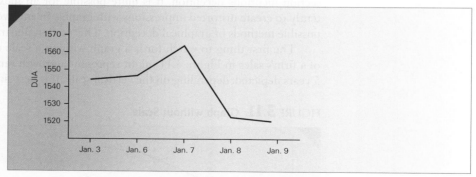

We now turn to some rather subtle methods of creating distorted impressions with graphs. Consider the graph in Figure 3.14, which depicts the growth in a firm's quarterly sales during the past year, from $100 million to $110 million. This 10% growth in quarterly sales can be made to appear more dramatic by stretching the vertical axis—a technique that involves changing the scale on the vertical axis so that a given dollar amount is represented by a greater height than before. As a result, the rise in sales appears to be greater because the slope of the graph is visually (but not numerically) steeper. The expanded scale is usually accommodated by employing a break in the vertical axis, as in Figure 3.15(a), or by truncating the vertical axis, as in Figure 3.15(b), so that the vertical scale begins at a point greater than zero. The effect of making slopes appear steeper can also be created by shrinking the horizontal axis, in which case points on the horizontal axis are moved closer together.

FIGURE **3.14** **Graph Showing Growth in Quarterly Sales 1**

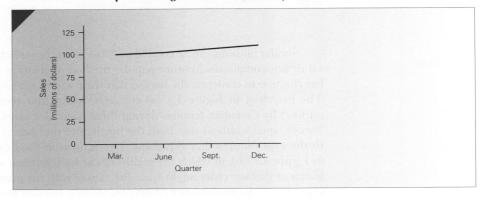

FIGURE **3.15** **Graph Showing Growth in Quarterly Sales 2**

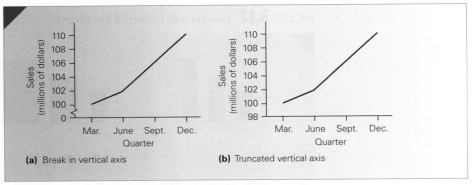

Just the opposite effect is obtained by stretching the horizontal axis; that is, spreading out the points on the horizontal axis to increase the distance between them so that slopes and trends will appear to be less steep. The graph of a firm's profits presented in Figure 3.16(a) shows considerable swings, both upward and downward in the profits from one quarter to the next. However, the firm could convey the impression of reasonable stability in profits from quarter to quarter by stretching the horizontal axis, as shown in Figure 3.16(b).

FIGURE **3.16** Graph Showing Considerable Swings or Relative Stability

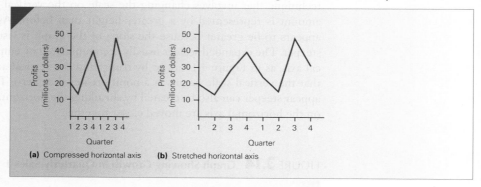

(a) Compressed horizontal axis   **(b)** Stretched horizontal axis

Similar illusions can be created with bar charts by stretching or shrinking the vertical or horizontal axis. Another popular method of creating distorted impressions with bar charts is to construct the bars so that their widths are proportional to their heights. The bar chart in Figure 3.17(a) correctly depicts the average weekly amount spent on food by Canadian families during three particular years. This chart correctly uses bars of equal width so that both the height and the area of each bar are proportional to the expenditures they represent. The growth in food expenditures is exaggerated in Figure 3.17(b), in which the widths of the bars increase with their heights. A quick glance at this bar chart might leave the viewer with the mistaken impression that food expenditures increased fourfold over the decade, because the 1995 bar is four times the size of the 1985 bar.

FIGURE **3.17** Correct and Distorted Bar Charts

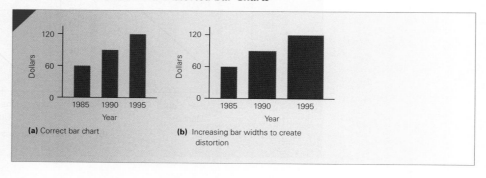

(a) Correct bar chart   **(b)** Increasing bar widths to create distortion

You should be on the lookout for size distortions, particularly in pictograms, which replace the bars with pictures of objects (such as bags of money, people, or animals) to enhance the visual appeal. Figure 3.18 displays the misuse of a pictogram—the snowman grows in width as well as height. The proper use of a pictogram is shown in Figure 3.19, which effectively uses pictures of Coca-Cola bottles.

FIGURE **3.18** Misuse of Pictogram

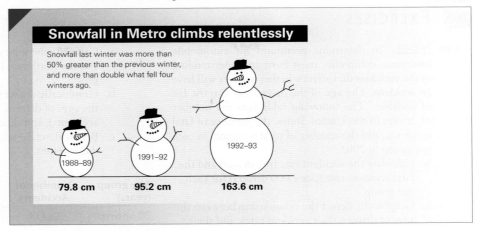

FIGURE **3.19** Correct Pictogram

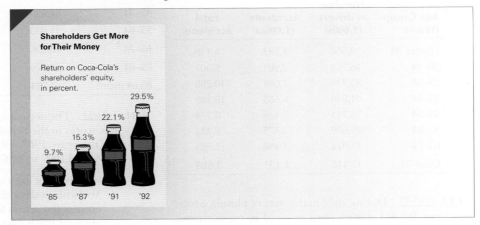

The preceding examples of creating a distorted impression using graphs are not exhaustive, but they include some of the more popular methods. They should also serve to make the point that graphical techniques are used to create a visual impression, and the impression you obtain may be a distorted one unless you examine the graph with care. You are less likely to be misled if you focus your attention on the numerical values that the graph represents. Begin by carefully noting the scales on both axes; graphs with unmarked axes should be ignored completely.

EXERCISES

3.82 Xr03-82 To determine premiums for automobile insurance, companies must have an understanding of the variables that affect whether a driver will have an accident. The age of the driver may top the list of variables. The following table lists the number of drivers in the United States, the number of fatal accidents, and the number of total accidents in each age group in 2002.

a. Calculate the accident rate (per driver) and the fatal accident rate (per 1,000 drivers) for each age group.
b. Graphically depict the relationship between the ages of drivers, their accident rates, and their fatal accident rates (per 1,000 drivers).
c. Briefly describe what you have learned.

Age Group (Years)	Number of drivers (1,000s)	Accidents (1,000s)	Fatal accidents
Under 20	9,508	3,543	6,118
20–24	16,768	2,901	5,907
25–34	33,734	7,061	10,288
35–44	41,040	6,665	10,309
45–54	38,711	5,136	8,274
55–64	25,609	2,775	5,322
65–74	15,812	1,498	2,793
Over 74	12,118	1,121	3,689

3.83 Xr03-83 During 2002 in the state of Florida, a total of 365,474 drivers were involved in car accidents. The accompanying table breaks down this number by the age group of the driver and whether the driver was injured or killed. (There were actually 371,877 accidents, but the driver's age was not recorded in 6,413 of these.)

a. Calculate the injury rate (per 100 accidents) and the death rate (per accident) for each age group.
b. Graphically depict the relationship between the ages of drivers, their injury rate (per 100 accidents), and their death rate.
c. Briefly describe what you have learned from these graphs.

Age group (years)	Number of Accidents	Drivers Injured	Drivers Killed
20 or less	52,313	21,762	217
21–24	38,449	16,016	185
25–34	78,703	31,503	324
35–44	76,152	30,542	389
45–54	54,699	22,638	260
55–64	31,985	13,210	167
65–74	18,896	7,892	133
75–84	11,526	5,106	138
85 or more	2,751	1,223	65

3.84 Xr03-84 The accompanying table lists the average test scores in the Scholastic Assessment Test (SAT) for the years 1967, 1970, 1975, 1980, 1985, 1990, 1995, and 1997 to 2007.

Draw a chart for each of the following.

a. You wish to show that both verbal and mathematics test scores for all students have not changed much over the years.
b. The exact opposite of part (a).
c. You want to claim that there are no differences between genders.
d. You want to "prove" that differences between genders exist.

Year	Verbal All	Verbal Male	Verbal Female	Math All	Math Male	Math Female
1967	543	540	545	516	535	495
1970	537	536	538	512	531	493
1975	512	515	509	498	518	479
1980	502	506	498	492	515	473
1985	509	514	503	500	522	480
1990	500	505	496	501	521	483
1995	504	505	502	506	525	490
1997	505	507	503	511	530	494
1998	505	509	502	512	531	496

1999	505	509	502	511	531	495
2000	505	507	504	514	533	498
2001	506	509	502	514	533	498
2002	504	507	502	516	534	500
2003	507	512	503	519	537	503
2004	508	512	504	518	537	501
2005	508	513	505	520	538	504
2006	503	505	502	518	536	502
2007	502	504	502	515	533	499
2008	502	504	500	515	533	500
2009	501	503	498	515	534	499

3.85 <u>Xr03-85</u> The monthly unemployment rate in one state for the past 12 months is listed here.
   a. Draw a bar chart of these data with 6.0% as the lowest point on the vertical axis.
   b. Draw a bar chart of these data with 0.0% as the lowest point on the vertical axis.
   c. Discuss the impression given by the two charts.
   d. Which chart would you use? Explain.

Month	1	2	3	4	5	6	7	8	9	10	11	12
Rate	7.5	7.6	7.5	7.3	7.2	7.1	7.0	6.7	6.4	6.5	6.3	6.0

CHAPTER SUMMARY

Histograms are used to describe a single set of interval data. Statistics practitioners examine several aspects of the shapes of histograms. These are symmetry, number of modes, and its resemblance to a bell shape. We described the difference between time-series data and cross-sectional data. Time series are graphed by line charts. To analyze the relationship between two interval variables, we draw a scatter diagram. We look for the direction and strength of the linear relationship.

To analyze the relationship between two interval variables, we draw a scatter diagram. We look for the direction and strength of the linear relationship.

IMPORTANT TERMS:

Classes   47
Histogram   48
Symmetric   51
Positively skewed   51
Negatively skewed   51
Modal class   52
Unimodal histogram   52
Bimodal histogram   52

Cross-sectional data   60
Time-series data   60
Line chart   60
Scatter diagram   66
Linear relationship   68
Positive linear relationship   68
Negative linear relationship   68
Graphical excellence   73
Graphical deception   73

EXCEL OUTPUT AND INSTRUCTIONS:

Graphical Technique	Excel
Histogram	48
Line chart	61
Scatter diagram	67

CHAPTER EXERCISES

The following exercises require a computer and software.

3.86 Xr03-86 Gold and precious metals have traditionally been considered a hedge against inflation. If
this is true, we would expect that a fund made up of
precious metals (gold, silver, platinum, and others)
would have a strong positive relationship with the
inflation rate. To see whether this is true, a statistics practitioner collected the monthly CPI and the
monthly precious metal subindex, which is based on
the prices of gold, silver, platinum, and so on for the
years 1975 to 2008. These figures were used to calculate the monthly inflation rate and the monthly
return on the precious metals subindex. Use a graphical technique to determine the nature of the relationship between the inflation rate and the return on
the subindex. What does the graph tell you?

Source: U.S. Treasury and Bridge Commodity Research Bureau.

3.87 Xr03-87 The monthly exchange rate of U.S. dollars
to one Australian dollar was recorded from 1971 to
2016. Draw a graph that shows how the exchange
rate has varied over the past 41 years.

Source: Federal Reserve Economic Data.

3.88 Xr03-88 Studies of twins may reveal more about
the "nature" or "nurture" debate. The issue being
debated is whether nature or the environment
has more effect on individual traits such as intelligence. Suppose that a sample of identical twins
was selected and their IQs measured. Use a suitable
graphical technique to display the data. Describe
what it tells you about the relationship between the
IQs of identical twins.

3.89 Xr03-89 An economist wanted to determine
whether a relationship existed between interest
rates and currencies (measured in U.S. dollars). He
recorded the monthly interest rate and the currency
indexes for the years 1982 to 2008. Graph the data
and describe the results.

Source: Bridge Commodity Research Bureau.

3.90 Xr03-90 SPAM is an unfortunate fact of life. A
random sample of university students was asked to
report the number of Spam e-mails they receive in
a typical day. Use an appropriate graphical method
to display these data.

3.91 Xr03-91 In Chapters 16, 17, and 18, we introduce
regression analysis, which addresses the relationships among variables. One of the first applications
of regression analysis was to analyze the relationship
between the heights of fathers and sons. Suppose
that in a sample of 80 father–son combinations their
heights were recorded.

a. Draw a graph that displays the relationship.
b. What is the direction of the relationship?
c. Does it appear that there is a linear relationship
   between the two variables? Explain.

3.92 Xr03-92 When the Dow-Jones Industrial Index
increases it usually means that the economy is growing, which in turn usually means that the unemployment rate is low. A statistics professor pointed out that
in numerous periods (including when this edition was
being written) the stock market has been booming
while the rest of the economy was performing poorly.
To learn more about the issue, the monthly closing
DJIA and the monthly unemployment rates were
recorded for the years 1950 to 2016. Draw a graph of
the data and report your results.

Source: Federal Reserve Economic Data and the Wall Street Journal.

3.93 Xr03-93 The monthly values of one British pound
measured in American dollars since 1971 were
recorded. Produce a graph that shows how the
exchange rate has varied over the past 45 years.

Source: Federal Reserve Economic Data.

3.94 Xr03-94 Do better golfers play faster than poorer
ones? To determine whether a relationship exists, a
sample of 125 foursomes was selected. Their total
scores and the amount of time taken to complete
the round were recorded. Graphically depict the
data and describe what they tell you about the relationship between total score and time.

3.95 Xr03-95 The value of monthly U.S. exports to
Mexico and imports from Mexico (in $ millions)
since 1985 were recorded.
a. Draw a chart that depicts exports.
b. Draw a chart that exhibits imports.
c. Compute the trade balance and graph these data.
d. What do these charts tell you?

Source: Federal Reserve Economic Data.

3.96 Xr03-96 An increasing number of consumers prefer
to use debit cards in place of both cash and credit
cards. To analyze the relationship between the
amounts of purchases made with debit and credit
cards, 240 people were interviewed and asked to
report the amount of money spent on purchases
using debit cards and the amount of money spent
using credit cards during the previous month. Draw
a graph of the data and summarize your findings.

3.97 Xr03-97 Most publicly traded companies have
boards of directors. The rate of pay varies considerably. A survey was undertaken by the *Globe and Mail*
wherein 100 companies were surveyed and asked to

report how much their directors were paid annually. Use a graphical technique to present these data.

3.98 Xr03-98   Refer to Exercise 3.97. In addition to reporting the annual payment per director, the survey recorded the number of meetings last year. Use a graphical technique to summarize and present these data.

3.99 Xr03-99   Is airline travel becoming safer? To help answer this question, a statistics professor recorded the number of fatal accidents involving airliners carrying at least 19 passengers that occurred in the years 1950 to 2014. Use a graphical method to answer the question.

Source: PlaneCrashInfo.com.

3.100 Xr03-100   Most car-rental companies keep their cars for about a year and then sell them to used car dealers. Suppose that one company decided to sell the used cars themselves. Because most used car buyers make their decision on what to buy and how much to spend based on the car's odometer reading, this would be an important issue for the car-rental company. To develop information about the mileage shown on the company's rental cars, the general manager took a random sample of 658 customers and recorded the average number of miles driven per day. Use a graphical technique to display these data.

3.101 Xr03-101   Several years ago the Barnes Exhibit toured major cities all over the world, with millions of people flocking to see it. Dr. Albert Barnes was a wealthy art collector who accumulated a large number of impressionist masterpieces; the total exceeds 800 paintings. Because of the size and value of the collection, it was predicted (correctly) that in each city a large number of people would come to view the paintings. Because space was limited, most galleries had to sell tickets that were valid at one time (much like a play). In this way, they were able to control the number of visitors at any one time. To judge how many people to let in at any time it was necessary to know the length of time people would spend at the exhibit; longer times would dictate smaller audiences; shorter times would allow for the sale of more tickets. The manager of a gallery that will host the exhibit realized her facility can comfortably and safely hold about 250 people at any one time. Although the demand will vary throughout the day and from weekday to weekend, she believes that the demand will not drop below 500 at any time. To help make a decision about how many tickets to sell she acquired the amount of time a sample of 400 people spent at the exhibit from another city. What ticket procedure should the museum management institute?

The following exercises are based on data sets that include additional data referenced in previously reported examples and exercises.

3.102 Xm03-03*, Xm03-04*   Examples 3.3 and 3.4 listed final marks in the business statistics course and the mathematical statistics course. The professor also provided the final marks in the first-year required calculus course. Graphically describe the relationship between calculus and statistics marks. What information were you able to develop?

3.103 Xm03-03*, Xm03-04*   In addition to the previously discussed data in Examples 3.3 and 3.4, the professor listed the midterm mark. Conduct an analysis of the relationship between the final exam mark and the midterm mark in each course. What does this analysis tell you?

3.104 Xr02-65*   Two other questions were asked in Exercise 2.65.

Number of weeks job searching?
Salary in ($ thousands)?

The placement office wants the following:
   a. Graphically describe salary.
   b. Is salary related to the number of weeks needed to land the job?

Message for United States residents: By the time that readers of this book get it in their hands the U.S. federal government debt will exceed $20 trillion. If you are a young American who will be paying tax in the near future the next three exercises should be of interest to you.

3.105 Xr03-105   The size of the U.S. federal government debt was recorded for every year starting in 1790. (Yes, the government was in debt even then.) Use a graphical technique to display these figures. Briefly describe what the graph tells you.

3.106 Xr03-106   Use the population of the United States from 1935 to 2015 to compute the per capita debt figures. Briefly describe what you have learned.

3.107 Xr03-107   Use the U.S. CPI Annual to adjust the per capita debt figures to 1982–1984 dollars. Graph these figures. Does removing the effect of inflation allay your concerns for the future? Explain.

Exercises 3.105 to 3.107 dealt with the United States government debt. The next three exercises should be of interest to Canadian students.

3.108 Xr03-108   The debt owed by the Canadian federal government was recorded for the years 1870 to 2015. Use a graph to present these figures. Should future tax-paying Canadians be concerned? Briefly explain.

3.109 Xr03-109   Use the population of Canada from 1870 to compute the per capita debt. Graph the results. What have you learned?

3.110 Xr03-110   Use the Canada CPI Annual to calculate the inflation adjusted (using 2002 as the base) per capita debt from 1915 to 2015. Briefly describe your results.

CASE 3.1   The Question of Global Warming

DATA
C03-01a
C03-01b

In the last part of the 20th century, scientists developed the theory that the planet was warming and the primary cause was the increasing amounts of carbon dioxide (CO_2), which is the product of burning oil, natural gas, and coal (fossil fuels). Although many climatologists believe in the so-called greenhouse effect, there are many others who do not subscribe to this theory. There are three critical questions that need to be answered in order to resolve the issue.

1. Is the earth actually warming? To answer this question, we need accurate temperature measurements over a large number of years. But how do we measure the temperature before the invention of accurate thermometers? Moreover, how do we go about measuring the earth's temperature even with accurate thermometers?

2. If the planet is warming, is there a manmade cause or is it natural fluctuation? The temperature of earth has increased and decreased many times in its long history. We've had higher temperatures and we've had lower temperatures, including various ice ages. In fact, a period called the "little ice age" ended around the middle to the end of the 19th century. Then the temperature rose until about 1940, at which point it decreased until 1975. An April 28, 1975, *Newsweek* article discussed the possibility of global cooling, which seemed to be the consensus among scientists.

3. If the planet is warming, is CO_2 the cause? There are greenhouse gases in the atmosphere without which the earth would be considerably colder. These gases include methane, water vapor, and carbon dioxide. All these gases occur naturally. Carbon dioxide is vital to our life on earth because it is necessary for growing plants. The amount of CO_2 produced by fossil fuels is relatively a small proportion of all the CO_2 in the atmosphere.

The generally accepted procedure is to record monthly temperature anomalies. To do so, we calculate the average for each month over many years. We then calculate any deviations between the latest month's temperature reading and its average. A positive anomaly would represent a month's temperature that is above the average. A negative anomaly indicates a month in which the temperature is less than the average. One key question is how we measure the temperature.

Although there are many different sources of data, we have chosen to provide you with one, the National Climatic Data Center (NCDC), which is affiliated with the National Oceanic and Atmospheric Administration (NOAA). (Other sources tend to agree with the NCDC's data.) C03-01a stores the monthly temperature anomalies from 1880 to 2016.

The best measures of CO_2 levels in the atmosphere come from the Mauna Loa Observatory in Hawaii, which started measuring this variable in December 1958 and continues to do so. However, attempts to estimate CO_2 levels prior to 1958 are as controversial as the methods used to estimate temperatures. These techniques include taking ice-core samples from the arctic and measuring the amount of CO_2 trapped in the ice from which estimates of atmospheric CO_2 are produced. To avoid this controversy, we will use the Mauna Loa Observatory numbers only. These data are stored in file C03-01b. (Note that some of the original data are missing and were replaced by interpolated values.)

a. Use whichever techniques you wish to determine whether there is global warming.

b. Use a graphical technique to determine whether there is a relationship between temperature anomalies and CO_2 levels.

CASE 3.2   Did Global Warming Cause Canada's Forest Fires?

DATA
C03-02a
C03-02b
C03-02c

In the summer of 2016, forest fires burned about a quarter of the homes and businesses in Fort McMurray Alberta. Some newspapers printed claims by scientists that the forest fires were the result of global warming. To examine this claim, we have recorded the number of forest fires and the areas burned (in hectares) annually from 1970 to 2015. Note: a hectare is equal to 10,000 square meters. It is about two and half times the size of an acre.) Use a graphical technique to graph the number of forest fires and the areas burned. Use annual temperature anomalies from 1970 to 2015 to see if there is a relationship between temperature and forest fires and areas burned. Briefly describe your results

CASE 3.3   Does Global Warming Increase the Frequency of Tornadoes?

DATA
C03-03a
C03-03b

If the earth is warming does it mean that we can expect an increase in extreme weather outcomes such as tornadoes? To answer the question we recorded the monthly number of tornadoes that occurred in the United States and monthly temperature anomalies between 2000 and 2015. Use a graphical technique to examine the relationship between temperature and the frequency of tornadoes.

CASE 3.4   Economic Freedom and Prosperity

DATA
C03-04a
C03-04b

Adam Smith published The Wealth of Nations in 1776 in which he argued that when institutions protect the liberty of individuals, greater prosperity results for all. Since 1995, the *Wall Street Journal* and the Heritage Foundation, a think tank in Washington D.C. have produced the Index of Economic Freedom for all countries in the world. The index is based on a subjective score for 10 freedoms. These are business, freedom, trade freedom, fiscal freedom, government size, monetary freedom, investment freedom, property rights freedom from corruption, and labor freedom. We downloaded the scores for the years 1995 to 2015 and stored them in C03-04a. From the CIA *Factbook* we determined the per capita gross domestic product (GDP), measured in terms purchasing power parity (PPP), which makes it possible to compare the GDP for all countries. The per capita GDP PPP figures for 2013 (the latest year available) are stored in C03-04b. Use the 2015 Freedom Index scores, the GDP PPP figures, and a graphical technique to see how freedom and prosperity are related.

lzf/Shutterstock.com

4

NUMERICAL DESCRIPTIVE TECHNIQUES

CHAPTER OUTLINE

The Cost of One More Win in Major League Baseball

Andrey Yurlov/Shutterstock.com

DATA
Xm04-00

In the era of free agency, professional sports teams must compete for the services of the best players. It is generally believed that only teams whose salaries place them in the top quarter have a chance of winning the championship. Efforts have been made to provide balance by establishing salary caps or some form of equalization. To examine the problem, we gathered data from the 2015 baseball season. For each team in major league baseball, we recorded the number of wins and the team payroll.

To make informed decisions, we need to know how the number of wins and the team payroll are related. After the statistical technique is presented, we return to this problem and solve it.

INTRODUCTION

In Chapters 2 and 3, we presented several graphical techniques that describe data. In this chapter, we introduce numerical descriptive techniques that allow the statistics practitioner to be more precise in describing various characteristics of a sample or population. These techniques are critical to the development of statistical inference.

As we pointed out in Chapter 2, arithmetic calculations can be applied to interval data only. Consequently, most of the techniques introduced here may be used only to numerically describe interval data. However, some of the techniques can be used for ordinal data, and one of the techniques can be employed for nominal data.

When we introduced the histogram, we commented that there are several bits of information that we look for. The first is the location of the center of the data. In Section 4-1, we will present **measures of central location**. Another important characteristic that we seek from a histogram is the spread of the data. The spread will be measured more precisely by measures of variability, which we present in Section 4-2. Section 4-3 introduces measures of relative standing.

In Section 3-3, we introduced the scatter diagram, which is a graphical method that we use to analyze the relationship between two interval variables. The numerical counterparts to the scatter diagram are called *measures of linear relationship*, and they are presented in Section 4-4.

Section 4.5 features an application in finance and in Section 4.6 we compare the information provided by graphical and numerical techniques. Finally, we complete this chapter by providing guidelines on how to explore data and retrieve information.

SAMPLE STATISTIC OR POPULATION PARAMETER

Recall the terms introduced in Chapter 1: population, sample, parameter, and statistic. A parameter is a descriptive measurement about a population, and a statistic is a descriptive measurement about a sample. In this chapter, we introduce a dozen descriptive measurements. For each one, we describe how to calculate both the population parameter and the sample statistic. However, in most realistic applications, populations are very large—in fact, virtually infinite. The formulas describing the calculation of parameters are not practical and are seldom used. They are provided here primarily to teach the concept and the notation. In Chapter 7, we introduce probability distributions, which describe populations. At that time we show how parameters are calculated from probability distributions. In general, small data sets of the type we feature in this book are samples.

4-1 / MEASURES OF CENTRAL LOCATION

4-1a Arithmetic Mean

There are three different measures that we use to describe the center of a set of data. The first is the best known, the *arithmetic mean*, which we'll refer to simply as the **mean**. Students may be more familiar with its other name, the *average*. The mean is computed by summing the observations and dividing by the number of observations. We label the observations in a sample $x_1, x_2, \ldots, x_n$, where x_1 is the first observation, x_2 is the second, and so on until x_n, where n is the sample size. As a result, the sample mean is denoted by $\bar{x}$. In a population, the number of observations is labeled N and the population mean is denoted by μ (Greek letter *mu*).

Mean

$$\text{Population mean: } \mu = \frac{\sum_{i=1}^{N} x_i}{N}$$

$$\text{Sample mean: } \bar{x} = \frac{\sum_{i=1}^{n} x_i}{n}$$

EXAMPLE 4.1

Mean Time Spent on the Internet

A sample of 10 adults was asked to report the number of hours they spent on the Internet the previous month. The results are listed here. Manually calculate the sample mean.

| 0 | 7 | 12 | 5 | 33 | 14 | 8 | 0 | 9 | 22 |

SOLUTION:

Using our notation, we have $x_1 = 0, x_2 = 7, \ldots, x_{10} = 22$, and $n = 10$. The sample mean is

$$\bar{x} = \frac{\sum_{i=1}^{n} x_i}{n} = \frac{0 + 7 + 12 + 5 + 33 + 14 + 8 + 0 + 9 + 22}{10} = \frac{110}{10} = 11.0$$

EXAMPLE 4.2

DATA
Xm03-01

Mean Age of ACBL Members

Refer to Example 3.1. Find the mean age of the sample of ACBL members.

SOLUTION:

To calculate the mean, we add the observations and divide by the size of the sample. Thus,

$$\bar{x} = \frac{\sum_{i=1}^{n} x_i}{n} = \frac{73 + 53 + 66 + \cdots + 17}{200} = \frac{10,753}{200} = 53.765$$

EXCEL Function

There are several ways to command Excel to compute the mean. If we simply want to compute the mean and no other statistics, we can use the AVERAGE function.

INSTRUCTIONS

Type or import the data into one or more columns. (Open Xm03-01.) Type into any empty cell

$$= \textbf{AVERAGE}([\text{Input Range}])$$

For Example 4.2, we would type into any empty cell

$$= \textbf{AVERAGE}(\text{A1:A201})$$

The active cell would store the mean as 53.765.

4-1b Median

The second most popular measure of central location is the *median*.

> **Median**
>
> The **median** is calculated by placing all the observations in order (ascending or descending). The observation that falls in the middle is the median. The sample and population medians are computed in the same way. When there is an even number of observations, the median is determined by averaging the two observations in the middle.

EXAMPLE 4.3

Median Time Spent on Internet

Find the median for the data in Example 4.1.

SOLUTION:

When placed in ascending order, the data appear as follows:

| 0 | 0 | 5 | 7 | 8 | 9 | 12 | 14 | 22 | 33 |

The median is the average of the fifth and sixth observations (the middle two), which are 8 and 9, respectively. Thus, the median is 8.5.

EXAMPLE 4.4

DATA
Xm03-01

Median Age of Sample of ACBL Members

Find the median of the 200 observations in Example 3.1.

SOLUTION:

Because there is an even number of observations the median is the average of the two middle observations. When all the observations are placed in order, the 100th and 101st observations are 54 and 55, respectively. Thus,

$$\text{Median} = \frac{54 + 55}{2} = 54.5$$

EXCEL Function

To calculate the median use the MEDIAN function. For Example 4.4 we typed into an empty cell

= MEDIAN(A1:201)

The result is 54.5.

INTERPRET

Half the observations are below 54.5 and half are above 54.5.

4-1c Mode

The third and last measure of central location that we present here is the *mode*.

> **Mode**
> The **mode** is defined as the observation (or observations) that occurs with the greatest frequency. Both the statistic and parameter are computed in the same way.

For populations and large samples, it is preferable to report the **modal class**, which we defined in Chapter 2. There are several problems with using the mode as a measure of central location. First, in a small sample it may not be a very good measure. Second, it may not be unique.

EXAMPLE 4.5 | Mode Time Spent on Internet

Find the mode for the data in Example 4.1.

SOLUTION:

All observations except 0 occur once. There are two 0s. Thus, the mode is 0. As you can see, this is a poor measure of central location. It is nowhere near the center of the data. Compare this with the mean 11.0 and median 8.5 and you can appreciate that in this example the mean and median are superior measures.

EXAMPLE 4.6 | Mode of Long-Distance Bill

DATA
Xm03-01

Determine the mode for Example 3.1.

SOLUTION:

The observation that occurs with the greatest frequency is 60, which occurs 8 times.

EXCEL Function

To compute the mode use the MODE function. Note that if there is more than one mode, Excel prints only the smallest one, without indicating that there are other modes.

Excel Printing All Measures of Central Location Plus Other Statistics Excel can produce the measures of central location and a variety of other statistics that we will introduce in later sections.

EXCEL Data Analysis

Excel Output for Examples 4.2, 4.4, and 4.6

	A	B
1	Ages	
2		
3	Mean	53.765
4	Standard Error	1.40
5	Median	54.5
6	Mode	60
7	Standard Deviation	19.76
8	Sample Variance	390.52
9	Kurtosis	−0.8851
10	Skewness	0.0025
11	Range	83
12	Minimum	16
13	Maximum	99
14	Sum	10753
15	Count	200

INSTRUCTIONS

1. Type or import the data into one column. (Open Xm03-01.)
2. Click **Data, Data Analysis**, and **Descriptive Statistics**.
3. Specify the **Input Range** (A1:A201) and click **Summary Statistics**.

4-1d Mean, Median, Mode: Which Is Best?

With three measures from which to choose, which one should we use? There are several factors to consider when making our choice of measure of central location. The mean is generally our first selection. However, there are several circumstances when the median is better. The mode is seldom the best measure of central location. One advantage the median holds is that it is not as sensitive to extreme values as is the mean. To illustrate, consider the data in Example 4.1. The mean was 11.0, and the median was 8.5. Now suppose that the respondent who reported 33 hours actually reported 133 hours (obviously an Internet addict). The mean becomes

$$\bar{x} = \frac{\sum_{i=1}^{n} x_i}{n} = \frac{0 + 7 + 12 + 5 + 133 + 14 + 8 + 0 + 22}{10} = \frac{210}{10} = 21.0$$

This value is exceeded by only 2 of the 10 observations in the sample, making this statistic a poor measure of central location. The median stays the same. When there is a relatively small number of extreme observations (either very small or very large, but not both), the median usually produces a better measure of the center of the data. To see another advantage of the median over the mean, suppose you and your classmates have written a statistics test and the instructor is returning the graded tests. What piece of information is most important to you? The answer, of course, is your mark. What is the next important bit of information? The answer is how well you performed relative to the class. Most students ask their instructor for the class mean. This is the wrong statistic to request. You want the median because it divides the class into two halves. This information allows you to identify which half of the class your mark falls into. The median provides this information; the mean does not. Nevertheless, the mean can also be useful in this scenario. If there are several sections of the course, the section means can be compared to determine whose class performed best (or worst).

4-1e Measures of Central Location for Ordinal and Nominal Data

When the data are interval, we can use any of the three measures of central location. However, for ordinal and nominal data, the calculation of the mean is not valid. Because the calculation of the median begins by placing the data in order, this statistic is appropriate for ordinal data. The mode, which is determined by counting the frequency of each observation, is appropriate for nominal data. However, nominal data do not have a "center," so we cannot interpret the mode of nominal data in that way. It is generally pointless to compute the mode of nominal data.

APPLICATIONS in FINANCE

Geometric Mean

The arithmetic mean is the single most popular and useful measure of central location. We noted certain situations, where the median is a better measure of central location. However, there is another circumstance where neither the mean nor the median is the best measure. When the variable is a growth rate or rate of change, such as the value of an investment over periods of time, we need another measure. This will become apparent from the following illustration.

Suppose you make a 2-year investment of $1,000, and it grows by 100% to $2,000 during the first year. During the second year, however, the investment suffers a 50% loss, from $2,000 back to $1,000. The rates of return for years 1 and 2 are $R_1 = 100\%$ and $R_2 = -50\%$, respectively. The arithmetic mean (and the median) is computed as

$$\bar{R} = \frac{R_1 + R_2}{2} = \frac{100 + (-50)}{2} = 25\%$$

But this figure is misleading. Because there was no change in the value of the investment from the beginning to the end of the 2-year period, the "average" compounded rate of return is 0%. As you will see, this is the value of the *geometric mean*.

Let R_i denote the rate of return (in decimal form) in period $i (i = 1, 2, \ldots, n)$. The **geometric mean** R_g of the returns $R_1, R_2, \ldots, R_n$ is defined such that

$$(1 + R_g)^n = (1 + R_1)(1 + R_2) \cdots (1 + R_n)$$

Solving for R_g, we produce the following formula:

$$R_g = \sqrt[n]{(1 + R_1)(1 + R_2) \cdots (1 + R_n)} - 1$$

The geometric mean of our investment illustration is

$$R_g = \sqrt[n]{(1 + R_1)(1 + R_2) \cdots (1 + R_n)} - 1 = \sqrt[2]{(1 + 1)(1 + [-.50])} - 1 = 1 - 1 = 0$$

The geometric mean is therefore 0%. This is the single "average" return that allows us to compute the value of the investment at the end of the investment period from the beginning value. Thus, using the formula for compound interest with the rate = 0%, we find

Value at the end of the investment period = $1,000(1 + R_g)^2 = 1,000(1 + 0)^2 = 1,000$

The geometric mean is used whenever we wish to find the "average" growth rate, or rate of change, in a variable *over time*. However, the arithmetic mean of n returns (or growth rates) is the appropriate mean to calculate if you wish to estimate the mean rate of return (or growth rate) for any *single* period in the future; that is, in the illustration above if we wanted to estimate the rate of return in year 3, we would use the arithmetic mean of the two annual rates of return, which we found to be 25%.

EXCEL Function

INSTRUCTIONS

1. Type or import the values of $1 + R_i$ into a column.
2. Follow the instructions to produce the mean (page 89) except substitute **GEOMEAN** in place of **AVERAGE**.
3. To determine the geometric mean, subtract 1 from the number produced.

Here is a summary of the numerical techniques introduced in this section and when to use them.

Factors That Identify When to Compute the Mean
1. **Objective**: Describe a single set of data
2. **Type of data**: Interval
3. **Descriptive measurement**: Central location

Factors That Identify When to Compute the Median
1. **Objective**: Describe a single set of data
2. **Type of data**: Ordinal or interval (with extreme observations)
3. **Descriptive measurement**: Central location

> **Factors That Identify When to Compute the Mode**
> 1. **Objective**: Describe a single set of data
> 2. **Type of data**: Nominal, ordinal, interval

> **Factors That Identify When to Compute the Geometric Mean**
> 1. **Objective**: Describe a single set of data
> 2. **Type of data**: Interval; growth rates

EXERCISES

4.1 A sample of 12 people was asked how much change they had in their pockets and wallets. The responses (in cents) are

| 52 | 25 | 15 | 0 | 104 | 44 |
| 60 | 30 | 33 | 81 | 40 | 5 |

Determine the mean, median, and mode for these data.

4.2 The number of sick days due to colds and flu last year was recorded by a sample of 15 adults. The data are

| 5 | 7 | 0 | 3 | 15 | 6 | 5 | 9 |
| 3 | 8 | 10 | 5 | 2 | 0 | 12 | |

Compute the mean, median, and mode.

4.3 A random sample of 12 joggers was asked to keep track and report the number of miles they ran last week. The responses are

| 5.5 | 7.2 | 1.6 | 22.0 | 8.7 | 2.8 |
| 5.3 | 3.4 | 12.5 | 18.6 | 8.3 | 6.6 |

a. Compute the three statistics that measure central location.
b. Briefly describe what each statistic tells you.

4.4 The midterm test for a statistics course has a time limit of 1 hour. However, like most statistics exams this one was quite easy. To assess how easy, the professor recorded the amount of time taken by a sample of nine students to hand in their test papers. The times (rounded to the nearest minute) are

33   29   45   60   42   19   52   38   36

a. Compute the mean, median, and mode.
b. What have you learned from the three statistics calculated in part (a)?

4.5 The professors at Wilfrid Laurier University are required to submit their final exams to the registrar's office 10 days before the end of the semester. The exam coordinator sampled 20 professors and recorded the number of days before the final exam that each submitted his or her exam. The results are

| 14 | 8 | 3 | 2 | 6 | 4 | 9 | 13 | 10 | 12 |
| 7 | 4 | 9 | 13 | 15 | 8 | 11 | 12 | 4 | 0 |

a. Compute the mean, median, and mode.
b. Briefly describe what each statistic tells you.

4.6 Compute the geometric mean of the following rates of return.

.25   −.10   .50

4.7 What is the geometric mean of the following rates of return?

.50   .30   −.50   −.25

4.8 The following returns were realized on an investment over a 5-year period.

Year	1	2	3	4	5
Rate of Return	.10	.22	.06	−.05	.20

a. Compute the mean and median of the returns.
b. Compute the geometric mean.
c. Which one of the three statistics computed in parts (a) and (b) best describes the return over the 5-year period? Explain.

4.9 An investment you made 5 years ago has realized the following rates of return.

Year	1	2	3	4	5
Rate of Return	−.15	−.20	.15	−.08	.50

NUMERICAL DESCRIPTIVE TECHNIQUES

a. Compute the mean and median of the rates of return.
b. Compute the geometric mean.
c. Which one of the three statistics computed in parts (a) and (b) best describes the return over the 5-year period? Explain.

4.10 An investment of $1,000 you made 4 years ago was worth $1,200 after the first year, $1,200 after the second year, $1,500 after the third year, and $2,000 today.
a. Compute the annual rates of return.
b. Compute the mean and median of the rates of return.
c. Compute the geometric mean.
d. Discuss whether the mean, median, or geometric mean is the best measure of the performance of the investment.

4.11 Suppose that you bought a stock 6 years ago at $12. The stock's price at the end of each year is shown here.

Year	1	2	3	4	5	6
Price	10	14	15	22	30	25

a. Compute the rate of return for each year.
b. Compute the mean and median of the rates of return.
c. Compute the geometric mean of the rates of return.
d. Explain why the best statistic to use to describe what happened to the price of the stock over the 6-year period is the geometric mean.

4.12 <u>Xr04-12</u> An auction house conducts an auction once every week listing items such as jewelry, furniture, art, coins, and many others. The number of bidders from each of the auctions over the last 3 years was recorded. Determine the mean and median of the weekly number of bidders. What do these statistics tell you about the sample of weekly bidders?

4.13 <u>Xr04-13</u> The starting salaries of a sample of 300 recent Bachelor of Business Administration graduates were recorded. Calculate the mean and median. Interpret the meaning of each statistic.

4.14 <u>Xr04-14</u> The amount of time spent commuting by residents of Washington D.C. was recorded for a sample of 235 commuters.
a. Compute the mean and median.
b. What do the mean and median tell you about this data set?

Source: U.S. Census Bureau.

4.15 <u>Xr04-15</u> According to a recent National Household Survey (NHS), roughly 15.4 million Canadians commuted to work. Overall, about four out of five Canadian commuters used private vehicles. Specifically, 74.0% of commuters, or 11.4 million workers, drove a vehicle to work. A random sample of these commuters was asked how long their typical commute was. Compute the mean and median and describe what each statistic tells you about these data.

Source: Statistics Canada.

4.16 <u>Xr04-16</u> In the United States, banks and financial institutions often require buyers to pay fees in order to arrange mortgages. In a survey conducted by the U.S. Federal Housing Finance Board, 400 buyers of new houses who received a mortgage from a bank were asked to report the amount of fees (fees include commissions, discounts, and points) they paid as a percentage of the entire mortgage.

Source: Adapted from Statistical Abstract of the United States 2012, Table 1193.

4.17 <u>Xr04-17</u> In an effort to slow drivers, traffic engineers painted a solid line 3 feet from the curb over the entire length of a road and filled the space with diagonal lines. The lines made the road look narrower. A sample of car speeds was taken after the lines were drawn.
a. Compute the mean and median of these data.
b. Briefly describe what information you acquired from each statistic.

4.18 <u>Xr04-18</u> A random sample of households was surveyed. Each was asked how old their refrigerators were (in months).
a. Compute the mean and median of these data.
b. What have you learned about this data set from the statistics?

GENERAL SOCIAL SURVEY EXERCISES

The following exercises are based on the General Social Survey of 2014.

4.19 <u>GSS2014*</u> Compute the mean and median of the ages (AGE) of the respondents. What information do these statistics give you?

4.20 <u>GSS2014*</u> Calculate the mean and median of the years of education (EDUC). Briefly summarize what these statistics tell you about the years of education of Americans in 2014.

4.21 <u>GSS2014*</u> How much television were Americans watching in 2014? Answer the question by calculating the mean and median of TVHOURS. What have you learned?

4.22 <u>GSS2014*</u> Calculate the mean and median of RINCOME. Is the mean greater than the median? If so, explain why.

SURVEY OF CONSUMER FINANCES EXERCISES

The following exercises are based on the Survey of Consumer Finances 2013.

4.23 <u>SCF2013:\All*</u> Compute the mean and median of the ages (AGE) of the respondents in the 2013 survey. Interpret each statistic.

4.24 <u>SCF2013:\All*</u> Find the mean and median of the incomes (INCOME) of the respondents. Briefly describe what the large difference between the two statistics tells you about the distribution of incomes of the respondents.

4.25 <u>SCF2013:\All*</u> Calculate the mean and median of the respondent's assets (ASSET). Is the mean greater than the median? If so, explain what that tells you about the distribution of assets.

4.26 <u>SCF2013:\All*</u> Determine the mean and median of the amount of debt (DEBT) owed by the respondents. Briefly describe what the two statistics tell you.

4-2 / MEASURES OF VARIABILITY

The statistics introduced in Section 4-1 serve to provide information about the central location of the data. However, as we have already discussed in Chapter 2, there are other characteristics of data that are of interest to practitioners of statistics. One such characteristic is the spread or variability of the data. In this section, we introduce four **measures of variability**. We begin with the simplest.

4-2a Range

> **Range**
>
> Range = Largest observation − Smallest observation

The advantage of the **range** is its simplicity. The disadvantage is also its simplicity. Because the range is calculated from only two observations, it tells us nothing about the other observations. Consider the following two sets of data.

Set 1:	4	4	4	4	4	50
Set 2:	4	8	15	24	39	50

The range of both sets is 46. The two sets of data are completely different, yet their ranges are the same. To measure variability, we need other statistics that incorporate all the data and not just two observations.

4-2b Variance

The **variance** and its related measure, the **standard deviation**, are arguably the most important statistics. They are used to measure variability, but, as you will discover, they play a vital role in almost all statistical inference procedures.

Variance

$$\text{Population variance:} \quad \sigma^2 = \frac{\sum\limits_{i=1}^{N}(x_i - \mu)^2}{N}$$

$$\text{Sample variance:}^* \quad s^2 = \frac{\sum\limits_{i=1}^{n}(x_i - \bar{x})^2}{n - 1}$$

The population variance is represented by σ^2 (Greek letter *sigma* squared).

Examine the formula for the sample variance s^2. It may appear to be illogical that in calculating s^2 we divide by $n - 1$ rather than by n.† However, we do so for the following reason. Population parameters in practical settings are seldom known. One objective of statistical inference is to estimate the parameter from the statistic. For example, we estimate the population mean μ from the sample mean $\bar{x}$. Although it is not obviously logical, the statistic created by dividing $\sum(x_i - \bar{x})^2$ by $n - 1$ is a better estimator than the one created by dividing by n. We will discuss this issue in greater detail in Section 10-1.

To compute the sample variance s^2, we begin by calculating the sample mean $\bar{x}$. Next we compute the difference (also call the **deviation**) between each observation and the mean. We square the deviations and sum. Finally, we divide the sum of squared deviations by $n - 1$.

We'll illustrate with a simple example. Suppose that we have the following observations of the numbers of hours five students spent studying statistics last week:

 8 4 9 11 3

The mean is

$$\bar{x} = \frac{8 + 4 + 9 + 11 + 3}{5} = \frac{35}{5} = 7$$

For each observation, we determine its deviation from the mean. The deviation is squared, and the sum of squares is determined as shown in Table 4.1.

TABLE **4.1**   **Calculation of Sample Variance**

x_i	$(x_i - \bar{x})$	$(x_i - \bar{x})^2$
8	$(8 - 7) = 1$	$(1)^2 = 1$
4	$(4 - 7) = -3$	$(-3)^2 = 9$
9	$(9 - 7) = 2$	$(2)^2 = 4$
11	$(11 - 7) = 4$	$(4)^2 = 16$
3	$(3 - 7) = -4$	$(-4)^2 = 16$
	$\sum\limits_{i=1}^{5}(x_i - \bar{x}) = 0$	$\sum\limits_{i=1}^{5}(x_i - \bar{x})^2 = 46$

---

†Technically, the variance of the sample is calculated by dividing the sum of squared deviations by n. The statistic computed by dividing the sum of squared deviations by $n - 1$ is called the sample variance corrected for the mean. Because this statistic is used extensively, we will shorten its name to sample variance.

The sample variance is

$$s^2 = \frac{\sum_{i=1}^{n}(x_i - \bar{x})^2}{n-1} = \frac{46}{5-1} = 11.5$$

The calculation of this statistic raises several questions. Why do we square the deviations before averaging? If you examine the deviations, you will see that some of the deviations are positive and some are negative. When you add them together, the sum is 0. This will always be the case because the sum of the positive deviations will always equal the sum of the negative deviations. Consequently, we square the deviations to avoid the "canceling effect."

Is it possible to avoid the canceling effect without squaring? We could average the *absolute* value of the deviations. In fact, such a statistic has already been invented. It is called the **mean absolute deviation** or MAD. However, this statistic has limited utility and is seldom calculated.

What is the unit of measurement of the variance? Because we squared the deviations, we also squared the units. In this illustration the units were hours (of study). Thus, the sample variance is 11.5 hours^2.

EXAMPLE 4.7

Summer Jobs

The following are the number of summer jobs a sample of six students applied for. Find the mean and variance of these data.

17   15   23   7   9   13

SOLUTION:

The mean of the six observations is

$$\bar{x} = \frac{17 + 15 + 23 + 7 + 9 + 13}{6} = \frac{84}{6} = 14 \text{ jobs}$$

The sample variance is

$$\begin{aligned} s^2 &= \frac{\sum_{i=1}^{n}(x_i - \bar{x})^2}{n-1} \\ &= \frac{(17-14)^2 + (15-14)^2 + (23-14)^2 + (7-14)^2 + (9-14)^2 + (13-14)^2}{6-1} \\ &= \frac{9 + 1 + 81 + 49 + 25 + 1}{5} = \frac{166}{5} = 33.2 \text{ jobs}^2 \end{aligned}$$

(Optional) Shortcut Method for Variance The calculations for larger data sets are quite time consuming. The following shortcut for the sample variance may help lighten the load.

Shortcut for Sample Variance

$$s^2 = \frac{1}{n-1}\left[\sum_{i=1}^{n}x_i^2 - \frac{\left(\sum_{i=1}^{n}x_i\right)^2}{n}\right]$$

To illustrate, we'll do Example 4.7 again.

$$\sum_{i=1}^{n} x_i^2 = 17^2 + 15^2 + 23^2 + 7^2 + 9^2 + 13^2 = 1{,}342$$

$$\sum_{i=1}^{n} x_i = 17 + 15 + 23 + 7 + 9 + 13 = 84$$

$$\left(\sum_{i=1}^{n} x_i\right)^2 = 84^2 = 7{,}056$$

$$s^2 = \frac{1}{n-1}\left[\sum_{i=1}^{n} x_i^2 - \frac{\left(\sum_{i=1}^{n} x_i\right)^2}{n}\right] = \frac{1}{6-1}\left[1342 - \frac{7056}{6}\right] = 33.2 \text{ jobs}^2$$

Notice that we produced the same exact answer.

EXCEL Function

INSTRUCTIONS

Follow the instructions to compute the mean (page 89) except type VAR instead of AVERAGE.

4-2c Interpreting the Variance

We calculated the variance in Example 4.7 to be 33.2 jobs^2. What does this statistic tell us? Unfortunately, the variance provides us with only a rough idea about the amount of variation in the data. However, this statistic is useful when comparing two or more sets of data of the same type of variable. If the variance of one data set is larger than that of a second data set, we interpret that to mean that the observations in the first set display more variation than the observations in the second set.

The problem of interpretation is caused by the way the variance is computed. Because we squared the deviations from the mean, the unit attached to the variance is the square of the unit attached to the original observations. In other words, in Example 4.7 the unit of the data is jobs; the unit of the variance is jobs squared. This contributes to the problem of interpretation. We resolve this difficulty by calculating another related measure of variability.

4-2d Standard Deviation

Standard Deviation

Population standard deviation: $\sigma = \sqrt{\sigma^2}$
Sample standard deviation: $s = \sqrt{s^2}$

The standard deviation is simply the positive square root of the variance. Thus, in Example 4.7, the sample standard deviation is

$$s = \sqrt{s^2} = \sqrt{33.2} = 5.76 \text{ jobs}$$

Notice that the unit associated with the standard deviation is the unit of the original data set.

EXAMPLE 4.8

DATA
Xm04-08

Comparing the Consistency of Two Types of Golf Clubs

Consistency is the hallmark of a good golfer. Golf equipment manufacturers are constantly seeking ways to improve their products. Suppose that a recent innovation is designed to improve the consistency of its users. As a test, a golfer was asked to hit 150 shots using a 7 iron, 75 of which were hit with his current club and 75 with the new innovative 7 iron. The distances were measured and recorded. Which 7 iron is more consistent?

SOLUTION:

To gauge the consistency, we must determine the standard deviations. (We could also compute the variances, but as we just pointed out, the standard deviation is easier to interpret.) We can get Excel and Minitab to print the sample standard deviations. Alternatively, we can calculate all the descriptive statistics, a course of action we recommend because we often need several statistics. The printouts for both 7 irons are shown here.

EXCEL Data Analysis

	A	B	C	D	E
1	Current			Innovation	
2					
3	Mean	150.55		Mean	150.15
4	Standard Error	0.67		Standard Error	0.36
5	Median	151		Median	150
6	Mode	150		Mode	149
7	Standard Deviation	5.79		Standard Deviation	3.09
8	Sample Variance	33.55		Sample Variance	9.56
9	Kurtosis	0.13		Kurtosis	−0.89
10	Skewness	−0.43		Skewness	0.18
11	Range	28		Range	12
12	Minimum	134		Minimum	144
13	Maximum	162		Maximum	156
14	Sum	11291		Sum	11261
15	Count	75		Count	75

INTERPRET

The standard deviation of the distances of the current 7 iron is 5.79 yards whereas that of the innovative 7 iron is 3.09 yards. Based on this sample, the innovative club is more consistent. Because the mean distances are similar it would appear that the new club is indeed superior.

Interpreting the Standard Deviation   Knowing the mean and standard deviation allows the statistics practitioner to extract useful bits of information. The information depends on the shape of the histogram. If the histogram is bell shaped, we can use the **Empirical Rule**.

> **Empirical Rule**
> 1. Approximately 68% of all observations fall within one standard deviation of the mean.
> 2. Approximately 95% of all observations fall within two standard deviations of the mean.
> 3. Approximately 99.7% of all observations fall within three standard deviations of the mean.

EXAMPLE 4.9 Using the Empirical Rule to Interpret Standard Deviation

After an analysis of the returns on an investment, a statistics practitioner discovered that the histogram is bell shaped and that the mean and standard deviation are 10% and 8%, respectively. What can you say about the way the returns are distributed?

SOLUTION:

Because the histogram is bell shaped, we can apply the Empirical Rule:

1. Approximately 68% of the returns lie between 2% (the mean minus one standard deviation = 10 − 8) and 18% (the mean plus one standard deviation = 10 + 8).
2. Approximately 95% of the returns lie between −6% [the mean minus two standard deviations = 10 − 2(8)] and 26% [the mean plus two standard deviations = 10 + 2(8)].
3. Approximately 99.7% of the returns lie between −14% [the mean minus three standard deviations = 10 − 3(8)] and 34% [the mean plus three standard deviations = 10 + 3(8)].

A more general interpretation of the standard deviation is derived from *Chebysheff's Theorem*, which applies to all shapes of histograms.

> **Chebysheff's Theorem**
> The proportion of observations in any sample or population that lie within k standard deviations of the mean is at least
> $$1 - \frac{1}{k^2} \text{ for } k > 1$$

When $k = 2$, **Chebysheff's Theorem** states that at least three-quarters (75%) of all observations lie within two standard deviations of the mean. With $k = 3$, Chebysheff's Theorem states that at least eight-ninths (88.9%) of all observations lie within three standard deviations of the mean.

Note that the Empirical Rule provides approximate proportions, whereas Chebysheff's Theorem provides lower bounds on the proportions contained in the intervals.

EXAMPLE 4.10

Using Chebysheff's Theorem to Interpret Standard Deviation

The annual salaries of the employees of a chain of computer stores produced a positively **skewed** histogram. The mean and standard deviation are $28,000 and $3,000, respectively. What can you say about the salaries at this chain?

SOLUTION:

Because the histogram is not bell shaped, we cannot use the Empirical Rule. We must employ Chebysheff's Theorem instead.

The intervals created by adding and subtracting two and three standard deviations to and from the mean are as follows:

1. At least 75% of the salaries lie between $22,000 [the mean minus two standard deviations = 28,000 − 2(3,000)] and $34,000 [the mean plus two standard deviations = 28,000 + 2(3,000)].

2. At least 88.9% of the salaries lie between $19,000 [the mean minus three standard deviations = 28,000 − 3(3,000)] and $37,000 [the mean plus three standard deviations = 28,000 + 3(3,000)].

4-2e Coefficient of Variation

Is a standard deviation of 10 a large number indicating great variability or a small number indicating little variability? The answer depends somewhat on the magnitude of the observations in the data set. If the observations are in the millions, then a standard deviation of 10 will probably be considered a small number. On the other hand, if the observations are less than 50, then the standard deviation of 10 would be seen as a large number. This logic lies behind yet another measure of variability, the *coefficient of variation*.

Coefficient of Variation

The **coefficient of variation** of a set of observations is the standard deviation of the observations divided by their mean:

$$\text{Population coefficient of variation: } CV = \frac{\sigma}{\mu}$$

$$\text{Sample coefficient of variation: } cv = \frac{s}{\bar{x}}$$

4-2f Measures of Variability for Ordinal and Nominal Data

The measures of variability introduced in this section can be used only for interval data. The next section will feature a measure that can be used to describe the variability of ordinal data. There are no measures of variability for nominal data.

4-2g Approximating the Mean and Variance from Grouped Data

The statistical methods presented in this chapter are used to compute descriptive statistics from data. However, in some circumstances, the statistics practitioner does not have the raw data but instead has a frequency distribution. This is often the case when data are supplied by government organizations. In the online appendix, Approximating Means and Variances for Grouped Data we provide the formulas used to approximate the sample mean and variance.

We complete this section by reviewing the factors that identify the use of measures of variability.

Factors That Identify When to Compute the Range, Variance, Standard Deviation, and Coefficient of Variation

1. **Objective**: Describe a single set of data
2. **Type of Data**: Interval
3. **Descriptive measurement**: Variability

EXERCISES

4.27 Calculate the variance of the following sample.

    9   3   7   4   1   7   5   4

4.28 Calculate the variance of the following sample.

    4   5   3   6   5   6   5   6

4.29 Determine the variance and standard deviation of the following sample.

    12 6 22 21 23 13 15 17 21

4.30 Find the variance and standard deviation of the following sample.

    0 −5 −3 6 4 −4 1 −5 0 3

4.31 Examine the three samples listed here. Without performing any calculations, indicate which sample has the largest amount of variation and which sample has the smallest amount of variation. Explain how you produced your answer.

a.	17	29	12	16	11
b.	22	18	23	20	17
c.	24	37	6	39	29

4.32 Refer to Exercise 4.31. Calculate the variance for each part. Was your answer in Exercise 4.31 correct?

4.33 A friend calculates a variance and reports that it is −25.0. How do you know that he has made a calculation error?

4.34 Create a sample of five observations whose mean is 6 and whose standard deviation is 0.

4.35 A set of data whose histogram is bell shaped yields a mean and standard deviation of 50 and 4, respectively. Approximately what proportion of observations
a. are between 46 and 54?
b. are between 42 and 58?
c. are between 38 and 62?

4.36 Refer to Exercise 4.35. Approximately what proportion of observations
a. are less than 46?
b. are less than 58?
c. are greater than 54?

4.37 A set of data whose histogram is extremely skewed yields a mean and standard deviation of 70 and 12, respectively. What is the minimum proportion of observations that
a. are between 46 and 94?
b. are between 34 and 106?

4.38 A statistics practitioner determined that the mean and standard deviation of a data set were 120 and 30, respectively. What can you say about the proportions of observations that lie between each of the following intervals?
a. 90 and 150
b. 60 and 180
c. 30 and 210

The following exercises require a computer and software.

4.39 <u>Xr04-39</u> There has been much media coverage of the high cost of medicinal drugs in the United States. One concern is the large variation from pharmacy to pharmacy. To investigate, a consumer advocacy group took a random sample of 100 pharmacies around the country and recorded the price (in dollars per 100 pills) of Prozac. Compute the range, variance, and standard deviation of the prices. Discuss what these statistics tell you.

4.40 <u>Xr04-40</u> Many traffic experts argue that the most important factor in accidents is not the average speed of cars but the amount of variation. Suppose that the speeds of a sample of 200 cars were taken over a stretch of highway that has seen numerous accidents. Compute the variance and standard deviation of the speeds, and interpret the results.

4.41 <u>Xr04-41</u> Three men are trying to make the football team as punters. The coach had each of them punt the ball 50 times, and the distances were recorded.
a. Compute the variance and standard deviation for each punter.
b. What do these statistics tell you about the punters?

4.42 <u>Xr04-42</u> Variance is often used to measure the quality in production-line products. Suppose that a sample of steel rods that are supposed to be exactly 100 cm long is taken. The length of each is determined, and the results are recorded. Calculate the variance and the standard deviation. Briefly describe what these statistics tell you.

4.43 <u>Xr04-43</u> To learn more about the size of withdrawals at a banking machine, the proprietor took a sample of 75 withdrawals and recorded the amounts. Determine the mean and standard deviation of these data, and describe what these two statistics tell you about the withdrawal amounts.

4.44 <u>Xr04-44</u> Everyone is familiar with waiting lines or queues. For example, people wait in line at a supermarket to go through the checkout counter. There are two factors that determine how long the queue becomes. One is the speed of service. The other is the number of arrivals at the checkout counter. The mean number of arrivals is an important number, but so is the standard deviation. Suppose that a consultant for the supermarket counts the number of arrivals per hour during a sample of 150 hours.
a. Compute the standard deviation of the number of arrivals.
b. Assuming that the histogram is bell shaped, interpret the standard deviation.

4.45 <u>Xr04-45</u> Flight delays in airplane travel is a fact of life for travelers. Suppose that the time for each of a sample of 125 delays in arriving (in minutes) was recorded. Early arrivals are shown as negative numbers and on-time arrivals are represented by zeroes. Calculate the mean and standard deviation of the times. Assuming that the distribution is approximately bell shaped describe what the mean and standard deviation tell you.

4.46 <u>Xr04-46</u> An amateur golf kept track of the scores of her last 100 rounds. Calculate the mean and standard deviation. Assuming that the distribution of scores is extremely skewed interpret the mean and standard deviation.

4.47 <u>Xr04-47</u> A random sample of homeowners was asked to report the amount of money they paid in property taxes last year. Compute the mean and standard deviation. Assuming that the amounts are highly positively skewed describe what the two statistics tell you.
Source: Adapted from Bureau of Labor Statistics 2015.

4.48 <u>Xr04-48</u> A sample of households was asked to report the amount of money they spend annually for fruits and vegetables. Compute the mean and standard deviation of these data. What do these statistics tell you about the distribution of the amounts?
Source: Adapted from Bureau of Labor Statistics 2015.

GENERAL SOCIAL SURVEY EXERCISES

The following exercises are based on the General Social Survey of 2014.

4.49 <u>GSS2014*</u> Calculate the mean and standard deviation of the ages of the respondents. What do these statistics tell you?

4.50 <u>GSS2014*</u> Respondents were asked about the number of years of education (EDUC). Calculate the mean and standard deviation. Histograms of this variable reveal an approximate bell shape. What do the mean and standard deviation tell you?

4.51 <u>GSS2014*</u> Determine the mean and standard deviation of the amount of television watched (TVHOURS). If we assume that the distribution is bell shaped what do the two statistics tell you?

4.52 <u>GSS2014*</u> Calculate the mean and standard deviation of the annual incomes (RINCOME). Assuming that the distribution of incomes is very skewed what information do the mean and standard deviation give you?

SURVEY OF CONSUMER FINANCES EXERCISES

The following exercises are based on the Survey of Consumer Finances 2013.

4.53 SCF2013:\All* Compute the mean and standard deviation of the ages (AGE) of the heads of households. Assuming that the distribution is bell shaped what do the mean and standard deviation tell you?

4.54 SCF2013:\All* Find the mean and standard deviation of the incomes (INCOME) of the heads of households. We know that the distribution of income is extremely positively skewed. Briefly describe what the two statistics tell you about the distribution of incomes.

4.55 SCF2013:\All* Calculate the mean and standard deviation of household assets (ASSET). Assuming that this variable is positively skewed interpret the two statistics.

4.56 SCF2013:\All* Find the mean and standard deviation of the household debt (DEBT) of the respondents in the 2013 survey. If we assume that debt is not bell shaped describe what the mean and standard deviation tell you.

4-3 / MEASURES OF RELATIVE STANDING

Measures of relative standing are designed to provide information about the position of particular values relative to the entire data set. We've already presented one measure of relative standing, the median, which is also a measure of central location. Recall that the median divides the data set into halves, allowing the statistics practitioner to determine which half of the data set each observation lies in. The statistics we're about to introduce will give you much more detailed information.

> **Percentile**
> The Pth **percentile** is the value for which P % are less than that value and $(100 - P)$% are greater than that value.

The scores and the percentiles of the Scholastic Achievement Test (SAT) and the Graduate Management Admission Test (GMAT), as well as various other admissions tests, are reported to students taking them. Suppose, for example, that your SAT score is reported to be at the 60th percentile. This means that 60% of all the other marks are below yours and 40% are above it. You now know exactly where you stand relative to the population of SAT scores.

We have special names for the 25th, 50th, and 75th percentiles. Because these three statistics divide the set of data into quarters, these measures of relative standing are also called **quartiles**. The *first* or *lower quartile* is labeled Q_1. It is equal to the 25th percentile. The *second quartile*, Q_2, is equal to the 50th percentile, which is also the median. The *third* or *upper quartile*, Q_3, is equal to the 75th percentile. Incidentally, many people confuse the terms *quartile* and *quarter*. A common error is to state that someone is in the lower *quartile* of a group when they actually mean that someone is in the lower *quarter* of a group.

Besides quartiles, we can also convert percentiles into quintiles and deciles. *Quintiles* divide the data into fifths, and *deciles* divide the data into tenths.

4-3a Locating Percentiles

The following formula allows us to approximate the location of any percentile.

Location of a Percentile

$$L_P = (n + 1)\frac{P}{100}$$

where L_P is the location of the Pth percentile.

EXAMPLE 4.11

Percentiles of Time Spent on Internet

Calculate the 25th, 50th, and 75th percentiles (first, second, and third quartiles) of the data in Example 4.1.

SOLUTION:

Placing the 10 observations in ascending order we get

0	0	5	7	8	9	12	14	22	33

The location of the 25th percentile is

$$L_{25} = (n + 1)\frac{25}{100} = (11)(.25) = 2.75$$

The 25th percentile is three-quarters of the distance between the second (which is 0) and the third (which is 5) observations. Three-quarters of the distance is

$$(.75)(5 - 0) = 3.75$$

Because the second observation is 0, the 25th percentile is $0 + 3.75 = 3.75$. To locate the 50th percentile, we substitute $P = 50$ and produce

$$L_{50} = (n + 1)\frac{50}{100} = (11)(.50) = 5.5$$

which means that the 50th percentile is halfway between the fifth and sixth observations. The fifth and sixth observations are 8 and 9, respectively. The 50th percentile is 8.5. This is the median calculated in Example 4.3.

The 75th percentile's location is

$$L_{75} = (n + 1)\frac{75}{100} = (11)(.75) = 8.25$$

Thus, it is located one-quarter of the distance between the eighth and ninth observations, which are 14 and 22, respectively. One-quarter of the distance is

$$(.25)(22 - 14) = 2$$

which means that the 75th percentile is

$$14 + 2 = 16$$

EXAMPLE 4.12

DATA
Xm03-01

Quartiles of the AGES of ACBL Members

Determine the quartiles for Example 3.1.

S O L U T I O N :

EXCEL Data Analysis

	A	B
1	Ages	
2		
3	Mean	53.765
4	Standard Error	1.40
5	Median	54.5
6	Mode	60
7	Standard Deviation	19.76
8	Sample Variance	390.52
9	Kurtosis	−0.885
10	Skewness	0.0025
11	Range	83
12	Minimum	16
13	Maximum	99
14	Sum	10753
15	Count	200
16	Largest(50)	69
17	Smallest(50)	36

INSTRUCTIONS

Follow the instructions for **Descriptive Statistics** (page 91). In the dialog box, click **Kth Largest** and type in the integer closest to $n/4$. Repeat for **Kth Smallest**, typing in the integer closest to $n/4$. Excel approximates the third and first quartiles in the following way. The Largest(50) is 69, which is the number such that 150 numbers are below it and 49 numbers are above it. The Smallest(50) is 36, which is the number such that 49 numbers are below it and 150 numbers are above it. The median is 54.5, a statistic we discussed in Example 4.4.

We can often get an idea of the shape of the histogram from the quartiles. For example, if the first and second quartiles are closer to each other than are the second and third quartiles, then the histogram is positively skewed. If the first and second quartiles are farther apart than the second and third quartiles, then the histogram is negatively skewed. If the difference between the first and second quartiles is approximately equal to the difference between the second and third quartiles, then the histogram is approximately symmetric.

4-3b Interquartile Range

The quartiles can be used to create another measure of variability, the **interquartile range**, which is defined as follows.

Interquartile Range

$$\text{Interquartile range} = Q_3 - Q_1$$

The interquartile range measures the spread of the middle 50% of the observations. Large values of this statistic mean that the first and third quartiles are far apart, indicating a high level of variability.

EXAMPLE **4.13**   **Interquartile Range for Ages of ACBL Members**

DATA
Xm03-01

Determine the interquartile range for Example 3.1.

SOLUTION:

Using Excel's approximations of the first and third quartiles, we find

Interquartile range $= Q_3 - Q_1 = 69 - 36 = 33$.

4-3c Measures of Relative Standing and Variability for Ordinal Data

Because the measures of relative standing are computed by ordering the data, these statistics are appropriate for ordinal as well as for interval data. Furthermore, because the interquartile range is calculated by taking the difference between the upper and lower quartiles, it too can be employed to measure the variability of ordinal data.

Here are the factors that tell us when to use the techniques presented in this section.

Factors That Identify When to Compute Percentiles and Quartiles
1. **Objective**: Describe a single set of data
2. **Type of data**: Interval or ordinal
3. **Descriptive measurement**: Relative standing

Factors That Identify When to Compute the Interquartile Range
1. **Objective**: Describe a single set of data
2. **Type of data**: Interval or ordinal
3. **Descriptive measurement**: Variability

EXERCISES

4.57 Determine the first, second, and third quartiles of the data shown next.

2 4 6 8 10 12 14 16 18 20

4.58 Calculate the first, second, and third quartiles of the following sample.

5 8 2 9 5 3 7 4 2 7 4 10 4 3 5

4.59 Find the third and eighth deciles (30th and 80th percentiles) of the following data set.

26 23 29 31 24
22 15 31 30 20

4.60 Find the first and second quintiles (20th and 40th percentiles) of the data shown here.

52 61 88 43 64
71 39 73 51 60

4.61 Determine the first, second, and third quartiles of the following data.

10.5 14.7 15.3 17.7 15.9 12.2 10.0
14.1 13.9 18.5 13.9 15.1 14.7

4.62 Calculate the 3rd and 6th deciles of the accompanying data.

7 18 12 17 29 18 4 27 30 2
4 10 21 5 8

4.63 Refer to Exercise 4.61. Determine the interquartile range.

4.64 Refer to Exercise 4.62. Determine the interquartile range.

4.65 Compute the interquartile range from the following data.

5 8 14 6 21 11 9 10 18 2

4.66 Find the interquartile range of the following sample.

9 28 15 21 12 22 29
20 23 31 11 19 24 16 13

4.67 <u>Xr04-67</u> Many automotive experts believe that speed limits on highways are too low. One particular expert has stated that he thinks that most drivers drive at speeds that they consider safe. He suggested that the "correct" speed limit should be set at the 85th percentile. Suppose that a random sample of 400 speeds on a highway where the limit is 60 mph was recorded. Find the "correct" speed limit.

4.68 <u>Xr04-68</u> Accountemps, a company that supplies temporary workers, sponsored a survey of 100 executives. Each was asked to report the number of minutes they spend screening each job resume they receive.
a. Compute the quartiles.
b. What information did you derive from the quartiles? What does this suggest about writing your resume?

4.69 <u>Xr04-69</u> How much do pets cost? A random sample of dog and cat owners was asked to compute the amounts of money spent on their pets (exclusive of pet food). Determine the quartiles and describe your findings.

4.70 <u>Xr04-70</u> The Travel Industry Association of America sponsored a poll that asked a random sample of people how much they spent in preparation for pleasure travel. Determine the quartiles and describe what they tell you.

4.71 <u>Xr04-71</u> The career-counseling center at a university wanted to learn more about the starting salaries of the university's graduates. They asked each graduate to report the highest salary offer received. The survey also asked each graduate to report the degree and starting salary (column A = BA, column B = BSc, column C = BBA, column D = other). For each degree find the quartiles and describe what they tell you about the four groups of graduates.

4.72 <u>Xr04-72</u> A random sample of Boston Marathon runners was drawn and the times to complete the race were recorded. Determine the quartiles and briefly describe what they tell you.

4.73 <u>Xr04-73</u> Do golfers who are members of private courses play faster than players on a public course? The amount of time taken for a sample of private-course and public-course golfers was recorded. Find the quartiles for each group and describe what you have learned.

4.74 <u>Xr04-74</u> For many restaurants, the amount of time customers linger over coffee and dessert negatively affects profits. To learn more about this variable, a sample of 200 restaurant groups was observed, and the amount of time customers spent in the restaurant was recorded.
a. Calculate the quartiles of these data.
b. What do these statistics tell you about the amount of time spent in this restaurant?

4.75 <u>Xr04-75</u> In the United States, taxpayers are allowed to deduct mortgage interest from their incomes before calculating the amount of income tax they are required to pay. The Internal Revenue Service sampled 500 tax returns that had a mortgage interest deduction and recorded the amounts. Find the quartiles and describe what they tell you.

4.76 <u>Xr04-76</u> A random sample of households was selected. Each was asked how much they spent in food away from home (restaurants, fast food, etc.) last year. Calculate the quartiles and describe what information you've extracted from them.

Source: Adapted from Bureau of Labor Statistics 2015.

GENERAL SOCIAL SURVEY EXERCISES

The following exercises are based on the General Social Survey of 2014.

4.77 <u>GSS2014*</u> Find the quartiles of the respondents' incomes (RINCOME). Describe what they tell you about incomes of the respondents.

4.78 <u>GSS2014*</u> Calculate the quartiles for the years of education (EDUC) completed by the respondents. What information do they provide?

4.79 <u>GSS2014*</u> Determine the quartiles of the amount of television watched (TVHOURS) by the respondents. Briefly describe what they tell you about this variable.

SURVEY OF CONSUMER FINANCES EXERCISES

The following exercises are based on the Survey of Consumer Finances 2013.

4.80 <u>SCF2013\All*</u> Find the quartiles of the incomes (INCOME) of the respondents. What do they tell you about incomes of the heads of households?

4.81 <u>SCF2013:\All*</u> Calculate the quartiles of household assets (ASSET). Interpret these statistics.

4.82 <u>SCF2013:\All*</u> Determine the quartiles of the household debt (DEBT) of the respondents in the 2013 survey. What information did you extract?

4-4 / MEASURES OF LINEAR RELATIONSHIP

In Chapter 3, we introduced the scatter diagram, a graphical technique that describes the relationship between two interval variables. At that time, we pointed out that we were particularly interested in the direction and strength of the linear relationship. We now present three numerical measures of linear relationship that provide this information: *covariance*, *coefficient of correlation*, and *coefficient of determination*. Later in this section, we discuss another related numerical technique, the *least squares line*.

4-4a Covariance

As we did in Chapter 3, we label one variable X and the other Y.

Covariance

$$\text{Population covariance: } \sigma_{xy} = \frac{\sum_{i=1}^{N}(x_i - \mu_x)(y_i - \mu_y)}{N}$$

$$\text{Sample covariance: } s_{xy} = \frac{\sum_{i=1}^{n}(x_i - \bar{x})(y_i - \bar{y})}{n - 1}$$

The denominator in the calculation of the sample **covariance** is $n - 1$, not the more logical n for the same reason we divide by $n - 1$ to calculate the sample variance (see page 97). If you plan to compute the sample covariance manually, here is a shortcut calculation.

Shortcut for Sample Covariance

$$s_{xy} = \frac{1}{n-1}\left[\sum_{i=1}^{n}x_iy_i - \frac{\sum_{i=1}^{n}x_i\sum_{i=1}^{n}y_i}{n}\right]$$

To illustrate how covariance measures the linear relationship, examine the following three sets of data.

Set 1

x_i	y_i	$(x_i - \bar{x})$	$(y_i - \bar{y})$	$(x_i - \bar{x})(y_i - \bar{y})$
2	13	−3	−7	21
6	20	1	0	0
7	27	2	7	14
$\bar{x} = 5$	$\bar{y} = 20$			$s_{xy} = 35/2 = 17.5$

Set 2

x_i	y_i	$(x_i - \bar{x})$	$(y_i - \bar{y})$	$(x_i - \bar{x})(y_i - \bar{y})$
2	27	−3	7	−21
6	20	1	0	0
7	13	2	−7	−14
$\bar{x} = 5$	$\bar{y} = 20$			$s_{xy} = -35/2 = -17.5$

Set 3

x_i	y_i	$(x_i - \bar{x})$	$(y_i - \bar{y})$	$(x_i - \bar{x})(y_i - \bar{y})$
2	20	−3	0	0
6	27	1	7	7
7	13	2	−7	−14
$\bar{x} = 5$	$\bar{y} = 20$			$s_{xy} = -7/2 = -3.5$

Notice that the values of x are the same in all three sets and that the values of y are also the same. The only difference is the *order* of the values of y.

In set 1, as x increases so does y. When x is larger than its mean, y is at least as large as its mean. Thus $(x_i - \bar{x})$ and $(y_i - \bar{y})$ have the same sign or 0. Their product is also positive or 0. Consequently, the covariance is a positive number. Generally, when two variables move in the same direction (both increase or both decrease), the covariance will be a large positive number.

If you examine set 2, you will discover that as x increases, y decreases. When x is larger than its mean, y is less than or equal to its mean. As a result when $(x_i - \bar{x})$ is positive, $(y_i - \bar{y})$ is negative or 0. Their products are either negative or 0. It follows that the covariance is a negative number. In general, when two variables move in opposite directions, the covariance is a large negative number.

In set 3, as x increases, y does not exhibit any particular direction. One of the products $(x_i - \bar{x})(y_i - \bar{y})$ is 0, one is positive, and one is negative. The resulting covariance is a small number. In general, when there is no particular pattern, the covariance is a small number.

We would like to extract two pieces of information. The first is the sign of the covariance, which tells us the nature of the relationship. The second is the magnitude, which describes the strength of the association. Unfortunately, the magnitude may be difficult to judge. For example, if you're told that the covariance between two variables is 500, does this mean that there is a strong linear relationship? The answer is that it is impossible to judge without additional statistics. Fortunately, we can improve on the information provided by this statistic by creating another one.

4-4b Coefficient of Correlation

The **coefficient of correlation** is defined as the covariance divided by the standard deviations of the variables.

Coefficient of Correlation

$$\text{Population coefficient of correlation: } \rho = \frac{\sigma_{xy}}{\sigma_x \sigma_y}$$

$$\text{Sample coefficient of correlation: } r = \frac{s_{xy}}{s_x s_y}$$

The population parameter is denoted by the Greek letter *rho*.

The advantage that the coefficient of correlation has over the covariance is that the former has a set lower and upper limit. The limits are −1 and +1, respectively—that is,

$$-1 \leq r \leq +1 \qquad \text{and} \qquad -1 \leq \rho \leq +1$$

When the coefficient of correlation equals −1, there is a negative linear relationship and the scatter diagram exhibits a straight line. When the coefficient of correlation equals +1, there is a perfect positive relationship. When the coefficient of correlation equals 0, there is no linear relationship. All other values of correlation are judged in relation to these three values. The drawback to the coefficient of correlation is that—except for the three values −1, 0, and +1—we cannot interpret the correlation. For example, suppose that we calculated the coefficient of correlation to be −.4. What does this tell us? It tells us two things. The minus sign tells us the relationship is negative and because .4 is closer to 0 than to 1, we judge that the linear relationship is weak. In many applications, we need a better interpretation than the "linear relationship is weak." Fortunately, there is yet another measure of the strength of a linear relationship, which gives us more information. It is the *coefficient of determination*, which we introduce later in this section.

EXAMPLE **4.14**

Calculating the Coefficient of Correlation

Calculate the coefficient of correlation for the three sets of data on page 111.

SOLUTION:

Because we've already calculated the covariances we need to compute only the standard deviations of X and Y.

$$\bar{x} = \frac{2 + 6 + 7}{3} = 5.0$$

$$\bar{y} = \frac{13 + 20 + 27}{3} = 20.0$$

$$s_x^2 = \frac{(2-5)^2 + (6-5)^2 + (7-5)^2}{3-1} = \frac{9+1+4}{2} = 7.0$$

$$s_y^2 = \frac{(13-20)^2 + (20-20)^2 + (27-20)^2}{3-1} = \frac{49+0+49}{2} = 49.0$$

The standard deviations are

$$s_x = \sqrt{7.0} = 2.65$$

$$s_y = \sqrt{49.0} = 7.00$$

The coefficients of correlation are:

Set 1: $r = \dfrac{s_{xy}}{s_x s_y} = \dfrac{17.5}{(2.65)(7.0)} = .943$

Set 2: $r = \dfrac{s_{xy}}{s_x s_y} = \dfrac{-17.5}{(2.65)(7.0)} = -.943$

Set 3: $r = \dfrac{s_{xy}}{s_x s_y} = \dfrac{-3.5}{(2.65)(7.0)} = -.189$

It is now easier to see the strength of the linear relationship between X and Y.

4-4c Comparing the Scatter Diagram, Covariance, and Coefficient of Correlation

The scatter diagram depicts relationships graphically; the covariance and the coefficient of correlation describe the linear relationship numerically. Figures 4.1, 4.2, and 4.3 depict three scatter diagrams. To show how the graphical and numerical techniques compare, we calculated the covariance and the coefficient of correlation for each. (The data are stored in files Fig04-01, Fig04-02, and Fig04-03.) As you can see, Figure 4.1 depicts a strong positive relationship between the two variables. The covariance is 36.87, and the coefficient of correlation is .9641. The variables in Figure 4.2 produced a relatively strong negative linear relationship; the covariance and coefficient of correlation are −34.18 and −.8791, respectively. The covariance and coefficient of correlation for the data in Figure 4.3 are 2.07 and .1206, respectively. There is no apparent linear relationship in this figure.

FIGURE **4.1** **Strong Positive Linear Relationship**

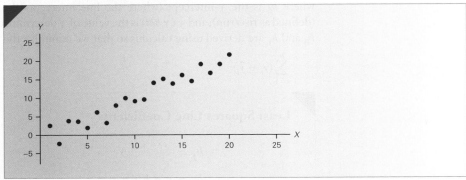

FIGURE **4.2** **Strong Negative Linear Relationship**

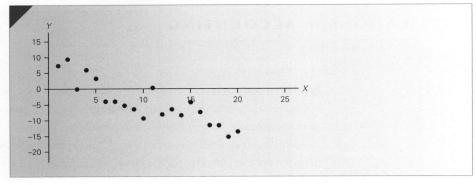

FIGURE **4.3** No Linear Relationship

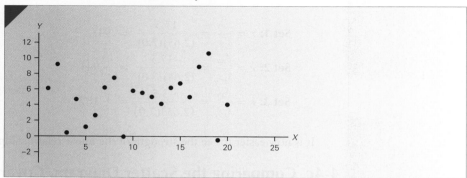

4-4d Least Squares Method

When we presented the scatter diagram in Section 3-3, we pointed out that we were interested in measuring the strength and direction of the linear relationship. Both can be more easily judged by drawing a straight line through the data. However, if different people draw a line through the same data set, it is likely that each person's line will differ from all the others. Moreover, we often need to know the equation of the line. Consequently, we need an objective method of producing a straight line. Such a method has been developed; it is called the **least squares method**.

The least squares method produces a straight line drawn through the points so that the sum of squared deviations between the points and the line is minimized. The line is represented by the equation:

$$\hat{y} = b_0 + b_1 x$$

where b_0 is the y-intercept (where the line intercepts the y-axis), and b_1 is the slope (defined as rise/run), and $\hat{y}$ (y *hat*) is the value of y determined by the line. The coefficients b_0 and b_1 are derived using calculus so that we minimize the sum of squared deviations:

$$\sum_{i=1}^{n} (y_i - \hat{y}_i)^2$$

Least Squares Line Coefficients

$$b_1 = \frac{s_{xy}}{s_x^2}$$
$$b_0 = \bar{y} - b_1 \bar{x}$$

APPLICATIONS in ACCOUNTING

Breakeven Analysis

Breakeven analysis is an extremely important business tool, one that you will likely encounter repeatedly in your course of studies. It can be used to determine how much sales volume your business needs to start making a profit.

Breakeven analysis is especially useful when managers are attempting to determine the appropriate price for the company's products and services.

A company's profit can be calculated simply as

Profit = (Price per unit – variable cost per unit) × (Number of units sold) – Fixed costs

The breakeven point is the number of units sold such that the profit is 0. Thus, the breakeven point is calculated as

Number of units sold = Fixed cost/(Price – Variable cost)

Managers can use the formula to help determine the price that will produce a profit. However, to do so requires knowledge of the fixed and variable costs. For example, suppose that a bakery sells only loaves of bread. The bread sells for $1.20, the variable cost is $0.40, and the fixed annual costs are $10,000. The breakeven point is

Number of units sold $= 10,000/(1.20 - 0.40) = 12,500$

The bakery must sell more than 12,500 loaves per year to make a profit.

In the next application box, we discuss fixed and variable costs.

APPLICATIONS in ACCOUNTING

Fixed and Variable Costs

Fixed costs are costs that must be paid whether or not any units are produced. These costs are "fixed" over a specified period of time or range of production. Variable costs are costs that vary directly with the number of products produced. For the previous bakery example, the fixed costs would include rent and maintenance of the shop, wages paid to employees, advertising costs, telephone, and any other costs that are not related to the number of loaves baked. The variable cost is primarily the cost of ingredients, which rises in relation to the number of loaves baked.

Some expenses are mixed. For the bakery example, one such cost is the cost of electricity. Electricity is needed for lights, which is considered a fixed cost, but also for the ovens and other equipment, which are variable costs.

There are several ways to break the mixed costs into fixed and variable components. One such method is the least squares line; that is, we express the total costs of some component as

$$y = b_0 + b_1 x$$

where y = total mixed cost, b_0 = fixed cost, b_1 = variable cost, and x is the number of units.

EXAMPLE **4.15**

Estimating Fixed and Variable Costs

A tool and die maker operates out of a small shop making specialized tools. He is considering increasing the size of his business and needs to know more about his costs. One such cost is electricity, which he needs to operate his machines and lights. (Some jobs require that he turn on extra bright lights to illuminate his work.) He keeps track of his daily electricity costs and the number of tools that he made that day. These data are listed next. Determine the fixed and variable electricity costs.

Day	1	2	3	4	5	6	7	8	9	10
Number of tools	7	3	2	5	8	11	5	15	3	6
Electricity cost	23.80	11.89	15.98	26.11	31.79	39.93	12.27	40.06	21.38	18.65

SOLUTION:

The dependent variable is the daily cost of electricity, and the independent variable is the number of tools. To calculate the coefficients of the least squares line and other statistics (calculated below), we need the sum of X, Y, XY, X^2, and Y^2.

Day	X	Y	XY	X^2	Y^2
1	7	23.80	166.60	49	566.44
2	3	11.89	35.67	9	141.37
3	2	15.98	31.96	4	255.36
4	5	26.11	130.55	25	681.73
5	8	31.79	254.32	64	1010.60
6	11	39.93	439.23	121	1594.40
7	5	12.27	61.35	25	150.55
8	15	40.06	600.90	225	1604.80
9	3	21.38	64.14	9	457.10
10	6	18.65	111.90	36	347.82
Total	65	241.86	1896.62	567	6810.20

Covariance:

$$s_{xy} = \frac{1}{n-1}\left[\sum_{i=1}^{n} x_i y_i - \frac{\sum_{i=1}^{n} x_i \sum_{i=1}^{n} y_i}{n}\right] = \frac{1}{10-1}\left[1896.62 - \frac{(65)(241.86)}{10}\right] = 36.06$$

Variance of X:

$$s_x^2 = \frac{1}{n-1}\left[\sum_{i=1}^{n} x_i^2 - \frac{\left(\sum_{i=1}^{n} x_i\right)^2}{n}\right] = \frac{1}{10-1}\left[567 - \frac{(65)^2}{10}\right] = 16.06$$

Sample means

$$\bar{x} = \frac{\sum x_I}{n} = \frac{65}{10} = 6.5$$

$$\bar{y} = \frac{\sum y_i}{n} = \frac{241.86}{10} = 24.19$$

The coefficients of the least squares line are as follows:

Slope:

$$b_1 = \frac{s_{xy}}{s_x^2} = \frac{36.06}{16.06} = 2.25$$

y-intercept:

$$b_0 = \bar{y} - b_1\bar{x} = 24.19 - (2.25)(6.5) = 9.57$$

The least squares line is

$$\hat{y} = 9.57 + 2.25x$$

EXCEL Chart

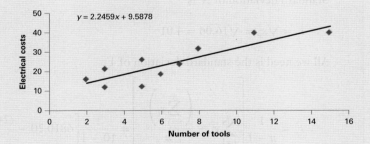

INSTRUCTIONS

1. Type or import the data into two columns where the first column stores the values of X and the second stores Y. (Open Xm04-15.) Highlight the columns containing the variables. Follow the instructions to draw a scatter diagram (page 67).

2. Click the + sign, click **Trendline** and arrow. Click More Options and Display Equation on chart.

INTERPRET

The slope is defined as rise/run, which means that it is the change in y (rise) for a one-unit increase in x (run). Put less mathematically, the slope measures the *marginal* rate of change in the dependent variable. The marginal rate of change refers to the effect of increasing the independent variable by one additional unit. In this example, the slope is 2.25, which means that in this sample, for each one-unit increase in the number of tools, the marginal increase in the electricity cost is $2.25. Thus, the estimated variable cost is $2.25 per tool.

The y-intercept is 9.57; that is, the line strikes the y-axis at 9.57. This is simply the value of $\hat{y}$ when $x = 0$. However, when $x = 0$, we are producing no tools and hence the estimated fixed cost of electricity is $9.57 per day.

Because the costs are estimates based on a straight line, we often need to know how well the line fits the data.

EXAMPLE 4.16

DATA
Xm04-15

Measuring the Strength of the Linear Relationship

Calculate the coefficient of correlation for Example 4.15.

SOLUTION:

To calculate the coefficient of correlation, we need the covariance and the standard deviations of both variables. The covariance and the variance of X were calculated in Example 4.15. The covariance is

$$s_{xy} = 36.06$$

and the variance of X is

$$s_x^2 = 16.06$$

Standard deviation of X is

$$s_x = \sqrt{s_x^2} = \sqrt{16.06} = 4.01$$

All we need is the standard deviation of Y.

$$s_y^2 = \frac{1}{n-1}\left[\sum_{i=1}^{n} y_i^2 - \frac{\left(\sum_{i=1}^{n} y_i\right)^2}{n}\right] = \frac{1}{10-1}\left[6810.20 - \frac{(241.86)^2}{10}\right] = 106.73$$

$$s_y = \sqrt{s_y^2} = \sqrt{106.73} = 10.33$$

The coefficient of correlation is

$$r = \frac{s_{XY}}{s_x s_y} = \frac{36.06}{(4.01)(10.33)} = .8705$$

EXCEL Function and Data Analysis

As with the other statistics introduced in this chapter, there is more than one way to calculate the coefficient of correlation and the covariance. Here are the instructions for both.

INSTRUCTIONS

1. Type or import the data into two columns. (Open Xm04-15.) Type the following into any empty cell.

= CORREL([Input range of one variable], [Input range of second variable])

In this example, we would enter

= CORREL(B1:B11, C1:C11)

To calculate the covariance, replace **CORREL** with **COVAR.**

Another method, which is also useful if you have more than two variables and would like to compute the coefficient of correlation or the covariance for each pair of variables, is to produce the correlation matrix and the variance–covariance matrix. We do the correlation matrix first.

	A	B	C
1		*Number of tools*	*Electrical costs*
2	Number of tools	1	
3	Electrical costs	0.8711	1

INSTRUCTIONS

1. Type or import the data into adjacent columns. (Open Xm04-15.)
2. Click **Data, Data Analysis**, and **Correlation**.
3. Specify the **Input Range (B1:C11).**

The coefficient of correlation between number of tools and electrical costs is .8711 (slightly different from the manually calculated value). (The two 1s on the diagonal of the matrix are the coefficients of number of tools and number of tools, and electrical costs and electrical costs, telling you the obvious.)

Incidentally, the formula for the population parameter ρ (Greek letter *rho*) and for the sample statistic r produce exactly the same value.

The variance–covariance matrix is shown next.

	A	B	C
1		*Number of tools*	*Electrical costs*
2	Number of tools	14.45	
3	Electrical costs	32.45	96.06

INSTRUCTIONS

1. Type or import the data into adjacent columns. (Open Xm04-15.)
2. Click **Data, Data Analysis**, and **Covariance**.
3. Specify the **Input Range (B1:C11).**

Unfortunately, Excel computes the population parameters. In other words, the variance of the number of tools is $\sigma_x^2 = 14.45$, the variance of the electrical costs is $\sigma_y^2 = 96.06$, and the covariance is $\sigma_{xy} = 32.45$. You can convert these parameters to statistics by multiplying each by $n/(n-1)$.

	D	E	F
1		*Number of tools*	*Electrical costs*
2	Number of tools	16.06	
3	Electrical costs	36.06	106.73

The coefficient of correlation is .8711, which tells us that there is a positive linear relationship between the number of tools and the electricity cost. The coefficient of correlation tells us that the linear relationship is quite strong and thus the estimates of the fixed and variable costs should be good.

4-4e Coefficient of Determination

When we introduced the coefficient of correlation (page 112), we pointed out that except for −1, 0, and +1 we cannot precisely interpret its meaning. We can judge the coefficient of correlation in relation to its proximity to only −1, 0, and +1. Fortunately, we have another measure that can be precisely interpreted. It is the coefficient of determination, which is calculated by squaring the coefficient of correlation. For this reason, we denote it R^2.

The coefficient of determination measures the amount of variation in the dependent variable that is explained by the variation in the independent variable. For example, if the coefficient of correlation is −1 or +1, a scatter diagram would display all the points lining up in a straight line. The coefficient of determination is 1, which we interpret to mean that 100% of the variation in the dependent variable Y is explained by the variation in the independent variable X. If the coefficient of correlation is 0, then there is no linear relationship between the two variables, $R^2 = 0$, and none of the variation in Y is explained by the variation in X. In Example 4.16, the coefficient of correlation was calculated to be $r = .8711$. Thus, the coefficient of determination is

$$r^2 = (.8711)^2 = .7588$$

This tells us that 75.88% of the variation in electrical costs is explained by the number of tools. The remaining 24.12% is unexplained.

EXCEL

You can use Excel to calculate the coefficient of correlation and then square the result. Alternatively, use Excel to draw the least squares line. After doing so, click **Trendline, More Options**, and **Display R-squared value on chart.**

The concept of explained variation is an extremely important one in statistics. We return to this idea repeatedly in Chapters 13, 14, 16, 17, and 18. In Chapter 16, we explain why we interpret the coefficient of determination in the way that we do.

Cost of One More Win: Solution

To determine the cost of an additional win, we must describe the relationship between two variables. To do so, we use the least squares method to produce a straight line through the data. Because we believe that the number of games a baseball team wins depends to some extent on its team payroll, we label Wins as the dependent variable and Payroll as the independent variable. Because of rounding problems, we expressed the payroll in the number of millions of dollars.

EXCEL Chart

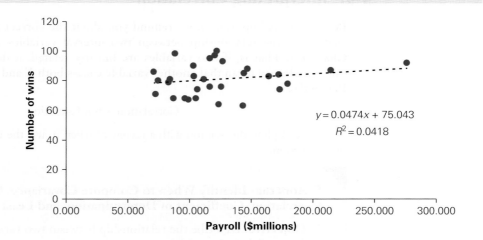

$y = 0.0474x + 75.043$
$R^2 = 0.0418$

As you can see, Excel outputs the least squares line and the coefficient of determination.

INTERPRET

The least squares line is:

$$\hat{y} = 75.043 + .0474\,x$$

The slope is equal to .0474, which is the marginal rate of change in games won for each 1-unit increase in payroll. Because payroll is measured in millions of dollars, we estimate that for each $1 million increase in the payroll the number of games won increases on average by .0474. Thus, to win one more game requires on average an additional expenditure of an incredible $21,097,705 (calculated as 1 million/.0474). In addition to analyzing the least squares line, we should determine the strength of the linear relationship. The coefficient of determination is .0418, which means that the variation in the teams' payroll explains 4.18% of the variation in the teams' number of games won. This tells us that there is virtually no linear relationship between team payroll and the number of wins in the 2015 season. This suggests that there are some teams that win a small number of games with large payrolls (e.g., Boston Red Sox, $179 million payroll, 78 wins), whereas others win a large number of games with small payrolls (e.g., Pittsburgh Pirates, $88 million payroll and 98 wins).

(Continued)

Here are the results of the 2006, 2009, and 2012 seasons.

2006:
$\hat{y} = 68.31 + .163x$; cost of one more win = \$6,134,969; coefficient of determination = 28.27%

2009:
$\hat{y} = 65.76 + .1725x$; cost of one more win = \$5,797,101; coefficient of determination = 25.12%

2012:
$\hat{y} = 74.77 + .0636x$; cost of one more win = \$15,723,270; coefficient of determination = 3.85%

4-4f Interpreting Correlation

Because of its importance, we remind you about the correct interpretation of the analysis of the relationship between two interval variables that we discussed in Chapter 3. That is, if two variables are linearly related, it does not mean that X causes Y. It may mean that another variable causes both X and Y or that Y causes X. Remember:

Correlation is not Causation

We complete this section with a review of when to use the techniques introduced in this section.

> **Factors that Identify When to Compute Covariance, Coefficient of Correlation, Coefficient of Determination, and Least Squares Line**
>
> 1. **Objective**: Describe the relationship between two variables
> 2. **Type of data**: Interval

EXERCISES

4.83 The covariance of two variables has been calculated to be −150. What does the statistic tell you about the two variables?

4.84 Refer to Exercise 4.83. You've now learned that the two sample standard deviations are 16 and 12.
  a. Calculate the coefficient of correlation. What does this statistic tell you about the relationship between the two variables?
  b. Calculate the coefficient of determination and describe what this says about the relationship between the two variables.

4.85 Xr04-85   A retailer wanted to estimate the monthly fixed and variable selling expenses. As a first step, she collected data from the past 8 months. The total selling expenses (\$1,000) and the total sales (\$1,000) were recorded and are listed below.

Total Sales	Selling Expenses
20	14
40	16
60	18
50	17
50	18
55	18
60	18
70	20

  a. Compute the covariance, the coefficient of correlation, and the coefficient of determination and describe what these statistics tell you.
  b. Determine the least squares line and use it to produce the estimates the retailer wants.

4.86 Xr04-86 Are the marks one receives in a course related to the amount of time spent studying the subject? To investigate this mysterious possibility, a student took a random sample of 10 students who had enrolled in an accounting class last semester. He asked each to report his or her mark in the course and the total number of hours spent studying accounting. These data are listed here.

Study										
time	40	42	37	47	25	44	41	48	35	28
Marks	77	63	79	86	51	78	83	90	65	47

a. Calculate the covariance.
b. Calculate the coefficient of correlation.
c. Calculate the coefficient of determination.
d. Determine the least squares line.
e. What do the statistics calculated earlier tell you about the relationship between marks and study time?

4.87 Xr04-87 Students who apply to MBA programs must take the Graduate Management Admission Test (GMAT). University admissions committees use the GMAT score as one of the critical indicators of how well a student is likely to perform in the MBA program. However, the GMAT may not be a very strong indicator for all MBA programs. Suppose that an MBA program designed for middle managers who wish to upgrade their skills was launched 3 years ago. To judge how well the GMAT score predicts MBA performance, a sample of 12 graduates was taken. Their grade point averages in the MBA program (values from 0 to 12) and their GMAT score (values range from 200 to 800) are listed here. Compute the covariance, the coefficient of correlation, and the coefficient of determination. Interpret your findings.

GMAT	599	689	584	631	594	643
GPA	9.6	8.8	7.4	10.0	7.8	9.2
GMAT	656	594	710	611	593	683
GPA	9.6	8.4	11.2	7.6	8.8	8.0

The following exercises require a computer and software.

4.88 Xr04-88 The unemployment rate is an important measure of a country's economic health. The unemployment rate measures the percentage of people who are looking for work and who are without jobs. Unfortunately, it can be a misleading statistic because it does not include people who are unemployed and would like to find work but have tried and failed and have become discouraged and are no longer looking for a job. Another way of measuring this economic variable is to calculate the labor participation rate, which is the percentage of adults who are employed. Here are the unemployment rates and labor participation rates (as of May

2016) for the largest economies. Calculate the coefficient of determination and describe what you have learned.

Country	Labor Participation Rate	Unemployment Rate
Australia	64.8	5.7
Brazil	61.5	11.2
Canada	65.8	7.1
Euro Area	56.9	10.2
France	56.1	10.2
Germany	60.6	4.2
India	52.5	4.9
Indonesia	65.76	5.5
Italy	64.5	11.7
Japan	59.8	3.2
Mexico	59.21	3.8
Netherlands	64.2	6.4
Russia	69.2	5.9
South Korea	62.8	3.7
Spain	59.29	21
United Kingdom	78.3	5.1
United States	62.6	4.7

4.89 Xr04-89 All Canadians have government-funded health insurance, which pays for any medical care they require. However, when traveling out of the country, Canadians usually acquire supplementary health insurance to cover the difference between the costs incurred for emergency treatment and what the government program pays. In the United States, this cost differential can be prohibitive. Until recently, private insurance companies (such as BlueCross BlueShield) charged everyone the same weekly rate, regardless of age. However, because of rising costs and the realization that older people frequently incur greater medical emergency expenses, insurers had to change their premium plans. They decided to offer rates that depend on the age of the customer. To help determine the new rates, one insurance company gathered data concerning the age and mean daily medical expenses of a random sample of 1,348 Canadians during the previous 12-month period.

a. Calculate the coefficient of determination.
b. What does the statistic calculated in part (a) tell you?
c. Determine the least squares line.
d. Interpret the coefficients.
e. What rate plan would you suggest?

4.90 Xr04-90 A real estate developer of single-family dwellings across the country is in the process of developing plans for the next several years. An analyst for the company believes that interest rates are likely to increase but remain at low levels. To help make decisions about the number of homes to build, the developer acquired the monthly bank prime rate and the number of new single-family homes sold monthly (thousands) from 1963 to 2016.

Calculate the coefficient of determination. Explain what this statistic tells you about the relationship between the prime bank rate and the number of single-family homes sold.

Source: Federal Reserve Statistics and U.S. Census Bureau.

4.91 <u>Xr04-91</u> When the price of crude oil increases, do oil companies drill more oil wells? To determine the strength and nature of the relationship, an economist recorded the price of a barrel of domestic crude oil (West Texas crude) and the number of exploratory oil wells drilled for each month from 1973 to 2010. Analyze the data and explain what you have discovered.

Source: U.S. Department of Energy.

4.92 <u>Xr04-92</u> One way of measuring the extent of unemployment is through the help wanted index, which measures the number of want ads in the nation's newspapers. The higher the index, the greater is the demand for workers. Another measure is the unemployment rate among insured workers. An economist wanted to know whether these two variables are related, and if so, how. He acquired the help wanted index and unemployment rates for each month between 1951 and 2006 (last year available). Determine the strength and direction of the relationship.

Source: U.S. Department of Labor Statistics.

4.93 <u>Xr04-93</u> A manufacturing firm produces its products in batches using sophisticated machines and equipment. The general manager wanted to investigate the relationship between direct labor costs and the number of units produced per batch. He recorded the data from the last 30 batches. Determine the fixed and variable labor costs.

4.94 <u>Xr04-94</u> A manufacturer has recorded its cost of electricity and the total number of hours of machine time for each of 52 weeks. Estimate the fixed and variable electricity costs.

4.95 <u>Xr04-95</u> The U.S. Census Bureau in conjunction with the Bureau of Labor Statistics conducts surveys that record a wide variety of subjects. In the Consumer Expenditure Survey of 2014–2015 respondents were asked their age and the amount of money spent in the previous year on alcoholic beverages. Compute whatever statistics you need to determine whether age and alcoholic expenditures are related.

4.96 <u>Xr04-96</u> Refer to Exercise 4.95. In another survey by the Bureau of Labor Statistics respondents who reported that they rent their dwelling were asked their age and how much they spend annually on rent. Use a statistical analysis to determine whether the data indicate that as renters grow older they spend less on rent.

4.97 <u>Xr04-97</u> To determine the relationship between age of cars and annual repair costs a random sample of car owners was drawn and the two variables were recorded. Calculate statistics to determine whether cost of repairs increase as the car ages and on average what is the cost.

4.98 <u>Xr04-98</u> A professional income tax preparer recorded the amount of tax rebate and the total taxable amount of a sample of 80 customers. Compute whichever statistics you need to determine whether tax rebates increase as the taxable income increases.

4.99 <u>Xr04-99</u> Carbon monoxide (CO) in the home is caused by faulty furnaces burning natural gas or heating oil. Concentrations above 35 parts per million (ppm) is considered dangerous. Suppose that a municipal home inspector randomly samples 180 houses around the city and records the age of the furnace and the carbon monoxide concentration during one day in the winter heating season. Conduct a statistical analysis to determine whether the age of the furnace and CO concentrations are related.

4.100 <u>Xr04-100</u> The U.S.–Canada exchange rate has fluctuated over the past 45 years. Can any single commodity explain these fluctuations? Is it oil, for example? Canada sells a lot of oil to the United States. It may be lumber or gold. A statistician set out to investigate the U.S.–Canada exchange rate and its underlying causes. We have stored the monthly exchange rate (the ratio of the value of the U.S. dollar to the value of the Canadian dollar) (Ch04: U.S.–Canada Exchange rate) from May 1986 to April 2016. The other prices we recorded are listed below. For each compute the coefficient of correlation with the U.S.–Canada exchange rate and briefly describe what the statistic tells you.

Price of West Texas crude oil (U.S. dollars per barrel)
Price of gold (U.S. dollars per troy ounce)
Price of silver (U.S. cents per troy ounce)
Price of copper (U.S. dollars per metric ton)
Price of beef (U.S. cents per pound)

4.101 <u>Xr04-101</u>* The chapter-opening example showed that there is a very weak linear relationship between a baseball teams' payroll and the number of wins.

This raises the question: Are success on the field and attendance related? If the answer is no, then profit-driven owners may not be inclined to spend money to improve their teams. The statistics practitioner recorded the number of wins and the average home attendance for the 2015 baseball season.
a. Calculate whichever parameters you wish to help guide baseball owners.
b. Estimate the marginal number of tickets sold for each additional game won.

4.102 Xr04-101* Refer to Exercise 4.101. The practitioner also recorded the average away attendance for each team in the 2015 season. Since visiting teams take a share of the gate, owners should be interested in this analysis.
a. Are visiting team attendance related to number of wins?
b. Estimate the marginal number of tickets sold for each additional game won.

4.103 Xr04-103 Repeat Exercise 4.101 for the 2012 baseball season.

4.104 Xr04-104 Repeat Exercise 4.102 for the 2012 baseball season.

4.105 Xr04-105 The number of wins, team payrolls, home attendance, and away attendance were recorded for the 2015–2016 National Basketball Association season.
a. Conduct an analysis to determine the marginal cost of winning one more game.

b. Analyze the relationship between games won and home attendance. What is the marginal number of tickets sold for each additional game won?
c. Repeat part (b) for away attendance.

4.106 Xr04-106 Repeat Exercise 4.105 for the 2012–2013 National Basketball Association season.

4.107 Xr04-107 The number of wins, team payrolls, home attendance, and away attendance were recorded for the 2015–2016 National Football League season.
a. Estimate the marginal cost of winning one more game.
b. Estimate the marginal number of tickets sold for each additional game won?
c. Repeat part (b) for away attendance.

4.108 Xr04-108 Repeat Exercise 4.107 for the 2012–2013 National Football League season

4.109 Xr04-109 We recorded the number of wins, team payrolls, home attendance, and away attendance for the 2015–2016 National Hockey League season.
a. Estimate the marginal cost of winning one more game.
b. Estimate the marginal number of tickets sold for each additional game won?
c. Repeat part (b) for away attendance.

4.110 Xr04-110 Repeat Exercise 4.109 for the 2012–2013 National Hockey league season.

4-5 (OPTIONAL) APPLICATIONS IN FINANCE: MARKET MODEL

In the Applications in Finance box on page 53, we introduced the terms *return on investment* and *risk*. We described two goals of investing. The first is to maximize the expected or mean return and the second is to minimize the risk. Financial analysts use a variety of statistical techniques to achieve these goals. Most investors are risk-averse, which means that for them minimizing risk is of paramount importance. In Section 4-2, we pointed out that variance and standard deviation are used to measure the risk associated with investments.

APPLICATIONS in FINANCE

Stock Market Indexes

Stock markets such as the New York Stock Exchange (NYSE), NASDAQ, Toronto Stock Exchange (TSE), and many others around the world calculate indexes to provide information about the prices of stocks on their exchanges. A stock market index is composed of a number of stocks that more or less represent the entire market. For example, the Dow Jones Industrial Average (DJIA) is the average price of a group of

30 NYSE stocks of large publicly traded companies. The Standard and Poor's 500 (S&P) is the average price of 500 NYSE stocks. These indexes represent their stock exchanges and give readers a quick view of how well the exchange is doing as well the economy of the country as a whole. The NASDAQ 100 is the average price of the 100 largest nonfinancial companies on the NASDAQ exchange. The S&P/TSX Composite Index is composed of 60 large companies on the TSE.

In this section, we describe one of the most important applications of the use of a least squares line. It is the well-known and often applied *market model*. This model assumes that the rate of return on a stock is linearly related to the rate of return on the stock market index. The return on the index is calculated in the same way the return on a single stock is computed. For example, if the index at the end of last year was 10,000 and the value at the end of this year is 11,000, the market index annual return is 10%. The return on the stock is the dependent variable Y and the return on the index is the independent variable X.

We use the least squares line to represent the linear relationship between X and Y. The coefficient b_1 is called the stock's *beta coefficient*, which measures how sensitive the stock's rate of return is to changes in the level of the overall market. For example, if b_1 is greater than 1, the stock's rate of return is more sensitive to changes in the level of the overall market than is the average stock. To illustrate, suppose that $b_1 = 2$. Then a 1% increase in the index results in an average increase of 2% in the stock's return. A 1% decrease in the index produces an average 2% decrease in the stock's return. Thus, a stock with a beta coefficient greater than 1 will tend to be more volatile than the market.

EXAMPLE 4.17

DATA
Xm04-17

Market Model for General Electric

The monthly rates of return for General Electric (Symbol GE) and the Standard and Poor's index (a measure of the overall NYSE stock market) were recorded for each month between January 2011 and December 2015. Some of these data are shown here. Estimate the market model and analyze the results.

Year	Month	S&P 500 Index	GE
2011	January	0.03196	0.04592
	February	−0.00105	−0.04159
	March	0.02850	0.01995
	April	−0.01350	−0.03961
2015	September	0.08298	0.14671
	October	0.00050	0.03527
	November	−0.01753	0.04820
	December	−0.05074	−0.06581

SOLUTION:

Excel's scatter diagram and least squares line are shown here. We included the equation and the coefficient of determination on the scatter diagram.

upon the quality of this information by computing the coefficient of correlation and drawing the least squares line.

Excel Output for Chapter 3 Opening Example: Coefficient of Correlation

	A	B	C
1		Price of Oil	Price of Gasoline
2	Price of Oil	1	
3	Price of Gasoline	0.9758	1

The coefficient of correlation seems to confirm what we learned from the scatter diagram. That is, there is a moderately strong positive linear relationship between the two variables.

Excel Output for Chapter 3 Opening Example: Least Squares Line

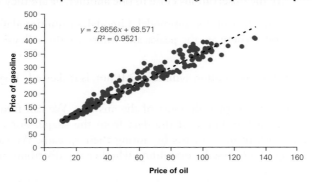

The slope coefficient tells us that for each dollar increase in the price of a barrel of oil, the price of a (U.S.) gallon of gasoline increases on average by 2.8656 cents. However, because there are 42 gallons per barrel, we would expect a dollar increase in a barrel of oil to yield a 2.4* cents per gallon (calculated as $1.00/42) increase. It does appear that the oil companies are taking some small advantage by adding an extra half cent per gallon. The coefficient of determination is .9521, which indicates that 95.21% of the variation in gasoline prices is explained by the variation in oil prices.

EXERCISES

4.132 Xr03-58 Calculate the coefficient of determination for Exercise 3.58. Is this more informative than the scatter diagram?

4.133 Xr03-59 Refer to Exercise 3.59. Compute the coefficients of the least squares line and compare your results with the scatter diagram.

The following exercises require a computer and statistical software.

4.134 Xr03-64 Compute the coefficient of determination and the least squares line for Exercise 3.64. Compare this information with that developed by the scatter diagram alone.

4.135 Xr03-67 Refer to Exercise 3.67. Calculate the coefficient of determination and the least squares line. Is this more informative than the scatter diagram?

4.136 Xm03-07 a. Calculate the coefficients of the least squares line for the data in Example 3.7.
b. Interpret the coefficients.
c. Is this information more useful than the information extracted from the scatter diagram?

4.137 Xr04-71 In Exercise 4.71 you calculated quartiles. Draw histograms instead and compare the results.

4.138 Xr04-74 Refer to Exercise 4.74. Draw histograms of the data. What have you learned?

---

*This is a simplification. In fact, a barrel of oil yields a variety of other profitable products. See Exercise 2.16.

4-7 / GENERAL GUIDELINES FOR EXPLORING DATA

The purpose of applying graphical and numerical techniques is to describe and summarize data. Statisticians usually apply graphical techniques as a first step because we need to know the shape of the distribution. The shape of the distribution helps answer the following questions:

1. Where is the approximate center of the distribution?

2. Are the observations close to one another, or are they widely dispersed?

3. Is the distribution unimodal, bimodal, or multimodal? If there is more than one mode, where are the peaks, and where are the valleys?

4. Is the distribution symmetric? If not, is it skewed? If symmetric, is it bell shaped?

Histograms provide most of the answers. We can frequently make several inferences about the nature of the data from the shape. For example, we can assess the relative risk of investments by noting their spreads. We can attempt to improve the teaching of a course by examining whether the distribution of final grades is bimodal or skewed.

The shape can also provide some guidance on which numerical techniques to use. As we noted in this chapter, the central location of highly skewed data may be more appropriately measured by the median. We may also choose to use the interquartile range instead of the standard deviation to describe the spread of skewed data.

When we have an understanding of the structure of the data, we may do additional analysis. For example, we often want to determine how one variable, or several variables, affects another. Scatter diagrams, covariance, and the coefficient of correlation are useful techniques for detecting relationships between variables. A number of techniques to be introduced later in this book will help uncover the nature of these associations.

CHAPTER SUMMARY

This chapter extended our discussion of descriptive statistics, which deals with methods of summarizing and presenting the essential information contained in a set of data. After constructing a frequency distribution to obtain a general idea about the distribution of a data set, we can use numerical measures to describe the central location and variability of interval data. Three popular measures of central location, or averages, are the mean, the median, and the mode. Taken by themselves, these measures provide an inadequate description of the data because they say nothing about the extent to which the data vary. Information regarding the variability of interval data is conveyed by such numerical measures as the range, variance, and standard deviation.

For the special case in which a sample of measurements has a mound-shaped distribution, the Empirical Rule provides a good approximation of the percentages of measurements that fall within one, two, and three standard deviations of the mean. Chebysheff's Theorem applies to all sets of data no matter the shape of the histogram.

Measures of relative standing that were presented in this chapter are percentiles and quartiles. The linear relationship between two interval variables is measured by the covariance, the coefficient of correlation, the coefficient of determination, and the least squares line.

IMPORTANT TERMS:

Measures of central location 87
Mean 87
Median 89
Mode 90
Modal class 90
Geometric mean 92
Measures of variability 96
Range 96
Variance 96
Standard deviation 96
Deviation 97

Mean absolute deviation 98
Empirical Rule 100
Chebysheff's Theorem 101
Skewed 102
Coefficient of variation 102
Percentiles 105
Quartiles 105
Interquartile range 107
Covariance 110
Coefficient of correlation 112
Least squares method 114

SYMBOLS:

Symbol	Pronounced	Represents
μ	mu	Population mean
σ^2	sigma squared	Population variance
σ	sigma	Population standard deviation
ρ	rho	Population coefficient of correlation
$\sum$	Sum of	Summation
$\sum_{i=1}^{n} x_i$	Sum of x_i from 1 to n	Summation of n numbers
$\hat{y}$	y hat	Fitted or calculated value of y
b_0	b zero	y-Intercept
b_1	b one	Slope coefficient

FORMULAS:

Population mean

$$\mu = \frac{\sum_{i=1}^{N} x_i}{N}$$

Sample mean

$$\bar{x} = \frac{\sum_{i=1}^{n} x_i}{n}$$

Range

Largest observation − Smallest observation

Population variance

$$\sigma^2 = \frac{\sum_{i=1}^{N} (x_i - \mu)^2}{N}$$

Sample variance

$$s^2 = \frac{\sum_{i=1}^{n} (x_i - \bar{x})^2}{n - 1}$$

Population standard deviation

$$\sigma = \sqrt{\sigma^2}$$

Sample standard deviation

$$s = \sqrt{s^2}$$

Population covariance

$$\sigma_{xy} = \frac{\sum_{i=1}^{N} (x_i - \mu_x)(y_i - \mu_y)}{N}$$

Sample covariance

$$s_{xy} = \frac{\sum_{i=1}^{n} (x_i - \bar{x})(y_i - \bar{y})}{n - 1}$$

Population coefficient of correlation

$$\rho = \frac{\sigma_{xy}}{\sigma_x \sigma_y}$$

Sample coefficient of correlation

$$r = \frac{s_{xy}}{s_x s_y}$$

Coefficient of determination

$$R^2 = r^2$$

Slope coefficient

$$b_1 = \frac{s_{xy}}{s_x^2}$$

y-intercept

$$b_0 = \bar{y} - b_1 \bar{x}$$

COMPUTER OUTPUT AND INSTRUCTIONS

Technique	Excel
Mean	97
Median	98
Mode	99
Variance	108
Standard deviation	109
Descriptive statistics	116
Least squares line	131
Covariance	133
Correlation	133
Coefficient of determination	135

CHAPTER EXERCISES

4.139 Xr04-139* Osteoporosis is a condition in which bone density decreases, often resulting in broken bones. Bone density usually peaks at age 30 and decreases thereafter. To understand more about the condition, a random sample of women aged 50 years and over was recruited. Each woman's bone density loss was recorded.
a. Compute the mean and median of these data.
b. Compute the standard deviation of the bone density losses.
c. Describe what you have learned from the statistics.

4.140 Xr04-140* The temperature in December in Buffalo, New York, is often below 40 degrees Fahrenheit (4 degrees Celsius). Not surprisingly, when the National Football League Buffalo Bills play at home in December, coffee is a popular item at the concession stand. The concession manager would like to acquire more information so that he can manage inventories more efficiently. The number of cups of coffee sold during 50 games played in December in Buffalo was recorded.

a. Determine the mean and median.
b. Determine the variance and standard deviation.
c. Briefly describe what you have learned from your statistical analysis.

4.141 Refer to Exercise 4.139. In addition to the bone density losses, the ages of the women were also recorded. Compute the coefficient of determination and describe what this statistic tells you.

4.142 Refer to Exercise 4.140. Suppose that in addition to recording the coffee sales, the manager also recorded the average temperature (measured in degrees Fahrenheit) during the game. These data together with the number of cups of coffee sold were recorded.
a. Compute the coefficient of determination.
b. Determine the coefficients of the least squares line.
c. What have you learned from the statistics calculated in parts a and b about the relationship between the number of cups of coffee sold and the temperature?

4.143 <u>Xr04-143*</u> Chris Golfnut loves the game of golf. Chris also loves statistics. Combining both passions, Chris records a sample of 100 scores.
a. What statistics should Chris compute to describe the scores?
b. Calculate the mean and standard deviation of the scores.
c. Briefly describe what the statistics computed in part b divulge.

4.144 <u>Xr04-144</u> Increasing tuition has resulted in some students being saddled with large debts upon graduation. To examine this issue, a random sample of recent graduates was asked to report whether they had student loans, and, if so, how much was the debt at graduation.
a. Compute all three measures of central location.
b. What do these statistics reveal about student loan debt at graduation?

GENERAL SOCIAL SURVEY EXERCISES

The following exercises are based on the General Social Survey of 2014.

4.145 <u>GSS2014*</u> Calculate the coefficient of correlation of the amount of education of the respondents and their spouses (EDUC and SPEDUC). What does this statistic tell you about the relationship between the two variables?

4.146 <u>GSS2014*</u> Is someone's education (EDUC) affected by his or her father's education (PAEDUC)? Use a statistical analysis to answer the following questions:
a. How strong is the linear relationship between the two variables?
b. What is the average marginal increase in the number of years of the respondent's education for each additional year of the father's education?

4.147 <u>GSS2014*</u> Repeat Exercise 4.146 for the respondents' mothers education (MAEDUC).

4.148 <u>GSS2014*</u> How does age (AGE) affect respondents' television viewing (TVHOURS)? Conduct a statistical analysis to determine whether the two variables are related and the average marginal increase in television viewing for each additional year of age.

4.149 <u>GSS2014*</u> We would expect that people with more education would postpone having children. To examine the relationship between years of education (EDUC) and the age at which one's first child is born (AGEKDBRN), perform a statistical analysis that answers the following questions.
a. How strong is the linear relationship between the two variables?
b. What is the average marginal increase in the age at which one's first child is born for each additional year of education.

4.150 <u>GSS2014*</u> Do more educated (EDUC) Americans watch less television (TVHOURS)?
a. To answer this question calculate a statistic that measures the strength of the linear relationship.
b. Calculate the average marginal decrease in the hours of television viewing for each additional year of education.

SURVEY OF CONSUMER FINANCES EXERCISES

The following exercises are based on the Survey of Consumer Finances 2013.

4.151 <u>SCF2013:\All*</u> The survey measured total household assets (ASSET) and total net worth of household (NETWORTH). Use a statistical technique to show that they should have just measured one of the two variables.

4.152 <u>SCF2013:\All*</u> Investigate the relationship between total household income (INCOME) and total value of household assets (ASSET). Conduct a statistical analysis to measure how well the two variables correlate. Estimate the average marginal increase in assets for each additional dollar of income.

4.153 <u>SCF2013:\All*</u> Repeat Exercise 4.152 using wage and salary income (WAGEINC) instead of income.

4.154 <u>SCF2013:\All*</u> We expect that older respondents will have few, if any, children living in the household. Perform a statistical analysis to determine whether the age (AGE) of the respondent is linearly related to the number of children in the household (KIDS).

Estimate the average marginal decrease in the number of children in the household for each additional year of age.

CASE 4.1   Return to the Global Warming Question

Now that we have presented techniques that allow us to conduct more precise analyses, we'll return to Case 3.1. Recall that there are two issues in this discussion. First, is there global warming and, second, if so, is carbon dioxide the cause? The only tools available at the end of Chapter 3 were graphical techniques including line charts and scatter diagrams. You are now invited to apply the more precise techniques used in this chapter to answer the same questions.

Here are the data sets you can work with:

C04-01a: Column 1: Months numbered 1 to 1637
Column 2: Temperature anomalies produced by the National Climatic Data Center

C04-01b: Column 1: Year
Column 2: Month
Column 3: Monthly carbon dioxide levels measured by the Mauna Loa Observatory

Column 4: Temperature anomalies produced by the National Climatic Data Center

a. Use the least squares method to estimate average monthly changes in temperature anomalies.

b. Calculate the least squares line and the coefficient of correlation between CO_2 levels and temperature anomalies and describe your findings.

DATA
C04-01a
C04-01b

CASE 4.2   Another Return to the Global Warming Question

Did you conclude in Case 4.1 that the earth has warmed since 1880 and that there is some linear relationship between CO_2 and temperature anomalies? If so, here is another look at the same data. C04-02a lists the temperature anomalies from 1880 to 1940, C04-02b lists the data from 1941 to 1975, C04-02c stores the temperature anomalies from 1976 to 1997, and C04-02d contains the data from 1998 to 2016. For each set of data, draw a line chart and report your findings.

DATA
C04-02a
C04-02b
C04-02c
C04-02d

CASE 4.3   The Effect of the Players' Strike in the 2004–2005 Hockey Season

The 2004–2005 hockey season was cancelled because of a player strike. The key issue in this labor dispute was a "salary cap." The team owners wanted a salary cap to cut their costs. The owners of small-market teams wanted the cap to help their teams be competitive. Of course, caps on salaries would lower the salaries of most players and as a result the players association fought against it. The team owners prevailed and the collective bargaining agreement specified

DATA
C04-03a
C04-03b

a salary cap of $39 million and a floor of $21.5 million for the 2005–2006 season.

Conduct an analysis of the 2003–2004 season (C04-02a) and the 2005–2006 season (C04-02b). For each season:

a. Estimate how much on average a team needs to spend to win one more game.

b. Measure the strength of the linear relationship.

c. Discuss the differences between the two seasons.

CASE 4.4
Quebec Referendum Vote: Was There Electoral Fraud?*

DATA
C04-04

Since the 1960s, Québécois have been debating whether to separate from Canada and form an independent nation. A referendum was held on October 30, 1995, in which the people of Quebec voted not to separate. The vote was extremely close, with the "no" side winning by only 52,448 votes. A large number of "No" votes was cast by the non-Francophone (non-French-speaking) people of Quebec, who make up about 20% of the population and who very much want to remain Canadians. The remaining 80% are Francophones, a majority of whom voted "yes."

After the votes were counted, it became clear that the tallied vote was much closer than it should have been. Supporters of the "no" side charged that poll scrutineers, all of whom were appointed by the pro-separatist provincial government, rejected a disproportionate number of ballots in ridings where the percentage of "yes" votes was low and where there are large numbers of Allophone (people whose first language is neither English nor French) and Anglophone (English-speaking) residents. (Electoral laws require the rejection of ballots that do not appear to be properly marked.) They were outraged that in a strong democracy such as Canada, votes would be rigged much as they are in many nondemocratic countries around the world.

If in ridings where there was a low percentage of "yes" votes there was a high percentage of rejected ballots, this would be evidence of electoral fraud. Moreover, if in ridings where there were large percentages of Allophone and/or Anglophone voters, there were high percentages of rejected ballots, this, too, would constitute evidence of fraud on the part of the scrutineers and possibly the government.

To determine the veracity of the charges, the following variables were recorded for each riding:

Percentage of rejected ballots in referendum

Percentage of "yes" votes

Percentage of Allophones

Percentage of Anglophones

Conduct a statistical analysis of these data to determine whether there are indications that electoral fraud took place.

---

*This case is based on "Voting Irregularities in the 1995 Referendum on Quebec Sovereignty" Jason Cawley and Paul Sommers, *Chance*, Vol. 9, No. 4, Fall, 1996. We are grateful to Dr. Paul Sommers, Middlebury College, for his assistance in writing this case.

APPENDIX 4 / REVIEW OF DESCRIPTIVE TECHNIQUES

Here is a list of the statistical techniques introduced in Chapters 2, 3, and 4. This is followed by a flowchart designed to help you select the most appropriate method to use to address any problem requiring a descriptive method.

To provide practice in identifying the correct descriptive method to use we have created a number of review exercises. These are in Keller's website Appendix, Descriptive Techniques Review Exercises.

Graphical Techniques

Histogram

Bar chart

Pie chart

Scatter diagram

Line chart (time series)

Numerical Techniques

Measures of Central Location

Mean

Median

Mode

Geometric mean (growth rates)

Measures of Variability

Range

Variance

Standard deviation

Coefficient of variation

Interquartile range

Measures of Relative Standing

Percentiles

Quartiles

Measures of Linear Relationship

Covariance

Coefficient of correlation

Coefficient of determination

Least squares line

Flowchart: Graphical and Numerical Techniques

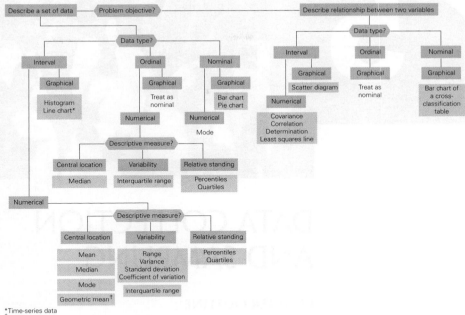

*Time-series data
†Growth rates

5

Rich Lindie/Shutterstock.com

DATA COLLECTION AND SAMPLING

CHAPTER OUTLINE

Sampling and the Census

The census, which is conducted every 10 years in the United States, serves an important function. It is the basis for deciding how many congressional representatives and how many votes in the electoral college each state will have. Businesses often use the information derived from the census to help make decisions about products, advertising, and plant locations.

    One of the problems with the census is the issue of undercounting, which occurs when some people are not included. For example, the 1990 census reported that 12.05% of adults were African American; the true value was 12.41%. To address undercounting, the Census Bureau adjusts the numbers it gets from the census. The adjustment is based

Spencer Grant/Age Fotostock

On page 150, you will find our answer.

on another survey. The mechanism is called the Accuracy and Coverage Evaluation. Using sampling methods described in this chapter, the Census Bureau is able to adjust the numbers in American subgroups. For example, the Bureau may discover that the number of Hispanics has been undercounted or that the number of people living in California has not been accurately counted.

Later in this chapter we'll discuss how the sampling is conducted and how the adjustments are made.

INTRODUCTION

In Chapter 1, we briefly introduced the concept of statistical inference—the process of inferring information about a population from a sample. Because information about populations can usually be described by parameters, the statistical technique used generally deals with drawing inferences about population parameters from sample statistics. (Recall that a parameter is a measurement about a population, and a statistic is a measurement about a sample.)

Working within the covers of a statistics textbook, we can assume that population parameters are known. In real life, however, calculating parameters is virtually impossible because populations tend to be very large. As a result, most population parameters are not only unknown but also unknowable. The problem that motivates the subject of statistical inference is that we often need information about the value of parameters in order to make decisions. For example, to make decisions about whether to expand a line of clothing, we may need to know the mean annual expenditure on clothing by North American adults. Because the size of this population is approximately 200 million, determining the mean is prohibitive. However, if we are willing to accept less than 100% accuracy, we can use statistical inference to obtain an estimate. Rather than investigating the entire population, we select a sample of people, determine the annual expenditures on clothing in this group, and calculate the sample mean. Although the probability that the sample mean will equal the population mean is very small, we would expect them to be close. For many decisions, we need to know how close. We postpone that discussion until Chapters 10 and 11. In this chapter, we will discuss the basic concepts and techniques of sampling itself. But first we take a look at various sources for collecting data.

5-1 / METHODS OF COLLECTING DATA

Most of this book addresses the problem of converting data into information. The question arises, where do data come from? The answer is that a large number of methods produce data. Before we proceed however, we'll remind you of the definition of data introduced in Section 2-1. Data are the observed values of a variable; that is, we define a variable or variables that are of interest to us and then proceed to collect observations of those variables.

5-1a Direct Observation

The simplest method of obtaining data is by direct observation. When data are gathered in this way, they are said to be **observational**. For example, suppose that a researcher for a pharmaceutical company wants to determine whether aspirin actually reduces the incidence of heart attacks. Observational data may be gathered by selecting a sample of men and women and asking each whether he or she has taken aspirin regularly over the past 2 years. Each person would be asked whether he or she had suffered a heart attack over the same period. The proportions reporting heart attacks would be compared and a statistical technique that is introduced in Chapter 13 would be used to determine whether aspirin is effective in reducing the likelihood of heart attacks. There are many drawbacks to this method. One of the most critical is that it is difficult to produce useful information in this way. For example, if the statistics practitioner concludes that people who take aspirin suffer fewer heart attacks, can we conclude that aspirin is effective? It may be that people who take aspirin tend to be more health conscious, and health-conscious people tend to have fewer heart attacks. The one advantage of direct observation is that it is relatively inexpensive.

5-1b Experiments

A more expensive but better way to produce data is through experiments. Data produced in this manner are called **experimental**. In the aspirin illustration, a statistics practitioner can randomly select men and women. The sample would be divided into two groups. One group would take aspirin regularly, and the other would not. After 2 years, the statistics practitioner would determine the proportion of people in each group who had suffered heart attacks, and statistical methods again would be used to determine whether aspirin works. If we find that the aspirin group suffered fewer heart attacks, then we may more confidently conclude that taking aspirin regularly is a healthy decision.

5-1c Surveys

One of the most familiar methods of collecting data is the **survey**, which solicits information from people concerning such things as their income, family size, and opinions on various issues. We're all familiar, for example, with opinion polls that accompany each political election. The Gallup Poll and the Harris Survey are two well-known surveys of public opinion whose results are often reported by the media. But the majority of surveys are conducted for private use. Private surveys are used extensively by market researchers to determine the preferences and attitudes of consumers and voters. The results can be used for a variety of purposes, from helping to determine the target market for an advertising campaign to modifying a candidate's platform in an election campaign. As an illustration, consider a television network that has hired a market research firm to provide the network with a profile of owners of luxury automobiles, including what they watch on television and at what times. The network could then use this information to develop a package of recommended time slots for Cadillac commercials, including costs, which it would present to General Motors. It is quite likely that many students reading this book will one day be marketing executives who will "live and die" by such market research data.

An important aspect of surveys is the **response rate**. The response rate is the proportion of all people who were selected who complete the survey. As we discuss in the next section, a low response rate can destroy the validity of any conclusion resulting from the statistical analysis. Statistics practitioners need to ensure that data are reliable.

Personal Interview Many researchers feel that the best way to survey people is by means of a personal interview, which involves an interviewer soliciting information from a respondent by asking prepared questions. A personal interview has the advantage of having a higher expected response rate than other methods of data collection. In addition, there will probably be fewer incorrect responses resulting from respondents misunderstanding some questions because the interviewer can clarify misunderstandings when asked to. But the interviewer must also be careful not to say too much for fear of biasing the response. To avoid introducing such biases, as well as to reap the potential benefits of a personal interview, the interviewer must be well trained in proper interviewing techniques and well informed on the purpose of the study. The main disadvantage of personal interviews is that they are expensive, especially when travel is involved.

Telephone Interview A telephone interview is usually less expensive, but it is also less personal and has a lower expected response rate. Unless the issue is of interest, many people will refuse to respond to telephone surveys. This problem is exacerbated by telemarketers trying to sell something.

Self-Administered Survey A third popular method of data collection is the self-administered questionnaire, which is usually mailed to a sample of people. This is an inexpensive method of conducting a survey and is therefore attractive when the number of people to be surveyed is large. But self-administered questionnaires usually have a low response rate and may have a relatively high number of incorrect responses due to respondents misunderstanding some questions.

Questionnaire Design Whether a questionnaire is self-administered or completed by an interviewer, it must be well designed. Proper questionnaire design takes knowledge, experience, time, and money. Some basic points to consider regarding questionnaire design follow.

1. First and foremost, the questionnaire should be kept as short as possible to encourage respondents to complete it. Most people are unwilling to spend much time filling out a questionnaire.

2. The questions themselves should also be short, as well as simply and clearly worded, to enable respondents to answer quickly, correctly, and without ambiguity. Even familiar terms such as "*unemployed*" and "*family*" must be defined carefully because several interpretations are possible.

3. Questionnaires often begin with simple demographic questions to help respondents get started and become comfortable quickly.

4. Dichotomous questions (questions with only two possible responses such as "yes" and "no" and multiple-choice questions) are useful and popular because of their simplicity, but they also have possible shortcomings. For example, a respondent's choice of yes or no to a question may depend on certain assumptions not stated in the question. In the case of a multiple-choice question, a respondent may feel that none of the choices offered is suitable.

5. Open-ended questions provide an opportunity for respondents to express opinions more fully, but they are time consuming and more difficult to tabulate and analyze.

6. Avoid using leading questions, such as "Wouldn't you agree that the statistics exam was too difficult?" These types of questions tend to lead the respondent to a particular answer.

7. Time permitting, it is useful to pretest a questionnaire on a small number of people in order to uncover potential problems such as ambiguous wording.

8. Finally, when preparing the questions, think about how you intend to tabulate and analyze the responses. First, determine whether you are soliciting values (i.e., responses) for an interval variable or a nominal variable. Then consider which type of statistical techniques—descriptive or inferential—you intend to apply to the data to be collected, and note the requirements of the specific techniques to be used. Thinking about these questions will help ensure that the questionnaire is designed to collect the data you need.

Whatever method is used to collect primary data, we need to know something about sampling, the subject of the next section.

EXERCISES

5.1 Briefly describe the difference between observational and experimental data.

5.2 A soft drink manufacturer has been supplying its cola drink in bottles to grocery stores and in cans to small convenience stores. The company is analyzing sales of this cola drink to determine which type of packaging is preferred by consumers.
   a. Is this study observational or experimental? Explain your answer.
   b. Outline a better method for determining whether a store will be supplied with cola in bottles or in cans so that future sales data will be more helpful in assessing the preferred type of packaging.

5.3 a. Briefly describe how you might design a study to investigate the relationship between smoking and lung cancer.
   b. Is your study in part (a) observational or experimental? Explain why.

5.4 a. List three methods of conducting a survey of people.
   b. Give an important advantage and disadvantage of each of the methods listed in part (a).

5.5 List five important points to consider when designing a questionnaire.

5-2 / SAMPLING

The chief motive for examining a sample rather than a population is cost. Statistical inference permits us to draw conclusions about a population parameter based on a sample that is quite small in comparison to the size of the population. For example, television executives want to know the proportion of television viewers who watch a network's programs. Because 100 million people may be watching television in the United States on a given evening, determining the actual proportion of the population that is watching certain programs is impractical and prohibitively expensive. The Nielsen ratings provide approximations of the desired information by observing what is watched by a sample of 5,000 television viewers. The proportion of households watching a particular program can be calculated for the households in the Nielsen sample. This sample proportion is then used as an **estimate** of the proportion of all households (the population proportion) that watched the program.

Another illustration of sampling can be taken from the field of quality management. To ensure that a production process is operating properly, the operations manager needs to know what proportion of items being produced is defective. If the quality technician must destroy the item to determine whether it is defective, then there is no alternative to sampling: A complete inspection of the product population would destroy the entire output of the production process.

We know that the sample proportion of television viewers or of defective items is probably not exactly equal to the population proportion we want to estimate. Nonetheless, the sample statistic can come quite close to the parameter it is designed to estimate if the **target population** (the population about which we want to draw inferences) and the **sampled population** (the actual population from which the sample has been taken) are the same. In practice, these may not be the same. One of statistics' most famous failures illustrates this phenomenon.

The *Literary Digest* was a popular magazine of the 1920s and 1930s that had correctly predicted the outcomes of several presidential elections. In 1936, the *Digest* predicted that the Republican candidate, Alfred Landon, would defeat the Democratic incumbent, Franklin D. Roosevelt, by a 3 to 2 margin. But in that election, Roosevelt defeated Landon in a landslide victory, garnering the support of 62% of the electorate. The source of this blunder was the sampling procedure, and there were two distinct mistakes.[*] First, the *Digest* sent out 10 million sample ballots to prospective voters. However, most of the names of these people were taken from the *Digest*'s subscription list and from telephone directories. Subscribers to the magazine and people who owned telephones tended to be wealthier than average and such people then, as today, tended to vote Republican. In addition, only 2.3 million ballots were returned resulting in a self-selected sample.

Self-selected samples are almost always biased because the individuals who participate in them are more keenly interested in the issue than are the other members of the population. You often find similar surveys conducted today when radio and television stations ask people to call and give their opinion on an issue of interest. Again, only listeners who are concerned about the topic and have enough patience to get through to the station will be included in the sample. Hence, the sampled population is composed entirely of people who are interested in the issue, whereas the target population is made up of all the people within the listening radius of the radio station. As a result, the conclusions drawn from such surveys are frequently wrong.

An excellent example of this phenomenon occurred on ABC's *Nightline* in 1984. Viewers were given a 900 telephone number (cost: 50 cents) and asked to phone in their responses to the question of whether the United Nations should continue to be located in the United States. More than 186,000 people called, with 67% responding "no." At the same time, a (more scientific) market research poll of 500 people revealed that 72% wanted the United Nations to remain in the United States. In general, because the true value of the parameter being estimated is never known, these surveys give the impression of providing useful information. In fact, the results of such surveys are likely to be no more accurate than the results of the 1936 *Literary Digest* poll or *Nightline*'s phone-in show. Statisticians have coined two terms to describe these polls: SLOP (self-selected opinion poll) and *Oy vey* (from the Yiddish lament), both of which convey the contempt that statisticians have for such data-gathering processes.

---

[*]Many statisticians ascribe the *Literary Digest*'s statistical debacle to the wrong causes. For an understanding of what really happened, read Maurice C. Bryson, "The Literary Digest Poll: Making of a Statistical Myth" *American Statistician* 30(4) (November 1976): 184–185.

Exercises

5.6 For each of the following sampling plans, indicate why the target population and the sampled population are not the same.

a. To determine the opinions and attitudes of customers who regularly shop at a particular mall, a surveyor stands outside a large department store in the mall and randomly selects people to participate in the survey.

b. A library wants to estimate the proportion of its books that have been damaged. The librarians decide to select one book per shelf as a sample by measuring 12 inches from the left edge of each shelf and selecting the book in that location.

c. Political surveyors visit 200 residences during one afternoon to ask eligible voters present in the house at the time whom they intend to vote for.

5.7 a. Describe why the *Literary Digest* poll of 1936 has become infamous.

b. What caused this poll to be so wrong?

5.8 a. What is meant by *self-selected sample*?

b. Give an example of a recent poll that involved a self-selected sample.

c. Why are self-selected samples not desirable?

5.9 A regular feature in a newspaper asks readers to respond via e-mail to a survey that requires a yes or no response. In the following day's newspaper, the percentage of yes and no responses are reported. Discuss why we should ignore these statistics.

5.10 Suppose your statistics professor distributes a questionnaire about the course. One of the questions asks, "Would you recommend this course to a friend?" Can the professor use the results to infer something about all statistics courses? Explain.

5-3 / SAMPLING PLANS

Our objective in this section is to introduce three different sampling plans: simple random sampling, stratified random sampling, and cluster sampling. We begin our presentation with the most basic design.

5-3a Simple Random Sampling

> **Simple Random Sample**
>
> A **simple random sample** is a sample selected in such a way that every possible sample with the same number of observations is equally likely to be chosen.

One way to conduct a simple random sample is to assign a number to each element in the population, write these numbers on individual slips of paper, toss them into a hat, and draw the required number of slips (the sample size, n) from the hat. This is the kind of procedure that occurs in raffles, when all the ticket stubs go into a large rotating drum from which the winners are selected.

Sometimes the elements of the population are already numbered. For example, virtually all adults have Social Security numbers (in the United States) or Social Insurance numbers (in Canada); all employees of large corporations have employee numbers; many people have driver's license numbers, medical plan numbers, student numbers, and so on. In such cases, choosing which sampling procedure to use is simply a matter of deciding how to select from among these numbers.

In other cases, the existing form of numbering has built-in flaws that make it inappropriate as a source of samples. Not everyone has a phone number, for example, so the telephone book does not list all the people in a given area. Many households have two (or more) adults but only one phone listing. It seems that everyone in the world has a cell phone. Many of these people have no land phone, so they do not appear on any list. Some people do not have phones, some have unlisted phone numbers, and some have more than one phone; these differences mean that each element of the population does not have an equal probability of being selected.

After each element of the chosen population has been assigned a unique number, sample numbers can be selected at random. A random number table can be used to select these sample numbers. (See, for example, *CRC Standard Management Tables*, W. H. Beyer, ed., Boca Raton FL: CRC Press.) Alternatively, we can use Excel to perform this function.

<table>
<tr><td>EXAMPLE 5.1</td><td></td></tr>
</table>

Random Sample of Income Tax Returns

A government income tax auditor has been given responsibility for 1,000 tax returns. A computer is used to check the arithmetic of each return. However, to determine whether the returns have been completed honestly, the auditor must check each entry and confirm its veracity. Because it takes, on average, 1 hour to completely audit a return and she has only 1 week to complete the task, the auditor has decided to randomly select 40 returns. The returns are numbered from 1 to 1,000. Use a computer random-number generator to select the sample for the auditor.

SOLUTION:

We generated 50 numbers between 1 and 1,000 even though we needed only 40 numbers. We did so because it is likely that there will be some duplicates. We will use the first 40 unique random numbers to select our sample. The following numbers were generated by Excel. The instructions are provided here. [Notice that the 24th and 36th (counting down the columns) numbers generated were the same—467.]

Computer-Generated Random Numbers

383	246	372	952	75
101	46	356	54	199
597	33	911	706	65
900	165	467	817	359
885	220	427	973	488
959	18	304	467	512
15	286	976	301	374
408	344	807	751	986
864	554	992	352	41
139	358	257	776	231

EXCEL Data Analysis

INSTRUCTIONS

1. Click **Data, Data Analysis**, and **Random Number Generation**.
2. Specify the **Number of Variables** (1) and the **Number of Random Numbers** (50).
3. Select **Uniform Distribution.**
4. Specify the range of the uniform distribution (**Parameters**) (0 and 1).
5. Click **OK**. Column A will fill with 50 numbers that range between 0 and 1.
6. Multiply column A by 1,000 and store the products in column B.

7. Make cell C1 active, and click f_x, **Math & Trig, ROUNDUP**, and **OK**.

8. Specify the first number to be rounded (B1).

9. Type the **number of digits** (decimal places) **(0)**. Click **OK**.

10. Complete column C.

The first five steps command Excel to generate 50 uniformly distributed random numbers between 0 and 1 to be stored in column A. Steps 6 through 10 convert these random numbers to integers between 1 and 1,000. Each tax return has the same probability (1/1,000 = .001) of being selected. Thus, each member of the population is equally likely to be included in the sample.

INTERPRET

The auditor would examine the tax returns selected by the computer. She would pick returns numbered 383, 101, 597, . . . , 352, 776, and 75 (the first 40 unique numbers). Each of these returns would be audited to determine whether it is fraudulent. If the objective is to audit these 40 returns, no statistical procedure would be employed. However, if the objective is to estimate the proportion of all 1,000 returns that are dishonest, then she would use one of the inferential techniques presented later in this book.

5-3b Stratified Random Sampling

In making inferences about a population, we attempt to extract as much information as possible from a sample. The basic sampling plan, simple random sampling, often accomplishes this goal at low cost. Other methods, however, can be used to increase the amount of information about the population. One such procedure is *stratified random sampling*.

> **Stratified Random Sample**
>
> A **stratified random sample** is obtained by separating the population into mutually exclusive sets, or strata, and then drawing simple random samples from each stratum.

Examples of criteria for separating a population into strata (and of the strata themselves) follow.

1. Gender
   male
   female

2. Age
   under 20
   20–30
   31–40
   41–50
   51–60
   over 60

3. Occupation
   professional
   clerical
   blue-collar
   other

4. Household income
   under $25,000
   $25,000–$39,999
   $40,000–$60,000
   over $60,000

To illustrate, suppose a public opinion survey is to be conducted to determine how many people favor a tax increase. A stratified random sample could be obtained by selecting a random sample of people from each of the four income groups we just described. We usually stratify in a way that enables us to obtain particular kinds of information. In this example, we would like to know whether people in the different income categories differ in their opinions about the proposed tax increase, because the tax increase will affect the strata differently. We avoid stratifying when there is no connection between the survey and the strata. For example, little purpose is served in trying to determine whether people within religious strata have divergent opinions about the tax increase.

One advantage of stratification is that, besides acquiring information about the entire population, we can also make inferences within each stratum or compare strata. For instance, we can estimate what proportion of the lowest income group favors the tax increase, or we can compare the highest and lowest income groups to determine whether they differ in their support of the tax increase.

Any stratification must be done in such a way that the strata are mutually exclusive: Each member of the population must be assigned to exactly one stratum. After the population has been stratified in this way, we can use simple random sampling to generate the complete sample. There are several ways to do this. For example, we can draw random samples from each of the four income groups according to their proportions in the population. Thus, if in the population the relative frequencies of the four groups are as listed here, our sample will be stratified in the same proportions. If a total sample of 1,000 is to be drawn, then we will randomly select 250 from stratum 1, 400 from stratum 2, 300 from stratum 3, and 50 from stratum 4.

Stratum	Income Categories ($)	Population Proportions (%)
1	Less than 25,000	25
2	25,000–39,999	40
3	40,000–60,000	30
4	More than 60,000	5

The problem with this approach, however, is that if we want to make inferences about the last stratum, a sample of 50 may be too small to produce useful information. In such cases, we usually increase the sample size of the smallest stratum to ensure that the sample data provide enough information for our purposes. An adjustment must then be made before we attempt to draw inferences about the entire population. The required procedure is beyond the level of this book. We recommend that anyone planning such a survey consult an expert statistician or a reference book on the subject. Better still, become an expert statistician yourself by taking additional statistics courses.

5-3c Cluster Sampling

> **Cluster Sample**
> A **cluster sample** is a simple random sample of groups or clusters of elements.

Cluster sampling is particularly useful when it is difficult or costly to develop a complete list of the population members (making it difficult and costly to generate a simple random sample). It is also useful whenever the population elements are widely dispersed geographically. For example, suppose we wanted to estimate the average annual household income in a large city. To use simple random sampling, we would need a complete list of households in the city from which to sample. To use stratified random sampling, we would need the list of households, and we would also need to have each household categorized by some other variable (such as age of household head) in order to develop the strata. A less-expensive alternative would be to let each block within the city represent a cluster. A sample of clusters could then be randomly selected, and every household within these clusters could be questioned to determine income. By reducing the distances the surveyor must cover to gather data, cluster sampling reduces the cost.

But cluster sampling also increases sampling error (see Section 5-4) because households belonging to the same cluster are likely to be similar in many respects, including household income. This can be partially offset by using some of the cost savings to choose a larger sample than would be used for a simple random sample.

5-3d Sample Size

Whichever type of sampling plan you select, you still have to decide what size sample to use. Determining the appropriate sample size will be addressed in detail in Chapters 10 and 12. Until then, we can rely on our intuition, which tells us that the larger the sample size is, the more accurate we can expect the estimates to be.

Sampling and the Census

To adjust for undercounting, the Census Bureau conducts cluster sampling. The clusters are geographic blocks. For the year 2000 census, the bureau randomly sampled 11,800 blocks, which contained 314,000 housing units. Each unit was intensively revisited to ensure that all residents were counted. From the results of this survey, the Census Bureau estimated the number of people missed by the first census in various subgroups, defined by several variables including gender, race, and age. Because of the importance of determining state populations, adjustments were made to state totals. For example, by comparing the results of the census and of the sampling, the Bureau determined that the undercount in the state of Texas was 1.7087%. The official census produced a state population of 20,851,820. Taking 1.7087% of this total produced an adjustment of 356,295. Using this method changed the population of the state of Texas to 21,208,115.

Spencer Grant/Age Fotostock

It should be noted that this process is contentious. The controversy concerns the way in which subgroups are defined. Changing the definition alters the undercounts, making this statistical technique subject to politicking.

EXERCISES

5.11 A statistics practitioner would like to conduct a survey to ask people their views on a proposed new shopping mall in their community. According to the latest census, there are 500 households in the community. The statistician has numbered each household (from 1 to 500), and she would like to randomly select 25 of these households to participate in the study. Use Excel to generate the sample.

5.12 A safety expert wants to determine the proportion of cars in his state with worn tire treads. The state license plate contains six digits. Use Excel to generate a sample of 20 cars to be examined.

5.13 A large university campus has 60,000 students. The president of the students' association wants to conduct a survey of the students to determine their views on an increase in the student activity fee. She would like to acquire information about all the students but would also like to compare the school of business, the faculty of arts and sciences, and the graduate school. Describe a sampling plan that accomplishes these goals.

5.14 A telemarketing firm has recorded the households that have purchased one or more of the company's products. These number in the millions. The firm would like to conduct a survey of purchasers to acquire information about their attitude concerning the timing of the telephone calls. The president of the company would like to know the views of all purchasers but would also like to compare the attitudes of people in the West, South, North, and East. Describe a suitable sampling plan.

5.15 The operations manager of a large plant with four departments wants to estimate the person-hours lost per month from accidents. Describe a sampling plan that would be suitable for estimating the plantwide loss and for comparing departments.

5.16 A statistics practitioner wants to estimate the mean age of children in his city. Unfortunately, he does not have a complete list of households. Describe a sampling plan that would be suitable for his purposes.

5-4 / SAMPLING AND NONSAMPLING ERRORS

Two major types of error can arise when a sample of observations is taken from a population: *sampling error* and *nonsampling error*. Anyone reviewing the results of sample surveys and studies, as well as statistics practitioners conducting surveys and applying statistical techniques, should understand the sources of these errors.

5-4a Sampling Error

Sampling error refers to differences between the sample and the population that exists only because of the observations that happened to be selected for the sample. Sampling error is an error that we expect to occur when we make a statement about a population that is based only on the observations contained in a sample taken from the population.

To illustrate, suppose that we wish to determine the mean annual income of North American blue-collar workers. To determine this parameter we would have to ask each North American blue-collar worker what his or her income is and then calculate the mean of all the responses. Because the size of this population is several million, the task is both expensive and impractical. We can use statistical inference to estimate the mean income μ of the population if we are willing to accept less than 100% accuracy. We record the incomes of a sample of the workers and find the mean $\bar{x}$ of this sample of incomes. This sample mean is an estimate of the desired population mean. But the value of the sample mean will deviate from the population mean simply by chance because the value of the sample mean depends on which incomes just happened to be selected for the sample. The difference between the true (unknown) value of the population mean and its estimate, the sample mean, is the sampling error. The size of this deviation may be large simply because of bad luck—bad luck that a particularly unrepresentative sample happened to be selected. The only way we can reduce the expected size of this error is to take a larger sample.

Given a fixed sample size, the best we can do is to state the probability that the sampling error is less than a certain amount (as we will discuss in Chapter 10). It is common today for such a statement to accompany the results of an opinion poll. If an opinion poll states that, based on sample results, the incumbent candidate for mayor has the support of 54% of eligible voters in an upcoming election, the statement may be accompanied by the following explanatory note: "This percentage is correct to within three percentage points, 19 times out of 20." This statement means that we estimate that the actual level of support for the candidate is between 51% and 57%, and that in the long run this type of procedure is correct 95% of the time.

5-4b Nonsampling Error

Nonsampling error is more serious than sampling error because taking a larger sample won't diminish the size, or the possibility of occurrence, of this error. Even a census can (and probably will) contain nonsampling errors. **Nonsampling errors** result from mistakes made in the acquisition of data or from the sample observations being selected improperly.

1. *Errors in data acquisition*. This type of error arises from the recording of incorrect responses. Incorrect responses may be the result of incorrect measurements being taken because of faulty equipment, mistakes made during transcription from primary sources, inaccurate recording of data because terms were misinterpreted, or inaccurate responses were given to questions concerning sensitive issues such as sexual activity or possible tax evasion.

2. *Nonresponse error*. **Nonresponse error** refers to error (or **bias**) introduced when responses are not obtained from some members of the sample. When this happens, the sample observations that are collected may not be representative of the target population, resulting in biased results (as was discussed in Section 5-2). Nonresponse can occur for a number of reasons. An interviewer may be unable to contact a person listed in the sample, or the sampled person may refuse to respond for some reason. In either case, responses are not obtained from a sampled person, and bias is introduced. The problem of nonresponse is even greater when self-administered questionnaires are used rather than an interviewer, who can attempt to reduce the nonresponse rate by means of callbacks. As noted previously, the *Literary Digest* fiasco was largely the result of a high nonresponse rate, resulting in a biased, self-selected sample.

3. *Selection bias*. **Selection bias** occurs when the sampling plan is such that some members of the target population cannot possibly be selected for inclusion in the sample. Together with nonresponse error, selection bias played a role in the *Literary Digest* poll being so wrong, as voters without telephones or without a subscription to *Literary Digest* were excluded from possible inclusion in the sample taken.

EXERCISES

5.17 a. Explain the difference between sampling error and nonsampling error.

b. Which type of error in part (a) is more serious? Why?

5.18 Briefly describe three types of nonsampling error.

5.19 Is it possible for a sample to yield better results than a census? Explain.

CHAPTER SUMMARY

Because most populations are very large, it is extremely costly and impractical to investigate each member of the population to determine the values of the parameters. As a practical alternative, we take a sample from the population and use the sample statistics to draw inferences about the parameters. Care must be taken to ensure that the **sampled population** is the same as the **target population**.

We can choose from among several different sampling plans, including **simple random sampling**, **stratified random sampling**, and **cluster sampling**. Whatever sampling plan is used, it is important to realize that both **sampling error** and **nonsampling error** will occur and to understand what the sources of these errors are.

IMPORTANT TERMS:

Observational   141
Experimental   142
Survey   142
Response rate   142
Estimate   144
Target population   145
Sampled population   145
Self-selected sample   145

Simple random sample   146
Stratified random sample   148
Cluster sample   150
Sampling error   151
Nonsampling error   152
Nonresponse error (bias)   152
Selection bias   152

![chapter number 6 graphic]

PROBABILITY

Dmitry Naumov/Shutterstock.com

CHAPTER OUTLINE

Auditing Tax Returns

Gary Buss/Taxi/Getty Images

Government auditors routinely check tax returns to determine whether calculation errors were made. They also attempt to detect fraudulent returns. There are several methods that dishonest taxpayers use to evade income tax. One method is not to declare various sources of income. Auditors have several detection methods, including spending patterns. Another form of tax fraud is to invent deductions that are not real. After analyzing the returns of thousands of self-employed taxpayers, an auditor has determined that 45% of fraudulent returns contain two suspicious deductions, 28% contain one suspicious deduction, and the rest no suspicious deductions. Among honest returns the rates are 11% for two deductions, 18% for one deduction, and 71% for no deductions. The auditor believes that 5% of the returns of self-employed individuals contain significant fraud. The auditor has just received a tax return for a self-employed individual that contains one suspicious expense deduction. What is the probability that this tax return contains significant fraud?

See page 183 for the answer.

154

INTRODUCTION

In Chapters 2, 3, and 4, we introduced graphical and numerical descriptive methods. Although the methods are useful on their own, we are particularly interested in developing statistical inference. As we pointed out in Chapter 1, statistical inference is the process by which we acquire information about populations from samples. A critical component of inference is *probability* because it provides the link between the population and the sample.

Our primary objective in this and the following two chapters is to develop the probability-based tools that are at the basis of statistical inference. However, probability can also play a critical role in decision making, a subject we explore in Chapter 22.

6-1/ASSIGNING PROBABILITY TO EVENTS

To introduce probability, we must first define a *random experiment*.

> **Random Experiment**
> A **random experiment** is an action or process that leads to one of several possible outcomes.

Here are six illustrations of random experiments and their outcomes.

Illustration 1. Experiment: Flip a coin.
Outcomes: Heads and tails

Illustration 2. Experiment: Record marks on a statistics test (out of 100).
Outcomes: Numbers between 0 and 100

Illustration 3. Experiment: Record grade on a statistics test.
Outcomes: A, B, C, D, and F

Illustration 4. Experiment: Record student evaluations of a course.
Outcomes: Poor, fair, good, very good, and excellent

Illustration 5. Experiment: Measure the time to assemble a computer.
Outcomes: Number whose smallest possible value is 0 seconds with no predefined upper limit

Illustration 6. Experiment: Record the party that a voter will vote for in an upcoming election.
Outcomes: Party A, Party B, . . .

The first step in assigning probabilities is to produce a list of the outcomes. The listed outcomes must be **exhaustive**, which means that all possible outcomes must be included. In addition, the outcomes must be **mutually exclusive**, which means that no two outcomes can occur at the same time.

To illustrate the concept of exhaustive outcomes consider this list of the outcomes of the toss of a die:

1   2   3   4   5

This list is not exhaustive, because we have omitted 6.

The concept of mutual exclusiveness can be seen by listing the following outcomes in illustration 2:

0–50　　50–60　　60–70　　70–80　　80–100

If these intervals include both the lower and upper limits, then these outcomes are not mutually exclusive because two outcomes can occur for any student. For example, if a student receives a mark of 70, both the third and fourth outcomes occur.

Note that we could produce more than one list of exhaustive and mutually exclusive outcomes. For example, here is another list of outcomes for illustration 3:

Pass and fail

A list of exhaustive and mutually exclusive outcomes is called a *sample space* and is denoted by *S*. The outcomes are denoted by $O_1, O_2, \ldots, O_k$.

Sample Space

A **sample space** of a random experiment is a list of all possible outcomes of the experiment. The outcomes must be exhaustive and mutually exclusive.

Using set notation, we represent the sample space and its outcomes as

$$S = \{O_1, O_2, \ldots, O_k\}$$

Once a sample space has been prepared we begin the task of assigning probabilities to the outcomes. There are three ways to assign probability to outcomes. However it is done, there are two rules governing probabilities as stated in the next box.

Requirements of Probabilities

Given a sample space $S = \{O_1, O_2, \ldots, O_k\}$, the probabilities assigned to the outcomes must satisfy two requirements.

1. The probability of any outcome must lie between 0 and 1; that is,

$$0 \le P(O_i) \le 1 \quad \text{for each } i$$

   [Note: $P(O_i)$ is the notation we use to represent the probability of outcome i.]

2. The sum of the probabilities of all the outcomes in a sample space must be 1. That is,

$$\sum_{i=1}^{k} P(O_i) = 1$$

6-1a Three Approaches to Assigning Probabilities

The **classical approach** is used by mathematicians to help determine probability associated with games of chance. For example, the classical approach specifies that the probabilities of heads and tails in the flip of a balanced coin are equal to each other. Because the sum of the probabilities must be 1, the probability of heads and the probability of tails are both 50%. Similarly, the six possible outcomes of the toss of a balanced die have the same probability; each is assigned a probability of 1/6. In some experiments, it is necessary to develop mathematical ways to count the number of outcomes. For example, to determine the probability of winning a lottery, we need to determine the number of possible combinations. For details on how to count events, see the online appendix Counting Formulas.

The **relative frequency approach** defines probability as the long-run relative frequency with which an outcome occurs. For example, suppose that we know that of the last 1,000 students who took the statistics course you're now taking, 200 received a grade of A. The relative frequency of A's is then 200/1000 or 20%. This figure represents an estimate of the probability of obtaining a grade of A in the course. It is only an estimate because the relative frequency approach defines probability as the "long-run" relative frequency. One thousand students do not constitute the long run. The larger the number of students whose grades we have observed, the better the estimate becomes. In theory, we would have to observe an infinite number of grades to determine the exact probability.

When it is not reasonable to use the classical approach and there is no history of the outcomes, we have no alternative but to employ the **subjective approach**. In the subjective approach, we define probability as the degree of belief that we hold in the occurrence of an event. An excellent example is derived from the field of investment. An investor would like to know the probability that a particular stock will increase in value. Using the subjective approach, the investor would analyze a number of factors associated with the stock and the stock market in general and, using his or her judgment, assign a probability to the outcomes of interest.

6-1b Defining Events

An individual outcome of a sample space is called a *simple event*. All other events are composed of the simple events in a sample space.

> **Event**
> An **event** is a collection or set of one or more simple events in a sample space.

In illustration 2, we can define the event, achieve a grade of A, as the set of numbers that lie between 80 and 100, inclusive. Using set notation, we have

$$A = \{80, 81, 82, \ldots, 99, 100\}$$

Similarly,

$$F = \{0, 1, 2, \ldots, 48, 49\}$$

6-1c Probability of Events

We can now define the probability of any event.

> **Probability of an Event**
>
> The probability of an event is the sum of the probabilities of the simple events that constitute the event.

For example, suppose that in illustration 3, we employed the relative frequency approach to assign probabilities to the simple events as follows:

$$P(A) = .20$$
$$P(B) = .30$$
$$P(C) = .25$$
$$P(D) = .15$$
$$P(F) = .10$$

The probability of the event, pass the course, is

$$P(\text{Pass the course}) = P(A) + P(B) + P(C) + P(D) = .20 + .30 + .25 + .15 = .90$$

6-1d Interpreting Probability

No matter what method was used to assign probability, we interpret it using the relative frequency approach for an infinite number of experiments. For example, an investor may have used the subjective approach to determine that there is a 65% probability that a particular stock's price will increase over the next month. However, we interpret the 65% figure to mean that if we had an infinite number of stocks with exactly the same economic and market characteristics as the one the investor will buy, 65% of them will increase in price over the next month. Similarly, we can determine that the probability of throwing a 5 with a balanced die is 1/6. We may have used the classical approach to determine this probability. However, we interpret the number as the proportion of times that a 5 is observed on a balanced die thrown an infinite number of times.

This relative frequency approach is useful to interpret probability statements such as those heard from weather forecasters or scientists. You will also discover that this is the way we link the population and the sample in statistical inference.

EXERCISES

6.1 The weather forecaster reports that the probability of rain tomorrow is 10%.
   a. Which approach was used to arrive at this number?
   b. How do you interpret the probability?

6.2 A sportscaster states that he believes that the probability that the New York Yankees will win the World Series this year is 25%.
   a. Which method was used to assign that probability?
   b. How would you interpret the probability?

6.3 A quiz contains a multiple-choice question with five possible answers, only one of which is correct. A student plans to guess the answer because he knows absolutely nothing about the subject.
   a. Produce the sample space for each question.
   b. Assign probabilities to the simple events in the sample space you produced.
   c. Which approach did you use to answer part (b)?
   d. Interpret the probabilities you assigned in part (b).

6.4 An investor tells you that in her estimation there is a 60% probability that the Dow Jones Industrial Averages index will increase tomorrow.
   a. Which approach was used to produce this figure?
   b. Interpret the 60% probability.

6.5 The sample space of the toss of a fair die is

$$S = \{1, 2, 3, 4, 5, 6\}$$

If the die is balanced each simple event has the same probability. Find the probability of the following events.
   a. An even number
   b. A number less than or equal to 4
   c. A number greater than or equal to 5

6.6 Four candidates are running for mayor. The four candidates are Adams, Brown, Collins, and Dalton. Determine the sample space of the results of the election.

6.7 Refer to Exercise 6.6. Employing the subjective approach a political scientist has assigned the following probabilities:

   $P(\text{Adams wins}) = .42$
   $P(\text{Brown wins}) = .09$
   $P(\text{Collins wins}) = .27$
   $P(\text{Dalton wins}) = .22$

Determine the probabilities of the following events.
   a. Adams loses.
   b. Either Brown or Dalton wins.
   c. Adams, Brown, or Collins wins.

6.8 The manager of a computer store has kept track of the number of computers sold per day. On the basis of this information, the manager produced the following list of the number of daily sales.

Number of Computers Sold	Probability
0	.08
1	.17
2	.26
3	.21
4	.18
5	.10

   a. If we define the experiment as observing the number of computers sold tomorrow, determine the sample space.
   b. Use set notation to define the event, sell more than three computers.
   c. What is the probability of selling five computers?
   d. What is the probability of selling two, three, or four computers?
   e. What is the probability of selling six computers?

6.9 Three contractors (call them contractors 1, 2, and 3) bid on a project to build a new bridge. What is the sample space?

6.10 Refer to Exercise 6.9. Suppose that you believe that contractor 1 is twice as likely to win as contractor 3 and that contractor 2 is three times as likely to win as contactor 3. What are the probabilities of winning for each contractor?

6.11 Shoppers can pay for their purchases with cash, a credit card, or a debit card. Suppose that the proprietor of a shop determines that 60% of her customers use a credit card, 30% pay with cash, and the rest use a debit card.
   a. Determine the sample space for this experiment.
   b. Assign probabilities to the simple events.
   c. Which method did you use in part (b)?

6.12 Refer to Exercise 6.11.
   a. What is the probability that a customer does not use a credit card?
   b. What is the probability that a customer pays in cash or with a credit card?
   c. Which method did you use in part (b)?

6.13 A survey asks adults to report their marital status. The sample space is

   $S = \{\text{single, married, divorced, widowed}\}$

Use set notation to represent the event the adult is not married.

6.14 Refer to Exercise 6.13. Suppose that in the city in which the survey is conducted, 50% of adults are married, 15% are single, 25% are divorced, and 10% are widowed.
   a. Assign probabilities to each simple event in the sample space.
   b. Which approach did you use in part (a)?

6.15 Refer to Exercises 6.13 and 6.14. Find the probability of each of the following events.
   a. The adult is single.
   b. The adult is not divorced.
   c. The adult is either widowed or divorced.

6.16 There are 62 million Americans who speak a language other than English at home. The languages are Spanish, Chinese Tagalog (Philippines language), Vietnamese, French, Korean, and others. Suppose that one of these individuals is selected at random. Use set notation to list the sample space.

6.17 Refer to Exercise 6.16. The numbers (in millions) of Americans speaking non-English languages at home are listed next.

Language Spoken at Home	Millions of Americans
Spanish	38.4
Chinese	3.0
Tagalog	1.6
Vietnamese	1.4
French	1.3
Korean	1.1
Other	15.2

Source: Center for Immigration Studies

If one individual is selected at random find the probability of the following events.

a. Individual speaks Spanish.

b. Individual speaks a language other than Spanish

c. Individual speaks Vietnamese or French

d. Individual speaks one of the other languages.

6.18 Uber, the ride-sharing service has been encountering protests mostly from taxi drivers. The taxi industry claims that Uber is more dangerous than other taxis because of the lack of government scrutiny. A survey was conducted where people were asked, "In your opinion how safe is Uber?" The responses are

Very safe; Somewhat safe; Somewhat unsafe; Very unsafe; Not sure

Create the sample space for this survey.

6.19 Refer to Exercise 6.18. The results of the survey are listed next.

How Safe is Uber?	Responses (%)
Very safe	17
Somewhat safe	28
Somewhat unsafe	21
Very unsafe	12
Not sure	22

If one person surveyed is selected at random find the following probabilities

a. Person selected said Very safe

b. Person selected said Very safe or Somewhat safe

c. Person said it was Very unsafe

6-2 / JOINT, MARGINAL, AND CONDITIONAL PROBABILITY

In the previous section, we described how to produce a sample space and assign probabilities to the simple events in the sample space. Although this method of determining probability is useful, we need to develop more sophisticated methods. In this section, we discuss how to calculate the probability of more complicated events from the probability of related events. Here is an illustration of the process.

The sample space for the toss of a die is

$$S = \{1, 2, 3, 4, 5, 6\}$$

If the die is balanced, the probability of each simple event is 1/6. In most parlor games and casinos, players toss two dice. To determine playing and wagering strategies, players need to compute the probabilities of various totals of the two dice. For example, the probability of tossing a total of 3 with two dice is 2/36. This probability was derived by creating combinations of the simple events. There are several different types of combinations. One of the most important types is the *intersection* of two events.

6-2a Intersection

> **Intersection of Events *A* and *B***
>
> The **intersection** of events *A* and *B* is the event that occurs when both *A* and *B* occur. It is denoted as
>
> *A* and *B*
>
> The probability of the intersection is called the **joint probability**.

For example, one way to toss a 3 with two dice is to toss a 1 on the first die *and* a 2 on the second die, which is the intersection of two simple events. Incidentally, to compute the probability of a total of 3, we need to combine this intersection with another intersection, namely, a 2 on the first die and a 1 on the second die. This type of combination is called a *union* of two events, and it will be described later in this section. Here is another illustration.

APPLICATIONS in **FINANCE**

Mutual Funds

A mutual fund is a pool of investments made on behalf of people who share similar objectives. In most cases, a professional manager who has been educated in finance and statistics manages the fund. He or she makes decisions to buy and sell individual stocks and bonds in accordance with a specified investment philosophy. For example, there are funds that concentrate on other publicly traded mutual fund companies. Other mutual funds specialize in Internet stocks (so-called dot-coms), whereas others buy stocks of biotechnology firms. Surprisingly, most mutual funds do not outperform the market; that is, the increase in the net asset value (NAV) of the mutual fund is often less than the increase in the value of stock indexes that represent their stock markets. One reason for this is the management expense ratio (MER), which is a measure of the costs charged to the fund by the manager to cover expenses, including the salary and bonus of the managers. The MERs for most funds range from .5% to more than 4%. The ultimate success of the fund depends on the skill and knowledge of the fund manager. This raises the question, Which managers do best?

EXAMPLE 6.1

Determinants of Success among Mutual Fund Managers—Part 1[*]

Why are some mutual fund managers more successful than others? One possible factor is the university where the manager earned his or her master of business administration (MBA). Suppose that a potential investor examined the relationship between how well the mutual fund performs and where the fund manager earned his or her MBA. After the analysis, Table 6.1, a table of joint probabilities, was developed. Analyze these probabilities and interpret the results.

TABLE **6.1** Joint Probabilities

	MUTUAL FUND OUTPERFORMS MARKET	MUTUAL FUND DOES NOT OUTPERFORM MARKET
Top-20 MBA program	.11	.29
Not top-20 MBA program	.06	.54

Table 6.1 tells us that the joint probability that a mutual fund outperforms the market *and* that its manager graduated from a top-20 MBA program is .11; that is, 11% of all mutual funds outperform the market and their managers graduated from a top-20 MBA program. The other three joint probabilities are defined similarly:

---

[*]This example is adapted from "Are Some Mutual Fund Managers Better than Others? Cross-Sectional Patterns in Behavior and Performance" by Judith Chevalier and Glenn Ellison, Working paper 5852, National Bureau of Economic Research.

The probability that a mutual fund outperforms the market and its manager did not graduate from a top-20 MBA program is .06.

The probability that a mutual fund does not outperform the market and its manager graduated from a top-20 MBA program is .29.

The probability that a mutual fund does not outperform the market and its manager did not graduate from a top-20 MBA program is .54.

To help make our task easier, we'll use notation to represent the events. Let

A_1 = Fund manager graduated from a top-20 MBA program

A_2 = Fund manager did not graduate from a top-20 MBA program

B_1 = Fund outperforms the market

B_2 = Fund does not outperform the market

Thus,

$$P(A_1 \text{ and } B_1) = .11$$
$$P(A_2 \text{ and } B_1) = .06$$
$$P(A_1 \text{ and } B_2) = .29$$
$$P(A_2 \text{ and } B_2) = .54$$

6-2b Marginal Probability

The joint probabilities in Table 6.1 allow us to compute various probabilities. **Marginal probabilities**, computed by adding across rows or down columns, are so named because they are calculated in the margins of the table.

Adding across the first row produces

$$P(A_1 \text{ and } B_1) + P(A_1 \text{ and } B_2) = .11 + .29 = .40$$

Notice that both intersections state that the manager graduated from a top-20 MBA program (represented by A_1). Thus, when randomly selecting mutual funds, the probability that its manager graduated from a top-20 MBA program is .40. Expressed as relative frequency, 40% of all mutual fund managers graduated from a top-20 MBA program.

Adding across the second row:

$$P(A_2 \text{ and } B_1) + P(A_2 \text{ and } B_2) = .06 + .54 = .60$$

This probability tells us that 60% of all mutual fund managers did not graduate from a top-20 MBA program (represented by A_2). Notice that the probability that a mutual fund manager graduated from a top-20 MBA program and the probability that the manager did not graduate from a top-20 MBA program add to 1.

Adding down the columns produces the following marginal probabilities.

Column 1: $P(A_1 \text{ and } B_1) + P(A_2 \text{ and } B_1) = .11 + .06 = .17$

Column 2: $P(A_1 \text{ and } B_2) + P(A_2 \text{ and } B_2) = .29 + .54 = .83$

These marginal probabilities tell us that 17% of all mutual funds outperform the market and that 83% of mutual funds do not outperform the market.

Table 6.2 lists all the joint and marginal probabilities.

6.25 Refer to Exercise 6.21. Compute the following.
a. $P(A_1 \text{ or } B_1)$
b. $P(A_1 \text{ or } B_2)$
c. $P(A_1 \text{ or } A_2)$

6.26 Suppose that you have been given the following joint probabilities. Are the events independent? Explain.

	A_1	A_2
B_1	.20	.60
B_2	.05	.15

6.27 Determine whether the events are independent from the following joint probabilities.

	A_1	A_2
B_1	.20	.15
B_2	.60	.05

6.28 Suppose we have the following joint probabilities.

	A_1	A_2	A_3
B_1	.15	.20	.10
B_2	.25	.25	.05

Compute the marginal probabilities.

6.29 Refer to Exercise 6.28.
a. Compute $P(A_2|B_2)$.
b. Compute $P(B_2|A_2)$.
c. Compute $P(B_1|A_2)$.

6.30 Refer to Exercise 6.28.
a. Compute $P(A_1 \text{ or } A_2)$.
b. Compute $P(A_2 \text{ or } B_2)$.
c. Compute $P(A_3 \text{ or } B_1)$.

6.31 Discrimination in the workplace is illegal, and companies that discriminate are often sued. The female instructors at a large university recently lodged a complaint about the most recent round of promotions from assistant professor to associate professor. An analysis of the relationship between gender and promotion produced the following joint probabilities.

	Promoted	Not Promoted
Female	.03	.12
Male	.17	.68

a. What is the rate of promotion among female assistant professors?
b. What is the rate of promotion among male assistant professors?
c. Is it reasonable to accuse the university of gender bias?

6.32 A department store analyzed its most recent sales and determined the relationship between the way the customer paid for the item and the price

category of the item. The joint probabilities in the following table were calculated.

	Cash	Credit Card	Debit Card
Less than $20	.09	.03	.04
$20–$100	.05	.21	.18
More than $100	.03	.23	.14

a. What proportion of purchases was paid by debit card?
b. Find the probability that a credit card purchase was more than $100.
c. Determine the proportion of purchases made by credit card or by debit card.

6.33 The following table lists the probabilities of unemployed females and males and their educational attainment.

	Female	Male
Less than high school	.057	.104
High school graduate	.136	.224
Some college/university—no degree	.132	.150
College/university graduate	.095	.103

Source: Statistical Abstract of the United States, 2012, Table 627.

a. If one unemployed person is selected at random, what is the probability that he or she did not finish high school?
b. If an unemployed female is selected at random, what is the probability that she has a college or university degree?
c. If an unemployed high school graduate is selected at random, what is the probability that he is a male?

6.34 The costs of medical care in North America are increasing faster than inflation, and with the baby boom generation soon to need health care, it becomes imperative that countries find ways to reduce both costs and demand. The following table lists the joint probabilities associated with smoking and lung disease among 60- to 65-year-old men.

	He is a Smoker	He is a Nonsmoker
He has lung disease	.12	.03
He does not have lung disease	.19	.66

One 60- to 65-year-old man is selected at random. What is the probability of the following events?
a. He is a smoker.
b. He does not have lung disease.
c. He has lung disease given that he is a smoker.
d. He has lung disease given that he does not smoke.

6.35 Refer to Exercise 6.34. Are smoking and lung disease among 60- to 65-year-old men related? Explain.

6.36 The method of instruction in college and university applied statistics courses is changing. Historically, most courses were taught with an emphasis on manual calculation. The alternative is to employ a computer and a software package to perform the calculations. An analysis of applied statistics courses investigated whether the instructor's educational background is primarily mathematics (or statistics) or some other field. The result of this analysis is the accompanying table of joint probabilities.

Education of Instructor	Statistics Course Emphasizes Manual Calculations	Statistics Course Computer and Software
Mathematics or statistics education	.23	.36
Other education	.11	.30

a. What is the probability that a randomly selected applied statistics course instructor whose education was in statistics emphasizes manual calculations?
b. What proportion of applied statistics courses employs a computer and software?
c. Are the educational background of the instructor and the way his or her course is taught independent?

6.37 A restaurant chain routinely surveys its customers. Among other questions, the survey asks each customer whether he or she would return and to rate the quality of food. Summarizing hundreds of thousands of questionnaires produced this table of joint probabilities.

Rating	Customer Will Return	Customer Will Not Return
Poor	.02	.10
Fair	.08	.09
Good	.35	.14
Excellent	.20	.02

a. What proportion of customers say that they will return and rate the restaurant's food as good?
b. What proportion of customers who say that they will return rate the restaurant's food as good?
c. What proportion of customers who rate the restaurant's food as good say that they will return?
d. Discuss the differences in your answers to parts (a), (b), and (c).

6.38 To determine whether drinking alcoholic beverages has an effect on the bacteria that cause ulcers, researchers developed the following table of joint probabilities.

Number of Alcoholic Drinks per Day	Ulcer	No Ulcer
None	.01	.22
One	.03	.19
Two	.03	.32
More than two	.04	.16

a. What proportion of people have ulcers?
b. What is the probability that a teetotaler (no alcoholic beverages) develops an ulcer?
c. What is the probability that someone who has an ulcer does not drink alcohol?
d. What is the probability that someone who has an ulcer drinks alcohol?

6.39 An analysis of fired or laid-off workers, their age, and the reasons for their departure produced the following table of joint probabilities.

Reason for job loss	Age Category			
	20–24	25–54	55–64	65 and older
Plant or company closed or moved	.015	.320	.089	.029
Insufficient work	.014	.180	.034	.011
Position or shift abolished	.006	.214	.071	.016

Source: Statistical Abstract of the United States, 2009, Table 593.

a. What is the probability that a 25- to 54-year-old employee was laid off or fired because of insufficient work?
b. What proportion of laid-off or fired workers is age 65 and older?
c. What is the probability that a laid-off or fired worker because the plant or company closed is 65 or older?

6.40 Many critics of television claim that there is too much violence and that it has a negative effect on society. There may also be a negative effect on advertisers. To examine this issue, researchers developed two versions of a cops-and-robbers made-for-television movie. One version depicted several violent crimes, and the other removed these scenes. In the middle of the movie, one 60-second commercial was shown advertising a new product and brand name. At the end of the movie, viewers were asked to name the brand. After observing the results, the researchers produced the following table of joint probabilities.

	Watch Violent Movie	Watch Nonviolent Movie
Remember brand name	.15	.18
Do not remember brand name	.35	.32

a. What proportion of viewers remember the brand name?

b. What proportion of viewers who watch the violent movie remember the brand name?

c. Does watching a violent movie affect whether the viewer will remember the brand name? Explain.

6.41 Is there a relationship between the male hormone testosterone and criminal behavior? To answer this question, medical researchers measured the testosterone level of penitentiary inmates and recorded whether they were convicted of murder. After analyzing the results, the researchers produced the following table of joint probabilities.

Testosterone Level	Murderer	Other Felon
Above average	.27	.24
Below average	.21	.28

a. What proportion of murderers have above-average testosterone levels?

b. Are levels of testosterone and the crime committed independent? Explain.

6.42 The issue of health care coverage in the United States is becoming a critical issue in American politics. A large-scale study was undertaken to determine who is and is not covered. From this study, the following table of joint probabilities was produced.

Age Category	Has Health Insurance	Does Not Have Health Insurance
25–34	.167	.085
35–44	.209	.061
45–54	.225	.049
55–64	.177	.026

Source: U.S. Department of Health and Human Services.

If one person is selected at random, find the following probabilities.

a. P(Person has health insurance)

b. P(Person 55–64 has no health insurance)

c. P(Person without health insurance is between 25 and 34 years old)

6.43 Violent crime in many American schools is an unfortunate fact of life. An analysis of schools and violent crime yielded the table of joint probabilities shown next.

Level	Violent Crime Committed This Year	No Violent Crime Committed This Year
Primary	.393	.191
Middle	.176	.010
High School	.134	.007
Combined	.074	.015

Source: Statistical Abstract of the United States, 2009, Table 237.

If one school is randomly selected find the following probabilities.

a. Probability of at least one incident of violent crime during the year in a primary school

b. Probability of no violent crime during the year

6.44 Refer to Exercise 6.43. A similar analysis produced these joint probabilities.

Enrollment	Violent Crime Committed This Year	No Violent Crime Committed This Year
Less than 300	.159	.091
300 to 499	.221	.065
500 to 999	.289	.063
1,000 or more	.108	.004

Source: Statistical Abstract of the United States, 2009, Table 237.

a. What is the probability that a school with an enrollment of less than 300 had at least one violent crime during the year?

b. What is the probability that a school that has at least one violent crime had an enrollment of less than 300?

6.45 A firm has classified its customers in two ways: (1) according to whether the account is overdue and (2) whether the account is new (less than 12 months) or old. An analysis of the firm's records provided the input for the following table of joint probabilities.

Account	Overdue	Not Overdue
New	.06	.13
Old	.52	.29

One account is randomly selected.

a. If the account is overdue, what is the probability that it is new?

b. If the account is new, what is the probability that it is overdue?

c. Is the age of the account related to whether it is overdue? Explain.

6.46 How are the size of a firm (measured in terms of the number of employees) and the type of firm related? To help answer the question, an analyst referred to the U.S. Census and developed the following.

Employees	Construction	Manufacturing	Retail
Fewer than 20	.464	.147	.237
20 to 99	.039	.049	.035
100 or more	.005	.019	.005

Source: Statistical Abstract of the United States, 2009, Table 737.

If one firm is selected at random, find the probability of the following events.
a. The firm employs fewer than 20 employees.
b. The firm is in the retail industry.
c. A firm in the construction industry employs between 20 and 99 workers.

6.47 Credit scorecards are used by financial institutions to help decide to whom loans should be granted. An analysis of the records of one bank produced the following probabilities.

| | **Score** | |
Loan Performance	**Under 400**	**400 or More**
Fully repaid	.19	.64
Defaulted	.13	.04

a. What proportion of loans are fully repaid?
b. What proportion of loans given to scorers of less than 400 fully repay?
c. What proportion of loans given to scorers of 400 or more fully repay?
d. Are score and whether the loan is fully repaid independent? Explain.

6.48 A retail outlet wanted to know whether its weekly advertisement in the daily newspaper works. To acquire this critical information, the store manager surveyed the people who entered the store and determined whether each individual saw the ad and whether a purchase was made. From the information developed, the manager produced the following table of joint probabilities. Are the ads effective? Explain.

	Purchase	**No Purchase**
See ad	.18	.42
Do not see ad	.12	.28

6.49 To gauge the relationship between education and unemployment, an economist turned to the U.S. Census from which the following table of joint probabilities was produced:

Education	**Employed**	**Unemployed**
Not a high school graduate	.075	.015
High school graduate	.257	.035
Some college, no degree	.155	.016
Associate's degree	.096	.008
Bachelor's degree	.211	.012
Advanced degree	.118	.004

Source: Statistical Abstract of the United States, 2012, Table 221.

a. What is the probability that a high school graduate is unemployed?

b. Determine the probability that a randomly selected individual is employed.
c. Find the probability that an unemployed person possesses an advanced degree.
d. What is the probability that a randomly selected person did not finish high school?

6.50 The decision about where to build a new plant is a major one for most companies. One of the factors that is often considered is the education level of the location's residents. Census information may be useful in this regard. After analyzing a recent census, a company produced the following joint probabilities:

Education	**Northeast**	**Midwest**	**South**	**West**
Not a high school graduate	.021	.022	.053	.032
High school graduate	.062	.075	.118	.058
Some college, no degree	.024	.038	.062	.044
Associate's degree	.015	.022	.032	.022
Bachelor's degree	.038	.040	.067	.050
Advanced degree	.024	.021	.036	.025

Source: Statistical Abstract of the United States, 2012, Table 231.

a. Determine the probability that a person living in the West has a bachelor's degree.
b. Find the probability that a high school graduate lives in the Northeast.
c. What is the probability that a person selected at random lives in the South?
d. What is the probability that a person selected at random does not live in the South?

6.51 A Gallup survey asked a sample of Americans how much confidence they had in the criminal justice system. After recording the responses as well as the race of the respondent, the following table of joint probabilities was created.

Confidence in Justice System	**White**	**Black**
A great deal or quite a lot	.240	.041
Some	.356	.048
Very little or none	.255	.060

a. Calculate the probability that a white person had some confidence in the justice system.
b. Find the probability that a black person would have very little or no confidence in the justice system
c. What is the probability that a person who has some confidence is white?

6.52 Arthritis is an inflammation of one or more joints. The symptoms are pain and stiffness, which usually worsen with age. Suppose that an analysis of age and incidence of arthritis produced the following table of joint probabilities.

Age Categories	Has Arthritis	Does not have Arthritis
50–60	.040	.360
60–70	.075	.225
70–80	.072	.088
Over 80	.105	.035

a. What is the probability that a person who is over 80 has arthritis?

b. Determine the probability that a person who is 55 years old does not have arthritis.

c. What is the probability that someone who has arthritis is between 60 and 70 years old?

6.53 There are three major political parties in Canada. They are Conservatives, Liberals, and New Democrats. Suppose that in one city the breakdown of the party preferences and gender produced the following table of joint probabilities.

Party	Men	Women
Conservative	.255	.215
Liberal	.191	.224
New Democrat	.044	.071

a. Find the probability that a man would support the New Democrats.

b. Calculate the probability that a Liberal supporter is a woman.

c. If we select one person at random what is the probability that he or she is a Conservative supporter?

6.54 There are no universally accepted definitions of the ages of Millennials and Generation Xers; the consensus is that the former are Americans born between 1984 and 2000 and the latter are Americans born between 1965 and 1984. Baby boomers are defined as people born between 1946 and 1964. An analysis conducted by the Pew Research Center produced the following table of joint probabilities relating marital status of the three groups defined here.

Marital Status	Millennial	Generation X	Baby Boomer
Single, never married	.195	.058	.030
Married	.089	.223	.201
Living with partner, not married	.030	.025	.009
Divorced, separated, widowed	.017	.054	.070

a. Find the probability that a Millennial is married.

b. Compute the probability that a Baby Boomer is single, never married.

c. Suppose that one person is selected at random. What is the probability that he or she is married?

d. What is the probability that someone who is living with a partner, but not married is a Generation X?

In Chapter 2 (Page 32), we introduced the Pew Research Center. The next four exercises are based on several Pew Research Center surveys. In October 2014, Pew investigated political polarization and media habits. A sample of Americans was selected and each person was placed in one of the following political categories.

Consistent Liberal, Mostly liberal, Mixed, Mostly conservative, Consistent conservative.

Each was also asked to what degree they trusted a variety of television networks for news about government and politics.

6.55 After tabulating the results for NBC news the table of joint probabilities was created.

NBC News	Consistent Liberal	Mostly Liberal	Mixed	Mostly Conservative	Consistent Conservative
Trust	0.0896	0.1386	0.1944	0.0629	0.0144
Distrust	0.0096	0.0154	0.0540	0.0595	0.0558
Neither	0.0576	0.0506	0.0864	0.0391	0.0153
DK	0.0032	0.0154	0.0252	0.0085	0.0045

a. Find the probability that one respondent selected at random would trust NBC News.

b. What is the probability that a consistent Conservative would distrust NBC News?

c. What is the probability that a consistent Liberal neither trusts nor distrusts NBC News?

d. If one person is randomly chosen, what is the probability that he or she is a consistent Liberal?

6.56 Here are the joint probabilities for MSNBC

MSNBC	Consistent Liberal	Mostly Liberal	Mixed	Mostly Conservative	Consistent Conservative
Trust	0.0832	0.1056	0.1404	0.0442	0.0063
Distrust	0.0144	0.0198	0.0540	0.0680	0.0675
Neither	0.0560	0.0682	0.1116	0.0442	0.0108
DK	0.0064	0.0264	0.0540	0.0136	0.0054

a. Compute the probability that a mostly Conservative would distrust MSNBC.

b. Find the probability that a mixed Liberal–Conservative would neither trust nor distrust MSNBC.

c. If one person is selected at random what is the probability that he or she trusts MSNBC?

d. If one person is chosen at random, what is the probability that he or she is a mostly Conservative?

6.57 We list the joint probabilities for Fox News.

Fox News	Consistent Liberal	Mostly Liberal	Mixed	Mostly Conservative	Consistent Conservative
Trust	0.0096	0.0616	0.1692	0.1224	0.0792
Distrust	0.1296	0.1188	0.1008	0.0187	0.0027
Neither	0.0128	0.0264	0.0540	0.0187	0.0045
DK	0.0080	0.0132	0.0360	0.0102	0.0036

a. Determine the probability that a consistent Liberal would distrust Fox News.

b. Find the probability that a mostly Conservative trusts Fox News

c. Find the probability that a consistent Conservative neither trusts nor distrusts Fox News

d. If one person is chosen randomly, find the probability that he or she is a consistent Conservative.

6.58 Here are the joint probabilities for CNN.

CNN	Consistent Liberal	Mostly Liberal	Mixed	Mostly Conservative	Consistent Conservative
Trust	0.0896	0.1452	0.2196	0.0663	0.0126
Distrust	0.0192	0.0242	0.0504	0.0561	0.0549
Neither	0.0480	0.0396	0.0612	0.0408	0.0171
DK	0.0032	0.0110	0.0288	0.0068	0.0054

a. If one person is selected at random what is the probability that he or she distrusts CNN?

b. Find the probability that a consistent Conservative trusts CNN.

c. Compute the probability that a mostly Liberal neither trusts nor distrusts CNN.

d. If one person is chosen at random determine the probability that that person is a mixed Liberal-Conservative.

6-3 / PROBABILITY RULES AND TREES

In Section 6-2, we introduced intersection and union and described how to determine the probability of the intersection and the union of two events. In this section, we present other methods of determining these probabilities. We introduce three rules that enable us to calculate the probability of more complex events from the probability of simpler events.

6-3a Complement Rule

The **complement** of event A is the event that occurs when event A does not occur. The complement of event A is denoted by A^C. The **complement rule** defined here derives from the fact that the probability of an event and the probability of the event's complement must sum to 1.

Complement Rule

$$P(A^C) = 1 - P(A)$$

for any event A.

We will demonstrate the use of this rule after we introduce the next rule.

6-3b Multiplication Rule

The **multiplication rule** is used to calculate the joint probability of two events. It is based on the formula for conditional probability supplied in the previous section; that is, from the following formula

$$P(A|B) = \frac{P(A \text{ and } B)}{P(B)}$$

we derive the multiplication rule simply by multiplying both sides by $P(B)$.

> **Multiplication Rule**
>
> The joint probability of any two events A and B is
>
> $$P(A \text{ and } B) = P(B)P(A|B)$$
>
> or, altering the notation,
>
> $$P(A \text{ and } B) = P(A)P(B|A)$$

If A and B are independent events, $P(A|B) = P(A)$ and $P(B|A) = P(B)$. It follows that the joint probability of two independent events is simply the product of the probabilities of the two events. We can express this as a special form of the multiplication rule.

> **Multiplication Rule for Independent Events**
>
> The joint probability of any two independent events A and B is
>
> $$P(A \text{ and } B) = P(A)P(B)$$

EXAMPLE **6.5***

Selecting Two Students without Replacement

A graduate statistics course has seven male and three female students. The professor wants to select two students at random to help her conduct a research project. What is the probability that the two students chosen are female?

SOLUTION:

Let A represent the event that the first student chosen is female and B represent the event that the second student chosen is also female. We want the joint probability $P(A \text{ and } B)$. Consequently, we apply the multiplication rule:

$$P(A \text{ and } B) = P(A)P(B|A)$$

Because there are 3 female students in a class of 10, the probability that the first student chosen is female is

$$P(A) = 3/10$$

---

*This example can be solved using the Hypergeometric distribution, which is described in the online appendix of the same name.

After the first student is chosen, there are only 9 students left. Given that the first student chosen was female, there are only 2 female students left. It follows that

$$P(B|A) = 2/9$$

Thus, the joint probability is

$$P(A \text{ and } B) = P(A)P(B|A) = \left(\frac{3}{10}\right)\left(\frac{2}{9}\right) = \frac{6}{90} = .067$$

EXAMPLE 6.6

Selecting Two Students with Replacement

Refer to Example 6.5. The professor who teaches the course is suffering from flu and will be unavailable for two classes. The professor's replacement will teach the next two classes. His style is to select one student at random and pick on him or her to answer questions during that class. What is the probability that the two students chosen are female?

S O L U T I O N :

The form of the question is the same as in Example 6.5: We wish to compute the probability of choosing two female students. However, the experiment is slightly different. It is now possible to choose the *same* student in each of the two classes taught by the replacement. Thus, A and B are independent events, and we apply the multiplication rule for independent events:

$$P(A \text{ and } B) = P(A)P(B)$$

The probability of choosing a female student in each of the two classes is the same; that is,

$$P(A) = 3/10 \text{ and } P(B) = 3/10$$

Hence,

$$P(A \text{ and } B) = P(A)P(B) = \left(\frac{3}{10}\right)\left(\frac{3}{10}\right) = \frac{9}{100} = .09$$

6-3c Addition Rule

The **addition rule** enables us to calculate the probability of the union of two events.

Addition Rule

The probability that event A, or event B, or both occur is

$$P(A \text{ or } B) = P(A) + P(B) - P(A \text{ and } B)$$

If you're like most students, you're wondering why we subtract the joint probability from the sum of the probabilities of A and B. To understand why this is necessary, examine Table 6.2 (page 163), which we have reproduced here as Table 6.3.

TABLE **6.3** Joint and Marginal Probabilities

	B_1	B_2	TOTALS
A_1	$P(A_1 \text{ and } B_1) = .11$	$P(A_1 \text{ and } B_2) = .29$	$P(A_1) = .40$
A_2	$P(A_2 \text{ and } B_1) = .06$	$P(A_2 \text{ and } B_2) = .54$	$P(A_2) = .60$
Totals	$P(B_1) = .17$	$P(B_2) = .83$	1.00

This table summarizes how the marginal probabilities were computed. For example, the marginal probability of A_1 and the marginal probability of B_1 were calculated as

$$P(A_1) = P(A_1 \text{ and } B_1) + P(A_1 \text{ and } B_2) = .11 + .29 = .40$$
$$P(B_1) = P(A_1 \text{ and } B_1) + P(A_2 \text{ and } B_1) = .11 + .06 = .17$$

If we now attempt to calculate the probability of the union of A_1 and B_1 by summing their probabilities, we find

$$P(A_1) + P(B_1) = .11 + .29 + .11 + .06$$

Notice that we added the joint probability of A_1 and B_1 (which is .11) twice. To correct the double counting, we subtract the joint probability from the sum of the probabilities of A_1 and B_1. Thus,

$$P(A_1 \text{ or } B_1) = P(A_1) + P(B_1) - P(A_1 \text{ and } B_1)$$
$$= [.11 + .29] + [.11 + .06] - .11$$
$$= .40 + .17 - .11 = .46$$

This is the probability of the union of A_1 and B_1, which we calculated in Example 6.4 (page 165).

As was the case with the multiplication rule, there is a special form of the addition rule. When two events are mutually exclusive (which means that the two events cannot occur together), their joint probability is 0.

Addition Rule for Mutually Exclusive Events
The probability of the union of two mutually exclusive events A and B is
$$P(A \text{ or } B) = P(A) + P(B)$$

EXAMPLE 6.7

Applying the Addition Rule

In a large city, two newspapers are published, the *Sun* and the *Post*. The circulation departments report that 22% of the city's households have a subscription to the *Sun* and 35% subscribe to the *Post*. A survey reveals that 6% of all households subscribe to both newspapers. What proportion of the city's households subscribe to either newspaper?

SOLUTION:

We can express this question as, What is the probability of selecting a household at random that subscribes to the *Sun*, the *Post*, or both? Another way of asking the question is, What is the probability that a randomly selected household subscribes to *at least one* of the newspapers? It is now clear that we seek the probability of the union, and we must apply the addition rule. Let A = household that subscribes to the *Sun* and B = the household that subscribes to the *Post*. We perform the following calculation:

$$P(A \text{ or } B) = P(A) + P(B) - P(A \text{ and } B) = .22 + .35 - .06 = .51$$

The probability that a randomly selected household subscribes to either newspaper is .51. Expressed as relative frequency, 51% of the city's households subscribe to either newspaper.

6-3d Probability Trees

An effective and simpler method of applying the probability rules is the probability tree, wherein the events in an experiment are represented by lines. The resulting figure resembles a tree, hence the name. We will illustrate the probability tree with several examples, including two that we addressed using the probability rules alone.

In Example 6.5, we wanted to find the probability of choosing two female students, where the two choices had to be different. The tree diagram in Figure 6.1 describes this experiment. Notice that the first two branches represent the two possibilities, female and male students, on the first choice. The second set of branches represents the two possibilities on the second choice. The probabilities of female and male student chosen first are 3/10 and 7/10, respectively. The probabilities for the second set of branches are conditional probabilities based on the choice of the first student selected.

We calculate the joint probabilities by multiplying the probabilities on the linked branches. Thus, the probability of choosing two female students is $P(F \text{ and } F) = (3/10)(2/9) = 6/90$. The remaining joint probabilities are computed similarly.

FIGURE **6.1** Probability Tree for Example 6.5

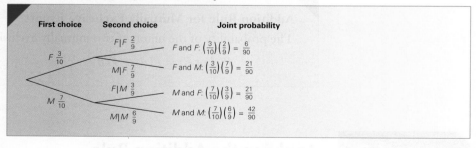

In Example 6.6, the experiment was similar to that of Example 6.5. However, the student selected on the first choice was returned to the pool of students and was eligible to be chosen again. Thus, the probabilities on the second set of branches remain the same as the probabilities on the first set, and the probability tree is drawn with these changes, as shown in Figure 6.2.

FIGURE **6.2** Probability Tree for Example 6.6

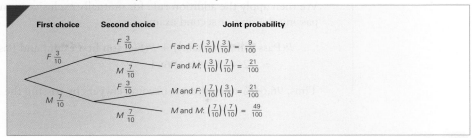

The advantage of a probability tree on this type of problem is that it restrains its users from making the wrong calculation. Once the tree is drawn and the probabilities of the branches inserted, virtually the only allowable calculation is the multiplication of the probabilities of linked branches. An easy check on those calculations is available. The joint probabilities at the ends of the branches must sum to 1 because all possible events are listed. In both figures, notice that the joint probabilities do indeed sum to 1.

The special form of the addition rule for mutually exclusive events can be applied to the joint probabilities. In both probability trees, we can compute the probability that one student chosen is female and one is male simply by adding the joint probabilities. For the tree in Example 6.5, we have

$$P(F \text{ and } M) + P(M \text{ and } F) = 21/90 + 21/90 = 42/90$$

In the probability tree in Example 6.6, we find

$$P(F \text{ and } M) + P(M \text{ and } F) = 21/100 + 21/100 = 42/100$$

EXAMPLE **6.8**

Probability of Passing the Bar Exam

Students who graduate from law schools must still pass a bar exam before becoming lawyers. Suppose that in a particular jurisdiction the pass rate for first-time test takers is 72%. Candidates who fail the first exam may take it again several months later. Of those who fail their first test, 88% pass their second attempt. Find the probability that a randomly selected law school graduate becomes a lawyer. Assume that candidates cannot take the exam more than twice.

SOLUTION:

The probability tree in Figure 6.3 is employed to describe the experiment. Note that we use the complement rule to determine the probability of failing each exam.

FIGURE **6.3** Probability Tree for Example 6.8

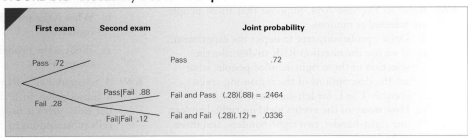

We apply the multiplication rule to calculate P(Fail and Pass), which we find to be .2464. We then apply the addition rule for mutually exclusive events to find the probability of passing the first or second exam:

P(Pass [on first exam]) + P(Fail [on first exam] and Pass [on second exam])
= .72 + .2464 = .9664

Thus, 96.64% of applicants become lawyers by passing the first or second exam.

EXERCISES

6.59 Given the following probabilities, compute all joint probabilities.

$P(A) = .9$ .... $P(A^C) = .1$
$P(B|A) = .4$ .... $P(B|A^C) = .7$

6.60 Determine all joint probabilities from the following.

$P(A) = .8$ .... $P(A^C) = .2$
$P(B|A) = .4$ .... $P(B|A^C) = .7$

6.61 Draw a probability tree to compute the joint probabilities from the following probabilities.

$P(A) = .5$ .... $P(A^C) = .5$
$P(B|A) = .4$ .... $P(B|A^C) = .7$

6.62 Given the following probabilities, draw a tree to compute the joint probabilities.

$P(A) = .8$ .... $P(A^C) = .2$
$P(B|A) = .3$ .... $P(B|A^C) = .3$

6.63 Given the following probabilities, find the joint probability $P(A \text{ and } B)$.

$P(A) = .7$ .... $P(B|A) = .3$

6.64 Approximately 10% of people are left-handed. If two people are selected at random, what is the probability of the following events?
a. Both are right-handed.
b. Both are left-handed.
c. One is right-handed and the other is left-handed.
d. At least one is right-handed.

6.65 Refer to Exercise 6.64. Suppose that three people are selected at random.
a. Draw a probability tree to depict the experiment.
b. If we use the notation RRR to describe the selection of three right-handed people, what are the descriptions of the remaining seven events? (Use L for left-hander.)
c. How many of the events yield no right-handers, one right-hander, two right-handers, and three right-handers?

d. Find the probability of no right-handers, one right-hander, two right-handers, and three right-handers.

6.66 Suppose there are 100 students in your accounting class, 10 of whom are left-handed. Two students are selected at random.
a. Draw a probability tree and insert the probabilities for each branch.

What is the probability of the following events?
b. Both are right-handed.
c. Both are left-handed.
d. One is right-handed and the other is left-handed.
e. At least one is right-handed

6.67 Refer to Exercise 6.66. Suppose that three people are selected at random.
a. Draw a probability tree and insert the probabilities of each branch.
b. What is the probability of no right-handers, one right-hander, two right-handers, and three right-handers?

6.68 An aerospace company has submitted bids on two separate federal government defense contracts. The company president believes that there is a 40% probability of winning the first contract. If they win the first contract, the probability of winning the second is 70%. However, if they lose the first contract, the president thinks that the probability of winning the second contract decreases to 50%.
a. What is the probability that they win both contracts?
b. What is the probability that they lose both contracts?
c. What is the probability that they win only one contract?

6.69 A telemarketer calls people and tries to sell them a subscription to a daily newspaper. On 20% of her calls, there is no answer or the line is busy. She sells subscriptions to 5% of the remaining calls. For what proportion of calls does she make a sale?

6.70 A foreman for an injection-molding firm admits that on 10% of his shifts, he forgets to shut off the injection machine on his line. This causes the machine to overheat, increasing the probability from 2% to 20% that a defective molding will be produced during the early morning run. What proportion of moldings from the early morning run is defective?

6.71 A study undertaken by the Miami-Dade Supervisor of Elections revealed that 44% of registered voters are Democrats, 37% are Republicans, and 19% are others. If two registered voters are selected at random, what is the probability that both of them have the same party affiliation?

6.72 Among many other pieces of information, the U.S. Census Bureau records the race or ethnicity of the residents of every county in every state. From these results, the bureau calculated a "diversity index" that measures the probability that two people chosen at random are of different races or ethnicities. Suppose that the census determined that in a county in Wisconsin 80% of its residents are white, 15% are black, and 5% are Asian. Calculate the diversity index for this county.

6.73 A survey of middle-aged men reveals that 28% of them are balding at the crown of their heads. Moreover, it is known that such men have an 18% probability of suffering a heart attack in the next 10 years. Men who are not balding in this way have an 11% probability of a heart attack. Find the probability that a middle-aged man will suffer a heart attack sometime in the next 10 years.

6.74 The chartered financial analyst (CFA) is a designation earned after a candidate has taken three annual exams (CFA I, II, and III). The exams are taken in early June. Candidates who pass an exam are eligible to take the exam for the next level in the following year. The pass rates for levels I, II, and III are .57, .73, and .85, respectively. Suppose that 3,000 candidates take the level I exam, 2,500 take the level II exam, and 2,000 take the level III exam. Suppose that one student is selected at random. What is the probability that he or she has passed the exam?

Source: Institute of Financial Analysts.

6.75 The Nickels restaurant chain regularly conducts surveys of its customers. Respondents are asked to assess food quality, service, and price. The responses are

Excellent   Good   Fair

Surveyed customers are also asked whether they would come back. After analyzing the responses, an expert in probability determined that 87% of customers say that they will return. Of those who so indicate, 57% rate the restaurant as excellent, 36% rate it as good, and the remainder rate it as fair. Of those who say that they won't return, the probabilities are 14%, 32%, and 54%, respectively. What proportion of customers rate the restaurant as good?

6.76 Researchers at the University of Pennsylvania School Of Medicine have determined that children under 2 years old who sleep with the lights on have a 36% chance of becoming myopic before they are 16 Children who sleep in darkness have a 21% of becoming myopic. A survey indicates that 28% of children under 2 sleep with some light on. Find the probability that a child under 16 is myopic.

6.77 All printed circuit boards (PCBs) that are manufactured at a certain plant are inspected. An analysis of the company's records indicates that 22% are flawed in some way. Of those that are flawed, 84% are reparable and the rest must be discarded. If a newly produced PCB is randomly selected, what is the probability that it does not have to be discarded?

6.78 A financial analyst has determined that there is a 22% probability that a mutual fund will outperform the market over a 1-year period provided that it outperformed the market the previous year. If only 15% of mutual funds outperform the market during any year, what is the probability that a mutual fund will outperform the market 2 years in a row?

6.79 An investor believes that on a day when the Dow Jones Industrial Average (DJIA) increases, the probability that the NASDAQ also increases is 77%. If the investor believes that there is a 60% probability that the DJIA will increase tomorrow, what is the probability that the NASDAQ will increase as well?

6.80 The controls of an airplane have several backup systems or redundancies so that if one fails the plane will continue to operate. Suppose that the mechanism that controls the flaps has two backups. If the probability that the main control fails is .0001 and the probability that each backup will fail is .01, what is the probability that all three fail to operate?

6.81 According to TNS Intersearch, 69% of wireless web users use it primarily for receiving and sending e-mail. Suppose that three wireless web users are selected at random. What is the probability that all of them use it primarily for e-mail?

6.82 A financial analyst estimates that the probability that the economy will experience a recession in the next 12 months is 25%. She also believes that if the economy encounters a recession, the probability that her mutual fund will increase in value is 20%. If there is no recession, the probability that the mutual fund will increase in value is 75%. Find the probability that the mutual fund's value will increase.

6.83 In June 2016, Britons were heading to the polls to vote in a referendum to decide whether the United Kingdom would leave the European Union. Pew Research Center conducted surveys in European countries to determine opinions about the possible "Brexit." Respondents were asked what the U.K.'s departure would mean for the EU. Responses were "Bad thing" or "Good thing." The number of respondents in each of the countries and the proportions who said it would be a bad thing are listed in the following table.

Country	Number of Respondents	Probability of Responding "Bad Thing"
France	630	62%
Germany	590	74%
Italy	480	57%

What is the probability that if we select one respondent at random he or she would say the U.K. leaving the EU is a bad thing?

6.84 Refer to Exercise 6.83. Respondents in Greece, Hungary, and Poland were asked whether they approved or disapproved of the way the EU was dealing with the refugee issue. The number of respondents and the percentage opting for disapprove are listed here.

Country	Number of Respondents	Probability of Disapprove (%)
Greece	385	942
Hungary	420	70
Poland	475	66

What is the probability that if we select one respondent at random he or she disapproves of the way the EU is handling the refugee issue?

6.85 How many Americans under the age of 40 have student debts? A Pew Research Center attempted to answer the question by asking whether respondents had student debt and in what was their occupation. The following probabilities were determined.

Occupation	Proportion (%)	Has Student Debt (%)
Managerial/ Professional	32	45
Technical, Sales, or Services	15	39
Other	53	27

Calculate the probability that a randomly selected respondent has student debt.

6.86 A statistics professor was in the process of comparing the pass rates (the percentage of entering students who graduate in 5 years or less) for B.A.'s, B.B.A.'s, B.Sc.'s, and B.Eng.'s. Delving into the record he finds the following probabilities.

Degree	Proportion of Entering Class (%)	Pass Rate (%)
B.A	38	79
B.B.A.	41	74
B.Sc	13	68
B.Eng	8	57

What is the probability that a student graduates in 5 years or less?

6-4 BAYES'S LAW

Conditional probability is often used to gauge the relationship between two events. In many of the examples and exercises you've already encountered, conditional probability measures the probability that an event occurs given that a possible cause of the event has occurred. In Example 6.2, we calculated the probability that a mutual fund outperforms the market (the effect) given that the fund manager graduated from a top-20 MBA program (the possible cause). There are situations, however, where we witness a particular event and we need to compute the probability of one of its possible causes. **Bayes's Law** is the technique we use.

EXAMPLE 6.9

Should an MBA Applicant Take a Preparatory Course?

The Graduate Management Admission Test (GMAT) is a requirement for all applicants of MBA programs. A variety of preparatory courses are designed to help applicants improve their GMAT scores, which range from 200 to 800. Suppose that a survey of MBA students reveals that among GMAT scorers above 650, 52% took a preparatory course; whereas among GMAT scorers of less than 650 only 23% took a preparatory course. An applicant to an MBA program has determined that he needs a score of more than 650 to get into a certain MBA program, but he feels that his probability of getting that high a score is quite low—10%. He is considering taking a preparatory course that costs $500. He is willing to do so only if his probability of achieving 650 or more doubles. What should he do?

SOLUTION:

The easiest way to address this problem is to draw a tree diagram. The following notation will be used:

A = GMAT score is 650 or more

A^C = GMAT score less than 650

B = Took preparatory course

B^C = Did not take preparatory course

The probability of scoring 650 or more is

$P(A) = .10$

The complement rule gives us

$P(A^C) = 1 - .10 = .90$

Conditional probabilities are

$P(B|A) = .52$

and

$P(B|A^C) = .23$

Again using the complement rule, we find the following conditional probabilities:

$P(B^C|A) = 1 - .52 = .48$

and

$P(B^C|A^C) = 1 - .23 = .77$

We would like to determine the probability that he would achieve a GMAT score of 650 or more given that he took the preparatory course; that is, we need to compute

$P(A|B)$

Using the definition of conditional probability (page 163), we have

$$P(A|B) = \frac{P(A \text{ and } B)}{P(B)}$$

Neither the numerator nor the denominator is known. The probability tree (Figure 6.4) will provide us with the probabilities.

FIGURE **6.4** **Probability Tree for Example 6.9**

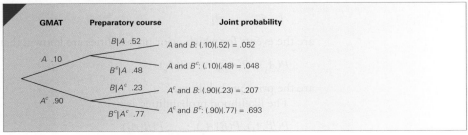

As you can see,

$$P(A \text{ and } B) = (.10)(.52) = .052$$
$$P(A^C \text{ and } B) = (.90)(.23) = .207$$

and

$$P(B) = P(A \text{ and } B) + P(A^C \text{ and } B) = .052 + .207 = .259$$

Thus,

$$P(A|B) = \frac{P(A \text{ and } B)}{P(B)} = \frac{.052}{.259} = .201$$

The probability of scoring 650 or more on the GMAT doubles when the preparatory course is taken.

Thomas Bayes first employed the calculation of conditional probability as shown in Example 6.9 during the eighteenth century. Accordingly, it is called Bayes's Law.

The probabilities $P(A)$ and $P(A^C)$ are called **prior probabilities** because they are determined *prior* to the decision about taking the preparatory course. The conditional probabilities are called **likelihood probabilities** for reasons that are beyond the mathematics in this book. Finally, the conditional probability $P(A|B)$ and similar conditional probabilities $P(A^C|B)$, $P(A|B^C)$, and $P(A^C|B^C)$ are called **posterior probabilities** or **revised probabilities** because the prior probabilities are revised *after* the decision about taking the preparatory course.

You may be wondering why we did not get $P(A|B)$ directly. In other words, why not survey people who took the preparatory course and ask whether they received a score of 650 or more? The answer is that using the likelihood probabilities and using Bayes's Law allows individuals to set their own prior probabilities, which can then be revised. For example, another MBA applicant may assess her probability of scoring 650 or more as .40. Inputting the new prior probabilities produces the following probabilities:

$$P(A \text{ and } B) = (.40)(.52) = .208$$
$$P(A^C \text{ and } B) = (.60)(.23) = .138$$
$$P(B) = P(A \text{ and } B) + P(A^C \text{ and } B) = .208 + .138 = .346$$
$$P(A|B) = \frac{P(A \text{ and } B)}{P(B)} = \frac{.208}{.346} = .601$$

The probability of achieving a GMAT score of 650 or more increases by a more modest 50% (from .40 to .601).

6-4a Bayes's Law Formula (Optional)

Bayes's Law can be expressed as a formula for those who prefer an algebraic approach rather than a probability tree. We use the following notation.

The event B is the given event and the events

$$A_1, A_2, \ldots, A_k$$

are the events for which prior probabilities are known; that is,

$$P(A_1),\ P(A_2), \ldots, P(A_k)$$

are the prior probabilities.

The likelihood probabilities are

$$P(B|A_1), P(B|A_2), \ldots, P(B|A_k)$$

and

$$P(A_1|B), P(A_2|B), \ldots, P(A_k|B)$$

are the posterior probabilities, which represent the probabilities we seek.

Bayes's Law Formula

$$P(A_i|B) = \frac{P(A_i)P(B|A_i)}{P(A_1)P(B|A_1) + P(A_2)P(B|A_2) + \cdots + P(A_k)P(B|A_k)}$$

To illustrate the use of the formula, we'll redo Example 6.9. We begin by defining the events.

A_1 = GMAT score is 650 or more
A_2 = GMAT score less than 650
B = Take preparatory course

The probabilities are

$$P(A_1) = .10$$

The complement rule gives us

$$P(A_2) = 1 - .10 = .90$$

Conditional probabilities are

$$P(B|A_1) = .52$$

and

$$P(B|A_2) = .23$$

Substituting the prior and likelihood probabilities into the Bayes's Law formula yields the following:

$$P(A_1|B) = \frac{P(A_1)P(B|A_1)}{P(A_1)P(B|A_1) + P(A_2)P(B|A_2)} = \frac{(.10)(.52)}{(.10)(.52) + (.90)(.23)}$$

$$= \frac{.052}{.052 + .207} = \frac{.052}{.259} = .201$$

As you can see, the calculation of the Bayes's Law formula produces the same results as the probability tree.

Auditing Tax Returns: Solution

We need to revise the prior probability that this return contains significant fraud. The tree shown in Figure 6.5 details the calculation.

F = Tax return is fraudulent
F^C = Tax return is honest
E_0 = Tax return contains no expense deductions

(Continued)

$E_1 =$ Tax return contains one expense deduction
$E_2 =$ tax return contains two expense deductions

$P(E_1) = P(F \text{ and } E_1) + P(F^C \text{ and } E_1) = .0140 + .1710 = .1850$
$P(F|E_1) = P(F \text{ and } E_1)/P(E_1) = .0140/.1850 = .0757$

The probability that this return is fraudulent is .0757.

FIGURE **6.5** **Probability Tree for Auditing Tax Returns**

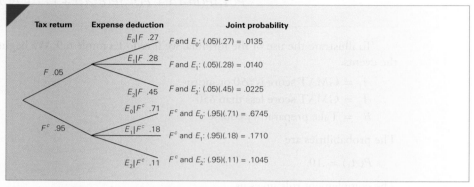

6-4b Applications in Medicine and Medical Insurance (Optional)

Physicians routinely perform medical tests, called *screenings*, on their patients. Screening tests are conducted for all patients in a particular age and gender group, regardless of their symptoms. For example, men in their 50s are advised to take a prostate-specific antigen (PSA) test to determine whether there is evidence of prostate cancer. Women undergo a Pap test for cervical cancer. Unfortunately, few of these tests are 100% accurate. Most can produce *false-positive* and *false-negative* results. A **false-positive** result is one in which the patient does not have the disease, but the test shows positive. A **false-negative** result is one in which the patient does have the disease, but the test produces a negative result. The consequences of each test are serious and costly. A false-negative test results in not detecting a disease in a patient, therefore postponing treatment, perhaps indefinitely. A false-positive test leads to apprehension and fear for the patient. In most cases, the patient is required to undergo further testing such as a biopsy. The unnecessary follow-up procedure can pose medical risks.

False-positive test results have financial repercussions. The cost of the follow-up procedure, for example, is usually far more expensive than the screening test. Medical insurance companies as well as government-funded plans are all adversely affected by false-positive test results. Compounding the problem is that physicians and patients are incapable of properly interpreting the results. A correct analysis can save both lives and money.

Bayes's Law is the vehicle we use to determine the true probabilities associated with screening tests. Applying the complement rule to the false-positive and false-negative rates produces the conditional probabilities that represent correct conclusions. Prior probabilities are usually derived by looking at the overall proportion of people with the diseases. In some cases, the prior probabilities may themselves have been revised because of heredity or demographic variables such as age or race. Bayes's Law allows us to revise the prior probability after the test result is positive or negative.

Example 6.10 is based on the actual false-positive and false-negative rates. Note however, that different sources provide somewhat different probabilities. The differences may be the result of the way positive and negative results are defined or the way technicians conduct the tests. Students who are affected by the diseases described in the example and exercises should seek clarification from their physicians.

EXAMPLE 6.10

Probability of Prostate Cancer

Prostate cancer is the most common form of cancer found in men. The probability of developing prostate cancer over a lifetime is 16%. (This figure may be higher since many prostate cancers go undetected.) Many physicians routinely perform a PSA test, particularly for men over age 50. PSA is a protein produced only by the prostate gland and thus is fairly easy to detect. Normally, men have PSA levels between 0 and 4 mg/ml. Readings above 4 may be considered high and potentially indicative of cancer. However, PSA levels tend to rise with age even among men who are cancer free. Studies have shown that the test is not very accurate. In fact, the probability of having an elevated PSA level given that the man does not have cancer (false positive) is .135. If the man does have cancer, the probability of a normal PSA level (false negative) is almost .300. (This figure may vary by age and by the definition of *high* PSA level.) If a physician concludes that the PSA is high, a biopsy is performed. Besides the concerns and health needs of the men, there are also financial costs. The cost of the blood test is low (approximately $50). However, the cost of the biopsy is considerably higher (approximately $1,000). A false-positive PSA test will lead to an unnecessary biopsy. Because the PSA test is so inaccurate, some private and public medical plans do not pay for it. Suppose you are a manager in a medical insurance company and must decide on guidelines for those who should be routinely screened for prostate cancer. An analysis of prostate cancer incidence and age produces the following table of probabilities. (The probability of a man under 40 developing prostate cancer is less than .0001, or small enough to treat as 0.)

Age	Probability of Developing Prostate Cancer
40–49	.010
50–59	.022
60–69	.046
70 and older	.079

Assume that a man in each of the age categories undergoes a PSA test with a positive result. Calculate the probability that each man actually has prostate cancer and the probability that he does not. Perform a cost–benefit analysis to determine the cost per cancer detected.

SOLUTION:

As we did in Example 6.9 and the chapter-opening example, we'll draw a probability tree (Figure 6.6). The notation is

C = Has prostate cancer

C^C = Does not have prostate cancer

PT = Positive test result

NT = Negative test result

Starting with a man between 40 and 50 years old, we have the following probabilities

Prior

$P(C)$ = .010

$P(C^C)$ = 1 − .010 = .990

Likelihood probabilities

False negative:	$P(NT\|C)$	$= .300$
True positive:	$P(PT\|C)$	$= 1 - .300 = .700$
False positive:	$P(PT\|C^C)$	$= .135$
True negative:	$P(NT\|C^C)$	$= 1 - .135 = .865$

FIGURE **6.6** Probability Tree for Example 6.10

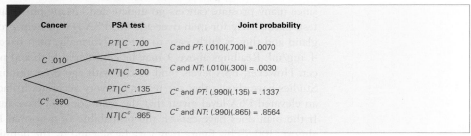

The tree allows you to determine the probability of obtaining a positive test result. It is

$$P(PT) = P(C \text{ and } PT) + P(C^C \text{ and } PT) = .0070 + .1337 = .1407$$

We can now compute the probability that the man has prostate cancer given a positive test result:

$$P(C|PT) = \frac{P(C \text{ and } PT)}{P(PT)} = \frac{.0070}{.1407} = .0498$$

The probability that he does not have prostate cancer is

$$P(C^C|PT) = 1 - P(C|PT) = 1 - .0498 = .9502$$

We can repeat the process for the other age categories. Here are the results.

	Probabilities Given a Positive PSA Test	
Age	Has Prostate Cancer	Does Not Have Prostate Cancer
40–49	.0498	.9502
50–59	.1045	.8955
60–69	.2000	.8000
70 and older	.3078	.6922

The following table lists the proportion of each age category wherein the PSA test is positive $[P(PT)]$.

Age	Proportion of Tests That Are Positive	Number of Biopsies Performed per Million	Number of Cancers Detected	Number of Biopsies per Cancer Detected
40–49	.1407	140,700	.0498(140,700) = 7,007	20.10
50–59	.1474	147,400	.1045(147,400) = 15,403	9.57
60–79	.1610	161,000	.2000(161,000) = 32,200	5.00
70 and older	.1796	179,600	.3078(179,600) = 55,281	3.25

If we assume a cost of $1,000 per biopsy, the cost per cancer detected is $20,100 for 40 to 50, $9,570 for 50 to 60, $5,000 for 60 to 70, and $3,250 for over 70.

We have created an Excel spreadsheet to help you perform the calculations in Example 6.10. Open the **Excel Workbooks** folder and select **Medical screening**. There are three cells that you may alter. In cell B5, enter a new prior probability for prostate cancer. Its complement will be calculated in cell B15. In cells D6 and D15, type new values for the false-negative and false-positive rates, respectively. Excel will do the rest. We will use this spreadsheet to demonstrate some terminology standard in medical testing.

Terminology We will illustrate the terms using the probabilities calculated for the 40 to 50 age category.

The false-negative rate is .300. Its complement is the likelihood probability $P(PT|C)$, called the *sensitivity*. It is equal to $1 - .300 = .700$. Among men with prostate cancer, this is the proportion of men who will get a positive test result.

The complement of the false-positive rate (.135) is $P(NT|C^C)$, which is called the *specificity*. This likelihood probability is $1 - .135 = .865$

The posterior probability that someone has prostate cancer given a positive test result $[P(C|PT) = .0498]$ is called the *positive predictive value*. Using Bayes's Law, we can compute the other three posterior probabilities.

The probability that the patient does not have prostate cancer given a positive test result is

$$P(C^C|PT) = .9502$$

The probability that the patient has prostate cancer given a negative test result is

$$P(C|NT) = .0035$$

The probability that the patient does not have prostate cancer given a negative test result:

$$P(C^C|NT) = .9965$$

This revised probability is called the *negative predictive value*.

6-4c Developing an Understanding of Probability Concepts

If you review the computations made previously, you'll realize that the prior probabilities are as important as the probabilities associated with the test results (the likelihood probabilities) in determining the posterior probabilities. The following table shows the prior probabilities and the revised probabilities.

Age	Prior Probabilities for Prostate Cancer	Posterior Probabilities Given a Positive PSA Test
40–49	.010	.0498
50–59	.022	.1045
60–69	.046	.2000
70 and older	.079	.3078

As you can see, if the prior probability is low, then unless the screening test is quite accurate, the revised probability will still be quite low.

To see the effects of different likelihood probabilities, suppose the PSA test is a perfect predictor. In other words, the false-positive and false-negative rates are 0. Figure 6.7 displays the probability tree.

FIGURE **6.7** Probability Tree for Example 6.10 with a Perfect Predictor Test

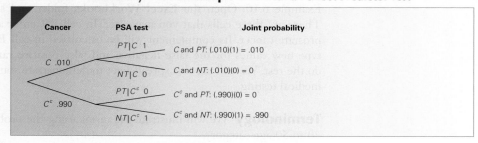

We find

$$P(PT) = P(C \text{ and } PT) + P(C^C \text{ and } PT) = .01 + 0 = .01$$

$$P(C|PT) = \frac{P(C \text{ and } PT)}{P(PT)} = \frac{.01}{.01} = 1.00$$

Now we calculate the probability of prostate cancer when the test is negative.

$$P(NT) = P(C \text{ and } NT) + P(C^C \text{ and } NT) = 0 + .99 = .99$$

$$P(C|NT) = \frac{P(C \text{ and } NT)}{P(NT)} = \frac{0}{.99} = 0$$

Thus, if the test is a perfect predictor and a man has a positive test, then as expected the probability that he has prostate cancer is 1.0. The probability that he does not have cancer when the test is negative is 0.

Now suppose that the test is always wrong; that is, the false-positive and false-negative rates are 100%. The probability tree is shown in Figure 6.8.

FIGURE **6.8** Probability Tree for Example 6.10 with a Test That Is Always Wrong

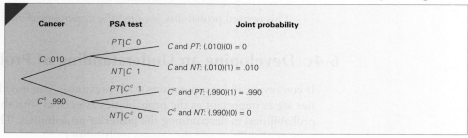

$$P(PT) = P(C \text{ and } PT) + P(C^C \text{ and } PT) = 0 + .99 = .99$$

$$P(C|PT) = \frac{P(C \text{ and } PT)}{P(PT)} \frac{0}{.99} = 0$$

and

$$P(NT) = P(C \text{ and } NT) + P(C^C \text{ and } NT) = .01 + 0 = .01$$

$$P(C|NT) = \frac{P(C \text{ and } NT)}{P(NT)} = \frac{.01}{.01} = 1.00$$

Notice we have another perfect predictor except that it is reversed. The probability of prostate cancer given a positive test result is 0, but the probability becomes 1.00 when the test is negative.

Finally we consider the situation when the set of likelihood probabilities are the same. Figure 6.9 depicts the probability tree for a 40- to 50-year-old male and the probability of a positive test is (say) .3 and the probability of a negative test is .7.

FIGURE **6.9** Probability Tree for Example 6.10 with Identical Likelihood Probabilities

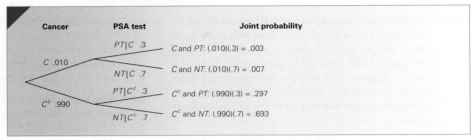

$$P(PT) = P(C \text{ and } PT) + P(C^C \text{ and } PT) = .003 + .297 = .300$$

$$P(C|PT) = \frac{P(C \text{ and } PT)}{P(PT)} = \frac{.003}{.300} = .01$$

and

$$P(NT) = P(C \text{ and } NT) + P(C^C \text{ and } NT) = .007 + .693 = .700$$

$$P(C|NT) = \frac{P(C \text{ and } NT)}{P(NT)} = .007/.700 = .01$$

As you can see, the posterior and prior probabilities are the same. That is, the PSA test does not change the prior probabilities. Obviously, the test is useless.

We could have used any probability for the false-positive and false-negative rates, including .5. If we had used .5, then one way of performing this PSA test is to flip a fair coin. One side would be interpreted as positive and the other side as negative. It is clear that such a test has no predictive power.

The exercises and Case 6.4 offer the probabilities for several other screening tests.

EXERCISES

6.87 Refer to Exercise 6.59. Determine $P(A|B)$.

6.88 Refer to Exercise 6.60. Find the following.
a. $P(A|B)$
b. $P(A^C|B)$
c. $P(A|B^C)$
d. $P(A^C|B^C)$

6.89 Refer to Example 6.9. An MBA applicant believes that the probability of scoring more than 650 on the GMAT without the preparatory course is .95. What is the probability of attaining that level after taking the preparatory course?

6.90 Refer to Exercise 6.70. The plant manager randomly selects a molding from the early morning run and discovers it is defective. What is the probability that the foreman forgot to shut off the machine the previous night?

6.91 The U.S. National Highway Traffic Safety Administration gathers data concerning the causes of highway crashes where at least one fatality has occurred. The following probabilities were determined from the 1998 annual study (BAC is blood-alcohol content).

$P(BAC = 0 \mid \text{Crash with fatality}) = .616$

$P(BAC \text{ is between } .01 \text{ and } .09 \mid \text{Crash with fatality}) = .300$

$P(BAC \text{ is greater than } .09 \mid \text{Crash with fatality}) = .084$

Over a certain stretch of highway during a 1-year period, suppose the probability of being involved in a crash that results in at least one fatality is .01. It has been estimated that 12% of the drivers on this highway drive while their BAC is greater than .09. Determine the probability of a crash with at least one fatality if a driver drives while legally intoxicated (BAC greater than .09).

6.92 Refer to Exercise 6.74. A randomly selected candidate who took a CFA exam tells you that he has passed the exam. What is the probability that he took the CFA I exam?

6.93 Bad gums may mean a bad heart. Researchers discovered that 85% of people who have suffered a heart attack had periodontal disease, an inflammation of the gums. Only 29% of healthy people have this disease. Suppose that in a certain community heart attacks are quite rare, occurring with only 10% ease, what is the probability that he or she will have a heart attack?

6.94 Refer to Exercise 6.93. If 40% of the people in a community will have a heart attack, what is the probability that a person with periodontal disease will have a heart attack?

6.95 Data from the Office on Smoking and Health, Centers for Disease Control and Prevention, indicate that 40% of adults who did not finish high school, 34% of high school graduates, 24% of adults who completed some college, and 14% of college graduates smoke. Suppose that one individual is selected at random, and it is discovered that the individual smokes. What is the probability that the individual is a college graduate? Use the probabilities in Exercise 6.45 to calculate the probability that the individual is a college graduate.

6.96 Three airlines serve a small town in Ohio. Airline A has 50% of all the scheduled flights, airline B has 30%, and airline C has the remaining 20%. Their on-time rates are 80%, 65%, and 40%, respectively. A plane has just left on time. What is the probability that it was airline A?

6.97 Your favorite team is in the final playoffs. You have assigned a probability of 60% that it will win the championship. Past records indicate that when teams win the championship, they win the first game of the series 70% of the time. When they lose the series, they win the first game 25% of the time. The first game is over; your team has lost. What is the probability that it will win the series?

6.98 Transplant operations have become routine. One common transplant operation is for kidneys. The most dangerous aspect of the procedure is the possibility that the body may reject the new organ. Several new drugs are available for such circumstances, and the earlier the drug is administered, the higher the probability of averting rejection. The *New England Journal of Medicine* recently reported the development of a new urine test to detect early warning signs that the body is rejecting a transplanted kidney.

However, like most other tests, the new test is not perfect. When the test is conducted on someone whose kidney will be rejected, approximately one out of five tests will be negative (i.e., the test is wrong). When the test is conducted on a person whose kidney will not be rejected, 8% will show a positive test result (i.e., another incorrect result). Physicians know that in about 35% of kidney transplants the body tries to reject the organ. Suppose that the test was performed and the test is positive (indicating early warning of rejection). What is the probability that the body is attempting to reject the kidney?

6.99 The Rapid Test is used to determine whether someone has HIV (the virus that causes AIDS). The false-positive and false-negative rates are .027 and .080, respectively. A physician has just received the Rapid Test report that his patient tested positive. Before receiving the result, the physician assigned his patient to the low-risk group (defined on the basis of several variables) with only a 0.5% probability of having HIV. What is the probability that the patient actually has HIV?

6.100 What are the sensitivity, specificity, positive predictive value, and negative predictive value in the previous exercise?

6.101 The Pap smear is the standard test for cervical cancer. The false-positive rate is .636; the false-negative rate is .180. Family history and age are factors that must be considered when assigning a probability of cervical cancer. Suppose that, after obtaining a medical history, a physician determines that 2% of women of his patient's age and with similar family histories have cervical cancer. Determine the effects a positive and a negative Pap smear test have on the probability that the patient has cervical cancer.

6.102 Refer to Exercise 6.76. The researchers examined a child under 16 and discovered that he is myopic. What is the probability that he slept with the lights when he was under 2?

6.103 Refer to Exercise 6.83. A respondent who said that the U.K. leaving the EU is a bad thing was selected. What is the probability that the respondent is from Italy?

6.104 Refer to Exercise 6.84. A respondent who disapproved of the way the EU handled the refugee issue was selected. Calculate the probability that the respondent is from Greece.

6.105 Refer to Exercise 6.85. An American under 40 tells you that he has student debt. What is the probability that he is managerial or professional?

6.106 Refer to Exercise 6.86. The professor meets a student who has just graduated in less than five year. Determine the probability that he graduated with B.B.A. degree.

6-5 / IDENTIFYING THE CORRECT METHOD

As we've previously pointed out, the emphasis in this book will be on identifying the correct statistical technique to use. In Chapters 2 and 4, we showed how to summarize data by first identifying the appropriate method to use. Although it is difficult to offer strict rules on which probability method to use, we can still provide some general guidelines.

In the examples and exercises in this text (and most other introductory statistics books), the key issue is whether joint probabilities are provided or are required.

6-5a Joint Probabilities Are Given

In Section 6-2, we addressed problems where the joint probabilities were given. In these problems, we can compute marginal probabilities by adding across rows and down columns. We can use the joint and marginal probabilities to compute conditional probabilities, for which a formula is available. This allows us to determine whether the events described by the table are independent or dependent.

We can also apply the addition rule to compute the probability that either of two events occur.

6-5b Joint Probabilities Are Required

The previous section introduced three probability rules and probability trees. We need to apply some or all of these rules in circumstances where one or more joint probabilities are required. We apply the multiplication rule (either by formula or through a probability tree) to calculate the probability of intersections. In some problems, we're interested in adding these joint probabilities. We're actually applying the addition rule for mutually exclusive events here. We also frequently use the complement rule. In addition, we can also calculate new conditional probabilities using Bayes's Law.

CHAPTER SUMMARY

The first step in assigning probability is to create an **exhaustive** and **mutually exclusive** list of outcomes. The second step is to use the **classical**, **relative frequency**, or **subjective approach** and assign probability to the outcomes. A variety of methods are available to compute the probability of other events. These methods include **probability rules** and **trees**.

An important application of these rules is **Bayes's Law**, which allows us to compute conditional probabilities from other forms of probability.

IMPORTANT TERMS:

Random experiment   155
Exhaustive   155
Mutually exclusive   155
Sample space   156
Classical approach   156
Relative frequency approach   157
Subjective approach   157
Event   157
Intersection   160
Joint probability   160
Marginal probability   162
Conditional probability   163

Independent events   164
Union   165
Complement   172
Complement rule   172
Multiplication rule   172
Addition rule   174
Bayes's Law   180
Prior probability   182
Likelihood probability   182
Posterior probability   182
False-positive   184
False-negative   184

FORMULAS:

Conditional probability

$$P(A|B) = \frac{P(A \text{ and } B)}{P(B)}$$

Complement rule

$$P(A^C) = 1 - P(A)$$

Multiplication rule

$$P(A \text{ and } B) = P(A|B)P(B)$$

Addition rule

$$P(A \text{ or } B) = P(A) + P(B) - P(A \text{ and } B)$$

CHAPTER EXERCISES

6.107 Pew Research Center conducted a survey of countries around the world and asked respondents whether they were having a typical day, a good day, or a bad day. The results and the number of respondents in Europe, Asia, and the United States are listed next.

Country	Number of Respondents	Typical Day (%)	Good Day (%)	Bad Day (%)
Asia	525	68	30	2
Europe	650	76	17	7
United States	390	49	41	10

One respondent is selected at random.

a. Find the probability that the respondent is having a good day.
b. The respondent is having a typical day. What is the probability that he is from the United States.

6.108 The following table lists the joint probabilities of achieving grades of A and not achieving A's in two MBA courses.

	Achieve a Grade of A in Marketing	Does Not Achieve a Grade of A in Marketing
Achieve a grade of A in statistics	.053	.130
Does not achieve a grade of A in statistics	.237	.580

a. What is the probability that a student achieves a grade of A in marketing?
b. What is the probability that a student achieves a grade of A in marketing, given that he or she does not achieve a grade of A in statistics?
c. Are achieving grades of A in marketing and statistics independent events? Explain.

6.109 A construction company has bid on two contracts. The probability of winning contract A is .3. If the company wins contract A, then the probability of winning contract B is .4. If the company loses contract A,

then the probability of winning contract B decreases to .2. Find the probability of the following events.
a. Winning both contracts
b. Winning exactly one contract
c. Winning at least one contract

6.110 Laser surgery to fix shortsightedness is becoming more popular. However, for some people, a second procedure is necessary. The following table lists the joint probabilities of needing a second procedure and whether the patient has a corrective lens with a factor (diopter) of minus 8 or less.

Factor	Vision Corrective Factor of More Than Minus 8	Vision Corrective Factor of Minus 8 or Less
First procedure is successful	.66	.15
Second procedure is required	.05	.14

a. Find the probability that a second procedure is required.
b. Determine the probability that someone whose corrective lens factor is minus 8 or less does not require a second procedure.
c. Are the events independent? Explain your answer.

6.111 The effect of an antidepressant drug varies from person to person. Suppose that the drug is effective on 80% of women and 65% of men. It is known that 66% of the people who take the drug are women. What is the probability that the drug is effective?

6.112 Refer to Exercise 6.111. Suppose that you are told that the drug is effective. What is the probability that the drug taker is a man?

6.113 In a four-cylinder engine there are four spark plugs. If any one of them malfunctions, the car will idle roughly and power will be lost. Suppose that for a certain brand of spark plugs the probability that a spark plug will function properly after 5,000 miles is .90. Assuming that the spark plugs operate independently, what is the probability that the car will idle roughly after 5,000 miles?

6.114 A telemarketer sells magazine subscriptions over the telephone. The probability of a busy signal or no answer is 65%. If the telemarketer does make contact, the probability of 0, 1, 2, or 3 magazine subscriptions is .5, .25, .20, and .05, respectively. Find the probability that in one call she sells no magazines.

6.115 A statistics professor believes that there is a relationship between the number of missed classes and the grade on his midterm test. After examining his records, he produced the following table of joint probabilities.

	Student Fails the Test	Student Passes the Test
Student misses fewer than 5 classes	.02	.86
Student misses 5 or more classes	.09	.03

a. What is the pass rate on the midterm test?
b. What proportion of students who miss five or more classes passes the midterm test?
c. What proportion of students who miss fewer than five classes passes the midterm test?
d. Are the events independent?

6.116 In Canada, criminals are entitled to parole after serving only one-third of their sentence. Virtually all prisoners, with several exceptions including murderers, are released after serving two-thirds of their sentence. The government has proposed a new law that would create a special category of inmates based on whether they had committed crimes involving violence or drugs. Such criminals would be subject to additional detention if the Correction Services judges them highly likely to reoffend. Currently, 27% of prisoners who are released commit another crime within 2 years of release. Among those who have reoffended, 41% would have been detained under the new law, whereas 31% of those who have not reoffended would have been detained.
a. What is the probability that a prisoner who would have been detained under the new law does commit another crime within 2 years?
b. What is the probability that a prisoner who would not have been detained under the new law does commit another crime within 2 years?

6.117 Casino Windsor conducts surveys to determine the opinions of its customers. Among other questions, respondents are asked to give their opinion about "Your overall impression of Casino Windsor." The responses are

Excellent Good Average Poor

In addition, the gender of the respondent is noted. After analyzing the results, the following table of joint probabilities was produced.

Rating	Women	Men
Excellent	.27	.22
Good	.14	.10
Average	.06	.12
Poor	.03	.06

a. What proportion of customers rate Casino Windsor as excellent?
b. Determine the probability that a male customer rates Casino Windsor as excellent.
c. Find the probability that a customer who rates Casino Windsor as excellent is a man.
d. Are gender and rating independent? Explain your answer.

6.118 A customer-service supervisor regularly conducts a survey of customer satisfaction. The results of the latest survey indicate that 8% of customers were not satisfied with the service they received at their last visit to the store. Of those who are not satisfied, only 22% return to the store within a year. Of those who are satisfied, 64% return within a year. A customer has just entered the store. In response to your question, he informs you that it is less than 1 year since his last visit to the store. What is the probability that he was satisfied with the service he received?

6.119 How does level of affluence affect health care? To address one dimension of the problem, a group of heart attack victims was selected. Each was categorized as a low-, medium-, or high-income earner. Each was also categorized as having survived or died. A demographer notes that in our society 21% fall into the low-income group, 49% are in the medium-income group, and 30% are in the high-income group. Furthermore, an analysis of heart attack victims reveals that 12% of low-income people, 9% of medium-income people, and 7% of high-income people die of heart attacks. Find the probability that a survivor of a heart attack is in the low-income group.

6.120 A statistics professor and his wife are planning to take a 2-week vacation in Hawaii, but they can't decide whether to spend 1 week on each of the islands of Maui and Oahu, 2 weeks on Maui, or 2 weeks on Oahu. Placing their faith in random chance, they insert two Maui brochures in one envelope, two Oahu brochures in a second envelope, and one brochure from each island in a third envelope. The professor's wife will select one envelope at random, and their vacation schedule will be based on the brochures of the islands so selected. After his wife randomly selects an envelope, the professor removes one brochure from the envelope (without looking at the second brochure) and observes that it is a Maui brochure. What is the probability that the other brochure in the envelope is a Maui brochure? (Proceed with caution: The problem is more difficult than it appears.)

6.121 The owner of an appliance store is interested in the relationship between the price at which an item is sold (regular or sale price) and the customer's decision on whether to purchase an extended warranty. After analyzing her records, she produced the following joint probabilities.

	Purchased Extended Warranty	Did Not Purchase Extended Warranty
Regular price	.21	.57
Sale price	.14	.08

a. What is the probability that a customer who bought an item at the regular price purchased the extended warranty?
b. What proportion of customers buy an extended warranty?
c. Are the events independent? Explain.

6.122 Researchers have developed statistical models based on financial ratios that predict whether a company will go bankrupt over the next 12 months. In a test of one such model, the model correctly predicted the bankruptcy of 85% of firms that did in fact fail, and it correctly predicted nonbankruptcy for 74% of firms that did not fail. Suppose that we expect 8% of the firms in a particular city to fail over the next year. Suppose that the model predicts bankruptcy

for a firm that you own. What is the probability that your firm will fail within the next 12 months?

6.123 A union's executive conducted a survey of its members to determine what the membership felt were the important issues to be resolved during upcoming negotiations with management. The results indicate that 74% of members felt that job security was an important issue, whereas 65% identified pension benefits as an important issue. Of those who felt that pension benefits were important, 60% also felt that job security was an important issue. One member is selected at random.

a. What is the probability that he or she felt that both job security and pension benefits were important?
b. What is the probability that the member felt that at least one of these two issues was important?

6.124 In a class on probability, a statistics professor flips two balanced coins. Both fall to the floor and roll under his desk. A student in the first row informs the professor that he can see both coins. He reports that at least one of them shows tails. What is the probability that the other coin is also tails? (Beware the obvious.)

6.125 Refer to Exercise 6.124. Suppose the student informs the professor that he can see only one coin and it shows tails. What is the probability that the other coin is also tails?

CASE 6.1   Let's Make a Deal

A number of years ago, there was a popular television game show called *Let's Make a Deal*. The host, Monty Hall, would randomly select contestants from the audience and, as the title suggests, he would make deals for prizes. Contestants would be given relatively modest prizes and would then be offered the opportunity to risk those prizes to win better ones.

Suppose that you are a contestant on this show. Monty has just given you a free trip touring toxic waste sites around the country. He now offers you a trade: Give up the trip in exchange for a gamble. On the stage are three curtains, A, B, and C. Behind one of them is a brand new car worth $50,000. Behind the other two curtains, the stage is empty. You decide to gamble and select curtain A. In an attempt to make things more interesting, Monty then exposes an empty stage by opening curtain C (he knows there is nothing behind curtain C). He then offers you the free trip again if you quit now or, if you like, he will propose another deal (i.e., you can keep your choice of curtain A or perhaps switch to curtain B). What do you do?

To help you answer that question, try first answering these questions.

1. Before Monty shows you what's behind curtain C, what is the probability that the car is behind curtain A? What is the probability that the car is behind curtain B?

2. After Monty shows you what's behind curtain C, what is the probability that the car is behind curtain A? What is the probability that the car is behind curtain B?

CASE 6.2 — To Bunt or Not to Bunt, That Is the Question

Kyodo News / ContributorKyodo News / Contributor/Getty Image

No sport generates as many statistics as baseball. Reporters, managers, and fans argue and discuss strategies on the basis of these statistics. An article in *Chance* ("A Statistician Reads the Sports Page," Hal S. Stern, Vol. 1, Winter 1997) offers baseball lovers another opportunity to analyze numbers associated with the game. Table 1 lists the probabilities of scoring at least one run in situations that are defined by the number of outs and the bases occupied. For example, the probability of scoring at least one run when there are no outs and a man is on first base is .39. If the bases are loaded with one out, then the probability of scoring any runs is .67. (Probabilities are based on results from the American League during the 1989 season. The results for the National League are also shown in the article and are similar.)

TABLE **1** **Probability of Scoring Any Runs**

Bases Occupied	0 Outs	1 Out	2 Outs
Bases empty	.26	.16	.07
First base	.39	.26	.13
Second base	.57	.42	.24
Third base	.72	.55	.28
First base and second base	.59	.45	.24
First base and third base	.76	.61	.37
Second base and third base	.83	.74	.37
Bases loaded	.81	.67	.43

Table 1 allows us to determine the best strategy in a variety of circumstances. This case will concentrate on the strategy of the sacrifice bunt. The purpose of the sacrifice bunt is to sacrifice the batter to move base runners to the next base. It can be employed when there are fewer than two outs and men on base. Ignoring the suicide squeeze, any of four outcomes can occur:

1. The bunt is successful. The runner (or runners) advances one base, and the batter is out.

2. The batter is out but fails to advance the runner.

3. The batter bunts into a double play.

4. The batter is safe (hit or error), and the runner advances.

Suppose that you are an American League manager. The game is tied in the middle innings of a game, and there is a runner on first base with no one out. Given the following probabilities of the four outcomes of a bunt for the batter at the plate, should you signal the batter to sacrifice bunt?

P(Outcome 1) = .75
P(Outcome 2) = .10
P(Outcome 3) = .10
P(Outcome 4) = .05

Assume for simplicity that after the hit or error in outcome 4, there will be men on first and second base and no one out.

CASE 6.3 — Should He Attempt to Steal a Base?

Otto Greule Jr/Getty Images

Refer to Case 6.2. Another baseball strategy is to attempt to steal second base. Historically the probability of a successful steal of second base is approximately 68%. The probability of being thrown out is 32%.

(We'll ignore the relatively rare event wherein the catcher throws the ball into center field allowing the base runner to advance to third base.) Suppose there is a runner on first base. For each of the possible number of outs (0, 1, or 2),

determine whether it is advisable to have the runner attempt to steal second base.

CASE 6.4 Maternal Serum Screening Test for Down Syndrome

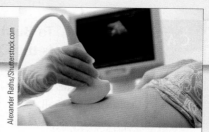

Alexander Raths/Shutterstock.com

Pregnant women are screened for a birth defect called Down syndrome. Down syndrome babies are mentally and physically challenged. Some mothers choose to abort the fetus when they are certain that their baby will be born with the syndrome. The most common screening is maternal serum screening, a blood test that looks for markers in the blood to indicate whether the birth defect may occur. The false-positive and false-negative rates vary according to the age of the mother.

Mother's Age	False-Positive Rate	False-Negative Rate
Under 30	.04	.376
30–34	.082	.290
35–37	.178	.269
Over 38	.343	.029

The probability that a baby has Down syndrome is primarily a function of the mother's age. The probabilities are listed here.

Age	Probability of Down Syndrome
25	1/1300
30	1/900
35	1/350
40	1/100
45	1/25
49	1/12

a. For each of the ages 25, 30, 35, 40, 45, and 49 determine the probability of Down syndrome if the maternity serum screening produces a positive result.

b. Repeat for a negative result.

CASE 6.5 Probability That at Least Two People in the Same Room Have the Same Birthday

Anna Jurkovska/Shutterstock.com

Suppose that there are two people in a room. The probability that they share the same birthday (date, not necessarily year) is 1/365, and the probability that they have different birthdays is 364/365. To illustrate, suppose that you're in a room with one other person and that your birthday is July 1. The probability that the other person does not have the same birthday is 364/365 because there are 364 days in the year that are not July 1. If a third person now enters the room, the probability that he or she has a different birthday from the first two people in the room is 363/365. Thus, the probability that three people in a room having different birthdays is (364/365)(363/365). You can continue this process for any number of people.

Find the number of people in a room so that there is about a 50%

probability that at least two have the same birthday.

Hint 1: Calculate the probability that they don't have the same birthday.

Hint 2: Excel users can employ the **product** function to calculate joint probabilities.

Baloncici/Shutterstock.com

RANDOM VARIABLES AND DISCRETE PROBABILITY DISTRIBUTIONS

CHAPTER OUTLINE

Investing to Maximize Returns and Minimize Risk

DATA
Xm07-00

An investor has $100,000 to invest in the stock market. She is interested in developing a stock portfolio made up of stocks on the New York Exchange (NYSE), the Toronto Stock Exchange (TSX), and the NASDAQ. The stocks she has chosen to analyze are Home Depot (HD) and Nike (NKE) on the NYSE, Canadian National Railway (CNR) on the TSX, and Expedia (EXPE) on the NASDAQ. However, she does not know how much to invest in each one. She would like to maximize her return while minimizing her risk. She has compiled the monthly returns for all four stocks during a 60-month period (January 2011 to December 2015). After some consideration, she has narrowed her choices down to the following three. What should she do?

1. Invest $25,000 in each stock
2. Home Depot: $10,000, Nike: $20,000, Canadian National Railway: $30,000, Expedia: $40,000
3. Home Depot: $30,000, Nike: $30,000, Canadian National Railway: $10,000, Expedia: $30,000

Terry Vine/Blend/Getty Images

We will provide our answer after we've developed the necessary tools in Section 7-3.

197

INTRODUCTION

In this chapter, we extend the concepts and techniques of probability introduced in Chapter 6. We present random variables and probability distributions, which are essential in the development of statistical inference.

Here is a brief glimpse into the wonderful world of statistical inference. Suppose that you flip a coin 100 times and count the number of heads. The objective is to determine whether we can infer from the count that the coin is not balanced. It is reasonable to believe that observing a large number of heads (say, 90) or a small number (say, 15) would be a statistical indication of an unbalanced coin. However, where do we draw the line? At 75 or 65 or 55? Without knowing the probability of the frequency of the number of heads from a balanced coin, we cannot draw any conclusions from the sample of 100 coin flips.

The concepts and techniques of probability introduced in this chapter will allow us to calculate the probability we seek. As a first step, we introduce random variables and probability distributions.

7-1 / RANDOM VARIABLES AND PROBABILITY DISTRIBUTIONS

Consider an experiment where we flip two balanced coins and observe the results. We can represent the events as

Heads on the first coin and heads on the second coin

Heads on the first coin and tails on the second coin

Tails on the first coin and heads on the second coin

Tails on the first coin and tails on the second coin

However, we can list the events in a different way. Instead of defining the events by describing the outcome of each coin, we can count the number of heads (or, if we wish, the number of tails). Thus, the events are now

2 heads

1 heads

1 heads

0 heads

The number of heads is called the **random variable**. We often label the random variable X, and we're interested in the probability of each value of X. Thus, in this illustration, the values of X are 0, 1, and 2.

Here is another example. In many parlor games as well as in the game of craps played in casinos, the player tosses two dice. One way of listing the events is to describe the number on the first die and the number on the second die as follows.

1, 1	1, 2	1, 3	1, 4	1, 5	1, 6
2, 1	2, 2	2, 3	2, 4	2, 5	2, 6
3, 1	3, 2	3, 3	3, 4	3, 5	3, 6
4, 1	4, 2	4, 3	4, 4	4, 5	4, 6
5, 1	5, 2	5, 3	5, 4	5, 5	5, 6
6, 1	6, 2	6, 3	6, 4	6, 5	6, 6

However, in almost all games, the player is primarily interested in the total. Accordingly, we can list the totals of the two dice instead of the individual numbers.

2	3	4	5	6	7
3	4	5	6	7	8
4	5	6	7	8	9
5	6	7	8	9	10
6	7	8	9	10	11
7	8	9	10	11	12

If we define the random variable X as the total of the two dice, then X can equal 2, 3, 4, 5, 6, 7, 8, 9, 10, 11, and 12.

> **Random Variable**
>
> A **random variable** is a function or rule that assigns a number to each outcome of an experiment.

In some experiments, the outcomes are numbers. For example, when we observe the return on an investment or measure the amount of time to assemble a computer, the experiment produces events that are numbers. Simply stated, the value of a random variable is a numerical event.

There are two types of random variables, discrete and continuous. A **discrete random variable** is one that can take on a countable number of values. For example, if we define X as the number of heads observed in an experiment that flips a coin 10 times, then the values of X are 0, 1, 2, . . . , 10. The variable X can assume a total of 11 values. Obviously, we counted the number of values; hence, X is discrete.

A **continuous random variable** is one whose values are uncountable. An excellent example of a continuous random variable is the amount of time to complete a task. For example, let X = time to write a statistics exam in a university where the time limit is 3 hours and students cannot leave before 30 minutes. The smallest value of X is 30 minutes. If we attempt to count the number of values that X can take on, we need to identify the next value. Is it 30.1 minutes? 30.01 minutes? 30.001 minutes? None of these is the second possible value of X because there exist numbers larger than 30 and smaller than 30.001. It becomes clear that we cannot identify the second, or third, or any other values of X (except for the largest value 180 minutes). Thus, we cannot count the number of values, and X is continuous.

A **probability distribution** is a table, formula, or graph that describes the values of a random variable and the probability associated with these values. We will address discrete probability distributions in the rest of this chapter and cover continuous distributions in Chapter 8.

As we noted earlier, an uppercase letter will represent the *name* of the random variable, usually X. Its lowercase counterpart will represent the value of the random variable. Thus, we represent the probability that the random variable X will equal x as

$P(X = x)$

or more simply

$P(x)$

7-1a Discrete Probability Distributions

The probabilities of the values of a discrete random variable may be derived by means of probability tools such as tree diagrams or by applying one of the definitions of probability. However, two fundamental requirements apply as stated in the box.

Requirements for a Distribution of a Discrete Random Variable

1. $0 \leq P(x) \leq 1$ for all x

2. $\displaystyle\sum_{\text{all } x} P(x) = 1$

where the random variable can assume values x and $P(x)$ is the probability that the random variable is equal to x.

These requirements are equivalent to the rules of probability provided in Chapter 6. To illustrate, consider the following example.

EXAMPLE 7.1

Probability Distribution of Persons per Household

The *Statistical Abstract of the United States* is published annually. It contains a wide variety of information based on the census as well as other sources. The objective is to provide information about a variety of different aspects of the lives of the country's residents. One of the questions asks households to report the number of persons living in the household. The following table summarizes the data. Develop the probability distribution of the random variable defined as the number of persons per household.

Number of Persons	Number of Households (Millions)
1	31.1
2	38.6
3	18.8
4	16.2
5	7.2
6	2.7
7 or more	1.4
Total	116.0

SOLUTION:

The probability of each value of X, the number of persons per household, is computed as the relative frequency. We divide the frequency for each value of X by the total number of households, producing the following probability distribution.

x	P(x)
1	31.1/116.0 = .268
2	38.6/116.0 = .333
3	18.8/116.0 = .162
4	16.2/116.0 = .140
5	7.2/116.0 = .062
6	2.7/116.0 = .023
7 or more	1.4/116.0 = .012
Total	1.000

As you can see, the requirements are satisfied. Each probability lies between 0 and 1, and the total is 1.

We interpret the probabilities in the same way we did in Chapter 6. For example, if we select one household at random, the probability that it has three persons is

$$P(3) = .162$$

We can also apply the addition rule for mutually exclusive events. (The values of X are mutually exclusive; a household can have 1, 2, 3, 4, 5, 6, or 7 or more persons.) The probability that a randomly selected household has four or more persons is

$$P(X \geq 4) = P(4) + P(5) + P(6) + P(7 \text{ or more})$$
$$= .140 + .062 + .023 + .012 = .237$$

In Example 7.1, we calculated the probabilities using census information about the entire population. The next example illustrates the use of the techniques introduced in Chapter 6 to develop a probability distribution.

EXAMPLE 7.2

Probability Distribution of the Number of Sales

A mutual fund salesperson has arranged to call on three people tomorrow. Based on past experience, the salesperson knows there is a 20% chance of closing a sale on each call. Determine the probability distribution of the number of sales the salesperson will make.

SOLUTION:

We can use the probability rules and trees introduced in Section 6-3. Figure 7.1 displays the probability tree for this example. Let X = the number of sales.

FIGURE **7.1**

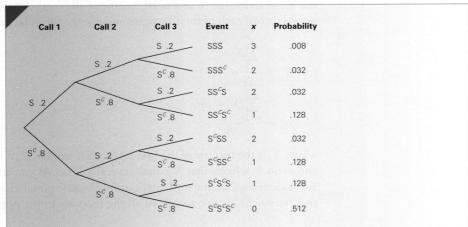

Call 1	Call 2	Call 3	Event	x	Probability
		S .2	SSS	3	.008
	S .2	S^C .8	SSS^C	2	.032
		S .2	$SS^C S$	2	.032
S .2	S^C .8	S^C .8	$SS^C S^C$	1	.128
		S .2	$S^C SS$	2	.032
S^C .8	S .2	S^C .8	$S^C SS^C$	1	.128
		S .2	$S^C S^C S$	1	.128
	S^C .8	S^C .8	$S^C S^C S^C$	0	.512

The tree exhibits each of the eight possible outcomes and their probabilities. We see that there is one outcome that represents no sales, and its probability is $P(0) = .512$. There are three outcomes representing one sale, each with probability .128, so we add these probabilities. Thus,

$$P(1) = .128 + .128 + .128 = 3(.128) = .384$$

The probability of two sales is computed similarly:

$$P(X) = 3(.032) = .096$$

There is one outcome where there are three sales:

$$P(3) = .008$$

The probability distribution of X is listed in Table 7.1.

TABLE **7.1** Probability Distribution of the Number of Sales in Example 7.2

x	P(x)
0	.512
1	.384
2	.096
3	.008

7-1b Probability Distributions and Populations

The importance of probability distributions derives from their use as representatives of populations. In Example 7.1, the distribution provided us with information about the population of numbers of persons per household. In Example 7.2, the population was the number of sales made in three calls by the salesperson. And as we noted before, statistical inference deals with inference about populations.

7-1c Describing the Population/Probability Distribution

In Chapter 4, we showed how to calculate the mean, variance, and standard deviation of a population. The formulas we provided were based on knowing the value of the random variable for each member of the population. For example, if we want to know the mean and variance of annual income of all North American blue-collar workers, we would record each of their incomes and use the formulas introduced in Chapter 4:

$$\mu = \frac{\sum_{i=1}^{N} X_i}{N}$$

$$\sigma^2 = \frac{\sum_{i=1}^{N} (X_i - \mu)^2}{N}$$

where X_1 is the income of the first blue-collar worker, X_2 is the second worker's income, and so on. It is likely that N equals several million. As you can appreciate, these formulas are seldom used in practical applications because populations are so large. It is unlikely that we would be able to record all the incomes in the population of North American blue-collar workers. However, probability distributions often represent populations. Rather than record each of the many observations in a population, we list the values and their associated probabilities as we did in deriving the probability distribution of the number of persons per household in Example 7.1 and the number of successes in three calls by the mutual fund salesperson. These can be used to compute the mean and variance of the population.

The population mean is the weighted average of all of its values. The weights are the probabilities. This parameter is also called the **expected value** of X and is represented by $E(X)$.

Population Mean

$$E(X) = \mu = \sum_{\text{all } x} x P(x)$$

The population variance is calculated similarly. It is the weighted average of the squared deviations from the mean.

Population Variance

$$V(X) = \sigma^2 = \sum_{\text{all } x} (x - \mu)^2 P(x)$$

There is a shortcut calculation that simplifies the calculations for the population variance. This formula is not an approximation; it will yield the same value as the formula above.

Shortcut Calculation for Population Variance

$$V(X) = \sigma^2 = \sum_{\text{all } x} x^2 P(x) - \mu^2$$

The standard deviation is defined as in Chapter 4.

Population Standard Deviation

$$\sigma = \sqrt{\sigma^2}$$

EXAMPLE 7.3

Describing the Population of the Number of Persons per Household

Find the mean, variance, and standard deviation for the population of the number of persons per household Example 7.1.

SOLUTION:

For this example, we will assume that the last category is exactly seven persons. The mean of X is

$$E(X) = \mu = \sum_{\text{all } x} xP(x) = 1P(1) + 2P(2) + 3P(3) + 4P(4) + 5P(5) + 6P(6) + 7P(7)$$
$$= 1(.268) + 2(.333) + 3(.162) + 4(.140) + 5(.062) + 6(.023) + 7(.012)$$
$$= 2.512$$

Notice that the random variable can assume integer values only, yet the mean is 2.513. The variance of X is

$$V(X) = \sigma^2 = \sum_{\text{all } x} (x - \mu)^2 P(x)$$
$$= (1 - 2.512)^2(.268) + (2 - 2.512)^2(.333) + (3 - 2.512)^2(.162)$$
$$+ (4 - 2.512)^2(.140) + (5 - 2.512)^2(.062) + (6 - 2.512)^2(.023)$$
$$+ (7 - 2.512)^2(.012)$$
$$= 1.954$$

To demonstrate the shortcut method, we'll use it to recompute the variance:

$$\sum_{\text{all } x} x^2 P(x) = 1^2(.268) + 2^2(.333) + 3^2(.162) + 4^2(.140) + 5^2(.062)$$
$$+ 6^2(.023) + 7^2(.012) = 8.264$$

and

$$\mu = 2.512$$

Thus,

$$\sigma^2 = \sum_{\text{all } x} x^2 P(x) - \mu^2 = 8.264 - (2.512)^2 = 1.954$$

The standard deviation is

$$\sigma = \sqrt{\sigma^2} = \sqrt{1.954} = 1.398$$

These parameters tell us that the mean and standard deviation of the number of persons per household are 2.512 and 1.398, respectively.

7-1d Laws of Expected Value and Variance

As you will discover, we often create new variables that are functions of other random variables. The formulas given in the next two boxes allow us to quickly determine the expected value and variance of these new variables. In the notation used here, X is the random variable and c is a constant.

Laws of Expected Value

1. $E(c) = c$
2. $E(X + c) = E(X) + c$
3. $E(cX) = cE(X)$

Laws of Variance

1. $V(c) = 0$
2. $V(X + c) = V(X)$
3. $V(cX) = c^2 V(X)$

EXAMPLE 7.4

Describing the Population of Monthly Profits

The monthly sales at a computer store have a mean of $25,000 and a standard deviation of $4,000. Profits are calculated by multiplying sales by 30% and subtracting fixed costs of $6,000. Find the mean and standard deviation of monthly profits.

SOLUTION:

We can describe the relationship between profits and sales by the following equation:

$$\text{Profit} = .30(\text{Sales}) - 6,000$$

The expected or mean profit is

$$E(\text{Profit}) = E[.30(\text{Sales}) - 6,000]$$

Applying the second law of expected value, we produce

$$E(\text{Profit}) = E[.30(\text{Sales})] - 6,000$$

Applying law 3 yields

$$E(\text{Profit}) = .30E(\text{Sales}) - 6,000 = .30(25,000) - 6,000 - 1,500$$

Thus, the mean monthly profit is $1,500.

The variance is

$$V(\text{Profit}) = V[.30(\text{Sales}) - 6,000]$$

The second law of variance states that

$$V(\text{Profit}) = V[.30(\text{Sales})]$$

and law 3 yields

$$V(\text{Profit}) = (.30)^2 V(\text{Sales}) = .09(4,000)^2 = 1,440,000$$

Thus, the standard deviation of monthly profits is

$$\sigma_{\text{Profit}} = \sqrt{1,440,000} = \$1,200$$

EXERCISES

7.1 The number of accidents that occur on a busy stretch of highway is a random variable.
   a. What are the possible values of this random variable?
   b. Are the values countable? Explain.
   c. Is there a finite number of values? Explain.
   d. Is the random variable discrete or continuous? Explain.

7.2 The distance a car travels on a tank of gasoline is a random variable.
   a. What are the possible values of this random variable?
   b. Are the values countable? Explain.
   c. Is there a finite number of values? Explain.
   d. Is the random variable discrete or continuous? Explain.

7.3 The amount of money students earn on their summer jobs is a random variable.
   a. What are the possible values of this random variable?
   b. Are the values countable? Explain.
   c. Is there a finite number of values? Explain.
   d. Is the random variable discrete or continuous? Explain.

7.4 The mark on a statistics exam that consists of 100 multiple-choice questions is a random variable.
   a. What are the possible values of this random variable?
   b. Are the values countable? Explain.
   c. Is there a finite number of values? Explain.
   d. Is the random variable discrete or continuous? Explain.

7.5 Determine whether each of the following is a valid probability distribution.

a.
x	0	1	2	3
$P(x)$	.1	.3	.4	.1

b.
x	5	−6	10	0
$P(x)$	.01	.01	.01	.97

c.
x	14	12	−7	13
$P(x)$	.25	.46	.04	.24

7.6 Let X be the random variable designating the number of spots that turn up when a balanced die is rolled. What is the probability distribution of X?

7.7 In a recent census, the number of color televisions per household was recorded.

Number of color televisions	0	1	2	3	4	5
Number of households (thousands)	1,218	32,379	37,961	19,387	7,714	2,842

   a. Develop the probability distribution of X, the number of color televisions per household.
   b. Determine the following probabilities.

   $$P(X \le 2)$$
   $$P(X > 2)$$
   $$P(X \ge 4)$$

7.8 Using historical records, the personnel manager of a plant has determined the probability distribution of X, the number of employees absent per day. It is

x	0	1	2	3	4	5	6	7
$P(x)$	.005	.025	.310	.340	.220	.080	.019	.001

   a. Find the following probabilities.

   $$P(2 \le X \le 5)$$
   $$P(X > 5)$$
   $$P(X < 4)$$

   b. Calculate the mean of the population.
   c. Calculate the standard deviation of the population.

7.9 Second-year business students at many universities are required to take 10 one-semester courses. The number of courses that result in a grade of A is a discrete random variable. Suppose that each value of this random variable has the same probability. Determine the probability distribution.

7.10 The random variable X has the following probability distribution.

x	−3	2	6	8
$P(x)$	.2	.3	.4	.1

Find the following probabilities.
   a. $P(X > 0)$
   b. $P(X \ge 1)$
   c. $P(X \ge 2)$
   d. $P(2 \le X \le 5)$

7.11 An Internet pharmacy advertises that it will deliver the over-the-counter products that customers purchase in 3–6 days. The manager of the company wanted to be more precise in its advertising. Accordingly, she recorded the number of days it took to deliver to customers. From the data, the following probability distribution was developed.

Number of days	0	1	2	3	4	5	6	7	8
Probability	0	0	.01	.04	.28	.42	.21	.02	.02

a. What is the probability that a delivery will be made within the advertised 3- to 6-day period?
b. What is the probability that a delivery will be late?
c. What is the probability that a delivery will be early?

7.12 A gambler believes that a strategy called "doubling up" is an effective way to gamble. The method requires the gambler to double the stake after each loss. Thus, if the initial bet is $1, after losing he will double the bet until he wins. After a win, he resorts back to a $1 bet. The result is that he will net $1 for every win. The problem, however, is that he will eventually run out of money or bump up against the table limit. Suppose that for a certain game the probability of winning is .5 and that losing six in a row will result in bankrupting the gambler. Find the probability of losing six times in a row.

7.13 The probability that a university graduate will be offered no jobs within a month of graduation is estimated to be 5%. The probability of receiving one, two, and three job offers has similarly been estimated to be 43%, 31%, and 21%, respectively. Determine the following probabilities.
a. A graduate is offered fewer than two jobs.
b. A graduate is offered more than one job.

7.14 Use a probability tree to compute the probability of the following events when flipping two fair coins.
a. Heads on the first coin and heads on the second coin
b. Heads on the first coin and tails on the second coin
c. Tails on the first coin and heads on the second coin
d. Tails on the first coin and tails on the second coin

7.15 Refer to Exercise 7.14. Find the following probabilities.
a. No heads
b. One head
c. Two heads
d. At least one head

7.16 Draw a probability tree to describe the flipping of three fair coins.

7.17 Refer to Exercise 7.16. Find the following probabilities.
a. Two heads
b. One head
c. At least one head
d. At least two heads

7.18 The random variable X has the following distribution.

x	−2	5	7	8
P(x)	.59	.15	.25	.01

a. Find the mean and variance for the probability distribution below.
b. Determine the probability distribution of Y where $Y = 5X$.
c. Use the probability distribution in part (b) to compute the mean and variance of Y.
d. Use the laws of expected value and variance to find the expected value and variance of Y from the parameters of X.

7.19 We are given the following probability distribution.

x	0	1	2	3
P(x)	.4	.3	.2	.1

a. Calculate the mean, variance, and standard deviation.
b. Suppose that $Y = 3X + 2$. For each value of X, determine the value of Y. What is the probability distribution of Y?
c. Calculate the mean, variance, and standard deviation from the probability distribution of Y.
d. Use the laws of expected value and variance to calculate the mean, variance, and standard deviation of Y from the mean, variance, and standard deviation of X. Compare your answers in parts (c) and (d). Are they the same (except for rounding)?

7.20 The number of pizzas delivered to university students each month is a random variable with the following probability distribution.

x	0	1	2	3
P(x)	.1	.3	.4	.2

a. Find the probability that a student has received delivery of two or more pizzas this month.
b. Determine the mean and variance of the number of pizzas delivered to students each month.

7.21 Refer to Exercise 7.20. If the pizzeria makes a profit of $3 per pizza, determine the mean and variance of the profits per student.

7.22 After watching a number of children playing games at a video arcade, a statistics practitioner estimated the following probability distribution of X, the number of games per visit.

x	1	2	3	4	5	6	7
P(x)	.05	.15	.15	.25	.20	.10	.10

a. What is the probability that a child will play more than four games?
b. What is the probability that a child will play at least two games?

7.23 Refer to Exercise 7.22. Determine the mean and variance of the number of games played.

7.24 Refer to Exercise 7.23. Suppose that each game costs the player 25 cents. Use the laws of expected value and variance to determine the expected value and variance of the amount of money the arcade takes in.

7.25 Refer to Exercise 7.22.
   a. Determine the probability distribution of the amount of money the arcade takes in per child.
   b. Use the probability distribution to calculate the mean and variance of the amount of money the arcade takes in.
   c. Compare the answers in part (b) with those of Exercise 7.24. Are they identical (except for rounding errors)?

7.26 A survey of Amazon.com shoppers reveals the following probability distribution of the number of books purchased per hit.

x	0	1	2	3	4	5	6	7
P(x)	.35	.25	.20	.08	.06	.03	.02	.01

   a. What is the probability that an Amazon.com visitor will buy four books?
   b. What is the probability that an Amazon.com visitor will buy eight books?
   c. What is the probability that an Amazon.com visitor will not buy any books?
   d. What is the probability that an Amazon.com visitor will buy at least one book?

7.27 A university librarian produced the following probability distribution of the number of times a student walks into the library over the period of a semester.

x	0	5	10	15	20	25	30	40	50	75	100
P(x)	.22	.29	.12	.09	.08	.05	.04	.04	.03	.03	.01

Find the following probabilities.
   a. $P(X \geq 20)$
   b. $P(X = 60)$
   c. $P(X > 50)$
   d. $P(X > 100)$

7.28 After analyzing the frequency with which cross-country skiers participate in their sport, a sportswriter created the following probability distribution for $X =$ number of times per year cross-country skiers ski.

x	0	1	2	3	4	5	6	7	8
P(x)	.04	.09	.19	.21	.16	.12	.08	.06	.05

Find the following.
   a. $P(3)$
   b. $P(X \geq 5)$
   c. $P(5 \leq X \leq 7)$

7.29 The natural remedy Echinacea is reputed to boost the immune system, which will reduce the number of flu and colds. A 6-month study was undertaken to determine whether the remedy works. From this study, the following probability distribution of the number of respiratory infections per year (X) for Echinacea users was produced.

x	0	1	2	3	4
P(x)	.45	.31	.17	.06	.01

Find the following probabilities.
   a. An Echinacea user has more than one infection per year.
   b. An Echinacea user has no infections per year.
   c. An Echinacea user has between one and three (inclusive) infections per year.

7.30 A shopping mall estimates the probability distribution of the number of stores mall customers actually enter, as shown in the table.

x	0	1	2	3	4	5	6
P(x)	.04	.19	.22	.28	.12	.09	.06

Find the mean and standard deviation of the number of stores entered.

7.31 Refer to Exercise 7.30. Suppose that, on average, customers spend 10 minutes in each store they enter. Find the mean and standard deviation of the total amount of time customers spend in stores.

7.32 When parking a car in a downtown parking lot, drivers pay according to the number of hours or parts thereof. The probability distribution of the number of hours cars are parked has been estimated as follows.

x	1	2	3	4	5	6	7	8
P(x)	.24	.18	.13	.10	.07	.04	.04	.20

Find the mean and standard deviation of the number of hours cars are parked in the lot.

7.33 Refer to Exercise 7.32. The cost of parking is $2.50 per hour. Calculate the mean and standard deviation of the amount of revenue each car generates.

7.34 You have been given the choice of receiving $500 in cash or receiving a gold coin that has a face value of $100. However, the actual value of the gold coin depends on its gold content. You are told that the coin has a 40% probability of being worth $400, a 30% probability of being worth $900, and a 30% probability of being worth its face value. Basing your decision on expected value, should you choose the coin?

7.35 The manager of a bookstore recorded the number of customers who arrive at a checkout counter every 5 minutes from which the following distribution was calculated. Calculate the mean and standard deviation of the random variable.

x	0	1	2	3	4
$P(x)$	.10	.20	.25	.25	.20

7.36 The owner of a small firm has just purchased a personal computer, which she expects will serve her for the next 2 years. The owner has been told that she "must" buy a surge suppressor to provide protection for her new hardware against possible surges or variations in the electrical current, which have the capacity to damage the computer. The amount of damage to the computer depends on the strength of the surge. It has been estimated that there is a 1% chance of incurring $400 damage, a 2% chance of incurring $200 damage, and 10% chance of $100 damage. An inexpensive suppressor, which would provide protection for only one surge can be purchased. How much should the owner be willing to pay if she makes decisions on the basis of expected value?

7.37 It cost one dollar to buy a lottery ticket, which has five prizes. The prizes and the probability that a player wins the prize are listed here. Calculate the expected value of the payoff.

Prize ($)	1 million	200,000	50,000
Probability	1/10 million	1/1 million	1/500,000

Prize ($)	10,000	1,000
Probability	1/50,000	1/10,000

7.38 After an analysis of incoming faxes, the manager of an accounting firm determined the probability distribution of the number of pages per facsimile as follows:

x	1	2	3	4	5	6	7
$P(x)$	.05	.12	.20	.30	.15	.10	.08

Compute the mean and variance of the number of pages per fax.

7.39 Refer to Exercise 7.38. Further analysis by the manager revealed that the cost of processing each page of a fax is $.25. Determine the mean and variance of the cost per fax.

7.40 To examine the effectiveness of its four annual advertising promotions, a mail-order company has sent a questionnaire to each of its customers, asking how many of the previous year's promotions prompted orders that would not otherwise have been made. The table lists the probabilities that were derived from the questionnaire, where X is the random variable representing the number of promotions that prompted orders. If we assume that overall customer behavior next year will be the same as last year, what is the expected number of promotions that each customer will take advantage of next year by ordering goods that otherwise would not be purchased?

x	0	1	2	3	4
$P(x)$	.10	.25	.40	.20	.05

7.41 Refer to Exercise 7.40. A previous analysis of historical records found that the mean value of orders for promotional goods is $20, with the company earning a gross profit of 20% on each order. Calculate the expected value of the profit contribution next year.

7.42 An expensive restaurant conducted an analysis of the number of people at tables from which the probability distribution was developed.

x	1	2	3	4	5	6	7	8
$P(x)$	.03	.32	.05	.28	.04	.15	.03	.10

If one table is selected at random determine the probability of the following events.
a. Table has more than 4 people
b. Table has fewer than 5 people
c. Table has between 4 and 6 people (inclusive)

7.43 Refer to Exercise 7.42. Compute the mean, variance, and standard deviation of the population.

7.44 At a private golf course known for its excellent golfers a statistician quizzed the members to determine how many holes in one each made in their lifetime. From his work the following probability distribution of the number of career holes in one.

x	0	1	2	3	4	5	6	7 or more
$P(x)$	.78	.10	.05	.03	.02	.01	.01	0

One member was selected at random. Find the following probabilities.
a. The member has more than 3 holes in one.
a. The member never had a hole in one.
b. The member has between 3 and 5 (inclusive) holes in one.

7-2 / BIVARIATE DISTRIBUTIONS

Thus far, we have dealt with the distribution of a *single* variable. However, there are circumstances where we need to know about the relationship between two variables. Recall that we have addressed this problem statistically in Chapter 3 by drawing the scatter diagram and in Chapter 4 by calculating the covariance and the coefficient of correlation. In this section, we present the **bivariate distribution**, which provides probabilities of combinations of two variables. Incidentally, when we need to distinguish between the bivariate distributions and the distributions of one variable, we'll refer to the latter as *univariate* distributions.

The joint probability that two variables will assume the values x and y is denoted $P(x, y)$. A bivariate (or joint) probability distribution of X and Y is a table or formula that lists the joint probabilities for all pairs of values of x and y. As was the case with univariate distributions, the joint probability must satisfy two requirements.

Requirements for a Discrete Bivariate Distribution

1. $0 \leq P(x, y) \leq 1$ for all pairs of values (x, y)

2. $\displaystyle\sum_{\text{all } x} \sum_{\text{all } y} P(x, y) = 1$

EXAMPLE 7.5

Bivariate Distribution of the Number of House Sales

Xavier and Yvette are real estate agents. Let X denote the number of houses that Xavier will sell in a month and let Y denote the number of houses Yvette will sell in a month. An analysis of their past monthly performances has the following joint probabilities.

Bivariate Probability Distribution

		X		
		0	**1**	**2**
	0	.12	.42	.06
Y	**1**	.21	.06	.03
	2	.07	.02	.01

We interpret these joint probabilities in the same way we did in Chapter 6. For example, the probability that Xavier sells 0 houses and Yvette sells 1 house in the month is $P(0, 1) = .21$.

7-2a Marginal Probabilities

As we did in Chapter 6, we can calculate the marginal probabilities by summing across rows or down columns.

Marginal Probability Distribution of X in Example 7.5

$$P(X = 0) = P(0, 0) + P(0, 1) + P(0, 2) = .12 + .21 + .07 = .4$$
$$P(X = 1) = P(1, 0) + P(1, 1) + P(1, 2) = .42 + .06 + .02 = .5$$
$$P(X = 2) = P(2, 0) + P(2, 1) + P(2, 2) = .06 + .03 + .01 = .1$$

The marginal probability distribution of X is

x	**P(x)**
0	.4
1	.5
2	.1

Marginal Probability Distribution of Y in Example 7.5

$$P(Y = 0) = P(0, 0) + P(1, 0) + P(2, 0) = .12 + .42 + .06 = .6$$
$$P(Y = 1) = P(0, 1) + P(1, 1) + P(2, 1) = .21 + .06 + .03 = .3$$
$$P(Y = 2) = P(0, 2) + P(1, 2) + P(2, 2) = .07 + .02 + .01 = .1$$

The marginal probability distribution of Y is

y	$P(y)$
0	.6
1	.3
2	.1

Notice that both marginal probability distributions meet the requirements; the probabilities are between 0 and 1, and they add to 1.

7-2b Describing the Bivariate Distribution

As we did with the univariate distribution, we often describe the bivariate distribution by computing the mean, variance, and standard deviation of each variable. We do so by utilizing the marginal probabilities.

Expected Value, Variance, and Standard Deviation of X in Example 7.5

$$E(X) = \mu_X = \sum xP(x) = 0(.4) + 1(.5) + 2(.1) = .7$$

$$V(X) = \sigma_X^2 = \sum (x - \mu_X)^2 P(x) = (0 - .7)^2(.4) + (1 - .7)^2(.5) + (2 - .7)^2(.1) = .41$$

$$\sigma_X = \sqrt{\sigma_X^2} = \sqrt{.41} = .64$$

Expected Value, Variance, and Standard Deviation of Y in Example 7.5

$$E(Y) = \mu_Y = \sum yP(y) = 0(.6) + 1(.3) + 2(.1) = .5$$

$$V(Y) = \sigma_Y^2 = \sum (y - \mu_Y)^2 P(y) = (0 - .5)^2(.6) + (1 - .5)^2(.3) + (2 - .5)^2(.1) = .45$$

$$\sigma_Y = \sqrt{\sigma_Y^2} = \sqrt{.45} = .67$$

There are two more parameters we can and need to compute. Both deal with the relationship between the two variables. They are the covariance and the coefficient of correlation. Recall that both were introduced in Chapter 4, where the formulas were based on the assumption that we knew each of the N observations of the population. In this chapter, we compute parameters like the covariance and the coefficient of correlation from the bivariate distribution.

Covariance

The covariance of two discrete variables is defined as

$$\text{COV}(X, Y) = \sigma_{xy} = \sum_{\text{all } x} \sum_{\text{all } y} (x - \mu_X)(y - \mu_Y)P(x, y)$$

Notice that we multiply the deviations from the mean for both X and Y and then multiply by the joint probability.

The calculations are simplified by the following shortcut method.

Shortcut Calculation for Covariance

$$\text{COV}(X,Y) = \sigma_{xy} = \sum_{\text{all }x} \sum_{\text{all }y} xyP(x,y) - \mu_X\mu_Y$$

The coefficient of correlation is calculated in the same way as in Chapter 4.

Coefficient of Correlation

$$\rho = \frac{\sigma_{xy}}{\sigma_x\sigma_y}$$

EXAMPLE 7.6

Describing the Bivariate Distribution

Compute the covariance and the coefficient of correlation between the numbers of houses sold by the two agents in Example 7.5.

SOLUTION:

We start by computing the covariance.

$$\sigma_{xy} = \sum_{\text{all }x} \sum_{\text{all }y} (x - \mu_X)(y - \mu_Y)P(x,y)$$
$$= (0 - .7)(0 - .5)(.12) + (1 - .7)(0 - .5)(.42) + (2 - .7)(0 - .5)(.06)$$
$$+ (0 - .7)(1 - .5)(.21) + (1 - .7)(1 - .5)(.06) + (2 - .7)(1 - .5)(.03)$$
$$+ (0 - .7)(2 - .5)(.07) + (1 - .7)(2 - .5)(.02) + (2 - .7)(2 - .5)(.01)$$
$$= -.15$$

As we did with the shortcut method for the variance, we'll recalculate the covariance using its shortcut method.

$$\sum_{\text{all }x} \sum_{\text{all }y} xyP(x,y) = (0)(0)(.12) + (1)(0)(.42) + (2)(0)(.06)$$
$$+ (0)(1)(.21) + (1)(1)(.06) + (2)(1)(.03)$$
$$+ (0)(2)(.07) + (1)(2)(.02) + (2)(2)(.01)$$
$$= .2$$

Using the expected values computed above, we find

$$\sigma_{xy} = \sum_{\text{all }x} \sum_{\text{all }y} xyP(x,y) - \mu_X\mu_Y = .2 - (.7)(.5) = -.15$$

We also computed the standard deviations above. Thus, the coefficient of correlation is

$$\rho = \frac{\sigma_{xy}}{\sigma_X \sigma_Y} = \frac{-.15}{(.64)(.67)} = -.35$$

There is a weak negative relationship between the two variables: the number of houses Xavier will sell in a month (X) and the number of houses Yvette will sell in a month (Y).

7-2c Sum of Two Variables

The bivariate distribution allows us to develop the probability distribution of any combination of the two variables. Of particular interest to us is the sum of two variables. The analysis of this type of distribution leads to an important statistical application in finance, which we present in the next section.

To see how to develop the probability distribution of the sum of two variables from their bivariate distribution, return to Example 7.5. The sum of the two variables X and Y is the total number of houses sold per month. The possible values of $X + Y$ are 0, 1, 2, 3, and 4. The probability that $X + Y = 2$, for example, is obtained by summing the joint probabilities of all pairs of values of X and Y that sum to 2:

$$P(X + Y = 2) = P(0, 2) + P(1, 1) + P(2, 0) = .07 + .06 + .06 = .19$$

We calculate the probabilities of the other values of $X + Y$ similarly, producing the following table.

Probability Distribution of $X + Y$ in Example 7.5

$x + y$	0	1	2	3	4
$P(x + y)$	.12	.63	.19	.05	.01

We can compute the expected value, variance, and standard deviation of $X + Y$ in the usual way.

$$E(X + Y) = 0(.12) + 1(.63) + 2(.19) + 3(.05) + 4(.01) = 1.2$$

$$V(X + Y) = \sigma_{X+Y}^2 = (0 - 1.2)^2(.12) + (1 - 1.2)^2(.63) + (2 - 1.2)^2(.19)$$
$$+ (3 - 1.2)^2(.05) + (4 - 1.2)^2(.01)$$
$$= .56$$

$$\sigma_{X+Y} = \sqrt{.56} = .75$$

We can derive a number of laws that enable us to compute the expected value and variance of the sum of two variables.

Laws of Expected Value and Variance of the Sum of Two Variables

1. $E(X + Y) = E(X) + E(Y)$
2. $V(X + Y) = V(X) + V(Y) + 2\text{COV}(X, Y)$

If X and Y are independent, $\text{COV}(X, Y) = 0$ and thus $V(X + Y) = V(X) + V(Y)$.

EXAMPLE 7.7

Describing the Population of the Total Number of House Sales

Use the rules of expected value and variance of the sum of two variables to calculate the mean and variance of the total number of houses sold per month in Example 7.5.

SOLUTION:

Using law 1 we compute the expected value of $X + Y$:

$$E(X + Y) = E(X) + E(Y) = .7 + .5 = 1.2$$

which is the same value we produced directly from the probability distribution of $X + Y$. We apply law 3 to determine the variance:

$$V(X + Y) = V(X) + V(Y) + 2COV(X, Y) = .41 + .45 + 2(-.15) = .56$$

This is the same value we obtained from the probability distribution of $X + Y$.

We will encounter several applications where we need the laws of expected value and variance for the sum of two variables. Additionally, we will demonstrate an important application in operations management where we need the formulas for the expected value and variance of the sum of more than two variables. See Exercises 7.57–7.60.

EXERCISES

7.45 The following table lists the bivariate distribution of X and Y.

| | x | |
y	1	2
1	.5	.1
2	.1	.3

a. Find the marginal probability distribution of X.
b. Find the marginal probability distribution of Y.
c. Compute the mean and variance of X.
d. Compute the mean and variance of Y.

7.46 Refer to Exercise 7.45. Compute the covariance and the coefficient of correlation.

7.47 Refer to Exercise 7.45. Use the laws of expected value and variance of the sum of two variables to compute the mean and variance of $X + Y$.

7.48 Refer to Exercise 7.45.
a. Determine the distribution of $X + Y$.
b. Determine the mean and variance of $X + Y$.
c. Does your answer to part (b) equal the answer to Exercise 7.45?

7.49 The bivariate distribution of X and Y is described here.

| | x | |
y	1	2
1	.28	.42
2	.12	.18

a. Find the marginal probability distribution of X.
b. Find the marginal probability distribution of Y.
c. Compute the mean and variance of X.
d. Compute the mean and variance of Y.

7.50 Refer to Exercise 7.49. Compute the covariance and the coefficient of correlation.

7.51 Refer to Exercise 7.49. Use the laws of expected value and variance of the sum of two variables to compute the mean and variance of $X + Y$.

7.52 Refer to Exercise 7.49.
a. Determine the distribution of $X + Y$.
b. Determine the mean and variance of $X + Y$.
c. Does your answer to part (b) equal the answer to Exercise 7.49?

7.53 The joint probability distribution of X and Y is shown in the following table.

		x	
y	1	2	3
1	.42	.12	.06
2	.28	.08	.04

a. Determine the marginal distributions of X and Y.
b. Compute the covariance and coefficient of correlation between X and Y.
c. Develop the probability distribution of $X + Y$.

7.54 The following distributions of X and of Y have been developed. If X and Y are independent, determine the joint probability distribution of X and Y.

x	0	1	2
$p(x)$	.6	.3	.1

y	1	2
$p(y)$	.7	.3

7.55 The distributions of X and of Y are described here. If X and Y are independent, determine the joint probability distribution of X and Y.

x	0	1
$p(x)$	.2	.8

y	1	2	3
$p(y)$	.2	.4	.4

7.56 After analyzing several months of sales data, the owner of an appliance store produced the following joint probability distribution of the number of refrigerators and stoves sold daily.

	Refrigerators		
Stoves	0	1	2
0	.08	.14	.12
1	.09	.17	.13
2	.05	.18	.04

a. Find the marginal probability distribution of the number of refrigerators sold daily.
b. Find the marginal probability distribution of the number of stoves sold daily.
c. Compute the mean and variance of the number of refrigerators sold daily.
d. Compute the mean and variance of the number of stoves sold daily.
e. Compute the covariance and the coefficient of correlation.

7.57 Canadians who visit the United States often buy liquor and cigarettes, which are much cheaper in the United States. However, there are limitations. Canadians visiting in the United States for more than 2 days are allowed to bring into Canada one bottle of liquor and one carton of cigarettes. A Canada customs agent has produced the following joint probability distribution of the number of bottles of liquor and the number of cartons of cigarettes imported by Canadians who have visited the United States for 2 or more days.

	Bottles of Liquor	
Cartons of Cigarettes	0	1
0	.63	.18
1	.09	.10

a. Find the marginal probability distribution of the number of bottles imported.
b. Find the marginal probability distribution of the number of cigarette cartons imported.
c. Compute the mean and variance of the number of bottles imported.
d. Compute the mean and variance of the number of cigarette cartons imported.
e. Compute the covariance and the coefficient of correlation.

7.58 Refer to Exercise 7.56. Find the following conditional probabilities.
a. $P(1 \text{ refrigerator} \mid 0 \text{ stoves})$
b. $P(0 \text{ stoves} \mid 1 \text{ refrigerator})$
c. $P(2 \text{ refrigerators} \mid 2 \text{ stoves})$

7.59 A fire inspector has conducted an extensive analysis of the number of smoke detectors and the number of carbon monoxide detectors in the homes in a large city. The analysis led to the creation of the following bivariate probability distribution.

	Carbon Monoxide Detectors		
Smoke Detectors	0	1	2
0	.42	.03	0
1	.15	.07	.01
2	.06	.10	.15
3	.05	.04	.02

a. What proportion of homes have no carbon monoxide detectors and two smoke detectors?
b. What proportion of homes have two carbon monoxide detectors and no smoke detectors?
c. What proportion of homes have at least one carbon monoxide detector and at least one smoke detector?

7.60 Refer to Exercise 7.59. (*Hint:* The answers to parts (a), (b), and (c) are all different.)
a. What proportions of homes have one carbon monoxide detector and two smoke detectors?
b. What proportion of homes with one carbon monoxide detector have two smoke detectors?
c. What proportion of homes with two smoke detectors have one carbon monoxide detector?

7.61 Refer to Exercise 7.59.
   a. Determine the probability distribution of carbon monoxide detectors.
   b. What is the mean, variance, and standard deviation of the number of carbon monoxide detectors?

7.62 Refer to Exercise 7.59.
   a. Determine the probability distribution of smoke detectors.
   b. What is the mean, variance, and standard deviation of the number of smoke detectors?

7.63 After watching several seasons of soccer a statistician produced the following bivariate distribution of scores.

Visiting team	Home team			
	0	1	2	3
0	.14	.11	.09	.10
1	.12	.10	.05	.02
2	.09	.07	.04	.01
3	.03	.02	.01	0

   a. What is the probability that the home team wins?
   b. What is the probability of a tie?
   c. What is the probability that the visiting team wins?

7.64 Refer to Exercise 7.63.
   a. Determine the probability distribution of the home team scores.
   b. Calculate the mean, variance, and standard deviation of the home team scores.

7.65 Refer to Exercise 7.63.
   a. Determine the probability distribution of the visiting team scores.
   b. Calculate the mean, variance, and standard deviation of the visiting team scores.

7.66 Refer to Exercise 7.63.
   a. Determine the probability distribution of the total scores for both teams.
   b. Calculate the mean, variance, and standard deviation of the total scores for both teams.
   c. Calculate the covariance and coefficient of correlation of the two variables.

APPLICATIONS in OPERATIONS MANAGEMENT

PERT/CPM

The Project Evaluation and Review Technique (**PERT**) and the Critical Path Method (**CPM**) are related management-science techniques that help operations managers control the activities and the amount of time it takes to complete a project. Both techniques are based on the order in which the activities must be performed. For example, in building a house the excavation of the foundation must precede the pouring of the foundation, which in turn precedes the framing. A **path** is defined as a sequence of related activities that leads from the starting point to the completion of a project. In most projects, there are several paths with differing amounts of time needed for their completion. The longest path is called the **critical path** because any delay in the activities along this path will result in a delay in the completion of the project. In some versions of PERT/CPM, the activity completion times are fixed and the chief task of the operations manager is to determine the critical path. In other versions, each activity's completion time is considered to be a random variable, where the mean and variance can be estimated. By extending the laws of expected value and variance for the sum of two variables to more than two variables, we produce the following, where $X_1, X_2, \ldots, X_k$ are the times for the completion of activities $1, 2, \ldots, k$, respectively. These times are independent random variables.

Laws of Expected Value and Variance for the Sum of More than Two Independent Variables

1. $E(X_1 + X_2 + \cdots + X_k) = E(X_1) + E(X_2) + \cdots + E(X_k)$
2. $V(X_1 + X_2 + \cdots + X_k) = V(X_1) + V(X_2) + g + V(X_k)$

Using these laws, we can then produce the expected value and variance for the complete project. Exercises 7.67–7.70 address this problem.

7.67 There are four activities along the critical path for a project. The expected values and variances of the completion times of the activities are listed here. Determine the expected value and variance of the completion time of the project.

Activity	Expected Completion Time (Days) activity	Variance
1	18	8
2	12	5
3	27	6
4	8	2

7.68 The operations manager of a large plant wishes to overhaul a machine. After conducting a PERT/CPM analysis he has developed the following critical path.

1. Disassemble machine
2. Determine parts that need replacing
3. Find needed parts in inventory
4. Reassemble machine
5. Test machine

He has estimated the mean (in minutes) and variances of the completion times as follows.

Activity	Mean	Variance
1	35	8
2	20	5
3	20	4
4	50	12
5	20	2

Determine the mean and variance of the completion time of the project.

7.69 In preparing to launch a new product, a marketing manager has determined the critical path for her department. The activities and the mean and variance of the completion time for each activity along the critical path are shown in the accompanying table. Determine the mean and variance of the completion time of the project.

Activity	Expected Completion Time (Days) activity	Variance
Develop survey questionnaire	8	2
Pretest the questionnaire	14	5
Revise the questionnaire	5	1
Hire survey company	3	1
Conduct survey analyze data	30	8
Analyze data	30	10
Prepare report	10	3

(Continued)

7.70 A professor of business statistics is about to begin work on a new research project. Because his time is quite limited, he has developed a PERT/CPM critical path, which consists of the following activities:

1. Conduct a search for relevant research articles.
2. Write a proposal for a research grant.
3. Perform the analysis.
4. Write the article and send to journal.
5. Wait for reviews.
6. Revise on the basis of the reviews and resubmit.

The mean (in days) and variance of the completion times are as follows:

Activity	Mean	Variance
1	10	9
2	3	0
3	30	100
4	5	1
5	100	400
6	20	64

Compute the mean and variance of the completion time of the entire project.

7-3 (OPTIONAL) APPLICATIONS IN FINANCE: PORTFOLIO DIVERSIFICATION AND ASSET ALLOCATION

In this section, we introduce an important application in finance that is based on the previous section.

In Example 3.2 (page 54) we described what we look for in a histogram of investment returns to gauge the risk associated with that investment. Most investors tend to be risk averse, which means that they prefer to have lower risk associated with their investments. One of the ways in which financial analysts lower the risk that is associated with the stock market is through **diversification**. This strategy was first mathematically developed by Harry Markowitz in 1952. His model paved the way for the development of modern portfolio theory (MPT), which is the concept underlying mutual funds (see page 161).

To illustrate the basics of portfolio diversification, consider an investor who forms a portfolio, consisting of only two stocks, by investing $4,000 in one stock and $6,000 in a second stock. Suppose that the results after 1 year are as listed here. (We've previously defined return on investment. See Applications in Finance: Return on Investment on page 53.)

One-Year Results

Stock	Initial Investment ($)	Value of Investment After One Year ($)	Rate of Return on Investment
1	4,000	5,000	$R_1 = .25$ (25%)
2	6,000	5,400	$R_2 = -.10$ (−10%)
Total	10,000	10,400	$R_p = .04$ (4%)

Another way of calculating the portfolio return R_p is to compute the weighted average of the individual stock returns R_1 and R_2, where the weights w_1 and w_2 are the proportions of the initial $10,000 invested in stocks 1 and 2, respectively. In this illustration,

$w_1 = .4$ and $w_2 = .6$. (Note that w_1 and w_2 must always sum to 1 because the two stocks constitute the entire portfolio.) The weighted average of the two returns is

$$R_p = w_1R_1 + w_2R_2$$
$$= (.4)(.25) + (.6)(-.10) = .04$$

This is how portfolio returns are calculated. However, when the initial investments are made, the investor does not know what the returns will be. In fact, the returns are random variables. We are interested in determining the expected value and variance of the portfolio. The formulas in the box were derived from the laws of expected value and variance introduced in the two previous sections.

Mean and Variance of a Portfolio of Two Stocks

$$E(R_p) = w_1E(R_1) + w_2E(R_2)$$
$$V(R_p) = w_1^2V(R_1) + w_2^2V(R_2) + 2w_1w_2\text{COV}(R_1, R_2)$$
$$= w_1^2\sigma_1^2 + w_2^2\sigma_2^2 + 2w_1w_2\rho\sigma_1\sigma_2$$

where w_1 and w_2 are the proportions or weights of investments 1 and 2, $E(R_1)$ and $E(R_2)$ are their expected values, σ_1 and σ_2 are their standard deviations, $\text{COV}(R_1, R_2)$ is the covariance, and ρ is the coefficient of correlation.

(Recall that $\rho = \dfrac{\text{COV}(R_1, R_2)}{\sigma_1\sigma_2}$, which means that $\text{COV}(R_1, R_2) = \rho\sigma_1\sigma_2$.)

EXAMPLE 7.8

Describing the Population of the Returns on a Portfolio

An investor has decided to form a portfolio by putting 25% of his money into McDonald's stock and 75% into Cisco Systems stock. The investor assumes that the expected returns will be 8% and 15%, respectively, and that the standard deviations will be 12% and 22%, respectively.

    a. Find the expected return on the portfolio.

    b. Compute the standard deviation of the returns on the portfolio assuming that

        i. the two stocks' returns are perfectly positively correlated.

        ii. the coefficient of correlation is .5.

        iii. the two stocks' returns are uncorrelated.

SOLUTION:

    a. The expected values of the two stocks are

$$E(R_1) = .08 \quad \text{and} \quad E(R_2) = .15$$

The weights are $w_1 = .25$ and $w_2 = .75$.

Thus,

$$E(R_p) = w_1E(R_1) + w_2E(R_2) = .25(.08) + .75(.15) = .1325$$

b. The standard deviations are

$$\sigma_1 = .12 \text{ and } \sigma_2 = .22$$

Thus,

$$
\begin{aligned}
V(R_p) &= w_1^2\sigma_1^2 + w_2^2\sigma_2^2 + 2w_1 w_2 \rho \sigma_1 \sigma_2 \\
&= (.25^2)(.12^2) + (.75^2)(.22^2) + 2(.25)(.75)\rho(.12)(.22) \\
&= .0281 + .0099\rho
\end{aligned}
$$

When $\rho = 1$

$$V(R_p) = .0281 + .0099(1) = .0380$$

Standard deviation $= \sqrt{V(R_p)} = \sqrt{.0380} = .1949$

When $\rho = .5$

$$V(R_p) = .0281 + .0099(.5) = .0331$$

Standard deviation $= \sqrt{V(R_p)} = \sqrt{.0331} = .1819$

When $\rho = 0$

$$V(R_p) = .0281 + .0099(0) = .0281$$

Standard deviation $= \sqrt{V(R_p)} = \sqrt{.0281} = .1676$

Notice that the variance and standard deviation of the portfolio returns decrease as the coefficient of correlation decreases.

7-3a Portfolio Diversification in Practice

The formulas introduced in this section require that we know the expected values, variances, and covariance (or coefficient of correlation) of the investments we're interested in. The question arises, How do we determine these parameters? (Incidentally, this question is rarely addressed in finance textbooks!) The most common procedure is to estimate the parameters from historical data, using sample statistics.

7-3b Portfolios with More Than Two Stocks

We can extend the formulas that describe the mean and variance of the returns of a portfolio of two stocks to a portfolio of any number of stocks.

Mean and Variance of a Portfolio of k Stocks

$$E(R_p) = \sum_{i=1}^{k} w_i E(R_i)$$

$$V(R_p) = \sum_{i=1}^{k} w_i^2 \rho_i^2 + 2\sum_{i=1}^{k}\sum_{j=i+1}^{k} w_i w_j \text{COV}(R_i, R_j)$$

where R_i is the return of the ith stock, w_i is the proportion of the portfolio invested in stock i, and k is the number of stocks in the portfolio.

When k is greater than 2, the calculations can be tedious and time consuming. For example, when $k = 3$, we need to know the values of the three weights, three expected values, three variances, and three covariances. When $k = 4$, there are four expected values, four variances, and six covariances. [The number of covariances required in general is $k(k - 1)/2$.] To assist you, we have created an Excel worksheet to perform the computations when $k = 2, 3$, or 4. To demonstrate, we'll return to the problem described in this chapter's introduction.

Investing to Maximize Returns and Minimize Risk: Solution

Because of the large number of calculations, we will solve this problem using only Excel. From the file, we compute the means of each stock's returns.

Excel Means

	A	B	C	D
1	0.02370	0.02147	0.01591	0.02315

Next we compute the variance-covariance matrix. (The commands are the same as those described in Chapter 4—simply include all the columns of the returns of the investments you wish to include in the portfolio.)

Excel Variance-Covariance Matrix

	A	B	C	D	E
		HD	NKE	CNR	EXPE
1					
2	HD	0.00221			
3	NKE	0.00051	0.00362		
4	CNR	0.00083	0.00067	0.00203	
5	EXPE	0.00063	0.00088	0.00111	0.01057

Notice that the variances of the returns are listed on the diagonal. Thus, for example, the variance of the 60 monthly returns of Nike is .00362. The covariances appear below the diagonal. The covariance between the returns of Home Depot and Nike is .00051.

The means and the variance-covariance matrix are copied to the spreadsheet using the commands described here. The weights are typed producing the accompanying output.

Excel Worksheet: Portfolio Diversification-Plan 1

	A	B	C	D	E	F
1	Portfolio of 4 Stocks					
2			HD	NKE	CNR	EXPE
3	Variance-Covariance Matrix	HD	0.00221			
4		NKE	0.00051	0.00362		
5		CNR	0.00083	0.00067	0.00203	
6		EXPE	0.00063	0.00088	0.00111	0.01057
7						
8	Expected Returns		0.02370	0.02147	0.01591	0.02315
9						
10	Weights		0.25000	0.25000	0.25000	0.25000
11						
12	Portfolio Return					
13	Expected Value	0.02106				
14	Variance	0.00173				
15	Standard Deviation	0.04158				

The expected return on the portfolio is .0211 and the variance is .0017.

(Continued)

INSTRUCTIONS

1. Open the file containing the returns. In this example, open file **Ch7:\ Xm07-00**
2. Compute the means of the columns containing the returns of the stocks in the portfolio.
3. Using the commands described in Chapter 4 (page 119) compute the variance-covariance matrix.
4. Open the **Portfolio Diversification** workbook. Use the tab to select the **4 Stocks** worksheet. DO NOT CHANGE ANY CELLS THAT APPEAR IN BOLD PRINT. DO NOT SAVE ANY WORKSHEETS.
5. Copy the means into cells C8 to F8. (Use **Copy, Paste Special** with **Values and number formats**.)
6. Copy the variance-covariance matrix (including row and column labels) into columns B, C, D, E, and F.
7. Type the weights into cells C10 to F10.

The mean, variance, and standard deviation of the portfolio will be printed. Use similar commands for 2 stock and 3 stock portfolios.

The results for Plan 2 are:

	A	B
12	Portfolio Return	
13	Expected Value	0.02070
14	Variance	0.00265
15	Standard Deviation	0.05145

The results for Plan 3 are:

	A	B
12	Portfolio Return	
13	Expected Value	0.02209
14	Variance	0.00201
15	Standard Deviation	0.04489

Plan 1 has the second smallest expected value and the smallest variance. Plan 2 has the smallest expected value and the second largest variance. Plan 3's expected value is the largest and the second largest variance. If the investor is like most investors, she would select Plan 1 because of its lower risk. Other more daring investors may choose Plan 3 to take advantage of its higher expected value.

In this example, we showed how to compute the expected return, variance, and standard deviation from a sample of returns on the investments for any combination of weights. (We illustrated the process with three sets of weights.) It is possible to determine the "optimal" weights that minimize risk for a given expected value or maximize expected return for a given standard deviation. This is an extremely important function of financial analysts and investment advisors. Solutions can be determined using a management science technique called *linear programming*, a subject taught by most schools of business and faculties of management.

EXERCISES

7.71 Describe what happens to the expected value and standard deviation of the portfolio returns when the coefficient of correlation decreases.

7.72 A portfolio is composed of two stocks. The proportion of each stock, their expected values, and standard deviations are listed next.

Stock	1	2
Proportion of portfolio	.30	.70
Mean	.12	.25
Standard deviation	.02	.15

For each of the following coefficients of correlation, calculate the expected value and standard deviation of the portfolio:

a. $\rho = .5$
b. $\rho = .2$
c. $\rho = 0$

7.73 An investor is given the following information about the returns on two stocks:

Stock	1	2
Mean	.09	.13
Standard deviation	.15	.21

a. If he is most interested in maximizing his returns, which stock should he choose?

b. If he is most interested in minimizing his risk, which stock should he choose?

7.74 Refer to Exercise 7.73. Compute the expected value and standard deviation of the portfolio composed of 60% stock 1 and 40% stock 2. The coefficient of correlation is .4.

7.75 Refer to Exercise 7.73. Compute the expected value and standard deviation of the portfolio composed of 30% stock 1 and 70% stock 2.

The following exercises require the use of a computer.

Xr07-NYSE *We have recorded the monthly returns for 26 of the 30 stocks that compose the Dow Jones Industrials 30 (These stocks are on the New York Stock Exchange; the other four are on the NASDAQ.) for the period January 2011 to December 2015:*

3M (MMM), American Express (AXP), Boeing (BA), Caterpillar (CAT), Chevron (CVX), Coca-Cola (KO), Disney (DIS), Du Pont (DD), Exxon (XOM), General Electric (GE), Goldman Sacks (GS), Home Depot (HD), International Business Machines (IBM), Johnson & Johnson (JNJ), JP Morgan Chase (JPM), McDonald's (MCD), Merck (MRK), Nike (NKE), Pfizer (PFE), Proctor & Gamble (PG), Travelers (TRV), United Technologies (UTX), United Health (UNH), Verizon Communications (VZ), Visa (V), Wal-Mart Stores (WMT).

For Exercises 7.76 to 7.82, calculate the mean and standard deviation of the portfolio. The proportions invested in each stock are shown.

7.76 a. American Express (AXP): 20%, Goldman Sachs (GS): 30%, JP Morgan Chase (JPM): 50%

b. AXP: 20%, GS: 60%, JPM: 20%

c. AXP: 50%, GS: 30%, JPM: 20%

d. Which portfolio would an investor who likes to gamble choose? Explain.

e. Which portfolio would a risk-averse investor choose? Explain.

7.77 a. 3M (MMM): 25%, Boeing (BA): 25%, Home Depot (HD): 25%, Travelers (TRV): 25%

b. MMM: 10%, HD: 50%, IBM: 20%, TRV: 20%

c. MMM: 30%, HD: 20%, IBM: 10%, TRV: 40%

d. Explain why the choice of which portfolio to invest in is obvious.

7.78 a. Chevron (CVX): 25%, Coca Cola (KO): 25%, Disney (DIS): 25%, Exxon Mobil (XOM): 25%

b. CVX: 10%, KO: 20%, DIS: 30%, XOM: 40%

c. CVX: 55%, KO: 15%, DIS: 15%, XOM: 15%

d. Explain why the choice of which portfolio to not invest in is obvious.

7.79 a. General Electric (GE): 25%, Johnson & Johnson (JNJ): 25%, McDonald's (MCD): 25%, Merck (MRK): 25%

b. GE: 5%, JNJ: 30%, MCD: 40%, MRK: 25%

c. GE: 10%, JNJ: 50%, MCD: 30%, MRK: 10%

d. Which portfolio would a gambler choose? Explain.

e. Which portfolio would a risk-averse investor choose? Explain.

7.80 a. Coca Cola (KO): 40%, Pfizer (PFE): 20%, Verizon Communications (VZ): 40%

b. KO: 60% PFE: 20%, (VZ): 20%

c. KO: 10%, PFE: 30%, VZ: 60%

d. Which portfolio would a gambler choose? Explain.

e. Which portfolio would a risk-averse investor choose? Explain.

7.81 a. Chevron (CVX): 25%, du Pont (DD): 25%, Procter & Gamble (PG): 25%, Travelers (TRV): 25%

b. CVX: 50%, DD: 20%, PG: 15%, TRV: 15%

c. CVX: 10%, DD: 20%, PG: 30%, TRV: 40%

d. Explain why the choice of which portfolio to invest in is obvious.

7.82 a. United Health (UNH): 25%, United Technologies (UTX): 25%, Verizon (VZ): 25%, Walmart (WMT): 25%

b. UNH: 10%, UTX: 20%, VZ: 30%, WMT: 40%

c. UNH: 40%, UTX: 30%, VZ: 20%, WMT: 10%

d. Which portfolio would a gambler choose? Explain.

e. Which portfolio would a risk-averse investor choose? Explain.

7.83 Refer to Exercise 7.82.

a. Try to find weights that produce an expected value of at least .0100.

b. Using trial and error find weights that produce an expected value of at least .0100 and the smallest variance.

7.84 Refer to Exercises 7.82 and 7.83.

a. Compute the expected value and variance of this portfolio:
UNH: .191, UTX: .213, VZ: .370, WMT: .226

b. Can you do better? That is, can you find a portfolio whose expected value is greater than or equal to .0100 and whose variance is less than the one you calculated in part (a)? (*Hint:* Don't spend too much time at this. You won't be able to do better. If you want to learn how we produced the portfolio above, take a course that teaches linear and nonlinear programming.)

XR07-TSE *Monthly returns for the following selected stocks on the Toronto Stock Exchange were recorded for the years 2011 to 2015:*

Agnico Eagle (AEM), Barrick Gold (ABX), Bombardier (BBD.B), Bell Canada Enterprises (BCE), Bank of Montreal (BMO), Bank of Nova Scotia (BNS), Canadian Imperial Bank of Commerce (CM), Canadian National Railways (CNR), Canadian Oil Sands (COS), Canadian Tire (CTC.A), Dollarama (DOL), Encana (ECA), Enbridge (ENB), Loblaw (L), Manulife Financial (MFC), Magna International (MG), Potash Corporation of Saskatchewan (POT), Power Corporation of Canada (POW), Rogers Communication (RCI.B), Royal Bank of Canada (RY), Suncor Energy (SU), Telus (T), George Weston Limited (WN)

7.85 An analyst recommends that you invest in a portfolio made up of Bank of Montreal (BMO), Bank of Nova Scotia (BNS), Canadian Imperial Bank of Commerce (CM), and Royal Bank (RY). Why would it not useful in diversification?

7.86 Refer to Exercise 7.85. Compute the correlation matrix of the returns of the four banks. Briefly describe what the correlations tell you.

For Exercises 7.87 to 7.91, calculate the mean and standard deviation of the portfolio. The proportions invested in each stock are shown in parentheses.

7.87 a. Agnico Eagle (AEM): 25%, Bell Canada Enterprises (BCE): 25%, Bank of Montreal (BMO: 25%, Dollarama (DOL): 25%
b. AEM: 30%, BCE: 30%, BMO: 20%, DOL: 20%
c. AEM: 40%, BCE: 15%, BMO: 15%, DOL: 30%
d. Explain why the choice of which portfolio to invest in is obvious.

7.88 a. Canadian National Railway (CNR): 10%, Enbridge (ENB): 40%, Loblaw (L): 40%, Manulife Financial (MFC): 10%
b. CNR: 50%, ENB: 30%, L: 10%, MFC: 10%
c. CNR: 70%, ENB: 10%, L: 10%, MFC: 10%
d. Which portfolio would a gambler choose? Explain.
e. Which portfolio would a risk-averse investor choose? Explain.

7.89 a. Bank of Montreal (BMO): 25%, Magna International (MG): 25%, Power (POW): 25%, Rogers Communication (RCL.B): 25%
b. BMO: 20%, MG: 60%, POW: 10%, RCL.B: 10%
c. BMO: 10%, MG: 20%, POW: 30%, RCL.B: 40%
d. Which portfolio would a gambler choose? Explain.
e. Which portfolio would a risk-averse investor choose? Explain.

7.90 a. Bank of Nova Scotia (BNS): 25%, Sun Energy (SU): 25%, Telus (T): 25%, George Weston (WN): 25%

b. BNS: 10%, SU: 10%, T: 70%, WN: 10%
c. BNS: 10%, SU: 50%, T: 10%, WN: 30%
d. Which portfolio would a gambler choose? Explain.
e. Which portfolio would a risk-averse investor choose? Explain.

7.91 a. Agnico Eagle (AEM): 25%, Canadian Imperial Bank of Commerce (CM): 25%, Canadian Tire (CTC.A): 25%, Royal Bank (RY): 25%
b. AEM: 10%, CM: 20%, CTC.A: 60%, RY: 10%
c. AEM: 10%, CM: 10%, CTC.A: 10%, RY: 70%
d. Which portfolio would a gambler choose? Explain.
e. Which portfolio would a risk-averse investor choose? Explain.

7.92 You have decided to invest in a portfolio made up of these four stocks: Bank of Nova Scotia (BNS), Canadian National Railway (CNR), Canadian Tire (CTC.A), and Magna International (MG). You have also decided that the expected monthly return should exceed .0100. Try several sets of proportions (remember they must add to 1.0) to see if you can find the portfolio with the smallest variance.

7.93 Refer to Exercise 7.92.
a. Compute the expected value and variance of the portfolio described next. BNS: 44.0%, CNR: 27.5%, CTC.A: 21.9%, MG: 6.6%
b. Can you do better? That is, can you find a portfolio whose expected value is greater than or equal to 1% and whose variance is less than the one you calculated in part (a)? (*Hint:* Don't spend too much time at this. You won't be able to do better. If you want to learn how we produced the portfolio above, take a course that teaches linear and nonlinear programming.

XR07-NASDAQ *We calculated the returns on the following selected stocks on the NASDAQ Exchange for the period January 2011 to December 2015:*

Adobe Systems (ADBE), Amazon (AMZN), Apple (AAPL), Bed Bath & Beyond (BBBY), Cisco Systems (CSCO), Comcast (CMCSA), Costco Wholesale (COST), Dollar Tree (DLTR), Expedia (EXPE), Garmin (GRMN), Intel (INTC), Microsoft (MSFT), Netflix (NFLX), Oracle (ORCL), ScanDisk (SNDK), Sirius XM Radio (SIRI), Staples (SPLS), Starbucks (SBUX)

For Exercises 7.94 to 7.97 calculate the mean and standard deviation of the portfolio. The proportions invested in each stock are shown in parentheses.

7.94 a. Adobe (ADBE): 25%, Cisco Systems (CSCO): 25%, Comcast (CMCSA): 25%, Garmin (GRMN): 25%
b. ADBE: 40%, CSCO: 10%, CMCSA: 40%, GRMN: 10%

c. ADBE: 10%, CSCO: 20%, CMCSA: 30%, GRMN: 40%

d. Which portfolio would a gambler choose? Explain.

e. Which portfolio would a risk-averse investor choose? Explain.

7.95 a. Amazon (AMZN): 25%, Apple (AAPL): 25%, Bed Bath and Beyond (BBBY): 25%, Dollar Tree (DLTR): 25%

b. AMZN: 10%, AAPL: 40%, BBBY: 10%, DLTR: 40%

c. AMZN: 40%, AAPL: 30%, BBBY: 20%, DLTR: 10%

d. Which portfolio would a gambler choose? Explain.

e. Which portfolio would a risk-averse investor choose? Explain.

7.96 a. Costco (COST): 25%, Dollar Tree (DLTR): 25%, Expedia (EXPE): 25%, ScanDisk (SNDK): 25%

b. COST: 10%, DLTR: 20%, EXPE: 30%, SNDK: 40%

c. COST: 10%, DLTR: 10%, EXPE: 70%, SNDK: 10%

d. Which portfolio would a gambler choose? Explain.

e. Which portfolio would a risk-averse investor choose? Explain.

7.97 a. Intel (INTC): 25%, Oracle (ORCL): 25%, Sirius (SIRI): 25%, Starbucks (SBUX): 25%

b. INTC: 10%, ORCL: 10%, SIRI: 10%, SBUX: 70%

c. INTC: 40%, ORCL: 30%, SIRI: 20%, SBUX: 10%

d. Which portfolio would a gambler choose? Explain.

e. Which portfolio would a risk-averse investor choose? Explain.

7.98 Refer to Exercise 7.97. Suppose you want the expected value to be at least 2%. Try several sets of proportions (remember they must add to 1.0) to see if you can find the portfolio with the smallest variance.

7.99 Refer to Exercise 7.97.

a. Compute the expected value and variance of the portfolio described next.
INTC: 20.9%, ORCL: 7.4%, SIRI: 11.9%, SBUX: 59.8%

b. Can you do better? That is, can you find a portfolio whose expected value is greater than or equal to 2% and whose variance is less than the one you calculated in part (a)? (*Hint:* Don't spend too much time at this. You won't be able to do better. If you want to learn how we produced the portfolio above, take a course that teaches linear and nonlinear programming.)

7-4 / BINOMIAL DISTRIBUTION

Now that we've introduced probability distributions in general, we need to introduce several specific probability distributions. In this section, we present the *binomial distribution*.

The binomial distribution is the result of a *binomial experiment*, which has the following properties.

Binomial Experiment

1. The **binomial experiment** consists of a fixed number of trials. We represent the number of trials by n.

2. Each trial has two possible outcomes. We label one outcome a *success*, and the other a *failure*.

3. The probability of success is p. The probability of failure is $1 - p$.

4. The trials are independent, which means that the outcome of one trial does not affect the outcomes of any other trials.

If properties 2, 3, and 4 are satisfied, we say that each trial is a **Bernoulli process**. Adding property 1 yields the binomial experiment. The random variable of a binomial experiment is defined as the number of successes in the n trials. It is called the **binomial random variable**. Here are several examples of binomial experiments.

1. Flip a coin 10 times. The two outcomes per trial are heads and tails. The terms *success* and *failure* are arbitrary. We can label either outcome success. However, generally, we call success anything we're looking for. For example, if we were betting on heads, we would label heads a success. If the coin is fair, the probability of heads is 50%. Thus, $p = .5$. Finally, we can see that the trials are independent because the outcome of one coin flip cannot possibly affect the outcomes of other flips.

2. Draw five cards out of a shuffled deck. We can label as success whatever card we seek. For example, if we wish to know the probability of receiving five clubs, a club is labeled a success. On the first draw, the probability of a club is $13/52 = .25$. However, if we draw a second card without replacing the first card and shuffling, the trials are not independent. To see why, suppose that the first draw is a club. If we draw again without replacement the probability of drawing a second club is $12/51$, which is not .25. In this experiment, the trials are *not* independent.[*] Hence, this is not a binomial experiment. However, if we replace the card and shuffle before drawing again, the experiment is binomial. Note that in most card games, we do not replace the card, and as a result the experiment is not binomial.

3. A political survey asks 1,500 voters who they intend to vote for in an approaching election. In most elections in the United States, there are only two candidates, the Republican and Democratic nominees. Thus, we have two outcomes per trial. The trials are independent because the choice of one voter does not affect the choice of other voters. In Canada, and in other countries with parliamentary systems of government, there are usually several candidates in the race. However, we can label a vote for our favored candidate (or the party that is paying us to do the survey) a success and all the others are failures.

As you will discover, the third example is a very common application of statistical inference. The actual value of p is unknown, and the job of the statistics practitioner is to estimate its value. By understanding the probability distribution that uses p, we will be able to develop the statistical tools to estimate p.

7-4a Binomial Random Variable

The binomial random variable is the number of successes in the experiment's n trials. It can take on values $0, 1, 2, \ldots, n$. Thus, the random variable is discrete. To proceed, we must be capable of calculating the probability associated with each value.

Using a probability tree, we draw a series of branches as depicted in Figure 7.2. The stages represent the outcomes for each of the n trials. At each stage, there are two branches representing success and failure. To calculate the probability that there are X successes in n trials, we note that for each success in the sequence, we must multiply by p. And if there are X successes, there must be $n - X$ failures. For each failure in the sequence, we multiply by $1 - p$. Thus, the probability for each sequence of branches that represent x successes and $n - x$ failures has probability

$$p^x(1 - p)^{n-x}$$

---

[*]The hypergeometric distribution described in the online appendix of the same name is used to calculate probabilities in such cases.

EXERCISES

7.100 Given a binomial random variable with $n = 10$ and $p = .3$, use the formula to find the following probabilities.
a. $P(X = 3)$
b. $P(X = 5)$
c. $P(X = 8)$

7.101 Repeat Exercise 7.100 using Table 1 in Appendix B.

7.102 Repeat Exercise 7.100 using Excel.

7.103 Given a binomial random variable with $n = 6$ and $p = .2$, use the formula to find the following probabilities.
a. $P(X = 2)$
b. $P(X = 3)$
c. $P(X = 5)$

7.104 Repeat Exercise 7.103 using Table 1 in Appendix B.

7.105 Repeat Exercise 7.103 using Excel.

7.106 Suppose X is a binomial random variable with $n = 25$ and $p = .7$. Use Table 1 to find the following.
a. $P(X = 18)$
b. $P(X = 15)$
c. $P(X \leq 20)$
d. $P(X \geq 16)$

7.107 Repeat Exercise 7.106 using Excel.

7.108 A sign on the gas pumps of a chain of gasoline stations encourages customers to have their oil checked with the claim that one out of four cars needs to have oil added. If this is true, what is the probability of the following events?
a. One out of the next four cars needs oil
b. Two out of the next eight cars need oil
c. Three out of the next 12 cars need oil

7.109 The leading brand of dishwasher detergent has a 30% market share. A sample of 25 dishwasher detergent customers was taken.
a. What is the probability that 10 or fewer customers chose the leading brand?
b. What is the probability that 11 or more customers chose the leading brand?
c. What is the probability that 10 customers chose the leading brand?

7.110 A certain type of tomato seed germinates 90% of the time. A backyard farmer planted 25 seeds.
a. What is the probability that exactly 20 germinate?
b. What is the probability that 20 or more germinate?
c. What is the probability that 24 or fewer germinate?
d. What is the expected number of seeds that germinate?

7.111 According to the American Academy of Cosmetic Dentistry, 75% of adults believe that an unattractive smile hurts career success. Suppose that 25 adults are randomly selected.
a. What is the probability that 15 or more of them would agree with the claim?
b. What is the probability that less than 14 would agree?
c. What is the probability that 15 would agree?

7.112 A student majoring in accounting is trying to decide on the number of firms to which he should apply. Given his work experience and grades, he can expect to receive a job offer from 70% of the firms to which he applies. The student decides to apply to only four firms. Determine the probability distribution. That is calculate the probability for each of the values 0, 1, 2, 3, and 4.

7.113 According to a Gallup poll 27% of American adults have confidence in banks. Suppose that you interview 5 Americans adults at random.
a. What is the probability that 2 or fewer have confidence in banks?
b. What is the probability that no one had confidence in banks?
c. What is the probability that 3 or more have confidence in banks?

7.114 According to a Pew Research Center survey 30% of graduates who had student loans are delinquent (90 or more days behind in their payments. Suppose that a survey of 10 such graduates is taken.
a. What is the probability that 3 are delinquent?
b. What is the probability that 3 or more are delinquent?

7.115 Dermatologists strongly recommend that people who are exposed to sunlight should either be covered up or put on sunscreen. Suppose that at a Florida condominium pool only a quarter of residents sit around the pool in the sun with no sunscreen.
a. What is the probability that in a random sample of 10 condo residents 3 or fewer have no sunscreen?
b. What is the expected number of residents who do not use sunscreen in a random sample of 100?

7.116 A statistics practitioner working for major league baseball determined the probability that the hitter will be out on ground balls is .75. In a game where there are 20 ground balls, find the probability that all of them were outs.

7.117 In a recent survey the Pew Research Center asked graduates of private universities whether they were satisfied with their current job and 72% said they were. Suppose you take a sample of four private university graduates and ask each whether they are satisfied with their current jobs.
   a. What is the probability that all four say they are satisfied?
   b. What is the probability that two say they are satisfied?
   c. Determine the expected number of people who are satisfied.

7.118 According to a recent Gallop poll only 29% of American adults said they were satisfied with the way things are going in the United States. Suppose you randomly select 10 American adults and ask each whether they are satisfied with the way things are going in the United States.
   a. What is the probability that three or fewer are satisfied?
   b. What is the probability that none are satisfied?
   c. What are the expected number of people in the sample who are satisfied?

Exercises 7.119 to 7.126 are best solved with a computer.

7.119 The probability of winning a game of craps (a dice-throwing game played in casinos) is 244/495.
   a. What is the probability of winning 5 or more times in 10 games?
   b. What is the probability of winning in 50 or more times in 100 games?

7.120 In the game of blackjack as played in casinos in Las Vegas, Atlantic City, and Niagara Falls, as well as in many other cities, the dealer has the advantage. Most players do not play very well. As a result, the probability that the average player wins a hand is about 45%. Find the probability that an average player wins.
   a. Twice in 5 hands.
   b. Ten or more times in 25 hands.

7.121 Several books teach blackjack players the "basic strategy," which increases the probability of winning any hand to 50%. Repeat Exercise 7.102, assuming the player plays the basic strategy.

7.122 The best way of winning at blackjack is to "case the deck," which involves counting 10s, non-10s, and aces. For card counters, the probability of winning a hand may increase to 52%. Repeat Exercise 7.102 for a card counter.

7.123 In the game of roulette, a steel ball is rolled onto a wheel that contains 18 red, 18 black, and 2 green slots. If the ball is rolled 25 times, find the probabilities of the following events.
   a. The ball falls into the green slots two or more times.
   b. The ball does not fall into the green slots.
   c. The ball falls into black slots 15 or more times.
   d. The ball falls into red slots 10 or fewer times.

7.124 According to a Gallup Poll 52% of American adults think that protecting the environment should be given priority over developing U.S. energy supplies. Thirty-six percent think that developing energy supplies is more important, and 6% believe the two are equally important. The rest had no opinion. Suppose that a sample of 100 American adults is quizzed on the subject. What is the probability of the following events?
   a. Fifty or more think that protecting the environment should be given priority.
   b. Thirty or fewer think that developing energy supplies is more important.
   c. Five or fewer have no opinion.

7.125 In a *Bon Appetit* poll, 38% of people said that chocolate was their favorite flavor of ice cream. A sample of 20 people was asked to name their favorite flavor of ice cream. What is the probability that half or more of them prefer chocolate?

7.126 The statistics practitioner in Exercise 7.116 also determined that if a batter hits a line drive, the probability of an out is 23%. Determine the following probabilities.
   a. In a game with 10 line drives, at least 5 are outs.
   b. In a game with 25 line drives, there are 5 outs or less.

7.127 In a recent Gallup poll 53% of American adults believed that Congress is doing a poor or bad job. Suppose that you randomly choose 100 American adults and ask their opinion about Congress.
   a. Determine the probability that more than half say that Congress is doing a poor or bad job.
   b. Compute the probability more than 60% say that congress is doing a poor or bad job.
   c. What is the expected number of American adults in your sample who would say that Congress is doing a poor or bad job?

7-5 / POISSON DISTRIBUTION

Another useful discrete probability distribution is the **Poisson distribution**, named after its French creator. Like the binomial random variable, the **Poisson random variable** is the number of occurrences of events, which we'll continue to call *successes*. The

RANDOM VARIABLES AND DISCRETE PROBABILITY DISTRIBUTIONS   233

difference between the two random variables is that a binomial random variable is the number of successes in a set number of trials, whereas a Poisson random variable is the number of successes in an interval of time or specific region of space. Here are several examples of Poisson random variables.

1. The number of cars arriving at a service station in 1 hour. (The interval of time is 1 hour.)

2. The number of flaws in a bolt of cloth. (The specific region is a bolt of cloth.)

3. The number of accidents in 1 day on a particular stretch of highway. (The interval is defined by both time, 1 day, and space, the particular stretch of highway.)

The Poisson experiment is described in the box.

Poisson Experiment

A **Poisson experiment** is characterized by the following properties:

1. The number of successes that occur in any interval is independent of the number of successes that occur in any other interval.
2. The probability of a success in an interval is the same for all equal-size intervals.
3. The probability of a success in an interval is proportional to the size of the interval.
4. The probability of more than one success in an interval approaches 0 as the interval becomes smaller.

Poisson Random Variable

The **Poisson random variable** is the number of successes that occur in a period of time or an interval of space in a Poisson experiment.

There are several ways to derive the probability distribution of a Poisson random variable. However, all are beyond the mathematical level of this book. We simply provide the formula and illustrate how it is used.

Poisson Probability Distribution

The probability that a Poisson random variable assumes a value of x in a specific interval is

$$P(x) = \frac{e^{-\mu}\mu^x}{x!} \quad \text{for } x = 0, 1, 2, \ldots$$

where μ is the mean number of successes in the interval or region and e is the base of the natural logarithm (approximately 2.71828). Incidentally, the variance of a Poisson random variable is equal to its mean; that is, $\sigma^2 = \mu$.

EXAMPLE 7.12

Probability of the Number of Typographical Errors in Textbooks

A statistics instructor has observed that the number of typographical errors in new editions of textbooks varies considerably from book to book. After some analysis, he concludes that the number of errors is Poisson distributed with a mean of 1.5 per 100 pages. The instructor randomly selects 100 pages of a new book. What is the probability that there are no typographical errors?

S O L U T I O N :

We want to determine the probability that a Poisson random variable with a mean of 1.5 is equal to 0. Using the formula

$$P(x) = \frac{e^{-\mu}\mu^x}{x!}$$

and substituting $x = 0$ and $\mu = 1.5$, we get

$$P(0) = \frac{e^{-1.5}1.5^0}{0!} = \frac{(2.71828)^{-1.5}(1)}{1} = .2231$$

The probability that in the 100 pages selected there are no errors is .2231.

Notice that in Example 7.12, we wanted to find the probability of 0 typographical errors in 100 pages given a mean of 1.5 typos in 100 pages. The next example illustrates how we calculate the probability of events where the intervals or regions do not match.

EXAMPLE 7.13

Probability of the Number of Typographical Errors in 400 Pages

Refer to Example 7.12. Suppose that the instructor has just received a copy of a new statistics book. He notices that there are 400 pages.
   a. What is the probability that there are no typos?
   b. What is the probability that there are five or fewer typos?

S O L U T I O N :

The specific region that we're interested in is 400 pages. To calculate Poisson probabilities associated with this region, we must determine the mean number of typos per 400 pages. Because the mean is specified as 1.5 per 100 pages, we multiply this figure by 4 to convert to 400 pages. Thus, $\mu = 6$ typos per 400 pages.
   a. The probability of no typos is

$$P(0) = \frac{e^{-6}6^0}{0!} = \frac{(2.71828)^{-6}(1)}{1} = .002479$$

   b. We want to determine the probability that a Poisson random variable with a mean of 6 is 5 or less; that is, we want to calculate

$$P(X \le 5) = P(0) + P(1) + P(2) + P(3) + P(4) + P(5)$$

To produce this probability, we need to compute the six probabilities in the summation.

$$P(0) = .002479$$

$$P(1) = \frac{e^{-\mu}\mu^x}{x!} = \frac{e^{-6}6^1}{1!} = \frac{(2.71828)^{-6}(6)}{1} = .01487$$

$$P(2) = \frac{e^{-\mu}\mu^x}{x!} = \frac{e^{-6}6^2}{2!} = \frac{(2.71828)^{-6}(36)}{2} = .04462$$

$$P(3) = \frac{e^{-\mu}\mu^x}{x!} = \frac{e^{-6}6^3}{3!} = \frac{(2.71828)^{-6}(216)}{6} = .08924$$

$$P(4) = \frac{e^{-\mu}\mu^x}{x!} = \frac{e^{-6}6^4}{4!} = \frac{(2.71828)^{-6}(1296)}{24} = .1339$$

$$P(5) = \frac{e^{-\mu}\mu^x}{x!} = \frac{e^{-6}6^5}{5!} = \frac{(2.71828)^{-6}(7776)}{120} = .1606$$

Thus,

$$P(X \le 5) = .002479 + .01487 + .04462 + .08924 + .1339 + .1606$$
$$= .4457$$

The probability of observing 5 or fewer typos in this book is .4457.

7-5a Poisson Table

As was the case with the binomial distribution, a table is available that makes it easier to compute Poisson probabilities of individual values of x as well as cumulative and related probabilities.

Table 2 in Appendix B provides cumulative Poisson probabilities for selected values of μ. This table makes it easy to find cumulative probabilities like those in Example 7.13, part (b), where we found $P(X \le 5)$.

To do so, find $\mu = 6$ in Table 2. The values in that column are $P(X \le x)$ for $x = 0, 1, 2, \ldots, 18$ which are shown in Table 7.3.

TABLE **7.3** Cumulative Poisson Probabilities for $\mu = 6$

x	$P(X \le x)$
0	.0025
1	.0174
2	.0620
3	.1512
4	.2851
5	.4457
6	.6063
7	.7440
8	.8472
9	.9161
10	.9574
11	.9799
12	.9912
13	.9964
14	.9986
15	.9995
16	.9998
17	.9999
18	1.0000

Theoretically, a Poisson random variable has no upper limit. The table provides cumulative probabilities until the sum is 1.0000 (using four decimal places).

The first cumulative probability is $P(X \leq 0)$, which is $P(0) = .0025$. The probability we need for Example 7.13, part (b), is $P(X \leq 5) = .4457$, which is the same value we obtained manually.

Like Table 1 for binomial probabilities, Table 2 can be used to determine probabilities of the type $P(X \geq x)$. For example, to find the probability that in Example 7.13 there are 6 or more typos, we note that $P(X \leq 5) + P(X \geq 6) = 1$. Thus,

$$P(X \geq 6) = 1 - P(X \leq 5) = 1 - .4457 = .5543$$

Using Table 2 to Find the Poisson Probability $P(X \geq x)$

$$P(X \geq x) = 1 - P(X \leq [x - 1])$$

We can also use the table to determine the probability of one individual value of X. For example, to find the probability that the book contains exactly 10 typos, we note that

$$P(X \leq 10) = P(0) + P(1) + \cdots + P(9) + P(10)$$

and

$$P(X \leq 9) = P(0) + P(1) + \cdots + P(9)$$

The difference between these two cumulative probabilities is $P(10)$. Thus,

$$P(10) = P(X \leq 10) - P(X \leq 9) = .9574 - .9161 = .0413$$

Using Table 2 to Find the Poisson Probability $P(X = x)$

$$P(x) = P(X \leq x) - P(X \leq [x - 1])$$

EXCEL Function

INSTRUCTIONS

Type the following into any empty cell:

= **POISSON**([x], [μ], [True] or [False])

We calculate the probability in Example 7.12 by typing

= **POISSON**(0, 1.5, False)

For Example 7.13, we type

= **POISSON**(5, 6, True)

EXERCISES

7.128 Given a Poisson random variable with $\mu = 2$, use the formula to find the following probabilities.
  a. $P(X = 0)$
  b. $P(X = 3)$
  c. $P(X = 5)$

7.129 Given that X is a Poisson random variable with $\mu = .5$, use the formula to determine the following probabilities.
  a. $P(X = 0)$
  b. $P(X = 1)$
  c. $P(X = 2)$

7.130 The number of accidents that occur at a busy intersection is Poisson distributed with a mean of 3.5 per week. Find the probability of the following events.
  a. No accidents in one week
  b. Five or more accidents in one week
  c. One accident today

7.131 Snowfalls occur randomly and independently over the course of winter in a Minnesota city. The average is one snowfall every 3 days.
  a. What is the probability of five snowfalls in 2 weeks?
  b. Find the probability of a snowfall today.

7.132 The number of students who seek assistance with their statistics assignments is Poisson distributed with a mean of two per day.
  a. What is the probability that no students seek assistance tomorrow?
  b. Find the probability that 10 students seek assistance in a week.

7.133 Hits on a personal website occur quite infrequently. They occur randomly and independently with an average of five per week.
  a. Find the probability that the site gets 10 or more hits in a week.
  b. Determine the probability that the site gets 20 or more hits in 2 weeks.

7.134 In older cities across North America, infrastructure is deteriorating, including water lines that supply homes and businesses. A report to the Toronto city council stated that there are on average 30 water line breaks per 100 kilometers per year in the city of Toronto. Outside of Toronto, the average number of breaks is 15 per 100 kilometers per year.

  a. Find the probability that in a stretch of 100 kilometers in Toronto there are 35 or more breaks next year.
  b. Find the probability that there are 12 or fewer breaks in a stretch of 100 kilometers outside of Toronto next year.

7.135 The number of bank robberies that occur in a large North American city is Poisson distributed with a mean of 1.8 per day. Find the probabilities of the following events.
  a. Three or more bank robberies in a day.
  b. Between 10 and 15 (inclusive) robberies during a 5-day period.

7.136 Flaws in a carpet tend to occur randomly and independently at a rate of one every 200 square feet. What is the probability that a carpet that is 8 feet by 10 feet contains no flaws?

7.137 At an auction of antique furniture a statistician kept track of the number of bids for each item. After an analysis of the figures she concludes that the number of bids is Poisson distributed with a mean of 2.5.
  a. Calculate the probability that on any item the number of bids is 5 or more.
  b. Compute the probability that there are no bids.
  c. What is the probability that there are 3 bids or less?

7.138 The random variable in Exercise 7.30 was the number of stores entered by customers at a mall. Suppose that the random variable is Poisson distributed with a mean of 4.
  a. What proportion of mall customers enter 5 stores or more?
  b. Compute the probability that a customer enters 3 or fewer stores.
  c. Calculate the probability that a customer enters exactly 4 stores.

7.139 At a public library one of the librarians surveys individuals reading online newspapers. After analyzing the data she concludes that the number of newspapers read online is Poisson distributed with a mean of 5.
  a. What proportion of library patrons read 3 or fewer newspapers online?
  b. What proportion of library patrons read 6 or more newspapers online?
  c. What proportion of library patrons read 8 or fewer newspapers online?

7.140 The random variable in Exercise 7.44 was the number of holes in one by the members of a private golf course. In fact, the number of holes in one is Poisson distributed with a mean of 1.

   a. What proportion of members never have had a hole in one?

   b. What proportion have score 5 or more holes in one?

7.141 After conducting a survey of golfers a statistician concludes that the number of lost balls in a round is Poisson distributed with a mean of 2. Find the probability of the following events.

   a. A golfer loses no golf balls

   b. A golfer loses 4 or more no golf balls

   c. A golfer loses 2 or fewer golf balls

APPLICATIONS in OPERATIONS MANAGEMENT

Waiting Lines

Everyone is familiar with waiting lines. We wait in line at banks, groceries, and fast-food restaurants. There are also waiting lines in firms where trucks wait to load and unload and on assembly lines where stations wait for new parts. Management scientists have developed mathematical models that allow managers to determine the operating characteristics of waiting lines.

Some of the operating characteristics are:

The probability that there are no units in the system

The average number of units in the waiting line

The average time a unit spends in the waiting line

The probability that an arriving unit must wait for service

The Poisson probability distribution is used extensively in waiting-line (also called *queuing*) models. Many models assume that the arrival of units for service is Poisson distributed with a specific value of μ. In the next chapter, we will discuss the operating characteristics of waiting lines. Exercises 7.142–7.144 require the calculation of the probability of a number of arrivals.

7.142 The number of trucks crossing at the Ambassador Bridge connecting Detroit, Michigan, and Windsor, Ontario, is Poisson distributed with a mean of 1.5 per minute.

   a. What is the probability that in any 1-minute time span two or more trucks will cross the bridge?

   b. What is the probability that fewer than four trucks will cross the bridge over the next 4 minutes?

7.143 Cars arriving for gasoline at a particular gas station follow a Poisson distribution with a mean of 5 per hour.

   a. Determine the probability that over the next hour only one car will arrive.

   b. Compute the probability that in the next 3 hours more than 20 cars will arrive.

7.144 The number of users of an automatic banking machine is Poisson distributed. The mean number of users per 5-minute interval is 1.5. Find the probability of the following events.

   a. No users in the next 5 minutes

   b. Five or fewer users in the next 15 minutes

   c. Three or more users in the next 10 minutes

CHAPTER SUMMARY

There are two types of random variables. A **discrete random variable** is one whose values are countable. A **continuous random variable** can assume an uncountable number of values. In this chapter, we discussed discrete random variables and their **probability distributions**. We defined the **expected value**, **variance**, and **standard deviation** of a population represented by a discrete probability distribution. Also introduced in this chapter were **bivariate discrete distributions** on which an important application in finance was based. Finally, the two most important discrete distributions—the **binomial** and the **Poisson**—were presented.

IMPORTANT TERMS:

Random variable   198
Discrete random variable   199
Continuous random variable   199
Probability distribution   199
Expected value   203
Bivariate distribution   209
PERT (Project Evaluation and Review Technique)   216
CPM (Critical Path Method)   216
Path   216
Critical path   216

Diversification   218
Binomial experiment   225
Bernoulli process   226
Binomial random variable   226
Binomial probability distribution   227
Cumulative probability   228
Poisson distribution   232
Poisson random variable   232
Poisson experiment   233

SYMBOLS:

Symbol	Pronounced	Represents
$\sum\limits_{\text{all } x} x$	Sum of x for all values of x	Summation
C_x^n	n choose x	Number of combinations
$n!$	n factorial	$n(n-1)(n-2)\cdots(3)(2)(1)$
e		$2.71828\ldots$

FORMULAS:

Expected value (mean)

$$E(X) = \mu = \sum_{\text{all } x} xP(x)$$

Variance

$$V(x) = \sigma^2 = \sum_{\text{all } x} (x-\mu)^2 P(x)$$

Standard deviation

$$\sigma = \sqrt{\sigma^2}$$

Covariance

$$\text{COV}(X,Y) = \sigma_{xy} = \sum (x-\mu_x)(y-\mu_y)P(x,y)$$

Coefficient of Correlation

$$\rho = \frac{\text{COV}(X,Y)}{\sigma_x\sigma_y} = \frac{\sigma_{xy}}{\sigma_x\sigma_y}$$

Laws of expected value

1. $E(c) = c$
2. $E(X + c) = E(X) + c$
3. $E(cX) = cE(X)$

Laws of variance

1. $V(c) = 0$
2. $V(X + c) = V(X)$
3. $V(cX) = c^2V(X)$

Laws of expected value and variance of the sum of two variables

1. $E(X + Y) = E(X) + E(Y)$
2. $V(X + Y) = V(X) + V(Y) + 2\text{COV}(X,Y)$

Laws of expected value and variance for the sum of k variables, where $k \geq 2$

1. $E(X_1 + X_2 + \cdots + X_k)$
    $= E(X_1) + E(X_2) + \cdots + E(X_k)$

2. $V(X_1 + X_2 + \cdots + X_k)$
    $= V(X_1) + V(X_2) + \cdots + V(X_k)$

if the variables are independent

Mean and variance of a portfolio of two stocks

$E(Rp) = w_1 E(R_1) + w_2 E(R_2)$

$V(R_p) = w_1^2 V(R_1) + w_2^2 V(R_2)$
$\qquad + 2 w_1 w_2 \text{COV}(R_1, R_2)$
$\qquad = w_1^2 \sigma_1^2 + w_2^2 \sigma_2^2 + 2 w_1 w_2 \rho \sigma_1 \sigma_2$

Mean and variance of a portfolio of k stocks

$$E(R_p) = \sum_{i=1}^{k} w_i E(R_i)$$

$$V(R_p) = \sum_{i=1}^{k} w_i^2 \sigma_i^2 + 2 \sum_{i=1}^{k} \sum_{j=i+1}^{k} w_i w_j \text{COV}(R_i, R_j)$$

Binomial probability

$$P(X = x) = \frac{n!}{x!(n-x)!} p^x (1-p)^{n-x}$$

$$\mu = np$$
$$\sigma^2 = np(1-p)$$
$$\sigma = \sqrt{np(1-p)}$$

Poisson probability

$$P(X = x) = \frac{e^{-\mu} \mu^x}{x!}$$

COMPUTER INSTRUCTIONS:

Probability Distribution	Excel
Binomial	230
Poisson	236

CHAPTER EXERCISES

7.145 In a Gallup poll 20% of adults said that they had a great deal or quite a lot of confidence in newspapers. If we take a random sample of 25 adults and ask each whether they had a great deal or quite a lot of confidence in newspapers determine probability of each of these events.
   a. 5 or fewer have confidence
   b. 7 or more have confidence
   c. Exactly 5 have confidence

7.146 A recent Pew Center Research survey revealed that 15% of American adults have used an online dating service. Suppose a statistician randomly selected 20 American adults.
   a. What is the probability that exactly 3 used an online dating service?
   b. What is the probability that 5 or fewer used an online dating service?
   c. What is the probability that 3 or more used an online dating service?

7.147 An airline boasts that 77.4% of its flights were on time. If we select five flights at random, what is the probability that all five are on time?

7.148 The final exam in a one-term statistics course is taken in the December exam period. Students who are sick or have other legitimate reasons for missing the exam are allowed to write a deferred exam scheduled for the first week in January. A statistics professor has observed that only 2% of all students legitimately miss the December final exam. Suppose that the professor has 40 students registered this term.
   a. How many students can the professor expect to miss the December exam?
   b. What is the probability that the professor will not have to create a deferred exam?

7.149 The number of magazine subscriptions per household is represented by the following probability distribution.

Magazine subscriptions per household	0	1	2	3	4
Probability	.48	.35	.08	.05	.04

   a. Calculate the mean number of magazine subscriptions per household.
   b. Find the standard deviation.

7.150 The number of arrivals at a car wash is Poisson distributed with a mean of eight per hour.
  a. What is the probability that 10 cars will arrive in the next hour?
  b. What is the probability that more than 5 cars will arrive in the next hour?
  c. What is the probability that fewer than 12 cars will arrive in the next hour?

7.151 Hikers and other outdoor enthusiasts have a new concern, the Zika virus. Physicians are recommending that people use a mosquito repellant while in areas where mosquitoes are present. A statistician estimated that 80% of hikers would be spraying themselves with mosquito repellant. Suppose that a sample of 10 hikers is asked whether they are using repellant. Find the following probabilities.
  a. 9 or more are using repellant
  b. Exactly 8 are using repellant
  c. 7 or fewer are using repellant

7.152 Lotteries are an important income source for various governments around the world. However, the availability of lotteries and other forms of gambling have created a social problem: gambling addicts. A critic of government-controlled gambling contends that 30% tickets are gambling addicts. If we randomly select 10 people among those who report that they regularly buy lottery tickets, what is the probability that more than 5 of them are addicts?

7.153 The distribution of the number of home runs in soft-ball games is shown here.

Number of home runs	0	1	2	3	4	5
Probability	.05	.16	.41	.27	.07	.04

  a. Calculate the mean number of home runs.
  b. Find the standard deviation.

7.154 The Powerball lottery is one of the most popular lotteries in the United States. From time to time, the jackpot exceeds $100 million. As a result so many more people buy Powerball tickets that there are frequent lineups at convenience stores. A statistician interviews hundreds of people in queues and asks how many tickets each person intends to buy. He concludes that the number of tickets is a Poisson random variable with a mean of 5.
  a. What proportion of people will buy only 1 ticket?
  b. What proportion of people will buy 5 or fewer tickets?
  c. What proportion of people will buy 8 or more tickets?

7.155 Ten percent of American adults devote so much time to playing video games either on a console, computer, or cell phone that they consider themselves to be "gamers" according to a Pew Research Center report. Suppose that a random sample of 25 American adults is drawn and each is asked whether they consider themselves to be gamers. Determine the probability of the following events.
  a. 3 or more consider themselves to be gamers
  b. Exactly 2 consider themselves to be gamers
  c. 3 or fewer consider themselves to be gamers

7.156 University and college students are relatively confident about finding a job after graduation.
  According to a Gallup survey 50% of students are say now is a good time to find a quality job. Suppose you randomly select 10 students and ask about their future job prospects.
  a. What is the probability that 6 of them believe that now is a good time to find a quality job?
  b. Calculate the probability that at least 8 believe that now is a good time to find a quality job?
  c. Calculate the probability that 4 or fewer believe that now is a good time to find a quality job?

7.157 Many cell phone service providers offer family plans wherein parents who subscribe can get discounts for other family members. Suppose that the number of cell phones per family is Poisson distributed with a mean of 1.5. If one family is randomly selected calculate the following probabilities.
  a. Family has only 1 cell phone.
  b. Family has 3 or more cell phones.
  c. Family has 4 or fewer cell phones.

7.158 An auditor is preparing for a physical count of inventory as a means of verifying its value. Items counted are reconciled with a list prepared by the storeroom supervisor. In one particular firm, 20% of the items counted cannot be reconciled without reviewing invoices. The auditor selects 10 items. Find the probability that 6 or more cannot be reconciled

7.159 Shutouts in the National Hockey League occur randomly and independently at a rate of 1 every 20 games. Calculate the probability of the following events.
  a. 2 shutouts in the next 10 games
  b. 25 shutouts in 400 games
  c. A shutout in tonight's game

7.160 Most Miami Beach restaurants offer "early-bird" specials. These are lower-priced meals that are available only from 4 to 6 P.M. However, not all customers who arrive between 4 and 6 P.M. order the special. In fact, only 70% do.
  a. Find the probability that of 80 customers between 4 and 6 P.M., more than 65 order the special.
  b. What is the expected number of customers who order the special?
  c. What is the standard deviation?

7.161 According to climatologists, the long-term average for Atlantic storms is 9.6 per season (June 1 to November 30), with 6 becoming hurricanes and 2.3 becoming intense hurricanes. Find the probability of the following events.
  a. Ten or more Atlantic storms
  b. Five or fewer hurricanes
  c. Three or more intense hurricanes

7.162 Researchers at the University of Pennsylvania School of Medicine theorized that children under 2 years old who sleep in rooms with the light on have a 40% probability of becoming myopic by age 16. Suppose that researchers found 25 children who slept with the light on before they were 2.
  a. What is the probability that 10 of them will become myopic before age 16?
  b. What is the probability that fewer than 5 of them will become myopic before age 16?
  c. What is the probability that more than 15 of them will become myopic before age 16?

7.163 A pharmaceutical researcher working on a cure for baldness noticed that middle-aged men who are balding at the crown of their head have a 45% probability of suffering a heart attack over the next decade. In a sample of 100 middle-age balding men, what are the following probabilities?
  a. More than 50 will suffer a heart attack in the next decade.
  b. Fewer than 44 will suffer a heart attack in the next decade.
  c. Exactly 45 will suffer a heart attack in the next decade.

7.164 Advertising researchers have developed a theory that states that commercials that appear in violent television shows are less likely to be remembered and will thus be less effective. After examining samples of viewers who watch violent and nonviolent programs and asking them a series of five questions about the commercials, the researchers produced the following probability distributions of the number of correct answers.

Viewers of violent shows

x	0	1	2	3	4	5
P(x)	.36	.22	.20	.09	.08	.05

Viewers of nonviolent shows

x	0	1	2	3	4	5
P(x)	.15	.18	.23	.26	.10	.08

  a. Calculate the mean and standard deviation of the number of correct answers among viewers of violent television programs.
  b. Calculate the mean and standard deviation of the number of correct answers among viewers of nonviolent television programs.

7.165 In 1941 Joe DiMaggio hit in 56 consecutive games, a record that is predicted to never be broken. To see how unlikely this streak was, assume that a player batting .350 gets to bat 5 times in a game (with no walks and hit by pitch).
  a. What is the probability that the player will get at least one hit in a game?
  b. Use the probability calculated in part (a) to determine the probability that a player can hit in 56 consecutive games.

7.166 In Basketball players are awarded free throw when they are fouled. Suppose that a player has a career percentage of making free throws 80% of the time. If the player is awarded 10 free throws determine the probability of the following events.
  a. He makes all 10.
  b. He makes 8 or more.
  c. He makes 8 or fewer.

7.167 An investor hears a radio report that says in 60% of the stocks on the New York Stock Exchange increased in value. He realizes that he owns 20 stocks on the NYSE. Determine the probability of the following events.
  a. 15 or more stocks increased in value.
  b. 12 or fewer stocks increased in value.
  c. 12 stocks increased in value.

7.168 When Earth traveled through the storm of meteorites trailing the comet Tempel-Tuttle on November 17, 1998, the storm was 1,000 times as intense as the average meteor storm. Before the comet arrived, telecommunication companies worried about the potential damage that might be inflicted on the approximately 650 satellites in orbit. It was estimated that each satellite had a 1% chance of being hit, causing damage to the satellite's electronic system. One company had five satellites in orbit at the time. Determine the probability distribution of the number of the company's satellites that would be damaged.

7.169 According to a Gallup Poll conducted in 2015 only 1% of Russians approved of U.S. leadership. To evaluate whether this claim has any merit a statistician took a random sample of 100 Russians. Determine the probability of these events.
  a. No one approved of U.S. leadership.
  b. One Russian approved of U.S. leadership.
  c. Two Russians approved of U.S. leadership.

7.170 It is recommended that women age 40 and older have a mammogram annually. A recent report indicated that if a woman has annual mammograms over a 10-year period, there is a 60% probability that there will be at least one false-positive result. (A false-positive mammogram test result is one that indicates the presence of cancer when, in fact, there is no cancer.) If the annual test results are independent, what is the probability that in any one year a mammogram will produce a false-positive result? (*Hint:* Find the value of p such that the probability that a binomial random variable with n = 10 is greater than or equal to 1 is .60.)

CASE 7.1   To Bunt or Not to Bunt, That Is the Question—Part 2

Debby Wong/Shutterstock.com

In Case 6.2, we presented the probabilities of scoring at least one run and asked you to determine whether the manager should signal for the batter to sacrifice bunt. The decision was made on the basis of comparing the probability of scoring at least one run when the manager signaled for the bunt and when he signaled the batter to swing away. Another factor that should be incorporated into the decision is the *number* of runs the manager expects his team to score. In the same article referred to in Case 6.2, the author also computed the expected number of runs scored for each situation. Table 1 lists the expected number of runs in situations that are defined by the number of outs and the bases occupied.

TABLE 1 Expected Number of Runs Scored

Bases Occupied	0 Out	1 Out	2 Outs
Bases empty	.49	.27	.10
First base	.85	.52	.23
Second base	1.06	.69	.34
Third base	1.21	.82	.38
First base and second base	1.46	1.00	.48
First base and third base	1.65	1.10	.51
Second base and third base	1.94	1.50	.62
Bases loaded	2.31	1.62	.82

Assume that the manager wishes to score as many runs as possible. Using the same probabilities of the four outcomes of a bunt listed in Case 6.2, determine whether the manager should signal the batter to sacrifice bunt.

8

Wavebreakmedia/Shutterstock.com

CONTINUOUS PROBABILITY DISTRIBUTIONS

CHAPTER OUTLINE

Minimum GMAT Score to Enter Executive MBA Program

A university has just approved a new Executive MBA Program. The new director believes that to maintain the prestigious image of the business school, the new program must be seen as having high standards. Accordingly, the Faculty Council decides that one of the entrance requirements will be that applicants must score in the top 1% of Graduate Management Admission Test (GMAT) scores. The director knows that GMAT scores are normally distributed with a mean of 490 and a standard deviation of 61. The only thing she doesn't know is what the minimum GMAT score for admission should be.

After introducing the normal distribution, we will return to this question and answer it.

wavebreakmedia/Shutterstock.com

See page 261.

INTRODUCTION

This chapter completes our presentation of probability by introducing continuous random variables and their distributions. In Chapter 7, we introduced discrete probability distributions that are employed to calculate the probability associated with discrete random variables. In Section 7-4, we introduced the binomial distribution, which allows us to determine the probability that the random variable equals a particular value (the number of successes). In this way we connected the population represented by the probability distribution with a sample of nominal data. In this chapter, we introduce continuous probability distributions, which are used to calculate the probability associated with an interval variable. By doing so, we develop the link between a population and a sample of interval data.

Section 8-1 introduces probability density functions and uses the uniform density function to demonstrate how probability is calculated. In Section 8-2, we focus on the normal distribution, one of the most important distributions because of its role in the development of statistical inference. Section 8-3 introduces the exponential distribution, a distribution that has proven to be useful in various management-science applications. Finally, in Section 8-4 we introduce three additional continuous distributions. They will be used in statistical inference throughout the book.

8-1 / PROBABILITY DENSITY FUNCTIONS

A continuous random variable is one that can assume an uncountable number of values. Because this type of random variable is so different from a discrete variable, we need to treat it completely differently. First, we cannot list the possible values because there is an infinite number of them. Second, because there is an infinite number of values, the probability of each individual value is virtually 0. Consequently, we can determine the probability of only a range of values. To illustrate how this is done, consider the histogram we created for the ages of ACBL members (Example 3.1), which is depicted in Figure 8.1.

FIGURE **8.1** Histogram for Example 3.1

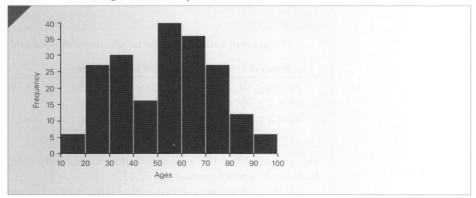

We found, for example, that the relative frequency of the interval 10–20 was 6/200. Using the relative frequency approach, we estimate that the probability that a randomly selected ACBL member will be between 10 and 20 years of age is 6/200 = .030. We can similarly estimate the probabilities of the other intervals in the histogram.

Interval	Relative Frequency
$10 \leq X \leq 20$	6/200
$20 < X \leq 30$	27/200
$30 < X \leq 40$	30/200
$40 < X \leq 50$	16/200
$50 < X \leq 60$	40/200
$60 < X \leq 70$	36/200
$70 < X \leq 80$	27/200
$80 < X \leq 90$	12/200
$90 < X \leq 100$	6/200
Total	200/200 = 1

Notice that the sum of the probabilities equals 1. To proceed, we set the values along the vertical axis so that the *area* in all the rectangles together adds to 1. We accomplish this by dividing each relative frequency by the width of the interval, which is 10. The result is a rectangle over each interval whose *area* equals the probability that the random variable will fall into that interval.

To determine probabilities of ranges other than the ones created when we drew the histogram, we apply the same approach. For example, the probability that an ACBL member is between 25 and 45 years of age is equal to the area between 25 and 45 as shown in Figure 8.2.

FIGURE 8.2 **Estimated Probability that an ACBL Member Will be Between 25 and 45**

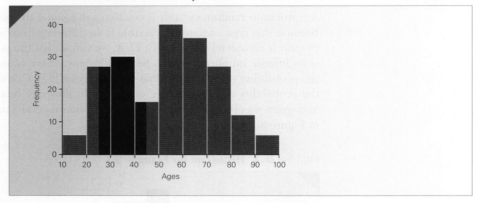

The areas in each shaded rectangle are calculated and added together as follows:

Interval	Height of Rectangle	Base Multiplied by Height
$25 < X \leq 30$	$27/(200 \times 10) = .0135$	$(30 - 25) \times .0135 = .0675$
$30 < X \leq 40$	$30/(200 \times 10) = .015$	$(40 - 30) \times .015 = .150$
$40 < X \leq 45$	$16/(200 \times 10) = .008$	$(45 - 40) \times .008 = .040$
		Total = .2575

We estimate that the probability that a randomly selected ACBL member will be between 25 and 45 years of age is .2575.

If the histogram is drawn with a large number of small intervals, we can smooth the edges of the rectangles to produce a smooth curve as shown in Figure 8.3. In many cases, it is possible to determine a function $f(x)$ that approximates the curve. The function is called a **probability density function**. Its requirements are stated in the following box.

FIGURE **8.3** **Density Function for Example 3.1**

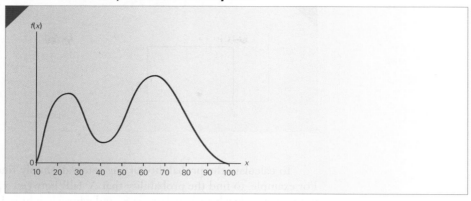

Requirements for a Probability Density Function

The following requirements apply to a probability density function $f(x)$ whose range is $a \leq x \leq b$.

1. $f(x) \geq 0$ for all x between a and b.

2. The total area under the curve between a and b is 1.0.

Integral calculus* can often be used to calculate the area under a curve. Fortunately, the probabilities corresponding to continuous probability distributions that we deal with do not require this mathematical tool. The distributions will be either simple or too complex for calculus. Let's start with the simplest continuous distribution.

8-1a Uniform Distribution

To illustrate how we find the area under the curve that describes a probability density function, consider the **uniform probability distribution**, also called the **rectangular probability distribution**.

Uniform Probability Density Function

The uniform distribution is described by the function

$$f(x) = \frac{1}{b - a} \quad \text{where } a \leq x \leq b$$

The function is graphed in Figure 8.4. You can see why the distribution is called *rectangular*.

---

*The online appendix Continuous Probability Distributions: Calculus Approach demonstrates how to use integral calculus to determine probabilities and parameters for continuous random variables.

FIGURE **8.4** **Uniform Distribution**

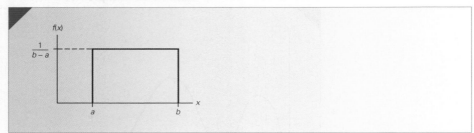

To calculate the probability of any interval, simply find the area under the curve. For example, to find the probability that X falls between x_1 and x_2 determine the area in the rectangle whose base is $x_2 - x_1$ and whose height is $1/(b - a)$. Figure 8.5 depicts the area we wish to find. As you can see, it is a rectangle and the area of a rectangle is found by multiplying the base times the height.

FIGURE **8.5** $P(x_1 < X < x_2)$

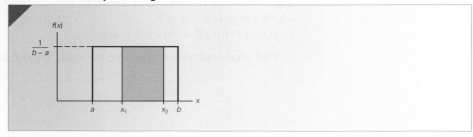

Thus,

$$P(x_1 < X < x_2) = \text{Base} \times \text{Height} = (x_2 - x_1) \times \frac{1}{b - a}$$

EXAMPLE **8.1**

Uniformly Distributed Gasoline Sales

The amount of gasoline sold daily at a service station is uniformly distributed with a minimum of 2,000 gallons and a maximum of 5,000 gallons.

    a. Find the probability that daily sales will fall between 2,500 and 3,000 gallons.

    b. What is the probability that the service station will sell at least 4,000 gallons?

    c. What is the probability that the station will sell exactly 2,500 gallons?

SOLUTION:

The probability density function is

$$f(x) = \frac{1}{5000 - 2000} = \frac{1}{3000} \quad 2000 \leq x \leq 5000$$

a. The probability that X falls between $2,500$ and $3,000$ is the area under the curve between $2,500$ and $3,000$ as depicted in Figure 8.6a. The area of a rectangle is the base times the height. Thus,

$$P(2,500 \leq X \leq 3,000) = (3,000 - 2,500) \times \left(\frac{1}{3,000}\right) = .1667$$

b. $P(X \geq 4,000) = (5,000 - 4,000) \times \left(\frac{1}{3,000}\right) = .3333$ [See Figure 8.6b.]

c. $P(X = 2,500) = 0$

Because there is an uncountable infinite number of values of X, the probability of each individual value is zero. Moreover, as you can see from Figure 8.6c, the area of a line is 0.

Because the probability that a continuous random variable equals any individual value is 0, there is no difference between $P(2,500 \leq X \leq 3,000)$ and $P(2,500 < X < 3,000)$. Of course, we cannot say the same thing about discrete random variables.

FIGURE **8.6** **Density Functions for Example 8.1**

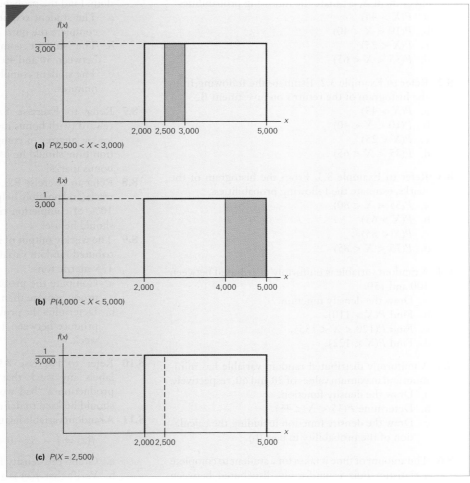

(a) $P(2,500 < X < 3,000)$

(b) $P(4,000 < X < 5,000)$

(c) $P(X = 2,500)$

8-1b Using a Continuous Distribution to Approximate a Discrete Distribution

In our definition of discrete and continuous random variables, we distinguish between them by noting whether the number of possible values is countable or uncountable. However, in practice, we frequently use a continuous distribution to approximate a discrete one when the number of values the variable can assume is countable but large. For example, the number of possible values of weekly income is countable. The values of weekly income expressed in dollars are 0, .01, .02, ... Although there is no set upper limit, we can easily identify (and thus count) all the possible values. Consequently, weekly income is a discrete random variable. However, because it can assume such a large number of values, we prefer to employ a continuous probability distribution to determine the probability associated with such variables. In the next section, we introduce the normal distribution, which is often used to describe discrete random variables that can assume a large number of values.

EXERCISES

8.1 Refer to Example 3.2. From the histogram for investment A, estimate the following probabilities.
- a. $P(X > 45)$
- b. $P(10 < X < 40)$
- c. $P(X < 25)$
- d. $P(35 < X < 65)$

8.2 Refer to Example 3.2. Estimate the following from the histogram of the returns on investment B.
- a. $P(X > 45)$
- b. $P(10 < X < 40)$
- c. $P(X < 25)$
- d. $P(35 < X < 65)$

8.3 Refer to Example 3.3. From the histogram of the marks, estimate the following probabilities.
- a. $P(55 < X < 80)$
- b. $P(X > 65)$
- c. $P(X < 85)$
- d. $P(75 < X < 85)$

8.4 A random variable is uniformly distributed between 100 and 150.
- a. Draw the density function.
- b. Find $P(X > 110)$.
- c. Find $P(120 < X < 135)$.
- d. Find $P(X < 122)$.

8.5 A uniformly distributed random variable has minimum and maximum values of 20 and 60, respectively.
- a. Draw the density function.
- b. Determine $P(35 < X < 45)$.
- c. Draw the density function including the calculation of the probability in part (b).

8.6 The amount of time it takes for a student to complete a statistics quiz is uniformly distributed between 30 and 60 minutes. One student is selected at random. Find the probability of the following events.
- a. The student requires more than 55 minutes to complete the quiz.
- b. The student completes the quiz in a time between 30 and 40 minutes.
- c. The student completes the quiz in exactly 37.23 minutes.

8.7 Refer to Exercise 8.6. The professor wants to reward (with bonus marks) students who are in the lowest quarter of completion times. What completion time should he use for the cutoff for awarding bonus marks?

8.8 Refer to Exercise 8.6. The professor would like to track (and possibly help) students who are in the top 10% of completion times. What completion time should he use?

8.9 The weekly output of a steel mill is a uniformly distributed random variable that lies between 110 and 175 metric tons.
- a. Compute the probability that the steel mill will produce more than 150 metric tons next week.
- b. Determine the probability that the steel mill will produce between 120 and 160 metric tons next week.

8.10 Refer to Exercise 8.9. The operations manager labels any week that is in the bottom 20% of production a "bad week." How many metric tons should be used to define a bad week?

8.11 A random variable has the following density function.

$$f(x) = 1 - .5x \quad 0 < x < 2$$

- a. Graph the density function.
- b. Verify that $f(x)$ is a density function.

c. Find $P(X > 1)$.
d. Find $P(X < .5)$.
e. Find $P(X = 1.5)$.

8.12 The following function is the density function for the random variable X:

$$f(x) = \frac{x - 1}{8} \quad 1 < x < 5$$

a. Graph the density function.
b. Find the probability that X lies between 2 and 4.
c. What is the probability that X is less than 3?

8.13 The following density function describes the random variable X.

$$f(x) = \begin{cases} \dfrac{x}{25} & 0 < x < 5 \\[2mm] \dfrac{10 - x}{25} & 5 < x < 10 \end{cases}$$

a. Graph the density function.
b. Find the probability that X lies between 1 and 3.
c. What is the probability that X lies between 4 and 8?
d. Compute the probability that X is less than 7.
e. Find the probability that X is greater than 3.

8.14 The following is a graph of a density function.

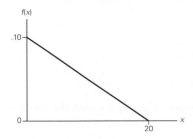

a. Determine the density function.
b. Find the probability that X is greater than 10.
c. Find the probability that X lies between 6 and 12.

8.15 Here is another density function.

$$f(x) = .40 \quad 0 < x < 1$$
$$= .05 \quad 1 < x < 13$$

a. Graph the density function.
b. Determine the probability that X is less than 8.
c. What is the probability that X lies between .4 and 10?

8.16 The following density function describes the random variable X.

$$f(x) = .10 \quad 0 < x < 2$$
$$= .20 \quad 2 < x < 5$$
$$= .15 \quad 5 < x < 6$$
$$= .05 \quad 6 < x < 7$$

a. Graph the density function.
b. Calculate the probability that X is less than 5.5.
c. Calculate the probability that X is greater than 3.5.
d. What is the probability that X lies between 1 and 6.5?

8.17 Here is another function.

$$f(x) = .2x \quad 0 < x < 2$$
$$= .4 \quad 2 < x < 3.5$$

a. Confirm that it is a density function.
b. Graph the function.
c. Determine the probability that X is less than 2.
d. Find the probability that X is less than 3.
e. What is the probability that X lies between 1 and 2.5?

8.18 The following density function describes the random variable X.

$$f(x) = .40 - .10x \quad 0 < x < 4$$
$$= .10x - .40 \quad 4 < x < 6$$

a. Graph the density function.
b. What is the probability that X is less than 2?
c. Find the probability that X is greater than 5.
d. Find the probability that X lies between 2.5 and 5.5.

8-2 / NORMAL DISTRIBUTION

The **normal distribution** is the most important of all probability distributions because of its crucial role in statistical inference.

Normal Density Function

The probability density function of a **normal random variable** is

$$f(x) = \frac{1}{\sigma\sqrt{2\pi}} e^{-\frac{1}{2}\left(\frac{x - \mu}{\sigma}\right)^2} \quad -\infty < x < \infty$$

where $e = 2.71828\ldots$ and $\pi = 3.14159\ldots$

Figure 8.7 depicts a normal distribution. Notice that the curve is symmetric about its mean and the random variable ranges between $-\infty$ and $+\infty$.

FIGURE **8.7** Normal Distribution

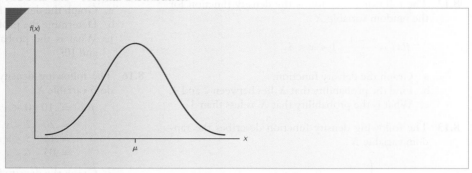

The normal distribution is described by two parameters, the mean μ and the standard deviation σ. In Figure 8.8, we demonstrate the effect of changing the value of μ. Obviously, increasing μ shifts the curve to the right and decreasing μ shifts it to the left.

FIGURE **8.8** Normal Distributions with the Same Variance but Different Means

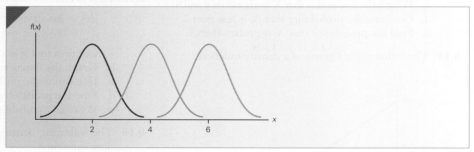

Figure 8.9 describes the effect of σ. Larger values of σ widen the curve and smaller ones narrow it.

FIGURE **8.9** Normal Distributions with the Same Means but Different Variances

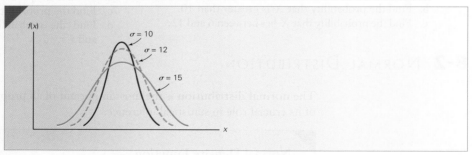

8-2a Calculating Normal Probabilities

To calculate the probability that a normal random variable falls into any interval, we must compute the area in the interval under the curve. Unfortunately, the function is not as simple as the uniform probability distribution, precluding the use of simple mathematics or even integral calculus. Instead we will resort to using a probability table similar to Tables 1 and 2 in Appendix B, which are used to calculate binomial and Poisson probabilities, respectively. Recall that to determine binomial probabilities from Table 1 we needed probabilities for selected values of n and p. Similarly, to find Poisson probabilities we needed probabilities for each value of μ that we chose to include in Table 2. It would appear then that we will need a separate table for normal probabilities for a selected set of values of μ and σ. Fortunately, this won't be necessary. Instead, we reduce the number of tables needed to one by standardizing the random variable. We standardize a random variable by subtracting its mean and dividing by its standard deviation. When the variable is normal, the transformed variable is called a **standard normal random variable** and denoted by Z; that is,

$$Z = \frac{X - \mu}{\sigma}$$

The probability statement about X is transformed by this formula into a statement about Z. To illustrate how we proceed, consider the following example.

EXAMPLE 8.2

Normally Distributed Gasoline Sales

Suppose that the daily demand for regular gasoline at another gas station is normally distributed with a mean of 1,000 gallons and a standard deviation of 100 gallons. The station manager has just opened the station for business and notes that there is exactly 1,100 gallons of regular gasoline in storage. The next delivery is scheduled later today at the close of business. The manager would like to know the probability that he will have enough regular gasoline to satisfy today's demands.

SOLUTION:

The amount of gasoline on hand will be sufficient to satisfy the demand if the demand is less than the supply. We label the demand for regular gasoline as X, and we want to find the probability:

$$P(X \leq 1{,}100)$$

Note that because X is a continuous random variable, we can also express the probability as

$$P(X < 1{,}100)$$

because the area for $X = 1{,}100$ is 0.

Figure 8.10 describes a normal curve with mean of 1,000 and standard deviation of 100, and the area we want to find.

FIGURE **8.10** $P(X < 1{,}100)$

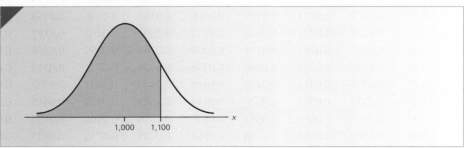

The first step is to standardize X. However, if we perform any operations on X, we must perform the same operations on 1,100. Thus,

$$P(X < 1{,}100) = P\left(\frac{X - \mu}{\sigma} < \frac{1{,}100 - 1{,}000}{100}\right) = P(Z < 1.00)$$

Figure 8.11 describes the transformation that has taken place. Notice that the variable X was transformed into Z, and 1,100 was transformed into 1.00. However, the area has not changed. In other words, the probability that we wish to compute $P(X < 1,100)$ is identical to $P(Z < 1.00)$.

FIGURE **8.11** $P(Z < 1.00)$

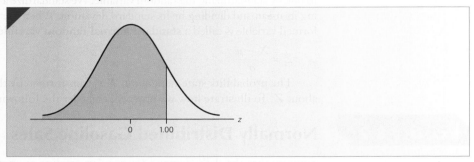

The values of Z specify the location of the corresponding value of X. A value of $Z = 1$ corresponds to a value of X that is 1 standard deviation above the mean. Notice as well that the mean of Z, which is 0, corresponds to the mean of X.

If we know the mean and standard deviation of a normally distributed random variable, we can always transform the probability statement about X into a probability statement about Z. Consequently, we need only one table, Table 3 in Appendix B, the standard normal probability table, which is reproduced here as Table 8.1.*

TABLE **8.1** Normal Probabilities (Table 3 in Appendix B)

Z	0.00	0.01	0.02	0.03	0.04	0.05	0.06	0.07	0.08	0.09
−3.0	0.0013	0.0013	0.0013	0.0012	0.0012	0.0011	0.0011	0.0011	0.0010	0.0010
−2.9	0.0019	0.0018	0.0018	0.0017	0.0016	0.0016	0.0015	0.0015	0.0014	0.0014
−2.8	0.0026	0.0025	0.0024	0.0023	0.0023	0.0022	0.0021	0.0021	0.0020	0.0019
−2.7	0.0035	0.0034	0.0033	0.0032	0.0031	0.0030	0.0029	0.0028	0.0027	0.0026
−2.6	0.0047	0.0045	0.0044	0.0043	0.0041	0.0040	0.0039	0.0038	0.0037	0.0036
−2.5	0.0062	0.0060	0.0059	0.0057	0.0055	0.0054	0.0052	0.0051	0.0049	0.0048
−2.4	0.0082	0.0080	0.0078	0.0075	0.0073	0.0071	0.0069	0.0068	0.0066	0.0064
−2.3	0.0107	0.0104	0.0102	0.0099	0.0096	0.0094	0.0091	0.0089	0.0087	0.0084
−2.2	0.0139	0.0136	0.0132	0.0129	0.0125	0.0122	0.0119	0.0116	0.0113	0.0110
−2.1	0.0179	0.0174	0.0170	0.0166	0.0162	0.0158	0.0154	0.0150	0.0146	0.0143
−2.0	0.0228	0.0222	0.0217	0.0212	0.0207	0.0202	0.0197	0.0192	0.0188	0.0183
−1.9	0.0287	0.0281	0.0274	0.0268	0.0262	0.0256	0.0250	0.0244	0.0239	0.0233
−1.8	0.0359	0.0351	0.0344	0.0336	0.0329	0.0322	0.0314	0.0307	0.0301	0.0294
−1.7	0.0446	0.0436	0.0427	0.0418	0.0409	0.0401	0.0392	0.0384	0.0375	0.0367
−1.6	0.0548	0.0537	0.0526	0.0516	0.0505	0.0495	0.0485	0.0475	0.0465	0.0455
−1.5	0.0668	0.0655	0.0643	0.0630	0.0618	0.0606	0.0594	0.0582	0.0571	0.0559
−1.4	0.0808	0.0793	0.0778	0.0764	0.0749	0.0735	0.0721	0.0708	0.0694	0.0681
−1.3	0.0968	0.0951	0.0934	0.0918	0.0901	0.0885	0.0869	0.0853	0.0838	0.0823
−1.2	0.1151	0.1131	0.1112	0.1093	0.1075	0.1056	0.1038	0.1020	0.1003	0.0985

*In previous editions we have used another table, which lists $P(0 < Z < z)$. The online appendix Determining Normal Probabilities using $P(0 < Z < z)$ provides instructions and examples using this table.

Z	0.00	0.01	0.02	0.03	0.04	0.05	0.06	0.07	0.08	0.09
−1.1	0.1357	0.1335	0.1314	0.1292	0.1271	0.1251	0.1230	0.1210	0.1190	0.1170
−1.0	0.1587	0.1562	0.1539	0.1515	0.1492	0.1469	0.1446	0.1423	0.1401	0.1379
−0.9	0.1841	0.1814	0.1788	0.1762	0.1736	0.1711	0.1685	0.1660	0.1635	0.1611
−0.8	0.2119	0.2090	0.2061	0.2033	0.2005	0.1977	0.1949	0.1922	0.1894	0.1867
−0.7	0.2420	0.2389	0.2358	0.2327	0.2296	0.2266	0.2236	0.2206	0.2177	0.2148
−0.6	0.2743	0.2709	0.2676	0.2643	0.2611	0.2578	0.2546	0.2514	0.2483	0.2451
−0.5	0.3085	0.3050	0.3015	0.2981	0.2946	0.2912	0.2877	0.2843	0.2810	0.2776
−0.4	0.3446	0.3409	0.3372	0.3336	0.3300	0.3264	0.3228	0.3192	0.3156	0.3121
−0.3	0.3821	0.3783	0.3745	0.3707	0.3669	0.3632	0.3594	0.3557	0.3520	0.3483
−0.2	0.4207	0.4168	0.4129	0.4090	0.4052	0.4013	0.3974	0.3936	0.3897	0.3859
−0.1	0.4602	0.4562	0.4522	0.4483	0.4443	0.4404	0.4364	0.4325	0.4286	0.4247
−0.0	0.5000	0.4960	0.4920	0.4880	0.4840	0.4801	0.4761	0.4721	0.4681	0.4641
0.0	0.5000	0.5040	0.5080	0.5120	0.5160	0.5199	0.5239	0.5279	0.5319	0.5359
0.1	0.5398	0.5438	0.5478	0.5517	0.5557	0.5596	0.5636	0.5675	0.5714	0.5753
0.2	0.5793	0.5832	0.5871	0.5910	0.5948	0.5987	0.6026	0.6064	0.6103	0.6141
0.3	0.6179	0.6217	0.6255	0.6293	0.6331	0.6368	0.6406	0.6443	0.6480	0.6517
0.4	0.6554	0.6591	0.6628	0.6664	0.6700	0.6736	0.6772	0.6808	0.6844	0.6879
0.5	0.6915	0.6950	0.6985	0.7019	0.7054	0.7088	0.7123	0.7157	0.7190	0.7224
0.6	0.7257	0.7291	0.7324	0.7357	0.7389	0.7422	0.7454	0.7486	0.7517	0.7549
0.7	0.7580	0.7611	0.7642	0.7673	0.7704	0.7734	0.7764	0.7794	0.7823	0.7852
0.8	0.7881	0.7910	0.7939	0.7967	0.7995	0.8023	0.8051	0.8078	0.8106	0.8133
0.9	0.8159	0.8186	0.8212	0.8238	0.8264	0.8289	0.8315	0.8340	0.8365	0.8389
1.0	0.8413	0.8438	0.8461	0.8485	0.8508	0.8531	0.8554	0.8577	0.8599	0.8621
1.1	0.8643	0.8665	0.8686	0.8708	0.8729	0.8749	0.8770	0.8790	0.8810	0.8830
1.2	0.8849	0.8869	0.8888	0.8907	0.8925	0.8944	0.8962	0.8980	0.8997	0.9015
1.3	0.9032	0.9049	0.9066	0.9082	0.9099	0.9115	0.9131	0.9147	0.9162	0.9177
1.4	0.9192	0.9207	0.9222	0.9236	0.9251	0.9265	0.9279	0.9292	0.9306	0.9319
1.5	0.9332	0.9345	0.9357	0.9370	0.9382	0.9394	0.9406	0.9418	0.9429	0.9441
1.6	0.9452	0.9463	0.9474	0.9484	0.9495	0.9505	0.9515	0.9525	0.9535	0.9545
1.7	0.9554	0.9564	0.9573	0.9582	0.9591	0.9599	0.9608	0.9616	0.9625	0.9633
1.8	0.9641	0.9649	0.9656	0.9664	0.9671	0.9678	0.9686	0.9693	0.9699	0.9706
1.9	0.9713	0.9719	0.9726	0.9732	0.9738	0.9744	0.9750	0.9756	0.9761	0.9767
2.0	0.9772	0.9778	0.9783	0.9788	0.9793	0.9798	0.9803	0.9808	0.9812	0.9817
2.1	0.9821	0.9826	0.9830	0.9834	0.9838	0.9842	0.9846	0.9850	0.9854	0.9857
2.2	0.9861	0.9864	0.9868	0.9871	0.9875	0.9878	0.9881	0.9884	0.9887	0.9890
2.3	0.9893	0.9896	0.9898	0.9901	0.9904	0.9906	0.9909	0.9911	0.9913	0.9916
2.4	0.9918	0.9920	0.9922	0.9925	0.9927	0.9929	0.9931	0.9932	0.9934	0.9936
2.5	0.9938	0.9940	0.9941	0.9943	0.9945	0.9946	0.9948	0.9949	0.9951	0.9952
2.6	0.9953	0.9955	0.9956	0.9957	0.9959	0.9960	0.9961	0.9962	0.9963	0.9964
2.7	0.9965	0.9966	0.9967	0.9968	0.9969	0.9970	0.9971	0.9972	0.9973	0.9974
2.8	0.9974	0.9975	0.9976	0.9977	0.9977	0.9978	0.9979	0.9979	0.9980	0.9981
2.9	0.9981	0.9982	0.9982	0.9983	0.9984	0.9984	0.9985	0.9985	0.9986	0.9986
3.0	0.9987	0.9987	0.9987	0.9988	0.9988	0.9989	0.9989	0.9989	0.9990	0.9990

This table is similar to the ones we used for the binomial and Poisson distributions; that is, this table lists cumulative probabilities

$$P(Z < z)$$

for values of z ranging from -3.09 to $+3.09$.

To use the table, we simply find the value of z and read the probability. For example, the probability $P(Z < 2.00)$ is found by finding 2.0 in the left margin and under the heading 0.00 finding 0.9772. The probability $P(Z < 2.01)$ is found in the same row but under the heading 0.01. It is .9778.

Returning to Example 8.2, the probability we seek is found in Table 8.1 by finding 1.0 in the left margin. The number to its right under the heading 0.00 is .8413. See Figure 8.12.

FIGURE **8.12** $P(Z < 1.00)$

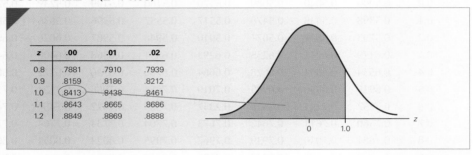

As was the case with Tables 1 and 2, we can also determine the probability that the standard normal random variable is greater than some value of z. For example, we find the probability that Z is greater than 1.80 by determining the probability that Z is less than 1.80 and subtracting that value from 1. By applying the complement rule, we get

$$P(Z > 1.80) = 1 - P(Z < 1.80) = 1 - .9641 = .0359$$

See Figure 8.13.

FIGURE **8.13** $P(Z > 1.80)$

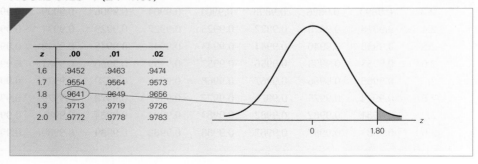

We can also easily determine the probability that a standard normal random variable lies between two values of z. For example, we find the probability

$$P(-0.71 < Z < 0.92)$$

by finding the two cumulative probabilities and calculating their difference; that is,

$$P(Z < -0.71) = .2389$$

and

$$P(Z < 0.92) = .8212$$

Hence,

$$P(-0.71 < Z < 0.92) = P(Z < 92) - P(Z < -0.71) = .8212 - .2389 = .5823$$

Figure 8.14 depicts this calculation.

FIGURE 8.14 $P(-0.71 < Z < 0.92)$

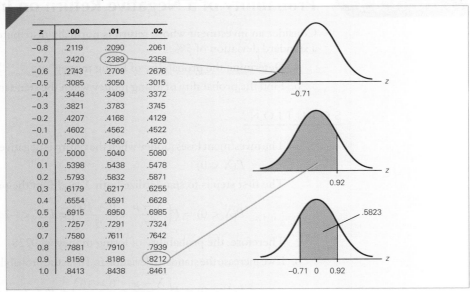

Notice that the largest value of z in the table is 3.09 and that $P(Z < 3.09) = .9990$. This means that

$$P(Z > 3.09) = 1 - .9990 = .0010$$

However, because the table lists no values beyond 3.09, we approximate any area beyond 3.10 as 0. In other words,

$$P(Z > 3.10) = P(Z < -3.10) \approx 0$$

Recall that in Tables 1 and 2 we were able to use the table to find the probability that X is *equal* to some value of x, but we won't do the same with the normal table. Remember that the normal random variable is continuous and the probability that a continuous random variable is equal to any single value is 0.

APPLICATIONS in FINANCE

Measuring Risk

In previous chapters, we discussed several probability and statistical applications in finance where we wanted to measure and perhaps reduce the risk
associated with investments. In Example 3.2, we drew histograms to gauge
the spread of the histogram of the returns on two investments. We repeated
this example in Chapter 4, where we computed the standard deviation and
variance as numerical measures of risk. In Section 7-3, we developed an important application in finance in which we emphasized reducing the variance of the
returns on a portfolio. However, we have not demonstrated why risk is measured by
the variance and standard deviation. The following example corrects this deficiency.

EXAMPLE **8.3**

Probability of a Negative Return on Investment

Consider an investment whose return is normally distributed with a mean of 10% and
a standard deviation of 5%.

   a. Determine the probability of losing money.

   b. Find the probability of losing money when the standard deviation is equal to 10%.

SOLUTION:

   a. The investment loses money when the return is negative. Thus, we wish to determine

$$P(X < 0)$$

The first step is to standardize both X and 0 in the probability statement:

$$P(X < 0) = P\left(\frac{X - \mu}{\sigma} < \frac{0 - 10}{5}\right) = P(Z < -2.00) = .0228$$

Therefore, the probability of losing money is .0228.

   b. If we increase the standard deviation to 10%, the probability of suffering a loss becomes

$$P(X < 0) = P\left(\frac{X - \mu}{\sigma} < \frac{0 - 10}{10}\right) = P(Z < -1.00) = .1587$$

As you can see, increasing the standard deviation increases the probability of
losing money. Note that increasing the standard deviation will also increase the
probability that the return will exceed some relatively large amount. However,
because investors tend to be risk averse, we emphasize the increased probability of
negative returns when discussing the effect of increasing the standard deviation.

8-2b Finding Values of Z

There is a family of problems that require us to determine the value of Z given a probability. We use the notation Z_A to represent the value of z such that the area to its right
under the standard normal curve is A; that is, Z_A is the value of a standard normal
random variable such that

$$P(Z > Z_A) = A$$

Figure 8.15 depicts this notation.

FIGURE **8.15** $P(Z > Z_A) = A$

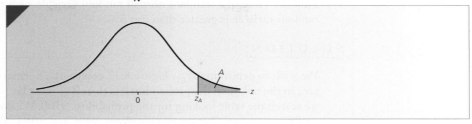

To find Z_A for any value of A requires us to use the standard normal table backward. As you saw in Example 8.2, to find a probability about Z, we must find the value of z in the table and determine the probability associated with it. To use the table backward, we need to specify a probability and then determine the z-value associated with it. We'll demonstrate by finding $Z_{.025}$. Figure 8.16 depicts the standard normal curve and $Z_{.025}$. Because of the format of the standard normal table, we begin by determining the area *less than* $Z_{.025}$, which is $1 - .025 = .9750$. (Notice that we expressed this probability with four decimal places to make it easier for you to see what you need to do.) We now search through the probability part of the table looking for .9750. When we locate it, we see that the z-value associated with it is 1.96.

Thus, $Z_{.025} = 1.96$, which means that $P(Z > 1.96) = .025$.

FIGURE **8.16** $Z_{.025}$

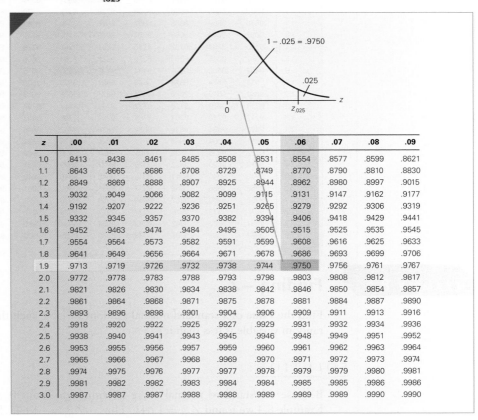

z	.00	.01	.02	.03	.04	.05	.06	.07	.08	.09
1.0	.8413	.8438	.8461	.8485	.8508	.8531	.8554	.8577	.8599	.8621
1.1	.8643	.8665	.8686	.8708	.8729	.8749	.8770	.8790	.8810	.8830
1.2	.8849	.8869	.8888	.8907	.8925	.8944	.8962	.8980	.8997	.9015
1.3	.9032	.9049	.9066	.9082	.9099	.9115	.9131	.9147	.9162	.9177
1.4	.9192	.9207	.9222	.9236	.9251	.9265	.9279	.9292	.9306	.9319
1.5	.9332	.9345	.9357	.9370	.9382	.9394	.9406	.9418	.9429	.9441
1.6	.9452	.9463	.9474	.9484	.9495	.9505	.9515	.9525	.9535	.9545
1.7	.9554	.9564	.9573	.9582	.9591	.9599	.9608	.9616	.9625	.9633
1.8	.9641	.9649	.9656	.9664	.9671	.9678	.9686	.9693	.9699	.9706
1.9	.9713	.9719	.9726	.9732	.9738	.9744	.9750	.9756	.9761	.9767
2.0	.9772	.9778	.9783	.9788	.9793	.9798	.9803	.9808	.9812	.9817
2.1	.9821	.9826	.9830	.9834	.9838	.9842	.9846	.9850	.9854	.9857
2.2	.9861	.9864	.9868	.9871	.9875	.9878	.9881	.9884	.9887	.9890
2.3	.9893	.9896	.9898	.9901	.9904	.9906	.9909	.9911	.9913	.9916
2.4	.9918	.9920	.9922	.9925	.9927	.9929	.9931	.9932	.9934	.9936
2.5	.9938	.9940	.9941	.9943	.9945	.9946	.9948	.9949	.9951	.9952
2.6	.9953	.9955	.9956	.9957	.9959	.9960	.9961	.9962	.9963	.9964
2.7	.9965	.9966	.9967	.9968	.9969	.9970	.9971	.9972	.9973	.9974
2.8	.9974	.9975	.9976	.9977	.9977	.9978	.9979	.9979	.9980	.9981
2.9	.9981	.9982	.9982	.9983	.9984	.9984	.9985	.9985	.9986	.9986
3.0	.9987	.9987	.9987	.9988	.9988	.9989	.9989	.9989	.9990	.9990

EXAMPLE 8.4

Finding $Z_{.05}$

Find the value of a standard normal random variable such that the probability that the random variable is greater than it is 5%.

SOLUTION:

We wish to determine $Z_{.05}$. Figure 8.17 depicts the normal curve and $Z_{.05}$. If .05 is the area in the tail, then the probability less than $Z_{.05}$ must be $1 - .05 = .9500$. To find $Z_{.05}$ we search the table looking for the probability .9500. We don't find this probability, but we find two values that are equally close: .9495 and .9505. The Z-values associated with these probabilities are 1.64 and 1.65, respectively. The average is taken as $Z_{.05}$. Thus, $Z_{.05} = 1.645$.

FIGURE 8.17 $Z_{.05}$

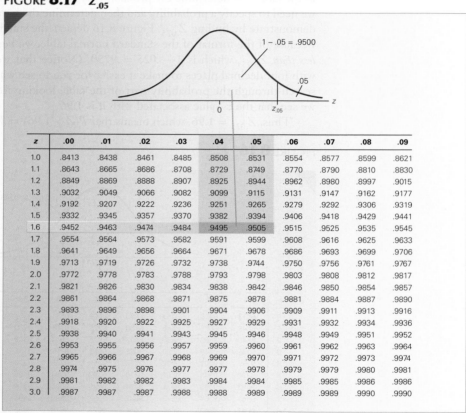

z	.00	.01	.02	.03	.04	.05	.06	.07	.08	.09
1.0	.8413	.8438	.8461	.8485	.8508	.8531	.8554	.8577	.8599	.8621
1.1	.8643	.8665	.8686	.8708	.8729	.8749	.8770	.8790	.8810	.8830
1.2	.8849	.8869	.8888	.8907	.8925	.8944	.8962	.8980	.8997	.9015
1.3	.9032	.9049	.9066	.9082	.9099	.9115	.9131	.9147	.9162	.9177
1.4	.9192	.9207	.9222	.9236	.9251	.9265	.9279	.9292	.9306	.9319
1.5	.9332	.9345	.9357	.9370	.9382	.9394	.9406	.9418	.9429	.9441
1.6	.9452	.9463	.9474	.9484	.9495	.9505	.9515	.9525	.9535	.9545
1.7	.9554	.9564	.9573	.9582	.9591	.9599	.9608	.9616	.9625	.9633
1.8	.9641	.9649	.9656	.9664	.9671	.9678	.9686	.9693	.9699	.9706
1.9	.9713	.9719	.9726	.9732	.9738	.9744	.9750	.9756	.9761	.9767
2.0	.9772	.9778	.9783	.9788	.9793	.9798	.9803	.9808	.9812	.9817
2.1	.9821	.9826	.9830	.9834	.9838	.9842	.9846	.9850	.9854	.9857
2.2	.9861	.9864	.9868	.9871	.9875	.9878	.9881	.9884	.9887	.9890
2.3	.9893	.9896	.9898	.9901	.9904	.9906	.9909	.9911	.9913	.9916
2.4	.9918	.9920	.9922	.9925	.9927	.9929	.9931	.9932	.9934	.9936
2.5	.9938	.9940	.9941	.9943	.9945	.9946	.9948	.9949	.9951	.9952
2.6	.9953	.9955	.9956	.9957	.9959	.9960	.9961	.9962	.9963	.9964
2.7	.9965	.9966	.9967	.9968	.9969	.9970	.9971	.9972	.9973	.9974
2.8	.9974	.9975	.9976	.9977	.9977	.9978	.9979	.9979	.9980	.9981
2.9	.9981	.9982	.9982	.9983	.9984	.9984	.9985	.9985	.9986	.9986
3.0	.9987	.9987	.9987	.9988	.9988	.9989	.9989	.9989	.9990	.9990

EXAMPLE 8.5

Finding $-Z_{.05}$

Find the value of a standard normal random variable such that the probability that the random variable is less than it is 5%.

SOLUTION:

Because the standard normal curve is symmetric about 0, we wish to find $-Z_{.05}$. In Example 8.4 we found $Z_{.05} = 1.645$. Thus, $-Z_{.05} = -1.645$. See Figure 8.18.

FIGURE **8.18** $-z_{.05}$

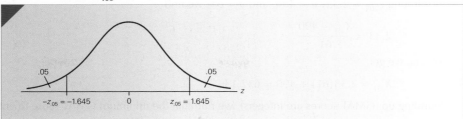

Minimum GMAT Score to Enter Executive MBA Program: Solution

Figure 8.19 depicts the distribution of GMAT scores. We've labeled the minimum score needed to enter the new MBA program $X_{.01}$ such that

$$P(X > X_{.01}) = .01$$

FIGURE **8.19** Minimum GMAT Score

z	.00	.01	.02	.03	.04
1.0	.8413	.8438	.8461	.8485	.8508
1.1	.8643	.8665	.8686	.8708	.8729
1.2	.8849	.8869	.8888	.8907	.8925
1.3	.9032	.9049	.9066	.9082	.9099
1.4	.9192	.9207	.9222	.9236	.9251
1.5	.9332	.9345	.9357	.9370	.9382
1.6	.9452	.9463	.9474	.9484	.9495
1.7	.9554	.9564	.9573	.9582	.9591
1.8	.9641	.9649	.9656	.9664	.9671
1.9	.9713	.9719	.9726	.9732	.9738
2.0	.9772	.9778	.9783	.9788	.9793
2.1	.9821	.9826	.9830	.9834	.9838
2.2	.9861	.9864	.9868	.9871	.9875
2.3	.9893	.9896	.9898	.9901	.9904
2.4	.9918	.9920	.9922	.9925	.9927
2.5	.9938	.9940	.9941	.9943	.9945
2.6	.9953	.9955	.9956	.9957	.9959
2.7	.9965	.9966	.9967	.9968	.9969
2.8	.9974	.9975	.9976	.9977	.9977
2.9	.9981	.9982	.9982	.9983	.9984
3.0	.9987	.9987	.9987	.9988	.9988

Above the normal curve, we depict the standard normal curve and $Z_{.01}$. We can determine the value of $Z_{.01}$ as we did in Example 8.4. In the standard normal table, we find $1 - .01 = .9900$ (its closest value in the table is .9901) and the Z-value 2.33. Thus, the standardized value of $X_{.01}$ is $Z_{.01} = 2.33$. To find $X_{.01}$, we must unstandardize $Z_{.01}$. We do so by solving for $X_{.01}$ in the equation

$$Z_{.01} = \frac{X_{.01} - \mu}{\sigma}$$

Substituting $Z_{.01} = 2.33$, $\mu = 490$, and $\sigma = 61$, we find

$$2.33 = \frac{X_{.01} - 490}{61}$$

Solving, we get

$$X_{.01} = 2.33(61) + 490 = 632.13$$

Rounding up (GMAT scores are integers), we find that the minimum GMAT score to enter the Executive MBA Program is 633.

8-2c Z_A and Percentiles

In Chapter 4, we introduced percentiles, which are measures of relative standing. The values of Z_A are the $100(1 - A)$th percentiles of a standard normal random variable. For example, $Z_{.05} = 1.645$, which means that 1.645 is the 95th percentile: 95% of all values of Z are below it, and 5% are above it. We interpret other values of Z_A similarly.

EXCEL Function

INSTRUCTIONS

We can use Excel to compute probabilities as well as values of X and Z. To compute cumulative normal probabilities $P(X < x)$, type (in any cell)

$$= \mathbf{NORMDIST}([X], [\mu], [\sigma], \text{True})$$

(Typing "True" yields a cumulative probability. Typing "False" will produce the value of the normal density function, a number with little meaning.)

If you type 0 for μ and 1 for σ, you will obtain standard normal probabilities. Alternatively, type

NORMSDIST instead of NORMDIST and enter the value of z.

In Example 8.2, we found $P(X < 1, 100) = P(Z < 1.00) = .8413$. To instruct Excel to calculate this probability, we enter

$$= \mathbf{NORMDIST}(1100, 1000, 100, \text{True})$$

or

$$= \mathbf{NORMSDIST}(1.00)$$

To calculate a value for Z_A, type

$$= \mathbf{NORMSINV}([1 - A])$$

In Example 8.4, we would type

$$= \mathbf{NORMSINV}(.95)$$

and produce 1.6449. We calculated $Z_{.05} = 1.645$.

To calculate a value of x given the probability $P(X > x) = A$, enter

$$= \mathbf{NORMINV}(1 - A, \mu, \sigma)$$

The chapter-opening example would be solved by typing

$$= \mathbf{NORMINV}(.99, 490, 61)$$

which yields 632.

APPLICATIONS in OPERATIONS MANAGEMENT

Inventory Management

Every organization maintains some inventory, which is defined as a stock of items. For example, grocery stores hold inventories of almost all the products they sell. When the total number of products drops to a specified level, the manager arranges for the delivery of more products. An automobile repair shop keeps an inventory of a large number of replacement parts. A school keeps stock of items that it uses regularly, including chalk, pens, envelopes, file folders, and paper clips. There are costs associated with inventories. These include the cost of capital, losses (theft and obsolescence), and warehouse space, as well as maintenance and record keeping. Management scientists have developed many models to help determine the optimum inventory level that balances the cost of inventory with the cost of shortages and the cost of making many small orders. Several of these models are deterministic—that is, they assume that the demand for the product is constant. However, in most realistic situations, the demand is a random variable. One commonly applied probabilistic model assumes that the demand during lead time is a normally distributed random variable. *Lead time* is defined as the amount of time between when the order is placed and when it is delivered.

The quantity ordered is usually calculated by attempting to minimize the total costs, including the cost of ordering and the cost of maintaining inventory. (This topic is discussed in most management-science courses.) Another critical decision involves the *reorder point*, which is the level of inventory at which an order is issued to its supplier. If the reorder point is too low, the company will run out of product, suffering the loss of sales and potentially customers who will go to a competitor. If the reorder point is too high, the company will be carrying too much inventory, which costs money to buy and store. In some companies, inventory has a tendency to walk out the back door or become obsolete. As a result, managers create a *safety stock*, which is the extra amount of inventory to reduce the times when the company has a shortage. They do so by setting a service level, which is the probability that the company will not experience a shortage. The method used to determine the reorder point will be demonstrated with Example 8.6.

Kzenon/Shutterstock.com

EXAMPLE 8.6

Determining the Reorder Point

During the spring, the demand for electric fans at a large home-improvement store is quite strong. The company tracks inventory using a computer system so that it knows how many fans are in the inventory at any time. The policy is to order a new shipment of 250 fans when the inventory level falls to the reorder point, which is 150. However, this policy has resulted in frequent shortages and thus lost sales because both lead time and demand are highly variable. The manager would like to reduce the incidence of shortages so that only 5% of orders will arrive after inventory drops to 0 (resulting in a shortage). This policy is expressed as a 95% service level. From previous periods, the company has determined that demand during lead time is normally distributed with a mean of 200 and a standard deviation of 50. Find the reorder point.

SOLUTION:

The reorder point is set so that the probability that demand during lead time exceeds this quantity is 5%. Figure 8.20 depicts demand during lead time and the reorder point. As we did in the solution to the chapter-opening example, we find the standard normal value such that the area to its right is .05. The standardized value of the reorder point (ROP) is $Z_{.05} = 1.645$. To find ROP, we must unstandardize $Z_{.05}$.

$$Z_{.05} = \frac{\text{ROP} - \mu}{\sigma}$$

$$1.645 = \frac{\text{ROP} - 200}{50}$$

$$\text{ROP} = 50(1.645) + 200 = 282.25$$

which we round up to 283. The policy is to order a new batch of fans when there are 283 fans left in inventory.

FIGURE **8.20** **Distribution of Demand During Lead Time**

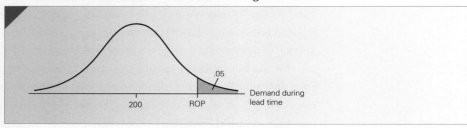

EXERCISES

In Exercises 8.15 to 8.30, find the probabilities.

8.19 $P(Z < 1.60)$

8.20 $P(Z < 1.61)$

8.21 $P(Z < 1.65)$

8.22 $P(Z < -1.39)$

8.23 $P(Z < -1.80)$

8.24 $P(Z < -2.16)$

8.25 $P(-1.30 < Z < .70)$

8.26 $P(Z > -1.24)$

8.27 $P(Z < 2.23)$

8.28 $P(Z > 1.87)$

8.29 $P(Z < 2.57)$

8.30 $P(1.04 < Z < 2.03)$

8.31 $P(-0.71 < Z < -0.33)$

8.32 $P(Z > 3.09)$

8.33 $P(Z > 0)$

8.34 $P(Z > 4.0)$

8.35 Find $z_{.03}$.

8.36 Find $z_{.065}$.

8.37 Find $z_{.28}$.

8.38 X is normally distributed with mean 100 and standard deviation 20. What is the probability that X is greater than 145?

8.39 X is normally distributed with mean 250 and standard deviation 40. What value of X does only the top 15% exceed?

8.40 X is normally distributed with mean 1,000 and standard deviation 250. What is the probability that X lies between 800 and 1, 100?

8.41 X is normally distributed with mean 50 and standard deviation 8. What value of X is such that only 8% of values are below it?

8.42 The long-distance calls made by the employees of a company are normally distributed with a mean of 6.3 minutes and a standard deviation of 2.2 minutes. Find the probability that a call
a. lasts between 5 and 10 minutes.
b. lasts more than 7 minutes.
c. lasts less than 4 minutes.

8.43 Refer to Exercise 8.42. How long do the longest 10% of calls last?

8.44 The lifetimes of lightbulbs that are advertised to last for 5,000 hours are normally distributed with a mean of 5,100 hours and a standard deviation of 200 hours. What is the probability that a bulb lasts longer than the advertised figure?

8.45 Refer to Exercise 8.44. If we wanted to be sure that 98% of all bulbs last longer than the advertised figure, what figure should be advertised?

8.46 SAT scores are normally distributed with a mean of 1,000 and a standard deviation of 300. Find the quartiles.

8.47 According to a PEW Research Center survey, the mean student loan at graduation is $25,000. Suppose that student loans are normally distributed with a standard deviation of $5,000. A graduate with a student loan is selected at random. Find the following probabilities.
a. The loan is greater than $30,000.
b. The loan is less than $22,500.
c. The loan falls between $20,000 and $32,000.

8.48 The Tesla Model S 85D is an electric car that the manufacturer claims can travel 270 miles on a single charge. However, the actual distance depends on a number of factors including speed and whether the car is driven in the city or on highways. Suppose that the distance is a normally distributed random variable with a mean of 200 miles and a standard deviation of 20 miles. An owner of this model intends to travel to a nearby city and return on the same charge. If the total distance is 210 miles, what is the probability that car makes it without running out of power?

8.49 Exercise 4.67 addressed the problem of setting an appropriate speed limit on highways. Automotive experts believe that the "correct" speed is the 85th percentile. Suppose that the speeds on a highway are normally distributed with a mean of 68 and a standard deviation of 5. Find the "correct" speed.

8.50 Economists frequently make use of quintiles (i.e., the 20th, 40th, 60th, and 80th percentiles) particularly when discussing incomes. Suppose that in a large city household incomes are normally distributed with a mean of $50,000 and a standard deviation of $10,000. An economist wishes to identify the quintiles. Unfortunately, he did not pass his statistics course. Help him by providing the quintiles.

8.51 The top-selling Red and Voss tire is rated 70,000 miles, which means nothing. In fact, the distance the tires can run until they wear out is a normally distributed random variable with a mean of 82,000 miles and a standard deviation of 6,400 miles.
a. What is the probability that a tire wears out before 70,000 miles?
b. What is the probability that a tire lasts more than 100,000 miles?

8.52 The heights of 2-year-old children are normally distributed with a mean of 32 inches and a standard deviation of 1.5 inches. Pediatricians regularly measure the heights of toddlers to determine whether there is a problem. There may be a problem when a child is in the top or bottom 5% of heights. Determine the heights of 2-year-old children that could be a problem.

8.53 Refer to Exercise 8.52. Find the probability of these events.
a. A 2-year-old child is taller than 36 inches.
b. A 2-year-old child is shorter than 34 inches.
c. A 2-year-old child is between 30 and 33 inches tall.

8.54 University and college students average 7.2 hours of sleep per night, with a standard deviation of 40 minutes. If the amount of sleep is normally distributed, what proportion of university and college students sleep for more than 8 hours?

8.55 Refer to Exercise 8.54. Find the amount of sleep that is exceeded by only 25% of students.

8.56 The amount of time devoted to studying statistics each week by students who achieve a grade of A in the course is a normally distributed random variable with a mean of 7.5 hours and a standard deviation of 2.1 hours.
   a. What proportion of A students study for more than 10 hours per week?
   b. Find the probability that an A student spends between 7 and 9 hours studying.
   c. What proportion of A students spend fewer than 3 hours studying?
   d. What is the amount of time below which only 5% of all A students spend studying?

8.57 The number of pages printed before replacing the cartridge in a laser printer is normally distributed with a mean of 11,500 pages and a standard deviation of 800 pages. A new cartridge has just been installed.
   a. What is the probability that the printer produces more than 12,000 pages before this cartridge must be replaced?
   b. What is the probability that the printer produces fewer than 10,000 pages?

8.58 Refer to Exercise 8.57. The manufacturer wants to provide guidelines to potential customers advising them of the minimum number of pages they can expect from each cartridge. How many pages should it advertise if the company wants to be correct 99% of the time?

8.59 The mean monthly income of graduates of professional and Ph.D. degrees is $6,000 according to a recent PEW Research Center survey. If these incomes are normally distributed with a standard deviation of $1,200,
   a. What proportion of incomes is greater than $4,900?
   b. Calculate the proportion of incomes that fall between $3,800 and $5,700.
   c. Calculate the proportion of incomes that are less than $6,500.

8.60 A golfer playing a new course encounters a hole that requires a drive of 145 yards to successfully clear a pond. She knows that her drives are normally distributed with a mean of 155 yards and a standard deviation of 9 yards. What is the probability that after her drive her golf ball will be at the bottom of the pond?

8.61 Battery manufacturers compete on the basis of the amount of time their products last in cameras and toys. A manufacturer of alkaline batteries has observed that its batteries last for an average of 26 hours when used in a toy racing car. The amount of time is normally distributed with a standard deviation of 2.5 hours.
   a. What is the probability that the battery lasts between 24 and 28 hours?
   b. What is the probability that the battery lasts longer than 28 hours?
   c. What is the probability that the battery lasts less than 24 hours?

8.62 Because of the relatively high interest rates, most consumers attempt to pay off their credit card bills promptly. However, this is not always possible. An analysis of the amount of interest paid monthly by a bank's Visa cardholders reveals that the amount is normally distributed with a mean of $27 and a standard deviation of $7.
   a. What proportion of the bank's Visa cardholders pay more than $30 in interest?
   b. What proportion of the bank's Visa cardholders pay more than $40 in interest?
   c. What proportion of the bank's Visa cardholders pay less than $15 in interest?
   d. What interest payment is exceeded by only 20% of the bank's Visa cardholders?

8.63 It is said that sufferers of a cold virus experience symptoms for 7 days. However, the amount of time is actually a normally distributed random variable whose mean is 7.5 days and whose standard deviation is 1.2 days.
   a. What proportion of cold sufferers experience fewer than 4 days of symptoms?
   b. What proportion of cold sufferers experience symptoms for between 7 and 10 days?

8.64 How much money does a typical family of four spend at a McDonald's restaurant per visit? The amount is a normally distributed random variable with a mean of $16.40 and a standard deviation of $2.75.
   a. Find the probability that a family of four spends less than $10.
   b. What is the amount below which only 10% of families of four spend at McDonald's?

8.65 The final marks in a statistics course are normally distributed with a mean of 70 and a standard deviation of 10. The professor must convert all marks to letter grades. She decides that she wants 10% A's, 30% B's, 40% C's, 15% D's, and 5% F's. Determine the cutoffs for each letter grade.

8.66 Mensa is an organization whose members possess IQs that are in the top 2% of the population. It is known that IQs are normally distributed with a mean of 100 and a standard deviation of 16. Find the minimum IQ needed to be a Mensa member.

8.67 The daily withdrawals from an ATM located at a service station is normally distributed with a mean of $50,000 and a standard deviation of $8,000. The operator of the ATM puts $64,000 in cash at the beginning of the day. What is the probability that the ATM will run out of money?

8.68 According to the *Statistical Abstract of the United States, 2012* (Table 721), the mean family net worth of families whose head is between 35 and 44 years old is approximately $325,600. If family net worth is normally distributed with a standard deviation of $100,000, find the probability that a randomly selected family whose head is between 35 and 44 years old has a net worth greater than $500,000.

8.69 A retailer of computing products sells a variety of computer-related products. One of his most popular products is an HP laser printer. The average weekly demand is 200. Lead time for a new order from the manufacturer to arrive is 1 week. If the demand for printers were constant, the retailer would reorder when there were exactly 200 printers in inventory. However, the demand is a random variable. An analysis of previous weeks reveals that the weekly demand standard deviation is 30. The retailer knows that if a customer wants to buy an HP laser printer but he has none available, he will lose that sale plus possibly additional sales. He wants the probability of running short in any week to be no more than 6%. How many HP laser printers should he have in stock when he reorders from the manufacturer?

8.70 The demand for a daily newspaper at a newsstand at a busy intersection is known to be normally distributed with a mean of 150 and a standard deviation of 25. How many newspapers should the newsstand operator order to ensure that he runs short on no more than 20% of days?

8.71 Every day a bakery prepares its famous marble rye. A statistically savvy customer determined that daily demand is normally distributed with a mean of 850 and a standard deviation of 90. How many loaves should the bakery make if it wants the probability of running short on any day to be no more than 30%?

8.72 Refer to Exercise 8.71. Any marble ryes that are unsold at the end of the day are marked down and sold for half-price. How many loaves should the bakery prepare so that the proportion of days that result in unsold loaves is no more than 60%?

8.73 The annual rate of return on a mutual fund is normally distributed with a mean of 14% and a standard deviation of 18%.
 a. What is the probability that the fund returns more than 25% next year?
 b. What is the probability that the fund loses money next year?

8.74 In a survey of consumer finances, it was determined that the average household debt is $250,000. If household debt is normally distributed with a standard deviation of $30,000 determine the quintiles.

APPLICATIONS in OPERATIONS MANAGEMENT

PERT/CPM

In the Applications in Operations Management box on page 216, we introduced PERT/CPM. The purpose of this powerful management-science procedure is to determine the critical path of a project. The expected value and variance of the completion time of the project are based on the expected values and variances of the completion times of the activities on the critical path. Once we have the expected value and variance of the completion time of the project, we can use these figures to determine the probability that the project will be completed by a certain date. Statisticians have established that the completion time of the project is approximately normally distributed, enabling us to compute the needed probabilities.

8.75 Refer to Exercise 7.67. Find the probability that the project will take more than 60 days to complete.

8.76 The mean and variance of the time to complete the project in Exercise 7.68 was 145 minutes and 31 minutes^2. What is the probability that it will take less than 2.5 hours to overhaul the machine?

(Continued)

Banana Stock/Jupiter Images

8.77 Refer to Exercise 7.69. Find the probability of the following events.
   a. The launch of the new product takes more than 105 days.
   b. The launch of the new product takes more than 92 days.
   c. The launch of the new product takes between 95 and 112 days.

8.78 Refer to Exercise 7.70. Find the quartiles of the time to complete the research project.

8-3 / (OPTIONAL) EXPONENTIAL DISTRIBUTION

Another important continuous distribution is the **exponential distribution**.

> **Exponential Probability Density Function**
>
> A random variable X is exponentially distributed if its probability density function is given by
>
> $$f(x) = \lambda e^{-\lambda x}, \quad x \geq 0$$
>
> where $e = 2.71828 \ldots$ and λ is the parameter of the distribution.

Statisticians have shown that the mean and standard deviation of an exponential random variable are equal to each other:

$$\mu = \sigma = 1/\lambda$$

Recall that the normal distribution is a two-parameter distribution. The distribution is completely specified once the values of the two parameters μ and σ are known. In contrast, the exponential distribution is a one-parameter distribution. The distribution is completely specified once the value of the parameter λ is known. Figure 8.21 depicts three exponential distributions, corresponding to three different values of the parameter λ. Notice that for any exponential density function $f(x)$, $f(0) = \lambda$ and $f(x)$ approaches 0 as x approaches infinity.

FIGURE **8.21** Exponential Distributions

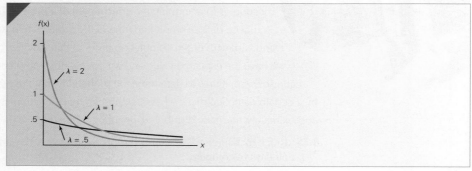

The exponential density function is easier to work with than the normal. As a result, we can develop formulas for the calculation of the probability of any range of values. Using integral calculus, we can determine the following probability statements.

> **Probability Associated with an Exponential Random Variable**
> If X is an exponential random variable,
> $$P(X > x) = e^{-\lambda x}$$
> $$P(X < x) = 1 - e^{-\lambda x}$$
> $$P(x_1 < X < x_2) = P(X < x_2) - P(X < x_1) = e^{-\lambda x_1} - e^{-\lambda x_2}$$

The value of $e^{-\lambda x}$ can be obtained with the aid of a calculator.

EXAMPLE 8.7

Lifetimes of Alkaline Batteries

The lifetime of an alkaline battery (measured in hours) is exponentially distributed with $\lambda = .05$.

 a. What is the mean and standard deviation of the battery's lifetime?
 b. Find the probability that a battery will last between 10 and 15 hours.
 c. What is the probability that a battery will last for more than 20 hours?

SOLUTION:

 a. The mean and standard deviation are equal to $1/\lambda$. Thus,
$$\mu = \sigma = 1/\lambda = 1/.05 = 20 \text{ hours}$$

 b. Let X denote the lifetime of a battery. The required probability is
$$\begin{aligned} P(10 < X < 15) &= e^{-.05(10)} - e^{-.05(15)} \\ &= e^{-.5} - e^{-.75} \\ &= .6065 - .4724 \\ &= .1341 \end{aligned}$$

 c. $\begin{aligned} P(X > 20) &= e^{-.05(20)} \\ &= e^{-1} \\ &= .3679 \end{aligned}$

Figure 8.22 depicts these probabilities.

FIGURE **8.22** **Probabilities for Example 8.7**

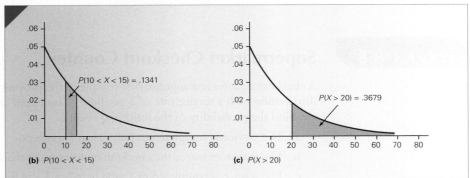

(b) $P(10 < X < 15)$ (c) $P(X > 20)$

EXCEL Function

INSTRUCTIONS

Type (in any cell)

= **EXPONDIST** ([X], [λ], True)

To produce the answer for Example 8.7c, we would find $P(X < 20)$ and subtract it from 1.

To find $P(X < 20)$, type

= **EXPONDIST**(20, .05, True)

which outputs .6321 and hence $P(X > 20) = 1 - .6321 = .3679$, which is exactly the number we produced manually.

APPLICATIONS in OPERATIONS MANAGEMENT

Waiting Lines

In Section 7-5, we described waiting-line models and how the Poisson distribution is used to calculate the probabilities of the number of arrivals per time period. To calculate the operating characteristics of waiting lines, management scientists often assume that the times to complete a service are exponentially distributed. In this application, the parameter λ is the service rate, which is defined as the mean number of service completions per time period.

For example, if service times are exponentially distributed with $\lambda = 5$/hour, this tells us that the service rate is 5 units per hour or 5 per 60 minutes. Recall that the mean of an exponential distribution is $\mu = 1/\lambda$. In this case, the service facility can complete a service in an average of 12 minutes. This was calculated as

$$\mu = \frac{1}{\lambda} = \frac{1}{5/\text{hour}} = \frac{1}{5/60 \text{ minutes}} = \frac{60 \text{ minutes}}{5} = 12 \text{ minutes}.$$

We can use this distribution to make a variety of probability statements.

EXAMPLE 8.8

Supermarket Checkout Counter

A checkout counter at a supermarket completes the process according to an exponential distribution with a service rate of 6 per hour. A customer arrives at the checkout counter. Find the probability of the following events.

a. The service is completed in fewer than 5 minutes.

b. The customer leaves the checkout counter more than 10 minutes after arriving.

c. The service is completed in a time between 5 and 8 minutes.

SOLUTION:

One way to solve this problem is to convert the service rate so that the time period is 1 minute. (Alternatively, we can solve by converting the probability statements so that the time periods are measured in fractions of an hour.) Let the service rate $= \lambda = .1/\text{minute}$.

  a. $P(X < 5) = 1 - e^{-\lambda x} = 1 - e^{-.1(5)} = 1 - e^{-.5} = 1 - .6065 = .3935$

  b. $P(X > 10) = e^{-\lambda x} = e^{-.1(10)} = e^{-1} = .3679$

  c. $P(5 < X < 8) = e^{-.1(5)} - e^{-.1(8)} = e^{-.5} - e^{-.8} = .6065 - .4493 = .1572$

EXERCISES

8.79 The random variable X is exponentially distributed with $\lambda = 3$. Sketch the graph of the distribution of X by plotting and connecting the points representing $f(x)$ for $x = 0, .5, 1, 1.5,$ and 2.

8.80 X is an exponential random variable with $\lambda = .25$. Sketch the graph of the distribution of X by plotting and connecting the points representing $f(x)$ for $x = 0, 2, 4, 6, 8, 10, 15, 20$.

8.81 Let X be an exponential random variable with $\lambda = .5$. Find the following probabilities.
  a. $P(X > 1)$
  b. $P(X > .4)$
  c. $P(X < .5)$
  d. $P(X < 2)$

8.82 X is an exponential random variable with $\lambda = .3$. Find the following probabilities.
  a. $P(X > 2)$
  b. $P(X < 4)$
  c. $P(1 < X < 2)$
  d. $P(X = 3)$

8.83 The production of a complex chemical needed for anticancer drugs is exponentially distributed with $\lambda = 6$ kilograms per hour. What is the probability that the production process requires more than 15 minutes to produce the next kilogram of drugs?

8.84 The time between breakdowns of aging machines is known to be exponentially distributed with a mean of 25 hours. The machine has just been repaired. Determine the probability that the next breakdown occurs more than 50 hours from now.

8.85 Canada and the United States are each other's largest trading partner. The two-way trade between these two countries is the largest in the world. This makes the Ambassador bridge linking Windsor Ontario and Detroit Michigan extremely busy. The Free Trade Agreement between Canada and the United States and the North American Free Trade Agreement (NAFTA) further increased trade. Trucks heading into Detroit and Windsor have on occasion been backed up for miles. When trucks arrive at the Ambassador Bridge connecting Windsor and Detroit, each truck must be checked by customs agents. Suppose that the times are exponentially distributed with a service rate of 10 per hour. What is the probability that a truck requires more than 15 minutes to be checked?

8.86 A bank wishing to increase its customer base advertises that it has the fastest service and that virtually all of its customers are served in less than 10 minutes. A management scientist has studied the service times and concluded that service times are exponentially distributed with a mean of 5 minutes. Determine what the bank means when it claims "virtually all" its customers are served in less than 10 minutes.

8.87 Toll booths on the New York State Thruway are often congested because of the large number of cars waiting to pay. A consultant working for the state concluded that if service times are measured from the time a car stops in line until it leaves, service times are exponentially distributed with a mean of 2.7 minutes. What proportion of cars can get through the toll booth in less than 3 minutes?

8.88 The manager of a gas station has observed that the times required by drivers to fill their car's tank and pay are quite variable. In fact, the times are exponentially distributed with a mean of 7.5 minutes. What is the probability that a car can complete the transaction in less than 5 minutes?

8.89 Because automatic banking machine (ABM) customers can perform a number of transactions, the times to complete them can be quite variable. A banking consultant has noted that the times are exponentially distributed with a mean of 125 seconds. What proportion of the ABM customers take more than 3 minutes to do their banking?

8.90 The manager of a supermarket tracked the amount of time needed for customers to be served by the cashier. After checking with his statistics professor, he concluded that the checkout times are exponentially distributed with a mean of 6 minutes. What proportion of customers require more than 10 minutes to check out?

APPLICATIONS in **OPERATIONS MANAGEMENT**

Determining the Service Rate

In some circumstances, the value of λ can be controlled by management. For example, in a supermarket, a manager can improve the service rate at a checkout counter by employing a worker to fill the shopper's bags. We can calculate the value of λ by specifying a value for x and its probability. To illustrate, suppose that the current service rate is 8 per hour. That is, $\lambda = 8$ and the mean of the exponential distribution is $1/\lambda = 1/8 = .125$ hour or 7.5 minutes. The manager would like the probability that a checkout takes longer than 15 minutes (.25 of an hour) to be less than 5%. With $\lambda = 8$ the probability that checkout will take longer than .25 of an hour is

$$P(X > .25) = e^{-\lambda x} = e^{-8(.25)} = e^{-2} = .1350$$

which the manager considers too large.

To solve for λ given x and the probability that X is greater than x, we solve the equation for λ

$$P(X > x) = e^{-\lambda x}$$

Thus,

$$ln[P(X > x)] = -\lambda x$$

or

$$\lambda = \frac{-ln[P(X > x)]}{x}$$

where ln is the natural logarithm (logarithm using the base e)
With $x = .25$ and the probability $= 5\%$, we find

$$\lambda = \frac{-ln[P(X > x)]}{x} = \frac{-ln(.05)}{.25} = 12$$

The manager can reduce the probability that a checkout will take longer than 15 minutes to .05 by increasing the service rate to 12 per hour.

8.91 Refer to Exercise 8.85. In order to improve the time spent by trucks waiting, both countries should improve the service rate by customs agents. Suppose that the governments decided that the probability that a truck spends more than 30 minutes being checked should be less than 1%. Find the service rate to accomplish this goal.

8.92 A Jiffy Lube franchise manager is concerned about the amount of time it takes for his technicians to change the oil and filters of cars. The current mean time for the complete operation is 18 minutes. He hasn't kept track of the number of times his employees took more than 30 minutes to complete a car but he knows that the probability is too high. There are several ways to reduce the mean time. Determine the mean time necessary to reduce the probability that a job takes longer than 30 minutes to 10%.

8-4 / OTHER CONTINUOUS DISTRIBUTIONS

In this section, we introduce three more continuous distributions that are used extensively in statistical inference.

8-4a Student *t* Distribution

The Student *t* distribution was first derived by William S. Gosset in 1908. (Gosset published his findings under the pseudonym "Student" and used the letter *t* to represent the random variable, hence the **Student *t* distribution**—also called the *Student's t distribution*.) It is very commonly used in statistical inference, and we will employ it in Chapters 12, 13, 14, 16, 17, and 18.

Student *t* Density Function

The density function of the Student *t* distribution is as follows:

$$f(t) = \frac{\Gamma[(\nu + 1)/2]}{\sqrt{\nu\pi}\,\Gamma(\nu/2)}\left[1 + \frac{t^2}{\nu} \right]^{-(\nu+1)/2}$$

where ν (Greek letter *nu*) is the parameter of the Student *t* distribution called the **degrees of freedom**, $\pi = 3.14159$ (approximately), and Γ is the gamma function (its definition is not needed here).

The mean and variance of a Student *t* random variable are

$$E(t) = 0$$

and

$$V(t) = \frac{\nu}{\nu - 2} \quad \text{for } \nu > 2$$

Figure 8.23 depicts the Student *t* distribution. As you can see, it is similar to the standard normal distribution. Both are symmetrical about 0. (Both random variables have a mean of 0.) We describe the Student *t* distribution as mound shaped, whereas the normal distribution is bell shaped.

FIGURE **8.23** Student *t* Distribution

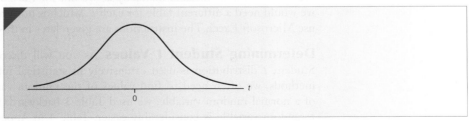

Figure 8.24 shows both the Student t and the standard normal distributions. The former is more widely spread out than the latter. [The variance of a standard normal random variable is 1, whereas the variance of a Student t random variable is $\nu/(\nu-2)$, which is greater than 1 for all ν.]

FIGURE 8.24 Student t and Normal Distributions

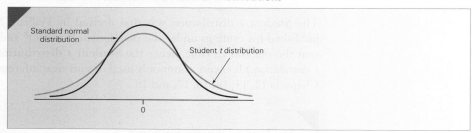

Figure 8.25 depicts Student t distributions with several different degrees of freedom. Notice that for larger degrees of freedom the Student t distribution's dispersion is smaller. For example, when $\nu = 10$, $V(t) = 1.25$; when $\nu = 50$, $V(t) = 1.042$; and when $\nu = 200$, $V(t) = 1.010$. As ν grows larger, the Student t distribution approaches the standard normal distribution.

FIGURE 8.25 Student t Distribution with $\nu = 2$, 10, and 30

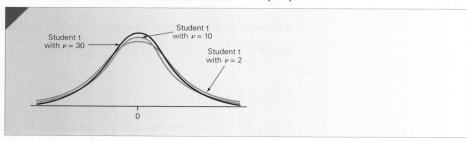

Student t Probabilities For each value of ν (the number of degrees of freedom), there is a different Student t distribution. If we wanted to calculate probabilities of the Student t random variable manually as we did for the normal random variable, then we would need a different table for each ν, which is not practical. Alternatively, we can use Microsoft Excel. The instructions are given later in this section.

Determining Student t Values As you will discover later in this book, the Student t distribution is used extensively in statistical inference. And for inferential methods, we often need to find values of the random variable. To determine values of a normal random variable, we used Table 3 backward. Finding values of a Student t random variable is considerably easier. Table 4 in Appendix B (reproduced here as Table 8.2) lists values of $t_{A,\nu}$, which are the values of a Student t random variable with ν degrees of freedom such that

$$P(t > t_{A,\nu}) = A$$

Figure 8.26 depicts this notation.

FIGURE **8.26** Student t Distribution with t_A

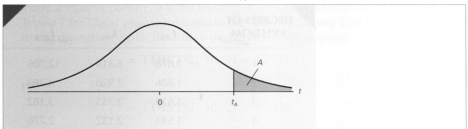

TABLE **8.2** Critical Values of t

ν	$t_{.100}$	$t_{.050}$	$t_{.025}$	$t_{.010}$	$t_{.005}$	ν	$t_{.100}$	$t_{.050}$	$t_{.025}$	$t_{.010}$	$t_{.005}$
1	3.078	6.314	12.71	31.82	63.66	29	1.311	1.699	2.045	2.462	2.756
2	1.886	2.920	4.303	6.965	9.925	30	1.310	1.697	2.042	2.457	2.750
3	1.638	2.353	3.182	4.541	5.841	35	1.306	1.690	2.030	2.438	2.724
4	1.533	2.132	2.776	3.747	4.604	40	1.303	1.684	2.021	2.423	2.704
5	1.476	2.015	2.571	3.365	4.032	45	1.301	1.679	2.014	2.412	2.690
6	1.440	1.943	2.447	3.143	3.707	50	1.299	1.676	2.009	2.403	2.678
7	1.415	1.895	2.365	2.998	3.499	55	1.297	1.673	2.004	2.396	2.668
8	1.397	1.860	2.306	2.896	3.355	60	1.296	1.671	2.000	2.390	2.660
9	1.383	1.833	2.262	2.821	3.250	65	1.295	1.669	1.997	2.385	2.654
10	1.372	1.812	2.228	2.764	3.169	70	1.294	1.667	1.994	2.381	2.648
11	1.363	1.796	2.201	2.718	3.106	75	1.293	1.665	1.992	2.377	2.643
12	1.356	1.782	2.179	2.681	3.055	80	1.292	1.664	1.990	2.374	2.639
13	1.350	1.771	2.160	2.650	3.012	85	1.292	1.663	1.988	2.371	2.635
14	1.345	1.761	2.145	2.624	2.977	90	1.291	1.662	1.987	2.368	2.632
15	1.341	1.753	2.131	2.602	2.947	95	1.291	1.661	1.985	2.366	2.629
16	1.337	1.746	2.120	2.583	2.921	100	1.290	1.660	1.984	2.364	2.626
17	1.333	1.740	2.110	2.567	2.898	110	1.289	1.659	1.982	2.361	2.621
18	1.330	1.734	2.101	2.552	2.878	120	1.289	1.658	1.980	2.358	2.617
19	1.328	1.729	2.093	2.539	2.861	130	1.288	1.657	1.978	2.355	2.614
20	1.325	1.725	2.086	2.528	2.845	140	1.288	1.656	1.977	2.353	2.611
21	1.323	1.721	2.080	2.518	2.831	150	1.287	1.655	1.976	2.351	2.609
22	1.321	1.717	2.074	2.508	2.819	160	1.287	1.654	1.975	2.350	2.607
23	1.319	1.714	2.069	2.500	2.807	170	1.287	1.654	1.974	2.348	2.605
24	1.318	1.711	2.064	2.492	2.797	180	1.286	1.653	1.973	2.347	2.603
25	1.316	1.708	2.060	2.485	2.787	190	1.286	1.653	1.973	2.346	2.602
26	1.315	1.706	2.056	2.479	2.779	200	1.286	1.653	1.972	2.345	2.601
27	1.314	1.703	2.052	2.473	2.771	∞	1.282	1.645	1.960	2.326	2.576
28	1.313	1.701	2.048	2.467	2.763						

Observe that $t_{A,\nu}$ is provided for degrees of freedom ranging from 1 to 200 and ∞. To read this table, simply identify the degrees of freedom and find that value or the closest number to it if it is not listed. Then locate the column representing the t_A value you wish. For example, if we want the value of t with 10 degrees of freedom such that the area under the Student t curve is .05, we locate 10 in the first column and move across this row until we locate the number under the heading $t_{.05}$. From Table 8.3, we find

$$t_{.05, 10} = 1.812$$

If the number of degrees of freedom is not shown, find its closest value. For example, suppose we wanted to find $t_{.025, 32}$. Because 32 degrees of freedom is not listed, we find the closest number of degrees of freedom, which is 30, and use $t_{.025, 30} = 2.042$ as an approximation.

The mean and variance of a chi-squared random variable are

$$E(\chi^2) = \nu$$

and

$$V(\chi^2) = 2\nu$$

Determining Chi-Squared Values The value of χ^2 with ν degrees of freedom such that the area to its right under the chi-squared curve is equal to A is denoted by $\chi^2_{A,\nu}$. We cannot use $-\chi^2_{A,\nu}$ to represent the point such that the area to its *left* is A (as we did with the standard normal and Student t values) because χ^2 is always greater than 0. To represent left-tail critical values, we note that if the area to the left of a point is A, the area to its right must be $1 - A$ because the entire area under the chi-squared curve (as well as all continuous distributions) must equal 1. Thus, $\chi^2_{1-A,\nu}$ denotes the point such that the area to its left is A. See Figure 8.29.

FIGURE **8.29** χ^2_A and χ^2_{1-A}

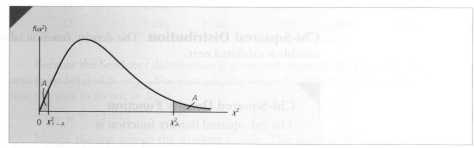

Table 5 in Appendix B (reproduced here as Table 8.4) lists critical values of the chi-squared distribution for degrees of freedom equal to 1 to 30, 40, 50, 60, 70, 80, 90, and 100. For example, to find the point in a chi-squared distribution with 8 degrees of freedom such that the area to its right is .05, locate 8 degrees of freedom in the left column and $\chi^2_{.050}$ across the top. The intersection of the row and column contains the number we seek as shown in Table 8.5; that is,

$$\chi^2_{.050, 8} = 15.5$$

To find the point in the same distribution such that the area to its *left* is .05, find the point such that the area to its *right* is .95. Locate $\chi^2_{.950}$ across the top row and 8 degrees of freedom down the left column (also shown in Table 8.5). You should see that

$$\chi^2_{.950, 8} = 2.73$$

TABLE **8.4** Critical Values of χ^2

ν	$\chi^2_{.995}$	$\chi^2_{.990}$	$\chi^2_{.975}$	$\chi^2_{.950}$	$\chi^2_{.900}$	$\chi^2_{.100}$	$\chi^2_{.050}$	$\chi^2_{.025}$	$\chi^2_{.010}$	$\chi^2_{.005}$
1	0.000039	0.000157	0.000982	0.00393	0.0158	2.71	3.84	5.02	6.63	7.88
2	0.0100	0.0201	0.0506	0.103	0.211	4.61	5.99	7.38	9.21	10.6
3	0.072	0.115	0.216	0.352	0.584	6.25	7.81	9.35	11.3	12.8

ν	$\chi^2_{.995}$	$\chi^2_{.990}$	$\chi^2_{.975}$	$\chi^2_{.950}$	$\chi^2_{.900}$	$\chi^2_{.100}$	$\chi^2_{.050}$	$\chi^2_{.025}$	$\chi^2_{.010}$	$\chi^2_{.005}$
4	0.207	0.297	0.484	0.711	1.06	7.78	9.49	11.1	13.3	14.9
5	0.412	0.554	0.831	1.15	1.61	9.24	11.1	12.8	15.1	16.7
6	0.676	0.872	1.24	1.64	2.20	10.6	12.6	14.4	16.8	18.5
7	0.989	1.24	1.69	2.17	2.83	12.0	14.1	16.0	18.5	20.3
8	1.34	1.65	2.18	2.73	3.49	13.4	15.5	17.5	20.1	22.0
9	1.73	2.09	2.70	3.33	4.17	14.7	16.9	19.0	21.7	23.6
10	2.16	2.56	3.25	3.94	4.87	16.0	18.3	20.5	23.2	25.2
11	2.60	3.05	3.82	4.57	5.58	17.3	19.7	21.9	24.7	26.8
12	3.07	3.57	4.40	5.23	6.30	18.5	21.0	23.3	26.2	28.3
13	3.57	4.11	5.01	5.89	7.04	19.8	22.4	24.7	27.7	29.8
14	4.07	4.66	5.63	6.57	7.79	21.1	23.7	26.1	29.1	31.3
15	4.60	5.23	6.26	7.26	8.55	22.3	25.0	27.5	30.6	32.8
16	5.14	5.81	6.91	7.96	9.31	23.5	26.3	28.8	32.0	34.3
17	5.70	6.41	7.56	8.67	10.09	24.8	27.6	30.2	33.4	35.7
18	6.26	7.01	8.23	9.39	10.86	26.0	28.9	31.5	34.8	37.2
19	6.84	7.63	8.91	10.12	11.65	27.2	30.1	32.9	36.2	38.6
20	7.43	8.26	9.59	10.85	12.44	28.4	31.4	34.2	37.6	40.0
21	8.03	8.90	10.28	11.59	13.24	29.6	32.7	35.5	38.9	41.4
22	8.64	9.54	10.98	12.34	14.04	30.8	33.9	36.8	40.3	42.8
23	9.26	10.20	11.69	13.09	14.85	32.0	35.2	38.1	41.6	44.2
24	9.89	10.86	12.40	13.85	15.66	33.2	36.4	39.4	43.0	45.6
25	10.52	11.52	13.12	14.61	16.47	34.4	37.7	40.6	44.3	46.9
26	11.16	12.20	13.84	15.38	17.29	35.6	38.9	41.9	45.6	48.3
27	11.81	12.88	14.57	16.15	18.11	36.7	40.1	43.2	47.0	49.6
28	12.46	13.56	15.31	16.93	18.94	37.9	41.3	44.5	48.3	51.0
29	13.12	14.26	16.05	17.71	19.77	39.1	42.6	45.7	49.6	52.3
30	13.79	14.95	16.79	18.49	20.60	40.3	43.8	47.0	50.9	53.7
40	20.71	22.16	24.43	26.51	29.05	51.8	55.8	59.3	63.7	66.8
50	27.99	29.71	32.36	34.76	37.69	63.2	67.5	71.4	76.2	79.5
60	35.53	37.48	40.48	43.19	46.46	74.4	79.1	83.3	88.4	92.0
70	43.28	45.44	48.76	51.74	55.33	85.5	90.5	95.0	100	104
80	51.17	53.54	57.15	60.39	64.28	96.6	102	107	112	116
90	59.20	61.75	65.65	69.13	73.29	108	113	118	124	128
100	67.33	70.06	74.22	77.93	82.36	118	124	130	136	140

TABLE **8.5** Critical Values of $\chi^2_{.05,\,8}$ and $\chi^2_{.950,\,8}$

DEGREES OF FREEDOM	$\chi^2_{.995}$	$\chi^2_{.990}$	$\chi^2_{.975}$	$\chi^2_{.950}$	$\chi^2_{.900}$	$\chi^2_{.100}$	$\chi^2_{.050}$	$\chi^2_{.025}$	$\chi^2_{.010}$	$\chi^2_{.005}$
1	0.000039	0.000157	0.000982	0.00393	0.0158	2.71	3.84	5.02	6.63	7.88
2	0.0100	0.0201	0.0506	0.103	0.211	4.61	5.99	7.38	9.21	10.6
3	0.072	0.115	0.216	0.352	0.584	6.25	7.81	9.35	11.3	12.8
4	0.207	0.297	0.484	0.711	1.06	7.78	9.49	11.1	13.3	14.9
5	0.412	0.554	0.831	1.15	1.61	9.24	11.1	12.8	15.1	16.7
6	0.676	0.872	1.24	1.64	2.20	10.6	12.6	14.4	16.8	18.5
7	0.989	1.24	1.69	2.17	2.83	12.0	14.1	16.0	18.5	20.3
8	1.34	1.65	2.18	2.73	3.49	13.4	15.5	17.5	20.1	22.0
9	1.73	2.09	2.70	3.33	4.17	14.7	16.9	19.0	21.7	23.6
10	2.16	2.56	3.25	3.94	4.87	16.0	18.3	20.5	23.2	25.2
11	2.60	3.05	3.82	4.57	5.58	17.3	19.7	21.9	24.7	26.8

For values of degrees of freedom greater than 100, the chi-squared distribution can be approximated by a normal distribution with $\mu = \nu$ and $\sigma = \sqrt{2\nu}$.

EXCEL Function

To calculate $P(\chi^2 > x)$, type into any cell

$$= \textbf{CHIDIST}([x], [\nu])$$

For example, **CHIDIST**$(6.25, 3) = .100$.

To determine $\chi_{A,\nu}$, type

$$= \textbf{CHIINV}([A], [\nu])$$

For example, $= \textbf{CHIINV}(.10, 3) = 6.25$

8-4b *F* Distribution

The density function of the *F* **distribution** is given in the following box.

F Density Function

$$f(F) = \frac{\Gamma\left(\dfrac{\nu_1 + \nu_2}{2}\right)}{\Gamma\left(\dfrac{\nu_1}{2}\right)\Gamma\left(\dfrac{\nu_2}{2}\right)} \left(\frac{\nu_1}{\nu_2}\right)^{\frac{\nu_1}{2}} \frac{F^{\frac{\nu_1 - 2}{2}}}{\left(1 + \dfrac{\nu_1 F}{\nu_2}\right)^{\frac{\nu_2 + \nu_2}{2}}} \quad F > 0$$

where *F* ranges from 0 to ∞ and ν_1 and ν_2 are the parameters of the distribution called degrees of freedom. For reasons that are clearer in Chapter 13, we call ν_1 the *numerator degrees of freedom* and ν_2 the *denominator degrees of freedom*.

The mean and variance of an F random variable are

$$E(F) = \frac{\nu_2}{\nu_2 - 2} \quad \nu_2 > 2$$

and

$$V(F) = \frac{2\nu_2^2(\nu_1 + \nu_2 - 2)}{\nu_1(\nu_2 - 2)^2(\nu_2 - 4)} \quad \nu_2 > 4$$

Notice that the mean depends only on the denominator degrees of freedom and that for large ν_2 the mean of the F distribution is approximately 1. Figure 8.30 describes the density function when it is graphed. As you can see, the F distribution is positively skewed. Its actual shape depends on the two numbers of degrees of freedom.

FIGURE **8.30** *F* **Distribution**

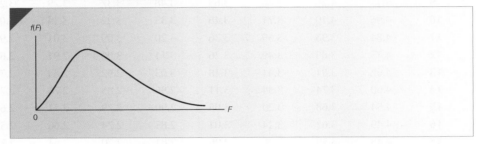

Determining Values of F We define F_{A,ν_1,ν_2} as the value of F with ν_1 and ν_2 degrees of freedom such that the area to its right under the curve is A; that is,

$$P(F > F_{A,\nu_1,\nu_2}) = A$$

Because the F random variable like the chi-squared can equal only positive values, we define F_{1-A,ν_1,ν_2} as the value such that the area to its left is A. Figure 8.31 depicts this notation. Table 6 in Appendix B provides values of F_{A,ν_1,ν_2} for $A = .05, .025, .01,$ and $.005$. Part of Table 6 is reproduced here as Table 8.6.

Values of F_{1-A,ν_1,ν_2} are unavailable. However, we do not need them because we can determine F_{1-A,ν_1,ν_2} from F_{A,ν_1,ν_2}. Statisticians can show that

$$F_{1-A,\nu_1,\nu_2} = \frac{1}{F_{A,\nu_2,\nu_1}}.$$

FIGURE **8.31** F_{1-A} **and** F_A

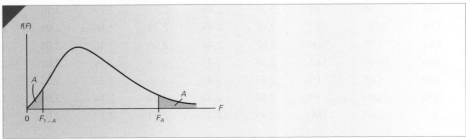

TABLE **8.6**   Critical Values of F_A for $A = .05$

ν_2	ν_1									
	1	2	3	4	5	6	7	8	9	10
1	161	199	216	225	230	234	237	239	241	242
2	18.5	19.0	19.2	19.2	19.3	19.3	19.4	19.4	19.4	19.4
3	10.1	9.55	9.28	9.12	9.01	8.94	8.89	8.85	8.81	8.79
4	7.71	6.94	6.59	6.39	6.26	6.16	6.09	6.04	6.00	5.96
5	6.61	5.79	5.41	5.19	5.05	4.95	4.88	4.82	4.77	4.74
6	5.99	5.14	4.76	4.53	4.39	4.28	4.21	4.15	4.10	4.06
7	5.59	4.74	4.35	4.12	3.97	3.87	3.79	3.73	3.68	3.64
8	5.32	4.46	4.07	3.84	3.69	3.58	3.50	3.44	3.39	3.35
9	5.12	4.26	3.86	3.63	3.48	3.37	3.29	3.23	3.18	3.14
10	4.96	4.10	3.71	3.48	3.33	3.22	3.14	3.07	3.02	2.98
11	4.84	3.98	3.59	3.36	3.20	3.09	3.01	2.95	2.90	2.85
12	4.75	3.89	3.49	3.26	3.11	3.00	2.91	2.85	2.80	2.75
13	4.67	3.81	3.41	3.18	3.03	2.92	2.83	2.77	2.71	2.67
14	4.60	3.74	3.34	3.11	2.96	2.85	2.76	2.70	2.65	2.60
15	4.54	3.68	3.29	3.06	2.90	2.79	2.71	2.64	2.59	2.54
16	4.49	3.63	3.24	3.01	2.85	2.74	2.66	2.59	2.54	2.49
17	4.45	3.59	3.20	2.96	2.81	2.70	2.61	2.55	2.49	2.45
18	4.41	3.55	3.16	2.93	2.77	2.66	2.58	2.51	2.46	2.41
19	4.38	3.52	3.13	2.90	2.74	2.63	2.54	2.48	2.42	2.38
20	4.35	3.49	3.10	2.87	2.71	2.60	2.51	2.45	2.39	2.35
22	4.30	3.44	3.05	2.82	2.66	2.55	2.46	2.40	2.34	2.30
24	4.26	3.40	3.01	2.78	2.62	2.51	2.42	2.36	2.30	2.25
26	4.23	3.37	2.98	2.74	2.59	2.47	2.39	2.32	2.27	2.22
28	4.20	3.34	2.95	2.71	2.56	2.45	2.36	2.29	2.24	2.19
30	4.17	3.32	2.92	2.69	2.53	2.42	2.33	2.27	2.21	2.16
35	4.12	3.27	2.87	2.64	2.49	2.37	2.29	2.22	2.16	2.11
40	4.08	3.23	2.84	2.61	2.45	2.34	2.25	2.18	2.12	2.08
45	4.06	3.20	2.81	2.58	2.42	2.31	2.22	2.15	2.10	2.05
50	4.03	3.18	2.79	2.56	2.40	2.29	2.20	2.13	2.07	2.03
60	4.00	3.15	2.76	2.53	2.37	2.25	2.17	2.10	2.04	1.99
70	3.98	3.13	2.74	2.50	2.35	2.23	2.14	2.07	2.02	1.97
80	3.96	3.11	2.72	2.49	2.33	2.21	2.13	2.06	2.00	1.95
90	3.95	3.10	2.71	2.47	2.32	2.20	2.11	2.04	1.99	1.94
100	3.94	3.09	2.70	2.46	2.31	2.19	2.10	2.03	1.97	1.93
120	3.92	3.07	2.68	2.45	2.29	2.18	2.09	2.02	1.96	1.91
140	3.91	3.06	2.67	2.44	2.28	2.16	2.08	2.01	1.95	1.90
160	3.90	3.05	2.66	2.43	2.27	2.16	2.07	2.00	1.94	1.89
180	3.89	3.05	2.65	2.42	2.26	2.15	2.06	1.99	1.93	1.88
200	3.89	3.04	2.65	2.42	2.26	2.14	2.06	1.98	1.93	1.88
∞	3.84	3.00	2.61	2.37	2.21	2.10	2.01	1.94	1.88	1.83

To determine any critical value, find the numerator degrees of freedom ν_1 across the top of Table 6 and the denominator degrees of freedom ν_2 down the left column. The intersection of the row and column contains the number we seek. To illustrate, suppose that we want to find $F_{.05, 5, 7}$. Table 8.7 shows how this point is found. Locate the numerator degrees of freedom, 5, across the top and the denominator degrees of freedom, 7, down the left column. The intersection is 3.97. Thus, $F_{.05, 5, 7} = 3.97$.

TABLE **8.7** $F_{.05, 5, 7}$

Denominator Degrees of Freedom

ν_1 ν_2	NUMERATOR DEGREES OF FREEDOM								
	1	2	3	4	5	6	7	8	9
1	161	199	216	225	230	234	237	239	241
2	18.5	19.0	19.2	19.2	19.3	19.3	19.4	19.4	19.4
3	10.1	9.55	9.28	9.12	9.01	8.94	8.89	8.85	8.81
4	7.71	6.94	6.59	6.39	6.26	6.16	6.09	6.04	6.00
5	6.61	5.79	5.41	5.19	5.05	4.95	4.88	4.82	4.77
6	5.99	5.14	4.76	4.53	4.39	4.28	4.21	4.15	4.1
7	5.59	4.74	4.35	4.12	3.97	3.87	3.79	3.73	3.68
8	5.32	4.46	4.07	3.84	3.69	3.58	3.5	3.44	3.39
9	5.12	4.26	3.86	3.63	3.48	3.37	3.29	3.23	3.18
10	4.96	4.10	3.71	3.48	3.33	3.22	3.14	3.07	3.02

Note that the order in which the degrees of freedom appear is important. To find $F_{.05, 7, 5}$ (numerator degrees of freedom = 7 and denominator degrees of freedom = 5), we locate 7 across the top and 5 down the side. The intersection is $F_{.05, 7, 5} = 4.88$.

Suppose that we want to determine the point in an F distribution with $\nu_1 = 4$ and $\nu_2 = 8$ such that the area to its right is .95. Thus,

$$F_{.95, 4, 8} = \frac{1}{F_{.05, 8, 4}} = \frac{1}{6.04} = .166$$

EXCEL Function

For probabilities, type

$$= \textbf{FDIST}([X],\ [\nu_1],\ [\nu_2])$$

For example, $= \textbf{FDIST}(3.97, 5, 7) = .05$.

To determine F_{A, ν_1, ν_2}, type

$$= \textbf{FINV}([A],\ [\nu_1],\ [\nu_2])$$

For example, $= \textbf{FINV}(.05, 5, 7) = 3.97$.

EXERCISES

Some of the following exercises require the use of a computer and software.

8.93 Use the t table (Table 4) to find the following values of t.

    a. $t_{.10, 15}$ b. $t_{.10, 23}$ c. $t_{.025, 83}$ d. $t_{.05, 195}$

8.94 Use the t table (Table 4) to find the following values of t.

    a. $t_{.005, 33}$ b. $t_{.10, 600}$ c. $t_{.05, 4}$ d. $t_{.01, 20}$

8.95 Use a computer to find the following values of t.

    a. $t_{.10, 15}$ b. $t_{.10, 23}$ c. $t_{.025, 83}$ d. $t_{.05, 195}$

8.96 Use a computer to find the following values of t.

    a. $t_{.05, 143}$ b. $t_{.01, 12}$ c. $t_{.025, \infty}$ d. $t_{.05, 100}$

8.97 Use a computer to find the following probabilities.

    a. $P(t_{64} > 2.12)$ c. $P(t_{159} > 1.33)$
    b. $P(t_{27} > 1.90)$ d. $P(t_{550} > 1.85)$

8.98 Use a computer to find the following probabilities.

    a. $P(t_{141} > .94)$ c. $P(t_{1000} > 1.96)$
    b. $P(t_{421} > 2.00)$ d. $P(t_{82} > 1.96)$

8.99 Use the χ^2 table (Table 5) to find the following values of χ^2.

    a. $\chi^2_{.10, 5}$ b. $\chi^2_{.01, 100}$ c. $\chi^2_{.95, 18}$ d. $\chi^2_{.99, 60}$

8.100 Use the χ^2 table (Table 5) to find the following values of χ^2.

    a. $\chi^2_{.90, 26}$ b. $\chi^2_{.01, 30}$ c. $\chi^2_{.10, 1}$ d. $\chi^2_{.99, 80}$

8.101 Use a computer to find the following values of χ^2.

    a. $\chi^2_{.25, 66}$ b. $\chi^2_{.40, 100}$ c. $\chi^2_{.50, 17}$ d. $\chi^2_{.10, 17}$

8.102 Use a computer to find the following values of χ^2.

    a. $\chi^2_{.99, 55}$ b. $\chi^2_{.05, 800}$ c. $\chi^2_{.99, 43}$ d. $\chi^2_{.10, 233}$

8.103 Use a computer to find the following probabilities.

    a. $P(\chi^2_{73} > 80)$
    b. $P(\chi^2_{200} > 125)$
    c. $P(\chi^2_{88} > 60)$
    d. $P(\chi^2_{1000} > 450)$

8.104 Use a computer to find the following probabilities.

    a. $P(\chi^2_{250} > 250)$ c. $P(\chi^2_{600} > 500)$
    b. $P(\chi^2_{36} > 25)$ d. $P(\chi^2_{120} > 100)$

8.105 Use the F table (Table 6) to find the following values of F.

    a. $F_{.05, 3, 7}$ b. $F_{.05, 7, 3}$ c. $F_{.025, 5, 20}$ d. $F_{.01, 12, 60}$

8.106 Use the F table (Table 6) to find the following values of F.

    a. $F_{.025, 8, 22}$ c. $F_{.01, 9, 18}$
    b. $F_{.05, 20, 30}$ d. $F_{..025, 24, 10}$

8.107 Use a computer to find the following values of F.

    a. $F_{.05, 70, 70}$ c. $F_{.025, 36, 50}$
    b. $F_{.01, 45, 100}$ d. $F_{.05, 500, 500}$

8.108 Use a computer to find the following values of F.

    a. $F_{.01, 100, 150}$ c. $F_{.01, 11, 33}$
    b. $F_{.05, 25, 125}$ d. $F_{.05, 300, 800}$

8.109 Use a computer to find the following probabilities.

    a. $P(F_{7, 20} > 2.5)$ c. $P(F_{34, 62} > 1.8)$
    b. $P(F_{18, 63} > 1.4)$ d. $P(F_{200, 400} > 1.1)$

8.110 Use a computer to find the following probabilities.

    a. $P(F_{600, 800} > 1.1)$
    b. $P(F_{35, 100} > 1.3)$
    c. $P(F_{66, 148} > 2.1)$
    d. $P(F_{17, 37} > 2.8)$

CHAPTER SUMMARY

This chapter dealt with **continuous random variables** and their distributions. Because a continuous random variable can assume an infinite number of values, the probability that the random variable equals any single value is 0. Consequently, we addressed the problem of computing the probability of a range of values. We showed that the probability of any interval is the area in the interval under the curve representing the **density function**.

We introduced the most important distribution in statistics and showed how to compute the probability that a **normal random variable** falls into any interval. Additionally, we demonstrated how to use the normal table backward to find values of a normal random variable given a probability. Next we introduced the **exponential distribution**, a distribution that is particularly useful in several management-science applications. Finally, we presented three more continuous random variables and their probability density functions. The **Student** *t*, **chi-squared**, and *F* **distributions** will be used extensively in statistical inference.

IMPORTANT TERMS:

Probability density function   246
Uniform probability distribution   247
Rectangular probability distribution   247
Normal distribution   251
Normal random variable   251
Standard normal random variable   253

Exponential distribution   268
Student *t* distribution   273
Degrees of freedom   273
Chi-squared distribution   277
F distribution   280

SYMBOLS:

Symbol	Pronounced	Represents
π	pi	3.14159 …
z_A	z-sub-*A* or z-*A*	Value of Z such that area to its right is A
ν	nu	Degrees of freedom
t_A	t-sub-*A* or t-*A*	Value of t such that area to its right is A
χ_A^2	chi-squared-sub-*A* or chi-squared-*A*	Value of chi-squared such that area to its right is A
F_A	F-sub-*A* or F-*A*	Value of F such that area to its right is A
ν_1	nu-sub-one or nu-one	Numerator degrees of freedom
ν_2	nu-sub-two or nu-two	Denominator degrees of freedom

COMPUTER OUTPUT AND INSTRUCTIONS:

Probability/Random Variable	Excel
Normal probability	262
Normal random variable	263
Exponential probability	270
Exponential random variable	270
Student *t* probability	277
Student *t* random variable	277
Chi-squared probability	280
Chi-squared random variable	280
F probability	283
F random variable	283

George Rudy/Shutterstock.com

9

SAMPLING DISTRIBUTIONS

CHAPTER OUTLINE

Salaries of a Business School's Graduates

Deans and other faculty members in professional schools often monitor how well the graduates of their programs fare in the job market. Information about the types of jobs and their salaries may provide useful information about the success of a program.

In the advertisements for a large university, the dean of the School of Business claims that the average salary of the school's graduates 1 year after graduation is $800 per week, with a standard deviation of $100. A second-year student in the business school who has just completed his statistics course would like to check whether the claim about the mean is correct. He does a survey of 25 people who graduated 1 year earlier and determines their weekly salary. He discovers the sample mean to be $750. To interpret his finding, he needs to calculate the probability that a sample of 25 graduates would have a mean of $750 or less when the population mean is $800 and the standard deviation is $100. After calculating the probability, he needs to draw some conclusion.

See page 294 for the answer.

Anton Gvozdikov/Shutterstock.com

This chapter introduces the *sampling distribution*, a fundamental element in statistical inference. We remind you that statistical inference is the process of converting data into information. Here are the parts of the process we have thus far discussed:

1. Parameters describe populations.
2. Parameters are almost always unknown.
3. We take a random sample of a population to obtain the necessary data.
4. We calculate one or more statistics from the data.

For example, to estimate a population mean, we compute the sample mean. Although there is very little chance that the sample mean and the population mean are identical, we would expect them to be quite close. However, for the purposes of statistical inference, we need to be able to measure *how* close. The sampling distribution provides this service. It plays a crucial role in the process because the measure of proximity it provides is the key to statistical inference.

9-1 / SAMPLING DISTRIBUTION OF THE MEAN

A **sampling distribution** is created by, as the name suggests, sampling. There are two ways to create a sampling distribution. The first is to actually draw samples of the same size from a population, calculate the statistic of interest, and then use descriptive techniques to learn more about the sampling distribution. The second method relies on the rules of probability and the laws of expected value and variance to derive the sampling distribution. We'll demonstrate the latter approach by developing the sampling distribution of the mean of two dice.

9-1a Sampling Distribution of the Mean of Two Dice

The population is created by throwing a fair die infinitely many times, with the random variable X indicating the number of spots showing on any one throw. The probability distribution of the random variable X is as follows:

x	1	2	3	4	5	6
$P(x)$	1/6	1/6	1/6	1/6	1/6	1/6

The population is infinitely large because we can throw the die infinitely many times (or at least imagine doing so). From the definitions of expected value and variance presented in Section 7-1, we calculate the population mean, variance, and standard deviation.

Population mean:

$$\mu = \sum x P(x)$$

$$= 1(1/6) + 2(1/6) + 3(1/6) + 4(1/6) + 5(1/6) + 6(1/6)$$

$$= 3.5$$

Population variance:

$$\sigma^2 = \sum (x - \mu)^2 P(x)$$
$$= (1 - 3.5)^2(1/6) + (2 - 3.5)^2(1/6) + (3 - 3.5)^2(1/6) + (4 - 3.5)^2(1/6)$$
$$+ (5 - 3.5)^2(1/6) + (6 - 3.5)^2(1/6)$$
$$= 2.92$$

Population standard deviation:

$$\sigma = \sqrt{\sigma^2} = \sqrt{2.92} = 1.71$$

The sampling distribution is created by drawing samples of size 2 from the population. In other words, we toss two dice. Figure 9.1 depicts this process in which we compute the mean for each sample. Because the value of the sample mean varies randomly from sample to sample, we can regard $\overline{X}$ as a new random variable created by sampling. Table 9.1 lists all the possible samples and their corresponding values of $\bar{x}$.

FIGURE **9.1** **Drawing Samples of Size 2 from a Population**

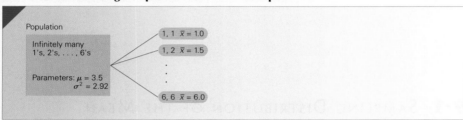

TABLE **9.1** **All Samples of Size 2 and Their Means**

SAMPLE	$\overline{X}$	SAMPLE	$\overline{X}$	SAMPLE	$\overline{X}$
1, 1	1.0	3, 1	2.0	5, 1	3.0
1, 2	1.5	3, 2	2.5	5, 2	3.5
1, 3	2.0	3, 3	3.0	5, 3	4.0
1, 4	2.5	3, 4	3.5	5, 4	4.5
1, 5	3.0	3, 5	4.0	5, 5	5.0
1, 6	3.5	3, 6	4.5	5, 6	5.5
2, 1	1.5	4, 1	2.5	6, 1	3.5
2, 2	2.0	4, 2	3.0	6, 2	4.0
2, 3	2.5	4, 3	3.5	6, 3	4.5
2, 4	3.0	4, 4	4.0	6, 4	5.0
2, 5	3.5	4, 5	4.5	6, 5	5.5
2, 6	4.0	4, 6	5.0	6, 6	6.0

There are 36 different possible samples of size 2; because each sample is equally likely, the probability of any one sample being selected is 1/36. However, $\bar{x}$ can assume only 11 different possible values: 1.0, 1.5, 2.0, . . . , 6.0, with certain values of $\bar{x}$ occurring more frequently than others. The value $\bar{x} = 1.0$ occurs only once, so its probability is 1/36. The value $\bar{x} = 1.5$ can occur in two ways—(1, 2) and (2, 1)—each having the same probability (1/36). Thus, $P(\bar{x} = 1.5) = 2/36$. The probabilities of the other values of $\bar{x}$ are determined in similar fashion, and the resulting **sampling distribution of the sample mean** is shown in Table 9.2.

TABLE **9.2** Sampling Distribution of $\bar{X}$

$\bar{x}$	$P(\bar{x})$
1.0	1/36
1.5	2/36
2.0	3/36
2.5	4/36
3.0	5/36
3.5	6/36
4.0	5/36
4.5	4/36
5.0	3/36
5.5	2/36
6.0	1/36

The most interesting aspect of the sampling distribution of $\bar{X}$ is how different it is from the distribution of X, as can be seen in Figure 9.2.

FIGURE **9.2** Distributions of X and $\bar{X}$

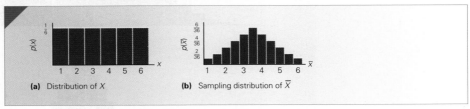

(a) Distribution of X (b) Sampling distribution of $\bar{X}$

We can also compute the mean, variance, and standard deviation of the sampling distribution. Once again using the definitions of expected value and variance, we determine the following parameters of the sampling distribution.

Mean of the sampling distribution of $\bar{X}$:

$$\mu_{\bar{x}} = \sum \bar{x} P(\bar{x})$$
$$= 1.0(1/36) + 1.5(2/36) + \cdots + 6.0(1/36)$$
$$= 3.5$$

Notice that the mean of the sampling distribution of $\bar{X}$ is equal to the mean of the population of the toss of a die computed previously.

Variance of the sampling distribution of $\bar{X}$:

$$\sigma_{\bar{x}}^2 = \sum (\bar{x} - \mu_{\bar{x}})^2 P(\bar{x})$$
$$= (1.0 - 3.5)^2(1/36) + (1.5 - 3.5)^2(2/36) + \cdots + (6.0 - 3.5)^2(1/36)$$
$$= 1.46$$

It is no coincidence that the variance of the sampling distribution of $\bar{X}$ is exactly half of the variance of the population of the toss of a die (computed previously as $\sigma^2 = 2.92$).

Standard deviation of the sampling distribution of $\bar{X}$:

$$\sigma_{\bar{x}} = \sqrt{\sigma_{\bar{x}}^2} = \sqrt{1.46} = 1.21$$

It is important to recognize that the distribution of $\overline{X}$ is different from the distribution of X as depicted in Figure 9.2. However, the two random variables are related. Their means are the same ($\mu_{\overline{x}} = \mu = 3.5$) and their variances are related ($\sigma_{\overline{x}}^2 = \sigma^2/2$).

Don't get lost in the terminology and notation. Remember that μ and σ^2 are the parameters of the population of X. To create the sampling distribution of $\overline{X}$, we repeatedly drew samples of size $n = 2$ from the population and calculated $\overline{x}$ for each sample. Thus, we treat $\overline{X}$ as a brand-new random variable, with its own distribution, mean, and variance. The mean is denoted by $\mu_{\overline{x}}$, and the variance is denoted by $\sigma_{\overline{x}}^2$.

If we now repeat the sampling process with the same population but with other values of n, we produce somewhat different sampling distributions of $\overline{X}$. Figure 9.3 shows the sampling distributions of $\overline{X}$ when $n = 5$, 10, and 25.

FIGURE 9.3 **Sampling Distributions of $\overline{X}$ for $n = 5$, 10, and 25**

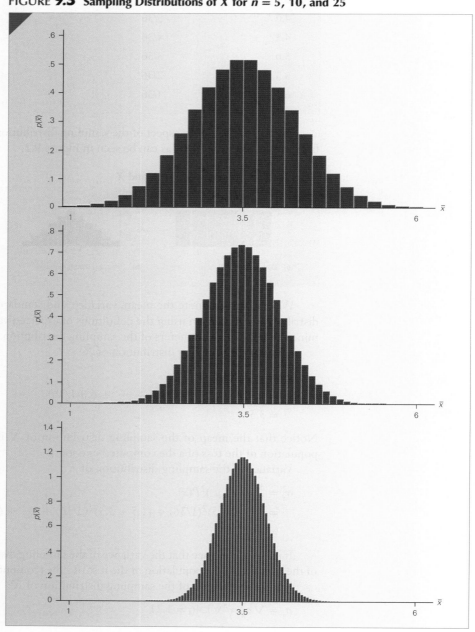

between -1.96 and 1.96 is $.95$. Figure 9.6 depicts this notation. We can express the notation algebraically as

$$P(-1.96 < Z < 1.96) = .95$$

FIGURE **9.6** $P(-1.96 < Z < 1.96) = .95$

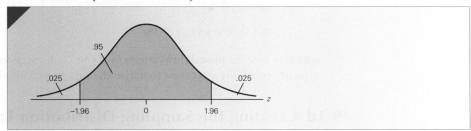

In this section, we established that

$$Z = \frac{\overline{X} - \mu}{\sigma/\sqrt{n}}$$

is standard normally distributed. Substituting this form of Z into the previous probability statement, we produce

$$P\left(-1.96 < \frac{\overline{X} - \mu}{\sigma/\sqrt{n}} < 1.96\right) = .95$$

With a little algebraic manipulation (multiply all three terms by $\sigma/\sqrt{n}$ and add μ to all three terms), we determine

$$P\left(\mu - 1.96\frac{\sigma}{\sqrt{n}} < \overline{X} < \mu + 1.96\frac{\sigma}{\sqrt{n}}\right) = .95$$

Returning to the chapter-opening example where $\mu = 800$, $\sigma = 100$, and $n = 25$, we compute

$$P\left(800 - 1.96\frac{100}{\sqrt{25}} < \overline{X} < 800 + 1.96\frac{100}{\sqrt{25}}\right) = .95$$

Thus, we can say that

$$P(760.8 < \overline{X} < 839.2) = .95$$

This tells us that there is a 95% probability that a sample mean will fall between 760.8 and 839.2. Because the sample mean was computed to be \$750, we would have to conclude that the dean's claim is not supported by the statistic.

Changing the probability from .95 to .90 changes the probability statement to

$$P\left(\mu - 1.645\frac{\sigma}{\sqrt{n}} < \overline{X} < \mu + 1.645\frac{\sigma}{\sqrt{n}}\right) = .90$$

We can also produce a general form of this statement:

$$P\left(\mu - z_{\alpha/2}\frac{\sigma}{\sqrt{n}} < \overline{X} < \mu + z_{\alpha/2}\frac{\sigma}{\sqrt{n}}\right) = 1 - \alpha$$

In this formula α (Greek letter *alpha*) is the probability that $\overline{X}$ does not fall into the interval. To apply this formula, all we need do is substitute the values for μ, σ, n, and α. For example, with $\mu = 800, \sigma = 100, n = 25$, and $\alpha = .01$, we produce

$$P\left(\mu - z_{.005}\frac{\sigma}{\sqrt{n}} < \overline{X} < \mu + z_{.005}\frac{\sigma}{\sqrt{n}}\right) = 1 - .01$$

$$P\left(800 - 2.575\frac{100}{\sqrt{25}} < \overline{X} < 800 + 2.575\frac{100}{\sqrt{25}}\right) = .99$$

$$P(748.5 < \overline{X} < 851.5) = .99$$

which is another probability statement about $\overline{X}$. In Section 10-2, we will use a similar type of probability statement to derive the first statistical inference technique.

9-1d Creating the Sampling Distribution Empirically by Computer Simulation

We can use Excel to approximate the theoretical sampling distribution. We'll start with the sampling distribution of the mean of the toss of two dice.

1. Set up the distribution of the toss of one die. In Column A, store the numbers 1, 2, 3, 4, 5, 6 and in Cell B1 type

    = 1/6

    (Do not type .1667 or any other version of 1/6 since the sum of the probabilities will not equal 1 causing Excel to issue an error warning at step 4.) Drag to fill cells B2–B6.

2. Click **Data, Data Analysis,** and **Random Number Generation**.

3. Type 2 to specify the **Number of Variables** and type 10000 to specify the **Number of Random Variables**.

4. Click **Discrete** distribution and in the **Parameters** box type A1:B6 to specify the **Value and Probability Input Range**.

5. Specify **New Worksheet Ply** and click **OK**. Columns A and B of the new worksheet ply will fill with the random numbers.

6. In column C row 1, type

    = AVERAGE(A1:B1)

7. Drag to fill the rest of Column C. Column C will now contain the values of the sample means.

It is important to understand that sampling distributions created in this way are only approximations of the theoretical sampling distributions. As a result, the histogram of the sample means will not look exactly like Figure 9.2 and the mean and standard deviation of the sample means will only approximate the theoretical values 3.5 and 1.71, respectively. Of course, if we increase the number of simulated tosses of the two dice to (say) a million, the approximations will be better.

EXERCISES

9.1 Draw the histogram of the sample means using bins 1.0, 1.5, 2.0, ... 6.0. Does it appear to be bell shaped? Explain.

9.2 Calculate the mean and standard deviation of the sample means stored in Column C. These are the mean and standard deviation of the simulated sampling distribution. Are they close to the theoretical values of 3.5 and 1.71?

9.3 Repeat the simulation using the sample size $n = 10$. Draw the histogram using bins 1.0, 1.5, 2.0, ... 6.0. Compare this histogram with the one you created in Exercise 9.1. Describe the differences between the two histograms.

9.4 Refer to Exercise 9.3. Compute the mean and standard deviation of the simulated sampling distribution. Compare them with the theoretical values of $\mu_{\bar{x}}$ and $\sigma_{\bar{x}}$, which are

$$\mu_{\bar{x}} = \mu = 3.5$$

$$\sigma_{\bar{x}} = \frac{\sigma}{\sqrt{n}} = \frac{1.71}{\sqrt{10}} = .54.$$

9.5 Repeat the simulation described earlier with the following changes. At step 3, specify 1 for the **Number of Variables** and 10000 for the **Number of Random Numbers**. At step 4, change the distribution to **Normal** and type the **Parameters Mean** 100 and **Standard deviation** 20. Calculate the mean and standard deviation of these numbers and draw a histogram. Describe your results.

9.6 Refer to Exercise 9.5. Create the sampling distribution of the mean from a normal population with mean 100 and standard deviation of 20 and a sample of size 9. Calculate the mean and standard deviation of these numbers and draw a histogram. Compare these results with those in Exercise 9.5.

9.7 Refer to Exercise 9.6. Determine the sampling distribution of the sample median. Draw the histogram and compute the mean and standard deviation of the sampling distribution. Compare the results of Exercise 9.6.

9.8 Repeat Exercise 9.6 calculating the sampling distribution of the sample variance.

9.9 Let X represent the result of the toss of a fair die. Find the following probabilities.
   a. $P(X = 1)$
   b. $P(X = 6)$

9.10 Let $\bar{X}$ represent the mean of the toss of two fair dice. Use the probabilities listed in Table 9.2 to determine the following probabilities.
   a. $P(\bar{X} = 1)$
   b. $P(\bar{X} = 6)$

9.11 An experiment consists of tossing five balanced dice. Find the following probabilities. (Determine the exact probabilities as we did in Tables 9.1 and 9.2 for two dice.)
   a. $P(\bar{X} = 1)$
   b. $P(\bar{X} = 6)$

9.12 Refer to Exercises 9.9–9.11. What do the probabilities tell you about the variances of X and $\bar{X}$?

9.13 A normally distributed population has a mean of 40 and a standard deviation of 12. What does the central limit theorem say about the sampling distribution of the mean if samples of size 100 are drawn from this population?

9.14 Refer to Exercise 9.13. Suppose that the population is not normally distributed. Does this change your answer? Explain.

9.15 A sample of $n = 16$ observations is drawn from a normal population with $\mu = 1,000$ and $\sigma = 200$. Find the following.
   a. $P(\bar{X} > 1,050)$
   b. $P(\bar{X} < 960)$
   c. $P(\bar{X} > 1,100)$

9.16 Repeat Exercise 9.15 with $n = 25$.

9.17 Repeat Exercise 9.15 with $n = 100$.

9.18 Given a normal population whose mean is 50 and whose standard deviation is 5, find the probability that a random sample of
   a. 4 has a mean between 49 and 52.
   b. 16 has a mean between 49 and 52.
   c. 25 has a mean between 49 and 52.

9.19 Repeat Exercise 9.18 for a standard deviation of 10.

9.20 Repeat Exercise 9.18 for a standard deviation of 20.

9.21 a. Calculate the finite population correction factor when the population size is $N = 1,000$ and the sample size is $n = 100$.
   b. Repeat part (a) when $N = 3,000$.
   c. Repeat part (a) when $N = 5,000$.
   d. What have you learned about the finite population correction factor when N is large relative to n?

9.22 a. Suppose that the standard deviation of a population with $N = 10,000$ members is 500. Determine the standard error of the sampling distribution of the mean when the sample size is 1,000.
   b. Repeat part (a) when $n = 500$.
   c. Repeat part (a) when $n = 100$.

9.23 The heights of North American women are normally distributed with a mean of 64 inches and a standard deviation of 2 inches.
   a. What is the probability that a randomly selected woman is taller than 66 inches?
   b. A random sample of four women is selected. What is the probability that the sample mean height is greater than 66 inches?
   c. What is the probability that the mean height of a random sample of 100 women is greater than 66 inches?

9.24 Refer to Exercise 9.23. If the population of women's heights is not normally distributed, which, if any, of the questions can you answer? Explain.

9.25 An automatic machine in a manufacturing process is operating properly if the lengths of an important subcomponent are normally distributed with mean = 117 cm and standard deviation = 5.2 cm.
   a. Find the probability that one selected subcomponent is longer than 120 cm.
   b. Find the probability that if four subcomponents are randomly selected, their mean length exceeds 120 cm.
   c. Find the probability that if four subcomponents are randomly selected, all four have lengths that exceed 120 cm.

9.26 Statisticians determined that the mortgages of homeowners in a city is normally distributed with a mean of $250,000 and a standard deviation of $50,000. A random sample of 100 homeowners was drawn. What is the probability that the mean is greater than $262,000?

9.27 Refer to Exercise 9.26. Does your answer change if you discover that mortgages are not normally distributed?

9.28 The amount of time the university professors devote to their jobs per week is normally distributed with a mean of 52 hours and a standard deviation of 6 hours.
   a. What is the probability that a professor works for more than 60 hours per week?
   b. Find the probability that the mean amount of work per week for three randomly selected professors is more than 60 hours.
   c. Find the probability that if three professors are randomly selected all three work for more than 60 hours per week.

9.29 The number of pizzas consumed per month by university students is normally distributed with a mean of 10 and a standard deviation of 3.
   a. What proportion of students consume more than 12 pizzas per month?
   b. What is the probability that in a random sample of 25 students more than 275 pizzas are consumed? (*Hint:* What is the mean number of pizzas consumed by the sample of 25 students?)

9.30 The marks on a statistics midterm test are normally distributed with a mean of 78 and a standard deviation of 6.
   a. What proportion of the class has a midterm mark of less than 75?
   b. What is the probability that a class of 50 has an average midterm mark that is less than 75?

9.31 The amount of time spent by North American adults watching television per day is normally distributed with a mean of 6 hours and a standard deviation of 1.5 hours.
   a. What is the probability that a randomly selected North American adult watches television for more than 7 hours per day?
   b. What is the probability that the average time watching television by a random sample of five North American adults is more than 7 hours?
   c. What is the probability that in a random sample of five North American adults, all watch television for more than 7 hours per day?

9.32 The manufacturer of cans of salmon that are supposed to have a net weight of 6 ounces tells you that the net weight is actually a normal random variable with a mean of 6.05 ounces and a standard deviation of .18 ounces. Suppose that you draw a random sample of 36 cans.
   a. Find the probability that the mean weight of the sample is less than 5.97 ounces.
   b. Suppose your random sample of 36 cans of salmon produced a mean weight that is less than 5.97 ounces. Comment on the statement made by the manufacturer.

9.33 The number of customers who enter a supermarket each hour is normally distributed with a mean of 600 and a standard deviation of 200. The supermarket is open 16 hours per day. What is the probability that the total number of customers who enter the supermarket in one day is greater than 10,000? (*Hint:* Calculate the average hourly number of customers necessary to exceed 10,000 in one 16-hour day.)

9.34 The sign on the elevator in an office tower states, "Maximum Capacity 1,140 kilograms (2,500 pounds) or 16 Persons." A professor of statistics wonders what the probability is that 16 persons would weigh more than 1,140 kilograms. Discuss what the professor needs (besides the ability to perform the calculations) in order to satisfy his curiosity.

9.35 Refer to Exercise 9.34. Suppose that the professor discovers that the weights of people who use the elevator are normally distributed with an average of 75 kilograms and a standard deviation of 10 kilograms. Calculate the probability that the professor seeks.

SAMPLING DISTRIBUTIONS **299**

9.36 The time it takes for a statistics professor to mark his midterm test is normally distributed with a mean of 4.8 minutes and a standard deviation of 1.3 minutes. There are 60 students in the professor's class. What is the probability that he needs more than 5 hours to mark all the midterm tests? (The 60 midterm tests of the students in this year's class can be considered a random sample of the many thousands of midterm tests the professor has marked and will mark.)

9.37 Refer to Exercise 9.36. Does your answer change if you discover that the times needed to mark a midterm test are not normally distributed?

9.38 The restaurant in a large commercial building provides coffee for the occupants in the building. The restaurateur has determined that the mean number of cups of coffee consumed in a day by all the occupants is 2.0 with a standard deviation of .6. A new tenant of the building intends to have a total of 125 new employees.

What is the probability that the new employees will consume more than 240 cups per day?

9.39 The number of pages produced by a fax machine in a busy office is normally distributed with a mean of 275 and a standard deviation of 75. Determine the probability that in 1 week (5 days) more than 1,500 faxes will be received?

9.40 The property tax paid by homeowners in a large city was determined to be normally distributed with a mean of $2,800 and a standard deviation of $400. A random sample of four homes was drawn.
  a. What is the probability distribution of the mean of the sample of four homes?
  b. Determine the probability that the sample mean falls between $2,500 and $2,900.

9.41 How would you answer Exercise 9.40 if property tax is not normally distributed?

9-2 / SAMPLING DISTRIBUTION OF A PROPORTION

In Section 7-4, we introduced the binomial distribution whose parameter is p, the probability of success in any trial. In order to compute binomial probabilities, we assumed that p was known. However, in the real world p is unknown, requiring the statistics practitioner to estimate its value from a sample. The estimator of a population proportion of successes is the sample proportion; that is, we count the number of successes in a sample and compute

$$\hat{P} = \frac{X}{n}$$

($\hat{P}$ is read as *p hat*) where X is the number of successes and n is the sample size. When we take a sample of size n, we're actually conducting a binomial experiment; as a result, X is binomially distributed. Thus, the probability of any value of $\hat{P}$ can be calculated from its value of X. For example, suppose that we have a binomial experiment with $n = 10$ and $p = .4$. To find the probability that the sample proportion $\hat{P}$ is less than or equal to .50, we find the probability that X is less than or equal to 5 (because $5/10 = .50$). From Table 1 in Appendix B we find with $n = 10$ and $p = .4$

$$P(\hat{P} \leq .50) = P(X \leq 5) = .8338$$

We can calculate the probability associated with other values of $\hat{P}$ similarly.

Discrete distributions such as the binomial do not lend themselves easily to the kinds of calculation needed for inference. And inference is the reason we need sampling distributions. Fortunately, we can approximate the binomial distribution by a normal distribution.

What follows is an explanation of how and why the normal distribution can be used to approximate a binomial distribution. Disinterested readers can skip to page 303, where we present the approximate **sampling distribution of a sample proportion**.

9-2a (Optional) Normal Approximation to the Binomial Distribution

Recall how we introduced continuous probability distributions in Chapter 8. We developed the density function by converting a histogram so that the total area in the rectangles equaled 1. We can do the same for a binomial distribution. To illustrate, let X

FIGURE **9.7**   **Binomial Distribution with** $n = 20$ **and** $p = .5$

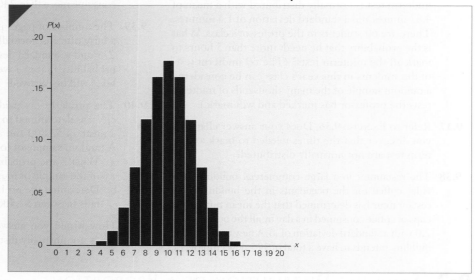

FIGURE **9.8**   **Binomial Distribution with** $n = 20$ **and** $p = .5$ **and Normal Approximation**

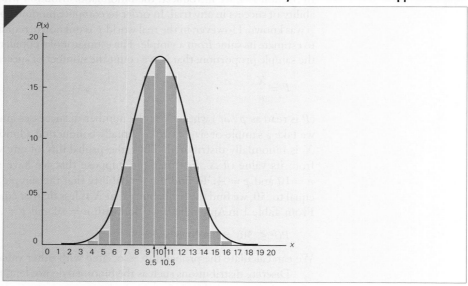

be a binomial random variable with $n = 20$ and $p = .5$. We can easily determine the probability of each value of X, where $X = 0, 1, 2, \cdots, 19, 20$. A rectangle representing a value of x is drawn so that its area equals the probability. We accomplish this by letting the height of the rectangle equal the probability and the base of the rectangle equal 1. Thus, the base of each rectangle for x is the interval $x - .5$ to $x + .5$. Figure 9.7 depicts this graph. As you can see, the rectangle representing $x = 10$ is the rectangle whose base is the interval 9.5 to 10.5 and whose height is $P(X = 10) = .1762$.

If we now smooth the ends of the rectangles, we produce a bell-shaped curve as seen in Figure 9.8. Thus, to use the normal approximation, all we need do is find the area under the *normal* curve between 9.5 and 10.5.

To find normal probabilities it is required to first standardize x by subtracting the mean and dividing by the standard deviation. The values for μ and σ are derived from the binomial distribution being approximated. In Section 7-4 we pointed out that

$$\mu = np$$

and

$$\sigma = \sqrt{np(1-p)}$$

For $n = 20$ and $p = .5$, we have

$$\mu = np = 20(.5) = 10$$

and

$$\sigma = \sqrt{np(1-p)} = \sqrt{20(.5)(1-.5)} = 2.24$$

To calculate the probability that $X = 10$ using the normal distribution requires that we find the area under the normal curve between 9.5 and 10.5; that is,

$$P(X = 10) \approx P(9.5 < Y < 10.5)$$

where Y is a normal random variable approximating the binomial random variable X. We standardize Y and use Table 3 of Appendix B to find

$$P(9.5 < Y < 10.5) = P\left(\frac{9.5 - 10}{2.24} < \frac{Y - \mu}{\sigma} < \frac{10.5 - 10}{2.24}\right)$$
$$= P(-.22 < Z < .22) = (Z < .22) - P(Z < -.22)$$
$$= .5871 - .4129 = .1742$$

The actual probability that X equals 10 is

$$P(X = 10) = .1762$$

As you can see, the approximation is quite good.

Notice that to draw a binomial distribution, which is discrete, it was necessary to draw rectangles whose bases were constructed by adding and subtracting .5 to the values of X. The .5 is called the **continuity correction factor**.

The approximation for any other value of X would proceed in the same manner. In general, the binomial probability $P(X = x)$ is approximated by the area under a normal curve between $x - .5$ and $x + .5$. To find the binomial probability $P(X \leq x)$, we calculate the area under the normal curve to the left of $x + .5$. For the same binomial random variable, the probability that its value is less than or equal to 8 is $P(X \leq 8) = .2517$. The normal approximation is

$$P(X \leq 8) \approx P(Y < 8.5) = P\left(\frac{Y - \mu}{\sigma} < \frac{8.5 - 10}{2.24}\right) = P(Z < -.67) = .2514$$

We find the area under the normal curve to the right of $x - .5$ to determine the binomial probability $P(X \geq x)$. To illustrate, the probability that the binomial random variable (with $n = 20$ and $p = .5$) is greater than or equal to 14 is $P(X \geq 14) = .0577$. The normal approximation is

$$P(X \geq 14) \approx P(Y > 13.5) = P\left(\frac{Y - \mu}{\sigma} > \frac{13.5 - 10}{2.24}\right) = P(Z > 1.56) = .0594$$

9-2b Omitting the Correction Factor for Continuity

When calculating the probability of *individual* values of X as we did when we computed the probability that X equals 10 earlier, the correction factor *must* be used. If we don't, we are left with finding the area in a line, which is 0. When computing the probability of a *range* of values of X, we can omit the correction factor. However, the omission of the correction factor will decrease the accuracy of the approximation. For example, if we approximate $P(X \leq 8)$ as we did previously except without the correction factor, we find

$$P(X \leq 8) \approx P(Y < 8) = P\left(\frac{Y - \mu}{\sigma} < \frac{8 - 10}{2.24}\right) = P(Z < -.89) = .1867$$

The absolute size of the error between the actual cumulative binomial probability and its normal approximation is quite small when the values of x are in the tail regions of the distribution. For example, the probability that a binomial random variable with $n = 20$ and $p = .5$ is less than or equal to 3 is

$$P(X \leq 3) = .0013$$

The normal approximation with the correction factor is

$$P(X \leq 3) \approx P(Y < 3.5) = P\left(\frac{Y - \mu}{\sigma} < \frac{3.5 - 10}{2.24}\right) = P(Z < -2.90) = .0019$$

The normal approximation without the correction factor is (using Excel)

$$P(X \leq 3) \approx P(Y < 3) = P\left(\frac{Y - \mu}{\sigma} < \frac{3 - 10}{2.24}\right) = P(Z < -3.13) = .0009$$

For larger values of n, the differences between the normal approximation with and without the correction factor are small even for values of X near the center of the distribution. For example, the probability that a binomial random variable with $n = 1,000$ and $p = .3$ is less than or equal to 260 is

$$P(X \leq 260) = .0029 \text{ (using Excel)}$$

The normal approximation with the correction factor is

$$P(X \leq 260) \approx P(Y < 260.5) = P\left(\frac{Y - \mu}{\sigma} < \frac{260.5 - 300}{14.49}\right) = P(Z < -2.73) = .0032$$

The normal approximation without the correction factor is

$$P(X \leq 260) \approx P(Y < 260) = P\left(\frac{Y - \mu}{\sigma} < \frac{260 - 300}{14.49}\right) = P(Z < -2.76) = .0029$$

As we pointed out, the normal approximation of the binomial distribution is made necessary by the needs of statistical inference. As you will discover, statistical inference generally involves the use of large values of n, and the part of the sampling distribution that is of greatest interest lies in the tail regions. The correction factor was a temporary tool that allowed us to convince you that a binomial distribution can be approximated by a normal distribution. Now that we have done so, we will use the normal approximation of the binomial distribution to approximate the sampling distribution of a sample proportion, and in such applications the correction factor will be omitted.

9-2c Approximate Sampling Distribution of a Sample Proportion

Using the laws of expected value and variance (see the online appendix Using the Laws of Expected Value and Variance to Derive the Parameters of Sampling Distributions), we can determine the mean, variance, and standard deviation of $\hat{P}$. We will summarize what we have learned.

Sampling Distribution of a Sample Proportion

1. $\hat{P}$ is approximately normally distributed provided that np and $n(1 - p)$ are greater than or equal to 5.

2. The expected value: $E(\hat{P}) = p$

3. The variance: $V(\hat{P}) = \sigma_{\hat{p}}^2 = \dfrac{p(1 - p)}{n}$

4. The standard deviation: $\sigma_{\hat{p}} = \sqrt{p(1 - p)/n}$*

(The standard deviation of $\hat{P}$ is called the **standard error of the proportion**.)

The sample size requirement is theoretical because, in practice, much larger sample sizes are needed for the normal approximation to be useful.

EXAMPLE 9.2

Political Survey

In the last election, a state representative received 52% of the votes cast. One year after the election, the representative organized a survey that asked a random sample of 300 people whether they would vote for him in the next election. If we assume that his popularity has not changed, what is the probability that more than half of the sample would vote for him?

SOLUTION:

The number of respondents who would vote for the representative is a binomial random variable with $n = 300$ and $p = .52$. We want to determine the probability that the sample proportion is greater than 50%. In other words, we want to find $P(\hat{P} > .50)$.

We now know that the sample proportion $\hat{P}$ is approximately normally distributed with mean $p = .52$ and standard deviation $= \sqrt{p(1 - p)/n} = \sqrt{(.52)(.48)/300} = .0288$. Thus, we calculate

$$P(\hat{P} > .50) = P\left(\frac{\hat{P} - p}{\sqrt{p(1 - p)/n}} > \frac{.50 - .52}{.0288}\right)$$

$$= P(Z > -.69) = 1 - P(Z < -.69) = 1 - .2451 = .7549$$

If we assume that the level of support remains at 52%, the probability that more than half the sample of 300 people would vote for the representative is .7549.

---

*As was the case with the standard error of the mean (page 291), the standard error of a proportion is $\sqrt{p(1 - p)/n}$ when sampling from infinitely large populations. When the population is finite, the standard error of the proportion must include the finite population correction factor, which can be omitted when the population is large relative to the sample size, a very common occurrence in practice.

EXERCISES

Use the normal approximation without the correction factor to find the probabilities in the following exercises.

9.42 a. In a binomial experiment with $n = 300$ and $p = .5$, find the probability that $\hat{P}$ is greater than 60%.
b. Repeat part (a) with $p = .55$.
c. Repeat part (a) with $p = .6$.

9.43 a. The probability of success on any trial of a binomial experiment is 25%. Find the probability that the proportion of successes in a sample of 500 is less than 22%.
b. Repeat part (a) with $n = 800$.
c. Repeat part (a) with $n = 1,000$.

9.44 Determine the probability that in a sample of 100 the sample proportion is less than .75 if $p = .80$.

9.45 A binomial experiment where $p = .4$ is conducted. Find the probability that in a sample of 60 the proportion of successes exceeds .35.

9.46 The proportion of eligible voters in the next election who will vote for the incumbent is assumed to be 55%. What is the probability that in a random sample of 500 voters less than 49% say they will vote for the incumbent?

9.47 The assembly line that produces an electronic component of a missile system has historically resulted in a 2% defective rate. A random sample of 800 components is drawn. What is the probability that the defective rate is greater than 4%? Suppose that in the random sample the defective rate is 4%. What does that suggest about the defective rate on the assembly line?

9.48 a. The manufacturer of aspirin claims that the proportion of headache sufferers who get relief with just two aspirins is 53%. What is the probability that in a random sample of 400 headache sufferers, less than 50% obtain relief? If 50% of the sample actually obtained relief, what does this suggest about the manufacturer's claim?
b. Repeat part (a) using a sample of 1,000.

9.49 The manager of a restaurant in a commercial building has determined that the proportion of customers who drink tea is 14%. What is the probability that in the next 100 customers at least 10% will be tea drinkers?

9.50 A commercial for a manufacturer of household appliances claims that 3% of all its products require a service call in the first year. A consumer protection association wants to check the claim by surveying 400 households that recently purchased one of the company's appliances. What is the probability that more than 5% require a service call within the first year? What would you say about the commercial's honesty if in a random sample of 400 households 5% report at least one service call?

9.51 The Laurier Company's brand has a market share of 30%. Suppose that 1,000 consumers of the product are asked in a survey which brand they prefer. What is the probability that more than 32% of the respondents say they prefer the Laurier brand?

9.52 A university bookstore claims that 50% of its customers are satisfied with the service and prices.
a. If this claim is true, what is the probability that in a random sample of 600 customers less than 45% are satisfied?
b. Suppose that in a random sample of 600 customers, 270 express satisfaction with the bookstore. What does this tell you about the bookstore's claim?

9.53 A psychologist believes that 80% of male drivers when lost continue to drive hoping to find the location they seek rather than ask directions. To examine this belief, he took a random sample of 350 male drivers and asked each what they did when lost. If the belief is true, determine the probability that less than 75% said they continue driving.

9.54 The Red Lobster restaurant chain regularly surveys its customers. On the basis of these surveys, the management of the chain claims that 75% of its customers rate the food as excellent. A consumer testing service wants to examine the claim by asking 460 customers to rate the food. What is the probability that less than 70% rate the food as excellent?

9.55 An accounting professor claims that no more than one-quarter of undergraduate business students will major in accounting. What is the probability that in a random sample of 1,200 undergraduate business students, 336 or more will major in accounting?

9.56 Refer to Exercise 9.55. A survey of a random sample of 1,200 undergraduate business students indicates that 336 students plan to major in accounting. What does this tell you about the professor's claim?

9.57 In 2014, approximately 13% of nonelderly Americans adults had no health insurance. Suppose that a random sample of 400 such individuals was drawn. What is the probability that 15% or more had no health insurance?

9.58 In a Gallup survey, Americans were asked about their main source of news about current events around the world. If 20% of the population report that their main source is television news, find the probability that in a sample of 500 at least 22% say that their source of news is television.

9.59 Most televised baseball games display a pitch tracker that shows whether the pitch was in the strike zone, which in turn shows whether the umpire made the correct call. Major League Baseball keeps track of how well each umpire calls games. Batters swing at approximately 47% of all pitches. As a result umpires need to make calls on the other 53%. The best umpires get 10% of their calls wrong and the worst get 15% wrong. Suppose that in an average game the best umpire makes calls on 150 pitches. If we assume that the calls in a game are random, what is the probability that he gets less than 8% wrong?

9.60 Repeat Exercise 9.59 for the worst umpire.

9-3 / SAMPLING DISTRIBUTION OF THE DIFFERENCE BETWEEN TWO MEANS

Another sampling distribution that you will soon encounter is that of the **difference between two sample means**. The sampling plan calls for independent random samples drawn from each of two normal populations. The samples are said to be independent if the selection of the members of one sample is independent of the selection of the members of the second sample. We will expand upon this discussion in Chapter 13. We are interested in the sampling distribution of the difference between the two sample means.

In Section 9-1, we introduced the central limit theorem, which states that in repeated sampling from a normal population whose mean is μ and whose standard deviation is σ, the sampling distribution of the sample mean is normal with mean μ and standard deviation $\sigma/\sqrt{n}$. Statisticians have shown that the difference between two independent normal random variables is also normally distributed. Thus, the difference between two sample means $\overline{X}_1 - \overline{X}_2$ is normally distributed if both populations are normal.

By using the laws of expected value and variance we derive the expected value and variance of the **sampling distribution of $\overline{X}_1 - \overline{X}_2$**:

$$\mu_{\overline{x}_1 - \overline{x}_2} = \mu_1 - \mu_2$$

and

$$\sigma^2_{\overline{x}_1 - \overline{x}_2} = \frac{\sigma^2}{n_1} + \frac{\sigma_2^2}{n_2}$$

Thus, it follows that in repeated independent sampling from two populations with means μ_1 and μ_2 and standard deviations σ_1 and σ_2, respectively, the sampling distribution of $\overline{X}_1 - \overline{X}_2$ is normal with mean

$$\mu_{\overline{x}_1 - \overline{x}_2} = \mu_1 - \mu_2$$

and standard deviation (which is the **standard error of the difference between two means**)

$$\sigma_{\overline{x}_1 - \overline{x}_2} = \sqrt{\frac{\sigma_1^2}{n_1} + \frac{\sigma_2^2}{n_2}}$$

If the populations are nonnormal, then the sampling distribution is only approximately normal for large sample sizes. The required sample sizes depend on the extent of nonnormality. However, for most populations, sample sizes of 30 or more are sufficient.

Figure 9.9 depicts the sampling distribution of the difference between two means.

FIGURE **9.9** Sampling Distribution of $\overline{X}_1 - \overline{X}_2$

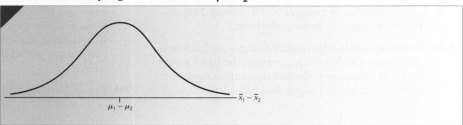

$\mu_1 - \mu_2$

$\overline{x}_1 - \overline{x}_2$

EXAMPLE 9.3

Starting Salaries of MBAs

Suppose that the starting salaries of MBAs at Wilfrid Laurier University (WLU) are normally distributed, with a mean of $62,000 and a standard deviation of $14,500. The starting salaries of MBAs at the University of Western Ontario (UWO) are normally distributed, with a mean of $60,000 and a standard deviation of $18,300. If a random sample of 50 WLU MBAs and a random sample of 60 UWO MBAs are selected, what is the probability that the sample mean starting salary of WLU graduates will exceed that of the UWO graduates?

SOLUTION:

We want to determine $P(\overline{X}_1 - \overline{X}_2 > 0)$. We know that $\overline{X}_1 - \overline{X}_2$ is normally distributed with mean $\mu_1 - \mu_2 = 62{,}000 - 60{,}000 = 2{,}000$ and standard deviation

$$\sqrt{\frac{\sigma_1^2}{n_1} + \frac{\sigma_2^2}{n_2}} = \sqrt{\frac{14{,}500^2}{50} + \frac{18{,}300^2}{60}} = 3{,}128$$

We can standardize the variable and refer to Table 3 of Appendix B:

$$P(\overline{X}_1 - \overline{X}_2 > 0) = P\left(\frac{(\overline{X}_1 - \overline{X}_2) - (\mu_1 - \mu_2)}{\sqrt{\frac{\sigma_1^2}{n_1} + \frac{\sigma_2^2}{n_2}}} > \frac{0 - 2{,}000}{3{,}128} \right)$$

$$= P(Z > -64) = 1 - P(Z < -64) = 1 - .2611 = .7389$$

There is a .7389 probability that for a sample of size 50 from the WLU graduates and a sample of size 60 from the UWO graduates, the sample mean starting salary of WLU graduates will exceed the sample mean of UWO graduates.

EXERCISES

9.61 Independent random samples of 10 observations each are drawn from normal populations. The parameters of these populations are

> Population 1: $\mu = 280$, $\sigma = 25$
> Population 2: $\mu = 270$, $\sigma = 30$

Find the probability that the mean of sample 1 is greater than the mean of sample 2 by more than 25.

9.62 Repeat Exercise 9.61 with samples of size 50.

9.63 Repeat Exercise 9.61 with samples of size 100.

9.64 Suppose that we have two normal populations with the means and standard deviations listed here. If random samples of size 25 are drawn from each population, what is the probability that the mean of sample 1 is greater than the mean of sample 2?

> Population 1: $\mu = 40$, $\sigma = 6$
> Population 2: $\mu = 38$, $\sigma = 8$

9.65 Repeat Exercise 9.64 assuming that the standard deviations are 12 and 16, respectively.

9.66 Repeat Exercise 9.64 assuming that the means are 140 and 138, respectively.

9.67 A factory's worker productivity is normally distributed. One worker produces an average of 75 units per day with a standard deviation of 20. Another worker produces at an average rate of 65 per day with a standard deviation of 21. What is the probability that in 1 week (5 working days), worker 1 will outproduce worker 2?

9.68 A professor of statistics noticed that the marks in his course are normally distributed. He has also noticed that his morning classes average 73%, with a standard deviation of 12% on their final exams. His afternoon classes average 77%, with a standard deviation of 10%. What is the probability that the mean mark of four randomly selected students from a morning class

is greater than the average mark of four randomly selected students from an afternoon class?

9.69 The manager of a restaurant believes that waiters and waitresses who introduce themselves by telling customers their names will get larger tips than those who don't. In fact, she claims that the average tip for the former group is 18%, whereas that of the latter is only 15%. If tips are normally distributed with a standard deviation of 3%, what is the probability that in a random sample of 10 tips recorded from waiters and waitresses who introduce themselves and 10 tips from waiters and waitresses who don't, the mean of the former will exceed that of the latter?

9.70 The average North American loses an average of 15 days per year to colds and flu. The natural remedy echinacea reputedly boosts the immune system. One manufacturer of echinacea pills claims that consumers of its product will reduce the number of days lost to colds and flu by one-third. To test the claim, a random sample of 50 people was drawn. Half took echinacea, and the other half took placebos. If we assume that the standard deviation of the number of days lost to colds and flu with and without echinacea is 3 days, find the probability that the mean number of days lost for echinacea users is less than that for nonusers.

9-4 FROM HERE TO INFERENCE

The primary function of the sampling distribution is statistical inference. To see how the sampling distribution contributes to the development of inferential methods, we need to briefly review how we got to this point.

In Chapters 7 and 8, we introduced probability distributions, which allowed us to make probability statements about values of the random variable. A prerequisite of this calculation is knowledge of the distribution and the relevant parameters. In Example 7.9, we needed to know that the probability that Pat Statsdud guesses the correct answer is 20% ($p = .2$) and that the number of correct answers (successes) in 10 questions (trials) is a binomial random variable. We could then compute the probability of any number of successes. In Example 8.3, we needed to know that the return on investment is normally distributed with a mean of 10% and a standard deviation of 5%. These three bits of information allowed us to calculate the probability of various values of the random variable.

Figure 9.10 symbolically represents the use of probability distributions. Simply put, knowledge of the population and its parameter(s) allows us to use the probability distribution to make probability statements about individual members of the population. The direction of the arrows indicates the direction of the flow of information.

FIGURE **9.10** Probability Distribution

In this chapter, we developed the sampling distribution, wherein knowledge of the parameter(s) and some information about the distribution allow us to make probability statements about a sample statistic. In Example 9.1(b), knowing the population mean and standard deviation and assuming that the population is not extremely nonnormal enabled us to calculate a probability statement about a sample mean. Figure 9.11 describes the application of sampling distributions.

FIGURE **9.11** Sampling Distribution

Notice that in applying both probability distributions and sampling distributions, we must know the value of the relevant parameters, a highly unlikely circumstance. In the real world, parameters are almost always unknown because they represent descriptive measurements about extremely large populations. Statistical inference addresses this problem. It does so by reversing the direction of the flow of knowledge in Figure 9.11. In Figure 9.12, we display the character of statistical inference. Starting in Chapter 10, we will assume that most population parameters are unknown. The statistics practitioner will sample from the population and compute the required statistic. The sampling distribution of that statistic will enable us to draw inferences about the parameter.

FIGURE **9.12** Sampling Distribution in Inference

You may be surprised to learn that, by and large, that is all we do in the remainder of this book. Why then do we need another 14 chapters? They are necessary because there are many more parameter and sampling distribution combinations that define the inferential procedures to be presented in an introductory statistics course. However, they all work in the same way. If you understand how one procedure is developed, then you will likely understand all of them. Our task in the next two chapters is to ensure that you understand the first inferential method. Your job is identical.

CHAPTER SUMMARY

The sampling distribution of a statistic is created by repeated sampling from one population. In this chapter, we introduced the sampling distribution of the mean, the proportion, and the difference between two means. We described how these distributions are created theoretically and empirically.

IMPORTANT TERMS:

SYMBOLS:

Symbol	Pronounced	Represents
$\mu_{\bar{x}}$	mu x bar	Mean of the sampling distribution of the sample mean
$\sigma_{\bar{x}}^2$	sigma squared x bar	Variance of the sampling distribution of the sample mean
$\sigma_{\bar{x}}$	sigma x bar	Standard deviation (standard error) of the sampling distribution of the sample mean
α	alpha	Probability
$\hat{P}$	p hat	Sample proportion
$\sigma_{\hat{p}}^2$	sigma squared p hat	Variance of the sampling distribution of the sample proportion
$\sigma_{\hat{p}}$	sigma p hat	Standard deviation (standard error) of the sampling distribution of the sample proportion
$\mu_{\bar{x}_1 - \bar{x}_2}$	mu x bar 1 minus x bar 2	Mean of the sampling distribution of the difference between two sample means
$\sigma_{\bar{x}_1 - \bar{x}_2}^2$	sigma squared x bar 1 minus x bar 2	Variance of the sampling distribution of the difference between two sample means
$\sigma_{\bar{x}_1 - \bar{x}_2}$	sigma x bar 1 minus x bar 2	Standard deviation (standard error) of the sampling distribution of the difference between two sample means

FORMULAS:

Expected value of the sample mean

$$E(\overline{X}) = \mu_{\bar{x}} = \mu$$

Variance of the sample mean

$$V(\overline{X}) = \sigma_{\bar{x}}^2 = \frac{\sigma^2}{n}$$

Standard error of the sample mean

$$\sigma_{\bar{x}} = \frac{\sigma}{\sqrt{n}}$$

Standardizing the sample mean

$$Z = \frac{\overline{X} - \mu}{\sigma/\sqrt{n}}$$

Expected value of the sample proportion

$$E(\hat{P}) = \mu_{\hat{p}} = p$$

Variance of the sample proportion

$$V(\hat{P}) = \sigma_{\hat{p}}^2 = \frac{p(1 - p)}{n}$$

Standard error of the sample proportion

$$\sigma_{\hat{p}} = \sqrt{\frac{p(1 - p)}{n}}$$

Standardizing the sample proportion

$$Z = \frac{\hat{P} - p}{\sqrt{p(1 - p)/n}}$$

Expected value of the difference between two means

$$E(\overline{X}_1 - \overline{X}_2) = \mu_{\bar{x}_1 - \bar{x}_2} = \mu_1 - \mu_2$$

Variance of the difference between two means

$$V(\overline{X}_1 - \overline{X}_2) = \sigma_{\bar{x}_1 - \bar{x}_2}^2 = \frac{\sigma_1^2}{n_1} + \frac{\sigma_2^2}{n_2}$$

Standard error of the difference between two means

$$\sigma_{\bar{x}_1 - \bar{x}_2} = \sqrt{\frac{\sigma_1^2}{n_1} + \frac{\sigma_2^2}{n_2}}$$

Standardizing the difference between two sample means

$$Z = \frac{(\overline{X}_1 - \overline{X}_2) - (\mu_1 - \mu_2)}{\sqrt{\frac{\sigma_1^2}{n_1} + \frac{\sigma_2^2}{n_2}}}$$

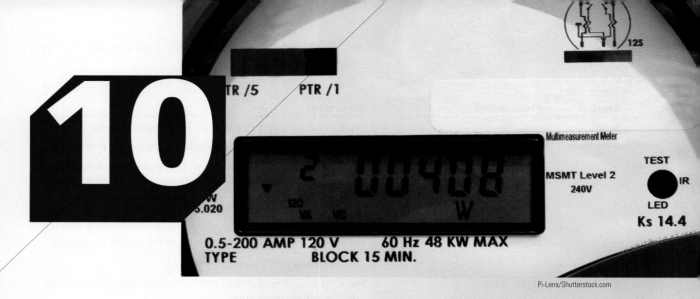

Pi-Lens/Shutterstock.com

10

INTRODUCTION TO ESTIMATION

CHAPTER OUTLINE

Determining the Sample Size to Estimate the Mean Tree Diameter

A lumber company has just acquired the rights to a large tract of land containing thousands of trees.

A lumber company needs to be able to estimate the amount of lumber it can harvest in a tract of land to determine whether the effort will be profitable. To do so, it must estimate the mean diameter of the trees. It decides to estimate that parameter to within 1 inch with 90% confidence. A forester familiar with the territory guesses that the diameters of the trees are normally distributed with a standard deviation of 6 inches. Using the formula on page 329, he determines that

Image.Art/Shutterstock.com

See page 330 for the solution.

he should sample 98 trees. After sampling those 98 trees, the forester calculates the sample mean to be 25 inches. Suppose that after he has completed his sampling and calculations, he discovers that the actual standard deviation is 12 inches. Will he be satisfied with the result?

INTRODUCTION

Having discussed descriptive statistics (Chapter 4), probability distributions (Chapters 7 and 8), and sampling distributions (Chapter 9), we are ready to tackle statistical inference. As we explained in Chapter 1, *statistical inference* is the process by which we acquire information and draw conclusions about populations from samples. There are two general procedures for making inferences about populations: *estimation* and *hypothesis testing*. In this chapter, we introduce the concepts and foundations of estimation and demonstrate them with simple examples. In Chapter 11, we describe the fundamentals of hypothesis testing. Because most of what we do in the remainder of this book applies the concepts of estimation and hypothesis testing, understanding Chapters 10 and 11 is vital to your development as a statistics practitioner.

10-1 / CONCEPTS OF ESTIMATION

As its name suggests, the objective of estimation is to determine the approximate value of a population parameter on the basis of a sample statistic. For example, the sample mean is employed to estimate the population mean. We refer to the sample mean as the *estimator* of the population mean. Once the sample mean has been computed, its value is called the *estimate*. In this chapter, we will introduce the statistical process whereby we estimate a population mean using sample data. In the rest of the book, we use the concepts and techniques introduced here for other parameters.

10-1a Point and Interval Estimators

We can use sample data to estimate a population parameter in two ways. First, we can compute the value of the estimator and consider that value as the estimate of the parameter. Such an estimator is called a *point estimator*.

Point Estimator

A **point estimator** draws inferences about a population by estimating the value of an unknown parameter using a single value or point.

There are three drawbacks to using point estimators. First, it is virtually certain that the estimate will be wrong. (The probability that a continuous random variable will equal a specific value is 0; that is, the probability that $\bar{x}$ will exactly equal μ is 0.) Second, we often need to know how close the estimator is to the parameter. Third, in drawing inferences about a population, it is intuitively reasonable to expect that a large sample will produce more accurate results because it contains more information than a smaller sample does. But point estimators don't have the capacity to reflect the effects of larger sample sizes. As a consequence, we use the second method of estimating a population parameter, the *interval estimator*.

> ### Interval Estimator
> An **interval estimator** draws inferences about a population by estimating the value of an unknown parameter using an interval.

As you will see, the interval estimator is affected by the sample size; because it possesses this feature, we will deal mostly with interval estimators in this text.

To illustrate the difference between point and interval estimators, suppose that a statistics professor wants to estimate the mean summer income of his second-year business students. Selecting 25 students at random, he calculates the sample mean weekly income to be $400. The point estimate is the sample mean. In other words, he estimates the mean weekly summer income of all second-year business students to be $400. Using the technique described subsequently, he may instead use an interval estimate; he estimates that the mean weekly summer income of second-year business students to lie between $380 and $420.

Numerous applications of estimation occur in the real world. For example, television network executives want to know the proportion of television viewers who are tuned in to their networks; an economist wants to know the mean income of university graduates; and a medical researcher wishes to estimate the recovery rate of heart attack victims treated with a new drug. In each of these cases, to accomplish the objective exactly, the statistics practitioner would have to examine each member of the population and then calculate the parameter of interest. For instance, network executives would have to ask each person in the country what he or she is watching to determine the proportion of people who are watching their shows. Because there are millions of television viewers, the task is both impractical and prohibitively expensive. An alternative would be to take a random sample from this population, calculate the sample proportion, and use that as an estimator of the population proportion. The use of the sample proportion to estimate the population proportion seems logical. The selection of the sample statistic to be used as an estimator, however, depends on the characteristics of that statistic. Naturally, we want to use the statistic with the most desirable qualities for our purposes.

One desirable quality of an estimator is *unbiasedness*.

> ### Unbiased Estimator
> An **unbiased estimator** of a population parameter is an estimator whose expected value is equal to that parameter.

This means that if you were to take an infinite number of samples and calculate the value of the estimator in each sample, the average value of the estimators would equal the parameter. This amounts to saying that, on average, the sample statistic is equal to the parameter.

We know that the sample mean $\overline{X}$ is an unbiased estimator of the population mean μ. In presenting the sampling distribution of $\overline{X}$ in Section 9-1, we stated that $E(\overline{X}) = \mu$. We also know that the sample proportion is an unbiased estimator of the population proportion because $E(\hat{P}) = p$ and that the difference between two sample means is an unbiased estimator of the difference between two population means because $E(\overline{X}_1 - \overline{X}_2) = \mu_1 - \mu_2$.

Recall that in Chapter 4 we defined the sample variance as

$$s^2 = \sum \frac{(x_i - \overline{x})^2}{n - 1}$$

At the time, it seemed odd that we divided by $n - 1$ rather than by n. The reason for choosing $n - 1$ was to make $E(s^2) = \sigma^2$ so that this definition makes the sample variance an unbiased estimator of the population variance. (The proof of this statement requires about a page of algebraic manipulation, which is more than we would be comfortable presenting here.) Had we defined the sample variance using n in the denominator, the resulting statistic would be a biased estimator of the population variance, one whose expected value is less than the parameter.

Knowing that an estimator is unbiased only assures us that its expected value equals the parameter; it does not tell us how close the estimator is to the parameter. Another desirable quality is that as the sample size grows larger, the sample statistic should come closer to the population parameter. This quality is called *consistency*.

> ### Consistency
> An unbiased estimator is said to be **consistent** if the difference between the estimator and the parameter grows smaller as the sample size grows larger.

The measure we use to gauge closeness is the variance (or the standard deviation). Thus, $\overline{X}$ is a consistent estimator of μ because the variance of $\overline{X}$ is σ^2/n. This implies that as n grows larger, the variance of $\overline{X}$ grows smaller. As a consequence, an increasing proportion of sample means falls close to μ.

Figure 10.1 depicts two sampling distributions of $\overline{X}$. One sampling distribution is based on samples of size 25, and the other is based on samples of size 100. The former is more spread out than the latter.

FIGURE **10.1** Sampling Distribution of $\overline{X}$ with $n = 25$ and $n = 100$

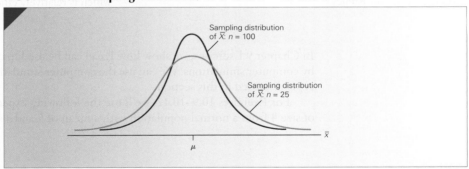

Similarly, $\hat{P}$ is a consistent estimator of p because it is unbiased and the variance of $\hat{P}$ is $p(1 - p)/n$, which grows smaller as n grows larger.

A third desirable quality is *relative efficiency*, which compares two unbiased estimators of a parameter.

> ### Relative Efficiency
> If there are two unbiased estimators of a parameter, the one whose variance is smaller is said to have **relative efficiency**.

We have already seen that the sample mean is an unbiased estimator of the population mean and that its variance is σ^2/n. In the next section, we will discuss the use of the sample median as an estimator of the population mean. Statisticians have established that the sample median is an unbiased estimator but that its variance is greater than that of the sample mean (when the population is normal). As a consequence, the sample mean is relatively more efficient than the sample median when estimating the population mean.

In the remaining chapters of this book, we will present the statistical inference of a number of different population parameters. In each case, we will select a sample statistic that is unbiased and consistent. When there is more than one such statistic, we will choose the one that is relatively efficient to serve as the estimator.

10-1b Developing an Understanding of Statistical Concepts

In this section, we described three desirable characteristics of estimators: unbiasedness, consistency, and relative efficiency. An understanding of statistics requires that you know that there are several potential estimators for each parameter, but that we choose the estimators used in this book because they possess these characteristics.

EXERCISES

10.1 How do point estimators and interval estimators differ?

10.2 Define unbiasedness.

10.3 Draw a sampling distribution of an unbiased estimator.

10.4 Draw a sampling distribution of a biased estimator.

10.5 Define consistency.

10.6 Draw diagrams representing what happens to the sampling distribution of a consistent estimator when the sample size increases.

10.7 Define relative efficiency.

10.8 Draw a diagram that shows the sampling distribution representing two unbiased estimators, one of which is relatively efficient.

In Chapter 9 Exercises, we show how Excel can be used to create sampling distributions by computer simulations. We can use the computer simulations to demonstrate the concepts discussed in this section.

For Exercises 10.9–10.12, we'll use the following experiment. Take 10,000 samples of size 4 from a normal population with a mean of 5 and a standard deviation of 1.

EXERCISES

10.9 For each sample calculate the sample mean. If the sample mean is an unbiased estimator of the population mean, what should you expect when you calculate the mean of the sample means? What did you observe?

10.10 Repeat the experiment calculating the sample medians. (Use Excel function MEDIAN.) If the sample median is an unbiased estimator of the population mean, what should you expect when you calculate

the mean of the sample medians? What did you observe?

The following exercises demonstrate why we defined the sample variance as

$$s^2 = \frac{\sum_{i=1}^{n} (x_i - \bar{x})^2}{n - 1}$$

10.11 Repeat the experiment calculating the sample variances (Excel function VAR). If the sample variance is an unbiased estimator of the population variance, what value should be observed when you calculate the mean of the sample variances? What did you actually observe?

10.12 Repeat the experiment calculating the following for each sample.

$$\frac{\sum_{i=1}^{n}(x_i - \bar{x})^2}{n}$$

The Excel function that produces this statistic is VARP. Calculate the mean of these statistics. Discuss why we define the sample variance by dividing the sum of squared deviations by $n-1$ rather than by n.

10-2 / ESTIMATING THE POPULATION MEAN WHEN THE POPULATION STANDARD DEVIATION IS KNOWN

We now describe how an interval estimator is produced from a sampling distribution. We choose to demonstrate estimation with an example that is unrealistic. However, this liability is offset by the example's simplicity. When you understand more about estimation, you will be able to apply the technique to more realistic situations.

Suppose we have a population with mean μ and standard deviation σ. The population mean is assumed to be unknown, and our task is to estimate its value. As we just discussed, the estimation procedure requires the statistics practitioner to draw a random sample of size n and calculate the sample mean $\bar{x}$.

The central limit theorem presented in Section 9-1 stated that $\overline{X}$ is normally distributed if X is normally distributed, or approximately normally distributed if X is nonnormal and n is sufficiently large. This means that the variable

$$Z = \frac{\overline{X} - \mu}{\sigma/\sqrt{n}}$$

is standard normally distributed (or approximately so). In Section 9-1 (page 295) we developed the following probability statement associated with the sampling distribution of the mean:

$$P\left(\mu - Z_{\alpha/2}\frac{\sigma}{\sqrt{n}} < \overline{X} < \mu + Z_{\alpha/2}\frac{\sigma}{\sqrt{n}}\right) = 1 - \alpha$$

which was derived from

$$P\left(-Z_{\alpha/2} < \frac{\overline{X} - \mu}{\sigma/\sqrt{n}} < Z_{\alpha/2}\right) = 1 - \alpha$$

Using a similar algebraic manipulation, we can express the probability in a slightly different form:

$$P\left(\overline{X} - Z_{\alpha/2}\frac{\sigma}{\sqrt{n}} < \mu < \overline{X} + Z_{\alpha/2}\frac{\sigma}{\sqrt{n}}\right) = 1 - \alpha$$

Notice that in this form the population mean is in the center of the interval created by adding and subtracting $Z_{\alpha/2}$ standard errors to and from the sample mean. It is important for you to understand that this is merely another form of probability statement about the sample mean. This equation says that, with repeated sampling from this population, the proportion of values of $\overline{X}$ for which the interval

$$\overline{X} - Z_{\alpha/2}\frac{\sigma}{\sqrt{n}}, \ \overline{X} + Z_{\alpha/2}\frac{\sigma}{\sqrt{n}}$$

includes the population mean μ is equal to $1 - \alpha$. This form of probability statement is very useful to us because it is the **confidence interval estimator of μ.**

Confidence Interval Estimator of μ[*]

$$\overline{x} - z_{\alpha/2}\frac{\sigma}{\sqrt{n}}, \ \overline{x} + z_{\alpha/2}\frac{\sigma}{\sqrt{n}}$$

The probability $1 - \alpha$ is called the **confidence level**.

$\overline{x} - z_{\alpha/2}\dfrac{\sigma}{\sqrt{n}}$ is called the **lower confidence limit (LCL)**.

$\overline{x} + z_{\alpha/2}\dfrac{\sigma}{\sqrt{n}}$ is called the **upper confidence limit (UCL)**.

We often represent the confidence interval estimator as

$$\overline{x} \pm z_{\alpha/2}\frac{\sigma}{\sqrt{n}}$$

where the minus sign defines the lower confidence limit and the plus sign defines the upper confidence limit.

To apply this formula, we specify the confidence level $1 - \alpha$, from which we determine α, $\alpha/2$, $z_{\alpha/2}$ (from Table 3 in Appendix B). Because the confidence level is the probability that the interval includes the actual value of μ, we generally set $1 - \alpha$ close to 1 (usually between .90 and .99).

In Table 10.1, we list four commonly used confidence levels and their associated values of $z_{\alpha/2}$. For example, if the confidence level is $1 - \alpha = .95$, $\alpha = .05$, $\alpha/2 = .025$,

---

[*]Since Chapter 7, we've been using the convention whereby an uppercase letter (usually X) represents a random variable and a lowercase letter (usually x) represents one of its values. However, in the formulas used in statistical inference, the distinction between the variable and its value becomes blurred. Accordingly, we will discontinue the notational convention and simply use lowercase letters except when we wish to make a probability statement.

and $z_{\alpha/2} = z_{.025} = 1.96$. The resulting confidence interval estimator is then called the **95% confidence interval estimator of μ**.

TABLE **10.1** **Four Commonly Used Confidence Levels and $z_{\alpha/2}$**

$1 - \alpha$	α	$\alpha/2$	$z_{\alpha/2}$
.90	.10	.05	$z_{.05} = 1.645$
.95	.05	.025	$z_{.025} = 1.96$
.98	.02	.01	$z_{.01} = 2.33$
.99	.01	.005	$z_{.005} = 2.575$

The following example illustrates how statistical techniques are applied. It also illustrates how we intend to solve problems in the rest of this book. The solution process that we advocate and use throughout this book is by and large the same one that statistics practitioners use to apply their skills in the real world. The process is divided into three stages. Simply stated, the stages are (1) the activities we perform before the calculations, (2) the calculations, and (3) the activities we perform after the calculations.

In stage 1, we determine the appropriate statistical technique to employ. Of course, for this example you will have no difficulty identifying the technique because you know only one at this point. (In practice, stage 1 also addresses the problem of *how* to gather the data. The methods used in the examples, exercises, and cases are described in the problem.)

In the second stage we calculate the statistics. We will do this in three ways.[*] To illustrate how the computations are completed, we will do the arithmetic manually with the assistance of a calculator. Solving problems by hand often provides insights into the statistical inference technique. However, at some point in our journey of discovery of statistical inference the arithmetic becomes so tedious that we use the computer exclusively.

The second method is a combination of the Analysis ToolPak (Data menu item Data Analysis that is part of Microsoft Excel) and the workbooks that we created. This combination will allow us to compute most, but not all of the inferential techniques introduced in this book. The rest will have to be done by additional software.

The third method uses XLSTAT, which is a commercial software add-in. XLSTAT calculates virtually all of the techniques covered in this book with the exception of forecasting (Chapter 20) and statistical process control (Chapter 21). Readers who need these topics can use Minitab or Data Analysis Plus, which was available in earlier editions of this book. Data Analysis Plus can still be downloaded; see Appendix 1.

In the third and last stage of the solution, we intend to interpret the results and deal with the question presented in the problem. To be capable of properly interpreting statistical results, one needs to have an understanding of the fundamental principles underlying statistical inference.

---

[*]We anticipate that students in most statistics classes will use only one of the three methods of computing statistics: the choice made by the instructor. If such is the case, readers are directed to ignore the other two.

APPLICATIONS in OPERATIONS MANAGEMENT

Inventory Management

Operations managers use inventory models to determine the stock level that minimizes total costs. In Section 8-2, we showed how the probabilistic model is used to make the inventory level decision (see page 263). One component of that model is the mean demand during lead time. Recall that *lead time* refers to the interval between the time an order is made and when it is delivered. Demand during lead time is a random variable that is often assumed to be normally distributed. There are several ways to determine mean demand during lead time, but the simplest is to estimate that quantity from a sample.

Comstock/Getty Images

EXAMPLE 10.1

Data
Xm 10-01

Doll Computer Company

The Doll Computer Company makes its own computers and delivers them directly to customers who order them via the Internet. Doll competes primarily on price and speed of delivery. To achieve its objective of speed, Doll makes each of its five most popular computers and transports them to warehouses across the country. The computers are stored in the warehouses from which it generally takes 1 day to deliver a computer to the customer. This strategy requires high levels of inventory that add considerably to the cost. To lower these costs, the operations manager wants to use an inventory model. He notes that both daily demand and lead time are random variables. He concludes that demand during lead time is normally distributed, and he needs to know the mean to compute the optimum inventory level. He observes 25 lead time periods and records the demand during each period. These data are listed here. The manager would like a 95% confidence interval estimate of the mean demand during lead time. From long experience, the manager knows that the standard deviation is 75 computers.

Demand During Lead Time

235	374	309	499	253
421	361	514	462	369
394	439	348	344	330
261	374	302	466	535
386	316	296	332	334

SOLUTION:

IDENTIFY

To ultimately determine the optimum inventory level, the manager must know the mean demand during lead time. Thus, the parameter to be estimated is μ. At this point, we have described only one interval estimator. Thus, the confidence interval estimator that we intend to use is

$$\bar{x} \pm z_{\alpha/2} \frac{\sigma}{\sqrt{n}}$$

The next step is to perform the calculations. As we discussed previously, we will perform the calculations in three ways: manually, using Excel, and using XLSTAT.

COMPUTE

MANUALLY:

We need four values to construct the confidence interval estimate of μ. They are

$$\bar{x}, z_{\alpha/2}, \sigma, n$$

Using a calculator, we determine the summation $\sum x_i = 9{,}254$. From this, we find

$$\bar{x} = \frac{\sum x_i}{n} = \frac{9{,}254}{25} = 370.16$$

The confidence level is set at 95%; thus, $1 - \alpha = .95$, $\alpha = 1 - .95 = .05$, and $\alpha/2 = .025$.

From Table 3 in Appendix B or from Table 10.1, we find

$$z_{\alpha/2} = z_{.025} = 1.96$$

The population standard deviation is $\sigma = 75$, and the sample size is 25. Substituting $\bar{x}$, $z_{\alpha/2}$, σ, and n into the confidence interval estimator, we find

$$\bar{x} \pm z_{\alpha/2}\frac{\sigma}{\sqrt{n}} = 370.16 \pm z_{.025}\frac{75}{\sqrt{25}} = 370.16 \pm 1.96\frac{75}{\sqrt{25}} = 370.16 \pm 29.40$$

The lower and upper confidence limits are LCL = 340.76 and UCL = 399.56, respectively.

EXCEL Workbook

	A	B	C	D	E
1	z-Estimate of a Mean				
2					
3	Sample mean	370.16	Confidence Interval Estimate		
4	Population standard deviation	75	370.16	±	29.40
5	Sample size	25	Lower confidence limit		340.76
6	Confidence level	0.95	Upper confidence limit		399.56

INSTRUCTIONS

1. Type or import the data into one column. (Open Xm10-01.) In any empty cell, calculate the sample mean (=AVERAGE(A1:A26)

2. Open the **Estimators Workbook** and click the **z-Estimate_Mean** tab. In cell B3, type or copy the value of the sample mean. If you use **Copy** also use **Paste Special** and **Values**). In cells B4–B6, type the value of σ (75), the value of n (25), and the confidence level (.95), respectively.

XLSTAT

	A	B	C	D
1	95% confidence interval on the mean:			
2	340.76	399.56		

Note: We have edited the printout deleting parts of the printout that are not needed for this technique.

INSTRUCTIONS

1. Type or import the data into one column. (Open Xm10-01.)

2. Click **XLSTAT** and **One-sample *t*-test and *z*-test**.

3. In the **Data:** dialog box type the input range (A1:A26). Click **Column labels** if the first row contains the name of the variable (as in this example). Check **z-test** and do not check **Student's *t*-test**.

4. Click the **Options** tab and choose **Mean ≠ Theoretical mean** in the **Alternative hypothesis:** box. Type the value of α (in percent) in the **Significance:** box (5). If there are blanks in the column (usually used to represent missing data) click **Missing data, Remove the observations.** For the **Variance for z-test:** check **User defined: Variance:** and type the value of σ^2 (5625). Click **OK** and then **Continue.**

INTERPRET

The operations manager estimates that the mean demand during lead time lies between 340.76 and 399.56. He can use this estimate as an input in developing an inventory policy. The model discussed in Section 8-2 computes the reorder point, assuming a particular value of the mean demand during lead time. In this example, he could have used the sample mean as a point estimator of the mean demand, from which the inventory policy could be determined. However, the use of the confidence interval estimator allows the manager to use both the lower and upper limits so that he can understand the possible outcomes.

10-2a Interpreting the Confidence Interval Estimate

Some people erroneously interpret the confidence interval estimate in Example 10.1 to mean that there is a 95% probability that the population mean lies between 340.76 and 399.56. This interpretation is wrong because it implies that the population mean is a variable about which we can make probability statements. In fact, the population mean is a fixed but unknown quantity. Consequently, we cannot interpret the confidence interval estimate of μ as a probability statement about μ. To translate the confidence interval estimate properly, we must remember that the confidence interval estimator was derived from the sampling distribution of the sample mean. In Section 9-1, we used the sampling distribution to make probability statements about the sample mean. Although the form has changed, the confidence interval estimator is also a probability statement about the sample mean. It states that there is $1 - \alpha$ probability that the sample mean will be equal to a value such that the interval $\bar{x} - z_{\alpha/2}\sigma/\sqrt{n}$ to $\bar{x} + z_{\alpha/2}\sigma/\sqrt{n}$ will include the population mean. Once the sample mean is computed, the interval acts as the lower and upper limits of the interval estimate of the population mean.

As an illustration, suppose we want to estimate the mean value of the distribution resulting from the throw of a fair die. Because we know the distribution, we also know that

$\mu = 3.5$ and $\sigma = 1.71$. Pretend now that we know only that $\sigma = 1.71$, that μ is unknown, and that we want to estimate its value. To estimate μ, we draw a sample of size $n = 100$ (we throw the die 100 times) and calculate $\bar{x}$. The confidence interval estimator of μ is

$$\bar{x} \pm z_{\alpha/2}\frac{\sigma}{\sqrt{n}}$$

The 90% confidence interval estimator is

$$\bar{x} + z_{\alpha/2}\frac{\sigma}{\sqrt{n}} = \bar{x} \pm 1.645\frac{1.71}{\sqrt{100}} = \bar{x} \pm .281$$

This notation means that if we repeatedly draw samples of size 100 from this population, 90% of the values of $\bar{x}$ will be such that μ would lie somewhere between $\bar{x} - .281$ and $\bar{x} + .281$, and 10% of the values of $\bar{x}$ will produce intervals that would not include μ. Now, imagine that we draw 40 samples of 100 observations each. The values of $\bar{x}$ and the resulting confidence interval estimates of μ are shown in Table 10.2. Notice that not all the intervals include the true value of the parameter. Samples 5, 16, 22, and 34 produce values of $\bar{x}$ that in turn produce intervals that exclude μ.

Students often react to this situation by asking, What went wrong with samples 5, 16, 22, and 34? The answer is nothing. Statistics does not promise 100% certainty. In fact, in this illustration, we expected 90% of the intervals to include μ and 10% to exclude μ. Since we produced 40 intervals, we expected that 4.0 (10% of 40) intervals would not contain $\mu = 3.5$.[*] It is important to understand that, even when the statistics practitioner performs experiments properly, a certain proportion (in this example, 10%) of the experiments will produce incorrect estimates by random chance.

TABLE **10.2** 90% Confidence Interval Estimates of μ

SAMPLE	$\bar{x}$	LCL = $\bar{x}$ − .281	UCL = $\bar{x}$ + .281	DOES INTERVAL INCLUDE $\mu = 3.5$?
1	3.550	3.269	3.831	Yes
2	3.610	3.329	3.891	Yes
3	3.470	3.189	3.751	Yes
4	3.480	3.199	3.761	Yes
5	3.800	3.519	4.081	No
6	3.370	3.089	3.651	Yes
7	3.480	3.199	3.761	Yes
8	3.520	3.239	3.801	Yes
9	3.740	3.459	4.021	Yes
10	3.510	3.229	3.791	Yes
11	3.230	2.949	3.511	Yes
12	3.450	3.169	3.731	Yes
13	3.570	3.289	3.851	Yes

(Continued)

---

[*]In this illustration, exactly 10% of the sample means produced interval estimates that excluded the value of μ, but this will not always be the case. Remember, we expect 10% of the sample means in the long run to result in intervals excluding μ. This group of 40 sample means does not constitute "the long run."

TABLE **10.2** 90% Confidence Interval Estimates of μ *(Continued)*

SAMPLE	$\bar{x}$	LCL = $\bar{x}$ − .281	UCL = $\bar{x}$ + .281	DOES INTERVAL INCLUDE μ = 3.5?
14	3.770	3.489	4.051	Yes
15	3.310	3.029	3.591	Yes
16	3.100	2.819	3.381	No
17	3.500	3.219	3.781	Yes
18	3.550	3.269	3.831	Yes
19	3.650	3.369	3.931	Yes
20	3.280	2.999	3.561	Yes
21	3.400	3.119	3.681	Yes
22	3.880	3.599	4.161	No
23	3.760	3.479	4.041	Yes
24	3.400	3.119	3.681	Yes
25	3.340	3.059	3.621	Yes
26	3.650	3.369	3.931	Yes
27	3.450	3.169	3.731	Yes
28	3.470	3.189	3.751	Yes
29	3.580	3.299	3.861	Yes
30	3.360	3.079	3.641	Yes
31	3.710	3.429	3.991	Yes
32	3.510	3.229	3.791	Yes
33	3.420	3.139	3.701	Yes
34	3.110	2.829	3.391	No
35	3.290	3.009	3.571	Yes
36	3.640	3.359	3.921	Yes
37	3.390	3.109	3.671	Yes
38	3.750	3.469	4.031	Yes
39	3.260	2.979	3.541	Yes
40	3.540	3.259	3.821	Yes

We can improve the confidence associated with the interval estimate. If we let the confidence level $1 - \alpha$ equal .95, the 95% confidence interval estimator is

$$\bar{x} \pm z_{\alpha/2}\frac{\sigma}{\sqrt{n}} = \bar{x} \pm 1.96\frac{1.71}{\sqrt{100}} = \bar{x} \pm .335$$

Because this interval is wider, it is more likely to include the value of μ. If you re-do Table 10.2, this time using a 95% confidence interval estimator, only samples 16, 22, and 34 will produce intervals that do not include μ. (Notice that we expected 5% of the intervals to exclude μ and that we actually observed 3/40 = 7.5%.) The 99% confidence interval estimator is

$$\bar{x} \pm z_{\alpha/2}\frac{\sigma}{\sqrt{n}} = \bar{x} \pm 2.575\frac{1.71}{\sqrt{100}} = \bar{x} \pm .440$$

Applying this interval estimate to the sample means listed in Table 10.2 would result in having all 40 interval estimates include the population mean $\mu = 3.5$. (We expected 1% of the intervals to exclude μ; we observed $0/40 = 0\%$.)

In actual practice, only one sample will be drawn, and thus only one value of $\bar{x}$ will be calculated. The resulting interval estimate will either correctly include the parameter or incorrectly exclude it. Unfortunately, statistics practitioners do not know whether they are correct in each case; they know only that, in the long run, they will incorrectly estimate the parameter some of the time. Statistics practitioners accept that as a fact of life.

We summarize our calculations in Example 10.1 as follows. We estimate that the mean demand during lead time falls between 340.76 and 399.56, and this type of estimator is correct 95% of the time. Thus, the confidence level applies to our estimation procedure and not to any one interval. Incidentally, the media often refer to the 95% figure as "19 times out of 20," which emphasizes the long-run aspect of the confidence level.

10-2b Information and the Width of the Interval

Interval estimation, like all other statistical techniques, is designed to convert data into information. However, a wide interval provides little information. For example, suppose that as a result of a statistical study we estimate with 95% confidence that the average starting salary of an accountant lies between $15,000 and $100,000. This interval is so wide that very little information was derived from the data. Suppose, however, that the interval estimate was $52,000 to $55,000. This interval is much narrower, providing accounting students more precise information about the mean starting salary.

The width of the confidence interval estimate is a function of the population standard deviation, the confidence level, and the sample size. Consider Example 10.1, where σ was assumed to be 75. The interval estimate was 370.16 ± 29.40. If σ equaled 150, the 95% confidence interval estimate would become

$$\bar{x} \pm z_{\alpha/2}\frac{\sigma}{\sqrt{n}} = 370.16 \pm z_{.025}\frac{150}{\sqrt{25}} = 370.16 \pm 1.96\frac{150}{\sqrt{25}} = 370.16 \pm 58.80$$

Thus, doubling the population standard deviation has the effect of doubling the width of the confidence interval estimate. This result is quite logical. If there is a great deal of variation in the random variable (measured by a large standard deviation), it is more difficult to accurately estimate the population mean. That difficulty is translated into a wider interval.

Although we have no control over the value of σ, we do have the power to select values for the other two elements. In Example 10.1, we chose a 95% confidence level. If we had chosen 90% instead, the interval estimate would have been

$$\bar{x} \pm z_{\alpha/2}\frac{\sigma}{\sqrt{n}} = 370.16 \pm z_{.05}\frac{75}{\sqrt{25}} = 370.16 \pm 1.645\frac{75}{\sqrt{25}} = 370.16 \pm 24.68$$

A 99% confidence level results in this interval estimate:

$$\bar{x} \pm z_{\alpha/2}\frac{\sigma}{\sqrt{n}} = 370.16 \pm z_{.005}\frac{75}{\sqrt{25}} = 370.16 \pm 2.575\frac{75}{\sqrt{25}} = 370.16 \pm 38.63$$

As you can see, decreasing the confidence level narrows the interval; increasing it widens the interval. However, a large confidence level is generally desirable because that means a larger proportion of confidence interval estimates that will be correct in the long run. There is a direct relationship between the width of the interval and the confidence level. This is because we need to widen the interval to be more confident in the estimate. (The analogy is that to be more likely to capture a butterfly, we need a larger butterfly net.) The trade-off between increased confidence and the resulting wider confidence interval estimates must be resolved by the statistics practitioner. As a general rule, however, 95% confidence is considered "standard."

The third element is the sample size. Had the sample size been 100 instead of 25, the confidence interval estimate would become

$$\bar{x} \pm z_{\alpha/2}\frac{\sigma}{\sqrt{n}} = 370.16 \pm z_{.025}\frac{75}{\sqrt{100}} = 370.16 \pm 1.96\frac{75}{\sqrt{100}} = 370.16 \pm 14.70$$

Increasing the sample size fourfold decreases the width of the interval by half. A larger sample size provides more potential information. The increased amount of information is reflected in a narrower interval. However, there is another trade-off: Increasing the sample size increases the sampling cost. We will discuss these issues when we present sample size selection in Section 10-3.

10-2c (Optional) Estimating the Population Mean Using the Sample Median

To understand why the sample mean is most often used to estimate a population mean, let's examine the properties of the sampling distribution of the sample median (denoted here as m). The sampling distribution of a sample median is normally distributed provided that the population is normal. Its mean and standard deviation are

$$\mu_m = \mu$$

and

$$\sigma_m = \frac{1.2533\sigma}{\sqrt{n}}$$

Using the same algebraic steps that we used above, we derive the confidence interval estimator of a population mean using the sample median

$$m \pm z_{\alpha/2}\frac{1.2533\sigma}{\sqrt{n}}$$

To illustrate, suppose that we have drawn the following random sample from a normal population whose standard deviation is 2.

$$1 \quad 1 \quad 1 \quad 3 \quad 4 \quad 5 \quad 6 \quad 7 \quad 8$$

The sample mean is $\bar{x} = 4$, and the sample median is $m = 4$.

The 95% confidence interval estimates using the sample mean and the sample median are

$$\bar{x} \pm z_{\alpha/2}\frac{\sigma}{\sqrt{n}} = 4.0 \pm 1.96\frac{2}{\sqrt{9}} = 4 \pm 1.307$$

$$m \pm z_{\alpha/2}\frac{1.2533\sigma}{\sqrt{n}} = 4.0 \pm 1.96\frac{(1.2533)(2)}{\sqrt{9}} = 4 \pm 1.638$$

As you can see, the interval based on the sample mean is narrower; as we pointed out previously, narrower intervals provide more precise information. To understand why the sample mean produces better estimators than the sample median, recall how the median is calculated. We simply put the data in order and select the observation that falls in the middle. Thus, as far as the median is concerned the data appear as

1   2   3   4   5   6   7   8   9

By ignoring the actual observations and using their ranks instead, we lose information. With less information, we have less precision in the interval estimators and so ultimately make poorer decisions.

Exercises

Developing an Understanding of Statistical Concepts

Exercises 10.13 to 10.20 are "what-if" analyses designed to determine what happens to the interval estimate when the confidence level, sample size, and standard deviation change. These problems can be solved manually or using the z-Estimate_Mean spreadsheet in the Estimators workbook.

10.13 a. A statistics practitioner took a random sample of 50 observations from a population with a standard deviation of 25 and computed the sample mean to be 100. Estimate the population mean with 90% confidence.
b. Repeat part (a) using a 95% confidence level.
c. Repeat part (a) using a 99% confidence level.
d. Describe the effect on the confidence interval estimate of increasing the confidence level.

10.14 a. The mean of a random sample of 25 observations from a normal population with a standard deviation of 50 is 200. Estimate the population mean with 95% confidence.
b. Repeat part (a) changing the population standard deviation to 25.
c. Repeat part (a) changing the population standard deviation to 10.
d. Describe what happens to the confidence interval estimate when the standard deviation is decreased.

10.15 a. A random sample of 25 was drawn from a normal distribution with a standard deviation of 5. The sample mean is 80. Determine the 95% confidence interval estimate of the population mean.
b. Repeat part (a) with a sample size of 100.
c. Repeat part (a) with a sample size of 400.
d. Describe what happens to the confidence interval estimate when the sample size increases.

10.16 a. Given the following information, determine the 98% confidence interval estimate of the population mean:
$\bar{x} = 500$ $\sigma = 12$ $n = 50$
b. Repeat part (a) using a 95% confidence level.
c. Repeat part (a) using a 90% confidence level.

d. Review parts (a)–(c) and discuss the effect on the confidence interval estimator of decreasing the confidence level.

10.17 a. The mean of a sample of 25 was calculated as $\bar{x} = 500$. The sample was randomly drawn from a population with a standard deviation of 15. Estimate the population mean with 99% confidence.
b. Repeat part (a) changing the population standard deviation to 30.
c. Repeat part (a) changing the population standard deviation to 60.
d. Describe what happens to the confidence interval estimate when the standard deviation is increased.

10.18 a. A statistics practitioner randomly sampled 100 observations from a population with a standard deviation of 5 and found that $\bar{x}$ is 10. Estimate the population mean with 90% confidence.
b. Repeat part (a) with a sample size of 25.
c. Repeat part (a) with a sample size of 10.
d. Describe what happens to the confidence interval estimate when the sample size decreases.

10.19 a. From the information given here determine the 95% confidence interval estimate of the population mean.
$\bar{x} = 100$ $\sigma = 20$ $n = 25$
b. Repeat part (a) with $\bar{x} = 200$.
c. Repeat part (a) with $\bar{x} = 500$.
d. Describe what happens to the width of the confidence interval estimate when the sample mean increases.

10.20 a. A random sample of 100 observations was randomly drawn from a population with a standard deviation of 5. The sample mean was calculated as $\bar{x} = 400$. Estimate the population mean with 99% confidence.
b. Repeat part (a) with $\bar{x} = 200$.
c. Repeat part (a) with $\bar{x} = 100$.
d. Describe what happens to the width of the confidence interval estimate when the sample mean decreases.

Exercises 10.21 to 10.24 are based on the optional subsection "Estimating the Population Mean Using the Sample Median." All exercises assume that the population is normal.

10.21 Is the sample median an unbiased estimator of the population mean? Explain.

10.22 Is the sample median a consistent estimator of the population mean? Explain.

10.23 Show that the sample mean is relatively more efficient than the sample median when estimating the population mean.

10.24 a. Given the following information, determine the 90% confidence interval estimate of the population mean using the sample median.

Sample median = 500, $\sigma = 12$, and $n = 50$

b. Compare your answer in part (a) to that produced in part (c) of Exercise 10.16. Why is the confidence interval estimate based on the sample median wider than that based on the sample mean?

Applications

The following exercises may be answered manually or with the assistance of a computer. The names of the files containing the data are shown.

10.25 Xr10-25 The following data represent a random sample of 9 marks (out of 10) on a statistics quiz. The marks are normally distributed with a standard deviation of 2. Estimate the population mean with 90% confidence.

7 9 7 5 4 8 3 10 9

10.26 Xr10-26 The following observations are the ages of a random sample of 8 men in a bar. It is known that the ages are normally distributed with a standard deviation of 10. Determine the 95% confidence interval estimate of the population mean. Interpret the interval estimate.

52 68 22 35 30 56 39 48

10.27 Xr10-27 How many rounds of golf do physicians (who play golf) play per year? A survey of 12 physicians revealed the following numbers:

3 41 17 1 33 37 18 15 17 12 29 51

Estimate with 95% confidence the mean number of rounds per year played by physicians, assuming that the number of rounds is normally distributed with a standard deviation of 12.

10.28 Xr10-28 Among the most exciting aspects of a university professor's life are the departmental meetings where such critical issues as the color of the walls will be painted and who gets a new desk are decided. A sample of 20 professors was asked how many hours per year are devoted to these meetings. The responses are listed here. Assuming that the variable is normally distributed with a standard deviation of 8 hours, estimate the mean number of hours spent at departmental meetings by all professors. Use a confidence level of 90%.

14 17 3 6 17 3 8 4 20 15
7 9 0 5 11 15 18 13 8 4

10.29 Xr10-29 The number of cars sold annually by used car salespeople is normally distributed with a standard deviation of 15. A random sample of 15 salespeople was taken, and the number of cars each sold is listed here. Find the 95% confidence interval estimate of the population mean. Interpret the interval estimate.

79 43 58 66 101 63 79 33 58
71 60 101 74 55 88

10.30 Xr10-30 It is known that the amount of time needed to change the oil on a car is normally distributed with a standard deviation of 5 minutes. The amount of time to complete a random sample of 10 oil changes was recorded and listed here. Compute the 99% confidence interval estimate of the mean of the population.

11 10 16 15 18 12 25 20 18 24

10.31 Xr10-31 Suppose that the amount of time teenagers spend weekly working at part-time jobs is normally distributed with a standard deviation of 40 minutes. A random sample of 15 teenagers was drawn, and each reported the amount of time spent at part-time jobs (in minutes). These are listed here. Determine the 95% confidence interval estimate of the population mean.

180 130 150 165 90 130 120 60 200
180 80 240 210 150 125

10.32 Xr10-32 One of the few negative side effects of quitting smoking is weight gain. Suppose that the weight gain in the 12 months following a cessation in smoking is normally distributed with a standard deviation of 6 pounds. To estimate the mean weight gain, a random sample of 13 quitters was drawn; their recorded weights are listed here. Determine the 90% confidence interval estimate of the mean 12-month weight gain for all quitters.

16 23 8 2 14 22 18 11 10 19 5 8 15

10.33 Xr10-33 Because of different sales ability, experience, and devotion, the incomes of real estate agents vary considerably. Suppose that in a large city the annual income is normally distributed with a standard deviation of $15,000. A random sample of 16 real estate agents was asked to report their annual income (in $1,000). The responses are listed here. Determine the 99% confidence interval estimate of the mean annual income of all real estate agents in the city.

65 94 57 111 83 61 50 73 68 80
93 84 113 41 60 77

The following exercises require the use of a computer and software. The answers may be calculated manually. See Appendix A for the sample statistics.

10.34 Xr10-34 A survey of 400 statistics professors was undertaken. Each professor was asked how much time was devoted to teaching graphical techniques. We believe that the times are normally distributed with a standard deviation of 30 minutes. Estimate the population mean with 95% confidence.

10.35 Xr10-35 In a survey conducted to determine, among other things, the cost of vacations, 64 individuals were randomly sampled. Each person was asked to compute the cost of her or his most recent vacation. Assuming that the standard deviation is $400, estimate with 95% confidence the average cost of all vacations.

10.36 Xr10-36 In an article about *disinflation*, various investments were examined. The investments included stocks, bonds, and real estate. Suppose that a random sample of 200 rates of return on real estate investments was computed and recorded. Assuming that the standard deviation of all rates of return on real estate investments is 2.1%, estimate the mean rate of return on all real estate investments with 90% confidence. Interpret the estimate.

10.37 Xr10-37 A statistics professor is in the process of investigating how many classes university students miss each semester. To help answer this question, she took a random sample of 100 university students and asked each to report how many classes he or she had missed in the previous semester. Estimate the mean number of classes missed by all students at the university. Use a 99% confidence level and assume that the population standard deviation is known to be 2.2 classes.

10.38 Xr10-38 As part of a project to develop better lawn fertilizers, a research chemist wanted to determine the mean weekly growth rate of Kentucky bluegrass, a common type of grass. A sample of 250 blades of grass was measured, and the amount of growth in 1 week was recorded. Assuming that weekly growth is normally distributed with a standard deviation of .10 inch, estimate with 99% confidence the mean weekly growth of Kentucky bluegrass. Briefly describe what the interval estimate tells you about the growth of Kentucky bluegrass.

10.39 Xr10-39 A time study of a large production facility was undertaken to determine the mean time required to assemble a cell phone. A random sample of the times to assemble 50 cell phones was recorded. An analysis of the assembly times reveals that they are normally distributed with a standard deviation of 1.3 minutes. Estimate with 95% confidence the mean assembly time for all cell phones. What do your results tell you about the assembly times?

10.40 Xr10-40 The image of the Japanese manager is that of a workaholic with little or no leisure time. In a survey, a random sample of 250 Japanese middle managers was asked how many hours per week they spent in leisure activities (e.g., sports, movies, television). The results of the survey were recorded. Assuming that the population standard deviation is 6 hours, estimate with 90% confidence the mean leisure time per week for all Japanese middle managers. What do these results tell you?

10.41 Xr10-41 One measure of physical fitness is the amount of time it takes for the pulse rate to return to normal after exercise. A random sample of 100 women age 40 to 50 exercised on stationary bicycles for 30 minutes. The amount of time it took for their pulse rates to return to pre-exercise levels was measured and recorded. If the times are normally distributed with a standard deviation of 2.3 minutes, estimate with 99% confidence the true mean pulse-recovery time for all 40- to 50-year-old women. Interpret the results.

10.42 Xr10-42 A survey of 80 randomly selected companies asked them to report the annual income of their presidents. Assuming that incomes are normally distributed with a standard deviation of $30,000, determine the 90% confidence interval estimate of the mean annual income of all company presidents. Interpret the statistical results.

10.43 Xr10-43 The rising cost of electricity is a concern for homeowners. An economist wanted to determine how much electricity has increased over the past 5 years. A survey was conducted with the percentage increase recorded. Assuming that the population standard deviation is known to be 20% estimate the mean percentage increase with 95% confidence.

APPLICATIONS in MARKETING

Advertising

One of the major tools in the promotion mix is advertising. An important decision to be made by the advertising manager is how to allocate the company's total advertising budget among the various competing media types, including television, radio, and newspapers. Ultimately, the manager wants to know, for example, which television programs are most watched by potential customers, and how effective it is to sponsor these programs through advertising. But first the manager must assess the size of the audience, which involves estimating the amount of exposure potential customers have to the various media types, such as television.

Sean Pavone/Shutterstock.com

10.44 Xr10-44 How much do American families spend on entertainment each month. A survey was conducted and the amounts spent on entertainment in the previous month were recorded. Assuming that the population standard deviation is $50 determine the 99% confidence interval estimate of the mean monthly amount of money spent by American families. Source: Adapted from the Bureau of Labor Statistics.

10.45 Xr10-45 Registered Retirement Savings Plan are retirement plans that defer taxes. Many Canadians rely on these plans for their retirement. To measure how these are doing, a random sample of 60-year-old Canadians was drawn and asked to report the total value of their RRSPs. If the population standard deviation is known to be $75,000, estimate the mean with 90% confidence.

10.46 Xr10-46 The sponsors of television shows targeted at the children's market wanted to know the amount of time children spend watching television because the types and number of programs and commercials are greatly influenced by this information. As a result, it was decided to survey 100 North American children and ask them to keep track of the number of hours of television they watch each week. From past experience, it is known that the population standard deviation of the weekly amount of television watched is $\sigma = 8.0$ hours. The television sponsors want an estimate of the amount of television watched by the average North American child. A confidence level of 95% is judged to be appropriate.

10-3 / SELECTING THE SAMPLE SIZE

As we discussed in the previous section, if the interval estimate is too wide, it provides little information. In Example 10.1 the interval estimate was 340.76 to 399.56. If the manager is to use this estimate as input for an inventory model, he needs greater precision. Fortunately, statistics practitioners can control the width of the interval by determining the sample size necessary to produce narrow intervals.

To understand how and why we can determine the sample size, we discuss the error of estimation.

10-3a Error of Estimation

In Chapter 5, we pointed out that sampling error is the difference between the sample and the population that exists only because of the observations that happened to be selected for the sample. Now that we have discussed estimation, we can define the sampling error as the difference between an estimator and a parameter. We can also define this difference as the **error of estimation**. In this chapter, this can be expressed as the difference between $\overline{X}$ and μ. In our derivation of the confidence interval estimator of μ (see page 316), we expressed the following probability,

$$P\left(-Z_{\alpha/2} < \frac{\overline{X} - \mu}{\sigma/\sqrt{n}} < Z_{\alpha/2}\right) = 1 - \alpha$$

which can also be expressed as

$$P\left(-Z_{\alpha/2}\frac{\sigma}{\sqrt{n}} < \overline{X} - \mu < +Z_{\alpha/2}\frac{\sigma}{\sqrt{n}}\right) = 1 - \alpha$$

This tells us that the difference between $\overline{X}$ and μ lies between $-Z_{\alpha/2}\sigma/\sqrt{n}$ and $+Z_{\alpha/2}\sigma/\sqrt{n}$ with probability $1 - \alpha$. Expressed another way, we have with probability $1 - \alpha$,

$$|\overline{X} - \mu| < Z_{\alpha/2}\frac{\sigma}{\sqrt{n}}$$

In other words, the error of estimation is less than $Z_{\alpha/2}\sigma/\sqrt{n}$. We interpret this to mean that $Z_{\alpha/2}\sigma/\sqrt{n}$ is the maximum error of estimation that we are willing to tolerate. We label this value B, which stands for the **bound on the error of estimation**; that is,

$$B = Z_{\alpha/2}\frac{\sigma}{\sqrt{n}}$$

10-3b Determining the Sample Size

We can solve the equation for n if the population standard deviation σ, the confidence level $1 - \alpha$, and the bound on the error of estimation B are known. Solving for n, we produce the following.

Sample Size to Estimate a Mean

$$n = \left(\frac{z_{\alpha/2}\sigma}{B}\right)^2$$

To illustrate, suppose that in Example 10.1, before gathering the data, the manager had decided that he needed to estimate the mean demand during lead time to within 16 units, which is the bound on the error of estimation. We also have $1 - \alpha = .95$ and $\sigma = 75$. We calculate

$$n = \left(\frac{z_{\alpha/2}\sigma}{B}\right)^2 = \left(\frac{(1.96)(75)}{16}\right)^2 = 84.41$$

Because n must be an integer and because we want the bound on the error of estimation to be *no more* than 16, any noninteger value must be rounded up. Thus, the value of n is rounded to 85, which means that to be 95% confident that the error of estimation will be no larger than 16, we need to randomly sample 85 lead time intervals.

Determining the Sample Size to Estimate the Mean Tree Diameter: Solution

Before the sample was taken, the forester determined the sample size as follows.

The bound on the error of estimation is $B = 1$. The confidence level is 90% $(1 - \alpha = .90)$. Thus $\alpha = .10$ and $\alpha / 2 = .05$. It follows that $z_{\alpha/2} = 1.645$. The population standard deviation is assumed to be $\sigma = 6$. Thus,

$$n = \left(\frac{z_{\alpha/2}\sigma}{B}\right)^2 = \left(\frac{1.645 \times 6}{1}\right)^2 = 97.42$$

which is rounded to 98.

However, after the sample is taken the forester discovered that $\sigma = 12$. The 90% confidence interval estimate is

$$\bar{x} \pm z_{\alpha/2}\frac{\sigma}{\sqrt{n}} = 25 \pm z_{.05}\frac{12}{\sqrt{98}} = 25 \pm 1.645\frac{12}{\sqrt{98}} = 25 \pm 2$$

As you can see, the bound on the error of estimation is 2 and not 1. The interval is twice as wide as it was designed to be. The resulting estimate will not be as precise as needed.

In this chapter, we have assumed that we know the value of the population standard deviation. In practice, this is seldom the case. (In Chapter 12, we introduce a more realistic confidence interval estimator of the population mean.) It is frequently necessary to "guesstimate" the value of σ to calculate the sample size; that is, we must use our knowledge of the variable with which we're dealing to assign some value to σ.

Unfortunately, we cannot be very precise in this guess. However, in guesstimating the value of σ, we prefer to err on the high side. For the chapter-opening example, if the forester had determined the sample size using $\sigma = 12$, he would have computed

$$n = \left(\frac{z_{\alpha/2}\sigma}{B}\right)^2 = \left(\frac{(1.645)(12)}{1}\right)^2 = 389.67 \,(\text{rounded to } 390)$$

Using $n = 390$ (assuming that the sample mean is again 25), the 90% confidence interval estimate is

$$\bar{x} \pm z_{\alpha/2}\frac{\sigma}{\sqrt{n}} = 25 \pm 1.645\frac{12}{\sqrt{390}} = 25 \pm 1$$

This interval is as narrow as the forester wanted.

What happens if the standard deviation is *smaller* than assumed? If we discover that the standard deviation is less than we assumed when we determined the sample size, the confidence interval estimator will be narrower and therefore more precise. Suppose that after the sample of 98 trees was taken (assuming again that $\sigma = 6$), the forester discovers that $\sigma = 3$. The confidence interval estimate is

$$\bar{x} \pm z_{\alpha/2}\frac{\sigma}{\sqrt{n}} = 25 \pm 1.645\frac{3}{\sqrt{98}} = 25 \pm 0.5$$

which is narrower than the forester wanted. Although this means that he would have sampled more trees than needed, the additional cost is relatively low when compared to the value of the information derived.

EXERCISES

Developing an Understanding of Statistical Concepts

10.47 a. Determine the sample size required to estimate a population mean to within 10 units given that the population standard deviation is 50. A confidence level of 90% is judged to be appropriate.
b. Repeat part (a) changing the standard deviation to 100.
c. Re-do part (a) using a 95% confidence level.
d. Repeat part (a) wherein we wish to estimate the population mean to within 20 units.

10.48 Review Exercise 10.47. Describe what happens to the sample size when
a. the population standard deviation increases.
b. the confidence level increases.
c. the bound on the error of estimation increases.

10.49 a. A statistics practitioner would like to estimate a population mean to within 50 units with 99% confidence given that the population standard deviation is 250. What sample size should be used?
b. Re-do part (a) changing the standard deviation to 50.
c. Re-do part (a) using a 95% confidence level.
d. Re-do part (a) wherein we wish to estimate the population mean to within 10 units.

10.50 Review the results of Exercise 10.49. Describe what happens to the sample size when
a. the population standard deviation decreases.
b. the confidence level decreases.
c. the bound on the error of estimation decreases.

10.51 a. Determine the sample size necessary to estimate a population mean to within 1 with 90% confidence given that the population standard deviation is 10.
b. Suppose that the sample mean was calculated as 150. Estimate the population mean with 90% confidence.

10.52 a. Repeat part (b) in Exercise 10.51 after discovering that the population standard deviation is actually 5.
b. Repeat part (b) in Exercise 10.45 after discovering that the population standard deviation is actually 20.

10.53 Review Exercises 10.51 and 10.52. Describe what happens to the confidence interval estimate when
a. the standard deviation is equal to the value used to determine the sample size.

b. the standard deviation is smaller than the one used to determine the sample size.
c. the standard deviation is larger than the one used to determine the sample size.

10.54 a. A statistics practitioner would like to estimate a population mean to within 10 units. The confidence level has been set at 95% and $\sigma = 200$. Determine the sample size.
b. Suppose that the sample mean was calculated as 500. Estimate the population mean with 95% confidence.

10.55 a. Repeat part (b) of Exercise 10.54 after discovering that the population standard deviation is actually 100.
b. Repeat part (b) of Exercise 10.48 after discovering that the population standard deviation is actually 400.

10.56 Review Exercises 10.54 and 10.55. Describe what happens to the confidence interval estimate when
a. the standard deviation is equal to the value used to determine the sample size.
b. the standard deviation is smaller than the one used to determine the sample size.
c. the standard deviation is larger than the one used to determine the sample size.

Applications

10.57 A medical statistician wants to estimate the average weight loss of people who are on a new diet plan. In a preliminary study, he guesses that the standard deviation of the population of weight losses is about 10 pounds. How large a sample should he take to estimate the mean weight loss to within 2 pounds, with 90% confidence?

10.58 The operations manager of a large production plant would like to estimate the average amount of time workers take to assemble a new electronic component. After observing a number of workers assembling similar devices, she guesses that the standard deviation is 6 minutes. How large a sample of workers should she take if she wishes to estimate the mean assembly time to within 20 seconds? Assume that the confidence level is to be 99%.

10.59 A statistics professor wants to compare today's students with those 25 years ago. All his current students' marks are stored on a computer so that he can easily determine the population mean. However, the marks 25 years ago reside only in his musty files. He does not want to retrieve all the marks and will be satisfied with a 95% confidence interval estimate of the mean mark 25 years ago. If he assumes that the population standard deviation is 12, how large a sample should he take to estimate the mean to within 2 marks?

10.60 A medical researcher wants to investigate the amount of time it takes for patients' headache to be relieved after taking a new prescription painkiller. She plans to use statistical methods to estimate the mean of the population of relief times. She believes that the population is normally distributed with a standard deviation of 20 minutes. How large a sample should she take to estimate the mean time to within 1 minute with 90% confidence?

10.61 The label on 1-gallon cans of paint states that the amount of paint in the can is sufficient to paint 400 square feet. However, this number is quite variable. In fact, the amount of coverage is known to be approximately normally distributed with a standard deviation of 25 square feet. How large a sample should be taken to estimate the true mean coverage of all 1-gallon cans to within 5 square feet with 95% confidence?

10.62 The operations manager of a plant making cellular telephones has proposed rearranging the production process to be more efficient. She wants to estimate the time to assemble the telephone using the new arrangement. She believes that the population standard deviation is 15 seconds. How large a sample of workers should she take to estimate the mean assembly time to within 2 seconds with 95% confidence?

CHAPTER SUMMARY

This chapter introduced the concepts of **estimation** and the **estimator** of a population mean when the population variance is known. It also presented a formula to calculate the sample size necessary to estimate a population mean.

IMPORTANT TERMS:

Point estimator   311
Interval estimator   312
Unbiased estimator   312
Consistency   313
Relative efficiency   313
Confidence interval estimator of μ 316

Confidence level   316
Lower confidence limit (LCL)   316
Upper confidence limit (UCL)   316
95% confidence interval estimator of μ 317
Error of estimation   328
Bound on the error of estimation   329

SYMBOLS:

Symbol	Pronounced	Represents
$1 - \alpha$	One minus alpha	Confidence level
B		Bound on the error of estimation
$z_{\alpha/2}$	z alpha by 2	Value of Z such that the area to its right is equal to $\alpha/2$

FORMULAS:

Confidence interval estimator of μ with σ known

$$\bar{x} \pm z_{\alpha/2}\frac{\sigma}{\sqrt{n}}$$

Sample size to estimate μ

$$n = \left(\frac{z_{\alpha/2}\sigma}{B}\right)^2$$

COMPUTER OUTPUT AND INSTRUCTIONS:

Technique	Excel
Confidence interval estimate of μ	319

Wavebreakmedia/Shutterstock.com

INTRODUCTION TO HYPOTHESIS TESTING

CHAPTER OUTLINE

SSA Envelope Plan

Data
Xm11-00

Federal Express (FedEx) sends invoices to customers requesting payment within 30 days. Each bill lists an address, and customers are expected to use their own envelopes to return their payments. Currently, the mean and standard deviation of the amount of time taken to pay bills are 24 days and 6 days, respectively. The chief financial officer (CFO) believes that including a stamped self-addressed (SSA) envelope would decrease the amount of time. She calculates that the improved cash flow from a 2-day decrease in the payment period would pay for the costs of the envelopes and stamps. Any further decrease in the payment period would generate a profit. To test her belief, she randomly selects 220 customers and includes an SSA envelope with their invoices. The numbers of days until payment is received were recorded. Can the CFO conclude that the plan will be profitable?

Franck Boston/Shutterstock.com

After we've introduced the required tools, we'll return to this question and answer it (see page 347).

333

INTRODUCTION

In Chapter 10, we introduced estimation and showed how it is used. Now we're going to present the second general procedure of making inferences about a population—hypothesis testing. The purpose of this type of inference is to determine whether enough statistical evidence exists to enable us to conclude that a belief or hypothesis about a parameter is supported by the data. You will discover that hypothesis testing has a wide variety of applications in business and economics, as well as many other fields. This chapter will lay the foundation upon which the rest of the book is based. As such it represents a critical contribution to your development as a statistics practitioner.

In the next section, we will introduce the concepts of hypothesis testing, and in Section 11-2 we will develop the method employed to test a hypothesis about a population mean when the population standard deviation is known. The rest of the chapter deals with related topics.

11-1 / CONCEPTS OF HYPOTHESIS TESTING

The term **hypothesis testing** is likely new to most readers, but the concepts underlying hypothesis testing are quite familiar. There are a variety of nonstatistical applications of hypothesis testing, the best known of which is a criminal trial.

When a person is accused of a crime, he or she faces a trial. The prosecution presents its case, and a jury must make a decision on the basis of the evidence presented. In fact, the jury conducts a test of hypothesis. There are actually two hypotheses that are tested. The first is called the **null hypothesis** and is represented by H_0 (pronounced *H nought*—*nought* is a British term for zero). It is

H_0:　The defendant is innocent.

The second is called the **alternative hypothesis** (or **research hypothesis**) and is denoted H_1. In a criminal trial it is

H_1:　The defendant is guilty.

Of course, the jury does not know which hypothesis is correct. The members must make a decision on the basis of the evidence presented by both the prosecution and the defense. There are only two possible decisions. Convict or acquit the defendant. In statistical parlance, convicting the defendant is equivalent to *rejecting the null hypothesis in favor of the alternative*; that is, the jury is saying that there was enough evidence to conclude that the defendant was guilty. Acquitting a defendant is phrased as *not rejecting the null hypothesis in favor of the alternative*, which means that the jury decided that there was not enough evidence to conclude that the defendant was guilty. Notice that we do not say that we accept the null hypothesis. In a criminal trial, that would be interpreted as finding the defendant *innocent*. Our justice system does not allow this decision.

There are two possible errors. A **Type I error** occurs when we reject a true null hypothesis. A **Type II error** is defined as not rejecting a false null hypothesis. In the criminal trial, a Type I error is made when an innocent person is wrongly convicted. A Type II error occurs when a guilty defendant is acquitted. The probability of a Type I error is denoted by α which is also called the **significance level**. The probability of a Type II error is denoted by β (Greek letter *beta*). The error probabilities α and β are inversely related, meaning that any attempt to reduce one will increase the other. Table 11.1 summarizes the terminology and the concepts.

TABLE **11.1** **Terminology of Hypothesis Testing**

DECISION	H_0 IS TRUE Defendant is innocent	H_0 IS FALSE Defendant is guilty
REJECT H_0 Convict defendant	TYPE I ERROR P(TYPE I ERROR) = α	CORRECT DECISION
DO NOT REJECT H_0 Acquit defendant	CORRECT DECISION	TYPE II ERROR P(TYPE II ERROR) = β

In our justice system, Type I errors are regarded as more serious. As a consequence, the system is set up so that the probability of a Type I error is small. This is arranged by placing the burden of proof on the prosecution (the prosecution must prove guilt—the defense need not prove anything) and by having judges instruct the jury to find the defendant guilty only if there is "evidence beyond a reasonable doubt." In the absence of enough evidence, the jury must acquit even though there may be some evidence of guilt. The consequence of this arrangement is that the probability of acquitting guilty people is relatively large. Oliver Wendell Holmes, a United States Supreme Court justice, once phrased the relationship between the probabilities of Type I and Type II errors in the following way: "Better to acquit 100 guilty men than convict one innocent one." In Justice Holmes's opinion, the probability of a Type I error should be 1/100 of the probability of a Type II error.

The critical concepts in hypothesis testing follow.

1. There are two hypotheses. One is called the null hypothesis, and the other the alternative or research hypothesis.

2. The testing procedure begins with the assumption that the null hypothesis is true.

3. The goal of the process is to determine whether there is enough evidence to infer that the alternative hypothesis is true.

4. There are two possible decisions:

   Conclude that there is enough evidence to support the alternative hypothesis.

   Conclude that there is not enough evidence to support the alternative hypothesis.

5. Two possible errors can be made in any test. A Type I error occurs when we reject a true null hypothesis, and a Type II error occurs when we don't reject a false null hypothesis. The probabilities of Type I and Type II errors are

$P(\text{Type I error}) = \alpha$

$P(\text{Type II error}) = \beta$

Let's extend these concepts to statistical hypothesis testing.

In statistics we frequently test hypotheses about parameters. The hypotheses we test are generated by questions that managers need to answer. To illustrate, suppose that in Example 10.1 (page 318) the operations manager did not want to estimate the mean demand during lead time but instead wanted to know whether the mean is different from 350, which may be the point at which the current inventory policy needs to be altered. In other words, the manager wants to determine whether he can infer that μ is not equal to 350. We can rephrase the question so that it now reads, Is there enough evidence to conclude that μ is not equal to 350? This wording is analogous to the criminal trial wherein the jury is asked to determine whether there is enough evidence to conclude that the defendant is guilty. Thus, the alternative (research) hypothesis is

$$H_1: \quad \mu \neq 350$$

In a criminal trial, the process begins with the assumption that the defendant is innocent. In a similar fashion, we start with the assumption that the parameter equals the value we're testing. Consequently, the operations manager would assume that $\mu = 350$, and the null hypothesis is expressed as

$$H_0: \quad \mu = 350$$

When we state the hypotheses, we list the null first followed by the alternative hypothesis. To determine whether the mean is different from 350, we test

$$H_0: \quad \mu = 350$$

$$H_1: \quad \mu \neq 350$$

Now suppose that in this illustration the current inventory policy is based on an analysis that revealed that the actual mean demand during lead time is 350. After a vigorous advertising campaign, the manager suspects that there has been an increase in demand and thus an increase in mean demand during lead time. To test whether there is evidence of an increase, the manager would specify the alternative hypothesis as

$$H_1: \quad \mu > 350$$

Because the manager knew that the mean was (and maybe still is) 350, the null hypothesis would state

$$H_0: \quad \mu = 350$$

Further suppose that the manager does not know the actual mean demand during lead time, but the current inventory policy is based on the assumption that the mean is *less than or equal to* 350. If the advertising campaign increases the mean to a quantity larger than 350, a new inventory plan will have to be instituted. In this scenario, the hypotheses become

$$H_0: \quad \mu \leq 350$$

$$H_1: \quad \mu > 350$$

Notice that in both illustrations the alternative hypothesis is designed to determine whether there is enough evidence to conclude that the mean is greater than 350. Although the two null hypotheses are different (one states that the mean is equal to 350, and the other states that the mean is less than or equal to 350), when the test is conducted, the process begins by assuming that the mean is *equal to* 350. In other words, no matter the form of the null hypothesis, we use the equal sign in the null hypothesis. Here is the reason. If there is enough evidence to conclude that the alternative hypothesis (the mean is greater than 350) is true when we assume that the mean is *equal to* 350, we would certainly draw the same conclusion when we assume that the mean is a value that is *less than* 350. As a result, the null hypothesis will always state that the parameter equals the value specified in the alternative hypothesis.

To emphasize this point, suppose the manager now wanted to determine whether there has been a decrease in the mean demand during lead time. We express the null and alternative hypotheses as

$$H_0: \quad \mu = 350$$

$$H_1: \quad \mu < 350$$

The hypotheses are often set up to reflect a manager's decision problem wherein the null hypothesis represents the *status quo*. Often this takes the form of some course of action such as maintaining a particular inventory policy. If there is evidence of an increase or decrease in the value of the parameter, a new course of action will be taken. Examples include deciding to produce a new product, switching to a better drug to treat an illness, or sentencing a defendant to prison.

The next element in the procedure is to randomly sample the population and calculate the sample mean. This is called the **test statistic**. The test statistic is the criterion on which we base our decision about the hypotheses. (In the criminal trial analogy, this is equivalent to the evidence presented in the case.) The test statistic is based on the best estimator of the parameter. In Chapter 10, we stated that the best estimator of a population mean is the sample mean.

If the test statistic's value is inconsistent with the null hypothesis, we reject the null hypothesis and infer that the alternative hypothesis is true. For example, if we're trying to decide whether the mean is greater than 350, a large value of $\bar{x}$ (say, 600) would provide enough evidence. If $\bar{x}$ is close to 350 (say, 355), we would say that this does not provide much evidence to infer that the mean is greater than 350. In the absence of sufficient evidence, we do not reject the null hypothesis in favor of the alternative. (In the absence of sufficient evidence of guilt, a jury finds the defendant not guilty.)

In a criminal trial, "sufficient evidence" is defined as "evidence beyond a reasonable doubt." In statistics, we need to use the test statistic's sampling distribution to define "sufficient evidence." We will do so in the next section.

EXERCISES

Exercises 11.1–11.5 feature nonstatistical applications of hypothesis testing. For each, identify the hypotheses, define Type I and Type II errors, and discuss the consequences of each error. In setting up the hypotheses, you will have to consider where to place the "burden of proof."

11.1 It is the responsibility of the federal government to judge the safety and effectiveness of new drugs. There are two possible decisions: approve the drug or disapprove the drug.

11.2 You are contemplating a Ph.D. in business or economics. If you succeed, a life of fame, fortune, and happiness awaits you. If you fail, you've wasted 5 years of your life. Should you go for it?

11.3 You are the centerfielder of the New York Yankees. It is the bottom of the ninth inning of the seventh game of the World Series. The Yanks lead by 2 with 2 outs and men on second and third. The batter is known to hit for high average and runs very well but only has mediocre power. A single will tie the game, and a hit over your head will likely result in the Yanks losing. Do you play shallow?

11.4 You are faced with two investments. One is very risky, but the potential returns are high. The other is safe, but the potential is quite limited. Pick one.

11.5 You are the pilot of a jumbo jet. You smell smoke in the cockpit. The nearest airport is less than 5 minutes away. Should you land the plane immediately?

11.6 Several years ago in a high-profile case, a defendant was acquitted in a double-murder trial but was subsequently found responsible for the deaths in a civil trial. (Guess the name of the defendant—the answer is in Appendix C.) In a civil trial the plaintiff (the victims' relatives) are required only to show that the preponderance of evidence points to the guilt of the defendant. Aside from the other issues in the cases, discuss why these results are logical.

11-2 TESTING THE POPULATION MEAN WHEN THE POPULATION STANDARD DEVIATION IS KNOWN

To illustrate the process, consider the following example.

EXAMPLE 11.1

Data
Xm11-01

Department Store's New Billing System

The manager of a department store is thinking about establishing a new billing system for the store's credit customers. After a thorough financial analysis, she determines that the new system will be cost-effective only if the mean monthly account is more than $170. A random sample of 400 monthly accounts is drawn, for which the sample mean is $178. The manager knows that the accounts are approximately normally distributed with a standard deviation of $65. Can the manager conclude from this that the new system will be cost-effective?

SOLUTION:

IDENTIFY

This example deals with the population of the credit accounts at the store. To conclude that the system will be cost-effective requires the manager to show that the mean account for all customers is greater than $170. Consequently, we set up the alternative hypothesis to express this circumstance:

H_1: $\mu > 170$ (Install new system)

If the mean is less than or equal to 170, then the system will not be cost-effective. The null hypothesis can be expressed as

H_0: $\mu \leq 170$ (Do not install new system)

However, as was discussed in Section 11-1, we will actually test $\mu = 170$, which is how we specify the null hypothesis:

H_0: $\mu = 170$

As we previously pointed out, the test statistic is the best estimator of the parameter. In Chapter 10, we used the sample mean to estimate the population mean. To conduct this test, we ask and answer the following question: Is a sample mean of 178 sufficiently greater than 170 to allow us to confidently infer that the population mean is greater than 170?

There are two approaches to answering this question. The first is called the *rejection region method*. It can be used in conjunction with the computer, but it is mandatory for those computing statistics manually. The second is the *p-value approach*, which in general can be employed only in conjunction with a computer and statistical software. We recommend, however, that users of statistical software be familiar with both approaches.

11-2a Rejection Region

It seems reasonable to reject the null hypothesis in favor of the alternative if the value of the sample mean is large relative to 170. If we had calculated the sample mean to be say, 500, it would be quite apparent that the null hypothesis is false and we would reject it.

On the other hand, values of $\bar{x}$ close to 170, such as 171, do not allow us to reject the null hypothesis because it is entirely possible to observe a sample mean of 171 from a population whose mean is 170. Unfortunately, the decision is not always so obvious. In this example, the sample mean was calculated to be 178, a value apparently neither very far away from nor very close to 170. To make a decision about this sample mean, we set up the *rejection region*.

Rejection Region

The **rejection region** is a range of values such that if the test statistic falls into that range, we decide to reject the null hypothesis in favor of the alternative hypothesis.

Suppose we define the value of the sample mean that is just large enough to reject the null hypothesis as $\bar{x}_L$. The rejection region is

$$\bar{x} > \bar{x}_L$$

Because a Type I error is defined as rejecting a true null hypothesis, and the probability of committing a Type I error is α, it follows that

$$\alpha = P(\text{rejecting } H_0 \text{ given that } H_0 \text{ is true})$$
$$= P(\bar{x} > \bar{x}_L \text{ given that } H_0 \text{ is true})$$

Figure 11.1 depicts the sampling distribution and the rejection region.

FIGURE **11.1** **Sampling Distribution for Example 11.1**

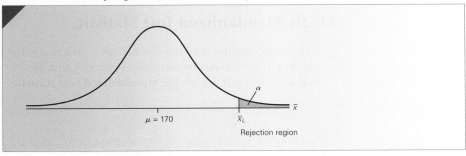

From Section 9-1, we know that the sampling distribution of $\bar{x}$ is normal or approximately normal, with mean μ and standard deviation $\sigma / \sqrt{n}$. As a result, we can standardize $\bar{x}$ and obtain the following probability:

$$P\left(\frac{\bar{x} - \mu}{\sigma / \sqrt{n}} > \frac{\bar{x}_L - \mu}{\sigma / \sqrt{n}}\right) = P\left(Z > \frac{\bar{x}_L - \mu}{\sigma / \sqrt{n}}\right) = \alpha$$

From Section 8-2, we defined z_α to be the value of a standard normal random variable such that

$$P(Z > z_\alpha) = \alpha$$

Because both probability statements involve the same distribution (standard normal) and the same probability (α), it follows that the limits are identical. Thus,

$$\frac{\bar{x}_L - \mu}{\sigma / \sqrt{n}} = z_\alpha$$

We know that $\sigma = 65$ and $n = 400$. Because the probabilities defined earlier are conditional on the null hypothesis being true, we have $\mu = 170$. To calculate the rejection region, we need a value of α at the significance level. Suppose that the manager chose α to be 5% It follows that $z_\alpha = z_{.05} = 1.645$. We can now calculate the value of $\bar{x}_L$:

$$\frac{\bar{x}_L - \mu}{\sigma / \sqrt{n}} = z_\alpha$$

$$\frac{\bar{x}_L - 170}{65 / \sqrt{400}} = 1.645$$

$$\bar{x}_L = 175.34$$

Therefore, the rejection region is

$$\bar{x} > 175.34$$

The sample mean was computed to be 178. Because the test statistic (sample mean) is in the rejection region (it is greater than 175.34), we reject the null hypothesis. Thus, there is sufficient evidence to infer that the mean monthly account is greater than $170.

Our calculations determined that any value of $\bar{x}$ above 175.34 represents an event that is quite unlikely when sampling (with $n = 400$) from a population whose mean is 170 (and whose standard deviation is 65). This suggests that the assumption that the null hypothesis is true is incorrect, and consequently we reject the null hypothesis in favor of the alternative hypothesis.

11-2b Standardized Test Statistic

The preceding test used the test statistic $\bar{x}$; as a result, the rejection region had to be set up in terms of $\bar{x}$. An easier method specifies that the test statistic be the standardized value of $\bar{x}$; that is, we use the **standardized test statistic**.

$$z = \frac{\bar{x} - \mu}{\sigma / \sqrt{n}}$$

and the rejection region consists of all values of z that are greater than z_α. Algebraically, the rejection region is

$$z > z_\alpha$$

We can redo Example 11.1 using the standardized test statistic. The rejection region is

$$z > z_\alpha = z_{.05} = 1.645$$

The value of the test statistic is calculated next:

$$z = \frac{\bar{x} - \mu}{\sigma / \sqrt{n}} = \frac{178 - 170}{65 / \sqrt{400}} = 2.46$$

Because 2.46 is greater than 1.645, reject the null hypothesis and conclude that there is enough evidence to infer that the mean monthly account is greater than $170.

As you can see, the conclusions we draw from using the test statistic $\bar{x}$ and the standardized test statistic z are identical. Figures 11.2 and 11.3 depict the two sampling distributions, highlighting the equivalence of the two tests.

FIGURE **11.2** Sampling Distribution of $\overline{X}$ for Example 11.1

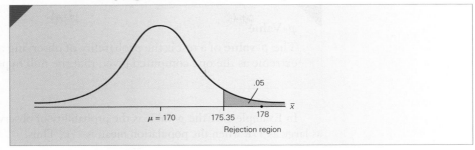

FIGURE **11.3** Sampling Distribution of Z for Example 11.1

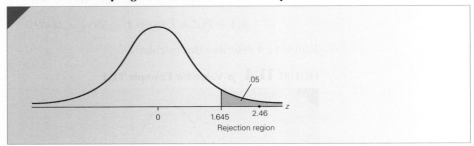

Because it is convenient and because statistical software packages employ it, the standardized test statistic will be used throughout this book. For simplicity, we will refer to the *standardized test statistic* simply as the *test statistic*.

Incidentally, when a null hypothesis is rejected, the test is said to be **statistically significant** at whatever significance level the test was conducted. Summarizing Example 11.1, we would say that the test was significant at the 5% significance level.

11-2c *p*-Value

There are several drawbacks to the rejection region method. Foremost among them is the type of information provided by the result of the test. The rejection region method produces a yes or no response to the question, Is there sufficient statistical evidence to infer that the alternative hypothesis is true? The implication is that the result of the test of hypothesis will be converted automatically into one of two possible courses of action: one action as a result of rejecting the null hypothesis in favor of the alternative and another as a result of not rejecting the null hypothesis in favor of the alternative. In Example 11.1, the rejection of the null hypothesis seems to imply that the new billing system will be installed.

In fact, this is not the way in which the result of a statistical analysis is utilized. The statistical procedure is only one of several factors considered by a manager when making a decision. In Example 11.1, the manager discovered that there was enough statistical evidence to conclude that the mean monthly account is greater than $170. However, before taking any action, the manager would like to consider a number of factors including the cost and feasibility of restructuring the billing system and the possibility of making an error, in this case a Type I error.

What is needed to take full advantage of the information available from the test result and make a better decision is a measure of the amount of statistical evidence supporting the alternative hypothesis so that it can be weighed in relation to the other factors, especially the financial ones. The *p-value of a test* provides this measure.

---

p-Value

The **p-value** of a test is the probability of observing a test statistic at least as extreme as the one computed given that the null hypothesis is true.

In Example 11.1 the *p*-value is the probability of observing a sample mean at least as large as 178 when the population mean is 170. Thus,

$$p\text{-value} = P(\overline{X} > 178) = P\left(\frac{\overline{X} - \mu}{\sigma / \sqrt{n}} > \frac{178 - 170}{65 / \sqrt{400}}\right) = P(Z > 2.46)$$

$$= 1 - P(Z < 2.46) = 1 - .9931 = .0069$$

Figure 11.4 describes this calculation.

FIGURE 11.4 *p*-Value for Example 11.1

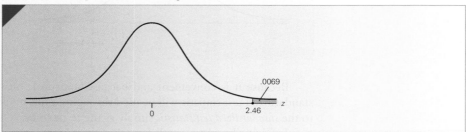

11-2d Interpreting the *p*-Value

To properly interpret the results of an inferential procedure, you must remember that the technique is based on the sampling distribution. The sampling distribution allows us to make probability statements about a sample statistic assuming knowledge of the population parameter. Thus, the probability of observing a sample mean at least as large as 178 from a population whose mean is 170 is .0069, which is very small. In other words, we have just observed an unlikely event, an event so unlikely that we seriously doubt the assumption that began the process—that the null hypothesis is true. Consequently, we have reason to reject the null hypothesis and support the alternative.

Students may be tempted to simplify the interpretation by stating that the *p*-value is the probability that the null hypothesis is true. Don't! As was the case with interpreting the confidence interval estimator, you cannot make a probability statement about a parameter. It is not a random variable.

The *p*-value of a test provides valuable information because it is a measure of the amount of statistical evidence that supports the alternative hypothesis. To understand this interpretation fully, refer to Table 11.2 where we list several values of $\overline{x}$, their *z*-statistics, and *p*-values for Example 11.1. Notice that the closer $\overline{x}$ is to the hypothesized mean, 170, the larger the *p*-value is. The farther $\overline{x}$ is above 170, the smaller the *p*-value is. Values of $\overline{x}$ far above 170 tend to indicate that the alternative hypothesis is true.

Thus, the smaller the p-value, the more the statistical evidence supports the alternative hypothesis. Figure 11.5 graphically depicts the information in Table 11.2.

TABLE 11.2   Test Statistics and p-Values for Example 11.1

SAMPLE MEAN $\bar{x}$	TEST STATISTIC $z = \dfrac{\bar{x} - \mu}{\sigma/\sqrt{n}} = \dfrac{\bar{x} - 170}{65/\sqrt{400}}$	p-VALUE
170	0	.5000
172	0.62	.2676
174	1.23	.1093
176	1.85	.0322
178	2.46	.0069
180	3.08	.0010

FIGURE 11.5 p-Values for Example 11.1

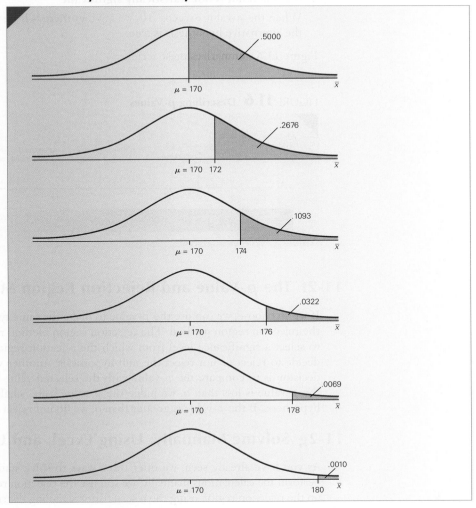

This raises the question, How small does the p-value have to be to infer that the alternative hypothesis is true? In general, the answer depends on a number of factors, including the costs of making Type I and Type II errors. In Example 11.1, a Type I error would occur if the manager adopts the new billing system when it is not cost-effective. If the cost of this error is high, we attempt to minimize its probability. In the rejection region method, we do so by setting the significance level quite low—say, 1%. Using the p-value method, we would insist that the p-value be quite small, providing sufficient evidence to infer that the mean monthly account is greater than $170 before proceeding with the new billing system.

11-2e Describing the p-Value

Statistics practitioners can translate p-values using the following descriptive terms:

If the p-value is less than .01, we say that there is *overwhelming* evidence to infer that the alternative hypothesis is true. We also say that the test is **highly significant**.

If the p-value lies between .01 and .05, there is *strong* evidence to infer that the alternative hypothesis is true. The result is deemed to be **significant**.

If the p-value is between .05 and .10, we say that there is *weak* evidence to indicate that the alternative hypothesis is true. When the p-value is greater than 5%, we say that the result is **not statistically significant**.

When the p-value exceeds .10, we say that there is little to no evidence to infer that the alternative hypothesis is true.

Figure 11.6 summarizes these terms.

FIGURE **11.6** Describing p-Values

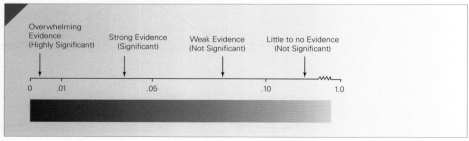

11-2f The p-Value and Rejection Region Methods

If we so choose, we can use the p-value to make the same type of decisions we make in the rejection region method. The rejection region method requires the decision maker to select a significance level from which the rejection region is constructed. We then decide to reject or not reject the null hypothesis. Another way of making that type of decision is to compare the p-value with the selected value of the significance level. If the p-value is less than α, we judge the p-value to be small enough to reject the null hypothesis. If the p-value is greater than α, we do not reject the null hypothesis.

11-2g Solving Manually, Using Excel, and Using XLSTAT

As you have already seen, we offer three ways to solve statistical problems. When we perform the calculations manually, we will use the rejection region approach. We will set up the rejection region using the test statistic's sampling distribution and associated table (in Appendix B). The calculations will be performed manually and a reject–do not reject decision will be made. In this chapter, it is possible to compute the p-value of the test manually. However, in later chapters we will be using test statistics that are not normally distributed, making it impossible to calculate the p-values manually. In these instances, manual calculations require the decision to be made via the rejection region method only.

Both Excel workbooks and XLSTAT output the value of the test statistic and the p-value of the test.

EXCEL Workbook

	A	B	C	D
1	z-Test of a Mean			
2				
3	Sample mean	178	z Stat	2.46
4	Population standard deviation	65	P(Z<=z) one-tail	0.0069
5	Sample size	400	z Critical one-tail	1.6449
6	Hypothesized mean	170	P(Z<=z) two-tail	0.0138
7	Alpha	0.05	z Critical two-tail	1.9600

INSTRUCTIONS

1. Type or import the data into one column. (Open Xm11-01.) In any empty cell, calculate the sample mean (=AVERAGE(A1:A401).)
2. Open the **Test Statistics Workbook** and click the **z-Test_Mean** tab. In Cell B3, type or copy the value of the sample mean. In cells B4–B7, type the value of σ (65), the value of n (400), the value of μ under the null hypothesis (170), and the value of α (.05), respectively.

The spreadsheet reports the value of the test statistic, $z = 2.46$. The p-value* of the test is .0069. Excel reports this probability as

$$P(Z < = z) \text{ one-tail}$$

XLSTAT

	A	B	C	D	E	F
1	Theoretical mean: 170					
2	Significance level (%): 5					
3						
4	Summary statistics:					
5	Variable	Observations	Minimum	Maximum	Mean	Std. deviation
6	Accounts	400	3.19	372.73	178.00	68.37
7						
8	One-sample z-test / Upper-tailed test:					
9	Difference	8.00				
10	z (Observed value)	2.46				
11	z (Critical value)	1.645				
12	p-value (one-tailed)	0.0069				
13	alpha	0.05				

Note: We have edited the printout deleting parts that are not needed for this procedure.

---

*Excel provides two probabilities in its printout. The way in which we determine the p-value of the test from the printout is somewhat more complicated. Interested students are advised to read the online appendix Converting Excel's Probabilities to p-Values.

INSTRUCTIONS

1. Type or import the data into one column. (Open Xm11-01.)
2. Click **XLSTAT** and **One-sample *t*-test** and **z-test**.
3. In the **Data**: dialog box type the input range (A1:A401). Click **Column labels** if the first row contains the name of the variable (as in this example). Check **z-test**. Do not check **Student's *t*-test**.
4. Click the **Options** tab and choose **Mean 1 > Theoretical mean** in the **Alternative hypothesis** box. Type the **Theoretical mean** (170) and the value of α (in percent) in the **Significance level:** box (5). In the **Variance for z-test:** box check **User defined: Variance:** and type the value of σ^2 (4225). Click **OK** and then **Continue.** If there are blanks in the column (usually used to represent missing data) click **Missing data** and click **Remove the observations.**

11-2h Interpreting the Results of a Test

In Example 11.1, we rejected the null hypothesis. Does this prove that the alternative hypothesis is true? The answer is no; because our conclusion is based on sample data (and not on the entire population), we can never *prove* anything by using statistical inference. Consequently, we summarize the test by stating that there is enough statistical evidence to infer that the null hypothesis is false and that the alternative hypothesis is true.

Now suppose that $\bar{x}$ had equaled 174 instead of 178. We would then have calculated $z = 1.23$ (*p*-value = .1093), which is not in the rejection region. Could we conclude on this basis that there is enough statistical evidence to infer that the null hypothesis is true and hence that $\mu = 170$? Again the answer is "no" because it is absurd to suggest that a sample mean of 174 provides enough evidence to infer that the population mean is 170. (If it proved anything, it would prove that the population mean is 174.) Because we're testing a single value of the parameter under the null hypothesis, we can never have enough statistical evidence to establish that the null hypothesis is true (unless we sample the entire population). (The same argument is valid if you set up the null hypothesis as $H_0 : \mu \leq 170$. It would be illogical to conclude that a sample mean of 174 provides enough evidence to conclude that the population mean is *less than or equal to 170*.)

Consequently, if the value of the test statistic does not fall into the rejection region (or the *p*-value is large), rather than say we accept the null hypothesis (which implies that we're stating that the null hypothesis is true), we state that we do not reject the null hypothesis, and we conclude that not enough evidence exists to show that the alternative hypothesis is true. Although it may appear to be the case, we are not being overly technical. Your ability to set up tests of hypotheses properly and to interpret their results correctly very much depends on your understanding of this point. The point is that the conclusion is based on the alternative hypothesis. In the final analysis, there are only two possible conclusions of a test of hypothesis.

> ### Conclusions of a Test of Hypothesis
>
> If we reject the null hypothesis, we conclude that there is enough statistical evidence to infer that the alternative hypothesis is true.
>
> If we do *not* reject the null hypothesis, we conclude that there is *not* enough statistical evidence to infer that the alternative hypothesis is true.

Observe that the alternative hypothesis is the focus of the conclusion. It represents what we are investigating, which is why it is also called the *research hypothesis*. Whatever you're trying to show statistically must be represented by the alternative hypothesis (bearing in mind that you have only three choices for the alternative hypothesis—the parameter is greater than, less than, or not equal to the value specified in the null hypothesis).

When we introduced statistical inference in Chapter 10, we pointed out that the first step in the solution is to identify the technique. When the problem involves hypothesis testing, part of this process is the specification of the hypotheses. Because the alternative hypothesis represents the condition we're researching, we will identify it first. The null hypothesis automatically follows because the null hypothesis must specify equality. However, by tradition, when we list the two hypotheses, the null hypothesis comes first, followed by the alternative hypothesis. All examples in this book will follow that format.

SSA Envelope Plan: Solution

IDENTIFY

The objective of the study is to draw a conclusion about the mean payment period. Thus, the parameter to be tested is the population mean μ. We want to know whether there is enough statistical evidence to show that the population mean is less than 22 days. Thus, the alternative hypothesis is

$$H_1: \quad \mu < 22$$

The null hypothesis is

$$H_0: \quad \mu = 22$$

The test statistic is the only one we've presented thus far. It is

$$z = \frac{\bar{x} - \mu}{\sigma / \sqrt{n}}$$

COMPUTE

MANUALLY:

To solve this problem manually, we need to define the rejection region, which requires us to specify a significance level. A 10% significance level is deemed to be appropriate. (We'll discuss our choice later.)

(Continued)

We wish to reject the null hypothesis in favor of the alternative only if the sample mean and hence the value of the test statistic is small enough. As a result, we locate the rejection region in the left tail of the sampling distribution. To understand why, remember that we're trying to decide whether there is enough statistical evidence to infer that the mean is less than 22 (which is the alternative hypothesis). If we observe a large sample mean (and hence a large value of z), do we want to reject the null hypothesis in favor of the alternative? The answer is an emphatic "no." It is illogical to think that if the sample mean is, say, 30, there is enough evidence to conclude that the mean payment period for all customers would be less than 22.

Consequently, we want to reject the null hypothesis only if the sample mean (and hence the value of the test statistic z) is small. How small is small enough? The answer is determined by the significance level and the rejection region. Thus, we set up the rejection region as

$$z < -z_\alpha = -z_{.10} = -1.28$$

Note that the direction of the inequality in the rejection region ($z < -z_\alpha$) matches the direction of the inequality in the alternative hypothesis ($\mu < 22$). Also note that we use the negative sign, because the rejection region is in the left tail (containing values of z less than 0) of the sampling distribution.

From the data, we compute the sum and the sample mean. They are

$$\sum x_i = 4,759$$

$$\bar{x} = \frac{\sum x_i}{220} = \frac{4,759}{220} = 21.63$$

We will assume that the standard deviation of the payment periods for the SSA plan is unchanged from its current value of $\sigma = 6$. The sample size is n = 220, and the value of μ is hypothesized to be 22. We compute the value of the test statistic as

$$z = \frac{\bar{x} - \mu}{\sigma/\sqrt{n}} = \frac{21.63 - 22}{6/\sqrt{220}} = -.91$$

Because the value of the test statistic, $z = -.91$, is not less than -1.28, we do not reject the null hypothesis and we do not conclude that the alternative hypothesis is true. There is insufficient evidence to infer that the mean is less than 22 days.

We can determine the p-value of the test as follows:

$$p\text{-value} = P(Z < -.91) = .1814$$

In this type of one-tail (left-tail) test of hypothesis, we calculate the p-value as $P(Z < z)$, where z is the actual value of the test statistic. Figure 11.7 depicts the sampling distribution, rejection region, and p-value.

EXCEL Workbook

	A	B	C	D
1	z-Test of a Mean			
2				
3	Sample mean	21.63	z Stat	-0.91
4	Population standard deviation	6	P(Z<=z) one-tail	0.1802
5	Sample size	220	z Critical one-tail	1.6449
6	Hypothesized mean	22	P(Z<=z) two-tail	0.3604
7	Alpha	0.05	z Critical two-tail	1.9600

XLSTAT

	A	B	C	D	E	F
1	Theoretical mean: 22					
2	Significance level (%): 10					
3						
4	Summary statistics:					
5	Variable	Observations	Minimum	Maximum	Mean	Std. deviation
6	Payment	220	9.00	39.00	21.632	5.835
7						
8	One-sample z-test / Lower-tailed test:					
9						
10	Difference	-0.368				
11	z (Observed value)	-0.910				
12	z (Critical value)	-1.282				
13	p-value (one-tailed)	0.1814				
14	alpha	0.10				

INTERPRET

The value of the test statistic is −.91, and its p-value is .1814, a figure that does not allow us to reject the null hypothesis. Because we were not able to reject the null hypothesis, we say that there is not enough evidence to infer that the mean payment period is less than 22 days. Note that there was some evidence to indicate that the mean of the entire population of payment periods is less than 22 days. We did calculate the sample mean to be 21.63. However, to reject the null hypothesis we need *enough* statistical evidence—and in this case we simply did not have enough reason to reject the null hypothesis in favor of the alternative. In the absence of evidence to show that the mean payment period for all customers sent a stamped self-addressed envelope would be less than 22 days, we cannot infer that the plan would be profitable.

A Type I error occurs when we conclude that the plan works when it actually does not. The cost of this mistake is not high. A Type II error occurs when we don't adopt the SSA envelope plan when it would reduce costs. The cost of this mistake can be high. As a consequence, we would like to minimize the probability of a Type II error. Thus, we chose a large value for the probability of a Type I error; we set

$$\alpha = .10$$

Figure 11.7 exhibits the sampling distribution for this example.

FIGURE **11.7** **Sampling Distribution for SSA Envelope Example**

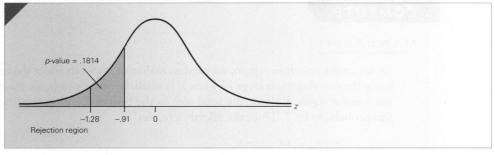

11-2i One- and Two-Tail Tests

The statistical tests conducted in Example 11.1 and the SSA envelope example are called **one-tail tests** because the rejection region is located in only one tail of the sampling distribution. The p-value is also computed by finding the area in one tail of the sampling distribution. The right tail in Example 11.1 is the important one because the alternative hypothesis specifies that the mean is *greater than* 170. In the SSA envelope example, the left tail is emphasized because the alternative hypothesis specifies that the mean is *less than* 22.

We now present an example that requires a **two-tail test**.

EXAMPLE 11.2

Data
Xm 11-02

Comparison of AT&T and Its Competitor

In recent years, several companies have been formed to compete with AT&T in long-distance calls. All advertise that their rates are lower than AT&T's, and as a result their bills will be lower. AT&T has responded by arguing that there will be no difference in billing for the average consumer. Suppose that a statistics practitioner working for AT&T determines that the mean and standard deviation of monthly long-distance bills for all its residential customers are $17.09 and $3.87, respectively. He then takes a random sample of 100 customers and recalculates their last month's bill using the rates quoted by a leading competitor. Assuming that the standard deviation of this population is the same as for AT&T, can we conclude at the 5% significance level that there is a difference between the average AT&T bill and that of the leading competitor?

SOLUTION:

IDENTIFY

In this problem, we want to know whether the mean monthly long-distance bill is different from $17.09. Consequently, we set up the alternative hypothesis to express this condition:

$$H_1: \quad \mu \neq 17.09$$

The null hypothesis specifies that the mean is equal to the value specified under the alternative hypothesis. Hence

$$H_0: \quad \mu = 17.09$$

COMPUTE

MANUALLY:

To set up the rejection region, we need to realize that we can reject the null hypothesis when the test statistic is large or when it is small. In other words, we must set up a *two-tail rejection region*. Because the total area in the rejection region must be α, we divide this probability by 2. Thus, the rejection region* is

$$z < -z_{\alpha/2} \quad \text{or} \quad z > z_{\alpha/2}$$

For $\alpha = .05$, $\alpha/2 = .025$, and $z_{\alpha/2} = z_{.025} = 1.96$.

$$z < -1.96 \quad \text{or} \quad z > 1.96$$

---

*Statistics practitioners often represent this rejection region as $|z| > z_{\alpha/2}$, which reads, "the absolute value of z is greater than $z_{\alpha/2}$." We prefer our method because it is clear that we are performing a two-tail test.

11.18 Research objective: The population mean is not equal to 0.

$\sigma = 50, n = 90, \bar{x} = -5.5$.

11.19 Research objective: The population mean is not equal to −5.

$\sigma = 5, n = 25, \bar{x} = -4.0$.

11.20 You are conducting a test to determine whether there is enough statistical evidence to infer that a population mean is greater than 100. You discover that the sample mean is 95.

a. Is it necessary to do any further calculations? Explain.
b. If you did calculate the p-value would it be smaller or larger than .5? Explain.

Exercises 11.21 to 11.35 are "what-if analyses" designed to determine what happens to the test statistic and p-value when the sample size, standard deviation, and sample mean change. These problems can be solved manually or by using the Excel spreadsheet.

11.21 a. Compute the p-value in order to test the following hypotheses given that $\bar{x} = 52$, $n = 9$, and $\sigma = 5$.

H_0: $\mu = 50$
H_1: $\mu > 50$

b. Repeat part (a) with $n = 25$.
c. Repeat part (a) with $n = 100$.
d. Describe what happens to the value of the test statistic and its p-value when the sample size increases.

11.22 a. A statistics practitioner formulated the following hypotheses

H_0: $\mu = 200$
H_1: $\mu < 200$

and learned that $\bar{x} = 190$, $n = 9$, and $\sigma = 50$ Compute the p-value of the test.
b. Repeat part (a) with $\sigma = 30$.
c. Repeat part (a) with $\sigma = 10$.
d. Discuss what happens to the value of the test statistic and its p-value when the standard deviation decreases.

11.23 a. Given the following hypotheses, determine the p-value when $\bar{x} = 21$, $n = 25$, and $\sigma = 5$.

H_0: $\mu = 20$
H_1: $\mu \neq 20$

b. Repeat part (a) with $\bar{x} = 22$.

c. Repeat part (a) with $\bar{x} = 23$.
d. Describe what happens to the value of the test statistic and its p-value when the value of $\bar{x}$ increases.

11.24 a. Test these hypotheses by calculating the p-value given that $\bar{x} = 99$, $n = 100$, and $\sigma = 8$.

H_0: $\mu = 100$
H_1: $\mu \neq 100$

b. Repeat part (a) with $n = 50$.
c. Repeat part (a) with $n = 20$.
d. What is the effect on the value of the test statistic and the p-value of the test when the sample size decreases?

11.25 a. Find the p-value of the following test given that $\bar{x} = 990$, $n = 100$, and $\sigma = 25$.

H_0: $\mu = 1000$
H_1: $\mu < 1000$

b. Repeat part (a) with $\sigma = 50$.
c. Repeat part (a) with $\sigma = 100$.
d. Describe what happens to the value of the test statistic and its p-value when the standard deviation increases.

11.26 a. Calculate the p-value of the test described here.

H_0: $\mu = 60$
H_1: $\mu > 60$
$\bar{x} = 72$, $n = 25$, $\sigma = 20$

b. Repeat part (a) with $\bar{x} = 68$.
c. Repeat part (a) with $\bar{x} = 64$.
d. Describe the effect on the test statistic and the p-value of the test when the value of $\bar{x}$ decreases.

11.27 Redo Example 11.1 with
a. $n = 200$
b. $n = 100$
c. Describe the effect on the test statistic and the p-value when n increases.

11.28 Redo Example 11.1 with
a. $\sigma = 35$
b. $\sigma = 100$
c. Describe the effect on the test statistic and the p-value when σ increases.

11.29 While conducting a test to determine whether a population mean is less than 900, you find that the sample mean is 1,050.

a. Can you make a decision on this information alone? Explain.
b. If you did calculate the p-value, would it be smaller or larger than .5? Explain.

11.30 Redo the SSA example with
  a. $n = 100$
  b. $n = 500$
  c. What is the effect on the test statistic and the p-value when n increases?

11.31 Redo the SSA example with
  a. $\sigma = 3$
  b. $\sigma = 12$
  c. Discuss the effect on the test statistic and the p-value when σ increases.

11.32 For the SSA example, create a table that shows the effect on the test statistic and the p-value of decreasing the value of the sample mean. Use $\bar{x} = 22.0, 21.8, 21.6, 21.4, 21.2, 21.0, 20.8, 20.6$, and 20.4.

11.33 Redo Example 11.2 with
  a. $n = 50$
  b. $n = 400$
  c. Briefly describe the effect on the test statistic and the p-value when n increases.

11.34 Redo Example 11.2 with
  a. $\sigma = 2$
  b. $\sigma = 10$
  c. What happens to the test statistic and the p-value when σ increases?

11.35 Refer to Example 11.2. Create a table that shows the effect on the test statistic and the p-value of changing the value of the sample mean. Use $\bar{x} = 15.0, 15.5, 16.0, 16.5, 17.0, 17.5, 18.0, 18.5$, and 19.0.

Applications

The following exercises may be answered manually or with the assistance of a computer. The files containing the data are given.

11.36 Xr11-36 A business student claims that, on average, an MBA student is required to prepare more than five cases per week. To examine the claim, a statistics professor asks a random sample of 10 MBA students to report the number of cases they prepare weekly. The results are exhibited here. Can the professor conclude at the 5% significance level that the claim is true, assuming that the number of cases is normally distributed with a standard deviation of 1.5?

    2   7   4   8   9   5   11   3   7   4

11.37 Xr11-37 A random sample of 18 young adult men (20–30 years old) was sampled. Each person was asked how many minutes of sports he watched on television daily. The responses are listed here. It is known that

$\sigma = 10$. Test to determine at the 5% significance level whether there is enough statistical evidence to infer that the mean amount of television watched daily by all young adult men is greater than 50 minutes.

50	48	65	74	66	37	45	68	64
65	58	55	52	63	59	57	74	65

11.38 Xr11-38 The club professional at a difficult public course boasts that his course is so tough that the average golfer loses a dozen or more golf balls during a round of golf. A dubious golfer sets out to show that the pro is fibbing. He asks a random sample of 15 golfers who just completed their rounds to report the number of golf balls each lost. Assuming that the number of golf balls lost is normally distributed with a standard deviation of 3, can we infer at the 10% significance level that the average number of golf balls lost is less than 12?

1	14	8	15	17	10	12	6
14	21	15	9	11	4	8	

11.39 Xr11-39 A random sample of 12 second-year university students enrolled in a business statistics course was drawn. At the course's completion, each student was asked how many hours he or she spent doing homework in statistics. The data are listed here. It is known that the population standard deviation is $\sigma = 8.0$. The instructor has recommended that students devote 3 hours per week for the duration of the 12-week semester, for a total of 36 hours. Test to determine whether there is evidence that the average student spent less than the recommended amount of time. Compute the p-value of the test.

  31 40 26 30 36 38 29 40 38 30 35 38

11.40 Xr11-40 The owner of a public golf course is concerned about slow play, which clogs the course and results in selling fewer rounds. She believes the problem lies in the amount of time taken to sink putts on the green. To investigate the problem, she randomly samples 10 foursomes and measures the amount of time they spend on the 18th green. The data are listed here. Assuming that the times are normally distributed with a standard deviation of 2 minutes, test to determine whether the owner can infer at the 5% significance level that the mean amount of time spent putting on the 18th green is greater than 6 minutes.

  8 11 5 6 7 8 6 4 8 3

11.41 Xr11-41 A machine that produces ball bearings is set so that the average diameter is .50 inch. A sample of 10 ball bearings was measured, with the results shown here. Assuming that the standard deviation is .05 inch, can we conclude at the 5% significance level that the mean diameter is not .50 inch?

.48 .50 .49 .52 .53 .48 .49 .47 .46 .51

11.42 Xr11-42 Spam e-mail has become a serious and costly nuisance. An office manager believes that the average amount of time spent by office workers reading and deleting spam exceeds 25 minutes per day. To test this belief, he takes a random sample of 18 workers and measures the amount of time each spends reading and deleting spam. The results are listed here. If the population of times is normal with a standard deviation of 12 minutes, can the manager infer at the 1% significance level that he is correct?

35 48 29 44 17 21 32 28 34
23 13   9 11 30 42 37 43 48

The following exercises require the use of a computer and software. The answers may be calculated manually. See Appendix A for the sample statistics.

11.43 Xr11-43 A manufacturer of lightbulbs advertises that, on average, its long-life bulb will last more than 5,000 hours. To test the claim, a statistician took a random sample of 100 bulbs and measured the amount of time until each bulb burned out. If we assume that the lifetime of this type of bulb has a standard deviation of 400 hours, can we conclude at the 5% significance level that the claim is true?

11.44 Xr11-44 In the midst of labor–management negotiations, the president of a company argues that the company's blue-collar workers, who are paid an average of $30,000 per year, are well paid because the mean annual income of all blue-collar workers in the country is less than $30,000. That figure is disputed by the union, which does not believe that the mean blue-collar income is less than $30,000. To test the company president's belief, an arbitrator draws a random sample of 350 blue-collar workers from across the country and asks each to report his or her annual income. If the arbitrator assumes that the blue-collar incomes are normally distributed with a standard deviation of $8,000, can it be inferred at the 5% significance level that the company president is correct?

11.45 Xr11-45 A dean of a business school claims that the Graduate Management Admission Test (GMAT) scores of applicants to the school's MBA program have increased during the past 5 years. Five years ago, the mean and standard deviation of GMAT scores of MBA applicants were 560 and 50, respectively. Twenty applications for this year's program were randomly selected and the GMAT scores recorded. If we assume that the distribution of GMAT scores of this year's applicants is the same as that of 5 years ago, with the possible exception of the mean, can we conclude at the 5% significance level that the dean's claim is true?

11.46 Xr11-46 Past experience indicates that the monthly long-distance telephone bill is normally distributed with a mean of $17.85 and a standard deviation of $3.87. After an advertising campaign aimed at increasing long-distance telephone usage, a random sample of 25 household bills was taken.
a. Do the data allow us to infer at the 10% significance level that the campaign was successful?
b. What assumption must you make to answer part (a)?

11.47 Xr11-47 In an attempt to reduce the number of person-hours lost as a result of industrial accidents, a large production plant installed new safety equipment. In a test of the effectiveness of the equipment, a random sample of 50 departments was chosen. The number of person-hours lost in the month before and the month after the installation of the safety equipment was recorded. The percentage change was calculated and recorded. Assume that the population standard deviation is $\sigma = 6$. Can we infer at the 10% significance level that the new safety equipment is effective?

11.48 Xr11-48 A highway patrol officer believes that the average speed of cars traveling over a certain stretch of highway exceeds the posted limit of 55 mph. The speeds of a random sample of 200 cars were recorded. Do these data provide sufficient evidence at the 1% significance level to support the officer's belief? What is the p-value of the test? (Assume that the standard deviation is known to be 5.)

11.49 Xr11-49 An automotive expert claims that the large number of self-serve gasoline stations has resulted in poor automobile maintenance, and that the average tire pressure is more than 4 pounds per square inch (psi) below its manufacturer's specification. As a quick test, 50 tires are examined, and the number of psi each tire is below specification is recorded. If we assume that tire pressure is normally distributed with $\sigma = 1.5$ psi, can we infer at the 10% significance level that the expert is correct? What is the p-value?

11.50 Xr11-50 For the past few years, the number of customers of a drive-up bank in New York has averaged 20 per hour, with a standard deviation of 3 per hour. This year, another bank 1 mile away opened a drive-up window. The manager of the first bank believes that this will result in a decrease in the number of customers. The number of customers who arrived during 36 randomly selected hours was recorded. Can we conclude at the 5% significance level that the manager is correct?

11.51 <u>Xr11-43</u> A fast-food franchiser is considering building a restaurant at a certain location. Based on financial analyses, a site is acceptable only if the number of pedestrians passing the location averages more than 100 per hour. The number of pedestrians observed for each of 40 hours was recorded. Assuming that the population standard deviation is known to be 16, can we conclude at the 1% significance level that the site is acceptable?

11.52 <u>Xr11-52</u> Many Alpine ski centers base their projections of revenues and profits on the assumption that the average Alpine skier skis four times per year. To investigate the validity of this assumption, a random sample of 63 skiers is drawn and each is asked to report the number of times he or she skied the previous year. If we assume that the standard deviation is 2, can we infer at the 10% significance level that the assumption is wrong?

11.53 <u>Xr11-53</u> The golf professional at a private course claims that members who have taken lessons from him lowered their handicap by more than five strokes. The club manager decides to test the claim by randomly sampling 25 members who have had lessons and asking each to report the reduction in handicap, where a negative number indicates an increase in the handicap. Assuming that the reduction in handicap is approximately normally distributed with a standard deviation of two strokes, test the golf professional's claim using a 10% significance level.

11.54 <u>Xr11-54</u> The current no-smoking regulations in office buildings require workers who smoke to take breaks and leave the building in order to satisfy their habits. A study indicates that such workers average 32 minutes per day taking smoking breaks. The standard deviation is 8 minutes. To help reduce the average break, rooms with powerful exhausts were installed in the buildings. To see whether these rooms serve their designed purpose, a random sample of 110 smokers was taken. The total amount of time away from their desks was measured for 1 day. Test to determine whether there has been a decrease in the mean

time away from their desks. Compute the *p*-value and interpret it relative to the costs of Type I and Type II errors.

11.55 <u>Xr11-55</u> A low-handicap golfer who uses Titleist brand golf balls observed that his average drive is 230 yards and the standard deviation is 10 yards. Nike has just introduced a new ball, which has been endorsed by Tiger Woods. Nike claims that the ball will travel farther than Titleist. To test the claim, the golfer hits 100 drives with a Nike ball and measures the distances. Conduct a test to determine whether Nike is correct. Use a 5% significance level.

11.56 <u>Xr11-56</u> An economist surveyed homeowners in a large city to determine the percentage increase in their heating bills over the last 5 years. The economist particularly wanted to know if there was enough evidence to infer that heating cost increases were greater than the rate of inflation, which was 10%. Assuming that percentage increase in heating is normally distributed with a standard deviation of 3% can the economist conclude at the 5% significance level that heating costs increased faster than inflation?

11.57 <u>Xr11-57</u> A survey of American consumers asked respondents to report the amount of money they spend on bakery products in a typical month. If we assume that the population standard deviation is $5, can we conclude at the 10% significance level that the mean monthly expenditures on bakery products for all Americans is not equal to $30?

11.58 <u>Xr11-58</u> Many Americans contributed to their 401k investment accounts. An economist wanted to determine how well these investments performed. A random sample of Americans with 401k investments were surveyed and asked to report the total amount invested. Can we infer at the 5% significance level that the mean amount for all Americans with 401k investments is greater than $125,000 assuming that investments are normally distributed with a standard deviation of $25,000?

11.59 <u>Xr11-59</u> A survey of 25- to 35-year-old Americans with professional or Ph.D. degrees was asked to report their monthly incomes. Can we conclude at the 10% significance level that the mean income exceeds $7,500 assuming that the incomes are normally distributed with a standard deviation of $1,200?

11-3 / CALCULATING THE PROBABILITY OF A TYPE II ERROR

To properly interpret the results of a test of hypothesis, you must be able to specify an appropriate significance level or to judge the *p*-value of a test. However, you also must understand the relationship between Type I and Type II errors. In this section, we describe how the probability of a Type II error is computed and interpreted.

Recall Example 11.1, where we conducted the test using the sample mean as the test statistic and we computed the rejection region (with $\alpha = .05$) as

$$\bar{x} > 175.34$$

A Type II error occurs when a false null hypothesis is not rejected. In Example 11.1, if $\bar{x}$ is less than 175.34, we will not reject the null hypothesis. If we do not reject the null hypothesis, we will not install the new billing system. Thus, the consequence of a Type II error in this example is that we will not install the new system when it would be cost-effective. The probability of this occurring is the probability of a Type II error. It is defined as

$$\beta = P(\overline{X} < 175.34, \text{ given that the null hypothesis is false})$$

The condition that the null hypothesis is false tells us only that the mean is not equal to 170. If we want to compute β, we need to specify a value for μ. Suppose that when the mean account is at least \$180, the new billing system's savings become so attractive that the manager would hate to make the mistake of not installing the system. As a result, she would like to determine the probability of not installing the new system when it would produce large cost savings. Because calculating probability from an approximately normal sampling distribution requires a value of μ (as well as σ and n), we will calculate the probability of not installing the new system when μ is *equal* to 180:

$$\beta = P(\overline{X} < 175.34, \text{ given that } \mu = 180)$$

We know that $\bar{x}$ is approximately normally distributed with mean μ and standard deviation $\sigma/\sqrt{n}$. To proceed, we standardize $\bar{x}$ and use the standard normal table (Table 3 in Appendix B):

$$\beta = P\left(\frac{\overline{X} - \mu}{\sigma/\sqrt{n}} < \frac{175.34 - 180}{65/\sqrt{400}}\right) = P(Z < -1.43) = .0764$$

This tells us that when the mean account is actually \$180, the probability of incorrectly not rejecting the null hypothesis is .0764. Figure 11.9 graphically depicts

FIGURE **11.9** Calculating β for $\mu = 180$, $\alpha = .05$, and n = 400

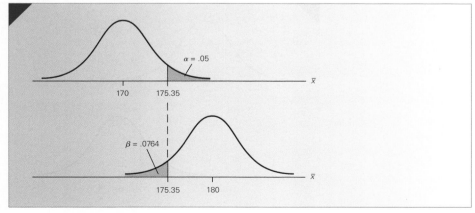

how the calculation was performed. Notice that to calculate the probability of a Type II error, we had to express the rejection region in terms of the unstandardized test statistic $\bar{x}$, and we had to specify a value for μ other than the one shown in the null hypothesis. In this illustration, the value of μ used was based on a financial analysis indicating that when μ is at least $180 the cost savings would be very attractive.

11-3a Effect on β of Changing α

Suppose that in the previous illustration we had used a significance level of 1% instead of 5%. The rejection region expressed in terms of the standardized test statistic would be

$$z > z_{.01} = 2.33$$

or

$$\frac{\bar{x} - 170}{65/\sqrt{400}} > 2.33$$

Solving for $\bar{x}$, we find the rejection region in terms of the unstandardized test statistic:

$$\bar{x} > 177.57$$

The probability of a Type II error when $\mu = 180$ is

$$\beta = P\left(\frac{\bar{x} - \mu}{\sigma/\sqrt{n}} < \frac{177.57 - 180}{65/\sqrt{400}}\right) = P(Z < -.75) = .2266$$

Figure 11.10 depicts this calculation. Compare this figure with Figure 11.9. As you can see, by decreasing the significance level from 5% to 1%, we have shifted the critical value of the rejection region to the right and thus enlarged the area where the null hypothesis is not rejected. The probability of a Type II error increases from .0764 to .2266.

FIGURE **11.10** Calculating β for $\mu = 180$, $\alpha = .01$, and $n = 400$

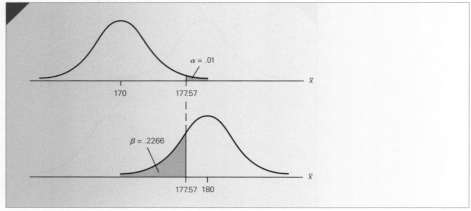

This calculation illustrates the inverse relationship between the probabilities of Type I and Type II errors alluded to in Section 11-1. It is important to understand this relationship. From a practical point of view, it tells us that if you want to decrease the probability of a Type I error (by specifying a small value of α), you increase the probability of a Type II error. In applications where the cost of a Type I error is considerably larger than the cost of a Type II error, this is appropriate. In fact, a significance level of 1% or less is probably justified. However, when the cost of a Type II error is relatively large, a significance level of 5% or more may be appropriate.

Unfortunately, there is no simple formula to determine what the significance level should be. The manager must consider the costs of both mistakes in deciding what to do. Judgment and knowledge of the factors in the decision are crucial.

11-3b Judging the Test

There is another important concept to be derived from this section. A statistical test of hypothesis is effectively defined by the significance level and the sample size, both of which are selected by the statistics practitioner. We can judge how well the test functions by calculating the probability of a Type II error at some value of the parameter. To illustrate, in Example 11.1 the manager chose a sample size of 400 and a 5% significance level on which to base her decision. With those selections, we found β to be .0764 when the actual mean is 180. If we believe that the cost of a Type II error is high and thus that the probability is too large, we have two ways to reduce the probability. We can increase the value of α; however, this would result in an increase in the chance of making a Type I error, which is very costly.

Alternatively, we can increase the sample size. Suppose that the manager chose a sample size of 1,000. We'll now recalculate β with $n = 1000$ (and $\alpha = .05$). The rejection region is

or

$$z > z_{.05} = 1.645$$

or

$$\frac{\bar{x} - 170}{65/\sqrt{1000}} > 1.645$$

which yields

$$\bar{x} > 173.38$$

The probability of a Type II error is

$$\beta = P\left(\frac{\bar{X} - \mu}{\sigma/\sqrt{n}} < \frac{173.38 - 180}{65/\sqrt{1000}}\right) = P(Z < -3.22) = 0 \text{ (approximately)}$$

In this case, we maintained the same value of $\alpha(.05)$, but we reduced the probability of not installing the system when the actual mean account is $180 to virtually 0.

11-3c Developing an Understanding of Statistical Concepts: Larger Sample Size Equals More Information Equals Better Decisions

Figure 11.11 displays the previous calculation. When compared with Figure 11.9, we can see that the sampling distribution of the mean is narrower because the standard error of the mean $\sigma/\sqrt{n}$ becomes smaller as n increases. Narrower distributions represent more information. The increased information is reflected in a smaller probability of a Type II error.

FIGURE **11.11** Calculating β for $\mu = 180$, $\alpha = .05$, and $n = 1,000$

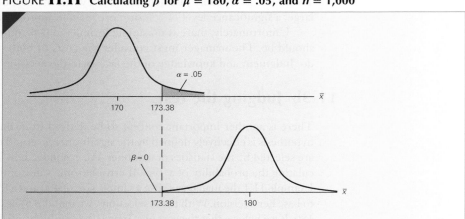

The calculation of the probability of a Type II error for $n = 400$ and for $n = 1,000$ illustrates a concept whose importance cannot be overstated. By increasing the sample size, we reduce the probability of a Type II error. By reducing the probability of a Type II error, we make this type of error less frequently. Hence, larger sample sizes allow us to make better decisions in the long run. This finding lies at the heart of applied statistical analysis and reinforces the book's first sentence: "Statistics is a way to get information from data."

Throughout this book we introduce a variety of applications in accounting, finance, marketing, operations management, human resources management, and economics. In all such applications, the statistics practitioner must make a decision, which involves converting data into information. The more information, the better the decision. Without such information, decisions must be based on guesswork, instinct, and luck. W. Edwards Deming, a famous statistician, said it best: "Without data you're just another person with an opinion."

11-3d Power of a Test

Another way of expressing how well a test performs is to report its *power*: the probability of its leading us to reject the null hypothesis when it is false. Thus, the power of a test is $1 - \beta$.

When more than one test can be performed in a given situation, we would naturally prefer to use the test that is correct more frequently. If (given the same alternative hypothesis, sample size, and significance level) one test has a higher power than a second test, the first test is said to be more powerful.

11-3e Operating Characteristic Curve

To compute the probability of a Type II error, we must specify the significance level, the sample size, and an alternative value of the population mean. One way to keep track of all these components is to draw the **operating characteristic (OC) curve**, which plots the values of β versus the values of μ. Because of the time-consuming nature of these calculations, the computer is a virtual necessity. To illustrate, we'll draw the OC curve for Example 11.1.

We used the Excel function NORMDIST to compute the probability of a Type II error in Example 11.1 for $\mu = 170, 171, \ldots, 184$, with $n = 400$.

EXCEL Function

With $\sigma = 65$ and $n = 400$, the standard error of the mean is

$$\sigma_{\bar{x}} = \frac{\sigma}{\sqrt{n}} = \frac{65}{\sqrt{400}} = 3.25$$

To calculate the probability of a Type II error in Example 11.1, we open Excel and in any empty cell type

= NORMDIST (175.35, [μ], 3.25, True)

For example, to compute β when $\mu = 180$, we type

= NORMDIST (175.35, 180, 3.25, True)

Figure 11.12 depicts this curve. Notice as the alternative value of μ increases the value of β decreases. This tells us that as the alternative value of μ moves farther from the value of μ under the null hypothesis, the probability of a Type II error decreases. In other words, it becomes easier to distinguish between $\mu = 170$ and other values of μ when μ is farther from 170. Notice that when $\mu = 170$ (the hypothesized value of μ), $\beta = 1 - \alpha$.

FIGURE **11.12** Operating Characteristic Curve for Example 11.1

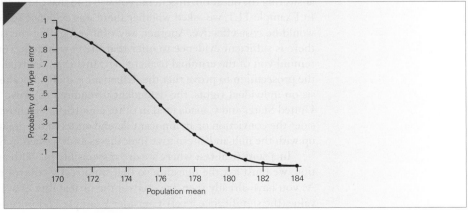

The OC curve can also be useful in selecting a sample size. Figure 11.13 shows the OC curve for Example 11.1 with $n = 100, 400, 1,000,$ and $2,000$. An examination of this chart sheds some light concerning the effect increasing the sample size has on how well the test performs at different values of μ. For example, we can see that smaller sample sizes will work well to distinguish between 170 and values of μ larger than 180. However, to distinguish between 170 and smaller values of μ requires larger sample sizes. Although the information is imprecise, it does allow us to select a sample size that is suitable for our purposes.

FIGURE **11.13**   **Operating Characteristic Curve for Example 11.1 for $n = 100, 400, 1,000,$ and 2,000**

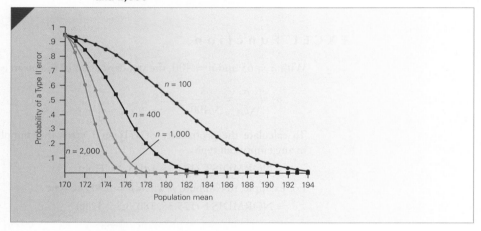

11-3f Determining the Alternative Hypothesis to Define Type I and Type II Errors

We've already discussed how the alternative hypothesis is determined. It represents the condition we're investigating. In Example 11.1, we wanted to know whether there was sufficient statistical evidence to infer that the new billing system would be cost-effective—that is, whether the mean monthly account is greater than $170. In this textbook, you will encounter many problems using similar phraseology. Your job will be to conduct the test that answers the question.

In real life, however, the manager (that's you 5 years from now) will be asking and answering the question. In general, you will find that the question can be posed in two ways. In Example 11.1, we asked whether there was evidence to conclude that the new system would be cost-effective. Another way of investigating the issue is to determine whether there is sufficient evidence to infer that the new system would *not* be cost-effective. We remind you of the criminal trial analogy. In a criminal trial, the burden of proof falls on the prosecution to prove that the defendant is guilty. In other countries with less emphasis on individual rights, the defendant is required to prove his or her innocence. In the United States and Canada (and in other countries), we chose the former because we consider the conviction of an innocent defendant to be the greater error. Thus, the test is set up with the null and alternative hypotheses as described in Section 11-1.

In a statistical test where we are responsible for both asking and answering a question, we must ask the question so that we directly control the error that is more costly. As you have already seen, we control the probability of a Type I error by specifying its value (the significance level). Consider Example 11.1 once again. There are two possible errors: (1) conclude that the billing system is cost-effective when it isn't and (2) conclude that the system is not cost-effective when it is. If the manager concludes that the billing plan is cost-effective, the company will install the new system. If, in reality, the system is not cost-effective, the company will incur a loss. On the other hand, if the manager concludes that the billing plan is not going to be cost-effective, the company will not install the system. However, if the system is actually cost-effective, the company will lose the potential gain from installing it. Which cost is greater?

Suppose we believe that the cost of installing a system that is not cost-effective is higher than the potential loss of not installing an effective system. The error we wish to avoid is the erroneous conclusion that the system is cost-effective. We define this as a Type I error. As a result, the burden of proof is placed on the system to deliver sufficient statistical evidence that the mean account is greater than \$170. The null and alternative hypotheses are as formulated previously:

$$H_0: \quad \mu = 170$$
$$H_1: \quad \mu > 170$$

However, if we believe that the potential loss of not installing the new system when it would be cost-effective is the larger cost, we would place the burden of proof on the manager to infer that the mean monthly account is less than \$170. Consequently, the hypotheses would be

$$H_0: \quad \mu = 170$$
$$H_1: \quad \mu < 170$$

This discussion emphasizes the need in practice to examine the costs of making both types of error before setting up the hypotheses. However, it is important for readers to understand that the questions posed in exercises throughout this book have already taken these costs into consideration. Accordingly, your task is to set up the hypotheses to answer the questions.

EXERCISES

Developing an Understanding of Statistical Concepts

11.60 Calculate the probability of a Type II error for the following test of hypothesis, given that $\mu = 203$.

$$H_0: \quad \mu = 200$$
$$H_1: \quad \mu \neq 200$$
$$\alpha = .05, \sigma = 10, n = 100$$

11.61 Find the probability of a Type II error for the following test of hypothesis, given that $\mu = 1,050$.

$$H_0: \quad \mu = 1,000$$
$$H_1: \quad \mu > 1,000$$
$$\alpha = .01, \sigma = 50, n = 25$$

11.62 Determine β for the following test of hypothesis, given that $\mu = 48$.

$$H_0: \quad \mu = 50$$
$$H_1: \quad \mu < 50$$
$$\alpha = .05, \sigma = 10, n = 40$$

11.63 For each of Exercises 11.60 to 11.62, draw the sampling distributions similar to Figure 11.9.

11.64 A statistics practitioner wants to test the following hypotheses with $\sigma = 20$ and $n = 100$:

$$H_0: \quad \mu = 100$$
$$H_1: \quad \mu > 100$$

a. Using $\alpha = .10$ find the probability of a Type II error when $\mu = 102$.
b. Repeat part (a) with $\alpha = .02$.
c. Describe the effect on β of decreasing α.

11.65 a. Calculate the probability of a Type II error for the following hypotheses when $\mu = 37$:

$$H_0: \quad \mu = 40$$
$$H_1: \quad \mu < 40$$

The significance level is 5%, the population standard deviation is 5, and the sample size is 25.

b. Repeat part (a) with $\alpha = 15\%$.

c. Describe the effect on β of increasing α.

11.66 Draw the figures of the sampling distributions for Exercises 11.64 and 11.65.

11.67 a. Find the probability of a Type II error for the following test of hypothesis, given that $\mu = 196$:

$$H_0: \quad \mu = 200$$
$$H_1: \quad \mu < 200$$

The significance level is 10%, the population standard deviation is 30, and the sample size is 25.

b. Repeat part (a) with $n = 100$.

c. Describe the effect on β of increasing n.

11.68 a. Determine β for the following test of hypothesis, given that $\mu = 310$:

$$H_0: \quad \mu = 300$$
$$H_1: \quad \mu > 300$$

The statistics practitioner knows that the population standard deviation is 50, the significance level is 5%, and the sample size is 81.

b. Repeat part (a) with $n = 36$.

c. Describe the effect on β of decreasing n.

11.69 For Exercises 11.67 and 11.68, draw the sampling distributions similar to Figure 11.9.

11.70 For the test of hypothesis

$$H_0: \quad \mu = 1,000$$
$$H_1: \quad \mu \neq 1,000$$
$$\alpha = .05, \sigma = 200$$

draw the operating characteristic curve for $n = 25$, 100, and 200.

11.71 Draw the operating characteristic curve for $n = 10$, 50, and 100 for the following test:

$$H_0: \quad \mu = 400$$
$$H_1: \quad \mu > 400$$
$$\alpha = .05, \sigma = 50$$

11.72 Suppose that in Example 11.1 we wanted to determine whether there was sufficient evidence to conclude that the new system would *not* be cost-effective. Set up the null and alternative hypotheses and discuss the consequences of Type I and Type II errors. Conduct the test. Is your conclusion the same as the one reached in Example 11.1? Explain.

Applications

11.73 In Exercise 11.47, we tested to determine whether the installation of safety equipment was effective in reducing person-hours lost to industrial accidents. The null and alternative hypotheses were

$$H_0: \quad \mu = 0$$
$$H_1: \quad \mu < 0$$

with $\sigma = 6$, $\alpha = .10$, $n = 50$, and $\mu =$ the mean percentage change. The test failed to indicate that the new safety equipment is effective. The manager is concerned that the test was not sensitive enough to detect small but important changes. In particular, he worries that if the true reduction in time lost to accidents is actually 2% (i.e., $\mu = -2$), then the firm may miss the opportunity to install very effective equipment. Find the probability that the test with $\sigma = 6$, $\alpha = .10$, and $n = 50$ will fail to conclude that such equipment is effective. Discuss ways to decrease this probability.

11.74 The test of hypothesis in the SSA example concluded that there was not enough evidence to infer that the plan would be profitable. The company would hate to not institute the plan if the actual reduction was as little as 3 days (i.e., $\mu = 21$). Calculate the relevant probability and describe how the company should use this information.

11.75 The fast-food franchiser in Exercise 11.51 was unable to provide enough evidence that the site is acceptable. She is concerned that she may be missing an opportunity to locate the restaurant in a profitable location. She feels that if the actual mean is 104, the restaurant is likely to be very successful. Determine the probability of a Type II error when the mean is 104. Suggest ways to improve this probability.

11.76 Refer to Exercise 11.54. A financial analyst has determined that a 2-minute reduction in the average break would increase productivity. As a result the company would hate to lose this opportunity. Calculate the probability of erroneously concluding that the renovation would not be successful when the average break is 30 minutes. If this probability is high, describe how it can be reduced.

11.77 A school-board administrator believes that the average number of days absent per year among students is less than 10 days. From past experience, he knows that the population standard deviation is 3 days. In testing to determine whether his belief is true, he could use one of the following plans:

i. $n = 100$, $\alpha = .01$
ii. $n = 75$, $\alpha = .05$
iii. $n = 50$, $\alpha = .10$

Which plan has the lowest probability of a Type II error, given that the true population average is 9 days?

11.78 The feasibility of constructing a profitable electricity-producing windmill depends on the mean velocity of the wind. For a certain type of windmill, the mean would have to exceed 20 miles per hour to warrant its construction. The determination of a site's feasibility is a two-stage process. In the first stage, readings of the wind velocity are taken and the mean is calculated. The test is designed to answer the question, "Is the site feasible?" In other words, is there sufficient evidence to conclude that the mean wind velocity exceeds 20 mph? If there is enough evidence, further testing is conducted. If there is not enough evidence, the site is removed from consideration. Discuss the consequences and potential costs of Type I and Type II errors.

11.79 The number of potential sites for the first-stage test in Exercise 11.78 is quite large and the readings can be expensive. Accordingly, the test is conducted with a sample of 25 observations. Because the second-stage cost is high, the significance level is set at 1%. A financial analysis of the potential profits and costs reveals that if the mean wind velocity is as high as 25 mph, the windmill would be extremely profitable. Calculate the probability that the first-stage test will not conclude that the site is feasible when the actual mean wind velocity is 25 mph. (Assume that σ is 8.) Discuss how the process can be improved.

11-4 / THE ROAD AHEAD

We had two principal goals to accomplish in Chapters 10 and 11. First, we wanted to present the concepts of estimation and hypothesis testing. Second, we wanted to show how to produce confidence interval estimates and conduct tests of hypotheses. The importance of both goals should not be underestimated. Almost everything that follows this chapter will involve either estimating a parameter or testing a set of hypotheses. Consequently, Sections 10-2 and 11-2 set the pattern for the way in which statistical techniques are applied. It is no exaggeration to state that if you understand how to produce and use confidence interval estimates and how to conduct and interpret hypothesis tests, then you are well on your way to the ultimate goal of being competent at analyzing, interpreting, and presenting data. It is fair for you to ask what more you must accomplish to achieve this goal. The answer, simply put, is much more of the same.

In the chapters that follow, we plan to present about three dozen different statistical techniques that can be (and frequently are) employed by statistics practitioners. To calculate the value of test statistics or confidence interval estimates requires nothing more than the ability to add, subtract, multiply, divide, and compute square roots. If you intend to use the computer, all you need to know are the commands. The key, then, to applying statistics is knowing which formula to calculate or which set of commands to issue. Thus, the real challenge of the subject lies in being able to define the problem and identify which statistical method is the most appropriate one to use.

Most students have some difficulty recognizing the particular kind of statistical problem they are addressing unless, of course, the problem appears among the exercises at the end of a section that just introduced the technique needed. Unfortunately, in practice, statistical problems do not appear already so identified. Consequently, we have adopted an approach to teaching statistics that is designed to help identify the statistical technique.

A number of factors determine which statistical method should be used, but two are especially important: the type of data and the purpose of the statistical inference. In Chapter 2, we pointed out that there are effectively three types of data—interval, ordinal, and nominal. Recall that nominal data represent categories such as marital status, occupation, and gender. Statistics practitioners often record nominal data by assigning numbers to the responses (e.g., 1 = Single, 2 = Married, 3 = Divorced, 4 = Widowed). Because these numbers are assigned completely arbitrarily, any calculations performed on them are meaningless. All that we can do with nominal data is count the number of times each category is observed. Ordinal data are obtained from questions whose answers represent a rating or ranking system. For example, if students are asked to rate a university professor, the responses may be excellent, good, fair, or poor. To draw inferences about such data, we convert the responses to numbers. Any numbering system is valid as long as the order of the responses is preserved. Thus "4 = Excellent, 3 = Good, 2 = Fair, 1 = Poor" is just as valid as "15 = Excellent, 8 = Good, 5 = Fair, 2 = Poor." Because of this feature, the most appropriate statistical procedures for ordinal data are ones based on a ranking process.

Interval data are real numbers, such as those representing income, age, height, weight, and volume. Computation of means and variances is permissible.

The second key factor in determining the statistical technique is the purpose of doing the work. Every statistical method has some specific objective. We address five such objectives in this book.

11-4a Problem Objectives

1. **Describe a population.** Our objective here is to describe some property of a population of interest. The decision about which property to describe is generally dictated by the type of data. For example, suppose the population of interest consists of all purchasers of computers. If we are interested in the purchasers' incomes (for which the data are interval), we may calculate the mean or the variance to describe that aspect of the population. But if we are interested in the brand of computer that has been bought (for which the data are nominal), all we can do is compute the proportion of the population that purchases each brand.

2. **Compare two populations.** In this case, our goal is to compare a property of one population with a corresponding property of a second population. For example, suppose the populations of interest are male and female purchasers of computers. We could compare the means of their incomes, or we could compare the proportion of each population that purchases a certain brand. Once again, the data type generally determines what kinds of properties we compare.

3. **Compare two or more populations.** We might want to compare the average income in each of several locations in order (for example) to decide where to build a new shopping center. Or we might want to compare the proportions of defective items in a number of production lines in order to determine which line is the best. In each case, the problem objective involves comparing two or more populations.

4. **Analyze the relationship between two variables.** There are numerous situations in which we want to know how one variable is related to another. Governments need to know what effect rising interest rates have on the unemployment rate. Companies want to investigate how the sizes of their advertising budgets influence sales volume. In most of the problems in this introductory text, the two variables to be analyzed will be of the same type; we will not attempt to cover the fairly large body of statistical techniques that has been developed to deal with two variables of different types.

5. **Analyze the relationship among two or more variables.** Our objective here is usually to forecast one variable (called the *dependent variable*) on the basis of several other variables (called *independent variables*). We will deal with this problem only in situations in which all variables are interval.

Table 11.3 lists the types of data and the five problem objectives. For each combination, the table specifies the chapter or section where the appropriate statistical technique

TABLE **11.3**   Guide to Statistical Inference Showing Where Each Technique Is Introduced

	DATA TYPE		
PROBLEM OBJECTIVE	**NOMINAL**	**ORDINAL**	**INTERVAL**
Describe a population	Sections 12-3, 15-1	Not covered	Sections 12-1, 12-2
Compare two populations	Sections 13-5, 15-2	Sections 19-1, 19-2	Sections 13-1, 13-3, 13-4, 19-1, 19-2
Compare two or more populations	Section 15-2	Section 19-3	Chapter 14 Section 19-3
Analyze the relationship between two variables	Section 15-2	Section 19-4	Chapter 16
Analyze the relationship among two or more variables	Not covered	Not covered	Chapters 17, 18

is presented. For your convenience, a more detailed version of this table is reproduced inside the front cover of this book.

11-4b Derivations

Because this book is about statistical applications, we assume that our readers have little interest in the mathematical derivations of the techniques described. However, it might be helpful for you to have some understanding about the process that produces the formulas.

As described previously, factors such as the problem objective and the type of data determine the parameter to be estimated and tested. For each parameter, statisticians have determined which statistic to use. That statistic has a sampling distribution that can usually be expressed as a formula. For example, in this chapter, the parameter of interest was the population mean μ, whose best estimator is the sample mean $\bar{x}$. Assuming that the population standard deviation σ is known, the sampling distribution of $\overline{X}$ is normal (or approximately so) with mean μ and standard deviation $\sigma/\sqrt{n}$. The sampling distribution can be described by the formula

$$Z = \frac{\overline{X} - \mu}{\sigma/\sqrt{n}}.$$

This formula also describes the test statistic for μ with σ known. With a little algebra, we were able to derive (in Section 10-2) the confidence interval estimator of μ.

In future chapters, we will repeat this process, which in several cases involves the introduction of a new sampling distribution (introduced in Chapter 8). Although its shape and formula will differ from the sampling distribution used in this chapter, the pattern will be the same. In general, the formula that expresses the sampling distribution will describe the test statistic. Then some algebraic manipulation (which we will not show) produces the interval estimator. Consequently, we will reverse the order of presentation of the two techniques. In other words, we will present the test of hypothesis first, followed by the confidence interval estimator.

CHAPTER SUMMARY

In this chapter, we introduced the concepts of hypothesis testing and applied them to testing hypotheses about a population mean. We showed how to specify the null and alternative hypotheses, set up the rejection region, compute the value of the test statistic, and, finally, to make a decision. Equally as important, we discussed how to interpret the test results. This chapter also demonstrated another way to make decisions; by calculating and using the p-value of the test. To help interpret test results, we showed how to calculate the probability of a Type II error. Finally, we provided a road map of how we plan to present statistical techniques.

IMPORTANT TERMS:

Hypothesis testing   334
Null hypothesis   334
Alternative or research hypothesis   334
Type I error   334
Type II error   334
Significance level   334
Test statistic   337
Rejection region   339
Standardized test statistic   340

Statistically significant   341
p-value of a test   342
Highly significant   344
Significant   344
Not statistically significant   344
One-tail test   349
Two-tail test   352
One-sided confidence interval estimator   353
Operating characteristic curve   363

SYMBOLS:

Symbol	Pronounced	Represents
H_0	H nought	Null hypothesis
H_1	H one	Alternative (research) hypothesis
α	alpha	Probability of a Type I error
β	beta	Probability of a Type II error
$\bar{x}_L$	X bar sub L or X bar L	Value of $\bar{x}$ large enough to reject H_0
$|z|$	Absolute z	Absolute value of z

FORMULA:

Test statistic for μ

$$Z = \frac{\bar{x} - \mu}{\sigma/\sqrt{n}}$$

COMPUTER OUTPUT AND INSTRUCTIONS:

Technique	Excel
Test of μ	345
Probability of a Type II error (and Power)	363

To calculate the value of the test statistic, we need to calculate the sample mean $\bar{x}$ and the sample standard deviation s. From the data, we determine

$$\sum x_i = 322.7 \text{ and } \sum x_i^2 = 845.1$$

Thus,

$$\bar{x} = \frac{\sum x_i}{n} = \frac{322.7}{148} = 2.18$$

$$s^2 = \frac{\sum x_i^2 - \frac{\left(\sum x_i\right)^2}{n}}{n-1} = \frac{845.1 - \frac{(322.7)^2}{148}}{148 - 1} = .962$$

and

$$s = \sqrt{s^2} = \sqrt{.962} = .981$$

The value of μ is to be found in the null hypothesis. It is 2.0. The value of the test statistic is

$$t = \frac{\bar{x} - \mu}{s/\sqrt{n}} = \frac{2.18 - 2.0}{.981/\sqrt{148}} = 2.23$$

Because 2.23 is not greater than 2.351, we cannot reject the null hypothesis in favor of the alternative. (Students performing the calculations manually can approximate the p-value. The online appendix Approximating the p-Value from the Student t Table describes how.)

EXCEL Workbook

	A	B	C	D
1	t-Test of a Mean			
2				
3	Sample mean	2.1804	t Stat	2.24
4	Sample standard deviation	0.9812	P(T<=t) one-tail	0.0134
5	Sample size	148	t Critical one-tail	2.3520
6	Hypothesized mean	2	P(T<=t) two-tail	0.0268
7	Alpha	0.01	t Critical two-tail	2.6097

INSTRUCTIONS

1. Type or import the data into one column. (Open Xm12-01.) In any empty cell, calculate the sample mean (=AVERAGE(A1:A149) and the sample standard deviation (=STDEV(A1:A149).

2. Open the **Test Statistics Workbook** and click the t-**Test_Mean** tab. Type or copy the sample mean and the sample standard deviation. Type the sample size, the value of μ under the null hypothesis and the value of α.

XLSTAT

	A	B	C	D	E	F
1	Theoretical mean: 2					
2	Significance level (%): 1					
3						
4	Summary statistics:					
5	Variable	Observations	Minimum	Maximum	Mean	Std. deviation
6	Newspaper	148	0.0	4.4	2.180	0.981
7						
8	One-sample t-test / Upper-tailed test:					
9	Difference	0.18				
10	t (Observed value)	2.24				
11	t (Critical value)	2.352				
12	DF	147				
13	p-value (one-tailed)	0.0134				
14	alpha	0.01				

INSTRUCTIONS

1. Type or import the data into one column. (Open Xm12-01.)

2. Click **XLSTAT, Parametric tests,** and **One-sample t-test and z-test**.

3. In the **Data**: dialog box type the input range (A1:A149). Check **Student's t-test**. Do not check **z-test**.

4. Click the **Options** tab and choose the **Mean 1 > Theoretical mean** in the **Alternative hypothesis** box.

   Type the **Theoretical mean** (2) and the value of α (in percent) in the **Significance level (%) box** (1). Click **OK**. If there are blanks in the column (usually used to represent missing data), click **Missing data** and click **Remove the observations**.

INTERPRET

The value of the test statistic is $t = 2.24$, and its p-value is .0134. There is not enough evidence to infer that the mean weight of discarded newspapers is greater than 2.0. Note that there is some evidence: The p-value is .0134. However, because we wanted the probability of a Type I error to be small, we insisted on a 1% significance level. Thus, we cannot conclude that the recycling plant would be profitable.

Figure 12.1 exhibits the sampling distribution for this example.

FIGURE **12.1** Sampling Distribution for Example 12.1

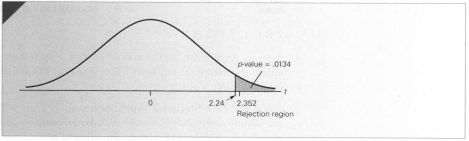

p-value = .0134

0   2.24   2.352 t

Rejection region

EXAMPLE 12.2

DATA
Xm12-02

Tax Collected from Audited Returns

In 2014 (the latest year reported), 146,861,217 tax returns were filed in the United States. The Internal Revenue Service (IRS) examined 1,228,117, of them to determine if they were correctly done. To determine how well the auditors are performing, a random sample of these returns was drawn and the additional tax was reported, which is listed next. Estimate with 95% confidence the mean additional income tax collected from the 1,228,117 files audited.

Additional Income Tax

13069.55	7773.87	6693.27	16293.73	11269.68	1599.52
6915.39	8310.68	21019.45	8625.75	9934.44	8375.89
16103.88	7897.67	10690.97	7844.23	7844.23	10824.18
1088.93	6063.57	3779.98	3483.38	10564.65	527.82
2895.24	9251.80	6725.38	7879.76	7434.50	9160.90
2365.28	9253.47	11285.80	10802.42	9033.40	11992.65
8811.64	10897.11	9191.01	14320.87	8505.35	12233.19
9876.18	2719.66	0.00	12149.66	5486.99	191.24
6811.01	6821.53	12276.66	17986.29	10377.83	8607.87
13736.62	2253.58	12228.93	17107.72	7717.48	9829.19
2324.17	14569.22	7820.71	9048.53	8500.15	12130.53
4969.44	4863.95	11639.65	14303.24	12801.99	4254.72
8440.77	10142.90	1540.58	0.00	5915.89	14102.22
15952.46	7207.52	20865.53	17197.05	7227.33	8598.93
6502.22	12728.47	4316.10	16913.57	12336.05	6983.37
19028.69	8298.02	10869.13	10460.38	12384.07	15452.72
6025.37	19269.79	15706.99	7731.24	10345.13	13577.00
17750.30	9827.53	9977.16	12469.07	8837.12	17295.55
7475.96	11112.31	4309.43	12434.39	8165.34	10436.96
11326.90	3178.42	5391.00	14913.03	10228.61	4896.92
12295.75	11393.22	14382.85	9025.67	9809.67	14203.49
7061.20	10198.69	6705.28	8743.87	8171.03	628.72
0.00	5462.37	8807.22	10359.81	4543.60	10685.24
12232.03	9736.53	16934.01	13157.66	7387.40	14358.06
8414.65	4323.51	14675.43	7327.91	12037.85	8126.13
17638.95	11831.65	8730.90	8133.98	5045.49	5276.17
7706.31	11313.89	6722.39	9821.58	14613.67	4440.67
2123.79	9254.80	10046.07	20814.39	18687.37	11392.17
8811.30	3396.21	13791.36	12901.52	10746.12	6742.86
9060.97	5817.56	8151.45	11263.38	14794.92	8508.47
2493.08	4025.66	17304.42	4989.82	12956.43	4580.93
15902.15	3685.81	11485.57	12164.60	10915.90	11788.37

Source: Adapted from U.S. Internal Revenue Service, IRS Data Book, annual, Publication 55B

SOLUTION:

IDENTIFY

The problem objective is to describe the population of additional income tax. The data are interval and hence, the parameter is the population mean μ. The question asks us to estimate this parameter. The confidence interval estimator is:

$$\bar{x} \pm t_{\alpha/2}\frac{s}{\sqrt{n}}$$

COMPUTE

MANUALLY:

From the data we determine:

$$\sum x_i = 1,829,247 \quad \text{and} \quad \sum x_i^2 = 21,293,389,277$$

Thus,

$$\bar{x} = \frac{\sum x_i}{n} = \frac{1,829,247}{192} = 9,527$$

and

$$s^2 = \frac{\sum x_i^2 - \dfrac{\left(\sum x_i\right)^2}{n}}{n-1} = \frac{21,293,389,277 - \dfrac{(1,829,247)^2}{192}}{192 - 1} = 20,238,531$$

Thus,

$$s = \sqrt{s^2} = \sqrt{20,238,531} = 4499$$

Because we want a 95% confidence interval estimate, $1 - \alpha = .95$, $\alpha = .05$, $\alpha/2 = .025$, and $t_{\alpha/2, n-1} = t_{.025,191} \approx t_{.025,190} = 1.973$. Thus, the 95% confidence interval estimate of μ is:

$$\bar{x} \pm t_{\alpha/2}\frac{s}{\sqrt{n}} = 9,527 \pm 1.973\frac{4499}{\sqrt{192}} = 9,527 \pm 641$$

or

$$\text{LCL} = \$8,886 \quad \text{UCL} = \$10,168$$

EXCEL Workbook

	A	B	C	D	E
1	t-Estimate of a Mean				
2					
3	Sample mean	9527	Confidence Interval Estimate		
4	Sample standard deviation	4499	9527	±	640
5	Sample size	192	Lower confidence limit		8887
6	Confidence level	0.95	Upper confidence limit		10168

INSTRUCTIONS

1. Type or import the data into one column. (Open Xm12-02.) In any empty cell, calculate the sample mean (=AVERAGE(A1:A193) and the sample standard deviation (=STDEV(A1:A193).

2. Open the **Estimators Workbook** and click the *t*-**Estimate_Mean tab**. Type or copy the sample mean and the sample standard deviation. Type the sample size and the confidence level.

XLSTAT

	A	B	C	D	E	F
1	Summary statistics:					
2	Variable	Observations	Minimum	Maximum	Mean	Std. deviation
3	Taxes	192	0.00	21019.45	9527	4499
4						
5	95% confidence interval of the mean:					
6	8,887	10,168				

INSTRUCTIONS

1. Type or import the data into one column. (Open Xm12-02.)

2. Click **XLSTAT**, **Parametric tests**, and **One-sample *t*-test and *z*-test**.

3. In the **Data:** dialog box type the input range (A1:A193). Check **Student's t-test**. Do not check *z*-**test**.

4. Click the **Options** tab and choose **Mean 1 ≠ Theoretical** in the **Alternative hypothesis** box. Type the value of α (in percent) in the **Significance level (%)** box (5).

INTERPRET

We estimate that the mean additional tax collected lies between $8,887 and $10,168. We can use this estimate to help decide whether the IRS is auditing the individuals who should be audited.

12-1a Checking the Required Conditions

When we introduced the Student *t*-distribution, we pointed out that the *t*-statistic is Student *t*-distributed if the population from which we've sampled is normal. However, statisticians have shown that the mathematical process that derived the Student *t*-distribution is **robust**, which means that if the population is nonnormal, the results of

FIGURE **12.2** Histogram for Example 12.1

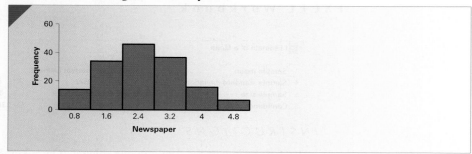

FIGURE **12.3** Histogram for Example 12.2

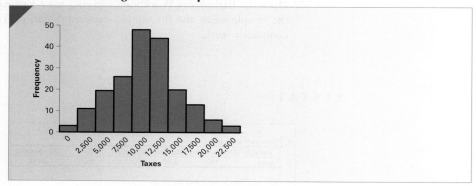

the *t*-test and confidence interval estimate are still valid provided that the population is not *extremely* nonnormal.* To check this requirement, we draw the histogram and determine whether it is far from bell-shaped. Figures 12.2 and 12.3 depict the histograms for Examples 12.1 and 12.2, respectively. Both histograms suggest that the variables are not extremely nonnormal, and in fact, may be normal.

12-1b Estimating the Totals of Finite Populations

The inferential techniques introduced thus far were derived by assuming infinitely large populations. In practice, however, most populations are finite. (Infinite populations are usually the result of some endlessly repeatable process, such as flipping a coin or selecting items with replacement.) When the population is small, we must adjust the test statistic and interval estimator using the finite population correction factor introduced in Chapter 9 (page 292). (On the online appendix Applications in Accounting: Auditing, we feature an application that requires the use of the correction factor.) However, in populations that are large relative to the sample size, we can ignore the correction factor. Large populations are defined as populations that are at least 20 times the sample size.

---

*Statisticians have shown that when the sample size is large, the results of a *t*-test and estimator of a mean are valid even when the population is extremely nonnormal. The sample size required depends on the extent of nonnormality.

Finite populations allow us to use the confidence interval estimator of a mean to produce a confidence interval estimator of the population total. To estimate the total, we multiply the lower and upper confidence limits of the estimate of the mean by the population size. Thus, the confidence interval estimator of the total is:

$$N\left[\bar{x} \pm t_{\alpha/2}\frac{s}{\sqrt{n}}\right]$$

For example, suppose that we wish to estimate the total amount of additional income tax collected from the 1,228,117 returns that were examined. The 95% confidence interval estimate of the total is:

$$N\left[\bar{x} \pm t_{\alpha/2}\frac{s}{\sqrt{n}}\right] = 1,228,117(9527 \pm 641)$$

which is

$$\text{LCL} = 10,913,047,662 \quad \text{and} \quad \text{UCL} = 12,487,493,656$$

12-1c Developing an Understanding of Statistical Concepts 1

This section introduced the term *degrees of freedom*. We will encounter this term many times in this book, so a brief discussion of its meaning is warranted. The Student *t*-distribution is based on using the sample variance to estimate the unknown population variance. The sample variance is defined as

$$s^2 = \frac{\sum (x_i - \bar{x})^2}{n - 1}$$

To compute s^2, we must first determine $\bar{x}$. Recall that sampling distributions are derived by repeated sampling from the same population. To repeatedly take samples to compute s^2, we can choose any numbers for the first $n - 1$ observations in the sample. However, we have no choice on the nth value because the sample mean must be calculated first. To illustrate, suppose that $n = 3$ and we find $\bar{x} = 10$. We can have x_1 and x_2 assume any values without restriction. However, x_3 must be such that $\bar{x} = 10$. For example, if $x_1 = 6$ and $x_2 = 8$, then x_3 must equal 16. Therefore, there are only two degrees of freedom in our selection of the sample. We say that we lose one degree of freedom because we had to calculate $\bar{x}$.

Notice that the denominator in the calculation of s^2 is equal to the number of degrees of freedom. This is not a coincidence and will be repeated throughout this book.

12-1d Developing an Understanding of Statistical Concepts 2

The *t*-statistic like the *z*-statistic measures the difference between the sample mean $\bar{x}$ and the hypothesized value of μ in terms of the number of standard errors. However, when the population standard deviation σ is unknown, we estimate the standard error by $s/\sqrt{n}$.

12-1e Developing an Understanding of Statistical Concepts 3

When we introduced the Student *t*-distribution in Section 8-4, we pointed out that it is more widely spread out than the standard normal. This circumstance is logical. The only variable in the z-statistic is the sample mean $\bar{x}$, which will vary from sample to sample. The t-statistic has two variables: the sample mean $\bar{x}$ and the sample standard deviation s, both of which will vary from sample to sample. Because of the greater uncertainty, the t-statistic will display greater variability. Exercises 12.15–12.22 address this concept.

We complete this section with a review of how we identify the techniques introduced in this section.

Factors That Identify the t-Test and Estimator of μ

1. **Problem objective**: Describe a population
2. **Data type**: Interval
3. **Type of descriptive measurement**: Central location

EXERCISES

Developing an Understanding of Statistical Concepts

The following exercises are "what-if" analyses designed to determine what happens to the test statistics and interval estimates when elements of the statistical inference change. These problems can be solved manually or using the Test Statistics or Estimators spreadsheets.

12.1 a. A statistics practitioner took a random sample of size 56. The sample mean and standard deviation are 70 and 12, respectively.

    b. Determine the 95% confidence interval estimate of the population mean.

    c. Repeat part (a) changing the sample mean to 30.

    d. Describe what happens to the width of the interval when the sample mean decreases.

12.2 a. The mean and standard deviation of a sample of 25 is 50 and 10, respectively.

    a. Estimate the population mean with 90% confidence.

    b. Repeat part (a) changing the sample mean to 100.

    c. Describe what happens to the width of the interval when the sample mean increases.

12.3 a. A random sample of 25 was drawn from a population. The sample mean and standard deviation are $\bar{x} = 510$ and $s = 125$. Estimate μ with 95% confidence.

    b. Repeat part (a) with $n = 50$.

    c. Repeat part (a) with $n = 100$.

    d. Describe what happens to the confidence interval estimate when the sample size increases.

12.4 a. The mean and standard deviation of a sample of 100 is $\bar{x} = 1500$ and $s = 300$. Estimate the population mean with 95% confidence.

    b. Repeat part (a) with $s = 200$.

    c. Repeat part (a) with $s = 100$.

    d. Discuss the effect on the confidence interval estimate of decreasing the standard deviation s.

12.5 a. A statistics practitioner drew a random sample of 400 observations and found that $\bar{x} = 700$ and $s = 100$. Estimate the population mean with 90% confidence.

    b. Repeat part (a) with a 95% confidence level.

    c. Repeat part (a) with a 99% confidence level.

    d. What is the effect on the confidence interval estimate of increasing the confidence level?

12.6 a. The mean and standard deviation of a sample of 100 are

$$\bar{x} = 10 \text{ and } s = 1.$$

Estimate the population mean with 95% confidence.

    b. Repeat part (a) with $s = 4$.

    c. Repeat part (a) with $s = 10$.

    d. Discuss the effect on the confidence interval estimate of increasing the standard deviation s.

12.7 a. A statistics practitioner calculated the mean and standard deviation from a sample of 51. They are $\bar{x} = 120$ and $s = 15$. Estimate the population mean with 95% confidence.

b. Repeat part (a) with a 90% confidence level.

c. Repeat part (a) with an 80% confidence level.

d. What is the effect on the confidence interval estimate of decreasing the confidence level?

12.8 a. The sample mean and standard deviation from a sample of 81 observations are $\bar{x} = 63$ and $s = 8$. Estimate μ with 95% confidence.

b. Repeat part (a) with $n = 64$.

c. Repeat part (a) with $n = 36$.

d. Describe what happens to the confidence interval estimate when the sample size decreases.

12.9 a. The sample mean and standard deviation from a random sample of 10 observations from a normal population were computed as $\bar{x} = 23$ and $s = 9$. Calculate the value of the test statistic (and for Excel users, the p-value) of the test required to determine whether there is enough evidence to infer at the 5% significance level that the population mean is greater than 20.

b. Repeat part (a) with $n = 30$.

c. Repeat part (a) with $n = 50$.

d. Describe the effect on the t-statistic (and for Excel users, the p-value) of increasing the sample size.

12.10 a. A statistics practitioner is in the process of testing to determine whether there is enough evidence to infer that the population mean is different from 180. She calculated the mean and standard deviation of a sample of 200 observations as $\bar{x} = 175$ and $s = 22$. Calculate the value of the test statistic (and for Excel users, the p-value) of the test required to determine whether there is enough evidence at the 5% significance level.

b. Repeat part (a) with $s = 45$.

c. Repeat part (a) with $s = 60$.

d. Discuss what happens to the t statistic (and for Excel users, the p-value) when the standard deviation increases.

12.11 a. Calculate the test statistic (and for Excel users, the p-value) when $\bar{x} = 145$, $s = 50$, and $n = 100$. Use a 5% significance level.

$$H_0: \quad \mu = 150$$
$$H_1: \quad \mu < 150$$

b. Repeat part (a) with $\bar{x} = 140$.

c. Repeat part (a) with $\bar{x} = 135$.

d. What happens to the t-statistic (and for Excel users, the p-value) when the sample mean decreases?

12.12 a. A random sample of 25 observations was drawn from a normal population. The sample mean and sample standard deviation are $\bar{x} = 52$ and $s = 15$. Calculate the test statistic (and for Excel users, the p-value) of a test to determine if there is enough evidence at the 10% significance level to infer that the population mean is not equal to 50.

b. Repeat part (a) with $n = 15$.

c. Repeat part (a) with $n = 5$.

d. Discuss what happens to the t-statistic (and for Excel users, the p-value) when the sample size decreases.

12.13 a. A statistics practitioner wishes to test the following hypotheses:

$$H_0: \quad \mu = 600$$
$$H_1: \quad \mu < 600$$

A sample of 50 observations yielded the statistics $\bar{x} = 585$ and $s = 45$. Calculate the test statistic (and for Excel users, the p-value) of a test to determine whether there is enough evidence at the 10% significance level to infer that the alternative hypothesis is true.

b. Repeat part (a) with $\bar{x} = 590$.

c. Repeat part (a) with $\bar{x} = 595$.

d. Describe the effect of increasing the sample mean.

12.14 a. To test the following hypotheses, a statistics practitioner randomly sampled 100 observations and found $\bar{x} = 106$ and $s = 35$. Calculate the test statistic (and for Excel users, the p-value) of a test to determine whether there is enough evidence at the 1% significance level to infer that the alternative hypothesis is true.

$$H_0: \quad \mu = 100$$
$$H_1: \quad \mu > 100$$

b. Repeat part (a) with $s = 25$.

c. Repeat part (a) with $s = 15$.

d. Discuss what happens to the t-statistic (and for Excel users, the p-value) when the standard deviation decreases.

12.15 A random sample of 8 observations was drawn from a normal population. The sample mean and sample standard deviation are $\bar{x} = 40$ and $s = 10$.

a. Estimate the population mean with 95% confidence.

b. Repeat part (a) assuming that you know that the population standard deviation is $\sigma = 10$.

c. Explain why the interval estimate produced in part (b) is narrower than that in part (a).

12.16 a. Estimate the population mean with 90% confidence given the following: $\bar{x} = 175$, $s = 30$, and $n = 5$.

b. Repeat part (a) assuming that you know that the population standard deviation is $\sigma = 30$.

c. Explain why the interval estimate produced in part (b) is narrower than that in part (a).

12.17 a. After sampling 1,000 members of a normal population, you find $\bar{x} = 15,500$ and $s = 9,950$. Estimate the population mean with 90% confidence.

b. Repeat part (a) assuming that you know that the population standard deviation is $\sigma = 9,950$.

c. Explain why the interval estimates were virtually identical.

12.18 a. In a random sample of 500 observations drawn from a normal population, the sample mean and sample standard deviation were calculated as $\bar{x} = 350$ and $s = 100$. Estimate the population mean with 99% confidence.

b. Repeat part (a) assuming that you know that the population standard deviation is $\sigma = 100$.

c. Explain why the interval estimates were virtually identical.

12.19 a. A random sample of 11 observations was taken from a normal population. The sample mean and standard deviation are $\bar{x} = 74.5$ and $s = 9$. Can we infer at the 5% significance level that the population mean is greater than 70?

b. Repeat part (a) assuming that you know that the population standard deviation is $\sigma = 90$.

c. Explain why the conclusions produced in parts (a) and (b) differ.

12.20 a. A statistics practitioner randomly sampled 10 observations and found $\bar{x} = 103$ and $s = 17$. Is there sufficient evidence at the 10% significance level to conclude that the population mean is less than 110?

b. Repeat part (a) assuming that you know that the population standard deviation is $\sigma = 17$.

c. Explain why the conclusions produced in parts (a) and (b) differ.

12.21 a. A statistics practitioner randomly sampled 1,500 observations and found $\bar{x} = 14$ and $s = 25$. Test to determine whether there is enough evidence at the 5% significance level to infer that the population mean is less than 15.

b. Repeat part (a) assuming that you know that the population standard deviation is $\sigma = 25$.

c. Explain why the conclusions produced in parts (a) and (b) are virtually identical.

12.22 a. Test the following hypotheses with $\alpha = .05$ given that $\bar{x} = 405$, $s = 100$, and $n = 1,000$.

$$H_0: \ \mu = 400$$
$$H_1: \ \mu > 400$$

b. Repeat part (a) assuming that you know that the population standard deviation is $\sigma = 100$.

c. Explain why the conclusions produced in parts (a) and (b) are virtually identical.

Applications

The following exercises may be answered manually or with the assistance of a computer. The data are stored in files. Assume that the random variable is normally distributed.

12.23 Xr12-23 A courier service advertises that its average delivery time is less than 6 hours for local deliveries. A random sample of times for 12 deliveries to an address across town was recorded. These data are shown here. Is this sufficient evidence to support the courier's advertisement, at the 5% level of significance?

| 3.03 | 6.33 | 6.50 | 5.22 | 3.56 | 6.76 |
| 7.98 | 4.82 | 7.96 | 4.54 | 5.09 | 6.46 |

12.24 Xr12-24 How much money do winners go home with from the television quiz show Jeopardy? To determine an answer, a random sample of winners was drawn; the recorded amount of money each won is listed here. Estimate with 95% confidence the mean winnings for all the show's players.

26,650	6,060	52,820	8,490	13,660
25,840	49,840	23,790	51,480	18,960
990	11,450	41,810	21,060	7,860

12.25 Xr12-25 A diet doctor claims that the average North American is more than 20 pounds overweight. To test his claim, a random sample of 20 North Americans was weighed, and the difference between their actual and ideal weights was calculated. The data are listed here. Do these data allow us to infer at the 5% significance level that the doctor's claim is true?

| 16 | 23 | 18 | 41 | 22 | 18 | 23 | 19 | 22 | 15 |
| 18 | 35 | 16 | 15 | 17 | 19 | 23 | 15 | 16 | 26 |

12.26 Xr12-26 A federal agency responsible for enforcing laws governing weights and measures routinely inspects packages to determine whether the weight of the contents is at least as great as that advertised on the package. A random sample of 18 containers whose packaging states that the contents weigh 8 ounces was drawn. The contents were weighed and the results follow. Can we conclude at the 1% significance level that on average the containers are mislabeled?

7.80	7.91	7.93	7.99	7.94	7.75
7.97	7.95	7.79	8.06	7.82	7.89
7.92	7.87	7.92	7.98	8.05	7.91

12.27 Xr12-27 A parking control officer is conducting an analysis of the amount of time left on parking meters. A quick survey of 15 cars that have just left their metered parking spaces produced the following times (in minutes). Estimate with 95% confidence the mean amount of time left for all the city's meters.

22	15	1	14	0	9	17	31
18	26	23	15	33	28	20	

12.28 Xr12-28 Part of a university professor's job is to publish his or her research. This task often entails reading a variety of journal articles to keep up to date. To help determine faculty standards, a dean of a business school surveyed a random sample of 12 professors across the country and asked them to count the number of journal articles they read in a typical month. These data are listed here. Estimate with 90% confidence the mean number of journal articles read monthly by professors.

9   17   4   23   56   30   41   45   21   10   44   20

12.29 Xr12-29 Most owners of digital cameras store their pictures on the camera. Some will eventually download these to a computer or print them using their own printers or a commercial printer. A film-processing company wanted to know how many pictures were stored on computers. A random sample of 10 digital camera owners produced the data given here. Estimate with 95% confidence the mean number of pictures stored on digital cameras.

25   6   22   26   31   18   13   20   14   2

12.30 Xr12-30 University bookstores order books that instructors adopt for their courses. The number of copies ordered matches the projected demand. However, at the end of the semester, the bookstore has too many copies on hand and must return them to the publisher. A bookstore has a policy that the proportion of books returned should be kept as small as possible. The average is supposed to be less than 10%. To see whether the policy is working, a random sample of book titles was drawn, and the fraction of the total originally ordered that are returned is recorded and listed here. Can we infer at the 10% significance level that the mean proportion of returns is less than 10%?

4   15   11   7   5   9   4   3   5   8

The following exercises require the use of a computer and software. The answers to Exercises 12.31 to 12.45 may be calculated manually. See Appendix A for the sample statistics. **Use a 5% significance level for all tests.**

12.31 Xr12-31* A growing concern for educators in the United States is the number of teenagers who have part-time jobs while they attend high school. It is generally believed that the amount of time teenagers spend working is deducted from the amount of time devoted to schoolwork. To investigate this problem, a school guidance counselor took a random sample of 200 15-year-old high school students and asked how many hours per week each worked at a part-time job. Estimate with 95% confidence the mean amount of time all 15-year-old high school students devote per week to part-time jobs.

12.32 Xr12-32 A company that produces universal remote controls wanted to determine the number of remote control devices American homes contain. The company hired a statistician to survey 240 randomly selected homes and determine the number of remote controls. If there are 100 million households, estimate with 99% confidence the total number of remote controls in the United States.

12.33 Xr12-33 A random sample of American adults was asked whether or not they smoked cigarettes. Those who responded affirmatively were asked how many cigarettes they smoked per day. Assuming that there are 50 million American adults who smoke, estimate with 95% confidence the number of cigarettes smoked per day in the United States.

Source: Adapted from the Statistical Abstract of the United States, 2009, Table 196 and Bloomberg News.

12.34 Xr12-34 Bankers and economists watch for signs that the economy is slowing. One statistic they monitor is consumer debt, particularly credit card debt. The Federal Reserve conducts surveys of consumer finances every 3 years. The last survey determined that 23.8% of American households have no credit cards and another 31.2% of the households paid off their most recent credit card bills. The remainder, approximately 50 million households, did not pay their credit card bills in the previous month. A random sample of these households was drawn. Each household in the sample reported how much credit card debt it currently carries. The Federal Reserve would like an estimate (with 95% confidence) of the total credit card debt in the United States.

12.35 Xr12-35* OfficeMax, a chain that sells a wide variety of office equipment often features sales of products whose prices are reduced because of rebates. Some rebates are so large that the effective price becomes $0. The goal is to lure customers into the store to buy other nonsale items. A secondary objective is to acquire addresses and telephone numbers to sell to telemarketers and other mass marketers. During one week in January, OfficeMax offered a 100-pack of CD-ROMs (regular price $29.99 minus $10 instant rebate, $12 manufacturer's rebate, and

$8 OfficeMax mail-in rebate). The number of packages was limited, and no rain checks were issued. In all OfficeMax stores, 2,800 packages were in stock. All were sold. A random sample of 122 buyers was undertaken. Each was asked to report the total value of the other purchases made that day. Estimate with 95% confidence the total spent on other products purchased by those who bought the CD-ROMs.

12.36 **Xr12-36** An increasing number of North Americans regularly take vitamins or herbal remedies daily. To gauge this phenomenon, a random sample of Americans was asked to report the number of vitamin and herbal supplements they take daily. Estimate with 95% confidence the mean number of vitamin and herbal supplements Americans take daily.

12.37 **Xr12-37** Generic drug sales make up about half of all prescriptions sold in the United States. The marketing manager for a pharmaceutical company wanted to acquire more information about the sales of generic prescription drugs. To do so, she randomly sampled 475 customers who recently filled prescriptions for generic drugs and recorded the cost of each prescription. Estimate with 95% confidence the mean cost of all generic prescription drugs.

Source: Adapted from the *Statistical Abstract of the United States*, 2012, Table 159.

12.38 **Xr12-38** Traffic congestion seems to worsen each year. This raises the question, How much does roadway congestion cost the United States annually? The Federal Highway Administration's Highway Performance Monitoring System conducts an analysis to produce an estimate of the total cost. Drivers in the 99 most congested areas in the United States were sampled and for each driver the congestion cost in time and gasoline was recorded. The total number of drivers in these 99 areas was 171,000,000. Estimate with 95% confidence the total cost of congestion in the 99 areas.

Source: Adapted from the *Statistical Abstract of the United States*, 2012, Table 1099.

12.39 **Xr12-39** To help estimate the size of the disposable razor market, a random sample of men was asked to count the number of shaves they used each razor for. Assume that each razor is used once per day. Estimate with 95% confidence the number of days a pack of 10 razors will last.

12.40 **Xr12-40** Because of the enormity of the viewing audience, firms that advertise during the Super Bowl create special commercials that tend to be quite entertaining. Thirty-second commercials cost several million dollars during the Super Bowl game. A random sample of people who watched the game was asked how many commercials they watched in their entirety.

Do these data allow us to infer that the mean number of commercials watched is greater than 15?

12.41 **Xr12-41** On a per capita basis, the United States spends far more on health than any other country. To help assess the costs, annual surveys are undertaken. One such survey asks a sample of Americans to report the number of times they visited a health care professional in the year. The data for 2009 (latest year available) were recorded. In 2009, the United States population was 307,439,000. Estimate with 95% confidence the total number of visits to a health care professional.

Source: Adapted from the *Statistical Abstract of the United States*, 2012, Table 166.

12.42 **Xr12-42** Companies that sell groceries over the Internet are called *e-grocers*. Customers enter their orders, pay by credit card, and receive delivery by truck. A potential e-grocer analyzed the market and determined that the average order would have to exceed $85 if the e-grocer were to be profitable. To determine whether an e-grocery would be profitable in one large city, she offered the service and recorded the size of the order for a random sample of customers. Can we infer from these data that an e-grocery will be profitable in this city?

12.43 **Xr12-43** During the last decade, many institutions dedicated to improving the quality of products and services in the United States have been formed. Many of these groups annually give awards to companies that produce high-quality goods and services. An investor believes that publicly traded companies that win awards are likely to outperform companies that do not win such awards. To help determine his return on investment in such companies, he took a random sample of 83 firms that won quality awards the previous year and computed the annual return he would have received had he invested. The investor would like an estimate of the returns he can expect. A 95% confidence level is deemed appropriate.

12.44 **Xr12-44** In 2010, most Canadian cities were experiencing a housing boom. As a consequence, home buyers were required to borrow more on their mortgages. To determine the extent of this problem, a survey of Canadian households was undertaken wherein household heads were asked to report their total debt. Assuming that there are 7 million households in Canada, estimate with 95% confidence the total household debt.

12.45 **Xr12-45** Refer to Exercise 12.44. In addition to household debt, the survey asked each household to report the debt-to-income ratio. Estimate with 90% confidence the mean debt-to-income ratio.

12.46 Xr12-46 Approximately 70% of students graduating from a 4-year program have student loan debt. To examine the problem, a random sample of graduates of 4-year colleges was taken and the amount of indebtedness was recorded. There are 43.3 million Americans with student loans. Estimate with 95% confidence the total amount owed by graduates with student loans.

12.47 Xr12-47 In another study on student loan indebtedness, a random sample of graduates 20–30 years old were asked the amount they paid monthly on their loans. Estimate with 99% confidence the mean monthly payment.

12.48 Xr12-48 A tax preparation company compiled the taxable income of a random sample of waiters and waitresses. The taxable income was based on their pay stubs from the restaurant where each worked.
   a. Estimate with 95% confidence the mean taxable income of waiters and waitresses.
   b. If we assume that each waiter and waitresses earns an additional 10% in tips, estimate the adjusted mean taxable income of waiters and waitresses.

12.49 Xr12-49 In the next 10 years, there will be the largest intergenerational wealth transfer in Canadian history, and the amount will likely grow over the next decade. There are 2.5 million Canadians 75 and older and when they pass on their sons, daughters, and grandchildren will inherit. To determine the size of the transfer, a random sample of Canadians 75 and older were asked for their net worth. Estimate with 95% confidence the total amount that will be transferred.

12.50 Xr12-50 Each year the Internal Revenue Service of the United States issues a migration report that shows how many tax filers moved from one state to another. In an effort to answer the question of why so many people are moving from states that usually vote for Democrats (so-called blue states) to states that usually elect Republicans (red states) an economist conducted a study. In the study, the economist learned that 112,236 tax filers left the state of New York. A random sample recorded the amount of money and potential taxable income of the emigrants from New York. Estimate with 95% confidence the total amount that left New York.

12.51 Xr12-51* It is a long-running joke that Britons have bad and missing teeth. However, Americans' dental problems may be worse. In a study reported in the *British Medical Journal* a random sample of Americans was drawn and the number of missing teeth was recorded. Estimate with 95% confidence the mean number of missing teeth in American adults.

12.52 Xr12-52 In the United States as well as most other countries, the income tax is progressive in that richer people pay not only more in absolute terms but more in percentage as well. Other taxes are regressive. One such tax is the tax on beer, wine, and liquor. To examine this issue, the National Center for Policy Analysis undertook a study of how much lower-income earners who purchase alcohol spend on beer, wine, and liquor. Estimate with 90% confidence the mean annual expenditures on alcohol by lower-income Americans.

12.53 Xr12-53 Last year 24 million Canadians made donations to charitable or nonprofit organizations. A random sample of donors was drawn and the amount of each respondent's donation was recorded. Estimate with 95% confidence the total donated by all Canadian donors.

GENERAL SOCIAL SURVEY EXERCISES

Conduct all tests at the 5% significance level. Use a 95% confidence level for all estimates.

12.54 GSS2014* The survey asked respondents to report the number of persons in the household who are related to the respondent and who earned any money from any job or employment (EARNRS).

   a. Estimate the mean number of earners per household in the United States.
   b. What is the required condition for your answer to part (a)?
   c. Is the required condition satisfied? Explain.

12.55 GSS2014* To help make a decision about how to advertise for a particular product, a marketing manager hypothesized that the average American had completed high school (To complete high school, one needs to complete grade 12).

a. Conduct an appropriate test on years of education (EDUC).

b. Is the required condition satisfied? Explain.

12.56 GSS2014*   Americans are getting married (if at all) at a higher age than in the past. A marketing manager for a baby food maker wanted an estimate of how old are Americans when they have their first child (AGEKDBRN). Estimate the mean and describe whether the required condition is satisfied.

12.57 GSS2014*   When the economy is healthy many firms ask their employees to put in overtime, which usually means working more than 40 hours per week. Is the average working American working for more than 40 hours per week (HRS1)?

a. Conduct a test to answer the question.

b. What is the required condition for the validity of the test?

c. Is the required condition satisfied? Explain.

12.58 GSS2014*   How well were American families doing in 2014? One very good guide is total family income (INCOME). Estimate the income for the average American family.

SURVEY OF CONSUMER FINANCES EXERCISES

Conduct all tests at the 5% significance level and estimates with 95% confidence.

12.59 SCF2013:\MC*   Because to be in the middle class requires a net worth of at least $67,300, we would expect the average age (AGE) of middle-class American adults to be greater than the average age of all American adults, which is 50.4.

a. Conduct a test to determine whether there is enough evidence to support this expectation.

b. Is the required condition satisfied? Explain.

12.60 SCF2013:\MC*   How much money do middle-class Americans keep in their checking account (CHECKING)?

a. Estimate the mean amount held in checking accounts.

b. What is the required condition?

c. Is it satisfied?

12.61 SCF2013:\MC*   A large number of American families are invested in the stock market. Many have various pension plans that use contributed funds to buy stocks. Many others have directly held shares in the stock market.

a. Estimate the mean total value of stocks held directly by the household (STOCKS).

b. What is the required condition for the test in part (a)?

c. Is the required condition satisfied? Explain.

12.62 SCF2013:\MC*   There are a variety of ways in which households have debt. The largest is probably the mortgage on the home they live in. Others include student debt, vehicle loans, and credit card debt.

a. To determine how much debt is carried by middle-class American families estimate the mean debt (DEBT).

b. Is the required condition satisfied? If not, why not?

12.63 SCF2013:\MC*   There is no single definition of the middle class in the United States. For the purposes of analyzing the data from the Survey of Consumer Finances we have defined middle class on the basis of net worth. However, many economists define middle class on the basis of income. Analyze middle-class income by estimating the mean (INCOME).

12.64 SCF2013:\MC*   In 2013, the housing market started picking up. Were people getting themselves too much into debt and hoping that the price of their homes would increase? One way to judge is to determine the size of mortgages (NH_MORT). Estimate the amount owed on mortgages in middle-class households.

12.65 SCF2013:\MC*   In the United States, there is no capital gains on houses until the last one is sold. Up to that point any gains are considered unrealized capital gains or losses on primary residence. Estimate the capital gains on the primary residence for middle class households (KGHOUSE).

12.66 SCF2013:\MC*   According to the United Census the average expenditure for food away from home was $2625. Is there enough evidence to infer that the average middle-class households spends less (FOODAWAY)?

12.67 SCF2013:\MC*   The interest rates charged by credit card companies is so high that consumers are advised to pay off their credit card debt as quickly as possible. To see if people are following this advice, estimate the credit card balance held by middle-class households (CCBAL).

12.68 <u>SCF2013:\MC*</u> How well educated are people in middle-class households? According to the U.S. Census the average American adult has completed 12.9 years of schooling. Is there enough evidence to conclude that the average middle class head of household has more education (EDUC)?

12.69 <u>SCF2013:\MC*</u> Because interest paid by banks on money left in savings accounts is so low, people are advised to keep very little in these accounts. To determine if people are following that advice, estimate the amount of money kept in savings accounts by middle-class households (SAVING).

12-2 / INFERENCE ABOUT A POPULATION VARIANCE

In Section 12-1, where we presented the inferential methods about a population mean, we were interested in acquiring information about the central location of the population. As a result, we tested and estimated the population mean. If we are interested instead in drawing inferences about a population's variability, the parameter we need to investigate is the population variance σ^2. Inference about the variance can be used to make decisions in a variety of problems. In an example illustrating the use of the normal distribution in Section 8-2, we showed why variance is a measure of risk. In Section 7-3, we described an important application in finance wherein stock diversification was shown to reduce the variance of a portfolio and, in so doing, reduce the risk associated with that portfolio. In both sections, we assumed that the population variances were known. In this section, we take a more realistic approach and acknowledge that we need to use statistical techniques to draw inferences about a population variance.

Another application of the use of variance comes from operations management. Quality technicians attempt to ensure that their company's products consistently meet specifications. One way of judging the consistency of a production process is to compute the variance of a product's size, weight, or volume; that is, if the variation in size, weight, or volume is large, it is likely that an unsatisfactorily large number of products will lie outside the specifications for that product. We will return to this subject later in this book. In Section 14-6, we discuss how operations managers search for and reduce the variation in production processes.

The task of deriving the test statistic and the interval estimator provides us with another opportunity to show how statistical techniques in general are developed. We begin by identifying the best estimator. That estimator has a sampling distribution, from which we produce the test statistic and the interval estimator.

12-2a Statistic and Sampling Distribution

The estimator of σ^2 is the sample variance introduced in Section 4-2. The statistic s^2 has the desirable characteristics presented in Section 10-1; that is, s^2 is an unbiased, consistent estimator of σ^2.

Statisticians have shown that the sum of squared deviations from the mean $\sum (x_i - \bar{x})^2$ [which is equal to $(n-1)s^2$] divided by the population variance is chi-squared distributed with $\nu = n - 1$ degrees of freedom provided that the sampled population is normal. The statistic

$$\chi^2 = \frac{(n-1)s^2}{\sigma^2}$$

is called the **chi-squared statistic** (χ^2-statistic). The chi-squared distribution was introduced in Section 8-4.

12-2b Testing and Estimating a Population Variance

As we discussed in Section 11-4, the formula that describes the sampling distribution is the formula of the test statistic.

Test Statistic for σ^2

The test statistic used to test hypotheses about σ^2 is

$$\chi^2 = \frac{(n-1)s^2}{\sigma^2}$$

which is chi-squared distributed with $\nu = n - 1$ degrees of freedom when the population random variable is normally distributed with variance equal to σ^2.

Using the notation introduced in Section 8-4, we can make the following probability statement:

$$P(\chi^2_{1-\alpha/2} < \chi^2 < \chi^2_{\alpha/2}) = 1 - \alpha$$

Substituting

$$\chi^2 = \frac{(n-1)s^2}{\sigma^2}$$

and with some algebraic manipulation, we derive the confidence interval estimator of a population variance.

Confidence Interval Estimator of σ^2

$$\text{Lower confidence limit (LCL)} = \frac{(n-1)s^2}{\chi^2_{\alpha/2}}$$

$$\text{Upper confidence limit (UCL)} = \frac{(n-1)s^2}{\chi^2_{1-\alpha/2}}$$

APPLICATIONS in OPERATIONS MANAGEMENT

Quality

A critical aspect of production is quality. The quality of a final product is a function of the quality of the product's components. If the components don't fit, the product will not function as planned and likely cease functioning before its customers expect it to. For example, if a car door is not made to its specifications, it will not fit. As a result, the door will leak both water and air.

Operations managers attempt to maintain and improve the quality of products by ensuring that all components are made so that there is as little variation as possible. As you have already seen, statisticians measure variation by computing the variance.

Incidentally, an entire chapter (Chapter 21) is devoted to the topic of quality.

EXAMPLE **12.3**

Consistency of a Container-Filling Machine, Part 1

Container-filling machines are used to package a variety of liquids, including milk, soft drinks, and paint. Ideally, the amount of liquid should vary only slightly because large variations will cause some containers to be underfilled (cheating the customer) and some to be overfilled (resulting in costly waste). The president of a company that developed a new type of machine boasts that this machine can fill 1-liter (1,000 cubic centimeters) containers so consistently that the variance of the fills will be less than 1 cubic centimeter^2. To examine the veracity of the claim, a random sample of 25 l-liter fills was taken and the results (cubic centimeters) recorded. These data are listed here. Do these data allow the president to make this claim at the 5% significance level?

Fills

999.6	1000.7	999.3	1000.1	999.5
1000.5	999.7	999.6	999.1	997.8
1001.3	1000.7	999.4	1000.0	998.3
999.5	1000.1	998.3	999.2	999.2
1000.4	1000.1	1000.1	999.6	999.9

SOLUTION:

IDENTIFY

The problem objective is to describe the population of l-liter fills from this machine. The data are interval, and we're interested in the variability of the fills. It follows that the parameter of interest is the population variance. Because we want to determine whether there is enough evidence to support the claim, the alternative hypothesis is

$$H_1: \quad \sigma^2 < 1$$

The null hypothesis is

$$H_0: \quad \sigma^2 = 1$$

and the test statistic we will use is

$$\chi^2 = \frac{(n-1)s^2}{\sigma^2}$$

COMPUTE

MANUALLY:

Using a calculator, we find

$$\sum x_i = 24{,}992.0 \quad \text{and} \quad \sum x_i^2 = 24{,}984{,}017.76$$

Thus,

$$s^2 = \frac{\sum x_i^2 - \dfrac{\left(\sum x_i\right)^2}{n}}{n-1} = \frac{24{,}984{,}017.76 - \dfrac{(24{,}992.0)^2}{25}}{25-1} = .6333$$

The value of the test statistic is

$$\chi^2 = \frac{(n-1)s^2}{\sigma^2} = \frac{(25-1)(.6333)}{1} = 15.20$$

The rejection region is

$$\chi^2 < \chi^2_{1-\alpha, n-1} = \chi^2_{1-.05, 25-1} = \chi^2_{.95, 24} = 13.85$$

Because 15.20 is not less than 13.85, we cannot reject the null hypothesis in favor of the alternative.

EXCEL Workbook

	A	B	C	D
1	Chi-squared Test of a Variance			
2				
3	Sample variance	0.6333	Chi-squared Stat	15.20
4	Sample size	25	P(CHI<=chi) one-tail	0.0852
5	Hypothesized variance	1	chi-squared Critical one-tail	36.42
6	Alpha	0.05	P(CHI<=chi) two-tail	0.1704
7			chi-squared Critical two-tail	12.40
8				39.36

INSTRUCTIONS

1. Type or import the data into one column. (Open Xm12-03.) In any empty cell, calculate the sample variance (=VAR(A1:A26).

2. Open the **Test Statistics Workbook** and click the **Chi-squared Test_Variance** tab. Type or copy the sample variance. Type the value of n, the value of σ^2 under the null hypothesis, and the value of α.

XLSTAT

	A	B	C	D	E	F
1	Theoretical variance: 1					
2	Significance level (%): 5					
3						
4	Summary statistics:					
5	Variable	Observations	Minimum	Maximum	Mean	Std. deviation
6	Fills	25	997.8	1001.3	999.68	0.80
7						
8	One-sample variance test / Lower-tailed test:					
9	Variance	0.633				
10	Chi-square (Observed value)	15.20				
11	Chi-square (Critical value)	13.85				
12	p-value (one-tailed)	0.0852				
13	alpha	0.05				

INSTRUCTIONS

1. Type or import the data into one column. (Open Xm12-03.)

2. Click **XLSTAT**, **Parametric tests**, and **One-sample variance test**.

3. In the **Data:** dialog box type the input range (A1:A26).

4. Click the **Options** tab and choose **Variance 1 < Theoretical variance** in the **Alternative hypothesis** box. Type the **Theoretical variance** (1) and the value of α (in percent) in the **Significance level (%)** box (5).

There is not enough evidence to infer that the claim is true. As we discussed before, the result does not say that the variance is equal to 1; it merely states that we are unable to show that the variance is less than 1. Figure 12.4 depicts the sampling distribution of the test statistic.

FIGURE **12.4** **Sampling Distribution for Example 12.3**

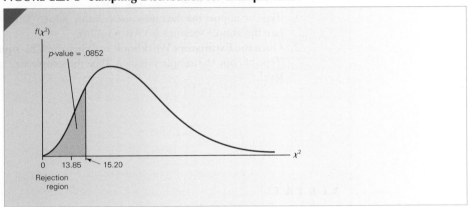

EXAMPLE 12.4

Consistency of a Container-Filling Machine, Part 2

Estimate with 99% confidence the variance of fills in Example 12.3.

SOLUTION:

COMPUTE

MANUALLY:

In the solution to Example 12.3, we found $(n - 1)s^2$ to be 15.20. From Table 5 in Appendix B, we find

$$\chi^2_{\alpha/2, n-1} = \chi^2_{.005, 24} = 45.6$$

$$\chi^2_{1-\alpha/2, n-1} = \chi^2_{.995, 24} = 9.89$$

Thus,

$$\text{LCL} = \frac{(n-1)s^2}{\chi^2_{\alpha/2}} = \frac{15.20}{45.6} = .3333$$

$$\text{UCL} = \frac{(n-1)s^2}{\chi^2_{1-\alpha/2}} = \frac{15.20}{9.89} = 1.537$$

We estimate that the variance of fills is a number that lies between .3333 and 1.537.

EXCEL Workbook

	A	B	C	D
1	Chi-Squared Estimate of a Variance			
2				
3	Sample variance	0.6333	Confidence Interval Estimate	
4	Sample size	25	Lower confidence limit	0.3336
5	Confidence level	0.99	Upper confidence limit	1.5374

INSTRUCTIONS

1. Type or import the data into one column. (Open Xm12-03.) In any empty cell, calculate the sample variance (=VAR(A1:A26).
2. Open the **Estimators Workbook** and click the **Chi-squared Estimate_Variance** tab. Type or copy the sample variance. Type the sample size and the value of the confidence level.

XLSTAT

	B	C	D	E
11	99% confidence interval on the variance:			
12	0.334	1.537		

INSTRUCTIONS

1. Type or import the data into one column. (Open Xm12-03.)
2. Click **XLSTAT**, **Parametric tests**, and **One-sample variance test**.
3. In the **Data:** dialog box type the input range (A1:A26).
4. Click the **Options** tab and choose **Variance 1 ≠ Theoretical variance** in the **Alternative hypothesis** box. Type the value of α (in percent) in the **Significance level (%)** box (1).

INTERPRET

In Example 12.3, we saw that there was not sufficient evidence to infer that the population variance is less than 1. Here we see that σ^2 is estimated to lie between .3336 and 1.5375. Part of this interval is above 1, which tells us that the variance may be larger than 1, confirming the conclusion we reached in Example 12.3. We may be able to use the estimate to predict the percentage of overfilled and underfilled bottles. This may allow us to choose among competing machines.

12-2c Checking the Required Condition

Like the t-test and estimator of μ introduced in Section 12-1, the chi-squared test and estimator of σ^2 theoretically require that the sample population be normal. In practice, however, the technique is valid so long as the population is not extremely nonnormal. We can gauge the extent of nonnormality by drawing the histogram as shown in Figure 12.5. As you can see, the fills appear to be somewhat asymmetric. However the variable does not appear to be very nonnormal. We conclude that the normality requirement is not seriously violated.

FIGURE **12.5** **Histogram for Examples 12.3 and 12.4**

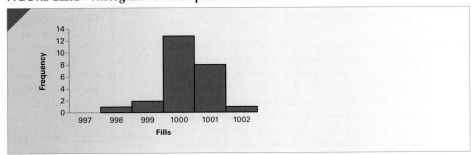

Here is how we recognize when to use the techniques introduced in this section.

Factors That Identify the Chi-Squared Test and Estimator of σ^2

1. **Problem objective**: Describe a population
2. **Data type**: Interval
3. **Type of descriptive measurement**: Variability

EXERCISES

Developing an Understanding of Statistical Concepts

The following three exercises are "what-if analyses" designed to determine what happens to the test statistics and interval estimates when elements of the statistical inference change. These problems can be solved manually or using the Excel spreadsheets.

12.70 a. A random sample of 100 observations was drawn from a normal population. The sample variance was calculated to be $s^2 = 220$. Test with $\alpha = .05$ to determine whether we can infer that the population variance differs from 300.

    b. Repeat Part a changing the sample size to 50.

    c. What is the effect of decreasing the sample size?

12.71 a. The sample variance of a random sample of 50 observations from a normal population was found to be $s^2 = 80$. Can we infer at the 1% significance level that σ^2 is less than 100?

b. Repeat part (a) increasing the sample size to 100.

c. What is the effect of increasing the sample size?

12.72 a. Estimate σ^2 with 90% confidence given that $n = 15$ and $s^2 = 12$.

b. Repeat part (a) with $n = 30$.

c. What is the effect of increasing the sample size?

Applications

12.73 **Xr12-73** The weights of a random sample of cereal boxes that are supposed to weigh 1 pound are listed here. Estimate the variance of the entire population of cereal box weights with 90% confidence.

1.05   1.03   .98   1.00   .99   .97   1.01   .96

12.74 **Xr12-74** After many years of teaching, a statistics professor computed the variance of the marks on her final exam and found it to be $\sigma^2 = 250$. She recently made changes to the way in which the final exam is marked and wondered whether this would result in a reduction in the variance. A random sample of this year's final exam marks are listed here. Can the professor infer at the 10% significance level that the variance has decreased?

57   92   99   73   62   64   75   70   88   60

12.75 **Xr12-75** With gasoline prices increasing, drivers are more concerned with their cars' gasoline consumption. For the past 5 years a driver has tracked the gas mileage of his car and found that the variance from fill-up to fill-up was $\sigma^2 = 23$ mpg². Now that his car is 5 years old, he would like to know whether the variability of gas mileage has changed. He recorded the gas mileage from his last eight fill-ups; these are listed here. Conduct a test at a 10% significance level to infer whether the variability has changed.

28   25   29   25   32   36   27   24

12.76 **Xr12-76** During annual checkups physicians routinely send their patients to medical laboratories to have various tests performed. One such test determines the cholesterol level in patients' blood. However, not all tests are conducted in the same way. To acquire more information, a man was sent to 10 laboratories and had his cholesterol level measured in each. The results are listed here. Estimate with 95% confidence the variance of these measurements.

188   193   186   184   190   195   187   190   192   196

The following exercises require the use of a computer and software. The answers may be calculated manually. See Appendix A for the sample statistics.

12.77 **Xr12-77** One important factor in inventory control is the variance of the daily demand for the product. A management scientist has developed the optimal order quantity and reorder point, assuming that the variance is equal to 250. Recently, the company has experienced some inventory problems, which induced the operations manager to doubt the assumption. To examine the problem, the manager took a sample of 25 days and recorded the demand.

a. Do these data provide sufficient evidence at the 5% significance level to infer that the management scientist's assumption about the variance is wrong?

b. What is the required condition for the statistical procedure in Part a?

c. Does it appear that the required condition is not satisfied?

12.78 **Xr12-78** Some traffic experts believe that the major cause of highway collisions is the differing speeds of cars. That is, when some cars are driven slowly while others are driven at speeds well in excess of the speed limit, cars tend to congregate in bunches, increasing the probability of accidents. Thus, the greater the variation in speeds, the greater will be the number of collisions that occur. Suppose that one expert believes that when the variance exceeds 18 mph², the number of accidents will be unacceptably high. A random sample of the speeds of 245 cars on a highway with one of the highest accident rates in the country is taken. Can we conclude at the 10% significance level that the variance in speeds exceeds 18 mph²?

12.79 **Xr12-79** The job placement service at a university observed the not unexpected result of the variance in marks and work experience of the university's graduates: Some graduates received numerous offers whereas others received far fewer. To learn more about the problem, a survey of 90 recent graduates was conducted wherein each was asked how many job offers they received. Estimate with 90% confidence the variance in the number of job offers made to the university's graduates.

12.80 **Xr12-80** One problem facing the manager of maintenance departments is when to change the bulbs in streetlamps. If bulbs are changed only when they burn out, it is quite costly to send crews out to change only one bulb at a time. This method also requires someone to report the problem and, in the meantime, the light is off. If each bulb lasts approximately the same amount of time, they can all be replaced periodically, producing significant cost savings in maintenance. Suppose that a financial analysis of the lights at Yankee Stadium has concluded that it will pay to replace all of the light bulbs at the same time if the variance of the lives of the bulbs is less than 200 hours^2. The lengths of life of the last 100 bulbs were recorded. What conclusion can be drawn from these data? Use a 5% significance level.

12.81 <u>Xr12-81</u> Home blood-pressure monitors have been on the market for several years. This device allows people with high blood pressure to measure their own and determine whether additional medication is necessary. Concern has been expressed about inaccurate readings. To judge the severity of the problem a laboratory technician measured his own blood pressure 25 times using the leading brand of monitors. Estimate the population variance with 95% confidence.

12-3 / INFERENCE ABOUT A POPULATION PROPORTION

In this section, we continue to address the problem of describing a population. However, we shift our attention to populations of nominal data, which means that the population consists of nominal or categorical values. For example, in a brand-preference survey in which the statistics practitioner asks consumers of a particular product which brand they purchase, the values of the random variable are the brands. If there are five brands, the values could be represented by their names, by letters (A, B, C, D, and E), or by numbers (1, 2, 3, 4, and 5). When numbers are used, it should be understood that the numbers only represent the name of the brand, are completely arbitrarily assigned, and cannot be treated as real numbers—that is, we cannot calculate means and variances.

12-3a Parameter

Recall the discussion of types of data in Chapter 2. When the data are nominal, all that we are permitted to do to describe the population or sample is count the number of occurrences of each value. From the counts, we calculate proportions. Thus, the parameter of interest in describing a population of nominal data is the population proportion p. In Section 7-4, this parameter was used to calculate probabilities based on the binomial experiment. One of the characteristics of the binomial experiment is that there are only two possible outcomes per trial. Most practical applications of inference about p involve more than two outcomes. However, in many cases we're interested in only one outcome, which we label a "success." All other outcomes are labeled as "failures." For example, in brand-preference surveys we are interested in our company's brand. In political surveys, we wish to estimate or test the proportion of voters who will vote for one particular candidate—likely the one who has paid for the survey.

12-3b Statistic and Sampling Distribution

The logical statistic used to estimate and test the population proportion is the sample proportion defined as

$$\hat{p} = \frac{x}{n}$$

where x is the number of successes in the sample and n is the sample size. In Section 9-2, we presented the approximate sampling distribution of $\hat{P}$. (The actual distribution is based on the binomial distribution, which does not lend itself to statistical inference.) The sampling distribution of $\hat{P}$ is approximately normal with mean p and standard deviation $\sqrt{p(1 - p/n)}$ [provided that np and $n(1 - p)$ are greater than 5]. We express this sampling distribution as

$$z = \frac{\hat{P} - p}{\sqrt{p(1 - p)/n}}$$

12-3c Testing and Estimating a Proportion

As you have already seen, the formula that summarizes the sampling distribution also represents the test statistic.

Test Statistic for p

$$z = \frac{\hat{P} - p}{\sqrt{p(1 - p)/n}}$$

which is approximately normal when np and $n(1 - p)$ are greater than 5.

Using the same algebra employed in Sections 10-2 and 12-1, we attempt to derive the confidence interval estimator of p from the sampling distribution. The result is

$$\hat{p} \pm z_{\alpha/2}\sqrt{p(1 - p)/n}$$

This formula, although technically correct, is useless. To understand why, examine the standard error of the sampling distribution $\sqrt{p(1 - p)/n}$. To produce the interval estimate, we must compute the standard error, which requires us to know the value of p, the parameter we wish to estimate. This is the first of several statistical techniques where we face the same problem: how to determine the value of the standard error. In this application, the problem is easily and logically solved: Simply estimate the value of p with $\hat{p}$.

Thus, we estimate the standard error with $\sqrt{\hat{p}(1 - \hat{p})/n}$.

Confidence Interval Estimator of p

$$\hat{p} \pm z_{\alpha/2}\sqrt{\hat{p}(1 - \hat{p})/n}$$

which is valid provided that $n\hat{p}$ and $n(1 - \hat{p})$ are greater than 5.

EXAMPLE 12.5

DATA
Xm12-05*

Election Day Exit Poll

When an election for political office takes place, the television networks cancel regular programming and instead provide election coverage. When the ballots are counted, the results are reported. However, for important offices such as president or senator in large states, the networks actively compete to see which will be the first to predict a winner. This is done through exit polls,* wherein a random sample of voters who exit the polling booth is asked for whom they voted. From the data, the sample proportion of voters supporting the candidates is computed. A statistical technique is applied to determine whether there is enough evidence to infer that the leading candidate will garner enough votes to win. Suppose that in the exit poll from the state of Florida during the 2000 year elections, the pollsters recorded only the votes of the two candidates who had any chance of winning, Democrat Albert Gore (code = 1) and Republican George W. Bush (code = 2). The polls close at 8:00 P.M. Can the networks conclude from these data that the Republican candidate will win the state? Should the network announce at 8:01 P.M. that the Republican candidate will win?

SOLUTION:

IDENTIFY

The problem objective is to describe the population of votes in the state. The data are nominal because the values are "Democrat" (code = 1) and "Republican" (code = 2). Thus the parameter to be tested is the proportion of votes in the entire state that are for the Republican candidate. Because we want to determine whether the network can declare the Republican to be the winner at 8:01 P.M., the alternative hypothesis is

$$H_1: \quad p > .5$$

which makes the null hypothesis

$$H_0: \quad p = .5$$

The test statistic is

$$z = \frac{\hat{p} - p}{\sqrt{p(1 - p)/n}}$$

COMPUTE

MANUALLY:

It appears that this is a "standard" problem that requires a 5% significance level. Thus, the rejection region is

$$z > z_\alpha = z_{.05} = 1.645$$

---

*Warren Mitofsky is generally credited for creating the election day exit poll in 1967 when he worked for CBS News. Mitofsky claimed to have correctly predicted 2,500 elections and only six wrong. Exit polls are considered so accurate that when the exit poll and the actual election result differ, some newspaper and television reporters claim that the election result is wrong! In the 2004 presidential election, exit polls showed John Kerry leading. However, when the ballots were counted, George Bush won the state of Ohio. Conspiracy theorists now believe that the Ohio election was stolen by the Republicans using the exit poll as their "proof." However, Mitofsky's own analysis found that the exit poll was improperly conducted, resulting in many Republican voters refusing to participate in the poll. Blame was placed on poorly trained interviewers (*Source: Amstat News*, December 2006).

From the file, we count the number of "successes," which is the number of votes cast for the Republican, and find $x = 407$. The sample size is 765. Hence, the sample proportion is

$$\hat{p} = \frac{x}{n} = \frac{407}{765} = .532$$

The value of the test statistic is

$$z = \frac{\hat{p} - p}{\sqrt{p(1-p)/n}} = \frac{.532 - .5}{\sqrt{.5(1-.5)/765}} = 1.77$$

Because the test statistic is (approximately) normally distributed, we can determine the p-value. It is

$$p\text{-value} = P(Z > 1.77) = 1 - p(Z < 1.77) = 1 - .9616 = .0384$$

There is enough evidence at the 5% significance level that the Republican candidate has won.

EXCEL Workbook

	A	B	C	D
1	z-Test of a Proportion			
2				
3	Sample proportion	0.532	z Stat	1.77
4	Sample size	765	P(Z<=z) one-tail	0.0384
5	Hypothesized proportion	0.5	z Critical one-tail	1.6449
6	Alpha	0.05	P(Z<=z) two-tail	0.0767
7			z Critical two-tail	1.9600

INSTRUCTIONS

1. Type or import the data into one column. (Open Xm12-05.) In any empty cell, calculate the number of "successes" (=COUNTIF A1:A766,2). Divide that number by the sample size to obtain the sample proportion.
2. Open the **Test Statistics Workbook** and click the **z-Test_Proportion** tab. Type or copy the sample proportion. Type the sample size, the value of p under the null hypothesis, and the value of α.

XLSTAT

	A	B
1	Proportion: 0.532	
2	Sample size: 765	
3	Test proportion: 0.5	
4	Hypothesized difference (D): 0	
5	Significance level (%): 5	
6		
7	z-test for one proportion / Upper-tailed test:	
8	Difference	0.032
9	z (Observed value)	1.77
10	z (Critical value)	1.645
11	p-value (one-tailed)	0.0384
12	alpha	0.05

1. Type or import the data into one column. (Open Xm12-05.) In any empty cell, calculate the number of "successes" (=COUNTIF A1:A766,2). Divide that number by the sample size to obtain the sample proportion.

2. Click **XLSTAT**, **Parametric tests**, and **Tests for one proportion**.

   Author's note: We find XLSTAT's terminology confusing. However, these instructions will produce the correct result.

3. Type the sample **Proportion:** (.532), the **Sample size:** (765), and the value of p under the null hypothesis – **Test proportion:** (.5). Under **Data format:** check **Proportion**. Click **z test**.

4. Click the **Options** tab and choose **Proportion – Test proportion > D**. Type the **Hypothesized difference (D):** (0) and type the **Significance level (%)** (5).

INTERPRET

The value of the test statistic is $z = 1.77$ and the one-tail p-value $= .0382$. Using a 5% significance level, we reject the null hypothesis and conclude that there is enough evidence to infer that George Bush won the presidential election in the state of Florida.

One of the key issues to consider here is the cost of Type I and Type II errors. A Type I error occurs if we conclude that the Republican will win when in fact he has lost. Such an error would mean that a network would announce at 8:01 P.M. that the Republican has won and then later in the evening would have to admit to a mistake. If a particular network were the only one that made this error, it would cast doubt on their integrity and possibly affect the number of viewers.

This is exactly what happened on the evening of the U.S. presidential elections in November 2000. Shortly after the polls closed at 8:00 P.M., all the networks declared that the Democratic candidate Albert Gore would win the state of Florida. A couple of hours later, the networks admitted that a mistake had been made and that Republican candidate George W. Bush had won. Several hours later, they again admitted a mistake and finally declared the race too close to call. Fortunately for each network, all the networks made the same mistake. However, if one network had not done this, it would have developed a better track record, which could have been used in future advertisements for news shows and would likely draw more viewers.

12-3d Missing Data

In real statistical applications, we occasionally find that the data set is incomplete. In some instances, the statistics practitioner may have failed to properly record some observations or some data may have been lost. In other cases, respondents may refuse to answer. For example, in political surveys where the statistics practitioner asks voters for whom they intend to vote in the next election, some people will answer that they haven't decided or that their vote is confidential and refuse to answer. In surveys where respondents are asked to report their income, people often refuse to divulge this information. This is a troublesome issue for statistics practitioners. We can't force people to answer our questions. However, if the number of nonresponses is high, the results of our analysis may be invalid because the sample is no longer truly random. To understand why, suppose that people who are in the top quarter of household incomes regularly refuse to answer questions about their incomes. The resulting estimate of the population household income mean will be lower than the actual value.

The issue can be complicated. There are several ways to compensate for non-responses. The simplest method is eliminating them. To illustrate, suppose that in a political survey respondents are asked for whom they intend to vote in a two-candidate race. Surveyors record the results as 1 = Candidate A, 2 = Candidate B, 3 = "Don't know," and 4 = "Refuse to say." If we wish to infer something about the proportion of decided voters who will vote for Candidate A, we can simply omit codes 3 and 4. If we're doing the work manually, we will count the number of voters who prefer Candidate A and the number who prefer Candidate B. The sum of these two numbers is the total sample size.

In the language of statistical software, nonresponses that we wish to eliminate are collectively called *missing data*. Software packages deal with missing data in different ways. The online appendix Excel and Minitab Instructions for Missing Data and Recoding Data describes how to address the problem of missing data in Excel and in Minitab as well as how to recode data.

We have deleted the nonresponses in the General Social Surveys (The Survey of Consumer Finances used a statistical technique to estimate the missing data.) In Excel, the nonresponses appear as blanks.

12-3e Estimating the Total Number of Successes in a Large Finite Population

As was the case with the inference about a mean, the techniques in this section assume infinitely large populations. When the populations are small, it is necessary to include the finite population correction factor. In our definition a population is small when it is less than 20 times the sample size. When the population is large and finite, we can estimate the total number of successes in the population.

To produce the confidence interval estimator of the total, we multiply the lower and upper confidence limits of the interval estimator of the proportion of successes by the population size. The confidence interval estimator of the total number of successes in a large finite population is

$$N\left(\hat{p} \pm z_{\alpha/2}\sqrt{\frac{\hat{p}(1 - \hat{p})}{n}} \right)$$

We will use this estimator in the chapter-opening example and several of this section's exercises.

12-3f Selecting the Sample Size to Estimate the Proportion

When we introduced the sample size selection method to estimate a mean in Section 10-3, we pointed out that the sample size depends on the confidence level and the bound on the error of estimation that the statistics practitioner is willing to tolerate. When the parameter to be estimated is a proportion, the bound on the error of estimation is

$$B = z_{\alpha/2}\sqrt{\frac{\hat{p}(1 - \hat{p})}{n}}$$

Solving for n, we produce the required sample size as indicated in the box.

Nielsen Ratings: Solution

IDENTIFY

The problem objective is to describe the population of television shows watched by viewers across the country. The data are nominal. The combination of problem objective and data type make the parameter to be estimated the proportion of the entire population of 18- to 49-year-olds that watched *Big Bang Theory* (code = 2). The confidence interval estimator of the proportion is:

$$\hat{p} \pm z_{\alpha/2}\sqrt{\frac{\hat{p}(1 - \hat{p})}{n}}$$

COMPUTE

MANUALLY:

To solve manually, we count the number of 2's in the file. We find this value to be 275. Thus,

$$\hat{p} = \frac{x}{n} = \frac{275}{5{,}000} = .0550$$

The confidence level is $1 - \alpha = .95$. It follows that $\alpha = .05$, $\alpha/2 = .025$, and $z_{\alpha/2} = z_{.025} = 1.96$. The 95% confidence interval estimate of p is:

$$\hat{p} \pm z_{\alpha/2}\sqrt{\frac{\hat{p}(1 - \hat{p})}{n}} = .0550 \pm 1.96\sqrt{\frac{(.0550)(1 - .0550)}{5{,}000}} = .0550 \pm .0063$$

$$\text{LCL} = .0487 \qquad \text{UCL} = .0613$$

EXCEL Workbook

	A	B	C	D	E
1	z-Estimate of a Proportion				
2					
3	Sample proportion	0.055	Confidence Interval Estimate		
4	Sample size	5000	0.055	±	0.0063
5	Confidence level	0.95	Lower confidence limit		0.0487
6			Upper confidence limit		0.0613

INSTRUCTIONS

1. Type or import the data into one column. (Open Xm12-00.) In any empty cell, calculate the number of "successes" (=COUNTIF A1:A5001, 2). Divide that number by the sample size to obtain sample proportion.

2. Open the **Estimators Workbook** and click the **z-Estimate_Proportion** tab. Type or copy the sample proportion. Type the value of the sample size and the value of α.

XLSTAT

	A	B	C	D	E
1	Proportion: 0.055				
2	Sample size: 5000				
3					
4	95% confidence interval on the proportion (Wald):				
5	0.0487	0.0613			

(*Continued*)

INSTRUCTIONS

1. Type or import the data into one column. (Open Xm12-00.) In any empty cell, calculate the number of "successes" (=COUNTIF A1:A5001,2). Divide that number by the sample size to obtain the sample proportion.

2. Click **XLSTAT**, **Parametric tests**, and **Tests for one proportion**.

3. Type the sample **Proportion:** (.0550), the **Sample size:** (5000), and any **Test proportion:** (This value will not affect the confidence interval estimate.) Under **Data format:** check **Proportion**. Click **z test**.

4. Click the **Options** tab and choose **Proportion – Test proportion ≠ D**. Type any **Hypothesized difference (D)**. (This too will not affect the confidence interval estimate). Type the **Significance level (%)** (5). Under the heading **Variance (confidence interval)**, click **Sample** and under **Confidence interval**, click **Wald**.

INTERPRET

We estimate that between 4.87% and 6.13% of all Americans who were between 18 and 49 years old were watching *Big Bang Theory* on Thursday, March 7, 2013, at 8:00 P.M. to 8:30 P.M. If we multiply these figures by the total number of Americans who were between 18 and 49 years old, 126.540 million, we produce an interval estimate of the number of American adults 18–49 were watching *Big Bang Theory*. Thus,

LCL = .0487 × 126.54 million = 6.16 million

and

UCL = .0613 × 126.54 million = 7.76 million

Sponsoring companies can then determine the value of any commercials that appeared on the show.

Sample Size to Estimate a Proportion

$$n = \left(\frac{z_{\alpha/2}\sqrt{\hat{p}(1 - \hat{p})}}{B} \right)^2$$

To illustrate the use of this formula, suppose that in a brand-preference survey we want to estimate the proportion of consumers who prefer our company's brand to within .03 with 95% confidence. This means that the bound on the error of estimation is $B = .03$. Because $1 - \alpha = .95$, $\alpha = .05$, $\alpha/2 = .025$, and $z_{\alpha/2} = z_{.025} = 1.96$,

$$n = \left(\frac{1.96\sqrt{\hat{p}(1 - \hat{p})}}{.03} \right)^2$$

To solve for n, we need to know $\hat{p}$. Unfortunately, this value is unknown, because the sample has not yet been taken. At this point, we can use either of two methods to solve for n.

Method 1 If we have no knowledge of even the approximate value of $\hat{p}$, we let $\hat{p} = .5$. We choose $\hat{p} = .5$ because the product $\hat{p}(1 - \hat{p})$ equals its maximum value at $\hat{p} = .5$.

(Figure 12.6 illustrates this point.) This, in turn, results in a conservative value of n; as a result, the confidence interval will be no wider than the interval $\hat{p} \pm .03$. If, when the sample is drawn, $\hat{p}$ does not equal .5, the confidence interval estimate will be better (that is, narrower) than planned. Thus,

$$n = \left(\frac{1.96\sqrt{(.5)(.5)}}{.03}\right)^2 = (32.67)^2 = 1,068$$

If it turns out that $\hat{p} = .5$, the interval estimate is $\hat{p} \pm .03$. If not, the interval estimate will be narrower. For instance, if it turns out that $\hat{p} = .2$, then the estimate is $\hat{p} \pm .024$, which is better than we had planned.

FIGURE **12.6**   Plot of $\hat{p}$ versus $\hat{p}(1 - \hat{p})$

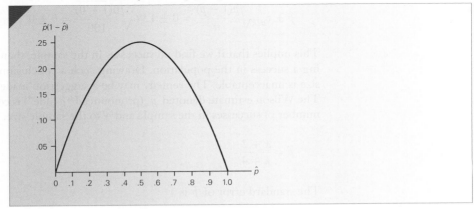

Method 2 If we have some idea about the value of $\hat{p}$, we can use that quantity to determine n. For example, if we believe that $\hat{p}$ will turn out to be approximately .2, we can solve for n as follows:

$$n = \left(\frac{1.96\sqrt{(.2)(.8)}}{.03}\right)^2 = (26.13)^2 = 683$$

Notice that this produces a smaller value of n (thus reducing sampling costs) than does method 1. If $\hat{p}$ actually lies between .2 and .8, however, the estimate will not be as good as we wanted, because the interval will be wider than desired.

Method 1 is often used to determine the sample size used in public opinion surveys reported by newspapers, magazines, television, and radio. These polls usually estimate proportions to within 3%, with 95% confidence. (The media often state the confidence level as "19 times out of 20.") If you've ever wondered why opinion polls almost always estimate proportions to within 3%, consider the sample size required to estimate a proportion to within 1%:

$$n = \left(\frac{1.96\sqrt{(.5)(.5)}}{.01}\right)^2 = (98)^2 = 9,604$$

The sample size 9,604 is 9 times the sample size needed to estimate a proportion to within 3%. Thus, to divide the width of the interval by 3 requires multiplying the sample size by 9. The cost would also increase considerably. For most applications, the increase in accuracy (created by decreasing the width of the confidence interval estimate) does not overcome the increased cost. Confidence interval estimates with 5% or 10% bounds (sample sizes 385 and 97, respectively) are generally considered too wide to be useful. Thus, the 3% bound provides a reasonable compromise between cost and accuracy.

12-3g Wilson Estimators (Optional)

When using the confidence interval estimator of a proportion when success is a relatively rare event, it is possible to find no successes, especially if the sample size is small. To illustrate, suppose that a sample of 100 produced $x = 0$, which means that $\hat{p} = 0$. The 95% confidence interval estimator of the proportion of successes in the population becomes

$$\hat{p} \pm z_{\alpha/2}\sqrt{\frac{\hat{p}(1 - \hat{p})}{n}} = 0 \pm 1.96\sqrt{\frac{0(1 - 0)}{100}} = 0 \pm 0$$

This implies that if we find no successes in the sample, then there is no chance of finding a success in the population. Drawing such a conclusion from virtually any sample size is unacceptable. The remedy may be a suggestion made by Edwin Wilson in 1927. The Wilson estimate denoted $\tilde{p}$ (pronounced "p tilde") is computed by adding 2 to the number of successes in the sample and 4 to the sample size. Thus,

$$\tilde{p} = \frac{x + 2}{n + 4}$$

The standard error of $\tilde{p}$ is

$$\sigma_{\tilde{p}} = \sqrt{\frac{\tilde{p}(1 - \tilde{p})}{n + 4}}$$

Confidence Interval Estimator of p Using the Wilson Estimate

$$\tilde{p} \pm z_{\alpha/2}\sqrt{\frac{\tilde{p}(1 - \tilde{p})}{n + 4}}$$

Exercises 12.100 To 12.102 require the use of this technique.

We complete this section by reviewing the factors that tell us when to test and estimate a population proportion.

Factors That Identify the z-Test and Interval Estimator of p

1. **Problem objective**: Describe a population
2. **Data type**: Nominal

EXERCISES

Developing an Understanding of Statistical Concepts

Exercises 12.82 to 12.85 are "what-if analyses" designed to determine what happens to the test statistics and interval estimates when elements of the statistical inference change. These problems can be solved manually or using an Excel spreadsheet.

12.82 a. In a random sample of 200 observations, we found the proportion of successes to be 48%. Estimate with 95% confidence the population proportion of successes.
b. Repeat part (a) with $n = 500$.
c. Repeat part (a) with $n = 1000$.
d. Describe the effect on the confidence interval estimate of increasing the sample size.

12.83 a. The proportion of successes in a random sample of 400 was calculated as 50%. Estimate the population proportion with 95% confidence.
b. Repeat part (a) with $\hat{p} = 33\%$.
c. Repeat part (a) with $\hat{p} = 10\%$.
d. Discuss the effect on the width of the confidence interval estimate of reducing the sample proportion.

12.84 a. Calculate the p-value of the test of the following hypotheses given that $\hat{p} = .63$ and $n = 100$:

$$H_0: \quad p = .60$$
$$H_1: \quad p > .60$$

b. Repeat part (a) with $n = 200$.
c. Repeat part (a) with $n = 400$.
d. Describe the effect on the p-value of increasing the sample size.

12.85 a. A statistics practitioner wants to test the following hypotheses:

$$H_0: \quad p = .70$$
$$H_1: \quad p > .70$$

A random sample of 100 produced $\hat{p} = .73$. Calculate the p-value of the test.
b. Repeat part (a) with $\hat{p} = .72$.
c. Repeat part (a) with $\hat{p} = .71$.
d. Describe the effect on the z-statistic and its p-value of decreasing the sample proportion.

12.86 Determine the sample size necessary to estimate a population proportion to within .03 with 90% confidence assuming you have no knowledge of the approximate value of the sample proportion.

12.87 Suppose that you used the sample size calculated in Exercise 12.86 and found $\hat{p} = .5$.
a. Estimate the population proportion with 90% confidence.
b. Is this the result you expected? Explain.

12.88 Suppose that you used the sample size calculated in Exercise 12.86 and found $\hat{p} = .75$.
a. Estimate the population proportion with 90% confidence.
b. Is this the result you expected? Explain.
c. If you were hired to conduct this analysis, would the person who hired you be satisfied with the interval estimate you produced? Explain.

12.89 Re-do Exercise 12.86 assuming that you know that the sample proportion will be no less than .75.

12.90 Suppose that you used the sample size calculated in Exercise 12.89 and found $\hat{p} = .75$.
a. Estimate the population proportion with 90% confidence.
b. Is this the result you expected? Explain.

12.91 Suppose that you used the sample size calculated in Exercise 12.89 and found $\hat{p} = .92$.
a. Estimate the population proportion with 90% confidence.
b. Is this the result you expected? Explain.
c. If you were hired to conduct this analysis, would the person who hired you be satisfied with the interval estimate you produced? Explain.

12.92 Suppose that you used the sample size calculated in Exercise 12.89 and found $\hat{p} = .5$.
a. Estimate the population proportion with 90% confidence.
b. Is this the result you expected? Explain.
c. If you were hired to conduct this analysis, would the person who hired you be satisfied with the interval estimate you produced? Explain.

Applications

12.93 A statistics practitioner working for major league baseball wants to supply radio and television commentators with interesting statistics. He observed several hundred games and counted the number of times a runner on first base attempted to steal second base. He found there were 373 such events of which 259 were successful. Estimate with 95% confidence the proportion of all attempted thefts of second base that are successful.

12.94 In some states, the law requires drivers to turn on their headlights when driving in the rain. A highway patrol officer believes that less than one-quarter of all drivers follow this rule. As a test, he randomly samples 200 cars driving in the rain and counts the number whose headlights are turned on. He finds this number to be 41. Does the officer have enough evidence at the 10% significance level to support his belief?

12.95 A dean of a business school wanted to know whether the graduates of her school used a statistical inference technique during their first year of employment after graduation. She surveyed 314 graduates and asked about the use of statistical techniques. After tallying up the responses, she found that 204 used statistical inference within one year of graduation. Estimate with 90% confidence the proportion of all business school graduates who use their statistical education within a year of graduation.

12.96 Has the recent drop in airplane passengers resulted in better on-time performance? Before the recent downturn one airline bragged that 92% of its flights were on time. A random sample of 165 flights completed this year reveals that 153 were on time. Can we conclude at the 5% significance level that the airline's on-time performance has improved?

12.97 What type of educational background do CEOs have? In one survey, 344 CEOs of medium and large companies were asked whether they had an MBA degree. There were 97 MBAs. Estimate with 95% confidence the proportion of all CEOs of medium and large companies who have MBAs.

12.98 The GO transportation system of buses and commuter trains operates on the honor system. Train travelers are expected to buy their tickets before boarding the train. Only a small number of people will be checked on the train to see whether they bought a ticket. Suppose that a random sample of 400 train travelers was sampled and 68 of them had failed to buy a ticket. Estimate with 95% confidence the proportion of all train travelers who do not buy a ticket.

12.99 Refer to Exercise 12.98. Assuming that there are 1 million travelers per year and the fare is $3.00 estimate with 95% confidence the amount of revenue lost each year.

The following three exercises require the use of the Wilson Estimator.

12.100 In Chapter 6, we discussed how an understanding of probability allows one to properly interpret the results of medical screening tests. The use of Bayes's Law requires a set of prior probabilities, which are based on historical records. Suppose that a physician wanted to estimate the probability that a woman under 35 years of age would give birth to a Down syndrome baby. She randomly sampled 200 births and discovered only one such case. Use the Wilson estimator to produce a 95% confidence interval estimate of the proportion of women under 35 who will have a Down syndrome baby.

12.101 Spam is of concern to anyone with an e-mail address. Several companies offer protection by eliminating spam e-mails as soon as they hit an inbox. To examine one such product, a manager randomly sampled his daily e-mails for 50 days after installing spam software. A total of 374 e-mails were received, of which 3 were spam. Use the Wilson estimator to estimate with 90% confidence the proportion of spam e-mails that get through.

12.102 A management professor was in the process of investigating the relationship between education and managerial level achieved. The source of his data was a survey of 385 CEOs of medium and large companies. He discovered that there was only one CEO who did not have at least one university degree. Estimate (using a Wilson estimator) with 99% confidence the proportion of CEOs of medium and large companies with no university degrees.

The following exercises require the use of a computer and software. The answers to Exercises 12.103 to 12.116 may be calculated manually. See Appendix A for the sample statistics. **Use a 5% significance level for all tests.**

12.103 Xr12-103 A national survey conducted by Pew Research asked a random sample of 974 American adults how they felt about doing their taxes. The responses are: 1 = Love it, 2 = Like it, 3 = Neither like nor dislike it, 4 = Dislike it, 5 = Hate it. There are 234,564,000 American adults. Estimate with 95% confidence the number of American adults who hates doing their taxes.

12.104 Xr12-104 Refer to Exercise 12.103. Those who hate or dislike doing their taxes were asked the reason. The responses are: 1 = Pay too much taxes, 2 = Complicated/too much paperwork, 3 = Inconvenient/time consuming, 4 = Don't like how government uses tax money, 5 = Owe the government money. 6 = Other. Estimate with 95% confidence the fraction of American adults who had indicated that they hated or disliked doing their taxes who hated or disliked it because they don't like how the government uses tax money.

12.105 Xr12-105* There is a looming crisis in universities and colleges across North America. In most places enrollments are increasing requiring more instructors. However, there are not enough PhDs to fill the vacancies now. Moreover, among current professors, a large proportion are nearing retirement age. On top of these problems, some universities allow professors over the age of 60 to retire early. To help devise a plan to deal with the crisis, a consultant surveyed 521 55- to 64-year-old professors and asked each whether he or she intended to retire before 65. The responses are 1 = No and 2 = Yes. Estimate with 95% confidence the proportion of professors who plan on early retirement.

12.106 Refer to Exercise 12.105. If the number of professors between the ages of 55 and 64 is 75,000, estimate the total number of such professors who plan to retire early.

12.107 Xr12-107 According to the Internal Revenue Service (IRS) in 2009 the top 5% of American income earners earned more than $153,542 and the top 1% earned more than $388,806. The top 1% pay slightly more than 40% of all federal income taxes. To determine whether Americans are aware of these figures Investor's Business Daily randomly sampled American adults and asked, "What share do you think the rich (earning more than $388,806) pay in income taxes. The categories are 1. 0% to 10%, 2. 10 to 20%, 3. 20% to 30%, 4. 30% to 40%, 5. Over 40%. The data are stored using the codes 1 to 5. Estimate with 95% confidence the proportion of Americans who knew that the rich pay more than 40% of all federal income taxes.

12.108 Xr12-108 The results of an annual Claimant Satisfaction Survey of policyholders who have had a claim with State Farm Insurance Company revealed a 90% satisfaction rate for claim service. To check the accuracy of this claim, a random sample of State Farm claimants was asked to rate whether they were satisfied with the quality of the service (1 = Satisfied and 2 = Unsatisfied). Can we infer that the satisfaction rate is less than 90%?

12.109 Xr12-109 An increasing number of people are giving gift certificates as Christmas presents. To measure the extent of this practice, a random sample of people was asked (survey conducted December 26–29) whether they had received a gift certificate for Christmas. The responses are recorded as 1 = No and 2 = Yes. Estimate with 95% confidence the proportion of people who received a gift certificate for Christmas.

12.110 Xr12-110* An important decision faces Christmas holiday celebrators: buy a real or artificial tree? A sample of 1,508 male and female respondents 18 years of age and over was interviewed. Respondents were asked whether they preferred a real (1) or artificial (2) tree. If there are 6 million Canadian households that buy Christmas trees, estimate with 95% confidence the total number of Canadian households that would prefer artificial Christmas trees.

12.111 Xr12-111* Because television audiences of newscasts tend to be older (and because older people suffer from a variety of medical ailments) pharmaceutical companies' advertising often appears on national news in the three networks (ABC, CBS, and NBC). The ads concern prescription drugs such as those to treat heartburn. To determine how effective the ads are, a survey was undertaken. Adults over 50 who regularly watch network newscasts were asked whether they had contacted their physician to ask about one of the prescription drugs advertised during the newscast. The responses (1 = No and 2 = Yes) were recorded. Estimate with 95% confidence the fraction of adults over 50 who have contacted their physician to inquire about a prescription drug.

12.112 Xr12-112 A professor of business statistics recently adopted a new textbook. At the completion of the course, 100 randomly selected students were asked to assess the book. The responses are as follows:

Excellent (1), Good (2), Adequate (3), Poor (4)

The results are stored using the codes in parentheses. Do the data allow us to conclude that more than 50% of all business students would rate the book as excellent?

12.113 Refer to Exercise 12.112. Do the data allow us to conclude that more than 90% of all business students would rate it as at least adequate?

12.114 Xm12-00 Refer to the chapter-opening example. Estimate with 95% confidence the number of Americans 18 to 49 years old who were tuned to the *American Idol*.

12.115 Xr12-115 According to the American Contract Bridge League (ACBL) bridge hands that contain two 4-card suits, one 3-card suit and one 2-card suit (4-4-3-2) occur with 21.55% probability. Suppose that a bridge-playing statistics professor with too much time on his hands tracked the number of hands over a one-year period and recorded the following hands with 4-4-3-2 distribution (Code 2) and some other distribution (Code 1). All hands were shuffled and dealt by the players at a bridge club. Test to determine whether the proportion of 4-4-3-2 hands differs from the theoretical probability. If the answer is yes, propose a reason to explain the result.

12.116 Xr12-116 Chlorofluorocarbons (CFCs) are used in air conditioners. However, CFCs damage the ozone layer, which protects us from the sun's harmful rays. As a result many jurisdictions have banned the production and use of CFCs. The latest jurisdiction to do so is the province of Ontario, which has banned the use of CFCs in car and truck air conditioners. However, it is not known how many vehicles will be affected by the new legislation. A survey of 650 vehicles was undertaken. Each vehicle was identified as either using CFCs (2) or not (1). If there are 5 million vehicles registered in Ontario, estimate with 95% confidence the number of vehicles affected by the new law.

Exercises 12.117 to 12.129 are based on the following tables listing percentages in the United States in 2010. Source: Statistical Abstract of the United States 2012.

Race

White	79.5
Black	12.9
Other	7.6

Marital status

	Never married	Married	Widowed	Divorced
Total	26.9	56.4	6.3	10.4
Race				
White	24.3	58.9	6.3	10.4
Black	42.8	38.8	6.7	11.7

Homeowner status

Owner-occupied	65.8
Renter-occupied	34.2

Educational attainment

Characteristic	Not a high school graduate	High school graduate	Some college no degree	Associate's degree	Bachelor's degree	Advanced degree
Total	12.9	31.2	16.8	9.1	19.4	10.5
Sex						
Male	13.4	31.9	16.8	8.0	19.4	10.9
Female	12.4	30.7	17.1	10.2	19.4	10.2
Race						
White	12.4	31.3	16.7	9.2	19.6	10.7
Black	15.8	35.2	19.8	9.4	13.3	6.5
Other	13.0	23.5	13.0	8.1	26.6	15.7
Marital status						
Never married	14.0	30.4	17.5	8.4	21.2	8.6
Married	10.5	30.0	16.2	9.5	21.2	12.6
Separated	23.3	34.4	18.0	8.6	10.6	5.2
Widowed	25.3	38.6	14.5	6.2	9.9	5.5
Divorced	11.3	33.7	21.0	10.5	15.7	7.7

GENERAL SOCIAL SURVEY EXERCISES

12.117 GSS2014* Is there sufficient evidence to infer that the proportion of White Americans has decreased since the 2010 census (RACE: 1 = White)?

12.118 GSS2014* Has the proportion of Americans who were never married changed since the census? Conduct a test to answer the question (MARITAL: 5 = Never married).

12.119 GSS2014* In 2010, the United States was just recovering from the housing debacle. The percentage of home ownership was 65.8%. Is there enough evidence to infer that the proportion of home ownership has changed since then (DWELOWN: 1 = Own)?

12.120 GSS2014* Since 2010 the number of jobs available for people who have not completed high school has decreased. Has this resulted in a change in the proportion of Americans who did not complete high school? Perform a statistical test to answer the question (DEGREE: 0 = Left high school).

12.121 GSS2014* In the 2010 census, the proportion of divorced White Americans was 10.4%. Has that percentage in 2014 increased? Conduct a statistical test to answer the question (RACE: 1 = White; MARITAL: 3 = Divorced).

12.122 GSS2014* An increasing number of women are attending university. Women now outnumber men in most college programs. In the 2010 census, the proportion of women with graduate degrees was 10.2% (The census used "advanced" to represent graduate degrees.) Can we infer from the General Social Survey of 2014 that the proportion is larger (SEX: 2 = Female; DEGREE" 4 = Graduate)?

12.123 GSS2014* According to the 2010 census, among people who were never married the percentage who did not finish high school was 14.0%. Has the proportion in 2014 increased? Perform a statistical test to answer the question (MARITAL: 5 = Never married; DEGREE: 0 = Left high school).

SURVEY OF CONSUMER FINANCES EXERCISES

12.124 SCF2013:\ALL* In the 2010 census, the proportion of Black/African Americans was 12.9%. Has that percentage decreased? Conduct a test using the Survey of Consumer Finances of 2013 to answer the question (RACE: 2 = Black/African American).

12.125 SCF2013:\ALL* The proportion of Americans living in homes that they owned in 2010 was 65.8%. Is there sufficient evidence to infer that that figure increased by 2013? (HOUSECL: 1 = Owns)

12.126 SCF2013:\ALL* In the 2010 census, 16.8% of American adults entered college but did not finish. Using the data from the Survey of Consumer Finances of 2013 test, determine whether that figure increased (EDCL: 3 = Some college).

12.127 SCF2013:\ALL* The proportion of women who did not finish high school was 12.4% according to the census in 2010. Is there enough statistical evidence to conclude that the proportion has decreased in 2013 (HHSEX: 2 = Female; EDCL: 1 = No high school diploma)?

12.128 SCF2013:\ALL* The 2010 census showed that the percentage of Black Americans who did not finish high school was 15.8%. Did this figure decrease by 2013? Conduct a test to determine whether there is enough evidence to infer that the proportion of Black Americans who did not finish high school had decreased (RACE: 2 = Black/African American; EDCL 1 = No high school diploma)?

12.129 SCF2013:\ALL The 2010 Census showed that the percentage of American adults who had an advanced degree (Read: graduate) was 10.5%. Is there sufficient evidence to infer that by 2013 that figure had been increased (EDUC: 17 = Graduate school)?

12-4 (OPTIONAL) APPLICATIONS IN MARKETING: MARKET SEGMENTATION

Mass marketing refers to the mass production and marketing by a company of a single product for the entire market. Mass marketing is especially effective for commodity goods such as gasoline, which are very difficult to differentiate from the competition, except through price and convenience of availability. Generally speaking, however, mass marketing has given way to target marketing, which focuses on satisfying the demands of a particular segment of the entire market. For example, the Coca-Cola Company has moved from the mass marketing of a single beverage to the production of several different beverages. Among the cola products are Coca-Cola Classic, Diet Coke, and Caffeine-Free Diet Coke. Each product is aimed at a different market segment.

Because there is no single way to segment a market, managers must consider several different variables (or characteristics) that could be used to identify segments. Surveys of customers are used to gather data about various aspects of the market, and statistical techniques are applied to define the segments. Market segmentation separates consumers of a product into different groups in such a way that members of each group are similar to each other, and there are differences between groups. Market segmentation grew out of the realization that a single product can seldom satisfy the needs and wants of all consumers. Managers must then formulate a strategy to target these profitable segments, using the four elements of the marketing mix: product, pricing, promotion, and placement.

There are many ways to segment a market. Table 12.1 lists several different segmentation variables and their market segments. For example, car manufacturers can use education levels to segment the market. It is likely that high school graduates would be quite similar to others in this group and that members of this group would differ from university graduates. We would expect those differences to include the types and brands of cars each group would choose to buy. However, it is likely that income level would differentiate more clearly between segments. Statistical techniques can be used to help determine the best way to segment the market. These statistical techniques are more advanced than this textbook. Consequently, we will focus our attention on other statistical applications.

TABLE **12.1** Market Segmentation

SEGMENTATION VARIABLE	SEGMENTS
Geographic	
Countries	Brazil, Canada, China, France, United States
Country regions	Midwest, Northeast, Southwest, Southeast
Demographic	
Age	Under 5, 5–12, 13–19, 20–29, 30–50, older than 50
Education	Some high school, high school graduate, some college, college or university graduate
Income	Under $20,000, $20,000–$29,999, $30,000–$49,999, more than $50,000
Marital status	Single, married, divorced, widowed
Social	
Religion	Catholic, Protestant, Jewish, Muslim, Buddhist
Class	Upper class, middle class, working class, lower class
Behavior	
Media usage	TV, Internet, newspaper, magazine
Payment method	Cash, check, Visa, Mastercard

It is important for marketing managers to know the size of the segment because the size (among other parameters) determines its profitability. Not all segments are worth pursuing. In some instances, the size of the segment is too small or the costs of satisfying it may be too high. The size can be determined in several ways. The census provides useful information. For example, we can determine the number of Americans in various age categories or the size of geographic residences. For other segments, we may need to survey members of a general population and use the inferential techniques introduced in the previous section, where we showed how to estimate the total number of successes.

In Section 12-3, we showed how to estimate the total number of successes in a large finite population. The confidence interval estimator is

$$N\left(\hat{p} \pm z_{\alpha/2}\sqrt{\frac{\hat{p}(1 - \hat{p})}{n}} \right)$$

The following example demonstrates the use of this estimator in market segmentation.

EXAMPLE 12.6

DATA
Xm12-06*

Segmenting the Breakfast Cereal Market

In segmenting the breakfast cereal market, a food manufacturer uses health and diet consciousness as the segmentation variable. Four segments are developed:

1. Concerned about eating healthy foods
2. Concerned primarily about weight
3. Concerned about health because of illness
4. Unconcerned

To distinguish between groups, surveys are conducted. On the basis of a questionnaire, people are categorized as belonging to one of these groups. A recent survey asked a random sample of 1,250 American adults (18 and older) to complete the questionnaire. The categories were recorded using the codes. The most recent census reveals that 244,137,873 Americans are 18 and older. Estimate with 95% confidence the number of American adults who are concerned about eating healthy foods.

SOLUTION:

IDENTIFY

The problem objective is to describe the population of American adults. The data are nominal. Consequently, the parameter we wish to estimate is the proportion p of American adults who classify themselves as concerned about eating healthy. The confidence interval estimator we need to employ is

$$\hat{p} \pm z_{\alpha/2}\sqrt{\frac{\hat{p}(1 - \hat{p})}{n}}$$

from which we will produce the estimate of the size of the market segment.

COMPUTE

MANUALLY:

To solve manually, we count the number of 1s in the file. We find this value to be 269. Thus,

$$\hat{p} = \frac{x}{n} = \frac{269}{1,250} = .2152$$

The confidence level is $1 - \alpha = .95$. It follows that $\alpha = .05$, $\alpha/2 = .025$, and $z_{\alpha/2} = z_{.025} = 1.96$. The 95% confidence interval estimate of p is

$$\hat{p} \pm z_{\alpha/2}\sqrt{\frac{\hat{p}(1 - \hat{p})}{n}} = .2152 \pm 1.96\sqrt{\frac{(.2152)(1 - .2152)}{1,250}} = .2152 \pm .0228$$

$$\text{LCL} = .1924 \qquad \text{UCL} = .2380$$

EXCEL Workbook

	A	B	C	D	E
1	z-Estimate of a Proportion				
2					
3	Sample proportion	0.2152	Confidence Interval Estimate		
4	Sample size	1250	0.2152	±	0.0228
5	Confidence level	0.95	Lower confidence limit		0.1924
6			Upper confidence limit		0.2380

XLSTAT

	B	C	D	E	F
17	95% confidence interval on the proportion (Wald):				
18	0.1924	0.2380			

INTERPRET

We estimate that the proportion of American adults who are in group 1 lies between .1924 and .2380. Because there are 244,137,873 adults in the population, we estimate that the number of adults who belong to group 1 falls between

$$\text{LCL} = N\left[\hat{p} - z_{\alpha/2}\sqrt{\frac{\hat{p}(1 - \hat{p})}{n}}\right] = 244,137,873 \,(.1924) \,=\, 46,972,127$$

and

$$\text{UCL} = N\left[\hat{p} + z_{\alpha/2}\sqrt{\frac{\hat{p}(1 - \hat{p})}{n}}\right] = 244{,}137{,}873\,(.2380) = 58{,}104{,}814$$

We will return to the subject of market segmentation in other chapters where we demonstrate how statistics can be used to determine whether differences actually exist between segments.

EXERCISES

The following exercises may be solved manually. See Appendix A for the sample statistics.

12.130 <u>Xr12-130</u> A new credit card company is investigating various market segments to determine whether it is profitable to direct its advertising specifically at each one. One of the market segments is composed of Hispanic people. According to the United States census, there are 41,580,000 Hispanic adults (18 and over) people in the United States. A survey of 475 Hispanics asked each how they usually pay for products that they purchase. The responses are:

1. Cash
2. Check
3. Visa
4. MasterCard
5. Other credit card

Estimate with 95% confidence the number of Hispanics in the United States who usually pay by credit card.

12.131 <u>Xr12-131*</u> A California university is investigating expanding its evening programs. It wants to target people between 25 and 55 years old who have completed high school but did not complete college or university. To help determine the extent and type of offerings, the university needs to know the size of its target market. A survey of 320 California adults was drawn and each person was asked to identify his or her highest educational attainment. The responses are:

1. Did not complete high school
2. Completed high school only
3. Some college or university
4. College or university graduate

The Public Policy Institute of California indicates that there are 16,015,493 Californians between the ages of 25 and 55. Estimate with 95% confidence the number of Californians between 25 and 55 years

of age who are in the market segment the university wishes to target.

12.132 <u>Xr12-132*</u> The JC Penney department store chain segments the market for women's apparel by its identification of values. The three segments are:

1. Conservative
2. Traditional
3. Contemporary

Questionnaires about personal and family values are used to identify which segment a woman falls into. Suppose that the questionnaire was sent to a random sample of 1,836 women. Each woman was classified using the codes 1, 2, and 3. The latest census reveals that there are 124,723,003 adult women in the United States. Use a 95% confidence level.

a. Estimate the proportion of adult American women who are classified as traditional.
b. Estimate the size of the traditional market segment.

12.133 <u>Xr12-133</u> Most life insurance companies are leery about offering policies to people over 64. When they do the premiums must be high enough to overcome the predicted length of life. The president of one life insurance company was thinking about offering special discounts to Americans over 64 who held full-time jobs. The plan was based on the belief that full-time workers over 64 are likely to be in good health and would likely live well into their eighties. To help decide what to do, he organized a survey of a random sample of the 44,679,192 American adults over 64. He asked a random sample of 325 Americans over 64 whether they currently hold a full-time job (1 = No and 2 = Yes).

a. Estimate with 95% confidence the size of this market segment.
b. Write a report to the executives of an insurance company detailing your statistical analysis.

Source: United States Census

12.134 <u>Xr12-134</u> An advertising company was awarded the contract to design advertising for Rolls Royce automobiles. An executive in the firm decided to pitch the product not only to the affluent in the United States but also to those who think they are in the top 1% of income earners in the country. A survey was undertaken, which among other questions asked respondents 25 and over where their annual income ranked. The following responses were given.

> 1 = Top 1%
> 2 = Top 5% but not top 1%
> 3 = Top 10% but not top 5%
> 4 = Top 25% but not top 10%
> 5 = Bottom 75%

Estimate with 90% confidence the number of Americans 25 and over who believe they are in the top 1% of income earners. The number of Americans over 25 is 211,306,936.

(Source: United States Census).

12.135 <u>Xr12-135</u> Suppose the survey in the previous exercise also asked those who were not in the top 1% whether they believed that within 5 years they would be in the top 1% (1 = will not be in top 1% within 5 years and 2 = will be in top 1% within 5 years). Estimate with 95% confidence the number of Americans who believe that they will be in the top 1% of income earners within 5 years.

CHAPTER SUMMARY

The inferential methods presented in this chapter address the problem of describing a single population. When the data are interval, the parameters of interest are the population mean μ and the population variance σ^2. The Student t-distribution is used to test and estimate the mean when the population standard deviation is unknown. The chi-squared distribution is used to make inferences about a population variance. When the data are nominal, the parameter

to be tested and estimated is the population proportion p. The sample proportion follows an approximate normal distribution, which produces the test statistic and the interval estimator. We also discussed how to determine the sample size required to estimate a population proportion. We introduced market segmentation and described how statistical techniques presented in this chapter can be used to estimate the size of a segment.

IMPORTANT TERMS:

t-statistic   373
Student t-distribution   373

Robust   379
Chi-squared statistic   389

SYMBOLS:

Symbol	Pronounced	Represents
ν	nu	Degrees of freedom
χ^2	chi squared	Chi-squared statistic
$\hat{p}$	p hat	Sample proportion
$\tilde{p}$	p tilde	Wilson estimator

FORMULAS:

Test statistic for μ

$$t = \frac{\bar{x} - \mu}{s/\sqrt{n}}$$

Confidence interval estimator of μ

$$\bar{x} \pm t_{\alpha/2}\frac{s}{\sqrt{n}}$$

Test statistic for σ^2

$$\chi^2 = \frac{(n-1)s^2}{\sigma^2}$$

Confidence interval estimator of σ^2

$$LCL = \frac{(n-1)s^2}{\chi^2_{\alpha/2}}$$

$$UCL = \frac{(n-1)s^2}{\chi^2_{1-\alpha/2}}$$

Test statistic for p

$$z = \frac{\hat{p} - p}{\sqrt{p(1-p)/n}}$$

Confidence interval estimator of p

$$\hat{p} \pm z_{\alpha/2}\sqrt{\hat{p}(1-\hat{p})/n}$$

Sample size to estimate p

$$n = \left(\frac{z_{\alpha/2}\sqrt{\hat{p}(1-\hat{p})}}{B}\right)^2$$

Wilson estimator

$$\tilde{p} = \frac{x+2}{n+4}$$

Confidence interval estimator of p using the Wilson estimator

$$\tilde{p} \pm z_{\alpha/2}\sqrt{\tilde{p}(1-\tilde{p})/(n+4)}$$

Confidence interval estimator of the total of a large finite population

$$N\left[\bar{x} \pm t_{\alpha/2}\frac{s}{\sqrt{n}}\right]$$

Confidence interval estimator of the total number of successes in a large finite population

$$N\left[\hat{p} \pm z_{\alpha/2}\sqrt{\frac{\hat{p}(1-\hat{p})}{n}}\right]$$

COMPUTER OUTPUT AND INSTRUCTIONS:

Technique	Excel
t-test of μ	375
t-estimator of μ	378
Chi-squared test of σ^2	392
Chi-squared estimator of σ^2	394
z-test of p	400
z-estimator of p	403

We present the flowchart in Figure 12.7 as part of our ongoing effort to help you identify the appropriate statistical technique. This flowchart shows the techniques introduced in this chapter only. As we add new techniques in the upcoming chapters, we will expand this flowchart until it contains all the statistical inference techniques covered in this book. Use the flowchart to select the correct method in the chapter exercises that follow.

FIGURE **12.7**   **Flowchart of Techniques: Chapter 12**

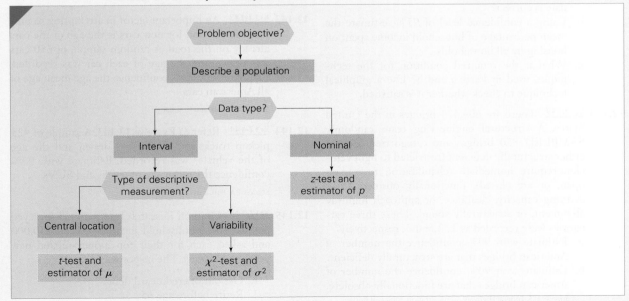

CHAPTER EXERCISES

The following exercises require the use of a computer and software.
Use a 5% significance level unless specified otherwise.

12.136 Xr12-136 The National Hockey League's Florida Panthers play in the BB&T center. The cost of parking is $20. However, Lexus occasionally pays the cost by offering free parking to drivers of Lexus cars. A statistician wanted to estimate the cost of this program. He randomly sampled 300 cars entering the parking lot and recorded whether the car was a Lexus (2) or not (1). By counting the number of empty parking spots he discovered that there were 4850 cars parked that night. Estimate with 95% confidence the amount of money Lexus had to pay the BB&T center.

12.137 Xr12-137 Hazardous materials are constantly being around the country. To help determine how dangerous these events are a statistics practitioner recorded the distances of a random sample of trucks, trains, airplanes, and boats carrying explosives. Estimate with 95% confidence the mean distance.

Source: Adapted from Statistical Abstract of the United States 2012, Table 1071.

12.138 Xr12-138 One of the issues that came up in a recent municipal election was the high cost of housing. A candidate seeking to unseat an incumbent claimed that the average family spends more than 30% of its annual income on housing. A housing expert was asked to investigate the claim. A random sample of 125 households was drawn, and each household was asked to report the percentage of household income spent on housing costs.

a. Is there enough evidence to infer that the candidate is correct?

b. Using a confidence level of 95%, estimate the mean percentage of household income spent on housing by all households.

c. What is the required condition for the techniques used in Parts a and b? Use a graphical technique to check whether it is satisfied.

12.139 Xr12-139 There are 604,474 bridges in the United States. A structural engineering team randomly SAMPLED 850 bridges and categorized each as either structurally deficient (restricted to light vehicles, require immediate rehabilitation to remain open, or are closed), functionally obsolete (load carrying capacity, clearance, or approach highway alignment, or structurally sound. These three categories were recorded as 1, 2, and 3, respectively.

a. Estimate with 99% confidence the number of American bridges that are structurally deficient.

b. Estimate with 90% confidence the number of American bridges that are functionally obsolete.

Source: U.S. Federal Highway Administration, Office of Bridge Technology

12.140 Xr12-140 Robots are being used with increasing frequency on production lines to perform monotonous tasks. To determine whether a robot welder should replace human welders in producing automobiles, an experiment was performed. The time for the robot to complete a series of welds was found to be 38 seconds. A random sample of 20 workers was taken, and the time for each worker to complete the welds was measured. The mean was calculated to be 38 seconds, the same as the robot's time. However, the robot's time did not vary, whereas there was variation among the workers' times. An analysis of the production line revealed that if the variance exceeds 17 seconds^2, there will be problems. Perform an analysis of the data, and determine whether problems using human welders are likely.

12.141 Xr12-141 According to FBI statistics, there were 354,520 robberies in the United States in 2012 (latest statistics available). A random sample of robberies was drawn and the amount of loss was recorded. Estimate with 95% confidence the total loss of all the robberies in the United States in 2012.

Source: Adapted from U.S. Department of Justice, Federal Bureau of Investigation, Uniform Crime Reports.

12.142 Xr12-142 Refer to Exercise 12.151. Also recorded was the weapon used (1 = firearm, 2 = knife or other cutting instrument, 3 = other, 4 = no weapon). Estimate with 90% confidence the number of crimes where a firearm was not used.

12.143 Xr12-143 An important factor in attempting to predict the demand for new cars is the age of the cars already on the road. A random sample of 650 cars was drawn and the age of each car was recorded. Estimate with 99% confidence the age mean age of all American cars.

Source: R.L. Polk and Company.

12.144 Xr12-144 Refer to Exercise 12.143. A sample of 425 pickup trucks and SUVs was drawn and the age of the vehicles was recorded. Estimate with 95% confidence the mean age of trucks and SUVs.

Source: R.L. Polk and Company.

12.145 Xr12-145 Opinion Research International surveyed people whose household incomes exceed $50,000 and asked each for their top money-related new year's resolutions. The responses are:

1. Get out of credit card debt
2. Retire before age 65
3. Die broke

12.187 SCF2013:\W* Do wealthy households have late payments? Estimate the proportion of wealthy households that had at least one late payment in the previous year (LATE: 1).

12.188 SCF2013:\W* Net worth is defined as the difference between total assets and total liabilities including debt. Does high net worth mean that these households have little or no debt?

a. Answer the question by estimating the mean debt of all wealthy households (DEBT).
b. Is the required condition satisfied? Explain.

12.189 SCF2013:\W* Checking accounts are often used for household expenditures. Because they pay no interest, most households including wealthy ones keep a minimum amount in these accounts.

a. Estimate the mean total value of checking accounts held by wealthy households (CHECKING).
b. Is the required condition satisfied? If not, why not?

12.190 SCF2013:\W* According to the Bureau of Labor Statistics, the average American family spent $2625 on food at restaurants. Is there enough evidence that wealthy households spend more than twice that figure (FOODAWAY)?

| CASE 12.1 | Pepsi's Exclusivity Agreement with a University |

DATA
C12-01

In the last few years, colleges and universities have signed exclusivity agreements with a variety of private companies. These agreements bind the university to sell that company's products exclusively on the campus. Many of the agreements involve food and beverage firms. A large university with a total enrollment of about 50,000 students has offered Pepsi-Cola an exclusivity agreement that would give Pepsi exclusive rights to sell its products at all university facilities for the next year and an option for future years. In return, the university would receive 35% of the on-campus revenues and an additional lump sum of $200,000 per year. Pepsi has been given 2 weeks to respond.

The management at Pepsi quickly reviews what it knows. The market for soft drinks is measured in terms of the equivalent of 12-ounce cans. Pepsi currently sells an average of 22,000 cans or their equivalents per week (over the 40 weeks of the year that the university operates). The cans sell for an average of one dollar each. The costs, including labor, amount to $.30 per can. Pepsi is unsure of its market share but suspects it is considerably less than 50%. A quick analysis reveals that if its current market share were 25%, then with an exclusivity agreement Pepsi would sell 88,000 cans per week. Thus, annual sales would be 3,520,000 cans per year (calculated as 88,000 cans per week × 40 weeks). The gross revenue would be computed as follows*:

Gross revenue = 3,520,000 cans × $1.00 revenue/can = $3,520,000

This figure must be multiplied by 65% because the university would rake in 35% of the gross. Thus, 65% × $3,520,000 = $2,288,000 The total cost of 30 cents per can (or $1,056,000) and the annual payment to the university of $200,000 is subtracted to obtain the net profit:

Net profit = $2,288,000−$1,056,000 − $200,000 = $1,032,000

Its current annual profit is

Current profit = 40 weeks × 22,000 cans/week × $.70/can = $616,000

---

*We have created an Excel spreadsheet that does the calculations for this case. To access it, click **Excel Workbooks** and **Case 12.1**. The only cell you may alter is cell C3, which contains the average number of soft drinks sold per week per student, assuming a total of 88,000 drinks sold per year.

If the current market share is 25%, the potential gain from the agreement is

$1,032,000 − $616,000 = $416,000

The only problem with this analysis is that Pepsi does not know how many soft drinks are sold weekly at the university. In addition, Coke is not likely to supply Pepsi with information about its sales, which together with Pepsi's line of products constitutes virtually the entire market.

A recent graduate of a business program believes that a survey of the university's students can supply the needed information. Accordingly, she organizes a survey that asks 500 students to keep track of the number of soft drinks they purchase on campus over the next 7 days.

Perform a statistical analysis to extract the needed information from the data. Estimate with 95% confidence the parameter that is at the core of the decision

problem. Use the estimate to compute estimates of the annual profit. Assume that Coke and Pepsi drinkers would be willing to buy either product in the absence of their first choice.

a. On the basis of maximizing profits from sales of soft drinks at the university, should Pepsi agree to the exclusivity agreement?

b. Write a report to the company's executives describing your analysis.

CASE 12.2   Pepsi's Exclusivity Agreement with a University: The Coke Side of the Equation

While the executives of Pepsi Cola are trying to decide what to do, the university informs them that a similar offer has gone out to the Coca-Cola Company. Furthermore, if both companies want exclusive rights, a bidding war will take

place. The executives at Pepsi would like to know how likely it is that Coke will want exclusive rights under the conditions outlined by the university.

Perform a similar analysis to the one you did in Case 12.1, but

this time from Coke's point of view. Is it likely that Coke will want to conclude an exclusivity agreement with the university? Discuss the reasons for your conclusions.

DATA
C12-0

CASE 12.3   Estimating Total Medical Costs

Virtually all countries have universal government-run health-care systems. The United States is one notable exception. This is an issue in every election, with some politicians pushing for the United States to adopt a program similar to Canada's.

In Canada, hospitals are financed and administered by provincial governments. Physicians are paid by the government for each patient service. As a result, Canadians pay nothing for these services. The revenues that support the system are derived through income taxes, corporate taxes, and sales taxes.

Despite higher taxes in Canada than those in the United States, the system is chronically underfunded, resulting in long waiting times for, sometimes, critical procedures. For example, in some provinces,

DATA
C12-0

newly diagnosed cancer victims must wait several weeks before treatments can begin. Virtually everyone agrees that more money is needed. No one can agree however, on how much is needed. Unfortunately, the problem is going to worsen. Canada, like the United States, has an aging population because of the large numbers of so-called baby boomers (those born between 1946 and 1966), and because medical costs are generally higher for older people.

One of the first steps in addressing the problem is to forecast medical costs, particularly for the 20-year period starting when the first baby boomers reached age 60 (in 2006). A statistics practitioner has been given the task of making these predictions. Accordingly, random samples of four groups of Canadians were drawn. They are

Group	Ages
1	45–64
2	65–74
3	75–84
4	85+

The medical expenses for the previous 12 months were recorded and stored in columns A to D, respectively, in C12-03.

Age Category	2023	2028	2033	2038
45–64	10,045	9,970	10,172	10,671
65–74	4,264	4,804	4,873	4,621
75–84	2,413	2,987	3,536	4,042
85+	924	1,095	1,429	1,793

Source: Statistics Canada.

Projections for 2023, 2028, 2033, and 2038 of the numbers of Canadians (in thousands) in each age category are listed here.

a. Determine the 95% confidence interval estimates of the mean medical costs for each of the four age categories.

b. For each year listed, determine 95% confidence interval estimates of the total medical costs for Canadians 45 years old and older.

CASE 12.4   Estimating the Number of Alzheimer's Cases

DATA
C12-04

As the U.S. population ages, the number of people needing medical care increases. Unless a cure is found in the next decade, one of the most expensive diseases requiring such care is Alzheimer's, a form of dementia.

To estimate the total number of Alzheimer's cases in the future, a survey was undertaken. The survey determined the age bracket where 1 = 65–74, 2 = 75–84, 3 = 85 and over and whether the individual had Alzheimer's (1 = no and 2 = yes).

(Adapted from the Alzheimer's Association, www.alz.org.)

Here are the projections for the number of Americans (thousands) in each of the three age categories.

Age Category	2020	2025	2030	2035	2040
65–74	33,076	37,093	39,227	38,162	36,644
75–84	16,639	21,345	25,750	29,162	31,067
85+	6,726	7,482	9,131	11,908	14,634

Source: United States Census.

a. Determine the 95% confidence interval estimates of the proportion of Alzheimer's patients in each of the three age categories.

b. For each year listed, determine 95% confidence interval estimates of the total number of Americans with Alzheimer's disease.

CASE 12.5 Bias in Roulette Betting

The game of roulette consists of a wheel with 38 colored and numbered slots. The numbers are 1 to 36, 0 and 00. Half of the slots numbered 1 to 36 are red and the other half are black. The two "zeros" are green. The wheel is spun and an iron ball is rolled, which eventually comes to rest in one of the slots. Gamblers can make several different kinds of bets. Most players bet on one or more numbers or on a color (black or red). Here is the layout of the roulette betting table:

```
 0   3  6  9 12 15 18 21 24 27 30 33 36
00   2  5  8 11 14 17 20 23 26 29 32 35
     1  4  7 10 13 16 19 22 25 28 31 34
```

Two statisticians recorded the bets on 904 spins. There were 21,731 bets.

Researchers wanted to use these data to examine *middle bias*, which is the tendency for guessers in multiple-choice exams to select the middle answers. For example, if there are five choices a, b, c, d, and e, guessers will tend to select answer c.

Most players stand on both sides of the betting table so that the middle numbers are 2, 5, 8, 11, 14, 17, 20, 23, 26, 29, 32, and 35.

a. If there is no middle bias, what proportion of the bets will be on 1 of the 12 middle numbers?

b. Conduct a test at the 5% significance level to determine whether middle bias exists.

c. The middle of the middle are the numbers 17 and 20. If there is no middle bias, what proportion of the bets will be either 17 or 20?

d. Test with a 5% significance level to determine whether middle of the middle bias exists.

Source: Maya Bar-Hillel and Ro'l Zultan, "We Sing the Praise of Good Displays: How Gamblers Bet in Casino Roulette," *Chance,* Volume 25, No. 2, 2012.

Pressmaster/Shutterstock.com

13

INFERENCE ABOUT COMPARING TWO POPULATIONS

CHAPTER OUTLINE

General Social Survey

Comparing Democrats and Republicans: Who is Likely to Have Completed a University Degree?

DATA
GSS2014*

In the business of politics it is important to be able to determine what differences exist between supporters and opponents. In 2014 the General Social Survey asked people what is the highest degree earned (DEGREE)?

The responses are:

0. Left high school

1. Completed high school

2. Completed junior college

3. Completed Bachelor's degree

4. Completed graduate degree

KamiGami/Shutterstock.com

On page 489, we will provide our answer.

(Continued)

427

The survey also asked, Do you think of yourself as Democrat, Independent, or Republican (PARTYID3)?

1. Democrat
2. Independent
3. Republican

Do these data allow us to infer that people who identify themselves as Republican Party supporters are more likely to have completed a Bachelor's or graduate degree than their Democratic counterparts?

INTRODUCTION

We can compare learning how to use statistical techniques to learning how to drive a car. We began by describing what you are going to do in this course (Chapter 1) and then presented the essential background material (Chapters 2–9). Learning the concepts of statistical inference and applying them the way we did in Chapters 10 and 11 is akin to driving a car in an empty parking lot. You're driving, but it's not a realistic experience. Learning Chapter 12 is like driving on a quiet side street with little traffic. The experience represents real driving, but many of the difficulties have been eliminated. In this chapter, you begin to drive for real, with many of the actual problems faced by licensed drivers, and the experience prepares you to tackle the next difficulty.

In this chapter, we present a variety of techniques used to compare two populations. In Sections 13-1 and 13-3, we deal with interval variables; the parameter of interest is the difference between two means. The difference between these two sections introduces yet another factor that determines the correct statistical method—the design of the experiment used to gather the data. In Section 13-1, the samples are independently drawn, whereas in Section 13-3, the samples are taken from a matched pairs experiment. In Section 13-2, we discuss the difference between observational and experimental data, a distinction that is critical to the way in which we interpret statistical results.

Section 13-4 presents the procedures employed to infer whether two population variances differ. The parameter is the ratio σ_1^2/σ_2^2. (When comparing two variances, we use the ratio rather than the difference because of the nature of the sampling distribution.)

Section 13-5 addresses the problem of comparing two populations of nominal data. The parameter to be tested and estimated is the difference between two proportions.

13-1 / INFERENCE ABOUT THE DIFFERENCE BETWEEN TWO MEANS: INDEPENDENT SAMPLES

In order to test and estimate the difference between two population means, the statistics practitioner draws random samples from each of two populations. In this section, we discuss independent samples. In Section 13-3, where we present the matched pairs experiment, the distinction between independent samples and matched pairs will be made clear. For now, we define independent samples as samples completely unrelated to one another.

Figure 13.1 depicts the sampling process. Observe that we draw a sample of size n_1 from population 1 and a sample of size n_2 from population 2. For each sample, we compute the sample means and sample variances.

FIGURE **13.1** **Independent Samples from Two Populations**

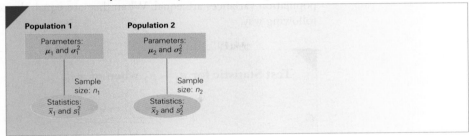

The best estimator of the difference between two population means, $\mu_1 - \mu_2$, is the difference between two sample means, $\bar{x}_1 - \bar{x}_2$. In Section 9-3 we presented the sampling distribution of $\bar{x}_1 - \bar{x}_2$.

Sampling Distribution of $\bar{x}_1 - \bar{x}_2$

1. $\bar{x}_1 - \bar{x}_2$ is normally distributed if the populations are normal and approximately normal if the populations are nonnormal and the sample sizes are large.

2. The expected value of $\bar{x}_1 - \bar{x}_2$ is

$$E(\bar{x}_1 - \bar{x}_2) = \mu_1 - \mu_2$$

3. The variance of $\bar{x}_1 - \bar{x}_2$ is

$$V(\bar{x}_1 - \bar{x}_2) = \frac{\sigma_1^2}{n_1} + \frac{\sigma_2^2}{n_2}$$

The standard error of $\bar{x}_1 - \bar{x}_2$ is

$$\sqrt{\frac{\sigma_1^2}{n_1} + \frac{\sigma_2^2}{n_2}}$$

Thus,

$$z = \frac{(\bar{x}_1 - \bar{x}_2) - (\mu_1 - \mu_2)}{\sqrt{\dfrac{\sigma_1^2}{n_1} + \dfrac{\sigma_2^2}{n_2}}}$$

is a standard normal (or approximately normal) random variable. It follows that the test statistic is

$$z = \frac{(\bar{x}_1 - \bar{x}_2) - (\mu_1 - \mu_2)}{\sqrt{\dfrac{\sigma_1^2}{n_1} + \dfrac{\sigma_2^2}{n_2}}}$$

The interval estimator is

$$(\bar{x}_1 - \bar{x}_2) \pm z_{\alpha/2}\sqrt{\frac{\sigma_1^2}{n_1} + \frac{\sigma_2^2}{n_2}}$$

However, these formulas are rarely used because the population variances σ_1^2 and σ_2^2 are virtually always unknown. Consequently, it is necessary to estimate the standard error of the sampling distribution. The way to do this depends on whether the two unknown population variances are equal. When they are equal, the test statistic is defined in the following way.

Test Statistic for $\mu_1 - \mu_2$ when $\sigma_1^2 = \sigma_2^2$

$$t = \frac{(\bar{x}_1 - \bar{x}_2) - (\mu_1 - \mu_2)}{\sqrt{s_p^2 \left(\frac{1}{n_1} + \frac{1}{n_2} \right)}} \qquad v = n_1 + n_2 - 2$$

where

$$s_p^2 = \frac{(n_1 - 1)s_1^2 + (n_2 - 1)s_2^2}{n_1 + n_2 - 2}$$

The quantity s_p^2 is called the **pooled variance estimator**. It is the weighted average of the two sample variances with the number of degrees of freedom in each sample used as weights. The requirement that the population variances be equal makes this calculation feasible because we need only one estimate of the common value of σ_1^2 and σ_2^2. It makes sense for us to use the pooled variance estimator because, in combining both samples, we produce a better estimate.

The test statistic is Student t distributed with $n_1 + n_2 - 2$ degrees of freedom, provided that the two populations are normal. The confidence interval estimator is derived by mathematics that by now has become routine.

Confidence Interval Estimator of $\mu_1 - \mu_2$ When $\sigma_1^2 = \sigma_2^2$

$$(\bar{x}_1 - \bar{x}_2) \pm t_{\alpha/2} \sqrt{s_p^2 \left(\frac{1}{n_1} + \frac{1}{n_2} \right)} \qquad v = n_1 + n_2 - 2$$

We will refer to these formulas as the **equal-variances test statistic** and **confidence interval estimator**, respectively.

When the population variances are unequal, we cannot use the pooled variance estimate. Instead, we estimate each population variance with its sample variance. Unfortunately, the sampling distribution of the resulting statistic

$$\frac{(\bar{x}_1 - \bar{x}_2) - (\mu_1 - \mu_2)}{\sqrt{\frac{s_1^2}{n_1} + \frac{s_2^2}{n_2}}}$$

is neither normally nor Student t distributed. However, it can be approximated by a Student t distribution with degrees of freedom equal to

$$v = \frac{(s_1^2/n_1 + s_2^2/n_2)^2}{\frac{(s_1^2/n_1)^2}{n_1 - 1} + \frac{(s_2^2/n_2)^2}{n_2 - 1}}$$

(It is usually necessary to round this number to the nearest integer.) The test statistic and confidence interval estimator are easily derived from the sampling distribution.

Test Statistic for $\mu_1 - \mu_2$ When $\sigma_1^2 \neq \sigma_2^2$

$$t = \frac{(\bar{x}_1 - \bar{x}_2) - (\mu_1 - \mu_2)}{\sqrt{\left(\dfrac{s_1^2}{n_1} + \dfrac{s_2^2}{n_2}\right)}} \qquad \nu = \frac{(s_1^2/n_1 + s_2^2/n_2)^2}{\dfrac{(s_1^2/n_1)^2}{n_1 - 1} + \dfrac{(s_2^2/n_2)^2}{n_2 - 1}}$$

Confidence Interval Estimator of $\mu_1 - \mu_2$ When $\sigma_1^2 \neq \sigma_2^2$

$$(\bar{x}_1 - \bar{x}_2) \pm t_{\alpha/2}\sqrt{\left(\frac{s_1^2}{n_1} + \frac{s_2^2}{n_2}\right)} \qquad \nu = \frac{(s_1^2/n_1 + s_2^2/n_2)^2}{\dfrac{(s_1^2/n_1)^2}{n_1 - 1} + \dfrac{(s_2^2/n_2)^2}{n_2 - 1}}$$

We will refer to these formulas as the **unequal-variances test statistic** and **confidence interval estimator**, respectively.

The question naturally arises, How do we know when the population variances are equal? The answer is that because σ_1^2 and σ_2^2 are unknown, we can't know for certain whether they're equal. However, we can perform a statistical test to determine whether there is evidence to infer that the population variances differ. We conduct the F-test of the ratio of two variances, which we briefly present here and save the details for Section 13-4.

Testing the Population Variances

The hypotheses to be tested are

H_0: $\sigma_1^2/\sigma_2^2 = 1$

H_1: $\sigma_1^2/\sigma_2^2 \neq 1$

The test statistic is the ratio of the sample variances s_1^2/s_2^2, which is F-distributed with degrees of freedom $v_1 = n_1 - 1$ and $v_2 = n_2 - 1$. Recall that we introduced the F-distribution in Section 8-4. The required condition is the same as that for the t-test of $\mu_1 - \mu_2$, which is that both populations are normally distributed.

This is a two-tail test so that the rejection region is

$$F > F_{\alpha/2, \nu_1, \nu_2} \qquad \text{or} \qquad F < F_{1 - \alpha/2, \nu_1, \nu_2}$$

Put simply, we will reject the null hypothesis that states that the population variances are equal when the ratio of the sample variances is large or if it is small. Table 6 in Appendix B, which lists the critical values of the F-distribution, defines "large" and "small."

13-1a Decision Rule: Equal-Variances or Unequal-Variances *t*-Tests and Estimators

Recall that we can never have enough statistical evidence to conclude that the null hypothesis is true. This means that we can only determine whether there is enough evidence to infer that the population variances *differ*. Accordingly, we adopt the following rule: We will use the equal-variances test statistic and confidence interval estimator unless there is evidence (based on the *F*-test of the population variances) to indicate that the population variances are unequal, in which case we will apply the unequal-variances test statistic and confidence interval estimator.

EXAMPLE **13.1***

DATA
Xm13-01

Direct and Broker-Purchased Mutual Funds

Millions of investors buy mutual funds (see page 161 for a description of mutual funds), choosing from thousands of possibilities. Some funds can be purchased directly from banks or other financial institutions whereas others must be purchased through brokers, who charge a fee for this service. This raises the question, Can investors do better by buying mutual funds directly than by purchasing mutual funds through brokers? To help answer this question, a group of researchers randomly sampled the annual returns from mutual funds that can be acquired directly and mutual funds that are bought through brokers and recorded the net annual returns, which are the returns on investment after deducting all relevant fees. These are listed next.

Direct					Broker				
9.33	4.68	4.23	14.69	10.29	3.24	3.71	16.4	4.36	9.43
6.94	3.09	10.28	−2.97	4.39	−6.76	13.15	6.39	−11.07	8.31
16.17	7.26	7.1	10.37	−2.06	12.8	11.05	−1.9	9.24	−3.99
16.97	2.05	−3.09	−0.63	7.66	11.1	−3.12	9.49	−2.67	−4.44
5.94	13.07	5.6	−0.15	10.83	2.73	8.94	6.7	8.97	8.63
12.61	0.59	5.27	0.27	14.48	−0.13	2.74	0.19	1.87	7.06
3.33	13.57	8.09	4.59	4.8	18.22	4.07	12.39	−1.53	1.57
16.13	0.35	15.05	6.38	13.12	−0.8	5.6	6.54	5.23	−8.44
11.2	2.69	13.21	−0.24	−6.54	−5.75	−0.85	10.92	6.87	−5.72
1.14	18.45	1.72	10.32	−1.06	2.59	−0.28	−2.15	−1.69	6.95

Can we conclude at the 5% significance level that directly purchased mutual funds outperform mutual funds bought through brokers?

SOLUTION:

IDENTIFY

To answer the question, we need to compare the population of returns from direct and the returns from broker-bought mutual funds. The data are obviously interval (we've recorded real numbers). This problem objective–data type combination tells us that the parameter to be tested is the difference between two means, $\mu_1 - \mu_2$. The hypothesis

*Source: D. Bergstresser, J. Chalmers, and P. Tufano, "Assessing the Costs and Benefits of Brokers in the Mutual Fund Industry."

to be tested is that the mean net annual return from directly purchased mutual funds (μ_1) is larger than the mean of broker-purchased funds (μ_2). Hence, the alternative hypothesis is

$$H_1: \quad (\mu_1 - \mu_2) > 0$$

As usual, the null hypothesis automatically follows:

$$H_0: \quad (\mu_1 - \mu_2) = 0$$

To decide which of the t-tests of $\mu_1 - \mu_2$ to apply, we conduct the F-test of σ_1^2/σ_2^2.

$$H_0: \quad \sigma_1^2/\sigma_2^2 = 1$$
$$H_1: \quad \sigma_1^2/\sigma_2^2 \neq 1$$

COMPUTE

MANUALLY:

From the data, we calculated the following statistics:

$$s_1^2 = 37.49 \quad \text{and} \quad s_2^2 = 43.34$$

Test statistic: $F = s_1^2/s_2^2 = 37.49/43.34 = 0.86$

Rejection region: $F > F_{\alpha/2,\nu_1,\nu_2} = F_{.025,49,49} \approx F_{.025,50,50} = 1.75$

or

$$F < F_{1-\alpha/2,\nu_1,\nu_2} = F_{.975,49,49} = 1/F_{.025,49,49} \approx 1/F_{.025,50,50} = 1/1.75 = .57$$

Because $F = .86$ is not greater than 1.75 or smaller than .57, we cannot reject the null hypothesis.

EXCEL Data Analysis

	A	B	C
1	F-Test: Two-Sample for Variances		
2			
3		Direct	Broker
4	Mean	6.63	3.72
5	Variance	37.49	43.34
6	Observations	50	50
7	df	49	49
8	F	0.8650	
9	P(F<=f) one-tail	0.3068	
10	F Critical one-tail	0.6222	

The value of the test statistic is $F = .8650$. Excel outputs the one-tail p-value. Because we're conducting a two-tail test, we double that value. Thus, the p-value of the test we're conducting is $2 \times .3068 = .6136$.

INSTRUCTIONS

1. Type or import the data into two columns. (Open Xm13-01.)
2. Click **Data, Data Analysis,** and **F-test Two-Sample for Variances.**
3. Specify the **Variable 1 Range** (A1:A51) and the **Variable 2 Range** (B1:B51). Type a value for α (.05).

XLSTAT

	B	C	D	E	F	G
1	Hypothesized ratio (R): 1					
2	Significance level (%): 5					
3						
4	Summary statistics:					
5	Variable	Observations	Minimum	Maximum	Mean	Std. deviation
6	Direct	50	-6.54	18.45	6.63	6.12
7	Broker	50	-11.07	18.22	3.72	6.58
8						
9	Fisher's F-test / Two-tailed test:					
10	Ratio	0.865				
11	F (Observed value)	0.865				
12	F (Critical value)	1.76				
13	DF1	49				
14	DF2	49				
15	p-value (Two-tailed)	0.8137				
16	alpha	0.05				

INSTRUCTIONS

1. Type or import the data into two columns. (Open Xm13-01.)
2. Click **XLSTAT, Parametric tests**, and **Two-sample comparison of variances**.
3. Check **One column per sample.** Type the input range for both samples. **Sample 1**(A1:A51) **Sample 2** (B1:B51). Click **Fisher's F-test**.
4. Click the **Options** tab and choose **Variance 1/Variance 2 ≠ R** in the **Alternative hypothesis** box. Type the **Hypothesized ratio (R)** (1). Type the value of α (in percent) in the **Significance level(%)** box (5). Click **OK**.

INTERPRET

There is not enough evidence to infer that the population variances differ. It follows that we must apply the equal-variances t-test of $\mu_1 - \mu_2$.

The hypotheses are

$$H_0: \quad (\mu_1 - \mu_2) = 0$$
$$H_1: \quad (\mu_1 - \mu_2) > 0$$

COMPUTE

MANUALLY:

From the data, we calculated the following statistics:

$$\bar{x}_1 = 6.63$$
$$\bar{x}_2 = 3.72$$
$$s_1^2 = 37.49$$
$$s_2^2 = 43.34$$

The pooled variance estimator is

$$s_p^2 = \frac{(n_1 - 1)s_1^2 + (n_2 - 1)s_2^2}{n_1 + n_2 - 2}$$

$$= \frac{(50 - 1)37.49 + (50 - 1)43.34}{50 + 50 - 2}$$

$$= 40.42$$

The number of degrees of freedom of the test statistic is

$$\nu = n_1 + n_2 - 2 = 50 + 50 - 2 = 98$$

The rejection region is

$$t > t_{\alpha, \nu} = t_{.05, 98} \approx t_{.05, 100} = 1.660$$

We determine that the value of the test statistic is

$$t = \frac{(\bar{x}_1 - \bar{x}_2) - (\mu_1 - \mu_2)}{\sqrt{s_p^2 \left(\frac{1}{n_1} + \frac{1}{n_2}\right)}}$$

$$= \frac{(6.63 - 3.72) - 0}{\sqrt{40.42 \left(\frac{1}{50} + \frac{1}{50}\right)}}$$

$$= 2.29$$

EXCEL Data Analysis

	A	B	C
1	t-Test: Two-Sample Assuming Equal Variances		
2			
3		Direct	Broker
4	Mean	6.63	3.72
5	Variance	37.49	43.34
6	Observations	50	50
7	Pooled Variance	40.41	
8	Hypothesized Mean Difference	0	
9	df	98	
10	t Stat	2.29	
11	P(T<=t) one-tail	0.0122	
12	t Critical one-tail	1.6606	
13	P(T<=t) two-tail	0.0243	
14	t Critical two-tail	1.9845	

INSTRUCTIONS

1. Type or import the data into two columns. (Open Xm13-01.)

2. Click **Data, Data Analysis,** and **t-Test: Two-Sample Assuming Equal Variances.**

3. Specify the **Variable 1 Range** (A1:A51) and the **Variable 2 Range** (B1:B51). Type the value of the **Hypothesized Mean Difference*** (0) and type a value for α(.05).

XLSTAT

	A	B	C	D
1	Hypothesized difference (D): 0			
2	Significance level (%): 5			
3	Population variances for the t-test: Assume equality			
4				
5	Summary statistics:			
6	Variable	Observations	Mean	Std. deviation
7	Direct	50	6.63	6.12
8	Broker	50	3.72	6.58
9				
10	t-test for two independent samples / Upper-tailed test:			
11	Difference	2.91		
12	t (Observed value)	2.29		
13	t (Critical value)	1.661		
14	DF	98		
15	p-value (one-tailed)	0.0122		
16	alpha	0.05		

---

*This term is technically incorrect. Because we're testing $\mu_1 - \mu_2$, Excel should ask for and output the "Hypothesized Difference between Means."

INSTRUCTIONS

1. Type or import the data into two columns. (Open Xm13-01.)
2. Click **XLSTAT**, **Parametric test**, and **Two-sample t-test and z-test**.
3. Check **One-column per sample**. Type the input range for both samples. **Sample 1** (A1:A51) **Sample 2** (B1:B51). Click **Student's t-test**. Do not click **z-test**.
4. Click the **Options** tab and choose **Mean 1 – Mean 2 > D** in the **Alternative hypothesis** box. Type **the Hypothesized difference (D) (0)**. Click **Assume equality** under **Population variances for the t-test**. (If you click **Use an F-test** you do not need to conduct a separate F-test of the two variances as a first step to testing the difference between two means.) Type the value of α in the **Significance level(%)** box (5). Click **OK**.

INTERPRET

The value of the test statistic is 2.29. The one-tail p-value is .0122. We observe that the p-value of the test is small (and the test statistic falls into the rejection region). As a result, we conclude that there is sufficient evidence to infer that on average directly purchased mutual funds outperform broker-purchased mutual funds.

Estimating $\mu_1 - \mu_2$: Equal-Variances

In addition to testing a value of the difference between two population means, we can also estimate the difference between means. Next we compute the 95% confidence interval estimate of the difference between the mean return for direct and broker mutual funds.

COMPUTE

MANUALLY:

The confidence interval estimator of the difference between two means with equal population variances is

$$(\bar{x}_1 - \bar{x}_2) \pm t_{\alpha/2}\sqrt{s_p^2\left(\frac{1}{n_1} + \frac{1}{n_2}\right)}$$

The 95% confidence interval estimate of the difference between the return for directly purchased mutual funds and the mean return for broker-purchased mutual funds is

$$(\bar{x}_1 - \bar{x}_2) \pm t_{\alpha/2}\sqrt{s_p^2\left(\frac{1}{n_1} + \frac{1}{n_2}\right)} = (6.63 - 3.72) \pm 1.984\sqrt{40.42\left(\frac{1}{50} + \frac{1}{50}\right)}$$

$$= 2.91 \pm 2.52$$

The lower and upper limits are .39 and 5.43.

EXCEL Workbook

	A	B	C	D	E	F
1	t-Estimate of the Difference Between Two Means (Equal-Variances)					
2						
3		Sample 1	Sample 2	Confidence Interval Estimate		
4	Mean	6.63	3.72	2.91	±	2.52
5	Variance	37.49	43.34	Lower confidence limit		0.39
6	Sample size	50	50	Upper confidence limit		5.43
7	Pooled Variance	40.42				
8	Confidence level	0.95				

INSTRUCTIONS

Type or import the data into two columns (Open Xm13-01). Calculate the mean and variance for each sample. Open the **Estimators Workbook** and select the **t-Estimate_2 Means (Eq-Var)** tab. Type the. mean and variance into the spreadsheet. Type the sample sizes and the confidence level.

XLSTAT

	B	C	D	E	F	G
13	95% confidence interval on the difference between the means:					
14	0.385	5.43				

INSTRUCTIONS

Follow the instructions for the t-test of the difference between two means. Make certain that you specify a two-tail test. That is, choose **Mean 1 – Mean 2 ≠ D** in the **Alternative hypothesis** box.

INTERPRET

We estimate that the return on directly purchased mutual funds is on average between .39 and 5.43 percentage points larger than broker-purchased mutual funds.

EXAMPLE 13.2[†]

DATA
Xm13-02

Effect of New CEO in Family-Run Businesses

What happens to the family-run business when the boss's son or daughter takes over? Does the business do better after the change if the new boss is the offspring of the owner, or does the business do better when an outsider is made chief executive officer (CEO)? In pursuit of an answer, researchers randomly selected 140 firms between 1994 and 2002, 30% of which passed ownership to an offspring and 70% of which appointed an outsider as CEO. For each company, the researchers calculated the operating income as a proportion of assets in the year before and the year after the new CEO took over. The change (operating income after—operating income before) in this variable

---

[†]*Source:* M. Bennedsen and K. Nielsen, Copenhagen Business School and D. Wolfenzon, New York University.

was recorded and is listed next. Do these data allow us to infer that the effect of making an offspring CEO is different from the effect of hiring an outsider as CEO?

Offspring			Outsider						
−1.95	0.91	−3.15	0.69	−1.05	1.58	−2.46	3.33	−1.32	−0.51
0	−2.16	3.27	−0.95	−4.23	−1.98	1.59	3.2	5.93	8.68
0.56	1.22	−0.67	−2.2	−0.16	4.41	−2.03	0.55	−0.45	1.43
1.44	0.67	2.61	2.65	2.77	4.62	−1.69	−1.4	−3.2	−0.37
1.5	−0.39	1.55	5.39	−0.96	4.5	0.55	2.79	5.08	−0.49
1.41	−1.43	−2.67	4.15	1.01	2.37	0.95	5.62	0.23	−0.08
−0.32	−0.48	−1.91	4.28	0.09	2.44	3.06	−2.69	−2.69	−1.16
−1.7	0.24	1.01	2.97	6.79	1.07	4.83	−2.59	3.76	1.04
−1.66	0.79	−1.62	4.11	1.72	−1.11	5.67	2.45	1.05	1.28
−1.87	−1.19	−5.25	2.66	6.64	0.44	−0.8	3.39	0.53	1.74
−1.38	1.89	0.14	6.31	4.75	1.36	1.37	5.89	3.2	−0.14
0.57	−3.7	2.12	−3.04	2.84	0.88	0.72	−0.71	−3.07	−0.82
3.05	−0.31	2.75	−0.42	−2.1	0.33	4.14	4.22	−4.34	0
2.98	−1.37	0.3	−0.89	2.07	−5.96	3.04	0.46	−1.16	2.68

SOLUTION:

IDENTIFY

The objective is to compare two populations, and the data are interval. It follows that the parameter of interest is the difference between two population means $\mu_1 - \mu_2$, where μ_1 is the mean difference for companies where the owner's son or daughter became CEO and μ_2 is the mean difference for companies who appointed an outsider as CEO.

To determine whether to apply the equal or unequal variances t-test, we use the F-test of two variances.

$$H_0: \ \sigma_1^2/\sigma_2^2 = 1$$
$$H_1: \ \sigma_1^2/\sigma_2^2 \neq 1$$

COMPUTE

MANUALLY:

From the data, we calculated the following statistics:

$$s_1^2 = 3.79 \quad \text{and} \quad s_2^2 = 8.03$$

Test statistic: $F = s_1^2/s_2^2 = 3.79/8.03 = 0.47$

The degrees of freedom are $\nu_1 = n_1 - 1 = 42 - 1 = 41$ and $\nu_2 = n_2 - 1 = 98 - 1 = 97$.

Rejection region: $F > F_{\alpha/2,\nu_1,\nu_2} = F_{.025,41,97} \approx F_{.025,40,100} = 1.64$

or

$$F < F_{1-\alpha/2,\nu_1,\nu_2} = F_{.975,41,97} \approx 1/F_{.025,97,41} \approx 1/F_{.025,100,40} = 1/1.74 = .57$$

Because $F = .47$ is less than $.57$, we reject the null hypothesis.

EXCEL Data Analysis

	A	B	C
1	F-Test: Two-Sample for Variances		
2			
3		*Offspring*	*Outsider*
4	Mean	−0.10	1.24
5	Variance	3.79	8.03
6	Observations	42	98
7	df	41	97
8	F	0.47	
9	P(F<=f) one-tail	0.0040	
10	F Critical one-tail	0.6314	

The value of the test statistic is $F = .47$, and the p-value $= 2 \times .0040 = .0080$.

XLSTAT

	A	B	C	D	E	F
1	Hypothesized ratio (R): 1					
2	Significance level (%): 5					
3						
4	Summary statistics:					
5	Variable	Observations	Minimum	Maximum	Mean	Std. deviation
6	Offspring	42	-5.25	3.27	-0.10	1.95
7	Outsider	98	-5.96	8.68	1.24	2.83
8						
9	Fisher's F-test / Two-tailed test:					
10	Ratio	0.471				
11	F (Observed value)	0.471				
12	F (Critical value)	1.639				
13	DF1	41				
14	DF2	97				
15	p-value (Two-tailed)	0.0081				
16	alpha	0.05				

INTERPRET

There is enough evidence to infer that the population variances differ. The appropriate technique is the unequal-variances t-test of $\mu_1 - \mu_2$.

Because we want to determine whether there is a *difference* between means, the alternative hypothesis is

$$H_1: \quad (\mu_1 - \mu_2) \neq 0$$

and the null hypothesis is

$$H_0: \quad (\mu_1 - \mu_2) = 0$$

COMPUTE

MANUALLY:

From the data, we calculated the following statistics:

$$\bar{x}_1 = -.10$$
$$\bar{x}_2 = 1.24$$
$$s_1^2 = 3.79$$
$$s_2^2 = 8.03$$

The number of degrees of freedom of the test statistic is

$$\nu = \frac{(s_1^2/n_1 + s_2^2/n_2)^2}{\dfrac{(s_1^2/n_1)^2}{n_1 - 1} + \dfrac{(s_2^2/n_2)^2}{n_2 - 1}}$$

$$= \frac{(3.79/42 + 8.03/98)^2}{\dfrac{(3.79/42)^2}{42 - 1} + \dfrac{(8.03/98)^2}{98 - 1}}$$

$$= 110.69 \text{ rounded to } 111$$

The rejection region is

$$t < -t_{\alpha/2,\nu} = -t_{.025,111} \approx -t_{.025,110} = -1.982 \quad \text{or} \quad t > t_{\alpha/2,\nu} = t_{.025,111} \approx 1.982$$

The value of the test statistic is computed next:

$$t = \frac{(\bar{x}_1 - \bar{x}_2) - (\mu_1 - \mu_2)}{\sqrt{\left(\dfrac{s_1^2}{n_1} + \dfrac{s_2^2}{n_2}\right)}}$$

$$= \frac{(-.10 - 1.24) - (0)}{\sqrt{\left(\dfrac{3.79}{42} + \dfrac{8.03}{98}\right)}} = -3.22$$

EXCEL Data Analysis

	A	B	C
1	t-Test: Two-Sample Assuming Unequal Variances		
2			
3		Offspring	Outsider
4	Mean	−0.10	1.24
5	Variance	3.79	8.03
6	Observations	42	98
7	Hypothesized Mean Difference	0	
8	df	111	
9	t Stat	−3.22	
10	P(T<=t) one-tail	0.0008	
11	t Critical one-tail	1.6587	
12	P(T<=t) two-tail	0.0017	
13	t Critical two-tail	1.9816	

INSTRUCTIONS

Follow the instructions for Example 13.1, except at step 2 click **Data, Data Analysis,** and **t-Test: Two-Sample Assuming Unequal Variances**.

XLSTAT

	A	B	C	D	E	F
1	Hypothesized difference (D): 0					
2	Significance level (%): 5					
3						
4	Summary statistics:					
5	Variable	Observations	Minimum	Maximum	Mean	Std. deviation
6	Offspring	42	-5.25	3.27	-0.10	1.95
7	Outsider	98	-5.96	8.68	1.24	2.83
8						
9	t-test for two independent samples / Two-tailed test:					
10	Difference	-1.34				
11	t (Observed value)	-3.22				
12	|t| (Critical value)	1.98				
13	DF	111				
14	p-value (Two-tailed)	0.0017				
15	alpha	0.05				

INSTRUCTIONS

Follow the instructions for Example 13.1 except do not click **Assume equality** under **Population variances for the t-test.**

INTERPRET

The t-statistic is -3.22, and its p-value is .0017. Accordingly, we conclude there is sufficient evidence to infer that the mean changes in operating income differ.

Estimating $\mu_1 - \mu_2$: Unequal-Variances

We can also draw inferences about the difference between the two population means by calculating the confidence interval estimator. We use the unequal-variances confidence interval estimator of $\mu_1 - \mu_2$ and a 95% confidence level.

COMPUTE

MANUALLY:

$$(\bar{x}_1 - \bar{x}_2) \pm t_{\alpha/2}\sqrt{\left(\frac{s_1^2}{n_1} + \frac{s_2^2}{n_2}\right)}$$

$$= (-.10 - 1.24) \pm 1.982\sqrt{\left(\frac{3.79}{42} + \frac{8.03}{98}\right)}$$

$$= -1.34 \pm .82$$

$$\text{LCL} = -2.16 \quad \text{and} \quad \text{UCL} = -.52$$

EXCEL Workbook

	A	B	C	D	E	F
1	t-Estimate of the Difference Between Two Means (Unequal-Variances)					
2						
3		Sample 1	Sample 2	Confidence Interval Estimate		
4	Mean	–0.1	1.2	–1.34	±	0.82
5	Variance	3.79	8.03	Lower confidence limit		-2.16
6	Sample size	42	98	Upper confidence limit		-0.52
7	Degrees of freedom	111				
8	Confidence level	0.95				

INSTRUCTIONS

Follow the instructions for Example 13.1 except use the **t-Estimate_2 Means (Uneq-Var)** tab.

XLSTAT

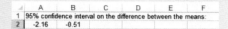

	A	B	C	D	E	F
1	95% confidence interval on the difference between the means:					
2	-2.16	-0.51				

INSTRUCTIONS

Follow the instructions for Example 13.1 except do not click **Assume equality** under **Population variances for the t-test.** Make certain to specify a two-tail test.

INTERPRET

We estimate that the mean change in operating incomes for outsiders exceeds the mean change in the operating income for offspring by between .52 and 2.16 percentage points.

13-1b Checking the Required Condition

Both the equal-variances and unequal-variances techniques require that the populations be normally distributed.[†] As before, we can check to see whether the requirement is satisfied by drawing the histograms of the data.

To illustrate, we used Excel to create the histograms for Example 13.1 (Figures 13.2 and 13.3) and Example 13.2 (Figures 13.4 and 13.5). Although the histograms are not

FIGURE **13.2** **Histogram of Rates of Return for Directly Purchased Mutual Funds in Example 13.1**

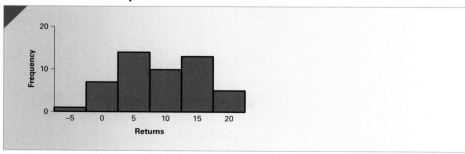

[†]As we pointed out in Chapter 12 large sample sizes can overcome the effects of extreme nonnormality.

perfectly bell shaped, it appears that in both examples the data are at least approximately normal. Because this technique is robust, we can be confident in the validity of the results.

FIGURE **13.3** **Histogram of Rates of Return for Broker-Purchased Mutual Funds in Example 13.1**

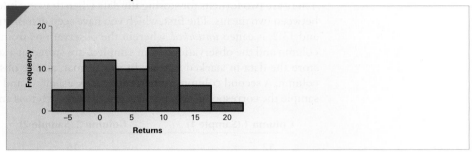

FIGURE **13.4** **Histogram of Change in Operating Income for Offspring-Run Businesses in Example 13.2**

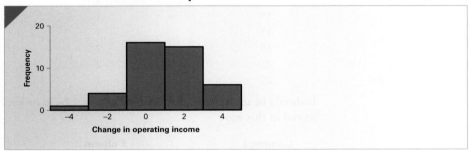

FIGURE **13.5** **Histogram of Change in Operating Income for Outsider-Run Businesses in Example 13.2**

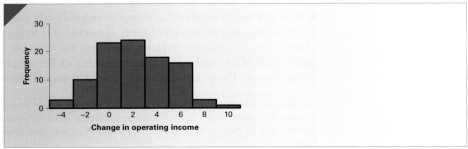

13-1c Violation of the Required Condition

When the normality requirement is unsatisfied, we can use a nonparametric technique: the Wilcoxon rank sum test (Chapter 19*) to replace the equal-variances test of $\mu_1 - \mu_2$. We have no alternative to the unequal-variances test of $\mu_1 - \mu_2$ when the populations are very nonnormal.

13-1d Data Formats

There are two formats for storing the data when drawing inferences about the difference between two means. The first, which you have seen demonstrated in both Examples 13.1 and 13.2, is called *unstacked*, wherein the observations from sample 1 are stored in one column and the observations from sample 2 are stored in a second column. We may also store the data in stacked format. In this format, all the observations are stored in one column. A second column contains the codes, usually 1 and 2, that indicate from which sample the corresponding observation was drawn. Here is an example of unstacked data.

Column 1 (Sample 1)	Column 2 (Sample 2)
12	18
19	23
13	25

Here are the same data in stacked form.

Column 1	Column 2
12	1
19	1
13	1
18	2
23	2
25	2

It should be understood that the data need not be in order. Hence, they could have been stored in this way:

Column 1	Column 2
18	2
25	2
13	1
12	1
23	2
19	1

If there are two populations to compare and only one variable, then it is probably better to record the data in unstacked form. However, it is frequently the case that we want to observe several variables and compare them. For example, suppose that we survey male and female MBAs and ask each to report his or her age, income, and number of years of experience. These data are usually stored in stacked form using the following format.

---

*Instructors who wish to teach the use of nonparametric techniques for testing the difference between two means when the normality requirement is not satisfied should use the online appendixes Introduction to Nonparametric Techniques and Wilcoxon Rank Sum Test and Wilcoxon Signed Rank Sum Test.

Column 1: Code identifying female (1) and male (2)

Column 2: Age

Column 3: Income

Column 4: Years of experience

To compare ages, we would use columns 1 and 2. Columns 1 and 3 are used to compare incomes, and columns 1 and 4 are used to compare experience levels.

Most statistical software requires one format or the other. Some but not all of Excel's techniques require unstacked data. Some of XLSTAT's procedures allow either format, whereas others specify only one. Fortunately, both of our software packages allow the statistics practitioner to alter the format. (See online appendix Excel Instructions for Stacking and Unstacking Data.) We say "fortunately" because this allowed us to store the data in either form on our website. In fact, we've used both forms to allow you to practice your ability to manipulate the data as necessary. You will need this ability to perform statistical techniques in this and other chapters in this book.

13-1e Developing an Understanding of Statistical Concepts 1

The formulas in this section are relatively complicated. However, conceptually both test statistics are based on the techniques we introduced in Chapter 11 and repeated in Chapter 12: The value of the test statistic is the difference between the statistic $\bar{x}_1 - \bar{x}_2$ and the hypothesized value of the parameter $\mu_1 - \mu_2$ measured in terms of the standard error.

13-1f Developing an Understanding of Statistical Concepts 2

The standard error must be estimated from the data for all inferential procedures introduced here. The method we use to compute the standard error of $\bar{x}_1 - \bar{x}_2$ depends on whether the population variances are equal. When they are equal we calculate and use the pooled variance estimator s_p^2. We are applying an important principle here, and we will do so again in Section 13-5 and in later chapters. The principle can be loosely stated as follows: Where possible, it is advantageous to pool sample data to estimate the standard error. In Example 13.1, we are able to pool because we assume that the two samples were drawn from populations with a common variance. Combining both samples increases the accuracy of the estimate. Thus, s_p^2 is a better estimator of the common variance than either s_1^2 or s_2^2 separately. When the two population variances are unequal, we cannot pool the data and produce a common estimator. We must compute s_1^2 and s_2^2 and use them to estimate σ_1^2 and σ_2^2, respectively.

Here is a summary of how we recognize the techniques presented in this section.

Factors that Identify the Equal-Variances t-Test and Estimator of $\mu_1 - \mu_2$

1. **Problem objective**: Compare two populations
2. **Data type**: Interval
3. **Descriptive measurement**: Central location
4. **Experimental design**: Independent samples
5. **Population variances**: Equal

> **Factors that Identify the Unequal-Variances t-Test and Estimator of $\mu_1 - \mu_2$**
> 1. **Problem objective**: Compare two populations
> 2. **Data type**: Interval
> 3. **Descriptive measurement**: Central location
> 4. **Experimental design**: Independent samples
> 5. **Population variances**: Unequal

EXERCISES

Developing an Understanding of Statistical Concepts

Exercises 13.1–13.6 are "what-if" analyses designed to determine what happens to the test statistics and interval estimates when elements of the statistical inference change. These problems can be solved manually, using an Excel spreadsheet.

13.1 In random samples of 25 from each of two normal populations, we found the following statistics:

$$\bar{x}_1 = 524 \qquad s_1 = 129$$
$$\bar{x}_2 = 469 \qquad s_2 = 141$$

a. Estimate the difference between the two population means with 95% confidence.
b. Repeat part (a) increasing the standard deviations to $s_1 = 255$ and $s_2 = 260$.
c. Describe what happens when the sample standard deviations get larger.
d. Repeat part (a) with samples of size 100.
e. Discuss the effects of increasing the sample size.

13.2 In random samples of 12 from each of two normal populations, we found the following statistics:

$$\bar{x}_1 = 74 \qquad s_1 = 18$$
$$\bar{x}_2 = 71 \qquad s_2 = 16$$

a. Test with $\alpha = .05$ to determine whether we can infer that the population means differ.
b. Repeat part (a) increasing the standard deviations to $s_1 = 210$ and $s_2 = 198$.
c. Describe what happens when the sample standard deviations get larger.
d. Repeat part (a) with samples of size 150.
e. Discuss the effects of increasing the sample size.
f. Repeat part (a) changing the mean of sample 1 to $\bar{x}_1 = 76$.
g. Discuss the effect of increasing $\bar{x}_1$.

13.3 Random sampling from two normal populations produced the following results:

$$\bar{x}_1 = 63 \qquad s_1 = 18 \qquad n_1 = 50$$
$$\bar{x}_2 = 60 \qquad s_2 = 7 \qquad n_2 = 45$$

a. Estimate with 90% confidence the difference between the two population means.
b. Repeat part (a) changing the sample standard deviations to 41 and 15, respectively.
c. What happens when the sample standard deviations increase?
d. Repeat part (a) doubling the sample sizes.
e. Describe the effects of increasing the sample sizes.

13.4 Random sampling from two normal populations produced the following results:

$$\bar{x}_1 = 412 \qquad s_1 = 128 \qquad n_1 = 150$$
$$\bar{x}_2 = 405 \qquad s_2 = 54 \qquad n_2 = 150$$

a. Can we infer at the 5% significance level that μ_1 is greater than μ_2?
b. Repeat part (a) decreasing the standard deviations to $s_1 = 31$ and $s_2 = 16$.
c. Describe what happens when the sample standard deviations get smaller.
d. Repeat part (a) with samples of size 20.
e. Discuss the effects of decreasing the sample size.
f. Repeat part (a) changing the mean of sample 1 to $\bar{x}_1 = 409$.
g. Discuss the effect of decreasing $\bar{x}_1$.

13.5 For each of the following, determine the number of degrees of freedom assuming equal population variances and unequal population variances.
a. $n_1 = 15, n_2 = 15, s_1^2 = 25, s_2^2 = 15$
b. $n_1 = 10, n_2 = 16, s_1^2 = 100, s_2^2 = 15$
c. $n_1 = 50, n_2 = 50, s_1^2 = 8, s_2^2 = 14$
d. $n_1 = 60, n_2 = 45, s_1^2 = 75, s_2^2 = 10$

13.6 Refer to Exercise 13.5.

    a. Confirm that in each case the number of degrees of freedom for the equal-variances test statistic and confidence interval estimator is larger than that for the unequal-variances test statistic and confidence interval estimator.

    b. Try various combinations of sample sizes and sample variances to illustrate that the number of degrees of freedom for the equal-variances test statistic and confidence interval estimator is larger than that for the unequal-variances test statistic and confidence interval estimator.

Applications

For Exercises 13.7 to 13.16 use a 10% significance level.

13.7 A human resources manager for a car company wanted to know whether production-line workers have more days absent than office workers. He took a random sample of eight workers from each category and recorded the number of days absent the previous year. Can we infer that there is a difference in days absent between the two groups of workers?

Production-line workers	4	0	6	8	3	11	13	5
Office workers	9	2	7	1	4	7	9	8

13.8 The owner of a small book-publishing company is concerned about the declining number of people who read books. To learn more about the problem she takes a random sample of customers in a retail book store and asked each how many books they read in the last 12 months. The following figures were recorded. Is there enough evidence to conclude that there are differences in the number of books purchased by females and males?

Females	5	18	11	3	7	5	9	13	15
Males	9	7	9	3	6	5			

13.9 The operations manager of a manufacturer of television remote controls wants to determine which batteries last the longest in his product. He took a random sample of his remote controls and tested two brands of batteries. Here are the number of minutes of continuous use before the batteries failed for each brand. Is there statistical evidence of a difference in longevity between the two batteries?

Battery 1	106	111	109	105
Battery 2	125	103	121	118

13.10 An avid golfer has just purchased a new putter with a money-back guarantee. She plays seven rounds with the new putter and seven rounds with her old putter and records the number of putts. Can the golfer conclude that the new putter is better?

Old putter	37	35	38	40	37	33
New putter	36	34	34	32	35	36

13.11 XR13-11 Every month a clothing store conducts an inventory and calculates losses from theft. The store would like to reduce these losses and is considering two methods. The first is to hire a security guard, and the second is to install cameras. To help decide which method to choose, the manager hired a security guard for 6 months. During the next 6-month period, the store installed cameras. The monthly losses were recorded and are listed here. The manager decided that because the cameras were cheaper than the guard, he would install the cameras unless there was enough evidence to infer that the guard was better. What should the manager do?

Security guard	355	284	401	398	477	254
Cameras	486	303	270	386	411	435

13.12 Xr13-12 A men's softball league is experimenting with a yellow baseball that is easier to see during night games. One way to judge the effectiveness is to count the number of errors. In a preliminary experiment, the yellow baseball was used in 10 games and the traditional white baseball was used in another 10 games. The number of errors in each game was recorded and is listed here. Can we infer that there are fewer errors on average when the yellow ball is used?

Yellow	5	2	6	7	2	5	3	8	4	9
White	7	6	8	5	9	11	8	3	6	10

13.13 Xr13-13 A number of restaurants feature a device that allows credit card users to swipe their cards at the table. It allows the user to specify a percentage or a dollar amount to leave as a tip. In an experiment to see how it works, a random sample of credit card users was drawn. Some paid the usual way, and some used the new device. The percent left as a tip was recorded and listed below. Can we infer that users of the device leave larger tips?

Usual	10.3	15.2	13.0	9.9	12.1	13.4	12.2	14.9	13.2	12.0
Device	13.6	15.7	12.9	13.2	12.9	13.4	12.1	13.9	15.7	15.4	17.4

13.14 Xr13-14 Who spends more on their vacations, golfers or skiers? To help answer this question, a travel agency surveyed 15 customers who regularly take their spouses on either a skiing or a golfing vacation. The amounts spent on vacations last year are shown here. Can we infer that golfers and skiers differ in their vacation expenses?

Golfer	2,450	3,860	4,528	1,944	3,166	3,275
	4,490	3,685	2,950			
Skier	3,805	3,725	2,990	4,357	5,550	4,130

13.15 Xr13-15   A growing concern among fans and owners is the amount of time to complete a major league baseball game. To assess the extent of the problem, a statistician recorded the amount of time (in minutes) to complete a random sample of games 5 years ago and this year. Can we conclude that games take longer to complete this year than 5 years ago.

5 Years Ago

169	160	174	161	187	172	177	187	153	169	161	194

This Year

153	182	162	190	163	189	171	197	159	180	197	178

13.16 Xr13-16   How do drivers react to sudden large increases in the price of gasoline? To help answer the question, a statistician recorded the speeds of cars as they passed a large service station. He recorded the speeds (mph) in the same location after the service station sign showed that the price of gasoline had risen by 15 cents. Can we conclude that the speeds differ?

Speeds Before Price Increase

43	36	31	30	28	36	27	36	35	30	32	36

Speeds After Price Increase

32	33	36	31	32	29	28	39	26	30	32	30

Exercises 13.17–13.53 require the use of a computer and software. The answers to may be calculated manually using the sample statistics listed in Appendix A. ***Use a 5% significance level unless specified otherwise.***

13.17 Xr13-17   The president of Tastee Inc., a baby-food producer, claims that her company's product is superior to that of her leading competitor because babies gain weight faster with her product. (This is a good thing for babies.) To test this claim, a survey was undertaken. Mothers of newborn babies were asked which baby food they intended to feed their babies. Those who responded Tastee or the leading competitor were asked to keep track of their babies' weight gains over the next 2 months. There were 15 mothers who indicated that they would feed their babies Tastee and 25 who responded that they would feed their babies the product of the leading competitor. Each baby's weight gain (in ounces) was recorded.

a. Can we conclude, using weight gain as our criterion, that Tastee baby food is indeed superior?

b. Estimate with 95% confidence the difference between the mean weight gains of the two products.

c. Check to ensure that the required condition(s) is satisfied.

13.18 Xr13-18   Is eating oat bran an effective way to reduce cholesterol? Early studies indicated that eating oat bran daily reduces cholesterol levels by 5% to 10%. Reports of this study resulted in the introduction of many new breakfast cereals with various percentages of oat bran as an ingredient. However, an experiment performed by medical researchers in Boston cast doubt on the effectiveness of oat bran. In that study, 120 volunteers ate oat bran for breakfast, and another 120 volunteers ate another grain cereal for breakfast. At the end of 6 weeks, the percentage of cholesterol reduction was computed for both groups. Can we infer that oat bran is different from other cereals in terms of cholesterol reduction?

13.19 Xr13-19*   In assessing the value of radio advertisements, sponsors consider not only the total number of listeners but also their ages. The 18 to 34 age group is considered to spend the most money. To examine the issue, the manager of an FM station commissioned a survey. One objective was to measure the difference in listening habits between the 18 to 34 age and 35 to 50 age groups. The survey asked 250 people in each age category how much time they spent listening to FM radio per day. The results (in minutes) were recorded and stored in stacked format (column 1 = Age group and column 2 = Listening times).

a. Can we conclude that a difference exists between the two groups?

b. Estimate with 95% confidence the difference in mean time listening to FM radio between the two age groups.

c. Are the required conditions satisfied for the techniques you used in parts (a) and (b)?

13.20 Xr13-20   The cruise ship business is rapidly increasing. Although cruises have long been associated with seniors, it now appears that younger people are choosing a cruise as their vacations. To determine whether this is true, an executive for a cruise line sampled passengers 2 years ago and this year and determined their ages.

a. Do these data allow the executive to infer that cruise ships are attracting younger customers?

b. Estimate with 99% confidence the difference in ages between this year and 2 years ago.

13.21 Xr13-21*   Automobile insurance companies take many factors into consideration when setting rates. These factors include age, marital status, and miles driven per year. To determine the effect of gender, a random sample of young (under 25, with at least 2 years of driving experience) male and female drivers was surveyed. Each was asked how many miles he or she had driven in the past year. The distances (in thousands of miles) are stored in stacked format (column 1 = driving distances and column 2 identifies the gender where 1 = male and code 2 = female).

a. Can we conclude that male and female drivers differ in the numbers of miles driven per year?
b. Estimate with 95% confidence the difference in mean distance driven by male and female drivers.
c. Check to ensure that the required condition(s) of the techniques used in parts (a) and (b) is satisfied.

13.22 Xr13-22 The president of a company that manufactures automobile air conditioners is considering switching his supplier of condensers. Supplier A, the current producer of condensers for the manufacturer, prices its product 5% higher than supplier B. Because the president wants to maintain his company's reputation for quality, he wants to be sure that supplier B's condensers last at least as long as supplier A's. After a careful analysis, the president decided to retain supplier A if there is sufficient statistical evidence that supplier A's condensers last longer on average than supplier B's. In an experiment, 30 midsize cars were equipped with air conditioners using type A condensers while another 30 midsize cars were equipped with type B condensers. The number of miles (in thousands) driven by each car before the condenser broke down was recorded. Should the president retain supplier A?

13.23 Xr13-23 An important function of a firm's human resources manager is to track worker turnover. As a general rule, companies prefer to retain workers. New workers frequently need to be trained, and it often takes time for new workers to learn how to perform their jobs. To investigate nationwide results, a human resources manager organized a survey wherein a random sample of men and women was asked how long they had worked for their current employers. Can we infer that men and women have different job tenures? (Adapted from the *Statistical Abstract of the United States, 2000*, Table 664).

13.24 Xr13-24 A statistics professor is about to select a statistical software package for her course. One of the most important features, according to the professor, is the ease with which students learn to use the software. She has narrowed the selection to two possibilities: software A, a menu-driven statistical package with some high-powered techniques, and software B, a spreadsheet that has the capability of performing most techniques. To help her decision, she asks 40 statistics students selected at random to choose one of the two packages. She gives each student a statistics problem to solve by computer and the appropriate manual. The amount of time (in minutes) each student needed to complete the assignment was recorded.

a. Can the professor conclude from these data that the two software packages differ in the amount of time needed to learn how to use them? (Use a 1% significance level.)
b. Estimate with 95% confidence the difference in the mean amount of time needed to learn to use the two packages.
c. What are the required conditions for the techniques used in parts (a) and (b)?
d. Check to see whether the required conditions are satisfied.

13.25 Xr13-25 One factor in low productivity is the amount of time wasted by workers. Wasted time includes time spent cleaning up mistakes, waiting for more material and equipment, and performing any other activity not related to production. In a project designed to examine the problem, an operations-management consultant took a survey of 200 workers in companies that were classified as successful (on the basis of their latest annual profits) and another 200 workers from unsuccessful companies. The amount of time (in hours) wasted during a standard 40-hour workweek was recorded for each worker.

a. Do these data provide enough evidence at the 1% significance level to infer that the amount of time wasted in unsuccessful firms exceeds that of successful ones?
b. Estimate with 95% confidence how much more time is wasted in unsuccessful firms than in successful ones.

13.26 Xr13-26 Recent studies seem to indicate that using a cell phone while driving is dangerous. One reason for this is that a driver's reaction time may slow while he or she is talking on the phone. Researchers at Miami (Ohio) University measured the reaction times of a sample of drivers who owned a cell phone. Half the sample was tested while on the phone and the other half was tested while not on the phone. Can we conclude that reaction times are slower for drivers using cell phones?

13.27 Xr13-27 Refer to Exercise 13.26. To determine whether the type of phone usage affects reaction times, another study was launched. A group of drivers was asked to participate in a discussion. Half the group engaged in simple chitchat, and the other half participated in a political discussion. Once again, reaction times were measured. Can we infer that the type of telephone discussion affects reaction times?

13.28 <u>Xr13-28</u> Most consumers who require someone to perform various professional services undertake research before making their selection. A random sample of people who recently selected a financial planner and a random sample of individuals who chose a stockbroker were asked to report the amount of time they spent researching before deciding. Can we infer that people spend more time researching for a financial planner than they do for a stockbroker? (*Source:* Yankelovich Partners.)

13.29 <u>Xr13-29</u> A study by researchers at North Carolina State University found thousands of errors in 12 of the most widely used high school science texts. For example, the Statue of Liberty is left-handed; volume is equal to length multiplied by depth. The books are so bad that Philip Sadler, director of science education at the Harvard-Smithsonian Center for Astrophysics, decided to conduct a study of their effects. He recorded the physics marks of college students who had used a textbook in high school and the marks of students who did not have a high school textbook. Do these data allow us to infer that students without high school textbooks in science outperform students who used textbooks?

13.30 <u>Xr13-30</u> Between Wendy's and McDonald's, which fast-food drive-through window is faster? To answer the question, a random sample of service times for each restaurant was measured. Can we infer from these data that there are differences in service times between the two chains?

(*Source:* QSR Drive-Thru Time Study.)

13.31 <u>Xr13-31</u> Lack of sleep is a serious medical problem. It has been linked to heart attacks and automobile collisions. A Statistics Canada study asked a random sample of Canadian adults to report the amount of sleep they normally get. Can we conclude from the data that men and women differ in the amount of sleep?

13.32 <u>Xr13-32</u> It is often useful for companies to know who their customers are and how they became customers. In a study of credit card use, random samples were drawn of cardholders who applied for the credit card and credit cardholders who were contacted by telemarketers or by mail. The total purchases made by each last month were recorded. Can we conclude from these data that differences exist on average between the two types of customers?

13.33 <u>Xr13-33</u> Tire manufacturers are constantly researching ways to produce tires that last longer. New innovations are tested by professional drivers on racetracks. However, any promising inventions are also test-driven by ordinary drivers. The latter tests are closer to what the tire company's customers will actually experience. Suppose that to determine whether a new steel-belted radial tire lasts longer than the company's current model, two new-design tires were installed on the rear wheels of 20 randomly selected cars and two existing-design tires were installed on the rear wheels of another 20 cars. All drivers were told to drive in their usual way until the tires wore out. The number of miles driven by each driver was recorded. Can the company infer that the new tire will last longer on average than the existing tire?

13.34 <u>Xr13-34</u> It is generally believed that salespeople who are paid on a commission basis outperform salespeople who are paid a fixed salary. Some management consultants argue, however, that in certain industries the fixed-salary salesperson may sell more because the consumer will feel less sales pressure and respond to the salesperson less as an antagonist. In an experiment to study this, a random sample of 180 salespeople from a retail clothing chain was selected. Of these, 90 salespeople were paid a fixed salary, and the remaining 90 were paid a commission on each sale. The total dollar amount of 1 month's sales for each was recorded. Can we conclude that the commission salesperson outperforms the fixed-salary salesperson?

13.35 <u>Xr13-35</u> Credit scorecards were designed to be used to help financial institutions make decisions about loan applications. However, some insurance companies have suggested that credit scores could also be used to determine insurance premiums, particularly car insurance. The Massachusetts Public Interest Research Group has come out against this proposal. To acquire more information, an executive for a car-insurance company gathered data about a random sample of the company's customers. She recorded whether the individual was involved in an accident in the last 3 years and determined the credit score. Can the executive infer that there is a difference in scores between those who did and those who did not have accidents in a 3-year period?

13.36 <u>Xr13-36*</u> Traditionally, wine has been sold in glass bottles with cork stoppers. The stoppers are supposed to keep air out of the bottle because oxygen is the enemy of wine, particularly red wine. Recent research appears to indicate that metal screw caps are more effective in keeping air out of the bottle. However, metal caps are perceived to be inferior and usually associated with cheaper brands of wine. To determine if this perception is wrong, a random sample of 130 people who drink at least one bottle per week on average was asked to participate in an experiment. All were given the same wine in two types of bottles. One group was given a corked bottle, and the other was given a bottle with a metal cap and asked to taste the wine and indicate what they think the retail price of the wine should be.

Determine whether there is enough evidence to conclude that bottles of wine with metal caps are perceived to be cheaper.

13.37 Xr13-37 Studies have shown that tired children have trouble learning because neurons become incapable of forming new synaptic connections that are necessary to encode memory. The problem is that the school day starts too early. Awakened at dawn, teenage brains are still releasing melatonin, which makes them sleepy. Several years ago, Edina, Minnesota, changed its high school start from 7:25 A.M. to 8:30 A.M. The SAT scores for a random sample of students taken before the change and a random sample of SAT scores after the change were recorded. Can we infer from the data that SAT scores increased after the change in the school start time?

Overeating Experiments

Obesity is not only a health problem but it is a financial one as well. Obesity leads to health problems such as diabetes, heart disease, and strokes. These result in increased medical costs to individuals and employers. About one-third of North Americans are obese. Why do we overeat? The reasons are complicated. However, a number of experiments have shed some light on the subject. In most of the experiments, subjects were not aware that an experiment was being conducted. **Conduct all tests at the 5% significance level.**

13.38 Xr13-38 Stale Popcorn Experiment

Students were invited to watch a newly released movie shortly after lunch. Half the students were given a medium-sized bucket of popcorn and the other half a large-sized bucket. The popcorn was not fresh. In fact, it was five days old and very stale. Both sizes of containers were large enough so that none of the students could finish. At the end of the movie the buckets were weighed and the results recorded. Do these data allow researchers to conclude that the larger the bucket the more people will eat?

(*Source:* Adapted from Brian Wansink and SeaBum Park, "At the Movies: How External Cues and Perceived Taste Impact Consumption Volume, *Food Quality and Preference* 12:1 (January 2001): 69–74.)

13.39 Xr13-39 Fake Wine Experiment

Diners at a restaurant were informed on entering that they would be receiving a free glass of wine, which they were told was Cabernet Sauvignon. However, it was not. It was a cheap wine sold for $2 a bottle, popularly known as Two Buck Chuck. Half of the diners were told that the wine was from a new California winery. The other half of diners were informed that the wine they would receive was from a new North Dakota winery. (There are no wineries in North Dakota and even

if there were the wine produced would not be considered excellent.) The restaurant featured a fixed menu so that all diners had exactly the same meal. The goal of the experiment was to determine whether the perceived quality of the wine affected their dining experience. The amount of food consumed (measured as a percentage of the amount originally served that was consumed by the diner, so that 100 represents a diner who cleaned his or her plate) and the amount of time spent in the restaurant were recorded.

a. Is there enough statistical evidence to infer that diners who believe they are drinking a fine wine (California wine) eat more than diners who believe they are drinking an inferior wine?

b. Can we conclude that diners who believe they are drinking a fine wine (California wine) spend more time in the restaurant than diners who believe they are drinking an inferior wine?

(*Source:* Adapted from Brian Wansink, Collin Payne, and Jill North, "Fine as North Dakota Wine: Sensory Experiences and the Intake of Companion Foods," *Physiology and Behavior* 90:5 (2007): 712–16.)

13.40 Xr13-40 Super Bowl Chicken Wings Experiment

A group of MBA students was invited to watch a Super Bowl game at a local sports bar. They were promised free chicken wings and free soda drinks. The students loaded up on the wings and when they were eaten could refill their plates. Waitresses were part of the experiment. For half the students they cleared the plates loaded with bones. The other half did not have their bone plates picked up. After the Super Bowl was over the number of wings consumed by each group of students was recorded. Is there sufficient statistical evidence to infer that people eat more when they are not aware of how much they have already eaten?

(*Source:* Adapted from Brian Wansink and Collin Payne, "Counting Bones: Environmental Cues that Decrease Food Intake," *Perceptual and Motor Skills* 104 (2007): 273–77.)

13.41 Xr13-41 Bags of M&M's Experiment

A researcher recruited 40 adults at a PTA meeting and asked them to view a video. To thank them for their participation, 20 adults were given a one-pound bag of M&Ms and the other half a half pound. All were told that they can snack on the M&Ms while they watched the video. The numbers of M&Ms eaten was recorded. Is there sufficient evidence to conclude that more M&M's would be eaten by people who were given the full pound?

(*Source:* Adapted from Brian Wansink, "Can Package Size Accelerate Usage Volume?" *Journal of Marketing* 60:3 (July 1996): 1–14.)

13.42 Xr13-42 Is it true that an apple a day keeps the doctor away? A study designed and conducted by the National Health and Nutrition Examination Study (results published in the *Journal of the American Medical Association*) considered 8,399 American adults of whom 756 reported that they ate a small apple a day. The rest did not eat apples or ate them infrequently. The number of healthcare visits in the previous 36 months was recorded. Conduct a test to determine whether the adage is true.

13.43 Xr13-43 In a Reason-Rupe poll, a random sample of people were asked, "Just a rough guess, what percent profit on each dollar of sales do you think the average company makes after taxes?" The results from 5 years ago and this year were recorded. Can we infer that the guesses this year are higher than they were 5 years ago?

13.44 Xr13-44 Michigan State's Collegiate Employment Research Institute collected data from mid-August to mid-September, tapping the employment offices at 200 schools, which gathered starting salary data from 3,300 employers. The starting salaries for a random sample of electrical engineers and the starting salary for a sample of mechanical engineers were recorded. Can we conclude that electrical engineers receive higher starting salaries than do mechanical engineers?

13.45 Xr13-45 Does drinking hot chocolate boost the memory in older people? A random sample of people around the age of 73 was recruited. All had some form of cognitive deterioration. Half the participants drank two cups of hot chocolate a day for 30 days. Each was tested by solving puzzles that required working memory. The amount of time needed to complete the puzzles was recorded. Is there sufficient evidence to conclude that chocolate helps improve cognitive memory?

13.46 Xr12-51* Refer to Exercise 12.51. The researchers also recorded the number of missing teeth of a random sample of Britons. Can we infer that, in fact, Americans have more missing teeth?

13.47 Xr13-47 Researchers at the University of California, San Diego conducted an experiment that studied the sleep of 164 American adults. The researchers used a device called a polysomnography machine to document slow-wave sleep, which is thought to be the most restorative period of sleep very important to good health. Generally, people are thought to spend 20 percent of their night in slow-wave sleep. The percentage of slow-wave sleep each individual experienced was recorded as was the race of the participants in the study. Can we infer that White American adults get more slow-wave sleep than Black American adults?

13.48 Xr13-48 How does exercise affect memory in older adults with mild cognitive impairment? A study published in the *Journal of Aging Research* asked a random sample of women aged 70–80 with subjective memory complaints to exercise twice a week for six months. At the end of the study all were given a test that measured verbal memory and learning. Also recorded were the results of the test for a control group that did not exercise. Can we conclude that exercise improves cognitive impairment?

13.49 Xr13-49 Is there a tax on the poor? The tax on income is progressive in that higher income individuals pay at a high rate than lower-income people. For example, the top 0.1 percent of taxpayers earn 9.1 percent of the income, but pay 17.4 percent of all federal taxes. The top 1 percent of taxpayers earn 19 percent of the income but pay 36.9 percent of the taxes. The top 5 percent earn 33.4 percent but pay 57.1 percent, while the bottom 50 percent earn 13.4 percent but only pay 3.3 percent of federal taxes. However, the so-called "sin taxes" are regressive. To measure how taxes on tobacco and alcohol are regressive the National Center for Policy Analysis randomly sampled low-income and high-income American adults who smoke (About one-third of low-income and one-fifth of high income individuals smoke.) and recorded their annual expenditures on tobacco. Is there sufficient statistical evidence to infer that low-income smokers spend more than high-income smokers?

13.50 Xr13-50 Refer to Exercise 13.49. The NCPA conducted another study, this one on alcohol. They randomly sample low-income and middle-income alcohol drinkers and determined how much each spends annually on alcoholic drinks. Can we infer that low-income alcoholic drinkers spend more than middle-income?

13.51 Xr13-51 Which Canadians give the most to charity? A Statistics Canada study took random samples of men and women and recorded the amount donated to charity in the previous year. Is there sufficient evidence to infer that there are differences between the two sexes?

13.52 Xr13-52* Are Canadian public servants gaming the system by taking more sick days than do private sector workers? To answer the question Statistics Canada took a random sample of white-collar public servants and a random sample of white collar private sector workers and recorded the number of sick days each took in the previous 12 months. Is there enough statistical evidence to infer that white-collar public servants take more sick days than do white-collar private sector workers?

13.53 Xr13-52* Refer to Exercise 13.52. The data for public servants' sick days 5 years ago was also recorded. Is there sufficient evidence to conclude that there are more sick days this year than 5 years ago?

GENERAL SOCIAL SURVEY EXERCISES

Use a 5% significance level for all tests. Use a 95% confidence level for all estimates.

13.54 GSS2014* Study after study indicate that men earn higher incomes than women (SEX: 1 = Male, 2 = Female).
  a. To determine the extent of the differential in 2014 estimate the difference between male and female annual incomes (RINCOME).
  b. What are the required conditions for the validity of your answer in part (a)?
  c. Are the required conditions satisfied? Explain.

13.55 GSS2014* Some economists have theorized that one of the reasons that men earn higher incomes than women (SEX: 1 = Male, 2 = Female) is that men work longer hours (HRS1).
  a. Conduct a statistical test to determine whether this contention is true.
  b. Are the required conditions satisfied? Explain.

13.56 GSS2014* Immigration has become an important topic in American politics. Some immigrants came to the United States to do jobs that Americans do not want to do. Many of these immigrants have little formal education. Other immigrants came to the United States with work permits. Many of these are highly educated.
  a. Conduct a test to determine if American-born residents (BORN: 1 = In the United States, 2 = Elsewhere) are more educated than those born outside the United States (EDUC).
  b. Are the required conditions satisfied? Explain.
  c. If the required conditions are not satisfied what other technique can be used to answer the question?

13.57 GSS2014* Because many immigrants come to the United States with little money they often are willing to take risks that can result in high incomes. However, is this enough to overcome language and culture difficulties?

  a. Is there sufficient evidence to infer that Americans born in the United States (BORN: 1 = In the United States, 2 = Elsewhere) have higher incomes than those born elsewhere (RINCOME)?
  b. Are the required conditions satisfied? Explain.
  c. If the required conditions are not satisfied what other technique can be used to answer the question?

13.58 GSS2014* In most countries including the United States, younger people tend to be on the left side of the political spectrum. If so, we would expect Republicans to be older than Democrats.
  a. Conduct a test to determine whether there is enough evidence to infer that Republicans (PARTYID3: 1 = Democrat; 3 = Republican) are older than Democrats (AGE).
  b. What are the required conditions? Are they satisfied?
  c. If the required conditions are not satisfied, what other technique should be used?

13.59 GSS2014* Republicans tend to prefer smaller less intrusive government and lower taxes. Is this because Republicans have higher incomes (PARTYID3: 1 = Democrat; 3 = Republican)?
  a. Do the data allow us to conclude that Republicans earn more income (RINCOME) than Democrats?
  b. Estimate how much more Republicans earn than do Democrats.
  c. What are the required conditions? Are they satisfied?
  d. If the required conditions are not satisfied, what other technique should be used?

13.60 GSS2014* Refer to Exercise 13.59. If it is true that Republicans (PARTYID3: 1 = Democrat; 3 = Republican) have higher incomes than Democrats, is it because they work harder?
  a. Conduct a statistical test to determine whether Republicans work longer hours (HRS1).

b. Are the required conditions satisfied?

c. If the required conditions are not satisfied, what other technique should be used?

13.61 <u>GSS2014*</u> Does education play a role to explain the results in Exercise 13.59.

a. Test to determine whether there is enough evidence to infer that Republicans (PARTYID3: 1 = Democrat; 3 = Republican) more educated than Democrats (EDUC).

b. Estimate the difference in years of education between Democrats and Republicans.

13.62 <u>GSS2014*</u> Perhaps another way to explain the outcome of the test in Exercise 13.59 is that Republicans wait longer to have children.

a. Test to determine whether Republicans are older than Democrats (PARTYID3: 1 = Democrat; 3 = Republican) when their first child is born (AGEKDBRN)

b. Are the required conditions satisfied?

c. If the required conditions are not satisfied, what other technique should be used?

13.63 <u>GSS2014*</u> As was the case with Democrats and Republicans we would expect that Conservatives would have higher incomes (POLVIEWS3: 1 = Liberal, 3 = Conservative)

a. Conduct a statistical test to determine whether we can conclude that Conservatives, income exceeds that of Liberals (RINCOME).

b. Are the required conditions satisfied?

c. If the required conditions are not satisfied, what other technique should be used?

13.64 <u>GSS2014*</u> We can attempt to explain the results in Exercise 13.63 by determining whether Conservatives are more educated than Liberals (POLVIEWS3: 1 = Liberal, 3 = Conservative). Test to determine whether Conservatives have more education than Liberals (EDUC). What does the *p*-value mean?

13.65 <u>GSS2012*</u> Another way to explain the results of Exercise 13.64 is to look at the differences in the number of hours of work.

a. Is there sufficient evidence to infer that Conservatives work longer hours than Liberals (POLVIEWS3: 1 = Liberal, 3 = Conservative) (HRS1)?

b. Are the required conditions satisfied?

c. If the required conditions are not satisfied, what other technique should be used?

13.66 <u>GSS2014*</u> Are government jobs more complex requiring more education than do private sector jobs?

a. Test to determine whether there is enough evidence to conclude that government workers (WRKGOVT: 1 = Government, 2 = Private) have more education than do private sector employees (EDUC).

b. Are the required conditions satisfied?

c. If the required conditions are not satisfied, what other technique should be used?

13.67 <u>GSS2014*</u> As a general rule government employees (WRKGOVT: 1 = Government, 2 = Private) have more job security than do private sector employees. Do they also have higher incomes RINCOME)?

a. Conduct a test to answer the question.

b. Are the required conditions satisfied?

c. If the required conditions are not satisfied, what other technique should be used?

13.68 <u>GSS2014*</u> The upside to working for self-employment is that there is virtually no upper limit to income. If so, we would expect self-employed individuals (WRKSLF: 1 = Self-employed, 2 = Someone else) to have higher incomes (RINCOME).

a. Conduct a test to determine whether the expectation is true.

b. Are the required conditions satisfied?

c. If the required conditions are not satisfied, what other technique should be used?

SURVEY OF CONSUMER FINANCES EXERCISES

Conduct all tests at the 5% significance level. Use a 95% confidence level for all estimates.
The following exercises deal with middle class households defined as those with net worth of between $67,430 and $293,900

13.69 <u>SCF2013:\MC*</u> Estimate the difference in total household debt between self-employed (OCCAT1: 1 = someone else, 2 = self-employed/partnership)

and heads of households who work for someone else (DEBT).

13.70 <u>SCF2013:\MC*</u> Incomes of people who work for themselves are likely more variable than people who work for someone else. That's because incomes for someone who is self-employed range from $0 to virtually unlimited.

a. Is there sufficient evidence that middle class heads of households who work for someone else (OCCAT1: 1 = someone else, 2 = self-employed/partnership) have higher incomes that heads of households who are self-employed (INCOME)?

b. Estimate how much more heads of households earn than heads of households who are self-employed.

13.71 SCF2013:\MC* Managing debt properly requires skill and education.

a. Conduct a test to determine whether there is enough evidence to conclude that heads of households who did finish high school (EDCL: 1 = no high school diploma, 2 = high school diploma) have more debt than those who did not finish high school (DEBT)?

b. What does the p-value tell you?

13.72 SCF2013:\MC* Estimate the difference in income between heads of households who did finish high school (EDCL: 1 = no high school diploma, 2 = high school diploma) and those who did not (INCOME).

13.73 SCF2013:\MC* Is there sufficient evidence to infer that there are differences in total unrealized capital gains (KGTOTAL) between heads of households who finished high school and those who did not (EDCL:1 = No high school diploma, 2 = High school diploma)?

13.74 SCF2013:\MC* Estimate the difference in net worth (NETWORTH) between households whose heads have completed a college degree and heads with some college only (EDCL: 3 = some college, 4 = college degree)

13.75 SCF2013:\MC* Estimate how much greater income (INCOME) is earned in households whose heads completed college (EDCL: 3 = some college, 4 = college degree) when compared to heads who only have some college.

13.76 SCF2013:\MC* Do college graduates have smaller unrealized capital gains (KGTOTAL) in their households than do households with only some college (EDCL: 3 = some college, 4 = college degree)? Conduct a test to answer the question.

13.77 SCF2013:\MC* In most countries including the United States, men have higher incomes than women. Does this hold when comparing middle class heads of households (HHSEX: 1 = male, 2 = female)?

a. Is there sufficient evidence that male heads of households have higher incomes than do female heads of households (INCOME)?

b. Estimate the difference between male and female heads of middle class households.

c. What are the required conditions? Are they satisfied?

13.78 SCF2013:\MC* Is there enough evidence to infer that heads of households who finish high school (EDCL: 1 = no high school diploma, 2 = high school diploma) have greater net worth than those who did not complete high school (NETWORTH)?

13.79 SCF2013:\MC* Do people who completed a college degree fare better financially than those who started college but never finished? One way to judge financial success is by measuring assets. Is there enough evidence to conclude that heads of households with college degrees (EDCL: 3 = some college, 4 = college degree) have more assets than those who have some college (ASSET)?

13.80 SCF2013:\MC* Is there enough evidence to conclude that households whose heads have some college (EDCL: 3 = some college, 4 = college degree) have less debt (DEBT) than households whose heads completed a college degree?

13-2 / OBSERVATIONAL AND EXPERIMENTAL DATA

As we've pointed out several times, the ability to properly interpret the results of a statistical technique is a crucial skill for students to develop. This ability is dependent on your understanding of Type I and Type II errors and the fundamental concepts that are part of statistical inference. However, there is another component that must be understood: the difference between **observational data** and **experimental data**. The difference results from the way the data are generated. The following example will demonstrate the difference between the two types.

EXAMPLE **13.3**

DATA
Xm13-03

Dietary Effects of High-Fiber Breakfast Cereals

Despite some controversy, scientists generally agree that high-fiber cereals reduce the likelihood of various forms of cancer. However, one scientist claims that people who eat high-fiber cereal for breakfast will consume, on average, fewer calories for lunch than people who don't eat high-fiber cereal for breakfast. If this is true, high-fiber cereal manufacturers will be able to claim another advantage of eating their product—potential weight reduction for dieters. As a preliminary test of the claim, 150 people were randomly selected and asked what they regularly eat for breakfast and lunch. Each person was identified as either a consumer or a nonconsumer of high-fiber cereal, and the number of calories consumed at lunch was measured and recorded. These data are listed here. Can the scientist conclude at the 5% significance level that his belief is correct?

Calories Consumed at Lunch by Consumers of High-Fiber Cereal

568	646	607	555	530	714	593	647	650
498	636	529	565	566	639	551	580	629
589	739	637	568	687	693	683	532	651
681	539	617	584	694	556	667	467	
540	596	633	607	566	473	649	622	

Calories Consumed at Lunch by Nonconsumers of High-Fiber Cereal

705	754	740	569	593	637	563	421	514	536
819	741	688	547	723	553	733	812	580	833
706	628	539	710	730	620	664	547	624	644
509	537	725	679	701	679	625	643	566	594
613	748	711	674	672	599	655	693	709	596
582	663	607	505	685	566	466	624	518	750
601	526	816	527	800	484	462	549	554	582
608	541	426	679	663	739	603	726	623	788
787	462	773	830	369	717	646	645	747	
573	719	480	602	596	642	588	794	583	
428	754	632	765	758	663	476	490	573	

SOLUTION:

The appropriate technique is the unequal-variances t-test of $\mu_1 - \mu_2$, where μ_1 is the mean of the number of calories for lunch by consumers of high-fiber cereal for breakfast and μ_2 is the mean of the number of calories for lunch by nonconsumers of high-fiber cereal for breakfast. [The F-test of the ratio of two variances (not shown here) yielded $F = .3845$ and p-value $= .0008$.]

The hypotheses are

$$H_0: \ (\mu_1 - \mu_2) = 0$$
$$H_1: \ (\mu_1 - \mu_2) < 0$$

The Excel printout is shown next. The manually calculated and XLSTAT-produced results are identical.

	A	B	C
1	t-Test: Two-Sample Assuming Unequal Variances		
2			
3		Consumers	Nonconsumers
4	Mean	604.02	633.23
5	Variance	4103	10670
6	Observations	43	107
7	Hypothesized Mean Difference	0	
8	df	123	
9	t Stat	−2.09	
10	P(T<=t) one-tail	0.0193	
11	t Critical one-tail	1.6573	
12	P(T<=t) two-tail	0.0386	
13	t Critical two-tail	1.9794	

INTERPRET

The value of the test statistic is −2.09. The one-tail p-value is .0193. We observe that the p-value of the test is small (and the test statistic falls into the rejection region). As a result, we conclude that there is sufficient evidence to infer that consumers of high-fiber cereal do eat fewer calories at lunch than do nonconsumers. From this result, we're inclined to believe that eating a high-fiber cereal at breakfast may be a way to reduce weight. However, other interpretations are plausible. For example, people who eat fewer calories are probably more health conscious, and such people are more likely to eat high-fiber cereal as part of a healthy breakfast. In this interpretation, high-fiber cereals do not necessarily lead to fewer calories at lunch. Instead, another factor, general health consciousness, leads to both fewer calories at lunch and high-fiber cereal for breakfast. Notice that the conclusion of the statistical procedure is unchanged. On average, people who eat high-fiber cereal consume fewer calories at lunch. However, because of the way the data were gathered, we have more difficulty interpreting this result.

Suppose that we redo Example 13.3 using the experimental approach. We randomly select 150 people to participate in the experiment. We randomly assign 75 to eat high-fiber cereal for breakfast and the other 75 to eat something else. We then record the number of calories each person consumes at lunch. Ideally, in this experiment both groups will be similar in all other dimensions, including health consciousness. (Larger sample sizes increase the likelihood that the two groups will be similar.) If the statistical result is about the same as in Example 13.3, we may have some valid reason to believe that high-fiber cereal at breakfast leads to a decrease in caloric intake at lunch.

Experimental data are usually more expensive to obtain because of the planning required to set up the experiment; observational data usually require less work to gather. Furthermore, in many situations it is impossible to conduct a controlled experiment. For example, suppose that we want to determine whether an undergraduate degree in engineering better prepares students for an MBA than does an arts degree. In a controlled experiment, we would randomly assign some students to achieve a degree in engineering and other students to obtain an arts degree. We would then make them sign up for an MBA program where we would record their grades. Unfortunately for statistical despots (and fortunately for the rest of us), we live in a democratic society, which makes the coercion necessary to perform this controlled experiment impossible.

To answer our question about the relative performance of engineering and arts students, we have no choice but to obtain our data by observational methods. We would take a random sample of engineering students and arts students who have already entered MBA programs and record their grades. If we find that engineering students do better, we may tend to conclude that an engineering background better prepares students for an MBA program. However, it may be true that better students tend to choose engineering as their undergraduate major and that better students achieve higher grades in all programs, including the MBA program.

Although we've discussed observational and experimental data in the context of the test of the difference between two means, you should be aware that the issue of how the data are obtained is relevant to the interpretation of all the techniques that follow.

EXERCISES

13.81 Refer to Exercise 13.17. If the data are observational, describe another conclusion other than the one that infers that Tastee is better for babies.

13.82 Are the data in Exercise 13.18 observational or experimental? Explain. If the data are observational, describe a method of producing experimental data.

13.83 Refer to Exercise 13.24.
   a. Are the data observational or experimental?
   b. If the data are observational, describe a method of answering the question with experimental data?
   c. If the data are observational, produce another explanation for the statistical outcome.

13.84 Suppose that you wish to test to determine whether one method of teaching statistics is better than another.
   a. Describe a data-gathering process that produces observational data.
   b. Describe a data-gathering process that produces experimental data.

13.85 Put yourself in place of the director of research and development for a pharmaceutical company. When a new drug is developed it undergoes a number of tests. One of the tests is designed to determine whether the drug is safe and effective. Your company has just developed a drug that is designed to alleviate the symptoms of degenerative diseases such as multiple sclerosis. Design an experiment that tests the new drug.

13.86 You wish to determine whether MBA graduates who majored in finance attract higher starting salaries than MBA graduates who majored in marketing.
   a. Describe a data-gathering process that produces observational data.
   b. Describe a data-gathering process that produces experimental data.
   c. If observational data indicate that finance majors attract higher salaries than do marketing majors, provide two explanations for this result.

13.87 Suppose that you are analyzing one of the hundreds of statistical studies linking smoking with lung cancer. The study analyzed thousands of randomly selected people, some of whom had lung cancer. The statistics indicate that those who have lung cancer smoked on average significantly more than those who did not have lung cancer.
   a. Explain how you know that the data are observational.
   b. Is there another interpretation of the statistics other than the obvious one that smoking causes lung cancer? If so, what is it? (Students who produce the best answers will be eligible for a job in the public relations department of a tobacco company.)
   c. Is it possible to conduct a controlled experiment to produce data that address the question of the relationship between smoking and lung cancer? If so, describe the experiment.

13-3 INFERENCE ABOUT THE DIFFERENCE BETWEEN TWO MEANS: MATCHED PAIRS EXPERIMENT

We continue our presentation of statistical techniques that address the problem of comparing two populations of interval data. In Section 13-1, the parameter of interest was the difference between two population means, where the data were generated from independent samples. In this section, the data are gathered from a matched pairs experiment. To illustrate why matched pairs experiments are needed and how we deal with data produced in this way, consider the following example.

EXAMPLE 13.4

DATA
Xm13-04

Comparing Salary Offers for Finance and Marketing MBA Majors, Part 1

In the last few years, a number of web-based companies that offer job placement services have been created. The manager of one such company wanted to investigate the job offers recent MBAs were obtaining. In particular, she wanted to know whether finance majors were being offered higher salaries than marketing majors. In a preliminary study, she randomly sampled 50 recently graduated MBAs, half of whom majored in finance and half in marketing. From each she obtained the highest salary offer (including benefits). These data are listed here. Can we infer that finance majors obtain higher salary offers than do marketing majors among MBAs?

Highest salary offer made to finance majors

61,228	51,836	20,620	73,356	84,186	79,782	29,523	80,645	76,125
62,531	77,073	86,705	70,286	63,196	64,358	47,915	86,792	75,155
65,948	29,392	96,382	80,644	51,389	61,955	63,573		

Highest salary offer made to marketing majors

73,361	36,956	63,627	71,069	40,203	97,097	49,442	75,188	59,854
79,816	51,943	35,272	60,631	63,567	69,423	68,421	56,276	47,510
58,925	78,704	62,553	81,931	30,867	49,091	48,843		

SOLUTION:

IDENTIFY

The objective is to compare two populations of interval data. The parameter is the difference between two means $\mu_1 - \mu_2$ (where μ_1 = mean highest salary offer to finance majors and μ_2 = mean highest salary offer to marketing majors). Because we want to determine whether finance majors are offered higher salaries, the alternative hypothesis will specify that μ_1 is greater than μ_2. The F-test for variances was conducted, and the results indicate that there is not enough evidence to infer that the population variances differ. Hence we use the equal-variances test statistic:

$$H_0: (\mu_1 - \mu_2) = 0$$
$$H_1: (\mu_1 - \mu_2) > 0$$

Test statistic: $t = \dfrac{(\bar{x}_1 - \bar{x}_2) - (\mu_1 - \mu_2)}{\sqrt{s_p^2\left(\dfrac{1}{n_1} + \dfrac{1}{n_2}\right)}}$

COMPUTE

MANUALLY:

From the data, we calculated the following statistics:

$$\bar{x}_1 = 65,624$$
$$\bar{x}_2 = 60,423$$
$$s_1^2 = 360,433,294$$
$$s_2^2 = 262,228,559$$
$$s_p^2 = \frac{(n_1 - 1)s_1^2 + (n_2 - 1)s_2^2}{n_1 + n_2 - 2}$$
$$= \frac{(25 - 1)(360,433,294) + (25 - 1)(262,228,559)}{25 + 25 - 2}$$
$$= 311,330,926$$

The value of the test statistic is computed next:

$$t = \frac{(\bar{x}_1 - \bar{x}_2) - (\mu_1 - \mu_2)}{\sqrt{s_p^2 \left(\dfrac{1}{n_1} + \dfrac{1}{n_2}\right)}}$$

$$= \frac{(65,624 - 60,423) - (0)}{\sqrt{311,330,926 \left(\dfrac{1}{25} + \dfrac{1}{25}\right)}}$$

$$= 1.04$$

The number of degrees of freedom of the test statistic is

$$\nu = n_1 + n_2 - 2 = 25 + 25 - 2 = 48$$

The rejection region is

$$t > t_{\alpha, \nu} = t_{.05,48} \approx 1.676$$

EXCEL Data Analysis

	A	B	C
1	t-Test: Two-Sample Assuming Equal Variances		
2			
3		Finance	Marketing
4	Mean	65,624	60,423
5	Variance	360,433,294	262,228,559
6	Observations	25	25
7	Pooled Variance	311,330,926	
8	Hypothesized Mean Difference	0	
9	df	48	
10	t Stat	1.04	
11	P(T<=t) one-tail	0.1513	
12	t Critical one-tail	1.6772	
13	P(T<=t) two-tail	0.3026	
14	t Critical two-tail	2.0106	

INTERPRET

The value of the test statistic ($t = 1.04$) and its p-value (.1513) indicate that there is very little evidence to support the hypothesis that finance majors receive higher salary offers than marketing majors.

Notice that we have some evidence to support the alternative hypothesis. The difference in sample means is

$$(\bar{x}_1 - \bar{x}_2) = (65{,}624 - 60{,}423) = 5{,}201$$

However, we judge the difference between sample means in relation to the standard error of $\bar{x}_1 - \bar{x}_2$. As we've already calculated,

$$s_p^2 = 311{,}330{,}926$$

and

$$\sqrt{s_p^2\left(\frac{1}{n_1} + \frac{1}{n_2}\right)} = 4{,}991$$

Consequently, the value of the test statistic is $t = 5{,}201/4{,}991 = 1.04$, a value that does not allow us to infer that finance majors attract higher salary offers. We can see that although the difference between the sample means was quite large, the variability of the data as measured by s_p^2 was also large, resulting in a small test statistic value.

EXAMPLE 13.5

DATA
Xm13-05

Comparing Salary Offers for Finance and Marketing MBA Majors, Part 2

Suppose now that we redo the experiment in the following way. We examine the transcripts of finance and marketing MBA majors. We randomly select a finance and a marketing major whose grade point average (GPA) falls between 3.92 and 4 (based on a maximum of 4). We then randomly select a finance and a marketing major whose GPA is between 3.84 and 3.92. We continue this process until the 25th pair of finance and marketing majors is selected whose GPA fell between 2.0 and 2.08. (The minimum GPA required for graduation is 2.0.) As we did in Example 13.4, we recorded the highest salary offer. These data, together with the GPA group, are listed here. Can we conclude from these data that finance majors draw larger salary offers than do marketing majors?

Group	Finance	Marketing
1	95,171	89,329
2	88,009	92,705
3	98,089	99,205
4	106,322	99,003
5	74,566	74,825
6	87,089	77,038
7	88,664	78,272
8	71,200	59,462
9	69,367	51,555

Group	Finance	Marketing
10	82,618	81,591
11	69,131	68,110
12	58,187	54,970
13	64,718	68,675
14	67,716	54,110
15	49,296	46,467
16	56,625	53,559
17	63,728	46,793
18	55,425	39,984
19	37,898	30,137
20	56,244	61,965
21	51,071	47,438
22	31,235	29,662
23	32,477	33,710
24	35,274	31,989
25	45,835	38,788

SOLUTION:

The experiment described in Example 13.4 is one in which the samples are independent. In other words, there is no relationship between the observations in one sample and the observations in the second sample. However, in this example the experiment was designed in such a way that each observation in one sample is matched with an observation in the other sample. The matching is conducted by selecting finance and marketing majors with similar GPAs. Thus, it is logical to compare the salary offers for finance and marketing majors in each group. This type of experiment is called a **matched pairs experiment**. We now describe how we conduct the test.

For each GPA group, we calculate the matched pair difference between the salary offers for finance and marketing majors.

Group	Finance	Marketing	Difference
1	95,171	89,329	5,842
2	88,009	92,705	−4,696
3	98,089	99,205	−1,116
4	106,322	99,003	7,319
5	74,566	74,825	−259
6	87,089	77,038	10,051
7	88,664	78,272	10,392
8	71,200	59,462	11,738
9	69,367	51,555	17,812
10	82,618	81,591	1,027
11	69,131	68,110	1,021
12	58,187	54,970	3,217
13	64,718	68,675	−3,957

Group	Finance	Marketing	Difference
14	67,716	54,110	13,606
15	49,296	46,467	2,829
16	56,625	53,559	3,066
17	63,728	46,793	16,935
18	55,425	39,984	15,441
19	37,898	30,137	7,761
20	56,244	61,965	−5,721
21	51,071	47,438	3,633
22	31,235	29,662	1,573
23	32,477	33,710	−1,233
24	35,274	31,989	3,285
25	45,835	38,788	7,047

In this experimental design, the parameter of interest is the **mean of the population of differences**, which we label μ_D. Note that μ_D does in fact equal $\mu_1 - \mu_2$, but we test μ_D because of the way the experiment was designed. Hence, the hypotheses to be tested are

$$H_0: \ \mu_D = 0$$
$$H_1: \ \mu_D > 0$$

We have already presented inferential techniques about a population mean. Recall that in Chapter 12 we introduced the t-test of μ. Thus, to test hypotheses about μ_D, we use the following test statistic.

Test Statistic for μ_D

$$t = \frac{\bar{x}_D - \mu_D}{s_D / \sqrt{n_D}}$$

which is Student t distributed with $v = n_D - 1$ degrees of freedom, provided that the differences are normally distributed.

Aside from the subscript D, this test statistic is identical to the one presented in Chapter 12. We conduct the test in the usual way.

COMPUTE

MANUALLY:

Using the differences computed above, we find the following statistics:

$$\bar{x}_D = 5,065$$
$$s_D = 6,647$$

from which we calculate the value of the test statistic:

$$t = \frac{\bar{x}_D - \mu_D}{s_D/\sqrt{n_D}} = \frac{5,065 - 0}{6,647/\sqrt{25}} = 3.81$$

The rejection region is

$$t > t_{\alpha, \nu} = t_{.05,24} = 1.711$$

EXCEL Data Analysis

	A	B	C
1	t-Test: Paired Two Sample for Means		
2			
3		Finance	Marketing
4	Mean	65,438	60,374
5	Variance	444,981,810	469,441,785
6	Observations	25	25
7	Pearson Correlation	0.9520	
8	Hypothesized Mean Difference	0	
9	df	24	
10	t Stat	3.81	
11	P(T<=t) one-tail	0.0004	
12	t Critical one-tail	1.7109	
13	P(T<=t) two-tail	0.0009	
14	t Critical two-tail	2.0639	

Excel prints the sample means, variances, and sample sizes for each sample (as well as the coefficient of correlation), which implies that the procedure uses these statistics. It doesn't. The technique is based on computing the paired differences from which the mean, variance, and sample size are determined. Excel should have printed these statistics.

INSTRUCTIONS

1. Type or import the data into two columns. (Open Xm13-05.)
2. Click **Data, Data Analysis,** and **t-Test: Paired Two-Sample for Means**.
3. Specify the **Variable 1 Range** (B1:B26) and the **Variable 2 Range** (C1:C26). Type the value of **the Hypothesized Mean Difference** (0) and specify a value for α (.05).

XLSTAT

	A	B	C	D	E	F
1	Hypothesized difference (D): 0					
2	Significance level (%): 5					
3						
4	Summary statistics:					
5	Variable	Observations	Minimum	Maximum	Mean	Std. deviation
6	Finance	25	31,235	106,322	65,438	21,095
7	Marketing	25	29,662	99,205	60,374	21,667
8						
9	t-test for two paired samples / Upper-tailed test:					
10	Difference	5065				
11	t (Observed value)	3.81				
12	t (Critical value)	1.711				
13	DF	24				
14	p-value (one-tailed)	0.0004				
15	alpha	0.05				

INSTRUCTIONS

Follow the instructions for either *t*-test of the difference between two means. Under **Data format**: click **Paired samples**.

INTERPRET

The value of the test statistic is $t = 3.81$ with a p-value of .0004. There is now overwhelming evidence to infer that finance majors obtain higher salary offers than marketing majors. By redoing the experiment as matched pairs, we were able to extract this information from the data.

13-3a Estimating the Mean Difference

We derive the confidence interval estimator of μ_D using the usual form for the confidence interval.

> **Confidence Interval Estimator of μ_D**
>
> $$\bar{x}_D \pm t_{\alpha/2}\frac{s_D}{\sqrt{n_D}}$$

EXAMPLE 13.6

Comparing Salary Offers for Finance and Marketing MBA Majors, Part 3

DATA
Xm13-05

Compute the 95% confidence interval estimate of the mean difference in salary offers between finance and marketing majors in Example 13.5.

SOLUTION:

COMPUTE

MANUALLY:

The 95% confidence interval estimate of the mean difference is

$$\bar{x}_D \pm t_{\alpha/2}\frac{s_D}{\sqrt{n_D}} = 5{,}065 \pm 2.064\frac{6{,}647}{\sqrt{25}} = 5{,}065 \pm 2{,}744$$

$$\text{LCL} = 2{,}321 \quad \text{and} \quad \text{UCL} = 7{,}809$$

EXCEL Workbook

	A	B	C	D	E
1	t-Estimate of a Mean				
2					
3	Sample mean	5065	Confidence Interval Estimate		
4	Sample standard deviation	6647	5065	±	2744
5	Sample size	25	Lower confidence limit		2321
6	Confidence level	0.95	Upper confidence limit		7808

1. Type or copy the data into two columns (Open Xm13-05). In each row calculate the paired differences. Calculate the mean and standard deviation of the paired differences.

2. Open the **Estimators Workbook** and click the **t-Estimate_Mean** tab. Type or copy the sample mean and the sample standard deviation. Type the sample size and the confidence level.

XLSTAT

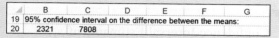

	B	C	D	E	F	G
19	95% confidence interval on the difference between the means:					
20	2321	7808				

INSTRUCTIONS

Follow the instructions for the t-test of the matched pairs difference. Choose the two-tail test.

INTERPRET

We estimate that the mean salary offer to finance majors exceeds the mean salary offer to marketing majors by an amount that lies between $2,321 and $7,809 (using the computer output).

13-3b Independent Samples or Matched Pairs: Which Experimental Design Is Better?

Examples 13.4 and 13.5 demonstrated that the experimental design is an important factor in statistical inference. However, these two examples raise several questions about experimental designs.

1. Why does the matched pairs experiment result in concluding that finance majors receive higher salary offers than do marketing majors, whereas the independent samples experiment could not?

2. Should we always use the matched pairs experiment? In particular, are there disadvantages to its use?

3. How do we recognize when a matched pairs experiment has been performed?

Here are our answers.

1. The matched pairs experiment worked in Example 13.5 by reducing the variation in the data. To understand this point, examine the statistics from both examples. In Example 13.4, we found $\bar{x}_1 - \bar{x}_2 = 5,201$. In Example 13.5, we computed $\bar{x}_D = 5,065$. Thus, the numerators of the two test statistics were quite similar. However, the test statistic in Example 13.5 was much larger than the

c. Check to ensure that the required condition(s) of the techniques used in parts (a) and (b) is satisfied.

d. Would it be advantageous to perform this experiment with independent samples? Explain why or why not.

13.96 Xr13-96 Because of the high cost of energy, homeowners in northern climates need to find ways to cut their heating costs. A building contractor wanted to investigate the effect on heating costs of increasing the insulation. As an experiment, he located a large subdevelopment built around 1970 with minimal insulation. His plan was to insulate some of the houses and compare the heating costs in the insulated homes with those that remained uninsulated. However, it was clear to him that the size of the house was a critical factor in determining heating costs. Consequently, he found 16 pairs of identical-sized houses ranging from about 1,200 to 2,800 square feet. He insulated one house in each pair (levels of R20 in the walls and R32 in the attic) and left the other house unchanged. The heating cost for the following winter season was recorded for each house.

a. Do these data allow the contractor to infer at the 10% significance level that the heating cost for insulated houses is less than that for the uninsulated houses?

b. Estimate with 95% confidence the mean savings due to insulating the house.

c. What is the required condition for the use of the techniques in parts (a) and (b)?

13.97 Xr13-97 The cost of health care is rising faster than most other items. To learn more about the problem a survey was undertaken to determine whether differences in health care expenditures exist between men and women. The survey randomly sampled men and women aged 21, 22,..., 65 and determined the total amount spent on health care. Do these data allow us to infer that men and women spend different amounts on health care?
(*Source:* Bureau of Labor Statistics, Consumer Expenditure Survey.)

13.98 Xr13-98 The fluctuations in the stock market induce some investors to sell and move their money into more stable investments. To determine the degree to which recent fluctuations affected ownership, a random sample of 170 people who confirmed that they owned some stock was surveyed. The values of the holdings were recorded at the end of last year and at the end of the year before. Can we infer that the value of the stock holdings has decreased?

13.99 Xr13-99 Are Americans more deeply in debt this year compared to last year? To help answer this question a statistics practitioner randomly sampled Americans this year and last year. The sampling was conducted so that the samples were matched by the age of the head of the household. For each, the ratio of debt payments to household income was recorded. Can we infer that the ratios are higher this year than last?

13.100 Xr13-100 Every April Americans and Canadians fill out their tax return forms. Many turn to tax preparation companies to do this tedious job. The question arises, Are there differences between companies? In an experiment two of the largest companies were asked to prepare the tax returns of a sample of 55 taxpayers. The amounts of tax payable were recorded. Can we conclude that company 1's service results in higher tax payable?

13.101 Xr13-101 Refer to Exercise 13.33. Suppose now we redo the experiment in the following way. On 20 randomly selected cars, one of each type of tire is installed on the rear wheels and as before, the cars are driven until the tires wear out. The number of miles until wear-out occurred was recorded. Can we conclude from these data that the new tire is superior?

13.102 Refer to Exercises 13.33 and 13.101. Explain why the matched pairs experiment produced significant results whereas the independent samples *t*-test did not.

13.103 Xr13-103 Refer to Examples 13.4 and 13.5. Suppose that another experiment is conducted. Finance and marketing MBA majors were matched according to their undergraduate GPA. As in the previous examples, the highest starting salary offers were recorded. Can we infer from these data that finance majors attract higher salary offers than marketing majors?

13.104 Discuss why the experiment in Example 13.5 produced a significant test result whereas the one in Exercise 13.103 did not.

13.105 Xr13-105 Refer to Example 13.2. The actual after and before operating incomes were recorded.
a. Test to determine whether there is enough evidence to infer that for companies where an offspring takes the helm there is a decrease in operating income.
b. Is there sufficient evidence to conclude that when an outsider becomes CEO the operating income increases?

GENERAL SOCIAL SURVEY EXERCISES

Use a 5% significance level.

13.106 GSS2014* The general trend over the last century is that each generation is more educated that its predecessor. Has this trend continued? To answer this question, determine whether there is sufficient evidence that Americans are more educated than their fathers (EDUC and PAEDUC)?

13.107 GSS2014* Is there sufficient evidence to infer that Americans are more educated than their mothers (EDUC and MAEDUC)?

13.108 GSS2014* The survey asks for total family income and respondents' income. The difference between them is the amount earned by the members of the respondent's family. Estimate with 95% confidence the mean income of the other members of the respondent's family (INCOME: total family income; RINCOME: respondent's income).

13.109 GSS2014* Do most two-income families try to have both spouses work the same number of hours? To answer the question conduct a test to determine whether there is sufficient evidence to infer that the respondent and his or her spouse differ in the number of hours per week of work (HRS1 and SPHRS1)?

SURVEY OF CONSUMER FINANCES EXERCISES

13.110 SCF2013:\MC* In terms of income, do heads of middle class households consider this to be a worse year than normal? Conduct a test to answer the question (INCOME = household; NORMINC = household normal income).

13.111 SCF2013:\MC* Capital gains can be produced in a number of ways. Most homeowners have unrealized capital gains on the homes. Estimate with 95% confidence the mean amount of all capital gains except the home (KGHOUSE = unrealized capital gains on the primary residence; KGTOTAL = total unrealized capital gains for the household).

13-4 / INFERENCE ABOUT THE RATIO OF TWO VARIANCES

In Sections 13-1 and 13-3, we dealt with statistical inference concerning the difference between two population means. The problem objective in each case was to compare two populations of interval data, and our interest was in comparing measures of central location. This section discusses the statistical technique to use when the problem objective and the data type are the same as in Sections 13-1 and 13-3, but our interest is in comparing variability. Here we will study the ratio of two population variances. We make inferences about the ratio because the sampling distribution is based on ratios rather than differences.

We have already encountered this technique when we used the F-test of two variances to determine which t-test and estimator of the difference between two means to use. In this section, we apply the technique to other problems where our interest is in comparing the variability in two populations.

In the previous chapter, we presented the procedures used to draw inferences about a single population variance. We pointed out that variance can be used to address problems where we need to judge the consistency of a production process. We also use variance to measure the risk associated with a portfolio of investments. In this section, we compare two variances, enabling us to compare the consistency of two production processes. We can also compare the relative risks of two sets of investments.

We will proceed in a manner that is probably becoming quite familiar.

13-4a Parameter

As you will see shortly, we compare two population variances by determining the ratio. Consequently, the parameter is σ_1^2 / σ_2^2.

13-4b Statistic and Sampling Distribution

We have previously noted that the sample variance (defined in Chapter 4) is an unbiased and consistent estimator of the population variance. Not surprisingly, the estimator of the parameter σ_1^2 / σ_2^2 is the ratio of the two sample variances drawn from their respective populations s_1^2 / s_2^2.

The sampling distribution of s_1^2 / s_2^2 is said to be F-distributed provided that we have independently sampled from two normal populations. (The F-distribution was introduced in Section 8-4.)

Statisticians have shown that the ratio of two independent chi-squared variables divided by their degrees of freedom is F-distributed. The degrees of freedom of the F-distribution are identical to the degrees of freedom for the two chi-squared distributions. In Section 12-2, we pointed out that $(n - 1)s^2/\sigma^2$ is chi-squared distributed, provided that the sampled population is normal. If we have independent samples drawn from two normal populations, then both $(n_1 - 1)s_1^2/\sigma_1^2$ and $(n_2 - 1)s_2^2/\sigma_2^2$ are chi-squared distributed. If we divide each by their respective number of degrees of freedom and take the ratio, we produce

$$\frac{\dfrac{(n_1 - 1)s_1^2/\sigma_1^2}{(n_1 - 1)}}{\dfrac{(n_2 - 1)s_2^2/\sigma_2^2}{(n_2 - 1)}}$$

which simplifies to

$$\frac{s_1^2/\sigma_1^2}{s_2^2/\sigma_2^2}$$

This statistic is F-distributed with $\nu_1 = n_1 - 1$ and $\nu_2 = n_2 - 1$ degrees of freedom. Recall that ν_1 is called the **numerator degrees of freedom** and ν_2 is called the **denominator degrees of freedom**.

13-4c Testing and Estimating a Ratio of Two Variances

In this book, our null hypothesis will always specify that the two variances are equal. As a result, the ratio will equal 1. Thus, the null hypothesis will always be expressed as

$$H_0: \quad \sigma_1^2/\sigma_2^2 = 1$$

The alternative hypothesis can state that the ratio σ_1^2/σ_2^2 is either not equal to 1, greater than 1, or less than 1. Technically, the test statistic is

$$F = \frac{s_1^2/\sigma_1^2}{s_2^2/\sigma_2^2}$$

However, under the null hypothesis, which states that $\sigma_1^2/\sigma_2^2 = 1$, the test statistic becomes as follows.

Test Statistic for σ_1^2/σ_2^2

The test statistic employed to test that σ_1^2/σ_2^2 is equal to 1 is

$$F = \frac{s_1^2}{s_2^2}$$

which is F-distributed with $\nu_1 = n_1 - 1$ and $\nu_2 = n_2 - 1$ degrees of freedom provided that the populations are normal.

With the usual algebraic manipulation, we can derive the confidence interval estimator of the ratio of two population variances.

Confidence Interval Estimator of σ_1^2/σ_2^2

$$\text{LCL} = \left(\frac{s_1^2}{s_2^2}\right)\frac{1}{F_{\alpha/2, \nu_1, \nu_2}}$$

$$\text{UCL} = \left(\frac{s_1^2}{s_2^2}\right)F_{\alpha/2, \nu_2, \nu_1}$$

where $\nu_1 = n_1 - 1$ and $\nu_2 = n_2 - 1$

EXAMPLE 13.7

DATA
Xm13-07

Testing the Quality of Two Bottle-Filling Machines

In Example 12.3, we applied the chi-squared test of a variance to determine whether there was sufficient evidence to conclude that the population variance was less than 1.0. Suppose that the statistics practitioner also collected data from another container-filling machine and recorded the fills of a randomly selected sample. Can we infer at the 5% significance level that the second machine is superior in its consistency?

SOLUTION:

IDENTIFY

The problem objective is to compare two populations where the data are interval. Because we want information about the consistency of the two machines, the parameter we wish to test is σ_1^2 / σ_2^2, where σ_1^2 is the variance of machine 1 and σ_2^2 is the variance for machine 2. We need to conduct the F-test of σ_1^2 / σ_2^2 to determine whether the variance of population 2 is less than that of population 1. Expressed differently, we wish to determine whether there is enough evidence to infer that σ_1^2 is larger than σ_2^2. Hence, the hypotheses we test are

$$H_0: \quad \sigma_1^2 / \sigma_2^2 = 1$$
$$H_1: \quad \sigma_1^2 / \sigma_2^2 > 1$$

COMPUTE

MANUALLY:

The sample variances are $s_1^2 = .6333$ and $s_2^2 = .4528$.
    The value of the test statistic is

$$F = \frac{s_1^2}{s_2^2} = \frac{.6333}{.4528} = 1.40$$

The rejection region is

$$F > F_{\alpha, \nu_1, \nu_2} = F_{.05, 24, 24} = 1.98$$

Because the value of the test statistic is not greater than 1.98, we cannot reject the null hypothesis.

EXCEL Data Analysis

	A	B	C
1	F-Test Two-Sample for Variances		
2			
3		Machine 1	Machine 2
4	Mean	999.7	999.8
5	Variance	0.6333	0.4528
6	Observations	25	25
7	df	24	24
8	F	1.3988	
9	P(F<=f) one-tail	0.2085	
10	F Critical one-tail	1.9838	

The value of the test statistic is $F = 1.3988$. Excel outputs the one-tail p-value, which is .2085.

INSTRUCTIONS

1. Type or import the data into two columns. (Open Xm13-07.)

2. Click **Data, Data Analysis**, and **F-test Two-Sample for Variances**.

3. Specify the **Variable 1 Range** (A1:A26) and the **Variable 2 Range** (B1:B26). Type a value for α (.05).

XLSTAT

	A	B	C	D	E	F
1	Hypothesized ratio (R): 1					
2	Significance level (%): 5					
3						
4	Summary statistics:					
5	Variable	Observations	Minimum	Maximum	Mean	Std. deviation
6	Machine 1	25	997.8	1001.3	999.7	0.796
7	Machine 2	25	998.5	1000.9	999.8	0.673
8						
9	Fisher's F-test / Upper-tailed test:					
10	Ratio	1.399				
11	F (Observed value)	1.399				
12	F (Critical value)	1.984				
13	DF1	24				
14	DF2	24				
15	p-value (one-tailed)	0.2085				
16	alpha	0.05				

INTERPRET

There is not enough evidence to infer that the variance of machine 2 is less than the variance of machine 1.

The histograms (not shown) appear to be sufficiently bell shaped to satisfy the normality requirement.

EXAMPLE 13.8

DATA
Xm13-07

Estimating the Ratio of the Variances in Example 13.7

Determine the 95% confidence interval estimate of the ratio of the two population variances in Example 13.7.

SOLUTION:

COMPUTE

MANUALLY:

We find

$$F_{\alpha/2, \nu_1, \nu_2} = F_{.025,24,24} = 2.27$$

Thus,

$$LCL = \left(\frac{s_1^2}{s_2^2}\right)\frac{1}{F_{\alpha/2,\nu_1,\nu_2}} = \left(\frac{.6333}{.4528}\right)\frac{1}{2.27} = .616$$

$$UCL = \left(\frac{s_1^2}{s_2^2}\right)F_{\alpha/2,\nu_2,\nu_1} = \left(\frac{.6333}{.4528}\right)2.27 = 3.17$$

We estimate that σ_1^2/σ_2^2 lies between .616 and 3.17.

EXCEL Workbook

	A	B	C	D	E
1	F-Estimate of the Ratio of Two Variances				
2					
3		Sample 1	Sample 2	Confidence Interval Estimate	
4	Sample variance	0.63	0.45	Lower confidence limit	0.6163
5	Sample size	25	25	Upper confidence limit	3.1739
6	Confidence level	0.95			

INSTRUCTIONS

1. Type or import the data into two columns (Open Xm13-07). Calculate the sample variances for each sample.
2. Open the **Estimators Workbook** and select the **F-Estimate_2 Variances** tab. Copy or type the sample variances, sample sizes, and confidence level.

XLSTAT

	A	B	C	D	E
1	95% confidence interval on the ratio of variances:				
2	0.616	3.174			

INSTRUCTIONS

Follow the instructions for the test of two variances. Select the two-tail test.

As we pointed out in Chapter 11, we can often use a confidence interval estimator to test the hypotheses. In this example, the interval estimate excludes the value of 1. Consequently, we can draw the same conclusion as we did in Example 13.7.

Factors that Identify the F-Test and Estimator of σ_1^2/σ_2^2

1. **Problem objective**: Compare two populations
2. **Data type**: Interval
3. **Descriptive measurement**: Variability

EXERCISES

Developing an Understanding of Statistical Concepts

Exercises 13.112 and 13.113 are "what-if analyses" designed to determine what happens to the test statistics and interval estimates when elements of the statistical inference change. These problems can be solved manually.

13.112 Random samples from two normal populations produced the following statistics:

$$s_1^2 = 350 \quad n_1 = 30 \quad s_2^2 = 700 \quad n_2 = 30$$

a. Can we infer at the 10% significance level that the two population variances differ?

b. Repeat part (a) changing the sample sizes to $n_1 = 15$ and $n_2 = 15$.

c. Describe what happens to the test statistic and the conclusion when the sample sizes decrease.

13.113 Random samples from two normal populations produced the following statistics:

$$s_1^2 = 28 \quad n_1 = 10 \quad s_2^2 = 19 \quad n_2 = 10$$

a. Estimate with 95% confidence the ratio of the two population variances.
b. Repeat part (a) changing the sample sizes to $n_1 = 25$ and $n_2 = 25$.
c. Describe what happens to the width of the confidence interval estimate when the sample sizes increase.

Applications

Use a 5% significance level in all tests, unless specified otherwise.

13.114 Xr13-114   The manager of a dairy is in the process of deciding which of two new carton-filling machines to use. The most important attripute is the consistency of the fills. In a preliminary study she measured the fills in the 1-liter carton and listed them here. Can the manager infer that the two machines differ in their consistency of fills?

Machine 1	.998	.997	1.003	1.000	.999	
	1.000	.998	1.003	1.004	1.000	
Machine 2	1.003	1.004	.997	.996	.999	1.003
	1.000	1.005	1.002	1.004	.996	

13.115 Xr13-115   An operations manager who supervises an assembly line has been experiencing problems with the sequencing of jobs. The problem is that bottlenecks are occurring because of the inconsistency of sequential operations. He decides to conduct an experiment wherein two different methods are used to complete the same task. He measures the times (in seconds). The data are listed here. Can he infer that the second method is more consistent than the first method?

Method 1	8.8	9.6	8.4	9.0	8.3	9.2	9.0	8.7	8.5	9.4
Method 2	9.2	9.4	8.9	9.6	9.7	8.4	8.8	8.9	9.0	9.7

13.116 Xr13-116   A statistics professor hypothesized that not only would the means vary, but also so would the variances if the business statistics course was taught in two different ways but had the same final exam. He organized an experiment wherein one section of the course was taught using detailed PowerPoint slides whereas the other required students to read the book and answer questions in class discussions. A sample of the marks was recorded and listed next. Can we infer that the variances of the marks differ between the two sections?

Class 1	64	85	80	64	48	62	75	77	50	81	90
Class 2	73	78	66	69	79	81	74	59	83	79	84

The following exercises require the use of a computer and software. The answers may be calculated manually. See Appendix A for the sample statistics. **Use a 5% significance level for all tests unless specified otherwise.**

13.117 Xr13-117   A new highway has just been completed and the government must decide on speed limits. There are several possible choices. However, on advice from police who monitor traffic the objective was to reduce the variation in speeds, which it is thought to contribute to the number of collisions. It has been acknowledged that speed contributes to the severity of collisions. It is decided to conduct an experiment to acquire more information. Signs are posted for 1 week indicating that the speed limit is 70 mph. A random sample of cars' speeds is measured. During the second week, signs are posted indicating that the maximum speed is 70 mph and that the minimum speed is 60 mph. Once again a random sample of speeds is measured. Can we infer that limiting the minimum and maximum speeds reduces the variation in speeds?

13.118 Xr13-118   In Exercise 12.80 we described the problem of whether to change all the light bulbs at Yankee Stadium or change them one by one as they burn out. There are two brands of bulbs that can be used. Because both the mean and the variance of the lengths of life are important, it was decided to test the two brands. A random sample of both brands was drawn and left on until they burned out. The times were recorded. Can the Yankee Stadium management conclude that the variances differ?

13.119 Xr13-119   In deciding where to invest her retirement fund, an investor recorded the weekly returns of two portfolios for 1 year. Can we conclude that portfolio 2 is riskier than portfolio 1?

13.120 Xr13-120   An important statistical measurement in service facilities (such as restaurants and banks) is the variability in service times. As an experiment, two bank tellers were observed, and the service times for each of 100 customers were recorded. Do these data allow us to infer at the 10% significance level that the variance in service times differs between the two tellers?

GENERAL SOCIAL SURVEY EXERCISES

Conduct tests at the 5% significance level.

13.121 GSS2014* There are advantages and disadvantages to working for one's self. The advantages are that the rewards can be substantial. However it is also possible to have nothing to show for a lot of work. In theory the variation in income for self-employed individuals is greater than the variation in income for people who work for someone else (WRKSLF: 1 = self-employed, 2 = work for someone else). Conduct a test to determine whether there is enough evidence to support the theory (RINCOME).

13.122 GSS2014* Most people who work for someone else are likely to have a set number of hours that does not vary. In most cases this will be around 40 hours per week. Self-employed people do not have the luxury of having a limit on the hours they work. As a result we would expect that the hours worked by the self-employed vary more than do the hours of employees (WRKSLF: 1 = self-employed, 2 = work for someone else). Is there sufficient evidence to support this theory (HRS1)?

SURVEY OF CONSUMER FINANCES EXERCISES

Conduct tests at the 5% significance level.

13.123 SCF2013:\MC* The financial rewards for self-employment can be considerable. The downside may be that one works long hours accruing debts with little or no financial return. As a result we theorize that the variance in compensation will be greater for the self-employed (OCCAT1: 1 = work for someone else, 2 = self-employed/partnership). Conduct a test to determine if the variation in income for the self-employed is greater than that of employees (INCOME).

13.124 SCF2013:\MC* Refer to Exercise 13.123. Is there enough evidence to conclude that the variation in net worth is greater for the self-employed than for employees (NETWORTH)?

13.125 SCF2013:\MC* Refer to Exercise 13.123. Is there more variation in the amount of debt of the self-employed than for employees (DEBT)?

13.126 SCF2013:\MC* Refer to Exercise 13.123. Do the data allow us to conclude that there is more variation in total capital gains (KGTOTAL) for self-employed individuals than for employees?

13-5 / INFERENCE ABOUT THE DIFFERENCE BETWEEN TWO POPULATION PROPORTIONS

In this section, we present the procedures for drawing inferences about the difference between populations whose data are nominal. The number of applications of these techniques is almost limitless. For example, pharmaceutical companies test new drugs by comparing the new and old or the new versus a placebo. Marketing managers compare market shares before and after advertising campaigns. Operations managers compare defective rates between two machines. Political pollsters measure the difference in popularity before and after an election.

13-5a Parameter

When data are nominal, the only meaningful computation is to count the number of occurrences of each type of outcome and calculate proportions. Consequently, the parameter to be tested and estimated in this section is the difference between two population proportions $p_1 - p_2$.

13-5b Statistic and Sampling Distribution

To draw inferences about $p_1 - p_2$, we take a sample of size n_1 from population 1 and a sample of size n_2 from population 2 (Figure 13.7 depicts the sampling process).

FIGURE 13.7 Sampling from Two Populations of Nominal Data

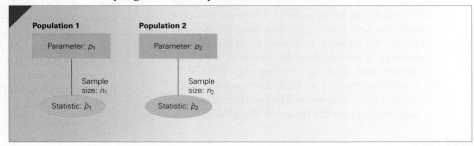

For each sample, we count the number of successes (recall that we call anything we're looking for a success), which we label x_1 and x_2, respectively. The sample proportions are then computed:

$$\hat{p}_1 = \frac{x_1}{n_1} \quad \text{and} \quad \hat{p}_2 = \frac{x_2}{n_2}$$

Statisticians have proven that the statistic $\hat{p}_1 - \hat{p}_2$ is an unbiased consistent estimator of the parameter $p_1 - p_2$. Using the same mathematics as we did in Chapter 9 to derive the sampling distribution of the sample proportion $\hat{p}$, we determine the sampling distribution of the difference between two sample proportions.

Sampling Distribution of $\hat{p}_1 - \hat{p}_2$

1. The statistic $\hat{p}_1 - \hat{p}_2$ is approximately normally distributed provided that the sample sizes are large enough so that $n_1 p_1$, $n_1(1 - p_1)$, $n_2 p_2$, and $n_2(1 - p_2)$ are all greater than or equal to 5. [Because p_1 and p_2 are unknown, we express the sample size requirement as $n_1\hat{p}_1$, $n_1(1 - \hat{p}_1)$, $n_2\hat{p}_2$, and $n_2(1 - \hat{p}_2)$ are greater than or equal to 5.]

2. The mean of $\hat{p}_1 - \hat{p}_2$ is

$$E(\hat{p}_1 - \hat{p}_2) = p_1 - p_2$$

3. The variance of $\hat{p}_1 - \hat{p}_2$ is

$$V(\hat{p}_1 - \hat{p}_2) = \frac{p_1(1 - p_1)}{n_1} + \frac{p_2(1 - p_2)}{n_2}$$

The standard error is

$$\sigma_{\hat{p}_1 - \hat{p}_2} = \sqrt{\frac{p_1(1 - p_1)}{n_1} + \frac{p_2(1 - p_2)}{n_2}}$$

Thus, the variable

$$z = \frac{(\hat{p}_1 - \hat{p}_2) - (p_1 - p_2)}{\sqrt{\dfrac{p_1(1 - p_1)}{n_1} + \dfrac{p_2(1 - p_2)}{n_2}}}$$

is approximately standard normally distributed.

13-5c Testing and Estimating the Difference between Two Proportions

We would like to use the z-statistic just described as our test statistic; however, the standard error of $\hat{p}_1 - \hat{p}_2$, which is

$$\sigma_{\hat{p}_1 - \hat{p}_2} = \sqrt{\frac{p_1(1 - p_1)}{n_1} + \frac{p_2(1 - p_2)}{n_2}}$$

is unknown because both p_1 and p_2 are unknown. As a result, the standard error of $\hat{p}_1 - \hat{p}_2$ must be estimated from the sample data. There are two different estimators of this quantity, and the determination of which one to use depends on the null hypothesis. If the null hypothesis states that $p_1 - p_2 = 0$, the hypothesized equality of the two population proportions allows us to pool the data from the two samples to produce an estimate of the common value of the two proportions p_1 and p_2. The **pooled proportion estimate** is defined as

$$\hat{p} = \frac{x_1 + x_2}{n_1 + n_2}$$

Thus, the estimated standard error of $\hat{p}_1 - \hat{p}_2$ is

$$\sqrt{\frac{\hat{p}(1 - \hat{p})}{n_1} + \frac{\hat{p}(1 - \hat{p})}{n_2}} = \sqrt{\hat{p}(1 - \hat{p})\left(\frac{1}{n_1} + \frac{1}{n_2}\right)}$$

The principle used in estimating the standard error of $\hat{p}_1 - \hat{p}_2$ is analogous to that applied in Section 13-1 to produce the pooled variance estimate s_p^2, which is used to test $\mu_1 - \mu_2$ with σ_1^2 and σ_2^2 unknown but equal. The principle roughly states that, where possible, pooling data from two samples produces a better estimate of the standard error. Here, pooling is made possible by hypothesizing (under the null hypothesis) that $p_1 = p_2$. (In Section 13-1, we used the pooled variance estimate because we assumed that $\sigma_1^2 = \sigma_2^2$.) We will call this application Case 1.

Test Statistic for $p_1 - p_2$: Case 1

If the null hypothesis specifies

$$H_0: \quad (p_1 - p_2) = 0$$

the test statistic is

$$z = \frac{(\hat{p}_1 - \hat{p}_2) - (p_1 - p_2)}{\sqrt{\hat{p}(1 - \hat{p})\left(\dfrac{1}{n_1} + \dfrac{1}{n_2}\right)}}$$

Because we hypothesize that $p_1 - p_2 = 0$, we simplify the test statistic to

$$z = \frac{(\hat{p}_1 - \hat{p}_2)}{\sqrt{\hat{p}(1 - \hat{p})\left(\dfrac{1}{n_1} + \dfrac{1}{n_2}\right)}}$$

The second case applies when, under the null hypothesis, we state that $p_1 - p_2 = D$, where D is some value other than 0. Under such circumstances, we cannot pool the sample data to estimate the standard error of $\hat{p}_1 - \hat{p}_2$. The appropriate test statistic is described next as Case 2.

Test Statistic for $p_1 - p_2$: Case 2

If the null hypothesis specifies

$$H_0: \quad (p_1 - p_2) = D \quad (D \neq 0)$$

the test statistic is

$$z = \frac{(\hat{p}_1 - \hat{p}_2) - (p_1 - p_2)}{\sqrt{\dfrac{\hat{p}_1(1 - \hat{p}_1)}{n_1} + \dfrac{\hat{p}_2(1 - \hat{p}_2)}{n_2}}}$$

which can also be expressed as

$$z = \frac{(\hat{p}_1 - \hat{p}_2) - D}{\sqrt{\dfrac{\hat{p}_1(1 - \hat{p}_1)}{n_1} + \dfrac{\hat{p}_2(1 - \hat{p}_2)}{n_2}}}$$

Notice that this test statistic is determined by simply substituting the sample statistics $\hat{p}_1$ and $\hat{p}_2$ in the standard error of $\hat{p}_1 - \hat{p}_2$.

You will find that, in most practical applications (including the exercises in this book), Case 1 applies—in most problems, we want to know whether the two population proportions differ: that is,

$$H_1: \quad (p_1 - p_2) \neq 0$$

or if one proportion exceeds the other; that is,

$$H_1: \quad (p_1 - p_2) > 0 \quad \text{or} \quad H_1: \quad (p_1 - p_2) < 0$$

In some other problems, however, the objective is to determine whether one proportion exceeds the other by a specific nonzero quantity. In such situations, Case 2 applies.

We derive the interval estimator of $p_1 - p_2$ in the same manner we have been using since Chapter 10.

Confidence Interval Estimator of $p_1 - p_2$

$$(\hat{p}_1 - \hat{p}_2) \pm z_{\alpha/2}\sqrt{\frac{\hat{p}_1(1 - \hat{p}_1)}{n_1} + \frac{\hat{p}_2(1 - \hat{p}_2)}{n_2}}$$

This formula is valid when $n_1\hat{p}_1, n_1(1 - \hat{p}_1), n_2\hat{p}_2$, and $n_2(1 - \hat{p}_2)$ are greater than or equal to 5.

Notice that the standard error is estimated using the individual sample proportions rather than the pooled proportion. In this procedure we cannot assume that the population proportions are equal as we did in the Case 1 test statistic.

APPLICATIONS in MARKETING

Test Marketing

Marketing managers frequently make use of test marketing to assess consumer reaction to a change in a characteristic (such as price or packaging) of an existing product, or to assess consumers' preferences regarding a proposed new product. *Test marketing* involves experimenting with changes to the marketing mix in a small, limited test market and assessing consumers' reaction in the test market before undertaking costly changes in production and distribution for the entire market.

EXAMPLE 13.9

DATA
Xm13-09

Test Marketing of Package Designs, Part 1

The General Products Company produces and sells a variety of household products. Because of stiff competition, one of its products, a bath soap, is not selling well. Hoping to improve sales, General Products decided to introduce more attractive packaging. The company's advertising agency developed two new designs. The first design features several bright colors to distinguish it from other brands. The second design is light green in color with just the company's logo on it. As a test to determine which design is better, the marketing manager selected two supermarkets. In one supermarket, the soap was packaged in a box using the first design; in the second supermarket, the second design was used. The product scanner at each supermarket tracked every buyer of soap over a 1-week period. The supermarkets recorded the last four digits of the scanner code for each of the five brands of soap the supermarket sold. The code for the General Products brand of soap is 9077 (the other codes are 4255, 3745, 7118, and 8855). After the trial period, the scanner data were transferred to a computer file. Because the first design is more expensive, management has decided to use this design only if there is sufficient evidence to allow it to conclude that design is better. Should management switch to the brightly colored design or the simple green one?

SOLUTION:

IDENTIFY

The problem objective is to compare two populations. The first is the population of soap sales in supermarket 1, and the second is the population of soap sales in supermarket 2. The data are nominal because the values are "buy General Products soap" and "buy other companies' soap." These two factors tell us that the parameter to be tested is the difference between two population proportions $p_1 - p_2$ (where p_1 and p_2 are the proportions of soap sales that are a General Products brand in supermarkets 1 and 2, respectively). Because we want to know whether there is enough evidence to adopt the brightly colored design, the alternative hypothesis is

$$H_1: \ (p_1 - p_2) > 0$$

The null hypothesis must be

$$H_0: \ (p_1 - p_2) = 0$$

which tells us that this is an application of Case 1. Thus, the test statistic is

$$z = \frac{(\hat{p}_1 - \hat{p}_2)}{\sqrt{\hat{p}(1 - \hat{p})\left(\dfrac{1}{n_1} + \dfrac{1}{n_2}\right)}}$$

COMPUTE

MANUALLY:

To compute the test statistic manually requires the statistics practitioner to tally the number of successes in each sample, where success is represented by the code 9077. Reviewing all the sales reveals that

$$x_1 = 180 \quad n_1 = 904 \quad x_2 = 155 \quad n_2 = 1,038$$

The sample proportions are

$$\hat{p}_1 = \frac{180}{904} = .1991$$

and

$$\hat{p}_2 = \frac{155}{1,038} = .1493$$

The pooled proportion is

$$\hat{p} = \frac{180 + 155}{904 + 1,038} = \frac{335}{1,942} = .1725$$

The value of the test statistic is

$$z = \frac{(\hat{p}_1 - \hat{p}_2)}{\sqrt{\hat{p}(1 - \hat{p})\left(\dfrac{1}{n_1} + \dfrac{1}{n_2}\right)}} = \frac{(.1991 - .1493)}{\sqrt{(.1725)(1 - .1725)\left(\dfrac{1}{904} + \dfrac{1}{1,038}\right)}} = 2.90$$

A 5% significance level seems to be appropriate. Thus, the rejection region is

$$z > z_\alpha = z_{.05} = 1.645$$

EXCEL Workbook

	A	B	C	D	E
1	z-Test of the Difference Between Two Proportions (Case 1)				
2					
3		Sample 1	Sample 2	z Stat	2.90
4	Sample proportion	0.1991	0.1493	P(Z<=z) one-tail	0.0019
5	Sample size	904	1038	z Critical one-tail	1.6449
6	Alpha	0.05		P(Z<=z) two-tail	0.0038
7				z Critical two-tail	1.9600

INSTRUCTIONS

1. Type or import the data into two columns (Open Xm13-07). Calculate the sample proportions for each sample.

2. Open the **Test Statistics Workbook** and select the **z-Test_2 Proportions (Case 1)** tab. Copy or type the sample proportions, sample sizes, and α.

XLSTAT

	B	C	D	E
2	Proportion 1: 0.1991			
3	Sample size 1: 904			
4	Proportion 2: 0.1493			
5	Sample size 2: 1038			
6	Hypothesized difference (D): 0			
7	Variance: pq(1/n1+1/n2)			
8				
9	z-test for two proportions / Upper-tailed test:			
14	Difference	0.050		
15	z (Observed value)	2.90		
16	z (Critical value)	1.645		
17	p-value (one-tailed)	0.0019		
18	alpha	0.05		

INSTRUCTIONS

1. Type or import the data into two columns (Open Xm13-09). Compute the frequencies for each sample.

2. Click **XLSTAT**, **Parametric tests**, and **Tests for two proportions**.

3. Click **Frequencies** and input the frequencies and sample sizes. Click **z test**.

4. Click **Options** and choose the **Alternative hypothesis: Proportion 1 – Proportion 2 > D** and type the value of D (0). Under **Variance** click **pq(1/n1 + 1/n2)**. Click **OK**.

INTERPRET

The value of the test statistic is $z = 2.90$; its p-value is .0019. There is enough evidence to infer that the brightly colored design is more popular than the simple design. As a result, it is recommended that management switch to the first design.

EXAMPLE 13.10

DATA
Xm13-09

Test Marketing of Package Designs, Part 2

Suppose that in Example 13.9 the additional cost of the brightly colored design requires that it outsell the simple design by more than 3%. Should management switch to the brightly colored design?

SOLUTION:

IDENTIFY

The alternative hypothesis is

$$H_1: \ (p_1 - p_2) > .03$$

and the null hypothesis follows as

$$H_0: \ (p_1 - p_2) = .03$$

Because the null hypothesis specifies a nonzero difference, we would apply the Case 2 test statistic.

COMPUTE

MANUALLY:

The value of the test statistic is

$$z = \frac{(\hat{p}_1 - \hat{p}_2) - (p_1 - p_2)}{\sqrt{\dfrac{\hat{p}_1(1 - \hat{p}_1)}{n_1} + \dfrac{\hat{p}_2(1 - \hat{p}_2)}{n_2}}} = \frac{(.1991 - .1493) - (.03)}{\sqrt{\dfrac{.1991(1 - .1991)}{904} + \dfrac{.1493(1 - .1493)}{1,038}}} = 1.15$$

EXCEL Workbook

	A	B	C	D	E
1	z-Test of the Difference Between Two Proportions (Case 2)				
2					
3		Sample 1	Sample 2	z Stat	1.15
4	Sample proportion	0.1991	0.1493	P(Z<=z) one-tail	0.1260
5	Sample size	904	1038	z Critical one-tail	1.6449
6	Hypothesized difference	0.03		P(Z<=z) two-tail	0.2520
7	Alpha	0.05		z Critical two-tail	1.9600

INSTRUCTIONS

1. Type or import the data into two columns (Open Xm13-07). Calculate the sample proportions for each sample.

2. Open the **Test Statistics Workbook** and select the **z-Test_2 Proportions (Case 2)** tab. Copy or type the sample proportions, sample sizes, the hypothesized difference (.03) and α.

XLSTAT

	B	C	D	E
2	Proportion 1: 0.1991			
3	Sample size 1: 904			
4	Proportion 2: 0.1493			
5	Sample size 2: 1038			
6	Hypothesized difference (D): 0.03			
7	Variance: p1q1/n1+p2q2/n2			
8				
9	z-test for two proportions / Upper-tailed test:			
10	Difference	0.050		
11	z (Observed value)	1.15		
12	z (Critical value)	1.645		
13	p-value (one-tailed)	0.1260		
14	alpha	0.05		

INSTRUCTIONS

Follow the first three steps shown in Example 13.9. At step 4 choose the **Alternative hypothesis: Proportion 1 – Proportion2 > D** and type the value of D (.03). Under **Variance** click **p1q1/n1 + p2q2/n2**. Click **OK**.

INTERPRET

There is not enough evidence to infer that the proportion of soap customers who buy the product with the brightly colored design is more than 3 % higher than the proportion of soap customers who buy the product with the simple design. In the absence of sufficient evidence, the analysis suggests that the product should be packaged using the simple design.

EXAMPLE 13.11

DATA

Xm13-09

Test Marketing of Package Designs, Part 3

To help estimate the difference in profitability, the marketing manager in Examples 13.9 and 13.10 would like to estimate the difference between the two proportions. A confidence level of 95 % is suggested.

SOLUTION:

IDENTIFY

The parameter is $p_1 - p_2$, which is estimated by the following confidence interval estimator:

$$(\hat{p}_1 - \hat{p}_2) \pm z_{\alpha/2}\sqrt{\frac{\hat{p}_1(1 - \hat{p}_1)}{n_1} + \frac{\hat{p}_2(1 - \hat{p}_2)}{n_2}}$$

COMPUTE

MANUALLY:

The sample proportions have already been computed. They are

$$\hat{p}_1 = \frac{180}{904} = .1991$$

and

$$\hat{p}_2 = \frac{155}{1038} = .1493$$

The 95% confidence interval estimate of $p_1 - p_2$ is

$$(\hat{p}_1 - \hat{p}_2) \pm z_{\alpha/2}\sqrt{\frac{\hat{p}_1(1 - \hat{p}_1)}{n_1} + \frac{\hat{p}_2(1 - \hat{p}_2)}{n_2}}$$

$$= (.1991 - .1493) \pm 1.96\sqrt{\frac{.1991(1 - .1991)}{904} + \frac{.1493(1 - .1493)}{1,038}}$$

$$= .0498 \pm .0339$$

$$\text{LCL} = .0159 \quad \text{and} \quad \text{UCL} = .0837$$

EXCEL Workbook

	A	B	C	D	E	F
1	z-Estimate of the Difference Between Two Proportions					
2						
3		Sample 1	Sample 2	Confidence Interval Estimate		
4	Sample proportion	0.1991	0.1493	0.0498	±	0.0339
5	Sample size	904	1038	Lower confidence limit		0.0159
6	Confidence level	0.95		Upper confidence limit		0.0837

INSTRUCTIONS

1. Type or import the data into two columns (Open Xm13-07). Calculate the sample proportions for each sample.

2. Open the **Estimators Workbook** and select the **z-Estimate_2 Proportions** tab. Copy or type the sample proportions, sample sizes, and α.

XLSTAT

	A	B	C	D	E	F	G
16	95% confidence interval on the difference between the proportions:						
17	0.0159	0.0837					

INSTRUCTIONS

Follow the first three steps shown in Example 13.9. At step 4 choose the **Alternative hypothesis: Proportion 1 – Proportion2 ≠ D** and type the value of D (0). Under **Variance** click **p1q1/n1 + p2q2/n2**. Click **OK**.

INTERPRET

We estimate that the market share for the brightly colored design is between 1.59% and 8.37% larger than the market share for the simple design.

General Social Survey

Comparing Democrats and Republicans: Who is more Likely to Have Completed a University Degree?

KamiGami/Shutterstock.com

SOLUTION:

The problem objective is to compare two populations, Democrats and Republicans. (PARTYID3: 1 = Democrat, 3 = Republican) The variable DEGREE is nominal. We've recoded the data so that all categories 3 and 4 are represented by 5, which will be our definition of success. The parameter is $p_1 - p_2$ where p_1 = proportion of Democrats with at least a Bachelor's degree and p_2 = proportion of Republicans with at least a Bachelor's degree. The hypotheses are:

$$H_0: (p_1 - p_2) = 0$$
$$H_1: (p_1 - p_2) < 0$$

The null hypothesis tells us that this is an application of Case 1. Thus, the test statistic is:

$$z = \frac{(\hat{p}_1 - \hat{p}_2)}{\sqrt{\hat{p}(1 - \hat{p})\left(\frac{1}{n_1} + \frac{1}{n_2}\right)}}$$

EXCEL Workbook

	A	B	C	D	E
1	z-Test of the Difference Between Two Proportions (Case 1)				
2					
3		Sample 1	Sample 2	z Stat	−0.73
4	Sample proportion	0.3200	0.3389	P(Z<=z) one-tail	0.2336
5	Sample size	825	537	z Critical one-tail	1.6449
6	Alpha	0.05		P(Z<=z) two-tail	0.4672
7				z Critical two-tail	1.9600

XLSTAT

	A	B
1	Frequency 1: 264	
2	Sample size 1: 825	
3	Frequency 2: 182	
4	Sample size 2: 537	
5	Hypothesized difference (D): 0	
6	Variance: pq(1/n1+1/n2)	
7	Significance level (%): 5	
8		
9	z-test for two proportions / Lower-tailed test:	
10	Difference	−0.019
11	z (Observed value)	−0.727
12	z (Critical value)	−1.645
13	p-value (one-tailed)	0.2336
14	alpha	0.05

INTERPRET

Although there is some evidence, there is not enough evidence at the 5% significance level to infer that the proportion of Republicans with at least a Bachelor's degree is greater than the proportion of Democrats with at least a Bachelor's degree.

The factors that identify the inference about the difference between two proportions are listed below.

Factors That Identify the z-Test and Estimator of $p_1 - p_2$

1. **Problem objective**: Compare two populations
2. **Data type**: Nominal

EXERCISES

Developing an Understanding of Statistical Concepts

Exercises 13.127–13.129 are "what-if analyses" designed to determine what happens to the test statistics and interval estimates when elements of the statistical inference change. These problems can be solved manually or by using an Excel spreadsheet.

13.127 Random samples from two binomial populations yielded the following statistics:

$$\hat{p}_1 = .45 \quad n_1 = 100 \quad \hat{p}_2 = .40 \quad n_2 = 100$$

a. Calculate the p-value of a test to determine whether we can infer that the population proportions differ.
b. Repeat part (a) increasing the sample sizes to 400.
c. Describe what happens to the p-value when the sample sizes increase.

13.128 These statistics were calculated from two random samples:

$$\hat{p}_1 = .60 \quad n_1 = 225 \quad \hat{p}_2 = .55 \quad n_2 = 225$$

a. Calculate the p-value of a test to determine whether there is evidence to infer that the population proportions differ.
b. Repeat part (a) with $\hat{p}_1 = .95$ and $\hat{p}_2 = .90$.
c. Describe the effect on the p-value of increasing the sample proportions.
d. Repeat part (a) with $\hat{p}_1 = .10$ and $\hat{p}_2 = .05$.
e. Describe the effect on the p-value of decreasing the sample proportions.

13.129 After sampling from two binomial populations we found the following.

$$\hat{p}_1 = .18 \quad n_1 = 100 \quad \hat{p}_2 = .22 \quad n_2 = 100$$

a. Estimate with 90% confidence the difference in population proportions.
b. Repeat part (a) increasing the sample proportions to .48 and .52, respectively.
c. Describe the effects of increasing the sample proportions.

Applications

13.130 Many stores sell extended warranties for products they sell. These are very lucrative for store owners. To learn more about who buys these warranties a random sample of a store's customers who recently purchased a product for which an extended warranty was available was drawn. Among other variables each respondent reported whether they paid the regular price or a sale price and whether they purchased an extended warranty.

	Regular price	Sale price
Sample size	229	178
Number who bought extended warranty	47	25

Can we conclude at the 10% significance level that those who paid the regular price are more likely to buy an extended warranty?

13.131 A firm has classified its customers in two ways: (1) according to whether the account is overdue and (2) whether the account is new (less than 12 months) or old. To acquire information about which customers are paying on time and which are overdue, a random sample of 292 customer accounts was drawn. Each was categorized as a new account (less than 12 months) and old, and whether the customer has paid or is overdue. The results are summarized next.

	New Account	Old Account
Sample size	83	209
Overdue account	12	49

Is there enough evidence at the 5% significance level to infer that new and old accounts are different with respect to overdue accounts?

Overeating Experiment (See page 451 for description.)

13.132 Chop Stick Experiment

One hundred normal-weight people and 100 obese people were observed at several Chinese-food buffets. For each researchers recorded whether the diner used chopsticks or knife and fork. The table shown here was created.

	Normal Weight	Obese
Used chop sticks	26	7
Used knife and fork	74	93

Is there sufficient evidence at the 10% significance level to conclude that obese Chinese food eaters are less likely to use chop sticks?
(*Source:* Brian Wansink and Collin R. Payne, "The Cues and Correlates of Overeating at the Chinese

Buffet," Cornell University Food and Brand Lab working paper.

13.133 Surveys have been widely used by politicians around the world as a way of monitoring the opinions of the electorate. Six months ago, a survey was undertaken to determine the degree of support for a national party leader. Of a sample of 1,100, 56% indicated that they would vote for this politician. This month, another survey of 800 voters revealed that 46% now support the leader.

   a. At the 5% significance level, can we infer that the national leader's popularity has decreased?

   b. At the 5% significance level, can we infer that the national leader's popularity has decreased by more than 5%?

   c. Estimate with 95% confidence the decrease in percentage support between now and 6 months ago.

13.134 The process that is used to produce a complex component used in medical instruments typically results in defective rates in the 40% range. Recently, two innovative processes have been developed to replace the existing process. Process 1 appears to be more promising, but it is considerably more expensive to purchase and operate than process 2. After a thorough analysis of the costs, management decides that it will adopt process 1 only if the proportion of defective components it produces is more than 8% smaller than that produced by process 2. In a test to guide the decision, both processes were used to produce 300 components. Of the 300 components produced by process 1, 33 were found to be defective, whereas 84 out of the 300 produced by process 2 were defective. Conduct a test using a significance level of 1% to help management make a decision.

APPLICATIONS in OPERATIONS MANAGEMENT

Pharmaceutical and Medical Experiments

When new products are developed, they are tested in several ways. First, does the new product work? Second, is it better than the existing product? Third, will customers buy it at a price that is profitable? Performing a customer survey or some other experiment that yields the information needed often tests the last question. This experiment is usually the domain of the marketing manager.

The other two questions are dealt with by the developers of the new product, which usually means the research department or the operations manager. When the product is a new drug, there are particular ways in which the data are gathered. The sample is divided into two groups. One group is assigned the new drug and the other is assigned a placebo, a pill that contains no medication. The experiment is often called "double-blind" because neither the subjects who take the drug nor the physician/scientist who provides the drug knows whether any individual is taking the drug or the placebo. At the end of the experiment the data that are compiled allow statistics practitioners to do their work. Exercises 13.135–13.139 are examples of this type of statistical application. Exercise 13.140 describes a health-related problem where the use of a placebo is not possible.

13.135 Cold and allergy medicines have been available for a number of years. One serious side effect of these medications is that they cause drowsiness, which makes them dangerous for industrial workers. In recent years, a nondrowsy cold and allergy medicine has been developed. One such product, Hismanal, is claimed by its manufacturer to be the first once-a-day nondrowsy allergy medicine. The nondrowsy part of the claim is based on a clinical experiment in which 1,604 patients were given Hismanal and 1,109 patients were given a placebo. Of the first group, 7.1% reported drowsiness; of the second group, 6.4% reported drowsiness. Do these results allow us to infer at the 5% significance level that Hismanal's claim is false?

13.136 Plavix is a drug that is given to angioplasty patients to help prevent blood clots. A researcher at McMaster University organized a study that involved 12,562 patients in 482 hospitals in 28 countries. All the patients had acute coronary syndrome, which produces mild heart attacks or unstable angina, chest pain that may precede a heart attack. The patients were divided into two equal groups. Group 1 received daily Plavix pills, while group 2 received a placebo. After 1 year 9.3% of patients on Plavix suffered a stroke or new heart attack, or had died of cardiovascular disease, compared with 11.5% of those who took the placebo.

a. Can we infer that Plavix is effective?

b. Describe your statistical analysis in a report to the marketing manager of the pharmaceutical company.

13.137 In a study that was highly publicized, doctors discovered that aspirin seems to help prevent heart attacks. The research project, which was scheduled to last for 5 years, involved 22,000 American physicians (all male). Half took an aspirin tablet three times per week, while the other half took a placebo on the same schedule. The researchers tracked each of the volunteers and updated the records regularly. Among the physicians who took aspirin, 104 suffered a heart attack; 189 physicians who took the placebo had a heart attack.

a. Determine whether these results indicate that aspirin is effective in reducing the incidence of heart attacks.

b. Write a report that describes the results of this experiment.

13.138 Exercise 13.137 described the experiment that determined that taking aspirin daily reduces one's probability of suffering a heart attack. The study was conducted in 1982 and at that time the mean age of the physicians was 50. In the years following the experiment the physicians were monitored for other medical conditions. One of these was the incidence of cataracts. There were 1,084 cataracts in the aspirin group and 997 in the placebo group. Do these statistics allow researchers to conclude that aspirin leads to more cataracts?

13.139 According to the Canadian Cancer Society more than 21,000 women will be diagnosed with breast cancer every year and more than 5,000 will die. (U.S. figures are more than 10 times those in Canada.) Surgery is generally considered the first method of treatment. However, many women suffer recurrences of cancer. For this reason many women are treated with Tamoxifen. But after 5 years, tumors develop a resistance to Tamoxifen. A new drug called Letrozole was developed by Novartis Pharmaceuticals to replace Tamoxifen. To determine its effectiveness, a study involving 5,187 breast cancer survivors from Canada, the United States, and Europe was undertaken. Half the sample received Letrozole and the other half a placebo. The study was to run for 5 years. However, after only 2.5 years it was determined that 132 women receiving the placebo and 75 taking the drug had recurrences of their cancers. The study was published in the *New England Journal of Medicine*.

a. Do these results provide sufficient evidence to infer that Letrozole works?

b. Prepare a presentation to the board of directors of Novartis describing your analysis.

13.140 A study described in the *British Medical Journal* (January 2004) sought to determine whether exercise would help extend the lives of patients with heart failure. A sample of 801 patients with heart failure was recruited; 395 received exercise training and 406 did not. There were 88 deaths among the exercise group and 105 among those who did not exercise. Can researchers infer that exercise training reduces mortality?

Exercises 13.141 -13.146 are based on the following experiment.

In attempt to understand the frustrations of driving in large cities an experiment was conducted. At a red light in a busy intersection the lead car hesitated for 2 seconds. The researchers recorded several variables and whether the driver in the following car honked his or her horn. The following tables were created from the recorded data. **Conduct all tests at the 5% significance level.**

13.141 Cell Phone Experiment 1

(*Source:* Statistics adapted from *Traffic*, Tom Vanderbilt.)

Driver in following car was female	Lead car driver using cell phone	Lead car driver not using cell phone
Honked horn	18	27
Did not honk horn	77	162

Is there enough evidence to infer that women drivers in a following car are more likely to honk when the lead car driver is using a cell phone?

13.142 Cell Phone Experiment 2

Driver in following car was male	Lead car driver used cell phone	Lead car driver did not use cell phone
Honked horn	35	34
Did not honk horn	103	170

Can we conclude that male drivers are more likely to honk when the lead car driver is using a cell phone?

13.143 Expensive Car Experiment

	Lead car was expensive (over $50,000)	Lead car was not expensive
Honked horn	33	49
Did not honk horn	122	118

Do these figures allow us to conclude that drivers behind expensive cars are less likely to honk?

13.144 Gender Experiment 1

	Lead car driver was female	Lead car driver was male
Honked horn	64	47
Did not honk horn	123	136

Is there sufficient evidence to infer that drivers behind a male driver are more likely to honk?

13.145 Gender Experiment 2

	Following car driver was female	Following car driver was male
Honked horn	68	105
Did not honk horn	143	135

Can we conclude from these statistics that women are less likely to honk?

13.146 Convertible Experiment

	Following car was a convertible	Following car was not a convertible
Honked horn	21	86
Did not honk horn	92	210

Is there enough evidence to draw the inference that drivers of convertibles are less likely to honk?

The following exercises require the use of a computer and software. The answers to Exercises 13.147–13.166 may be calculated manually. See Appendix A for the sample statistics. **Use a 5% significance level, unless specified otherwise.**

13.147 Xr13-147 Automobile magazines often compare models and rate them in various ways. One question that is often asked of car owners, Would you buy the same model again? Suppose that a researcher for one magazine asked a random sample of Lexus owners and a random sample of Acura owners whether they plan to buy another Lexus/Acura the next time they shop for a new car. The responses (1 = No, 2 = Yes) were recorded. Do these data allow the researcher to infer that the two populations of car owners differ in their satisfaction levels?

13.148 Xr13-148 An insurance company is thinking about offering discounts on its life insurance policies to nonsmokers. As part of its analysis, the company randomly selects 200 men who are 60 years old and asks them whether they smoke at least one pack of cigarettes per day and if they have ever suffered from heart disease. (2 = Suffer from heart disease, 1 = Do not suffer from heart disease).

a. Can the company conclude at the 10% significance level that smokers have a higher incidence of heart disease than nonsmokers?

b. Estimate with 90% confidence the difference in the proportions of men suffering from heart disease between smokers and nonsmokers.

13.149 Xr13-149 Has the illicit use of drugs decreased over the past 10 years? Government agencies have undertaken surveys of Americans 12 years of age and older. Each was asked whether he or she used drugs at least once in the previous month. The results of this year's survey and the results of the survey completed 10 years ago were recorded as 1 = No and 2 = Yes. Can we infer that the use of illicit drugs in the United States has increased in the past decade? (*Source:* Adapted from the U.S. Substance Abuse and Mental Health Services Administration, National Household Survey on Drug Abuse.)

13.150 Xr13-150 It has been estimated that the oil sands in Alberta Canada contains 2 trillion barrels of oil. However, recovering the oil damages the environment. A survey of Canadians and Americans asked, What is more important to you with regard to the oil-sands, environmental concerns (1), or the potential as a secure non-foreign supply of oil to North America(2)? Do these data allow you to conclude that Canadians and Americans differ in their responses to this question? (*Source:* Flieshman-Hillard Oilsands Survey.)

13.151 Xr13-151 An operations manager of a computer chip maker is in the process of selecting a new machine to replace several older ones. Although technological innovations have improved the production process, it is quite common for the machines to produce defective chips. The operations manager must choose between two machines. The cost of machine A is several thousand dollars greater than the cost of machine B. After an analysis of the costs it was determined that machine A is warranted provided that its defective rate is more than 2% less than that of machine B. To help decide both machines are used to produce 200 chips each. Each chip was examined and whether it was defective (code = 2) or not (code = 1) was recorded. Should the operations manager select machine A?

13.152 Xr13-152 Parents often urge their children to get more education, not only for the increased income but to perhaps work less hard. In a survey, a random sample of Canadians were asked whether they work 11 or more hours a day (1 = No, 2 = Yes) and whether they completed high school only or completed post-secondary education. Can we infer that those with more education are less likely to work 11 hours or more per day? (*Source:* Harris/Decima survey.)

13.153 Xr13-153 Are Americans becoming more unhappy at work? A survey of Americans in 2008 and again this year asked whether he or she was satisfied with their jobs (1 = No, 2 = Yes). Can we infer that more Americans are unhappy compared to 2008?

13.154 Xr13-154 In Chapters 3 and 4, we described the issue of global warming pointing out that the Earth has not warmed since 1998, explaining why the media now refer to the problem as climate change, and that there is a weak linear relationship between temperature anomalies and CO_2 levels. In the last few years news stories have appeared that seem to cast doubt on the entire theory. To measure the effect on public opinion several surveys have been conducted by Pew Research Center. Approximately 1,000 American adults were asked the following question in March 2012 and March 2013.

How serious a problem is global warming? The responses are:

1. Very serious
2. Somewhat serious
3. Not too serious
4. Not a problem

Is there sufficient evidence to infer that the proportion of American adults who believe that global warming is a very serious problem decreased between 2012 and 2013?

13.155 Xr13-155 One of the issues in the U.S. presidential election in 2016 was the Keystone XL pipeline, which would send Canadian oil to the refineries in Texas. Pew Research Center conducted a survey of American adults and asked each whether he or she was in favor (1) or opposed (2) to the pipeline. The survey identified each respondent as either male or female. Is there sufficient evidence to infer that men and women differ in their support of the pipeline?

13.156 Xr13-156* An experiment conducted by members of the Religious Affiliation and Hiring Discrimination Organization to determine what shouldn't be in the resume should be of interest to students preparing resumes in search of summer or permanent jobs. The experiment consisted of submitting 6400 resumes to employers that had advertised 1,600 job openings. The jobs included positions in customer service, hospitality, media, retail, real estate, shipping, and clerical duties. The postings only required an e-mailed resume. The fake job applicants were presented as young people recently graduated from college who earned a 3.7 or higher grade point average. Half of the resumes included mentions of religious activities and half made no reference to religion at all. For each resume the researchers recorded whether the prospective employer called the applicant back for more information or to schedule an interview (code = 1) or no call back (code = 2). Is there sufficient evidence to infer that including a reference to religious activity reduces the probability of a call back?

13.157 Xr13-156* Refer to Exercise 13.156. In 2700 of the resumes the religion mentioned was one of the mainstream religions. However, 500 resumes made reference to a made-up religion – Wallonian. The religious designation (1 = mainstream religion, 2 = Wallonian) was recorded. Is there sufficient evidence to infer that the Wallonians had a higher call back frequency than did the main stream religions?

13.158 Xr13-158 To measure the cardiovascular health of Canadians, cardiologists developed the Cardiovascular Health in Ambulatory Care Research Team (CANHEART) health index. A score of 1 is assigned for each of the following cardiovascular health factors and behaviors:

Do not smoke

Physical activity equivalent to walking 30 minutes per day

Consumption of 5 servings of fruit and vegetables per day

Body mass index of less than 25

Not diabetic

Normal blood pressure (less than 140 over 90)

A score of 6 is ideal, 4 to 5 is considered to be intermediate, and a score between 0 and 3 is considered poor cardiovascular health. The scores and sex (1 = female, 2 = male) of a random sample of Canadian adults were recorded. Can we infer from the data that females are more likely to be in ideal cardiovascular health than males?

13.159 Xr13-159   In Exercise 9.59 we pointed out that most televised baseball games display a pitch tracker that shows whether the pitch was a ball or a strike, which in turn shows whether the umpire made the correct call. Suppose a fan kept track of a random sample of calls made by two of the more experienced umpires. In this exercise he tracked pitches that were not in the strike zone and the batter did not swing. He recorded whether the umpire's call (1= ball, 2 = strike). Is there sufficient evidence that there is a difference in the error rate of making calls on pitches that were not in the strike zone between the two umpires? (Source: Adapted from SB Nation)

13.160 Xr13-160   Refer to Exercise 13.159. The fan also recorded the calls on pitches that were in the strike zone and the batter did not swing (1 = ball, 2 = strike). Can we infer from the data that there is a difference in the error rate of making calls on pitches in the strike zone between the two umpires?

13.161 Xr13-161   In June 2016 the United Kingdom voted to leave the European Union. As is the case in the United States, pollsters conducted exit polls and asked how each respondent voted (1 = remain, 2 = leave) and recorded the age category (1 = 18 – 24, 2 = 25 – 49, 3 = 50 – 64 0, 4 = 65 and older).

a. Is there sufficient evidence to conclude that there is a difference in the vote between Britons aged 50 to 64 and those 65 and over?

b. Can we infer that there is a difference in the vote between 18 to 24 year old Britons and those between 25 and 49?

13.162 Xr13-162   Surveys of workers asked a series of questions from which each was categorized as either 1 = thriving, 2 = struggling, 3 = suffering. Each respondent was also asked whether they worked for the federal government or a private sector employer. Is there sufficient evidence to infer that government workers are more likely to be thriving when compared to other workers?

13.163 Xr13-163   A Gallup survey asks a random sample of American adults this question. "In this country, are you satisfied or dissatisfied with your freedom to choose what you do with your life?" The responses are 1 = satisfied, 2 = dissatisfied. The survey results from this year and one 5 years ago were recorded. Is there enough statistical evidence to infer that American adults are less satisfied with the freedom to choose what do to with their lives than they were 5 years ago?

APPLICATIONS in MARKETING

Market Segmentation

In Section 12-4 we introduced market segmentation and described how the size of market segments can be estimated. Once the segments have been defined we can use statistical techniques to determine whether members of the segments differ in their purchases of a firm's products.

13.164 Xr13-164*   The market for breakfast cereals has been divided into several segments related to health. One company identified a segment as those adults who are health conscious. The marketing manager would like to know whether this segment is more likely to purchase its Special X cereal that is pitched toward the health conscious segment. A survey of adults was undertaken. On the basis of several probing questions each was classified as either a member of the health-conscious group (code = 1) or not (code = 2). Each respondent was also asked whether he or she buys Special X (1 = No, 2 = Yes). The data were recorded in stacked format. Can we infer from these data that health-conscious adults are more likely to buy Special X?

13.165 XR13-165*   Quik Lube is a company that offers oil change service while the customer waits. Its market has been broken down into the following segments:
1. Working men and women too busy to wait at a dealer or service center
2. Spouses who work in the home
3. Retired persons
4. Other

A random sample of car owners was drawn. Each owner classified his or her market segment and also reported whether they usually use the services like Quik Lube (1 = Yes, 2 = No). These data are stored in stacked format.
a. Determine whether members of segment 1 are more likely than members of segment 4 to respond that they usually use the service?
b. Can we infer that retired persons and spouses who work in the home differ in their use of services such as Quik Lube?

13.166 XR13-166   Telemarketers obtain names and telephone numbers from several sources. To determine whether one particular source is better than a second, a random sample of names and numbers from the two different sources was obtained. For each potential customer, a statistics practitioner recorded whether that individual made a purchase (code = 2) or not (code = 1). Can we infer that differences exist between the two sources?

GENERAL SOCIAL SURVEY EXERCISES

13.167 GSS2014*   A generation ago men were more likely to attend university and acquire a graduate degree than women. However, women now appear to be attending university in greater numbers than men. To gauge the extent of the difference, test to determine whether men and women (SEX: 1 = Male, 2 = Female) differ in completing a graduate degree (DEGREE: 4 = Graduate).

13.168 GSS2014*   The deep recession of 2008–2010 may have changed patterns of employment. Because of the large number of layoffs an increasing number of individuals have chosen to work for themselves. Does this apply equally to men and women (SEX: 1 = Male, 2 = Female)? Conduct a test to determine whether there is enough evidence to conclude that men and women differ in their decision to work for themselves (WRKSLF: 1 = Self-employed).

13.169 GSS2014*   Is there sufficient evidence to conclude that foreign-born people (BORN: 1 = In the United

States, 2 = Elsewhere) are more likely to have a graduate degree (DEGREE: 4 = Graduate) than people born in the United States?

13.170 GSS2014*   Is there a difference between men and women in their preference for working for some government agency? Conduct a test to determine whether there is enough evidence to infer that women (SEX: 1 = Male, 2 = Female) are more likely to work for the government (WRKGOVT: 1 = Government) than men?

13.171 GSS2014*   Can we infer from the data that Democrats (PARTYID3: 1 = Democrat; 3 = Republican) are more likely to work for the government (WRKGOVT: 1 = Government, 2 = Private enterprise)?

13.172 GSS2014*   Is working full time and earning more money than part time workers the prime reason why some people are Republicans. This raises the question, Is there sufficient evidence to conclude that Republicans (PARTYID3: 1 = Democrat,

3 = Republican) are more likely to be working full time (WRKSTAT: 1 = Full time) than Democrats?

13.173 <u>GSS2014*</u>   In theory, Republicans are more supportive of free enterprise. Do the data allow us to infer that Republicans (PARTYID3 1 = Democrat, 3 = Republican) are more likely to work for themselves (WRKSLF: 1 = Work for themselves, 2 = Other) than Democrats?

13.174 <u>GSS2014*</u>   Are married people more likely to be working full time (WRKSTAT: 1 = Full time,)?

Conduct a test to determine whether there are differences between married and never married (MARITAL: 1 = Married, 5 = Never married) American adults.

13.175 <u>GSS2014*</u>   Is there enough statistical evidence to conclude that married people (MARITAL: 1 = Married, 5 = Never married) are more likely to work for themselves (WRKSLF: 1 = Work for themselves, 2 = Work for someone else) than married people?

13.176 <u>GSS2014*</u>   Half a century ago men were far more likely to be the breadwinner and women were far more likely to be homemakers. There are now many households where women are the breadwinners and many households where both work outside the home. Is there a difference in the proportion of men and women (SEX: 1 = Male, 2 = Female) working fulltime outside the home (WRKSTAT: 1 = Working full time, 2–8 = Other)? Perform a statistical test to answer the question.

13.177 <u>GSS2014*</u>   Can we infer from the data that married and never married people (MARITAL: 1 = Married, 5 = Never married) differ in their completion of a graduate degree (DEGREE: 4 = Graduate degree)?

13.178 <u>GSS2014*</u>   It is generally understood that working for the government means more job security than working for private enterprise. Are married people

(MARITAL: 1 = Married, 5 = Never married) more likely to work for the government (WRKGOVT: 1 = Government) than do never married people?

13.179 <u>GSS2014*</u>   Is there enough statistical evidence to conclude that people born (BORN: 1 = In the United States, 2 = Elsewhere) in the United States are more likely to work for the government (WRKGVT: 1 = Government, 2 = Other) than people born outside the United States?

13.180 <u>GSS2014*</u>   Are foreign-born people (BORN: 1 = In the United States, 2 = Elsewhere) more likely to work for themselves (WRKSLF: 1 = Work for themselves, 2 = Work for someone else) than Americans born in the United States? Conduct a test to answer the question.

For each of the following four exercises, determine whether men and women are likely to differ in answering each question correctly.

13.181 <u>GSS2014*</u>   A doctor tells a couple that there is one chance in four that their child will have an inherited disease. Does this mean that if the first child has the illness, the next three will not (ODDS1: 1 = Yes, 2 = No)? Correct answer: No.

13.182 <u>GSS2014*</u>   A doctor tells a couple that there is one chance in four that their child will have an inherited disease. Does this mean that each of the couple's children will have the same risk of suffering the illness (ODDS2: 1 = Yes, 2 = No)? Correct answer: Yes.

13.183 <u>GSS2014*</u>   True or false, the center of the earth is very hot (HOTCORE: 1 = True, 2 = False)? Correct answer: True.

13.184 <u>GSS2014*</u>   Does the Earth go around the Sun, or does the Sun go around the Earth (EARTHSUN: 1 = Earth around Sun, 2 = Sun around Earth)? Correct answer: Earth around Sun.

SURVEY OF CONSUMER FINANCES EXERCISES

Conduct all tests at the 5% significance level.

13.185 <u>SCF2013:\ALL*</u>   Many studies show that women are more likely to have a college degree than men. However, does this apply to female and male heads (HHSEX: 1 = male, 2 = female) of households? Is there enough evidence to conclude that male heads of households are more likely to have a college degree than female heads of households (EDCL: 4 = College degree)?

13.186 <u>SCF2013:\ALL*</u>   If male heads of households (HHSEX: 1 = male, 2 = female) are more likely to have a college degree does it follow that they have a higher employment rate (LF: 1 = Working in some way)? Conduct a test to answer the question.

13.187 <u>SCF2013:\ALL*</u>   Is there sufficient evidence to conclude that male heads of households (HHSEX: 1 = male, 2 = female) are more likely to own the home they live in (HOUSECL: 1 = Owns)?

13.188 SCF2013:\ALL* Is there enough statistical evidence to infer that male heads of households (HHSEX: 1 = male, 2 = female) are more likely to be married (or living with partner) than female heads of households (MARRIED: 1 = Married or living with partner)?

13.189 What conclusions can you draw from the results of the four previous exercises?

13.190 SCF2013:\ALL* Are married heads of households (MARRIED: 1 =married or living with partner, 2 = not married or living with partner) more likely to have a college degree (EDCL: 4 = College degree)? Conduct a test to answer the question.

13.191 SCF2013:\ALL* With marriage comes financial responsibilities. If so, we would expect married heads of households (MARRIED: 1 = married or living with partner, 2 = not married or living with partner) to be less likely to be unemployed (LF: 0 = Not working). Is there sufficient evidence to support this expectation?

13.192 SCF2013:\ALL* Is there enough evidence to infer that married heads of households (MARRIED: 1 =married or living with partner, 2 = not married or living with partner) are more likely to be self-employed (OCCAT1: 2 = Self-employed/partnership)?

13.193 SCF2013:\ALL* Are married heads of households (MARRIED: 1 =married or living with partner, 2 = not married or living with partner) less likely to have declared bankruptcy in the last five years? Conduct a test to answer the question (BNKRUPLAST5: 1 = Yes).

CHAPTER SUMMARY

In this chapter, we presented a variety of techniques that allow statistics practitioners to compare two populations. When the data are interval and we are interested in measures of central location, we encountered two more factors that must be considered when choosing the appropriate technique. When the samples are independent, we can use either the **equal-variances** or **unequal-variances formulas**. When the samples are **matched pairs**, we have only one set of formulas. We introduced the **F-statistic**, which is used to make inferences about two population variances. When the data are nominal, the parameter of interest is the difference between two proportions. For this parameter, we had two test statistics and one interval estimator. Finally, we discussed **observational** and **experimental data**, important concepts in attempting to interpret statistical findings.

IMPORTANT TERMS:

Pooled variance estimator   430
Equal-variances test statistic   430
Equal-variances confidence interval estimator   430
Unequal-variances test statistic   431
Unequal-variances confidence interval estimator   431
Observational data   455

Experimental data   455
Matched pairs experiment   462
Mean of the population of differences   463
Numerator degrees of freedom   473
Denominator degrees of freedom   473
Pooled proportion estimate   481

SYMBOLS:

Symbol	Pronounced	Represents
s_p^2	s sub p squared	Pooled variance estimator
μ_D	mu sub D or mu D	Mean of the paired differences
$\overline{x}_D$	x bar sub D or x bar D	Sample mean of the paired differences
s_D	s sub D or s D	Sample standard deviation of the paired differences
n_D	n sub D or n D	Sample size of the paired differences
$\hat{p}$	p hat	Pooled proportion

FORMULAS:

Equal-variances t-test of $\mu_1 - \mu_2$

$$t = \frac{(\bar{x}_1 - \bar{x}_2) - (\mu_1 - \mu_2)}{\sqrt{s_p^2\left(\dfrac{1}{n_1} + \dfrac{1}{n_2}\right)}} \quad \nu = n_1 + n_2 - 2$$

Equal-variances interval estimator of $(\mu_1 - \mu_2)$

$$(\bar{x}_1 - \bar{x}_2) \pm t_{\alpha/2}\sqrt{s_p^2\left(\frac{1}{n_1} + \frac{1}{n_2}\right)} \quad \nu = n_1 + n_2 - 2$$

Unequal-variances t-test of $\mu_1 - \mu_2$

$$t = \frac{(\bar{x}_1 - \bar{x}_2) - (\mu_1 - \mu_2)}{\sqrt{\left(\dfrac{s_1^2}{n_1} + \dfrac{s_2^2}{n_2}\right)}} \quad \nu = \frac{(s_1^2/n_1 + s_2^2/n_2)^2}{\dfrac{(s_1^2/n_1)^2}{n_1 - 1} + \dfrac{(s_2^2/n_2)^2}{n_2 - 1}}$$

Unequal-variances interval estimator of $\mu_1 - \mu_2$

$$(\bar{x}_1 - \bar{x}_2) \pm t_{\alpha/2}\sqrt{\frac{s_1^2}{n_1} + \frac{s_2^2}{n_2}} \quad \nu = \frac{(s_1^2/n_1 + s_2^2/n_2)^2}{\dfrac{(s_1^2/n_1)^2}{n_1 - 1} + \dfrac{(s_2^2/n_2)^2}{n_2 - 1}}$$

t-test of μ_D

$$t = \frac{\bar{x}_D - \mu_D}{s_D/\sqrt{n_D}} \quad \nu = n_D - 1$$

t-estimator of μ_D

$$t = \frac{\bar{x}_D - \mu_D}{s_D/\sqrt{n_D}} \quad \nu = n_D - 1$$

F-test of σ_1^2/σ_2^2

$$F = \frac{s_1^2}{s_2^2} \quad \nu_1 = n_1 - 1 \text{ and } \nu_2 = n_2 - 1$$

F-estimator of σ_1^2/σ_2^2

$$\text{LCL} = \left(\frac{s_1^2}{s_2^2}\right)\frac{1}{F_{\alpha/2, \nu_1, \nu_2}}$$

$$\text{UCL} = \left(\frac{s_1^2}{s_2^2}\right)F_{\alpha/2, \nu_1, \nu_2}$$

z-test and estimator of $p_1 - p_2$

Case 1: $z = \dfrac{(\hat{p}_1 - \hat{p}_2)}{\sqrt{\hat{p}(1 - \hat{p})\left(\dfrac{1}{n_1} + \dfrac{1}{n_2}\right)}}$

Case 2: $z = \dfrac{(\hat{p}_1 - \hat{p}_2) - (p_1 - p_2)}{\sqrt{\dfrac{\hat{p}_1(1 - \hat{p}_1)}{n_1} + \dfrac{\hat{p}_2(1 - \hat{p}_2)}{n_2}}}$

z-estimator of $p_1 - p_2$

$$(\hat{p}_1 - \hat{p}_2) \pm z_{\alpha/2}\sqrt{\frac{\hat{p}_1(1 - \hat{p}_1)}{n_1} + \frac{\hat{p}_2(1 - \hat{p}_2)}{n_2}}$$

COMPUTER OUTPUT AND INSTRUCTIONS:

CHAPTER EXERCISES

The following exercises require the use of a computer and software.
*Use a 5% **significance level unless specified otherwise.***

13.194 Xr13-194 Obesity among children is quickly becoming an epidemic across North America. Television and video games are part of the problem. To gauge to what extent nonparticipation in organized sports contributes to the crisis surveys of children 5 to 14 years old were conducted this year and 10 years ago. The gender of the child and whether he or she participated in organized sports (1 = No, 2 = Yes) were recorded.

   a. Can we conclude that there has been a decrease in participation among boys over the past 10 years?

   b. Repeat part (a) for girls.

   c. Can we infer that girls are less likely to participate than boys this year?

13.195 Xr13-195 A restaurant located in an office building decides to adopt a new strategy for attracting customers to the restaurant. Every week it advertises in the city newspaper. To assess how well the advertising is working, the restaurant owner recorded the weekly gross sales for the 15 weeks after the campaign began and the weekly gross sales for the 24 weeks immediately prior to the campaign. Can the restaurateur conclude that the advertising campaign is successful?

13.196 Xr13-196 Every year, the Bureau of Labor Statistics administers a survey of American households called the American Time Use Survey. Respondents are asked to report their activities during an entire 24-hour day. The results are used to determine the number of hours respondents work in a typical week. The results for government and private-sector workers were recorded. Is there sufficient evidence to infer that government employees work less than private-sector workers?

13.197 Xr13-197 How important to your health are regular vacations? In a study a random sample of men and women were asked how frequently they take vacations. The men and women were divided into two groups each. The members of group 1 had suffered a heart attack; the members of group 2 had not. The number of days of vacation last year was recorded for each person. Can we infer that men and women who suffer heart attacks vacation less than those who did not suffer a heart attack?

13.198 Xr13-198 Research scientists at a pharmaceutical company have recently developed a new nonprescription sleeping pill. They decide to test its effectiveness by measuring the time it takes for people to fall asleep after taking the pill. Preliminary analysis indicates that the time to fall asleep varies considerably from one person to another. Consequently, they organize the experiment in the following way. A random sample of 100 volunteers who regularly suffer from insomnia is chosen. Each person is given one pill containing the newly developed drug and one placebo. (They do not know whether the pill they are taking is the placebo or the real thing, and the order of use is random.) Each participant is fitted with a device that measures the time until sleep occurs. Can we conclude that the new drug is effective?

13.199 Xr13-199 The city of Toronto boasts four daily newspapers. Not surprisingly, competition is keen. To help learn more about newspaper readers, an advertiser selected a random sample of people who bought their newspapers from a street vendor and people who had the newspaper delivered to their homes. Each was asked how many minutes they spent reading their newspapers. Can we infer that the amount of time reading differs between the two groups?

13.200 Xr13-200 In recent years, a number of state governments have passed mandatory seat-belt laws. Although the use of seat belts is known to save lives and reduce serious injuries, compliance with seat-belt laws is not universal. In an effort to increase the use of seat belts, a government agency sponsored a 2-year study. Among its objectives was to determine whether there was enough evidence to infer that seat-belt usage increased between last year and this year. To test this belief, random samples of drivers last year and this year were asked whether they always use their seat belts (2 = Wear seat belt, 1 = Do not wear seat belt). Can we infer that seat belt usage has increased over the last year?

13.201 Xr13-201 An important component of the cost of living is the amount of money spent on housing. Housing costs include rent (for tenants), mortgage payments and property tax (for home owners), heating, electricity, and water. An economist undertook a 5-year study to determine how housing costs have changed. Five years ago, he took a random sample of 200 households and recorded the percentage of total income spent on housing. This year, he took another sample of 200 households.

a. Conduct a test (with $\alpha = .10$) to determine whether the economist can infer that housing cost as a percentage of total income has increased over the last 5 years.

b. Use whatever statistical method you deem appropriate to check the required condition(s) of the test used in part (a).

13.202 Xr13-202   In designing advertising campaigns to sell magazines, it is important to know how much time each of a number of demographic groups spends reading magazines. In a preliminary study, 40 people were randomly selected. Each was asked how much time per week he or she spends reading magazines; additionally, each was categorized by gender and by income level (high or low). The data are stored in the following way: column 1 = Time spent reading magazines per week in minutes for all respondents; column 2 = Gender (1 = Male, 2 = Female); column 3 = Income level (1 = Low, 2 = High).

a. Is there sufficient evidence at the 10% significance level to conclude that men and women differ in the amount of time spent reading magazines?

b. Is there sufficient evidence at the 10% significance level to conclude that high-income individuals devote more time to reading magazines than low-income people?

13.203 Xr13-203   In a study to determine whether gender affects salary offers for graduating MBA students, 25 pairs of students were selected. Each pair consisted of a female and a male student who were matched according to their GPAs, courses taken, ages, and previous work experience. The highest salary offered (in thousands of dollars) to each graduate was recorded.

a. Is there enough evidence at the 10% significance level to infer that gender is a factor in salary offers?

b. Discuss why the experiment was organized in the way it was.

c. Is the required condition for the test in part (a) satisfied?

13.204 Xr13-204   Have North Americans grown to distrust television and newspaper journalists? A study was conducted this year to compare what Americans currently think of the press versus what they said 3 years ago. The survey asked respondents whether they agreed that the press tends to favor one side when reporting on political and social issues. A random sample of people was asked to participate in this year's survey. The results of a survey of another random sample taken 3 years ago are also available. The responses are 2 = Agree and 1 = Disagree.

Can we conclude at the 10% significance level that Americans have become more distrustful of television and newspaper reporting this year than they were 3 years ago?

13.205 Xr13-205   Before deciding which of two types of stamping machines should be purchased, the plant manager of an automotive parts manufacturer wants to determine the number of units that each produces. The two machines differ in cost, reliability, and productivity. The firm's accountant has calculated that machine A must produce 25 more non-defective units per hour than machine B to warrant buying machine A. To help decide, both machines were operated for 24 hours. The total number of units and the number of defective units produced by each machine per hour were recorded. These data are stored in the following way. Column 1 = Total number of units produced by machine A and column 2 = Number of defectives produced by machine A; column 3 = Total number of units produced by machine B; column 4 = Number of defectives produced by machine B). Determine which machine should be purchased.

13.206 Refer to Exercise 13.205. Can we conclude that the defective rate differs between the two machines?

13.207 Xr13-207   The growing use of bicycles to commute to work has caused many cities to create exclusive bicycle lanes. These lanes are usually created by disallowing parking on streets that formerly allowed curbside parking. Merchants on such streets complain that the removal of parking will cause their businesses to suffer. To examine this problem, the mayor of a large city decided to launch an experiment on one busy street that had 1-hour parking meters. The meters were removed and a bicycle lane was created. The mayor asked the three businesses (a dry cleaner, a doughnut shop, and a convenience store) in one block to record daily sales for two complete weeks (Sunday to Saturday) prior to the change and two complete weeks after the change. The data are stored as follows: column 1 = Day of the week; column 2 = Sales before change for dry cleaner; column 3 = Sales after change for dry cleaner; column 4 = Sales before change for doughnut shop; column 5 = Sales after change for doughnut shop; column 6 = Sales before change for convenience store; and column 7 = Sales after change for convenience store. What conclusions can you draw from these data?

13.208 Xr13-208   Researchers at the University of Ohio surveyed 219 students and found that 148 had Facebook accounts. All students were asked how for their current GPA. Do the data allow us to infer that Facebook users have lower GPAs?

13.209 Xr13-209   Clinical depression is linked to several other diseases. Scientists at Johns Hopkins University undertook a study to determine whether heart disease is one of these. A group of 1190 male medical students was tracked over a 40-year period. Of these, 132 had suffered clinically diagnosed depression. For each student, the scientists recorded whether the student died of a heart attack (code = 2) or did not (code = 1).

a. Can we infer at the 1% significance level that men who are clinically depressed are more likely to die from heart diseases?

b. If the answer to part (a) is "yes" can you interpret this to mean that depression causes heart disease? Explain.

13.210 Xr13-210   High blood pressure (hypertension) is a leading cause of strokes. Medical researchers are constantly seeking ways to treat patients suffering from this condition. A specialist in hypertension claims that regular aerobic exercise can reduce high blood pressure just as successfully as drugs, with none of the adverse side effects. To test the claim, 50 patients who suffer from high blood pressure were chosen to participate in an experiment. For 60 days, half the sample exercised three times per week for 1 hour and did not take medication; the other half took the standard medication. The percentage reduction in blood pressure was recorded for each individual.

a. Can we conclude at the 1% significance level that exercise is more effective than medication in reducing hypertension?

b. Estimate with 95% confidence the difference in mean percentage reduction in blood pressure between drugs and exercise programs.

c. Check to ensure that the required condition(s) of the techniques used in parts (a) and (b) is satisfied.

13.211 Xr13-211   Most people exercise in order to lose weight. To determine better ways to lose weight, a random sample of male and female exercisers was divided into groups. The first group exercised vigorously twice a week. The second group exercised moderately four times per week. The weight loss for each individual was recorded. Can we infer that people who exercise moderately more frequently lose more weight than people who exercise vigorously?

13.212 Xr13-212   After observing the results of the test in Exercise 13.211, a statistics practitioner organized another experiment. People were matched according to gender, height, and weight. One member of each matched pair then exercised vigorously twice a week and the other member exercised moderately four times per week. The weight losses were recorded. Can we infer that people who exercise moderately lose more weight?

13.213 Xr13-213   Personal spending is usually an indicator of the health of the overall economy. An increase tends to indicate that consumers are optimistic; a decrease indicates pessimism. Gallup tracks the spending of a random sample of American adults. The results for this month and last month were recorded. Do these data allow us to conclude that these consumers are optimistic about the state of the economy?

13.214 Xr13-214   There are currently 121,678 people waiting for lifesaving organ transplants in the United States. Of these, 100,791 await kidney transplants. (as of January 2016). The median wait time for an individual's first kidney transplant is 3.6 years and can vary depending on health, compatibility, and availability of organs. In 2014, 17,107 kidney transplants took place in the United States. Of these, 11,570 came from deceased donors and 5,537 came from living donors (Source: National Kidney Foundation). This raises the question, Are kidneys from living donors better than kidneys from deceased donors? A study conducted by the Barnes Jewish Hospital in St Louis may provide an answer. A random sample of kidney recipients was drawn and the number of years until the transplanted kidney needed replacement. Do these data provide enough evidence to infer that kidneys from living donors last longer than do kidneys from deceased donors?

13.215 Xr13-215   Most English professors complain that students don't write very well. In particular they point out that students often confuse quality and quantity. A study at the University of Texas examined this claim. In the study undergraduate students were asked to compare the cost benefits of Japanese and American cars. All wrote their analyses on computers. Unbeknownst to the students, the computers were rigged so that some students would have to type twice as many words to fill a single page. The number of words used by each student was recorded. Can we conclude that students write in such a way as to fill the allotted space?

13.216 Xr13-216   Approximately 20 million Americans work for themselves. Most run single-person businesses out of their homes. One-quarter of these individuals use personal computers in their businesses. A market research firm, Computer Intelligence InfoCorp, wanted to know whether single-person businesses that use personal computers are more successful than those with no computer. They surveyed 150 single-person firms and recorded their annual incomes. Can we infer at the 10% significance level that single-person businesses that use a personal computer earn more than those that do not?

13.217 Xr13-217   Many small retailers advertise in their neighborhoods by sending out flyers. People deliver these to homes and are paid according to the number of flyers delivered. Each deliverer is given several streets whose homes become their responsibility. One of the ways retailers use to check the performance of deliverers is to randomly sample some of the homes and ask the home owner whether he or she received the flyer. Recently university students started a new delivery service. They have promised better service at a competitive price. A retailer wanted to know whether the new company's delivery rate is better than that of the existing firm. She had both companies deliver her flyers. Random samples of homes were drawn and each was asked whether he or she received the flyer (2 = Yes, 1 = No). Can the retailer conclude that the new company is better? (Test with α = .10.)

13.218 Xr13-218   Medical experts advocate the use of vitamin and mineral supplements to help fight infections. A study undertaken by researchers at Memorial University recruited 96 men and women age 65 and older. One-half of them received daily supplements of vitamins and minerals, whereas the other half received placebos. The supplements contained the daily recommended amounts of 18 vitamins and minerals, including vitamins B-6, B-12, C, and D, thiamine, riboflavin, niacin, calcium, copper, iodine, iron, selenium, magnesium, and zinc. The doses of vitamins A and E were slightly less than the daily requirements. The supplements included four times the amount of beta-carotene than the average person ingests daily. The number of days of illness from infections (ranging from colds to pneumonia) was recorded for each person. Can we infer that taking vitamin and mineral supplements daily increases the body's immune system?

13.219 Xr13-219   An inspector for the Atlantic City Gaming Commission suspects that a particular blackjack dealer may be cheating (in favor of the casino) when he deals at expensive tables. To test her belief, she observed 500 hands each at the $100-limit table and the $3,000-limit table. For each hand, she recorded whether the dealer won (code = 2) or lost (code = 1). When a tie occurs, there is no winner or loser. Can the inspector conclude at the 10% significance level that the dealer is cheating at the more expensive table?

13.220 Xr13-220   In 2005 Larry Summers, then president of Harvard University received an avalanche of criticism for his attempt to explain why in mathematics there are more male professors than female professors. His suggested that there were innate differences that might permanently thwart the search for a more perfect gender balance. In an attempt to refute Dr Summers' hypothesis several researchers conducted large-scale mathematics tests of male and female students. Suppose the results were recorded. Conduct whatever tests you deem necessary to draw conclusions from these data. (Note that the data are simulated but represent actual results.)

13.221 Xr13-221   Refer to Exercise 12.143. The researchers also took a random sample of 702 cars last year. Is there sufficient evidence to conclude that American cars this year are on average older than cars last year?

13.222 Xr13-222   Are Americans more generous than Canadians? Random samples of American and Canadian tax returns were examined and whether it included a charitable donation were recorded (2 = Yes, 1 = No). Conduct a statistical test to answer the question. (*Source:* Adapted from a Fraser Institute study.)

Overeating Experiments (See page 451.)

13.223 Xr13-223   Music Experiment

A researcher convinced a restaurant to experiment with two different kinds of music. One was faster upbeat music and the second was soft relaxing music. A random sample of diners was drawn and the type of music, the amount of time spent in the restaurant, and the amount spent on drinks were recorded. Is there sufficient evidence to conclude that when the soft relaxing music was played diners spent more time in the restaurant and spent more money on drinks? (*Source:* Adapted from Ronald E. Milliman, "The Influence of Background Music on the Behavior of Restaurant Patrons," *Journal of Consumer Research* 13:1 (1986): 286–89.)

13.224 Xr13-224   Cinderella Makeover Experiment

A television program in conjunction with a researcher conducted a makeover of a Hardee's Restaurant. The main room had bright lights and loud music. In a separate room, the renovation brought in plants, paintings, indirect lighting, and white tablecloths and candles on the tables. The amount of time a random sample of patrons spent in the restaurant for each room was recorded. Is there enough evidence to infer that when the restaurant features bright lights and loud music customers spend less time in the restaurant?

13.225 Xr13-225   Refer to Exercise 13.224. Customers were also asked how likely they would return to the restaurant (2 = Likely, 1 = Unlikely). Is there enough evidence to infer that when the restaurant features bright lights and loud music customers are less likely to return?

13.226 <u>Xr13-226</u>   Glass Size Experiment

At a camp cafeteria teenagers were randomly given a tall skinny glass or a short wide glass. As they proceeded through the line they loaded up on the food they wanted and poured whatever drink they chose. At the end of the line the quantity of drink they had in their glasses was recorded. Can we infer that the quantities in the short wide glass contained were greater than the quantities in the tall skinny glasses? (*Source:* Adapted from Abby Ellin, "For Overweight Children, Are 'Fat Camps' a Solution?" *New York Times*, June 2005.)

Exercises 13.227 and 13.228 require access to the data files introduced in previous exercises.

13.227 <u>Xr12-31*</u>   Exercise 12.31 dealt with the amount of time high school students spend per week at part-time jobs. In addition to the hours of part-time work the school guidance counselor recorded the gender of the student surveyed (1 = Female, 2 = Male). Can we conclude that female and male high school students differ in the amount of time spent at part-time jobs?

13.228 <u>Xm12-01*</u>   The company that organized the survey to determine the amount of discarded newspaper (Example 12.1) kept track of the type of neighborhood (1 = City, 2 = Suburbs). Do these data allow the company management to infer that city households discard more newspaper than do suburban households?

APPLICATIONS in MARKETING

Market Segmentation

In Section 12-4 we introduced market segmentation. The following exercises address the problem of determining whether two market segments differ in their pattern of purchases of a particular product or service.

13.229 <u>Xr13-219</u> Movie studios segment their markets by age. Two segments that are particularly important to this industry are teenagers and 20- to 30-year-olds. To assess markets and guide the making of movies, a random sample of teenagers and 20- to 30-year-olds was drawn. Each was asked to report the number of movies they saw in theaters last year. Do these data allow us to infer that teenagers see more movies than 20- to 30-year-olds?

The following exercises employ data files associated with examples and exercises seen previously in this book.

13.230 <u>Xr12-131*</u> In addition to asking about educational attainment the survey conducted in Exercise 12.131 also asked whether the respondent had plans in the next 2 years to take a course (1 = No, 2 = Yes). Can we conclude that Californians who did not complete high school are less likely to take a course in the university's evening program?

13.231 <u>Xm12-06*</u> The objective in the survey conducted in Example 12.6 was to estimate the size of the market segment of adults who are concerned about eating healthy foods. As part of the survey each respondent was asked how much they spend on breakfast cereal in an average month. The marketing manager of a company that produces several breakfast cereals would like to know whether on average the market segment concerned about eating health foods outspends the other market segments. Write a brief report detailing your findings.

13.232 <u>Xr12-35*</u> In Exercise 12.35, we described how the office equipment chain OfficeMax offers rebates on some products. The goal in that exercise was to estimate the total amount spent by customers who bought the package of 100 CD-ROMS. In addition to tracking these amounts an executive also determined

(Continued)

the amounts spent in the store by another sample of customers who purchased a fax machine/copier (regular price $89.99 minus $40 manufacturer's rebate and $10 OfficeMax mail-in rebate). Can OfficeMax conclude that those who buy the fax/copier outspend those who buy the package of CD-ROMs? Write a brief memo to the executives of OfficeMax describing your findings and any possible recommendations.

13.233 Xr12-105* In addition to recording whether faculty members who are between 55 and 64 plan to retire before they reach 65 in Exercise 12.105, the consultant asked each to report his or her annual salary. Can the president infer that professors aged 55 to 64 who plan to retire early have higher salaries than those who don't plan to retire early?

13.234 Xr12-110* In Exercise 12.110, the statistics practitioner also recorded the gender of the respondents, where 1 = Female and 2 = Male. Can we infer that men and women differ in their choices of Christmas trees?

GENERAL SOCIAL SURVEY EXERCISES

13.235 GSS2014* In recent years, women have made up an increasing proportion of university students.
a. Is there sufficient evidence to conclude that females and males (SEX: 1 = Male, 2 = Female) differ in their years of education (EDUC)?
b. What are the required conditions for the validity of your answer in part (a)?
c. Are the required conditions satisfied? Explain.
d. If the required conditions are not satisfied how do you answer the question?

13.236 GSS2008* GSS2014* During difficult economic times governments stimulate the economy to reduce the unemployment rate. Governments do this by hiring more workers. Did this process take place between 2008 and 2014? Conduct a test to determine whether there is enough evidence to conclude that the fraction of Americans working for the government (WRKGOVT) increased between 2008 and 2014.

13.237 GSS2014* Men are often accused of being couch potatoes by spending too much time watching television. However, do men watch more TV than women (SEX: 1 = Male, 2 = Female)?
a. Conduct a test to answer the question (TVHOURS).
b. Are the required conditions satisfied? Explain.
c. If the required conditions are not satisfied what other techniques can you use?

13.238 GSS2012* GSS2014* The United States has one of the highest rates of post-secondary education. However, is the rate increasing? Can we infer from the data that the Americans were more educated (EDUC) in 2014 than they were in 2012?

13.239 GSS2012* GSS2014* The amount of money television networks charge the advertisers is very much dependent on how many people see the commercials. Thus, any decrease in viewers is a problem. Is there a downward trend in viewers? Were American adults watching less television (TVHOURS) in 2014 than they did in 2012? Conduct a test to answer the question.

13.240 GSS2012* GSS2014* Judging from rising enrollments there are more people attending colleges and universities. However, does this include students going on their masters and doctoral degrees? Is there enough statistical evidence to conclude that the percentage of American adults with graduate degrees (DEGREE = 4) changed between 2012 and 2014?

13.241 GSS2010* GSS2014* One measure of the health of the economy is the number of hours of work. Using this gauge can we conclude that the economy improved between 2010 and 2014? That is, can we conclude that Americans were working longer hours (HRS1) in 2014 than they did in 2010?

13.242 GSS2014* The fertility rate among Americans is falling. A rate of 2.1 children for each woman is needed to keep populations stable. As societies become more affluent, families tend to be smaller. Does this mean that immigrants (BORN: 1 = In the United States, 2 = Elsewhere) will have more children (CHILDS)?

a. Conduct a test to answer the question.
b. Are the required conditions satisfied? Explain.
c. If the required conditions are not satisfied what other technique can you use?

13.243 GSS2012* GSS2014* Estimate with 95% confidence the difference in income (RINCOME) between 2014 and 2012.

13.244 GSS2014* Americans work longer hours than residents of most other countries. Does this mean that American-born workers work more than do immigrants?

a. Conduct a statistical test to determine whether American-born workers (BORN: 1 = In the United States, 2 = Elsewhere) work longer hours than immigrants (HRS1).
b. Are the required conditions satisfied? Explain.
c. If the required conditions are not satisfied what other technique can you use?

13.245 GSS2014* Who watches more television (TVHOURS), Democrats or Republicans (PARTYID3: 1 = Democrat; 3 = Republican)? Conduct a test to determine whether Democrats beat Republicans in this category.

13.246 GSS2014* Do Americans become more Conservative as they grow older? If this is true we would expect that Conservatives would be older than Liberals (POLVIEWS3: 1 = Liberal, 3 = Conservative).

a. Test to determine whether there is enough evidence to conclude that Conservatives are older than liberals (AGE).
b. Are the required conditions satisfied?
c. If the required conditions are not satisfied, what other technique should be used?

13.247 GSS2012* GSS2014* Estimate with 95% confidence the change in the percentage of Americans who were working for themselves (WRKSLF: 1 = Self-employed)) between 2012 and 2014.

13.248 GSS2014* The perception among many voters is that public servants don't work very hard.

a. Is there enough evidence to draw the conclusion that public sector employees (WRKGOVT: 1 = Government, 2 = Private) work fewer hours than do their counterparts in the private sector (HRS1)?
b. Are the required conditions satisfied?

13.249 GSS2014* If government workers (WRKGOVT: 1 = Government, 2 = Private) have more education it follows that they begin their careers later than do private sector employees. Does this mean that government workers are older (AGE)?

a. Conduct a test to answer the question.
b. Are the required conditions satisfied?
c. If the required conditions are not satisfied, what other technique should be used?

13.250 GSS2014* One of the advantages of working for someone else is that the number of hours of work per week is limited as opposed to the number of hours for self-employed people.

a. Is there sufficient evidence to infer that self-employed individuals (WRKSLF: 1 = Self-employed, 2 = Someone else) work longer hours (HRS1)? What does the p-value tell you?
b. Are the required conditions satisfied?
c. If the required conditions are not satisfied, what other technique should be used?

13.251 GSS2014* Do you need more education (EDUC) to be self-employed (WRKSLF: 1 = Self-employed, 2 = Someone else)?

a. Conduct a test to answer the question.
b. Are the required conditions satisfied?

13.252 GSS2004* GSS2014* With a declining birth rate and increasing longevity most countries are aging. The consequences are serious. Aging societies mean that there will be fewer taxpayers supporting an increasing population of retirees. Because older people require more medical care the cost of health care will increase substantially. One way of measuring an aging society is to compute the average age.

a. Is there statistical evidence that the United States has aged in the decade 2004–2014 (AGE)?
b. Are the required conditions satisfied?
c. What alternative technique can be used if the required condition is unsatisfied?

13.253 GSS2004* GSS2014* Another way of measuring an aging society is to compute the number of children per family.

a. Is there enough evidence to infer that the number of children per family has decreased in the decade 2004–2014 (CHILDS)?
b. Are the required conditions satisfied?

13.254 GSS2004* GSS2014* If the number of children per family is decreasing is it because families are postponing the start of a family?

a. Conduct a test to determine if the age at which families have their first child has increased between 2004 and 2014 (AGEKDBRN).
b. Check the required conditions.

13.255 GSS2004* GSS2014* Innovation may be the key to creating high-value jobs. And innovation depends on education.

a. Is there sufficient evidence to infer that the United States in 2014 is more educated than it was in 2004?

b. Are the required conditions satisfied?

13.256 GSS2004* GSS2014* Are workers in 2014 working less than they did in 2004 (HRS1)?

a. Test to determine whether there is enough evidence to answer the question affirmatively.

b. Check the required conditions.

13.257 GSS2004* GSS2014* There are many other forms of electronic entertainment available. This may impact television.

a. Is there sufficient evidence to conclude that the amount of time watching television (TVHOURS) differs between 2004 and 2014?

b. Are the required conditions satisfied?

c. If the conditions are not satisfied what other technique is available?

SURVEY OF CONSUMER FINANCES EXERCISES

13.258 SCF2013:\MC* Is there sufficient evidence to infer that self-employed heads of households (OCCAT1: 1 = someone else, 2 = self-employed/partnership) have less net worth than heads of household who work for someone else (NETWORTH)?

13.259 SCF2013:\MC* If people who work for someone else have more assets and greater net worth than self-employed people (OCCAT1: 1 = someone else, 2 = self-employed/partnership) we would expect them to have larger unrealized capital

gains (KGTOTAL). Conduct a test to determine whether there is enough evidence to support this expectation.

13.260 SCF2013:\MC* As a general rule more education leads to more professional and financial success. Test to determine whether heads of households with a high school diploma (EDCL: 1 = no high school diploma, 2 = high school diploma) have more household assets than those who did not finish high school (ASSET).

| CASE 13.1 | Comparing Incomes in the 2000–2014 General Social Surveys |

In the years 2000–2014, the economy took two major hits. The first was the combination of the dotcom collapse that occurred in 2000 and the attacks on the World Trade Center and on the Pentagon in 2001. These two events precipitated the stock market crash in 2001. The second hit was the subprime mortgage industry collapse that caused a financial meltdown all over the world in 2008.

The effect on American incomes has been used as a political

football by both the Democrats and the Republicans. The Democrats accused the Bush administration of causing incomes to stagnate during his administration (2001–2008). In turn, the Republicans accuse the Obama administration of the same during his administration (2009–2016).

The General Social Survey allows you to determine the truth by performing inferential methods on the reported incomes (RINCOME) in the surveys. All you need to do is answer the following questions.

a. Is there sufficient evidence to infer that incomes rose between 2000 and 2008?

b. Is there sufficient evidence to infer that incomes rose between 2008 and 2014?

c. Is there sufficient evidence to infer that incomes rose between 2000 and 2008 after adjusting for inflation?

d. Is there sufficient evidence to infer that incomes rose between 2008 and 2014 after adjusting for inflation?

e. Describe what you have learned.

DATA
GSS20●
GSS20●
GSS20?
Chapte
\U.S. C
Annua?

| CASE 13.2 | Testing Eli Lilly's Latest Drug Evacetrapib |

The National Center for Health Statistics provided the following list of the top 10 killers in the United States and the numbers it killed in the 2014.

Heart disease: 614,348
Cancer: 591,699
Chronic lower respiratory diseases: 147,101
Accidents (unintentional injuries): 136,053
Stroke (cerebrovascular diseases): 133,103
Alzheimer's disease: 93,541
Diabetes: 76,488
Influenza and pneumonia: 55,227
Nephritis, nephrotic syndrome, and nephrosis: 48,146
Intentional self-harm (suicide): 42,773

Source: Health United States, 2015, Table 19.

Not surprisingly, virtually every drug manufacturer is constantly looking for drugs to reduce any of the diseases on the list, with particular emphasis on the heart disease and stroke, killers 1 and 5. After spending a decade on the development of Evacetrapib, a drug was designed to reduce bad cholesterol and increase good cholesterol. Here is a brief summary of the problem.

Cholesterol can't dissolve in the blood. It must be transported through your bloodstream by carriers called lipoproteins, which got their name because they're made of fat (lipid) and proteins.

The two types of lipoproteins that carry cholesterol to and from cells are low-density lipoprotein, or LDL, and high-density lipoprotein, or HDL. LDL cholesterol and HDL cholesterol, along with one-fifth of your triglyceride level, make up your total cholesterol count, which can be determined through a blood test.

LDL cholesterol is considered the "bad" cholesterol because it contributes to plaque, a thick, hard deposit that can clog arteries and make them less flexible. This condition is known as atherosclerosis. If a clot forms and blocks a narrowed artery, heart attack or stroke can result. Another condition called peripheral artery disease can develop when plaque buildup narrows an artery supplying blood to the legs.

HDL cholesterol is considered "good" cholesterol because it helps remove LDL cholesterol from the arteries. Experts believe HDL acts as a scavenger, carrying LDL cholesterol away from the arteries and back to the liver, where it is broken down and passed from the body. One-fourth to one-third of blood cholesterol is carried by HDL. A healthy level of HDL cholesterol may also protect against heart attack and stroke, while low levels of HDL cholesterol have been shown to increase the risk of heart disease.

When pharmaceutical companies develop a new drug it is tested extensively. The final stage of the testing protocol is actual patients.

A random sample of adult volunteers was divided so that one half took the drug and the other half took a placebo, so that neither the physician nor the volunteer knew which they were taking. The researchers tracked the results of the study and recorded the following for the drug group and the placebo group.

LDL before the study
LDL after the study
HDL before the study
HDL after the study
Heart attack occurred (0 = no heart attack, 1 = heart attack)
Stroke (0 = no stroke, 1 stroke)
Death (0 = alive, 1 = died)

Help the researchers decide whether the drug Evacetrapib works, by answering these questions.

a. Does the drug reduce LDL?
b. Does the drug increase HDL?
c. Does the drug reduce the heart attack rate?
d. Does the drug reduce the rate of stroke?
e. Does the drug reduce the death rate?

APPENDIX 13 / REVIEW OF CHAPTERS 12 AND 13

As you may have already discovered, the ability to identify the correct statistical technique is critical; any calculation performed without it is useless. When you solved problems at the end of each section in the preceding chapters (you *have* been solving problems at the end of each section covered, haven't you?), you probably had no great difficulty identifying the correct technique to use. You used the statistical technique introduced in that section. Although those exercises provided practice in setting up hypotheses, producing computer output of tests of hypothesis and confidence interval estimators, and interpreting the results, you did not address a fundamental question faced by statistics practitioners: Which technique should I use? If you still do not appreciate the dimension of this problem, examine Table A13.1, which lists all the inferential methods covered thus far.

TABLE **A13.1**   Summary of Statistical Techniques in Chapters 12 and 13

t-test of μ

Estimator of μ (including estimator of $N\mu$)

z-test of p

Estimator of p (including estimator of Np)

χ^2-test of σ^2

Estimator of σ^2

Equal-variances t-test of $\mu_1 - \mu_2$

Equal-variances estimator of $\mu_1 - \mu_2$

Unequal-variances t-test of $\mu_1 - \mu_2$

Unequal-variances estimator of $\mu_1 - \mu_2$

t-test of μ_D

Estimator of μ_D

F-test of σ_1^2/σ_2^2

Estimator of σ_1^2/σ_2^2

z-test of $p_1 - p_2$ (Case 1)

z-test of $p_1 - p_2$ (Case 2)

Estimator of $p_1 - p_2$

Counting tests and confidence interval estimators of a parameter as two different techniques, a total of 17 statistical procedures have been presented thus far, and there is much left to be done. Faced with statistical problems that require the use of some of these techniques (such as in real-world applications or on a quiz or midterm test), most students need some assistance in identifying the appropriate method. In this appendix and the appendixes of five more chapters, you will have the opportunity to practice your decision skills; we've provided exercises and cases that require all the inferential techniques introduced in Chapters 12 and 13. Solving these problems will require you to do what statistics practitioners must do: analyze the problem, identify the technique or techniques, employ statistical software and a computer to yield the required statistics, and interpret the results.

The flowchart in Figure A13.1 represents the logical process that leads to the identification of the appropriate method. Of course, it only shows the techniques covered to this point. Chapters 14, 15, 16, 17, and 19 will include appendixes that review all the techniques introduced up to that chapter. The list and the flowchart will be expanded in each appendix, and all appendixes will contain review exercises. (Some will contain cases.)

FIGURE **A13.1** **Flowchart of Techniques in Chapters 12 and 13**

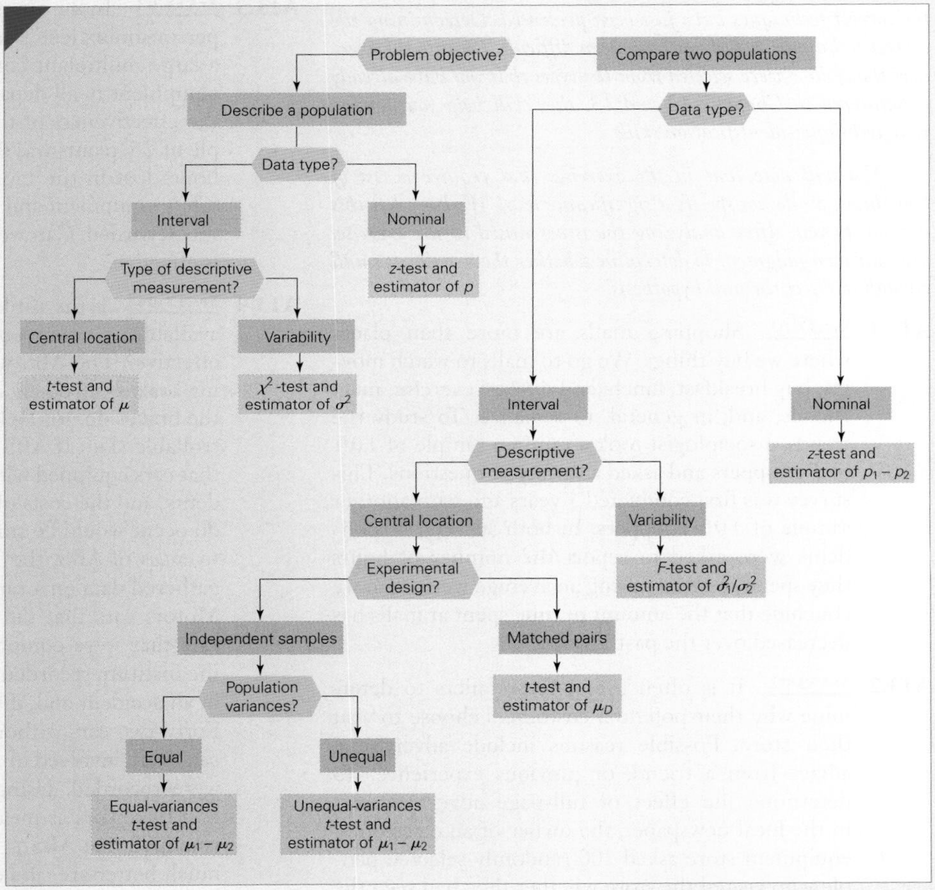

As we pointed out in Chapter 11, the two most important factors in determining the correct statistical technique are the problem objective and the data type. In some situations, once these have been recognized, the technique automatically follows. In other cases, however, several additional factors must be identified before you can proceed. For example, when the problem objective is to compare two populations and the data are interval, three other significant issues must be addressed: the descriptive measurement (central location or variability), whether the samples are independently drawn, and, if so, whether the unknown population variances are equal.

EXERCISES

The purpose of the exercises that follow is twofold. First, the exercises provide you with practice in the critical skill of identifying the correct technique. Second, they allow you to improve your ability to determine the statistics needed to answer the question and interpret the results. We believe that the first skill is underdeveloped because up to now you have had little practice. The exercises you've worked on have appeared at the end of sections and chapters where the correct techniques have just been presented. Determining the correct technique should not have been difficult. Because the exercises that follow were selected from the types that you have already encountered in Chapters 12 and 13, they will help you develop your technique-identification skills.

You will note that in the exercises that require a test of hypothesis, we do not specify a significance level. We have left this decision to you. After analyzing the issues raised in the exercise, use your own judgment to determine whether the p-value is small enough to reject the null hypothesis.

A13.1 XrA13-01 Shopping malls are more than places where we buy things. We go to malls to watch movies; buy breakfast, lunch, and dinner; exercise; meet friends; and, in general, to socialize. To study the trends, a sociologist took a random sample of 100 mall shoppers and asked a variety of questions. This survey was first conducted 3 years ago with another sample of 100 shoppers. In both surveys, respondents were asked to report the number of hours they spend in malls during an average week. Can we conclude that the amount of time spent at malls has decreased over the past 3 years?

A13.2 XrA13-02 It is often useful for retailers to determine why their potential customers choose to visit their store. Possible reasons include advertising, advice from a friend, or previous experience. To determine the effect of full-page advertisements in the local newspaper, the owner of an electronic-equipment store asked 200 randomly selected people who visited the store whether they had seen the ad. He also determined whether the customers had bought anything, and, if so, how much they spent. There were 113 respondents who saw the ad. Of these, 49 made a purchase. Of the 87 respondents who did not see the ad, 21 made a purchase. The amounts spent were recorded.

    a. Can the owner conclude that customers who see the ad are more likely to make a purchase than those who do not see the ad?

    b. Can the owner conclude that customers who see the ad spend more than those who do not see the ad (among those who make a purchase)?

    c. Estimate with 95% confidence the proportion of all customers who see the ad and then make a purchase.

    d. Estimate with 95% confidence the mean amount spent by customers who see the ad and make a purchase.

A13.3 XrA13-03 In an attempt to reduce the number of person-hours lost as a result of industrial accidents, a large multiplant corporation installed new safety equipment in all departments and all plants. To test the effectiveness of the equipment, a random sample of 25 plants was drawn. The number of person-hours lost in the month before installation of the safety equipment and in the month after installation was recorded. Can we conclude that the equipment is effective?

A13.4 XrA13-04 Is the antilock braking system (ABS) now available as a standard feature on many cars really effective? The ABS works by automatically pumping brakes extremely quickly on slippery surfaces so the brakes do not lock and thus avoiding an uncontrollable skid. If ABS is effective, we would expect that cars equipped with ABS would have fewer accidents, and the costs of repairs for the accidents that do occur would be smaller. To investigate the effectiveness of ABS, the Highway Loss Data Institute gathered data on a random sample of 500 General Motors cars that did not have ABS and 500 GM cars that were equipped with ABS. For each year, the institute recorded whether the car was involved in an accident and, if so, the cost of making repairs. Forty-two cars without ABS and 38 ABS-equipped cars were involved in accidents. The costs of repairs were recorded. Using frequency of accidents and cost of repairs as measures of effectiveness, can we conclude that ABS is effective? If so, estimate how much better are cars equipped with ABS compared to cars without ABS.

A13.5 XrA13-05 The electric company is considering an incentive plan to encourage its customers to pay their bills promptly. The plan is to discount the bills 1% if the customer pays within 5 days as opposed to the usual 25 days. As an experiment, 50 customers are offered the discount on their September bill. The amount of time each takes to pay his or her bill is recorded. The amount of time a random sample of 50 customers not offered the discount take to pay their bills is also recorded. Do these data allow us to infer that the discount plan works?

A13.6 XrA13-06 Traffic experts are always looking for ways to control automobile speeds. Some communities have experimented with "traffic-calming" techniques. These include speed bumps and various obstructions that force cars to slow down to drive around them. Critics point out that the techniques are counterproductive because they cause drivers to speed on other parts of these roads. In an analysis of the effectiveness of speed bumps, a statistics practitioner organized a study over a 1-mile stretch of city road that had 10 stop signs. He then took a random sample of 100 cars and recorded their average speed (the speed limit was 30 mph) and the number of proper stops at the stop signs. He repeated the observations for another sample of 100 cars after speed bumps were placed on the road. Do these data allow the statistics practitioner to conclude that the speed bumps are effective?

A13.7 XrA13-07 The proliferation of self-serve pumps at gas stations has generally resulted in poorer automobile maintenance. One feature of poor maintenance is low tire pressure, which results in shorter tire life and higher gasoline consumption. To examine this problem, an automotive expert took a random sample of cars across the country and measured the tire pressure. The difference between the recommended tire pressure and the observed tire pressure was recorded. [A recording of 8 means that the pressure of the tire is 8 pounds per square inch (psi) less than the amount recommended by the tire manufacturer.] Suppose that for each psi below recommendation, tire life decreases by 100 miles and gasoline consumption increases by 0.1 gallon per mile. Estimate with 95% confidence the effect on tire life and gasoline consumption.

A13.8 XrA13-08 Many North American cities encourage the use of bicycles as a way to reduce pollution and traffic congestion. So many people now regularly use bicycles to get to work and for exercise that some jurisdictions have enacted bicycle helmet laws that specify that all bicycle riders must wear helmets to protect against head injuries. Critics of these laws complain that it is a violation of individual freedom and that helmet laws tend to discourage bicycle usage. To examine this issue, a researcher randomly sampled 50 bicycle users and asked each to record the number of miles he or she rode weekly. Several weeks later, the helmet law was enacted. The number of miles each of the 50 bicycle riders rode weekly was recorded for the week after the law was passed. Can we infer from these data that the law discourages bicycle usage?

A13.9 XrA13-09 Cardizem CD is a prescription drug that is used to treat high blood pressure and angina.

One common side effect of such drugs is the occurrence of headaches and dizziness. To determine whether its drug has the same side effects, the drug's manufacturer, Marion Merrell Dow, Inc., undertook a study. A random sample of 908 high-blood-pressure sufferers was recruited; 607 took Cardizem CD and 301 took a placebo. Each reported whether they suffered from headaches or dizziness (2 = yes, 1 = no). Can the pharmaceutical company scientist infer that Cardizem CD users are more likely to suffer headache and dizziness side effects than nonusers?

A13.10 XrA13-10 A fast-food franchiser is considering building a restaurant at a downtown location. Based on a financial analysis, a site is acceptable only if the number of pedestrians passing the location during the work day averages more than 200 per hour. To help decide whether to build on the site, a statistics practitioner observes the number of pedestrians who pass the site each hour over a 40-hour workweek. Should the franchiser build on this site?

A13.11 XrA13-11 Most people who quit smoking cigarettes do so for health reasons. However, some quitters find that they gain weight after quitting, and scientists estimate that the health risks of smoking two packs of cigarettes per day or carrying 65 extra pounds of weight are about equivalent. In an attempt to learn more about the effects of quitting smoking, the U.S. Centers for Disease Control conducted a study (reported in *Time*, March 25, 1991). A sample of 1,885 smokers was taken. During the course of the experiment, some of the smokers quit their habit. The amount of weight gained by all the subjects was recorded. Do these data allow us to conclude that quitting smoking results in weight gains?

A13.12 XrA13-12 Golf-equipment manufacturers compete against one another by offering a bewildering array of new products and innovations. Oversized clubs, square grooves, and graphite shafts are examples of such innovations. The effect of these new products on the average golfer is, however, much in doubt. One product, a perimeter-weighted iron, was designed to increase the consistency of distance and accuracy. The most important aspect of irons is consistency, which means that ideally there should be no variation in distance from shot to shot. To examine the relative merits of two brands of perimeter-weighted irons, an average golfer used the 7-iron, hitting 100 shots using each of two brands. The distance in yards was recorded. Can the golfer conclude that brand B is superior to brand A?

A13.13 XrA13-13 Managers are frequently called on to negotiate in a variety of settings. This calls for an ability to think logically, which requires an ability to concentrate and ignore distractions. In a study of the effect of distractions, a random sample of 208 students was drawn by psychologists at McMaster University (reported in the *National Post*, December 11, 2003). The male students were shown pictures of women of varying attractiveness. The female students were shown pictures of men of varying attractiveness. All students were then offered a choice of an immediate reward of $15 or a wait of 8 months for a reward of $75. The choices of the male and of the female students (1 = immediate reward, 2 = larger reward 8 months later) were recorded. The results are stored in the following way:

Column 1: Choices of males shown most attractive women

Column 2: Choices of males shown less attractive women

Column 3: Choices of females shown most attractive men

Column 4: Choices of females shown less attractive men

a. Can we infer that men's choices are affected by the attractiveness of women's pictures?
b. Can we infer that women's choices are affected by the attractiveness of men's pictures?

A13.14 XrA13-14 Throughout the day, many exercise shows appear on television. These usually feature attractive and fit men and women performing various exercises and urging viewers to duplicate the activity at home. Some viewers are exercisers. However, some people like to watch the shows without exercising (which explains why attractive people are used as demonstrators). Various companies sponsor the shows, and there are commercial breaks. One sponsor wanted to determine whether there are differences between exercisers and non-exercisers in terms of how well they remember the sponsor's name. A random sample of viewers was selected and called after the exercise show was over. Each was asked to report whether he or she exercised or only watched. They were also asked to name the sponsor's brand name (2 = yes, they could; 1 = no, they couldn't). Can the sponsor conclude that exercisers are more likely to remember the sponsor's brand name than those who only watch?

A13.15 XrA13-15 According to the latest census, the number of households in a large metropolitan

area is 425,000. The home-delivery department of the local newspaper reports that 104,320 households receive daily home delivery. To increase home-delivery sales, the marketing department launches an expensive advertising campaign. A financial analyst tells the publisher that for the campaign to be successful, home-delivery sales must increase to more than 110,000 households. Anxious to see whether the campaign is working, the publisher authorizes a telephone survey of 400 households within 1 week of the beginning of the campaign and asks each household head whether he or she has the newspaper delivered. The responses were recorded where 2 = yes and 1 = no.

a. Do these data indicate that the campaign will increase home-delivery sales?
b. Do these data allow the publisher to conclude that the campaign will be successful?

A13.16 XrA13-16 The Scholastic Aptitude Test (SAT), which is organized by the Educational Testing Service (ETS), is important to high school students seeking admission to colleges and universities throughout the United States. A number of companies offer courses to prepare students for the SAT. The Stanley H. Kaplan Educational Center claims that its students gain, on average, more than 110 points by taking its course. ETS, however, insists that preparatory courses can improve a score by no more than 40 points. (The minimum and maximum scores of the SAT are 400 and 1,600, respectively.) Suppose a random sample of 40 students wrote the exam, then took the Kaplan preparatory course, and then took the exam again.

a. Do these data provide sufficient evidence to refute the ETS claim?
b. Do these data provide sufficient evidence to refute Kaplan's claim?

A13.17 XrA13-17 A potato chip manufacturer has contracted for the delivery of 15,000,000 kilograms of potatoes. The supplier agrees to deliver the potatoes in 15,000 equal truckloads. The manufacturer suspects that the supplier will attempt to cheat him. He has the weight of the first 50 truckloads recorded.

a. Can the manufacturer conclude from these data that the supplier is cheating him?
b. Estimate with 95% confidence the total weight of potatoes for all 15,000 truckloads.

GENERAL SOCIAL SURVEY EXERCISES

Conduct all tests at the 5% significance level. Use a 95% confidence level for estimates.

In 2012, there were 221,963,000 Americans aged 21 or more, of whom 115,219,000 were female and 106,744,000 were male.

A13.18 GSS2012* The number of private sector employees who belong to unions has been steadily decreasing in the United States for decades. However, the number of government workers who belong to unions is growing. To determine the number, the survey asked whether the respondent and/or spouse belong to unions (UNION: 1 = Respondent belongs, 2 = Spouse belongs, 3 = Both belong, 4 = Neither belong). Estimate the number of Americans who belong to unions.

A13.19 GSS2012* The survey asked respondents the following question, "A doctor tells a couple that there is one chance in four that their child will have an inherited disease. Does this mean that if the first child has the illness, the next three will not? (ODDS1:1 = Yes, 2 = No, 8 = Don't know, 9 = No answer)?" The correct answer is 2. Is there sufficient evidence to infer that Republicans are more likely to answer this question correctly than Democrats (PARTYID3: 1 = Democrat, 3 = Republican)?

A13.20 GSS2012* Although most high paying jobs require at least a university degree there are still many people who have not completed high school. Estimate the number of American men who did not complete high school (SEX: 1 = Male, DEGREE: 0 = Left high school).

A13.21 GSS2012* The United States like many other countries is aging. That is, each year the average age increases. Estimate the average age of American adults (AGE).

A13.22 GSS2012* Every year the readership of newspapers declines. To measure the extent of the problem, the survey asked respondents, "Do you read newspapers?" Estimate the number of people who never read newspapers (NEWS: 5 = Never).

A13.23 GSS2012* Television advertising depends on viewers. If there are fewer people watching television then advertisers will pay less for their television commercials. Estimate the average number of hours people are watching television (TVHOURS).

A13.24 GSS2012* According to the U.S. Census in 2012 women made up 51.909% of the adult population. Is there enough evidence to conclude that women are over represented in the 2012 General Social Survey of 2012 (SEX: 1 = Male, 2 = Female)?

A13.25 GSS2012* The second amendment has been part of the political debate. Can we infer from the data that the majority of Americans support gun control (GUNLAW: 1 = Favor, 2 = Oppose)?

A13.26 GSS2012* The survey asked the following question. The center of the earth is very hot, true or false? Estimate the number of Americans who know the correct answer is 1 (HOTCORE: 1 = True, 2 = False, 8 = Don't know, 9 = No answer).

A13.27 GSS2012* In many college disciplines women outnumber men. Does that mean that women have more years of education than men (EDUC)? Conduct a test to answer the question (SEX: 1 = Male, 2 = Female).

A13.28 GSS2012* How well do public sector workers fare against private sector workers (WRKGOVT: 1 = Government, 2 = Private)? In particular, are they paid better than private sector workers (RINCOME). Conduct a test to answer the question.

SURVEY OF CONSUMER FINANCES

Conduct all tests at the 5% significance level. Use a 95% confidence level for estimates.

According to the U.S. Census there were 220,958,853 adults in the United States in 2010.

A13.29 SCF2010:\MC* Numerous studies have shown that men make higher income (INCOME) than women (HHSEX: 1 = male, 2 = female). However, does this apply to male and female middle-class heads of households? Test to determine whether there is enough evidence to conclude that male heads of middle-class households have higher incomes than female heads of middle-class households.

A13.30 SCF2010:\UC The upper class in the 2010 survey had a household net worth between $1,345,975 and $7,402,095. We would expect people in the upper class to have achieved this level of financial success to be somewhat older. Estimate the mean age of members of the upper class (AGE).

A13.31 SCF2010:\ALL*　In the United States, one of the most popular university programs is business administration. The result will be an increase in the number of people working as managers or professionals. Estimate the number of people working as managers or professional (OCCAT2: 1)

A13.32 SCF2010:\UC*　High net worth households often have high expenses and large regular payments. Estimate the total value of monthly debt payments made by upper class households (TPAY).

A13.33 SCF2010:\MC*　The middle class in the 2010 Survey of Consumer Finances had a net worth of between $61,215 and $270,603. In 2010, the average amount spent on food at home was $3624 (*Source*: Bureau of Labor Statistics). Is there enough evidence to infer that the average middle-class household spent more than that amount in 2010 (FOODHOME)?

A13.34 SCF2010:\ALL*　Because of immigration and birth rates there is a growing number of Hispanics in the United States. Estimate the number of Hispanic adults (21 and over) in the United States (RACE: 3 = Hispanic).

A13.35 SCF2010:\MC*　Do middle-class household heads with college degrees get more heavily into debt (DEBT) than those without college degrees (EDCL: 1 = No high school diploma, 2 = High school diploma, 3 = Some college, 4 = College degree)? Conduct a test to answer the question.

A13.36 SCF2010:\ALL*　Estimate the number of household heads who declared bankruptcy in the previous 5 years (BNKRUPLAST5: 1).

A13.37 SCF2010:\ALL*　Is there enough statistical evidence to infer that female heads of households (HHSEX: 1 = Male, 2 = Female) are less likely to have completed a college degree than their male counterparts (EDCL: 4 = College degree)?

A13.38 SCF2010:\ALL*　Are male heads of households more likely than female heads (HHSEX: 1 = Male, 2 = Female) of households to be self-employed (OCCAT1: 2 = Self-employed)? Conduct a statistical test to answer the question.

Kzenon/Shutterstock.com

ANALYSIS OF VARIANCE

CHAPTER OUTLINE

General Social Survey: Liberal–Conservative Spectrum and Income

DATA
GSS2014*

Are Americans' political views affected by their incomes, or perhaps vice versa? If so, we would expect that incomes would differ between groups who define themselves somewhere on the following scale (POLVIEWS).

1 = Extremely liberal

2 = Liberal

3 = Slightly liberal

4 = Moderate

5 = Slightly conservative

6 = Conservative

7 = Extremely conservative

Maxh Herman/Shutterstock.com

The question to be answered (on page 529) is, Are there differences in income between the seven groups of political views?

INTRODUCTION

The technique presented in this chapter allows statistics practitioners to compare two or more populations of interval data. The technique is called the **analysis of variance**, and it is an extremely powerful and commonly used procedure. The analysis of variance technique determines whether differences exist between population means. Ironically, the procedure works by analyzing the sample variance, hence the name. We will examine several different forms of the technique.

One of the first applications of the analysis of variance was conducted in the 1920s to determine whether different treatments of fertilizer produced different crop yields. The terminology of that original experiment is still used. No matter what the experiment, the procedure is designed to determine whether there are significant differences between the **treatment means**.

14-1 / ONE-WAY ANALYSIS OF VARIANCE

The analysis of variance is a procedure that tests to determine whether differences exist between two or more population means. The name of the technique derives from the way in which the calculations are performed; that is, the technique analyzes the variance of the data to determine whether we can infer that the population means differ. As in Chapter 13, the experimental design is a determinant in identifying the proper method to use. In this section, we describe the procedure to apply when the samples are independently drawn. The technique is called the **one-way analysis of variance**. Figure 14.1 depicts the sampling process for drawing independent samples. The mean and variance of population j ($j = 1, 2, \ldots, k$) are labeled μ_j and σ_j^2, respectively. Both parameters are unknown. For each population, we draw independent random samples. For each sample, we can compute the mean $\bar{x}_j$ and the variance s_j^2.

FIGURE **14.1** Sampling Scheme for Independent Samples

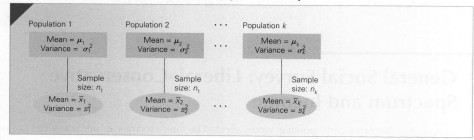

EXAMPLE 14.1*

DATA
Xm14-01

Proportion of Total Assets Invested in Stocks

In the last decade, stockbrokers have drastically changed the way they do business. Internet trading has become quite common, and online trades can cost as little as $7. It is now easier and cheaper to invest in the stock market than ever before. What are the effects of these changes? To help answer this question, a financial analyst randomly sampled 366 American households and asked each to report the age category of the

---

*Adapted from U.S. Census Bureau, "Asset Ownership of Households, May 2003," *Statistical Abstract of the United States*, 2006 , Table 700.

head of the household and the proportion of its financial assets that are invested in the stock market. The age categories are

Young (less than 35)

Early middle age (35 to 49)

Late middle age (50 to 65)

Senior (older than 65)

The analyst was particularly interested in determining whether the ownership of stocks varied by age. Some of the data are listed next. Do these data allow the analyst to determine that there are differences in stock ownership between the four age groups?

Young	Early Middle Age	Late Middle Age	Senior
24.8	28.9	81.5	66.8
35.5	7.3	0.0	77.4
68.7	61.8	61.3	32.9
42.2	53.6	0.0	74.0
⋮	⋮	⋮	⋮

SOLUTION:

You should confirm that the data are interval (percentage of total assets invested in the stock market) and that the problem objective is to compare four populations (age categories). The parameters are the four population means: $\mu_1, \mu_2, \mu_3,$ and μ_4. The null hypothesis will state that there are no differences between the population means. Hence,

$$H_0: \quad \mu_1 = \mu_2 = \mu_3 = \mu_4$$

The analysis of variance determines whether there is enough statistical evidence to show that the null hypothesis is false. Consequently, the alternative hypothesis will always specify the following:

$$H_1: \quad \text{At least two means differ}$$

The next step is to determine the test statistic, which is somewhat more involved than the test statistics we have introduced thus far. The process of performing the analysis of variance is facilitated by the notation in Table 14.1.

TABLE **14.1** Notation for the One-Way Analysis of Variance

	TREATMENT					
	1	**2**		**j**		**k**
	x_{11}	x_{12}	$\cdots$	x_{1j}	$\cdots$	x_{1k}
	x_{21}	x_{22}	$\cdots$	x_{2j}	$\cdots$	x_{2k}
	$\vdots$	$\vdots$		$\vdots$		$\vdots$
	$x_{n_1 1}$	$x_{n_2 2}$		$x_{n_j j}$		$x_{n_k k}$
Sample size	n_1	n_2		n_j		n_k
Sample mean	$\bar{x}_1$	$\bar{x}_2$		$\bar{x}_j$		$\bar{x}_k$

x_{ij} = ith observation of the jth sample

n_j = number of observations in the sample taken from the jth population

$\bar{x}_j$ = mean of the jth sample = $\dfrac{\displaystyle\sum_{i=1}^{n_j} x_{ij}}{n_j}$

$\bar{\bar{x}}$ = grand mean of all the observations = $\dfrac{\displaystyle\sum_{j=1}^{k}\sum_{i=1}^{n_j} x_{ij}}{n}$ where $n = n_1 + n_2 + \cdots + n_k$, and k is the number of populations

The variable X is called the **response variable**, and its values are called **responses**. The unit that we measure is called an **experimental unit**. In this example, the response variable is the percentage of assets invested in stocks, and the experimental units are the heads of households sampled. The criterion by which we classify the populations is called a **factor**. Each population is called a factor **level**. The factor in Example 14.1 is the age category of the head of the household and there are four levels. Later in this chapter, we'll discuss an experiment where the populations are classified using two factors. In this section, we deal with single-factor experiments only.

Test Statistic

The test statistic is computed in accordance with the following rationale. If the null hypothesis is true, the population means would all be equal. We would then expect that the sample means would be close to one another. If the alternative hypothesis is true, however, there would be large differences between some of the sample means. The statistic that measures the proximity of the sample means to each other is called the **between-treatments variation**; it is denoted **SST**, which stands for **sum of squares for treatments**.

Sum of Squares for Treatments

$$SST = \sum_{j=1}^{k} n_j(\bar{x}_j - \bar{\bar{x}})^2$$

As you can deduce from this formula, if the sample means are close to each other, all of the sample means would be close to the grand mean; as a result, SST would be small. In fact, SST achieves its smallest value (zero) when all the sample means are equal. In other words, if

$$\bar{x}_1 = \bar{x}_2 = \cdots = \bar{x}_k$$

then

$$SST = 0$$

It follows that a small value of SST supports the null hypothesis. In this example, we compute the sample means and the grand mean as

$$\bar{x}_1 = 44.40$$
$$\bar{x}_2 = 52.47$$
$$\bar{x}_3 = 51.14$$
$$\bar{x}_4 = 51.84$$
$$\bar{\bar{x}} = 50.18$$

The sample sizes are

$$n_1 = 84$$
$$n_2 = 131$$
$$n_3 = 93$$
$$n_4 = 58$$
$$n = n_1 + n_2 + n_3 + n_4 = 84 + 131 + 93 + 58 = 366$$

Then,

$$\begin{aligned}
\text{SST} &= \sum_{j=1}^{k} n_j(\bar{x}_j - \bar{\bar{x}})^2 \\
&= 84(44.40 - 50.18)^2 + 131(52.47 - 50.18)^2 \\
&\quad + 93(51.14 - 50.18)^2 + 58(51.84 - 50.18)^2 \\
&= 3{,}738.8
\end{aligned}$$

If large differences exist between the sample means, at least some sample means differ considerably from the grand mean, producing a large value of SST. It is then reasonable to reject the null hypothesis in favor of the alternative hypothesis. The key question to be answered in this test (as in all other statistical tests) is, How large does the statistic have to be for us to justify rejecting the null hypothesis? In our example, SST = 3,738.8. Is this value large enough to indicate that the population means differ? To answer this question, we need to know how much variation exists in the percentage of assets, which is measured by the **within-treatments variation**, which is denoted by **SSE (sum of squares for error)**. The within-treatments variation provides a measure of the amount of variation in the response variable that is not caused by the treatments. In this example, we are trying to determine whether the percentages of total assets invested in stocks vary by the age of the head of the household. However, other variables also affect the responses variable. We would expect that variables such as household income, occupation, and the size of the family would play a role in determining how much money families invest in stocks. All of these (as well as others we may not even be able to identify) are sources of variation, which we would group together and call the error. This source of variation is measured by the sum of squares for error.

Sum of Squares for Error

$$\text{SSE} = \sum_{j=1}^{k} \sum_{i=1}^{n_j} (x_{ij} - \bar{x}_j)^2$$

When SSE is partially expanded, we get

$$\text{SSE} = \sum_{i=1}^{n_1} (x_{i1} - \bar{x}_1)^2 + \sum_{i=1}^{n_2} (x_{i2} - \bar{x}_2)^2 + \cdots + \sum_{i=1}^{n_k} (x_{ik} - \bar{x}_k)^2$$

If you examine each of the k components of SSE, you'll see that each is a measure of the variability of that sample. If we divide each component by $n_j - 1$, we obtain the sample variances. We can express this by rewriting SSE as

$$\text{SSE} = (n_1 - 1)s_1^2 + (n_2 - 1)s_2^2 + \cdots + (n_k - 1)s_k^2$$

where s_j^2 is the sample variance of sample j. SSE is thus the combined or pooled variation of the k samples. This is an extension of a calculation we made in Section 13-1, where we tested and estimated the difference between two means using the pooled estimate of the common population variance (denoted s_p^2). One of the required conditions for that statistical technique is that the population variances are equal. That same condition is now necessary for us to use SSE; that is, we require that

$$\sigma_1^2 = \sigma_2^2 = \cdots = \sigma_k^2$$

Returning to our example, we calculate the sample variances as follows:

$$s_1^2 = 386.55$$
$$s_2^2 = 469.44$$
$$s_3^2 = 471.82$$
$$s_4^2 = 444.79$$

Thus,

$$\begin{aligned} \text{SSE} &= (n_1 - 1)s_1^2 + (n_2 - 1)s_2^2 + (n_3 - 1)s_3^2 + (n_4 - 1)s_4^2 \\ &= (84 - 1)(386.55) + (131 - 1)(469.44) \\ &\quad + (93 - 1)(471.82) + (58 - 1)(444.79) \\ &= 161{,}871.3 \end{aligned}$$

The next step is to compute quantities called the **mean squares**. The **mean square for treatments** is computed by dividing SST by the number of treatments minus 1.

Mean Square for Treatments

$$\text{MST} = \frac{\text{SST}}{k - 1}$$

The **mean square for error** is determined by dividing SSE by the total sample size (labeled n) minus the number of treatments.

Mean Square for Error

$$\text{MSE} = \frac{\text{SSE}}{n - k}$$

Finally, the test statistic is defined as the ratio of the two mean squares.

Test Statistic

$$F = \frac{\text{MST}}{\text{MSE}}$$

Sampling Distribution of the Test Statistic

The test statistic is F-distributed with $k - 1$ and $n - k$ degrees of freedom, provided that the response variable is normally distributed. In Section 8-4, we introduced the F-distribution, and in Section 13-4 we used it to test and estimate the ratio of two population variances. The test statistic in that application was the ratio of two sample variances s_1^2 and s_2^2. If you examine the definitions of SST and SSE, you will see that both measure variation similar to the numerator in the formula used to calculate the sample variance s^2 used throughout this book. When we divide SST by $k - 1$ and SSE by $n - k$

to calculate MST and MSE, respectively, we're actually computing unbiased estimators of the common population variance, assuming (as we do) that the null hypothesis is true. Thus, the ratio $F = MST/MSE$ is the ratio of two sample variances. The degrees of freedom for this application are the denominators in the mean squares; that is, $\nu_1 = k - 1$ and $\nu_2 = n - k$. For Example 14.1, the degrees of freedom are

$$\nu_1 = k - 1 = 4 - 1 = 3$$
$$\nu_2 = n - k = 366 - 4 = 362$$

In our example, we found

$$MST = \frac{SST}{k-1} = \frac{3{,}738.8}{3} = 1{,}246.27$$

$$MSE = \frac{SSE}{n-k} = \frac{161{,}871.3}{362} = 447.16$$

$$F = \frac{MST}{MSE} = \frac{1{,}246.27}{447.16} = 2.79$$

Rejection Region and *p*-Value

The purpose of calculating the **F-statistic** is to determine whether the value of SST is large enough to reject the null hypothesis. As you can see, if SST is large, F will be large. Hence, we reject the null hypothesis only if

$$F > F_{\alpha,k-1,n-k}$$

If we let $\alpha = .05$, the rejection region for Example 14.1 is

$$F > F_{\alpha,k-1,n-k} = F_{.05,3,362} \approx F_{.05,3,\infty} = 2.61$$

We found the value of the test statistic to be $F = 2.79$. Thus, there is enough evidence to infer that the mean percentage of total assets invested in the stock market differs between the four age groups.

The *p*-value of this test is

$$P(F > 2.79)$$

A computer is required to calculate this value, which is .0405.

Figure 14.2 depicts the sampling distribution for Example 14.1.

FIGURE **14.2** **Sampling Distribution for Example 14.1**

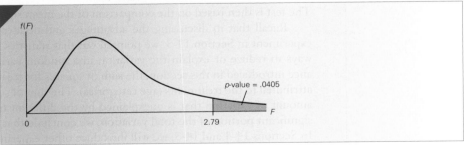

The results of the analysis of variance are usually reported in an **analysis of variance (ANOVA) table**. Table 14.2 shows the general organization of the ANOVA table, and Table 14.3 shows the ANOVA table for Example 14.1.

TABLE **14.2** ANOVA Table for the One-Way Analysis of Variance

SOURCE OF VARIATION	DEGREES OF FREEDOM	SUMS OF SQUARES	MEAN SQUARES	F-STATISTIC
Treatments	$k - 1$	SST	$MST = SST/(k - 1)$	$F = MST/MSE$
Error	$n - k$	SSE	$MSE = SSE/(n - k)$	
Total	$n - 1$	SS(Total)		

TABLE **14.3** ANOVA Table for Example 14.1

SOURCE OF VARIATION	DEGREES OF FREEDOM	SUMS OF SQUARES	MEAN SQUARES	F-STATISTIC
Treatments	3	3,738.8	1,246.27	2.79
Error	362	161,871.3	447.16	
Total	365	165,610.1		

The terminology used in the ANOVA table (and for that matter, in the test itself) is based on the partitioning of the sum of squares. Such partitioning is derived from the following equation (whose validity can be demonstrated by using the rules of summation):

$$\sum_{j=1}^{k} \sum_{i=1}^{n_j} (x_{ij} - \bar{\bar{x}})^2 = \sum_{j=1}^{k} n_j (\bar{x}_j - \bar{\bar{x}})^2 + \sum_{j=1}^{k} \sum_{i=1}^{n_j} (x_{ij} - \bar{x}_j)^2$$

The term on the left represents the **total variation** of all the data. This expression is denoted **SS(Total)**. If we divide SS(Total) by the total sample size minus 1 (that is, by $n - 1$), we would obtain the sample variance (assuming that the null hypothesis is true). The first term on the right of the equal sign is SST, and the second term is SSE. As you can see, the total variation SS(Total) is partitioned into two sources of variation. The sum of squares for treatments (SST) is the variation attributed to the differences between the treatment means, whereas the sum of squares for error (SSE) measures the variation within the samples. The preceding equation can be restated as

SS(Total) = SST + SSE

The test is then based on the comparison of the mean squares of SST and SSE.

Recall that in discussing the advantages and disadvantages of the matched pairs experiment in Section 13-3, we pointed out that statistics practitioners frequently seek ways to reduce or explain the variation in a random variable. In the analysis of variance introduced in this section, the sum of squares for treatments explains the variation attributed to the treatments (age categories). The sum of squares for error measures the amount of variation that is unexplained by the different treatments. If SST explains a significant portion of the total variation, we conclude that the population means differ. In Sections 14-4 and 14-5, we will introduce other experimental designs of the analysis of variance—designs that attempt to reduce or explain even more of the variation.

If you've felt some appreciation of the computer and statistical software sparing you the need to manually perform the statistical techniques in earlier chapters, your appreciation should now grow, because the computer will allow you to avoid the incredibly time-consuming and boring task of performing the analysis of variance by hand. As usual, we've solved Example 14.1 using Excel and XLSTAT, whose outputs are shown here.

COMPUTE

EXCEL Data Analysis

	A	B	C	D	E	F	G
1	Anova: Single Factor						
2							
3	SUMMARY						
4	Groups	Count	Sum	Average	Variance		
5	Young	84	3,729.5	44.40	386.55		
6	Early Middle Age	131	6,873.9	52.47	469.44		
7	Late Middle Age	93	4,755.9	51.14	471.82		
8	Senior	58	3,006.6	51.84	444.79		
9							
10							
11	ANOVA						
12	Source of Variation	SS	df	MS	F	P-value	F crit
13	Between Groups	3,741	3	1,247.1	2.79	0.0405	2.63
14	Within Groups	161,871	362	447.2			
15							
16	Total	165,612	365				

INSTRUCTIONS

1. Type or import the data into adjacent columns. (Open Xm14-01 and click the **Unstacked** tab.)

2. Click **Data, Data Analysis**, and **Anova: Single Factor.**

3. Specify the **Input Range** (A1:D132) and a value for α (.05).

XLSTAT

	B	C	D	E	F	G
26	Analysis of variance (Pct Stocks):					
27	Source	DF	Sum of squares	Mean squares	F	Pr > F
28	Model	3	3,741	1247.1	2.79	0.0405
29	Error	362	161,871	447.2		
30	Corrected Total	365	165,612			

INSTRUCTIONS

1. Type or import the data in stacked format. (Open Xm14-01 and click the **Stacked** tab.)

2. Click **XLSTAT, Modeling data**, and **ANOVA.**

3. In the **Quantitative** box type the input range (A1:A367). In the **X Explanatory variables** and **Qualitative** box type the input range (B1:B367).

4. Click **Outputs** and select **Analysis of variance.** Click **OK.**

INTERPRET

The value of the test statistic is $F = 2.79$, and its p-value is .0405, which means there is evidence to infer that the percentage of total assets invested in stocks are different in at least two of the age categories.

Note that in this example the data are observational. We cannot conduct a controlled experiment. To do so would require the financial analyst to randomly assign households to each of the four age groups, which is impossible.

Incidentally, when the data are obtained through a controlled experiment in the one-way analysis of variance, we call the experimental design the **completely randomized design** of the analysis of variance.

14-1a Checking the Required Conditions

The F-test of the analysis of variance requires that the random variable be normally distributed with equal variances. The normality requirement is easily checked graphically by producing the histograms for each sample. From the Excel histograms in Figure 14.3, we can see that there is no reason to believe that the requirement is not satisfied.

The equality of variances is examined by printing the sample variances, statistics that Excel includes in its printout. The similarity of sample variances allows us to assume that the population variances are equal. An online appendix presents Bartlett's Test, which is a procedure designed to test for the equality of variances.

14-1b Violation of the Required Conditions

If the data are not normally distributed, we can replace the one-way analysis of variance with its nonparametric counterpart, which is the Kruskal–Wallis Test. (See Section 19-3.*)

FIGURE **14.3** Histograms for Example 14.1

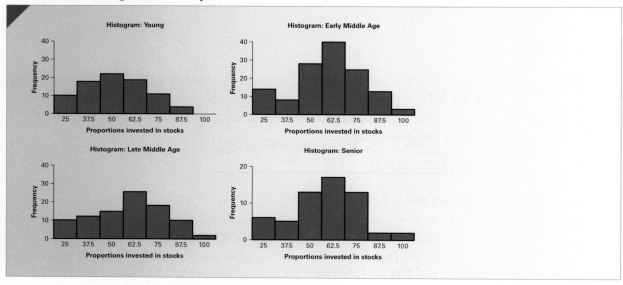

*Instructors who wish to teach the use of nonparametric techniques for testing the difference between two or more means when the normality requirement is not satisfied should use the online appendix Kruskal–Wallis Test and Friedman Test.

If the population variances are unequal, we can use several methods to correct the problem. However, these corrective measures are beyond the level of this book.

14-1c Can We Use the t-Test of the Difference between Two Means Instead of the Analysis of Variance?

The analysis of variance tests to determine whether there is evidence of differences between two or more population means. The t-test of $\mu_1 - \mu_2$ determines whether there is evidence of a difference between two population means. The question arises, Can we use t-tests instead of the analysis of variance? In other words, instead of testing all the means in one test as in the analysis of variance, why not test each pair of means? In Example 14.1, we would test $(\mu_1 - \mu_2)$, $(\mu_1 - \mu_3)$, $(\mu_1 - \mu_4)$, $(\mu_2 - \mu_3)$, $(\mu_2 - \mu_4)$, and $(\mu_3 - \mu_4)$. If we find no evidence of a difference in each test, we would conclude that none of the means differ. If there was evidence of a difference in at least one test, we would conclude that some of the means differ.

There are two reasons why we don't use multiple t-tests instead of one F-test. First, we would have to perform many more calculations. Even with a computer, this extra work is tedious. Second, and more important, conducting multiple tests increases the probability of making Type I errors. To understand why, consider a problem where we want to compare six populations, all of which are identical. If we conduct an analysis of variance where we set the significance level at 5%, there is a 5% chance that we would reject the true null hypothesis; that is, there is a 5% chance that we would conclude that differences exist when, in fact, they don't.

To replace the F-test, we would perform 15 t-tests. [This number is derived from the number of combinations of pairs of means to test, which is $C_2^6 = (6 \times 5)/2 = 15$.] Each test would have a 5% probability of erroneously rejecting the null hypothesis. The probability of committing one or more Type I errors is about 54%.*

One remedy for this problem is to decrease the significance level. In this illustration, we would perform the t-tests with $\alpha = .05/15$, which is equal to .0033. (We will use this procedure in Section 14-2 when we discuss multiple comparisons.) Unfortunately, this would increase the probability of a Type II error. Regardless of the significance level, performing multiple t-tests increases the likelihood of making mistakes. Consequently, when we want to compare more than two populations of interval data, we use the analysis of variance.

Now that we've argued that the t-tests cannot replace the analysis of variance, we need to argue that the analysis of variance cannot replace the t-test.

14-1d Can We Use the Analysis of Variance Instead of the t-Test of $\mu_1 - \mu_2$?

The analysis of variance is the first of several techniques that allow us to compare two or more populations. Most of the examples and exercises deal with more than two populations. However, it should be noted that, like all other techniques whose objective is to compare two or more populations, the analysis of variance can be used to compare only two populations. If that's the case, then why do we need techniques to compare exactly two populations? Specifically, why do we need the t-test of $\mu_1 - \mu_2$ when the analysis of variance can be used to test two population means?

---

*The probability of committing at least one Type I error is computed from a binomial distribution with $n = 15$ and $p = .05$. Thus, $P(X \geq 1) = 1 - P(X = 0) = 1 - .463 = .537$.

To understand why, we still need the t-test to make inferences about $\mu_1 - \mu_2$. Suppose that we plan to use the analysis of variance to test two population means. The null and alternative hypotheses are

$$H_0: \quad \mu_1 = \mu_2$$
$$H_1: \quad \text{At least two means differ}$$

Of course, the alternative hypothesis specifies that $\mu_1 \neq \mu_2$. However, if we want to determine whether μ_1 is greater than μ_2 (or vice versa), we cannot use the analysis of variance because this technique allows us to test for a difference only. Thus, if we want to test to determine whether one population mean exceeds the other, we must use the t-test of $\mu_1 - \mu_2$ (with $\sigma_1^2 = \sigma_2^2$). Moreover, the analysis of variance requires that the population variances are equal. If they are not, we must use the unequal variances test statistic.

14-1e Relationship between the F-Statistic and the t-Statistic

It is probably useful for you to understand the relationship between the t-statistic and the F-statistic. The test statistic for testing hypotheses about $\mu_1 - \mu_2$ with equal variances is

$$t = \frac{(\bar{x}_1 - \bar{x}_2) - (\mu_1 - \mu_2)}{\sqrt{s_p^2\left(\dfrac{1}{n_1} + \dfrac{1}{n_2}\right)}}$$

If we square this quantity, the result is the F-statistic: $F = t^2$. To illustrate this point, we'll redo the calculation of the test statistic in Example 13.1 using the analysis of variance. Recall that because we were able to assume that the population variances were equal, the test statistic was as follows:

$$t = \frac{(6.63 - 3.72) - 0}{\sqrt{40.42\left(\dfrac{1}{50} + \dfrac{1}{50}\right)}} = 2.29$$

Using the analysis of variance (the Excel output is shown here), we find that the value of the test statistic is $F = 5.23$, which is $(2.29)^2$. Notice though that the analysis of variance p-value is .0243, which is twice the t-test p-value, which is .0122. The reason: The analysis of variance is conducting a test to determine whether the population means *differ*. If Example 13.1 had asked to determine whether the means differ, we would have conducted a two-tail test and the p-value would be .0243, the same as the analysis of variance p-value.

Excel Data Analysis: Analysis of Variance for Example 13.1

	A	B	C	D	E	F	G
1	Anova: Single Factor						
2							
3	SUMMARY						
4	Groups	Count	Sum	Average	Variance		
5	Direct	50	331.56	6.63	37.49		
6	Broker	50	186.16	3.72	43.34		
7							
8							
9	ANOVA						
10	Source of Variation	SS	df	MS	F	P-value	F crit
11	Between Groups	211.4	1	211.41	5.23	0.0243	3.94
12	Within Groups	3960.5	98	40.41			
13							
14	Total	4172.0	99				

14-1f Developing an Understanding of Statistical Concepts

Conceptually and mathematically, the F-test of the independent samples' single-factor analysis of variance is an extension of the t-test of $\mu_1 - \mu_2$. Moreover, if we simply want to determine whether a difference between two means exists, we can use the analysis of variance. The advantage of using the analysis of variance is that we can partition the total sum of squares, which enables us to measure how much variation is attributable to differences between populations and how much variation is attributable to differences within populations. As we pointed out in Section 13-3, explaining the variation is an extremely important topic, one that we will see again in other experimental designs of the analysis of variance and in regression analysis (Chapters 16, 17, and 18).

General Social Survey: Liberal–Conservative Spectrum and Income: Solution

Maxh Herman/Shutterstock.com

IDENTIFY

The variable is income (RINCOME) of American adults, which is interval. The problem objective is to compare seven populations (the political views) and the experimental design is independent samples. Thus, we apply the one-way analysis of variance.

COMPUTE

EXCEL Data Analysis

	A	B	C	D	E	F	G
1	Anova: Single Factor						
2							
3	SUMMARY						
4	*Groups*	*Count*	*Sum*	*Average*	*Variance*		
5	E Liberal	66	2,995,000	45,379	1,454,819,697		
6	Liberal	197	9,597,250	48,717	2,098,667,911		
7	S Liberal	178	7,879,750	44,268	1,644,593,238		
8	Moderate	591	23,837,250	40,334	1,182,540,642		
9	S Conservative	191	9,639,750	50,470	1,739,834,944		
10	Conservative	202	10,489,500	51,928	1,620,508,503		
11	E Conservative	53	3,258,000	61,472	3,452,330,914		
12							
13	ANOVA						
14	*Source of Variation*	*SS*	*df*	*MS*	*F*	*P-value*	*F crit*
15	Between Groups	44,532,904,466	6	7,422,150,744	4.68	9.89E-05	2.10
16	Within Groups	2,330,506,229,161	1471	1,584,300,632			
17							
18	Total	2,375,039,133,627	1477				

(Continued)

INTERPRET

Note the use of scientific notation for the *p*-value. The number 9.89 E−05 (E stands for *exponent*) is 9.89 multiplied by 10 raised to the power −5, that is, 9.89×10^{-5}. You can increase or decrease the number of decimal places, and you can convert the number into a regular number. In some cases, you would need many decimal places, which is why Excel uses scientific notation when the number is very small. (Excel also uses scientific notation for very large numbers.)

The *p*-value is .0000989. There is overwhelming evidence to infer that the incomes differ between the seven political views. It appears that conservatives have higher incomes than liberals.

Factors That Identify the One-Way Analysis of Variance

1. **Problem objective**: Compare two or more populations
2. **Data type**: Interval
3. **Experimental design**: Independent samples

EXERCISES

Developing an Understanding of Statistical Concepts

Exercises 14.1–14.3 are "what-if" analyses designed to determine what happens to the test statistic when the means, variances, and sample sizes change. These problems can be solved manually or by creating an Excel worksheet.

14.1 A statistics practitioner calculated the following statistics:

Statistic	Treatment 1	2	3
n	5	5	5
$\bar{x}$	10	15	20
s^2	50	50	50

a. Complete the ANOVA table.
b. Repeat part (a) changing the sample sizes to 10 each.
c. Describe what happens to the *F*-statistic when the sample sizes increase.

14.2 You are given the following statistics:

Statistic	Treatment 1	2	3
n	4	4	4
$\bar{x}$	20	22	25
s^2	10	10	10

a. Complete the ANOVA table.
b. Repeat part (a) changing the variances to 25 each.
c. Describe the effect on the *F*-statistic of increasing the sample variances.

14.3 The following statistics were calculated:

Statistic	Treatment 1	2	3	4
n	10	14	11	18
$\bar{x}$	30	35	33	40
s^2	10	10	10	10

a. Complete the ANOVA table.
b. Repeat part (a) changing the sample means to 130, 135, 133, and 140.
c. Describe the effect on the F-statistic of increasing the sample means by 100.

Applications

14.4 <u>Xr14-04</u> How does an MBA major affect the number of job offers received? An MBA student randomly sampled four recent graduates, one each in finance, marketing, and management, and asked them to report the number of job offers. Can we conclude at the 5% significance level that there are differences in the number of job offers between the three MBA majors?

Finance	Marketing	Management
3	1	8
1	5	5
4	3	4
1	4	6

14.5 <u>Xr14-05</u> A consumer organization was concerned about the differences between the advertised sizes of containers and the actual amount of product. In a preliminary study, six packages of three different brands of margarine that are supposed to contain 500 ml were measured. The differences from 500 ml are listed here. Do these data provide sufficient evidence to conclude that differences exist between the three brands? Use $\alpha = .01$.

Brand 1	Brand 2	Brand 3
1	2	1
3	2	2
3	4	4
0	3	2
1	0	3
0	4	4

14.6 <u>Xr14-06</u> Many college and university students obtain summer jobs. A statistics professor wanted to determine whether students in different degree programs earn different amounts. A random sample of 5 students in the B.A., B.Sc., and B.B.A. programs were asked to report what they earned the previous summer. The results (in $1,000s) are listed here. Can the professor infer at the 5% significance level that students in different degree programs differ in their summer earnings?

B.A.	B.Sc.	B.B.A.
3.3	3.9	4.0
2.5	5.1	6.2
4.6	3.9	6.3
5.4	6.2	5.9
3.9	4.8	6.4

14.7 <u>Xr14-07</u> Spam is the price we pay for being able to easily communicate by e-mail. Does spam affect everyone equally? In a preliminary study, university professors, administrators, and students were randomly sampled. Each person was asked to count the number of spam messages received that day. The results follow. Can we infer at the 2.5% significance level that the differing university communities differ in the amount of spam they receive in their e-mails?

Professors	Administrators	Students
7	5	12
4	9	4
0	12	5
3	16	18
18	10	15

14.8 <u>Xr14-08</u> A management scientist believes that one way of judging whether a computer came equipped with enough memory is to determine the age of the computer. In a preliminary study, random samples of computer users were asked to identify the brand of computer and its age (in months). The categorized responses are shown here. Do these data provide sufficient evidence to conclude that there are differences in age between the computer brands? (Use $\alpha = .05$.)

IBM	Dell	Hewlett-Packard	Other
17	8	6	24
10	4	15	12
13	21	8	15

Exercises 14.9–14.22 require the use of a computer and software. The answers may be calculated manually. See Appendix A for the sample statistics. **Use a 5% significance level unless specified otherwise.**

14.9 <u>Xr14-09</u> Because there are no national or regional standards, it is difficult for university admission committees to compare graduates of different high schools. University administrators have noted that an 80% average at a high school with low standards may be equivalent to a 70% average at another school with higher standards of grading. In an effort to more equitably compare applications, a pilot study was initiated. Random samples of students who were admitted the previous year from four local high schools were drawn. All the students entered the business program with averages between 70% and 80%. Their average grades in the first year at the university were computed.

a. Can the university admissions officer conclude that there are differences in grading standards between the four high schools?

b. What are the required conditions for the test conducted in part (a)?

c. Does it appear that the required conditions of the test in part (a) are satisfied?

14.10 Xr14-10 The friendly folks at the Internal Revenue Service (IRS) in the United States and Canada Revenue Agency (CRA) are always looking for ways to improve the wording and format of its tax return forms. Three new forms have been developed recently. To determine which, if any, are superior to the current form, 120 individuals were asked to participate in an experiment. Each of the three new forms and the currently used form were filled out by 30 different people. The amount of time (in minutes) taken by each person to complete the task was recorded.

a. What conclusions can be drawn from these data?

b. What are the required conditions for the test conducted in part (a)?

c. Does it appear that the required conditions of the test in part (a) are satisfied?

14.11 Xr14-11 Are proficiency test scores affected by the education of the child's parents? (Proficiency tests are administered to a sample of students in private and public schools. Test scores can range from 0 to 500.) To answer this question, a random sample of 9-year-old children was drawn. Each child's test score and the educational level of the parent with the higher level were recorded. The education categories are less than high school, high school graduate, some college, and college graduate. Can we infer that there are differences in test scores between children whose parents have different educational levels? (Adapted from the *Statistical Abstract of the United States*, 2000, Table 286.)

14.12 Xr14-12 A manufacturer of outdoor brass lamps and mailboxes has received numerous complaints about premature corrosion. The manufacturer has identified the cause of the problem as the low-quality lacquer used to coat the brass. He decides to replace his current lacquer supplier with one of five possible alternatives. To judge which is best, he uses each of the five lacquers to coat 25 brass mailboxes and puts all 125 mailboxes outside. He records, for each, the number of days until the first sign of corrosion is observed.

a. Is there sufficient evidence at the 1% significance level to allow the manufacturer to conclude that differences exist between the five lacquers?

b. What are the required conditions for the test conducted in part (a)?

c. Does it appear that the required conditions of the test in part (a) are satisfied?

14.13 Xr14-13 In early 2001, the economy was slowing down and companies were laying off workers. A Gallup poll asked a random sample of workers how long it would be before they had significant financial hardships if they lost their jobs and couldn't find new ones. They also classified their income. The classifications are

> More than $50,000
> $30,000 to $50,000
> $20,000 to $30,000
> Less than $20,000

Can we infer that differences exist between the four groups?

14.14 Xr14-14 In the introduction to this chapter, we mentioned that the first use of the analysis of variance was in the 1920s. It was employed to determine whether different amounts of fertilizer yielded different amounts of crop. Suppose that a scientist at an agricultural college wanted to redo the original experiment using three different types of fertilizer. Accordingly, she applied fertilizer A to 20 1-acre plots of land, fertilizer B to another 20 plots, and fertilizer C to yet another 20 plots of land. At the end of the growing season, the crop yields were recorded. Can the scientist infer that differences exist between the crop yields?

14.15 Xr14-15 A study performed by a Columbia University professor (described in *Report on Business*, August 1991) counted the number of times per minute professors from three different departments said "uh" or "ah" during lectures to fill gaps between words. The data derived from observing 100 minutes from each of the three departments were recorded. If we assume that the more frequent use of "uh" and "ah" results in more boring lectures, can we conclude that some departments' professors are more boring than others?

14.16 Xr14-16 Does the level of success of publicly traded companies affect the way their board members are paid? Publicly traded companies were divided into four quarters using the rate of return in their stocks to differentiate among the companies. The annual payment (in $1,000s) to their board members was recorded. Can we infer that the amount of payment differs between the four groups of companies?

14.17 Xr14-17 In 1994, the chief executive officers of the major tobacco companies testified before a U.S. Senate subcommittee. One of the accusations made was that tobacco firms added nicotine to their cigarettes, which made them even more addictive to smokers. Company scientists argued that the amount of nicotine in cigarettes depended completely on the size of the tobacco leaf: During poor growing seasons, the tobacco leaves would be smaller than in normal or good growing seasons. However, because the amount of nicotine in a leaf is a fixed quantity, smaller leaves would result in cigarettes having more nicotine (because a greater fraction of the leaf would be used to make a cigarette). To examine the issue, a university chemist took random samples of tobacco leaves that were grown in greenhouses where the amount of water was allowed to vary. Three different groups of tobacco leaves were grown. Group 1 leaves were grown with about an average season's rainfall. Group 2 leaves were given about 67% of group 1's water, and group 3 leaves were given 33% of group 1's water. The size of the leaf (in grams) and the amount of nicotine in each leaf were measured.

a. Test to determine whether the leaf sizes differ between the three groups.
b. Test to determine whether the amounts of nicotine differ in the three groups.

14.18 Xr14-18 There is a bewildering number of breakfast cereals on the market. Each company produces several different products in the belief that there are distinct markets. For example, there is a market composed primarily of children, another for diet-conscious adults, and another for health-conscious adults. Each cereal the companies produce has at least one market as its target. However, consumers make their own decisions, which may or may not match the target predicted by the cereal maker. In an attempt to distinguish between consumers, a survey of adults between the ages of 25 and 65 was undertaken. Each was asked several questions, including age, income, and years of education, as well as which brand of cereal they consumed most frequently. The cereal choices are

1. Sugar Smacks, a children's cereal
2. Special K, a cereal aimed at dieters
3. Fiber One, a cereal that is designed and advertised as healthy
4. Cheerios, a combination of healthy and tasty

The results of the survey were recorded using the following format:

Column 1: Cereal choice
Column 2: Age of respondent
Column 3: Annual household income
Column 4: Years of education

a. Determine whether there are differences between the ages of the consumers of the four cereals.
b. Determine whether there are differences between the incomes of the consumers of the four cereals.
c. Determine whether there are differences between the educational levels of the consumers of the four cereals.
d. Summarize your findings in parts (a) through (c) and prepare a report describing the differences between the four groups of cereal consumers.

APPLICATIONS in MARKETING

Test Marketing

In Chapter 13, we introduced test marketing, which allows us to determine whether changing some of the elements of the marketing mix yields different sales. In the next exercise, we apply the technique to discover the effect of different prices.

14.19 Xr14-19 A manufacturer of novelty items is undecided about the price to charge for a new product. The marketing manager knows that it should sell for about $10 but is unsure of whether sales will vary significantly if it is priced at either $9 or $11. To conduct a pricing experiment, she distributes the new product to a sample of 60 stores belonging to a certain chain of variety stores. These 60 stores are all located in similar neighborhoods. The manager randomly selects 20 stores in which to sell the item at $9, 20 stores to sell it at $10, and the remaining 20 stores to sell it at $11. Sales at the end of the trial period were recorded. What should the manager conclude?

Pavel L Photo and Video/Shutterstock.com

APPLICATIONS in MARKETING

Marketing Segmentation

Section 12-4 introduced market segmentation. In Chapter 13 we demonstrated how to use statistical analyses to determine whether two segments differ in their buying behavior. The next exercise requires you to apply the analysis of variance to determine whether several segments differ.

14.20 Xr14-20   After determining in Exercise 13.229 that teenagers watch more movies than do 20–30-year-olds, teenagers were further segmented into three age groups: 12 to 14, 15 to 16, and 17 to 19. Random samples were drawn from each segment, and the number of movies each teenager saw last year was recorded. Do these data allow a marketing manager of a movie studio to conclude that differences exist between the three segments?

14.21 Xr14-21   As large cities grow larger, traffic congestion also increases. To measure how commuting time differs between California, New York, and Texas, random samples of commuters in each state were drawn. Is there sufficient evidence to infer that differences in commuting time exists between the three states?

Source: Adapted from *Statistical Abstract of the United States* 2012, Table 1100.

14.22 Xr14-22   The Program for International Student Assessment (PISA) conducts tests of 15-year-olds. The tests jointly developed by the participating countries are tests for reading literary test, mathematical literacy test, and scientific literary test. Random samples from the United States, Canada, and the United Kingdom were recorded. For each test, determine whether there are differences between the three countries.

Source: Adapted from *Statistical Abstract of the United States* 2012, Table 1371.

GENERAL SOCIAL SURVEY EXERCISES

Conduct all statistical tests at the 5% significance level.

The next seven exercises compare the eight categories of political parties (PARTYID: 0 = Strong Democrat, 1 = Not strong Democrat, 2 = Independent near Democrat, 3 = Independent, 4 = Independent near Republican, 5 = Not strong Republican, 6 = Strong Republican, 7 = Other party).

14.23 GSS2014*   Which political party is more educated? Conduct a test to determine whether differences in education (EDUC) actually exist among some of the eight political categories.

14.24 GSS2014*   Does income affect the way Americans choose which party to support? Conduct a statistical procedure to determine whether there are differences in income (RINCOME) between some or all of the eight political groups.

14.25 GSS2014*   Refer to Exercise 14.24. If differences in income exist, is it because higher-income Americans

work harder? Can we conclude from the data that there are differences in the hours worked (HRS1) between the eight political groups?

Exercises 14.26–14.29 examine whether differences exist between the eight political groupings with respect to the role of government.

14.26 GSS2014*   The survey asked the question, "Should government reduce income differences between rich and poor (EQWLTH: 1 = Government should reduce differences; 2, 3, 4, 5, 6, 7 = No government action)? Is there enough evidence to infer that there are differences among some or all of the eight political groups?

14.27 GSS2014*   Is there enough statistical evidence to conclude that the eight political categories differ in their responses to this question, "Should government improve standard of living of poor people

(HELPPOOR: 1 = Government act; 2, 3, 4, 5 = People should help themselves)?

14.28 GSS2014* The question that the survey asked is, "Should government do more or less to solve country's problems (HELPNOT: 1 = Government should do more; 2, 3, 4, 5 = Government does too much)? Can we infer from the data that there are differences among some or all of the eight political categories in their answer to the question?

14.29 GSS2014* With government-funded health insurance in the air the next question may be particularly relevant. Is it government's responsibility to help pay for doctor and hospital bills HELPSICK: 1 = Government should help; 2, 3, 4, 5 = People should help themselves)? Is there enough evidence to conclude that differences exist between the eight political categories?

Exercises 14.30–14.37 compare the seven political views (POLVIEWS: 1 = Extremely liberal, 2 = Liberal, 3 = Slightly liberal, 4 = Moderate, 5 = Slightly conservative, 6 = Conservative, 7 = Extremely conservative).

14.30 GSS2014* Are liberals, moderates, and conservatives all equally educated? Test to determine whether differences exist among the seven political views in the amount of education (EDUC).

14.31 GSS2014* What happens to Americans' political philosophies as they grow richer? If they change we would expect differences in income (RINCOME) between the seven groups. Is there enough evidence to conclude that such differences exist?

14.32 GSS2014* Is it a myth that conservatives work harder than do liberals and moderates? Test to determine whether there are differences in number of hours of work per week (HRS1) among some or all of the seven political points of view.

14.33 GSS2014* Is it true that younger Americans tend to be liberal and older Americans more conservative? To help discover the truth, start by determining whether there is enough statistical evidence to conclude that there are differences in age (AGE) among the seven political viewpoints.

Exercises 14.34–14.37 examine whether differences exist between the seven political viewpoints (POLVIEWS) with respect to the role of government.

14.34 GSS2014* Is there enough evidence to infer that there are differences between the seven political viewpoints in their answers to the question. "Should government reduce income differences between rich and poor (EQWLTH: 1 = Government should

reduce differences; 2, 3, 4, 5, 6, 7 = No government action)?

14.35 GSS2014* The survey asked, "Should government improve standard of living of poor people (HELPPOOR: 1 = Government act; 2, 3, 4, 5 = People should help themselves)?" Is there enough statistical evidence to conclude that some or all of the seven groups differ in their responses to this question?

14.36 GSS2014* Can we infer from the data that there are differences between the seven political viewpoints in their answer to the question? "Should government do more or less to solve country's problems (HELPNOT: 1 = Government should do more; 2, 3, 4, 5 = Government does too much)?

14.37 GSS2014* The survey asked, "Is it government's responsibility to help pay for doctor and hospital bills (HELPSICK: 1 = Government should help; 2, 3, 4, 5 = People should help themselves)? Is there enough evidence to conclude that differences exist among some or all of the seven groups?

14.38 GSS2014* How does acquiring additional degrees contribute to higher incomes? Conduct a test to determine whether the degree holders (DEGREE: 0 = Left high school, 1 = High school, 2 = Junior college, 3 = Bachelor's degree, 4 = Graduate degree) differ in income (RINCOME).

14.39 GSS2014* Television networks and their advertisers are constantly surveying viewers to determine their likes and dislikes and how much time adults spend watching television per day. Do the data allow us to infer that the amount of television (TVHOURS) differs by race (RACE)?

14.40 GSS2014* Do educated people work longer or shorter hours than do less-educated individuals? Conduct a test to determine whether there is enough evidence to conclude that differences exist in the number of hours per week (HRS1) between the five groups of educational attainment (DEGREE: 0 = Left high school, 1 = High school, 2 = Junior college, 3 = Bachelor's degree, 4 = Graduate degree)

Exercises 14.41–14.44 test differences between the four classes (CLASS: 1 = Lower class, 2 = Working class, 3 = Middle class, 4 = Upper class) with respect to the role of government. Does the way in which respondents self-identify the class their family is in affect each one of the questions listed here?

14.41 GSS2014* Should government reduce income differences between rich and poor EQWLTH: 1 = Government should reduce differences; 2, 3, 4, 5, 6, 7 = No government action)?

14.42 <u>GSS2014*</u> Should government improve standard of living of poor people (HELPPOOR: 1 = Government act; 2, 3, 4, 5 = People should help themselves)?

14.43 <u>GSS2014*</u> Should government do more or less to solve country's problems (HELPNOT: 1 = Government should do more; 2, 3, 4, 5 = Government does too much)?

14.44 <u>GSS2014*</u> Is it government's responsibility to help pay for doctor and hospital bills (HELPSICK: 1 = Government should help; 2, 3, 4, 5 = People should help themselves)?

14.45 <u>GSS2006* GSS2008* GSS2010* GSS2012* GSS2014*</u> Has educational levels kept uniform over the years 2006, 2008, 2010, 2012, and 2014? Conduct a test to determine whether the number of years of education (EDUC) differs in the 8-year period.

14.46 <u>GSS2006* GSS2008* GSS2010* GSS2012* GSS2014*</u> Has the amount of television American adults watch been constant over the years 2006, 2008, 2010, 2012, and 2014 or has the amount varied. Test to determine whether the number of hours of television per day (TVHOURS) changed over the 8-year span.

SURVEY OF CONSUMER FINANCES EXERCISES

Conduct all tests at the 5% significance level.

Exercises 14.47–14.56 are based on all the observations in the 2013 survey. Exercises 14.47–14.52 compare the four categories of the educational attainment of the household head (EDCL: 1 = No high school diploma, 2 = High school diploma, 3 = Some college, 4 = College graduate).

14.47 <u>SCF2013:\All*</u> How much evidence is there that more education leads to higher incomes and more financial success? Test to determine whether differences in income (INCOME) exist between the four education categories.

14.48 <u>SCF2013:\All*</u> Does the education category affect the net worth of households? Is so, there should be differences in net worth between the four categories of education. Conduct a test to determine whether there are such differences (NETWORTH).

14.49 <u>SCF2013:\All*</u> Are more educated individuals likely to have more unrealized capital gains? Is there enough evidence to infer that there are differences in total unrealized capital gains (KGTOTAL)?

14.50 <u>SCF2013:\All*</u> Is education a factor in the amount of debt carried by heads of households? Conduct a statistical test to determine whether the amount of debt (DEBT) differs between the four categories.

14.51 <u>SCF2013:\All*</u> Do households headed by a more educated person spend their food dollars differently from households headed by less-educated people? Is there enough evidence to conclude that there are differences in the annual expenditures on food at home between the four categories of education (FOODHOME)?

14.52 <u>SCF2013:\All*</u> Is there enough evidence to conclude that there are differences in total annual amount spent on food away from home between the four categories (FOODAWAY)?

Exercises 14.53–14.56 compare the three categories of industry classification (INDCAT: 1 = Mining + construction + manufacturing, 2 = Transportation + communications + utilities and sanitary services + wholesale trade + finance, insurance and real estate, 3 = Agriculture + retail trade + services + public transportation) Note that there are only three categories.

14.53 <u>SCF2013:\All*</u> Are some industries better than others in terms of financial remuneration? Conduct a test to determine whether there are differences in income (INCOME) between the three categories of industry.

14.54 <u>SCF2013:\All*</u> Can we infer from the data that there are differences in net worth (NETWORTH) between the heads of households whose jobs are in one of the three industry classifications?

14.55 <u>SCF2013:\All*</u> Can we infer from the data that there are differences in the amount of debt (DEBT) between the three industry classifications?

14.56 <u>SCF2013:\ALL*</u> Can we infer from the data that there are differences in the total unrealized capital gains (KGTOTAL) between the three industry classifications?

14-2 / MULTIPLE COMPARISONS

When we conclude from the one-way analysis of variance that at least two treatment means differ, we often need to know which treatment means are responsible for these differences. For example, if an experiment is undertaken to determine whether different locations within a store produce different mean sales, the manager would be keenly interested in determining which locations result in significantly higher sales and which locations result in lower sales. Similarly, a stockbroker would like to know which one of several mutual funds outperforms the others, and a television executive would like to know which television commercials hold the viewers' attention and which are ignored.

Although it may appear that all we need to do is examine the sample means and identify the largest or the smallest to determine which population means are largest or smallest, this is not the case. To illustrate, suppose that in a five-treatment analysis of variance, we discover that differences exist and that the sample means are as follows:

$$\bar{x}_1 = 20 \quad \bar{x}_2 = 19 \quad \bar{x}_3 = 25 \quad \bar{x}_4 = 22 \quad \bar{x}_5 = 17$$

The statistics practitioner wants to know which of the following conclusions are valid:

1. μ_3 is larger than the other means.

2. μ_3 and μ_4 are larger than the other means.

3. μ_5 is smaller than the other means.

4. μ_5 and μ_2 are smaller than the other means.

5. μ_3 is larger than the other means, and μ_5 is smaller than the other means.

From the information we have, it is impossible to determine which, if any, of the statements are true. We need a statistical method to make this determination. The technique is called **multiple comparisons**.

EXAMPLE 14.2

DATA
Xm14-02

Comparing the Costs of Repairing Car Bumpers

Because of foreign competition, North American automobile manufacturers have become more concerned with quality. One aspect of quality is the cost of repairing damage caused by accidents. A manufacturer is considering several new types of bumpers. To test how well they react to low-speed collisions, 10 bumpers of each of four different types were installed on mid-size cars, which were then driven into a wall at 5 miles per hour. The cost of repairing the damage in each case was assessed. The data are shown below.

a. Is there sufficient evidence at the 5% significance level to infer that the bumpers differ in their reactions to low-speed collisions?

b. If differences exist, which bumpers differ?

Bum per 1	Bumper 2	Bumper 3	Bumper 4
610	404	599	272
354	663	426	405
234	521	429	197
399	518	621	363
278	499	426	297
358	374	414	538
379	562	332	181
548	505	460	318
196	375	494	412
444	438	637	499

SOLUTION:

IDENTIFY

The problem objective is to compare four populations. The data are interval, and the samples are independent. The correct statistical method is the one-way analysis of variance, which we perform using Excel.

COMPUTE

EXCEL Data Analysis

	A	B	C	D	E	F	G
1	Anova: Single Factor						
2							
3	SUMMARY						
4	*Groups*	*Count*	*Sum*	*Average*	*Variance*		
5	Bumper 1	10	3800	380.0	16,924		
6	Bumper 2	10	4859	485.9	8,197		
7	Bumper 3	10	4838	483.8	10,426		
8	Bumper 4	10	3482	348.2	14,049		
9							
10							
11	ANOVA						
12	*Source of Variation*	*SS*	*df*	*MS*	*F*	*P-value*	*F crit*
13	Between Groups	150,884	3	50,295	4.06	0.0139	2.87
14	Within Groups	446,368	36	12,399			
15							
16	Total	597,252	39				

INTERPRET

The test statistic is $F = 4.06$ and the p-value = .0139. There is enough statistical evidence to infer that there are differences between some of the bumpers. The question is now, Which bumpers differ?

There are several statistical inference procedures that deal with this problem. We will present three methods that allow us to determine which population means differ. All three methods apply to the one-way experiment only.

14-2a Fisher's Least Significant Difference Method

To determine which population means differ, we could perform a series of t-tests of the difference between two means on all pairs of population means to determine which are significantly different. In Chapter 13, we introduced the equal-variances t-test of the difference between two means. The test statistic and confidence interval estimator are, respectively,

$$t = \frac{(\bar{x}_1 - \bar{x}_2) - (\mu_1 - \mu_2)}{\sqrt{s_p^2\left(\frac{1}{n_1} + \frac{1}{n_2}\right)}}$$

$$(\bar{x}_1 - \bar{x}_2) \pm t_{\alpha/2}\sqrt{s_p^2\left(\frac{1}{n_1} + \frac{1}{n_2}\right)}$$

with degrees of freedom $\nu = n_1 + n_2 - 2$.

Recall that s_p^2 is the pooled variance estimate, which is an unbiased estimator of the variance of the two populations. (Recall that the use of these techniques requires that the population variances be equal.) In this section, we modify the test statistic and interval estimator.

Earlier in this chapter, we pointed out that MSE is an unbiased estimator of the common variance of the populations we're testing. Because MSE is based on all the observations in the k samples, it will be a better estimator than s_p^2 (which is based on only two samples). Thus, we could draw inferences about every pair of means by substituting MSE for s_p^2 in the formulas for test statistic and confidence interval estimator shown previously. The number of degrees of freedom would also change to $\nu = n - k$ (where n is the total sample size). The test statistic to determine whether μ_i and μ_j differ is

$$t = \frac{(\bar{x}_i - \bar{x}_j) - (\mu_i - \mu_j)}{\sqrt{MSE\left(\frac{1}{n_i} + \frac{1}{n_j}\right)}}$$

The confidence interval estimator is

$$(\bar{x}_i - \bar{x}_j) \pm t_{\alpha/2}\sqrt{MSE\left(\frac{1}{n_i} + \frac{1}{n_j}\right)}$$

with degrees of freedom $\nu = n - k$.

We define the **least significant difference LSD** as

$$LSD = t_{\alpha/2}\sqrt{MSE\left(\frac{1}{n_i} + \frac{1}{n_j}\right)}$$

A simple way of determining whether differences exist between each pair of population means is to compare the absolute value of the difference between their two sample means and LSD. In other words, we will conclude that μ_i and μ_j differ if

$$|\bar{x}_i - \bar{x}_j| > LSD$$

LSD will be the same for all pairs of means if all k sample sizes are equal. If some sample sizes differ, LSD must be calculated for each combination.

In Section 14-1 we argued that this method is flawed because it will increase the probability of committing a Type I error. That is, it is more likely than the analysis of variance to conclude that a difference exists in some of the population means when in fact none differ. On page 527, we calculated that if $k = 6$ and all population means are equal, the probability of erroneously inferring at the 5% significance level that at least two means differ is about 54%. The 5% figure is now referred to as the *comparisonwise Type I error rate*. The true probability of making at least one Type I error is called the *experimentwise Type I error rate*, denoted α_E. The experimentwise Type I error rate can be calculated as

$$\alpha_E = 1 - (1 - \alpha)^C$$

Here C is the number of pairwise comparisons, which can be calculated by $C = k(k - 1)/2$. Mathematicians have proven that

$$\alpha_E \leq C\alpha$$

which means that if we want the probability of making at least one Type I error to be no more than α_E, we simply specify $\alpha = \alpha_E/C$. The resulting procedure is called the **Bonferroni adjustment**.

14-2b Bonferroni Adjustment to LSD Method

The adjustment is made by dividing the specified experimentwise Type I error rate by the number of combinations of pairs of population means. For example, if $k = 6$, then

$$C = \frac{k(k - 1)}{2} = \frac{6(5)}{2} = 15$$

If we want the true probability of a Type I error to be no more than 5%, we divide this probability by C. Thus, for each test we would use a value of α equal to

$$\alpha = \frac{\alpha_E}{C} = \frac{.05}{15} = .0033$$

We use Example 14.2 to illustrate Fisher's LSD method and the Bonferroni adjustment. The four sample means are

$$\bar{x}_1 = 380.0$$
$$\bar{x}_2 = 485.9$$
$$\bar{x}_3 = 483.8$$
$$\bar{x}_4 = 348.2$$

The pairwise absolute differences are

$$|\bar{x}_1 - \bar{x}_2| = |380.0 - 485.9| = |-105.9| = 105.9$$
$$|\bar{x}_1 - \bar{x}_3| = |380.0 - 483.8| = |-103.8| = 103.8$$
$$|\bar{x}_1 - \bar{x}_4| = |380.0 - 348.2| = |31.8| = 31.8$$
$$|\bar{x}_2 - \bar{x}_3| = |485.9 - 483.8| = |2.1| = 2.1$$
$$|\bar{x}_2 - \bar{x}_4| = |485.9 - 348.2| = |137.7| = 137.7$$
$$|\bar{x}_3 - \bar{x}_4| = |483.8 - 348.2| = |135.6| = 135.6$$

From the computer output, we learn that MSE $= 12,399$ and $\nu = n - k = 40 - 4 = 36$. If we conduct the LSD procedure with $\alpha = .05$ we find $t_{\alpha/2, n-k} = t_{.025, 36} \approx t_{.025, 35} = 2.030$. Thus,

$$t_{\alpha/2}\sqrt{\text{MSE}\left(\frac{1}{n_i} + \frac{1}{n_j}\right)} = 2.030\sqrt{12,399\left(\frac{1}{10} + \frac{1}{10}\right)} = 101.09$$

We can see that four pairs of sample means differ by more than 101.09. In other words, $|\bar{x}_1 - \bar{x}_2| = 105.9$, $|\bar{x}_1 - \bar{x}_3| = 103.8$, $|\bar{x}_2 - \bar{x}_4| = 137.7$, and $|\bar{x}_3 - \bar{x}_4| = 135.6$. Hence, μ_1 and μ_2, μ_1 and μ_3, μ_2 and μ_4, and μ_3 and μ_4 differ. The other two pairs—μ_1 and μ_4, and μ_2 and μ_3—do not differ.

If we perform the LSD procedure with the Bonferroni adjustment, the number of pairwise comparisons is 6 (calculated as $C = k(k-1)/2 = 4(3)/2$). We set $\alpha = .05/6 = .0083$. Thus $t_{\alpha/2,36} = t_{.0042,36} = 2.794$ (available from Excel and difficult to approximate manually) and

$$\text{LSD} = t_{\alpha/2}\sqrt{\text{MSE}\left(\frac{1}{n_i} + \frac{1}{n_j}\right)} = 2.794\sqrt{12,399\left(\frac{1}{10} + \frac{1}{10}\right)} = 139.13$$

Now no pair of means differ because all the absolute values of the differences between sample means are less than 139.19.

The drawback to the LSD procedure is that we increase the probability of at least one Type I error. The Bonferroni adjustment corrects this problem. However, recall that the probabilities of Type I and Type II errors are inversely related. The Bonferroni adjustment uses a smaller value of α, which results in an increased probability of a Type II error. A Type II error occurs when a difference between population means exists, yet we cannot detect it. This may be the case in this example. The next multiple comparison method addresses this problem.

14-2c Tukey's Multiple Comparison Method

A more powerful test is **Tukey's multiple comparison method**. This technique determines a critical number similar to LSD for Fisher's test, denoted by ω (Greek letter *omega*), such that if any pair of sample means has a difference greater than ω, we conclude that the pair's two corresponding population means are different.

The test is based on the Studentized range, which is defined as the variable

$$q = \frac{\bar{x}_{\text{max}} - \bar{x}_{\text{min}}}{s/\sqrt{n}}$$

where $\bar{x}_{\text{max}}$ and $\bar{x}_{\text{min}}$ are the largest and smallest sample means, respectively, assuming that there are no differences between the population means. We define ω as follows.

Critical Number ω

$$\omega = q_\alpha(k, \nu)\sqrt{\frac{\text{MSE}}{n_g}}$$

where

$k = $ Number of treatments

$n = $ Number of observations $(n = n_1 + n_2 + \ldots + n_k)$

$$\nu = \text{Number of degrees of freedom associated with}$$
$$\text{MSE } (\nu = n - k)$$
$$n_g = \text{Number of observations in each of } k \text{ samples}$$
$$\alpha = \text{Significance level}$$
$$q_\alpha(k, \nu) = \text{Critical value of the Studentized range}$$

Theoretically, this procedure requires that all sample sizes be equal. However, if the sample sizes are different, we can still use this technique provided that the sample sizes are at least similar. The value of n_g used previously is the *harmonic mean* of the sample sizes; that is,

$$n_g = \frac{k}{\dfrac{1}{n_1} + \dfrac{1}{n_2} + \cdots + \dfrac{1}{n_k}}$$

Table 7 in Appendix B provides values of $q_\alpha(k, \nu)$ for a variety of values of k and ν, and for $\alpha = .01$ and $.05$. Applying Tukey's method to Example 14.2, we find

$$k = 4$$
$$n_1 = n_2 = n_3 = n_4 = n_g = 10$$
$$\nu = n - k = 40 - 4 = 36$$
$$\text{MSE} = 12,399$$
$$q_{.05}(4, 36) \approx q_{.05}(4, 40) = 3.79$$

Thus,

$$\omega = q_\alpha(k, \nu)\sqrt{\frac{\text{MSE}}{n_g}} = (3.79)\sqrt{\frac{12,399}{10}} = 133.45$$

There are two absolute values larger than 133.45. Hence, we conclude that μ_2 and μ_4, and μ_3 and μ_4 differ. The other four pairs do not differ.

EXCEL Workbook

	A	B	C	D	E
1	LSD Method				
2			Sample i	Sample j	|Difference|	105.90
3	Sample means	380.0	485.9		
4	Sample sizes	10	10	LSD	100.99
5	Number of treatments	4			
6	Degrees of freedom	36			
7	MSE	12,399			
8	Alpha	0.05			

	A	B	C	D	E
1	Bonferroni Adjustment LSD				
2			Sample i	Sample j	|Difference|	105.90
3	Sample means	380.0	485.9		
4	Sample sizes	10	10	Bonferroni LSD	139.03
5	Number of treatments	4			
6	Degrees of freedom	36			
7	MSE	12,399			
8	Alpha	0.05			

A	B	C	D	E
Tukey's Method $\alpha = 5\%$				
		Sample i	Sample j	|Difference|	105.90
Sample means	380.0	485.9		
Sample size	10		ω (Omega)	134.12
Number of treatments	4			
Degrees of freedom	36			
MSE	12,399			

INSTRUCTIONS

1. Conduct the analysis of variance.

2. Open the **Multiple comparisons** worksheet and click the **LSD** tab.

3. Copy or type the value of MSE (MS: Within Groups) into cell B7. Type the sample means and sample sizes of the treatments you wish to compare. Type the number of degrees of freedom in cell B6 and the value of α in cell B8.

4. For the Bonferroni Adjustment click the **Bonferroni** tab and type the number of treatments into cell B5.

5. For Tukey's method click the tab that uses the value of α you wish to use. Type the number of treatments in cell B5 and the observations in cell B4. If the sample sizes differ calculate the harmonic mean (**=HARMEAN ([Input range]**) and type that into cell B4. The number of degrees of freedom will be calculated automatically.

XLSTAT

	A	B	C	D	E	F
1	Bumper / Fisher (LSD)					
2						
3	Contrast	Difference	Standardized difference	Critical value	Pr > Diff	Significant
4	2 vs 4	137.700	2.765	2.028	0.009	Yes
5	2 vs 1	105.900	2.127	2.028	0.040	Yes
6	2 vs 3	2.100	0.042	2.028	0.967	No
7	3 vs 4	135.600	2.723	2.028	0.010	Yes
8	3 vs 1	103.800	2.084	2.028	0.044	Yes
9	1 vs 4	31.800	0.639	2.028	0.527	No
10	LSD-value:			100.995		

	A	B	C	D	E	F
1	Bumper / Bonferroni					
2						
3	Contrast	Difference	Standardized difference	Critical value	Pr > Diff	Significant
4	2 vs 4	137.700	2.765	2.792	0.009	No
5	2 vs 1	105.900	2.127	2.792	0.040	No
6	2 vs 3	2.100	0.042	2.792	0.967	No
7	3 vs 4	135.600	2.723	2.792	0.010	No
8	3 vs 1	103.800	2.084	2.792	0.044	No
9	1 vs 4	31.800	0.639	2.792	0.527	No
10	Modified significance level:			0		

	A	B	C	D	E	F
1	Bumper / Tukey (HSD)					
2						
3	Contrast	Difference	Standardized difference	Critical value	Pr > Diff	Significant
4	2 vs 4	137.7	2.765	2.693	0.042	Yes
5	2 vs 1	105.9	2.127	2.693	0.164	No
6	2 vs 3	2.1	0.042	2.693	1.000	No
7	3 vs 4	135.6	2.723	2.693	0.047	Yes
8	3 vs 1	103.8	2.084	2.693	0.178	No
9	1 vs 4	31.8	0.639	2.693	0.919	No
10	Tukey's d critical value:			3.809		

INSTRUCTIONS

1. Run the analysis of variance.

2. Click **Outputs** and **Means**.

3. Click **Multiple comparisons** and click **Tukey (HSD)**, **Fisher (LSD)** and **Bonferroni**.

4. Click **Options** and specify 95% for the **Confidence interval (%)**.

INTERPRET

Using the Bonferroni adjustment of Fisher's LSD method, we discover that none of the bumpers differ. (This is not a surprising result; since we used a very small probability of making a Type I error (.0033), the probability of making a Type II error became large.) Tukey's method tells us that bumper 4 differs from both bumpers 2 and 3. Based on this sample, bumper 4 appears to have the lowest cost of repair. Because there was not enough evidence to conclude that bumpers 1 and 4 differ, we would consider using bumper 1 if it has other advantages over bumper 4.

14-2d Which Multiple Comparison Method to Use

Unfortunately, no one procedure works best in all types of problems. Most statisticians agree with the following guidelines:

If you have identified two or three pairwise comparisons that you wish to make before conducting the analysis of variance, use the Bonferroni method. This means that if there are 10 populations in a problem but you're particularly interested in comparing, say, populations 3 and 7 and populations 5 and 9, use Bonferroni with $C = 2$.

If you plan to compare all possible combinations, use Tukey.

When do we use Fisher's LSD? If the purpose of the analysis is to point to areas that should be investigated further, Fisher's LSD method is indicated.

Incidentally, to employ Fisher's LSD or the Bonferroni adjustment, you must perform the analysis of variance first. Tukey's method can be employed instead of the analysis of variance.

EXERCISES

Developing an Understanding of Statistical Concepts

14.57 a. Use Fisher's LSD method with $\alpha = .05$ to determine which population means differ in the following problem.

$k = 3$ $n_1 = 10$ $n_2 = 10$ $n_3 = 10$
MSE = 700 $\bar{x}_1 = 128.7$ $\bar{x}_2 = 101.4$ $\bar{x}_3 = 133.7$

    b. Repeat Part a using the Bonferroni adjustment.
    c. Repeat Part a using Tukey's multiple comparison method.

14.58 a. Use Fisher's LSD procedure with $\alpha = .05$ to determine which population means differ given the following statistics:

$k = 5$ $n_1 = 5$ $n_2 = 5$ $n_3 = 5$
MSE = 125 $\bar{x}_1 = 227$ $\bar{x}_2 = 205$ $\bar{x}_3 = 219$
$n_4 = 5$ $n_5 = 5$
$\bar{x}_4 = 248$ $\bar{x}_5 = 202$

    b. Repeat Part a using the Bonferroni adjustment.
    c. Repeat Part a using Tukey's multiple comparison method

Applications

Unless specified otherwise, use a 5% significance level.

14.59 Apply Tukey's method to determine which brands differ in Exercise 14.5.

14.60 Refer to Exercise 14.6.
    a. Employ Fisher's LSD method to determine which degrees differ (use $\alpha = .10$).
    b. Repeat Part a using the Bonferroni adjustment.

The following exercises require the use of a computer and software. The answers may be calculated manually. See Appendix A for the sample statistics.

14.61 Xr14-09 a. Apply Fisher's LSD method with the Bonferroni adjustment to determine which schools differ in Exercise 14.9.
    b. Repeat Part a applying Tukey's method instead.

14.62 Xr14-10 a. Apply Tukey's multiple comparison method to determine which forms differ in Exercise 14.10.
    b. Repeat Part a applying the Bonferroni adjustment.

14.63 <u>Xr14-63</u> Police cars, ambulances, and other emergency vehicles are required to carry road flares. One of the most important features of flares is their burning times. To help decide which of four brands on the market to use, a police laboratory technician measured the burning time for a random sample of 10 flares of each brand. The results were recorded to the nearest minute.

    a. Can we conclude that differences exist between the burning times of the four brands of flares?

    b. Apply Fisher's LSD method with the Bonferroni adjustment to determine which flares are better.

    c. Repeat Part b using Tukey's method.

14.64 <u>Xr14-64</u> Refer to Exercise 14.12.

    a. Apply Fisher's LSD method with the Bonferroni adjustment to determine which lacquers differ.

    b. Repeat Part a applying Tukey's method instead.

14.65 <u>Xr14-65</u> An engineering student who is about to graduate decided to survey various firms in Silicon Valley to see which offered the best chance for early promotion and career advancement. He surveyed 30 small firms (size level is based on gross revenues), 30 medium-sized firms, and 30 large firms, and determined how much time must elapse before an average engineer can receive a promotion.

    a. Can the engineering student conclude that speed of promotion varies between the three sizes of engineering firms?

    b. If differences exist, which of the following is true? Use Tukey's method.

        i. Small firms differ from the other two.

        ii. Medium-sized firms differ from the other two.

        iii. Large firms differ from the other two.

        iv. All three firms differ from one another.

        v. Small firms differ from large firms.

14.66 <u>Xr14-14</u> a. Apply Tukey's multiple comparison method to determine which fertilizers differ in Exercise 14.14.

    b. Repeat Part a applying the Bonferroni adjustment.

GENERAL SOCIAL SURVEY EXERCISES

Use a 5% significance level for all procedures.

14.67 <u>GSS2014*</u> Refer to Exercise 14.23.

    a. Apply Tukey's multiple comparison method to determine which pairs of means differ.

    b. Use the Bonferroni adjustment test to determine whether there are differences between each of the following pairs: PARTYID: 0 and 1, 0 and 2, 1 and 2.

    c. Use the Bonferroni adjustment test to determine whether there is enough evidence to infer that there are differences between each of the following pairs: PARTYID: 4 and 5, 4 and 6, 5 and 6.

14.68 <u>GSS2014*</u> Refer to Exercise 14.24. Suppose that all you want to know is whether there are statistically significant differences in income between the three Independents (PARTYID: 2, 3, and 4). Perform the appropriate statistical procedure.

14.69 <u>GSS2014*</u> Refer to Exercise 14.25.

    a. Apply Tukey's multiple comparison method to determine whether any means differ

    b. Is this result different from analysis of variance *F*-test?

14.70 <u>GSS2014*</u> Refer to Exercise 14.26.

    a. Apply Tukey's multiple comparison method to determine which pairs of means differ.

    b. Use the Bonferroni adjustment test to determine whether there are differences between each of the following pairs of Independents: PARTYID: 2 and 3, 2 and 4, 3 and 4.

14.71 <u>GSS2014*</u> Refer to Exercise 14.27.

    a. Use Tukey's multiple comparison method to determine which pairs of political parties differ.

    b. Use an appropriate method the compare the three Independents with the other. That is, test for the following pairs of means PARTYID: 2 and 3, 2 and 4, and 3 and 4.

14.72 <u>GSS2014*</u> a. Apply the analysis of variance to determine whether there is enough evidence to conclude that there are differences in income (RINCOME) between the races (RACE: 1 = White, 2 = Black, 3 = Other).

    b. Use Tukey's method to determine which means differ.

14.73 <u>GSS2014*</u> a. Use the analysis of variance to test for differences in the number of hours worked (HRS1) between races (RACE: 1 = White, 2 = Black, 3 = Other).

    b. Apply Tukey's method to determine whether there are differences.

    c. Describe what you have discovered.

14.74 <u>GSS2014*</u> Is it a myth that Democrats are more educated than Republicans and Independents?
  a. Use the analysis of variance to determine whether the years of education (EDUC) differ among Democrats, Independents, and Republicans (PARTYID3: 1 = Democrat, 2 = Independent, 3 = Republican)
  b. Use Tukey's multiple comparison method to test for each pair of differences.

14.75 <u>GSS2014*</u> Refer to Exercise 14.29. If you wanted to determine whether the following pairs of means differ: PARTYID: 1 and 3, 1 and 5, 3 and 5, which multiple comparison method would you select? What value of α would you use? Perform the test.

14.76 <u>GSS2014*</u> Refer to Exercise 14.30. Suppose that you want to determine whether there are differences in the amount of education between each pair of liberals: POLVIEWS: 1 = Extremely liberal, 2 = Liberal, 3 = Slightly liberal.
  a. Which procedure should you use?
  b. Use the technique and report the results.

14.77 <u>GSS2014*</u> Refer to Exercise 14.31. Apply Tukey's multiple comparison method to test for differences in income for each pair of political views.

14.78 <u>GSS2014*</u> a. Use the analysis of variance to determine whether there is enough evidence to conclude that there are differences in the years of education (EDUC) between the liberals, moderates, and conservatives (POLVIEWS3: 1 = Liberal, 2 = Moderate, 3 = Conservative).
  b. Use Tukey's method to determine which pairs differ.

14.79 <u>GSS2014*</u> Refer to Exercise 14.39. Use Tukey's multiple comparison method to determine which pairs differ.

14.80 <u>GSS2014*</u> Refer to Exercise 14.34. Suppose that you want to determine which of the following pairs of means differ (POLVIEWS: 1 and 2, 1 and 3, 2 and 3).
  a. Which technique should you use?
  b. Use the technique and describe your results.

SURVEY OF CONSUMER FINANCES EXERCISES

14.81 <u>SCF2013:\All*</u> Refer to Exercise 14.51. Use Tukey's multiple comparison method to determine which pairs of means differ.

14.82 <u>SCF2013:\All*</u> Refer to Exercise 14.52. Apply Tukey's method to determine whether there is enough statistical evidence to infer that each pair of means differ.

14-3 / ANALYSIS OF VARIANCE EXPERIMENTAL DESIGNS

Since we introduced the matched pairs experiment in Section 13-3, the experimental design has been one of the factors that determines which technique we use. Statistics practitioners often design experiments to help extract the information they need to assist them in making decisions. The one-way analysis of variance introduced in Section 14-1 is only one of many different experimental designs of the analysis of variance. For each type of experiment, we can describe the behavior of the response variable using a mathematical expression or model. Although we will not exhibit the mathematical expressions in this chapter (we introduce models in Chapter 16), we think it is useful for you to be aware of the elements that distinguish one experimental design or model from another. In this section, we present some of these elements; in so doing, we introduce two of the experimental designs that will be presented later in this chapter.

14-3a Single-Factor and Multifactor Experimental Designs

As we pointed out in Section 14-1, the criterion by which we identify populations is called a *factor*. The experiment described in Section 14-1 is a single-factor analysis of variance because it addresses the problem of comparing two or more populations defined on the basis of only one factor. A **multifactor experiment** is one in which two or more factors define the treatments. The experiment described in Example 14.1 is a single-factor design because we had one treatment: age of the head of the household. In other words, the factor is the age, and the four age categories were the levels of this factor.

Suppose that we can also look at the gender of the household head in another study. We would then develop a two-factor analysis of variance in which the first factor, age, has four levels, and the second factor, gender, has two levels. We will discuss two-factor experiments in Section 14-5.

14-3b Independent Samples and Blocks

In Section 13-3, we introduced statistical techniques where the data were gathered from a matched pairs experiment. This type of experimental design reduces the variation within the samples, making it easier to detect differences between the two populations. When the problem objective is to compare more than two populations, the experimental design that is the counterpart of the matched pairs experiment is called the **randomized block design**. The term *block* refers to a matched group of observations from each population. Suppose that in Examples 13.4 and 13.5 we had wanted to compare the salary offers for finance, marketing, accounting, and operations management majors. To redo Example 13.5 we would conduct a randomized block experiment where the blocks are the 25 GPA groups and the treatments are the four MBA majors.

Once again, the experimental design should reduce the variation in each treatment to make it easier to detect differences.

We can also perform a blocked experiment by using the same subject (person, plant, and store) for each treatment. For example, we can determine whether sleeping pills are effective by giving three brands of pills to the same group of people to measure the effects. Such experiments are called **repeated measures** designs. Technically, this is a different design than the randomized block. However, the data are analyzed in the same way for both designs. Hence, we will treat repeated measures designs as randomized block designs.

The randomized block experiment is also called the **two-way analysis of variance**. In Section 14-4, we introduce the technique used to calculate the test statistic for this type of experiment.

14-3c Fixed and Random Effects

If our analysis includes all possible levels of a factor, the technique is called a **fixed-effects analysis of variance**. If the levels included in the study represent a random sample of all the levels that exist, the technique is called a **random-effects analysis of variance**. In Example 14.2, there were only four possible bumpers. Consequently, the study is a fixed-effects experiment. However, if there were other bumpers besides the four described in the example, and we wanted to know whether there were differences in repair costs between all bumpers, the application would be a random-effects experiment. Here's another example.

To determine whether there is a difference in the number of units produced by the machines in a large factory, 4 machines out of 50 in the plant are randomly selected for study. The number of units each produces per day for 10 days will be recorded.

This experiment is a random-effects experiment because we selected a random sample of four machines and the statistical results thus allow us to determine whether there are differences between the 50 machines.

In some experimental designs, there are no differences in calculations of the test statistic between fixed and random effects. However, in others, including the two-factor experiment presented in Section 14-5, the calculations are different.

14-4 / RANDOMIZED BLOCK (TWO-WAY) ANALYSIS OF VARIANCE

The purpose of designing a randomized block experiment is to reduce the within-treatments variation to more easily detect differences between the treatment means. In the one-way analysis of variance, we partitioned the total variation into the between-treatments and the within-treatments variation; that is,

SS(Total) = SST + SSE

In the randomized block design of the analysis of variance, we partition the total variation into three sources of variation,

SS(Total) = SST + SSB + SSE

where **SSB**, the **sum of squares for blocks**, measures the variation between the blocks. When the variation associated with the blocks is removed, SSE is reduced, making it easier to determine whether differences exist between the treatment means.

At this point in our presentation of statistical inference, we will deviate from our usual procedure of solving examples in three ways: manually, using Excel, and using XLSTAT. The calculations for this experimental design and for the experiment presented in the next section are so time consuming that solving them by hand adds little to your understanding of the technique. Consequently, although we will continue to present the concepts by discussing how the statistics are calculated, we will solve the problems only by computer.

To help you understand the formulas, we will use the following notation:

$\bar{x}[T]_j$ = Mean of the observations in the jth treatment ($j = 1, 2, \ldots, k$)

$\bar{x}[B]_i$ = Mean of the observations in the ith block ($i = 1, 2, \ldots, b$)

b = Number of blocks

Table 14.4 summarizes the notation we use in this experimental design.

TABLE 14.4 Notation for the Randomized Block Analysis of Variance

BLOCK	TREATMENTS				BLOCK MEAN
	1	2		k	
1	x_{11}	x_{12}	$\cdots$	x_{1k}	$\bar{x}[B]_1$
2	x_{21}	x_{22}	$\cdots$	x_{2k}	$\bar{x}[B]_2$
$\vdots$	$\vdots$	$\vdots$		$\vdots$	$\vdots$
b	x_{b1}	x_{b2}	$\cdots$	x_{bk}	$\bar{x}[B]_b$
Treatment mean	$\bar{x}[T]_1$	$\bar{x}[T]_2$	$\cdots$	$\bar{x}[T]_k$	

The definitions of SS(Total) and SST in the randomized block design are identical to those in the independent samples design. SSE in the independent samples design is equal to the sum of SSB and SSE in the randomized block design.

Sums of Squares in the Randomized Block Experiment

$$SS(\text{Total}) = \sum_{j=1}^{k} \sum_{i=1}^{b} (x_{ij} - \bar{\bar{x}})^2$$

$$SST = \sum_{j=1}^{k} b(\bar{x}[T]_j - \bar{\bar{x}})^2$$

$$SSB = \sum_{i=1}^{b} k(\bar{x}[B]_i - \bar{\bar{x}})^2$$

$$SSE = \sum_{j=1}^{k} \sum_{i=1}^{b} (x_{ij} - \bar{x}[T]_j - \bar{x}[B]_i + \bar{\bar{x}})^2$$

The test is conducted by determining the mean squares, which are computed by dividing the sums of squares by their respective degrees of freedom.

Mean Squares for the Randomized Block Experiment

$$MST = \frac{SST}{k - 1}$$

$$MSB = \frac{SSB}{b - 1}$$

$$MSE = \frac{SSE}{n - k - b + 1}$$

Finally, the test statistic is the ratio of mean squares, as described in the box.

Test Statistic for the Randomized Block Experiment

$$F = \frac{MST}{MSE}$$

which is F-distributed with $\nu_1 = k - 1$ and $\nu_2 = n - k - b + 1$ degrees of freedom.

An interesting, and sometimes useful, by-product of the test of the treatment means is that we can also test to determine whether the block means differ. This will allow us to determine whether the experiment should have been conducted as a randomized block design. (If there are no differences between the blocks, the randomized block design is less likely to detect real differences between the treatment means.) Such a discovery could be useful in future similar experiments. The test of the block means is almost identical to that of the treatment means except the test statistic is

$$F = \frac{MSB}{MSE}$$

which is F-distributed with $\nu_1 = b - 1$ and $\nu_2 = n - k - b + 1$ degrees of freedom.

As with the one-way experiment, the statistics generated in the randomized block experiment are summarized in an ANOVA table, whose general form is exhibited in Table 14.5.

TABLE **14.5** ANOVA Table for the Randomized Block Analysis of Variance

SOURCE OF VARIATION	DEGREES OF FREEDOM	SUMS OF SQUARES	MEAN SQUARES	F-STATISTIC
Treatments	$k - 1$	SST	MST = SST/$(k - 1)$	F = MST/MSE
Blocks	$b - 1$	SSB	MSB = SSB/$(b - 1)$	F = MSB/MSE
Error	$n - k - b + 1$	SSE	MSE = SSE/$(n - k - b + 1)$	
Total	$n - 1$	SS(Total)		

EXAMPLE **14.3**

Comparing Cholesterol-Lowering Drugs

Many North Americans suffer from high levels of cholesterol, which can lead to heart attacks. For those with very high levels (above 280), doctors prescribe drugs to reduce cholesterol levels. A pharmaceutical company has recently developed four such drugs. To determine whether any differences exist in their benefits, an experiment was organized. The company selected 25 groups of four men, each of whom had cholesterol levels in excess of 280. In each group, the men were matched according to age and weight. The drugs were administered over a 2-month period, and the reduction in cholesterol was recorded. Do these results allow the company to conclude that differences exist between the four new drugs?

Group	Drug 1	Drug 2	Drug 3	Drug 4
1	6.6	12.6	2.7	8.7
2	7.1	3.5	2.4	9.3
3	7.5	4.4	6.5	10
4	9.9	7.5	16.2	12.6
5	13.8	6.4	8.3	10.6
6	13.9	13.5	5.4	15.4
7	15.9	16.9	15.4	16.3
8	14.3	11.4	17.1	18.9
9	16	16.9	7.7	13.7
10	16.3	14.8	16.1	19.4
11	14.6	18.6	9	18.5
12	18.7	21.2	24.3	21.1
13	17.3	10	9.3	19.3
14	19.6	17	19.2	21.9
15	20.7	21	18.7	22.1
16	18.4	27.2	18.9	19.4

Group	Drug 1	Drug 2	Drug 3	Drug 4
17	21.5	26.8	7.9	25.4
18	20.4	28	23.8	26.5
19	21.9	31.7	8.8	22.2
20	22.5	11.9	26.7	23.5
21	21.5	28.7	25.2	19.6
22	25.2	29.5	27.3	30.1
23	23	22.2	17.6	26.6
24	23.7	19.5	25.6	24.5
25	28.4	31.2	26.1	27.4

SOLUTION:

IDENTIFY

The problem objective is to compare four populations, and the data are interval. Because the researchers recorded the cholesterol reduction for each drug for each member of the similar groups of men, we identify the experimental design as randomized block. The response variable is the cholesterol reduction, the treatments are the drugs, and the blocks are the 25 similar groups of men. The hypotheses to be tested are as follows.

H_0: $\mu_1 = \mu_2 = \mu_3 = \mu_4$

H_1: At least two means differ

COMPUTE

EXCEL Data Analysis

	A	B	C	D	E	F	G
36	ANOVA						
37	Source of Variation	SS	df	MS	F	P-value	F crit
38	Rows	3848.66	24	160.36	10.11	9.7E-15	1.67
39	Columns	195.95	3	65.32	4.12	0.0094	2.73
40	Error	1142.56	72	15.87			
41							
42	Total	5187.17	99				

The output includes block and treatment statistics (sums, averages, and variances, which are not shown here), and the ANOVA table. The F-statistic to determine whether differences exist between the four drugs (**Columns**) is 4.12. Its p-value is .0094. The other F-statistic, 10.11 (p-value $= 9.70 \times 10^{-15} =$ virtually 0), indicates that there are differences between the groups of men (**Rows**).

INSTRUCTIONS

1. Type or import the data into adjacent columns.* (Open Xm14-03 and click the **Unstacked** tab.)

2. Click **Data, Data Analysis . . .**, and **Anova: Two-Factor Without Replication**.

3. Specify the **Input Range** (A1:E26). Click **Labels** if applicable. If you do, both the treatments and blocks must be labeled (as in Xm14-03). Specify the value of α (.05).

---

*If one or more columns contain an empty cell (representing missing data), the entire row must be removed. See online appendix Removing Empty Cells in Excel.

XLSTAT

	A	B	C	D	E	F
35	Type I Sum of Squares analysis (C. Level):					
36						
37	Source	DF	Sum of squares	Mean squares	F	Pr > F
38	Drug	3	195.95	65.32	4.12	0.009
39	Group	24	3848.66	160.36	10.11	< 0.0001

INSTRUCTIONS

1. Type or import the data in stacked format. (Open Xm14-03 and click the **Stacked** tab.)
2. Click **XLSTAT**, **Modeling data**, and **ANOVA**.
3. In the **Quantitative** box type the input range (A1:A101). In the **X Explanatory variables** and **Qualitative** box type the input range (B1:C101).
4. Click **Outputs** and select **Analysis of variance** and **Type I/II/III SS**. Click **OK**.

INTERPRET

A Type I error occurs when you conclude that differences exist when, in fact, they do not. A Type II error is committed when the test reveals no difference when at least two means differ. It would appear that both errors are equally costly. Accordingly, we judge the p-value against a standard of 5%. Because the p-value = .0094, we conclude that there is sufficient evidence to infer that at least two of the drugs differ. An examination reveals that cholesterol reduction is greatest using drugs 2 and 4. Further testing is recommended to determine which is better.

14-4a Checking the Required Conditions

The F-test of the randomized block design of the analysis of variance has the same requirements as the independent samples design. That is, the random variable must be normally distributed and the population variances must be equal. The histograms (not shown) appear to support the validity of our results; the reductions appear to be normal. The equality of variances requirement also appears to be met.

14-1b Violation of the Required Conditions

When the response is not normally distributed, we can replace the randomized block analysis of variance with the Friedman test, which is introduced in Section 19-4.

14-4c Criteria for Blocking

In Section 13-3, we listed the advantages and disadvantages of performing a matched pairs experiment. The same comments are valid when we discuss performing a blocked experiment. The purpose of blocking is to reduce the variation caused by differences between the experimental units. By grouping the experimental units into homogeneous blocks with respect to the response variable, the statistics practitioner increases the chances of detecting actual differences between the treatment means. Hence, we need to find criteria for blocking that significantly affect the response variable. For example, suppose that a statistics professor wants to determine which of four methods of teaching statistics is best. In a one-way experiment, he might take four samples of 10 students, teach each sample by a different method, grade the students at the end of the course, and perform an F-test to determine whether differences exist. However, it is likely that there are very large differences between the students within each class that may hide differences between classes. To reduce this variation, the statistics professor must identify variables that are linked to a student's grade in statistics. For example, overall ability of the student, completion of mathematics courses, and exposure to other statistics courses are all related to performance in a statistics course.

The experiment could be performed in the following way. The statistics professor selects four students at random whose average grade before statistics is 95–100. He then randomly assigns the students to one of the four classes. He repeats the process with students whose average is 90–95, 85–90, . . ., and 50–55. The final grades would be used to test for differences between the classes.

Any characteristics that are related to the experimental units are potential blocking criteria. For example, if the experimental units are people, we may block according to age, gender, income, work experience, intelligence, residence (country, county, or city), weight, or height. If the experimental unit is a factory and we're measuring number of units produced hourly, blocking criteria include workforce experience, age of the plant, and quality of suppliers.

14-4d Developing an Understanding of Statistical Concepts

As we explained previously, the randomized block experiment is an extension of the matched pairs experiment discussed in Section 13-3. In the matched pairs experiment, we simply remove the effect of the variation caused by differences between the experimental units. The effect of this removal is seen in the decrease in the value of the standard error (compared to the standard error in the test statistic produced from independent samples) and the increase in the value of the t-statistic. In the randomized block experiment of the analysis of variance, we actually measure the variation between the blocks by computing SSB. The sum of squares for error is reduced by SSB, making it easier to detect differences between the treatments. In addition, we can test to determine whether the blocks differ—a procedure we were unable to perform in the matched pairs experiment.

To illustrate, let's return to Examples 13.4 and 13.5, which were experiments to determine whether there was a difference in starting salaries offered to finance and marketing MBA majors. (In fact, we tested to determine whether finance majors draw higher salary offers than do marketing majors. However, the analysis of variance can test only for differences.) In Example 13.4 (independent samples), there was insufficient evidence to infer a difference between the two types of majors. In Example 13.5 (matched pairs experiment), there was enough evidence to infer a difference. As we pointed out in Section 13-3, matching by grade point average allowed the statistics practitioner to more easily discern a difference between the two types of majors. If we repeat Examples 13.4 and 13.5 using the analysis of variance, we come to the same conclusion. The Excel outputs are shown here.

EXCEL Data Analysis: Analysis of Variance for Example 13.4

	A	B	C	D	E	F	G
1	Anova: Single Factor						
2							
3	SUMMARY						
4	Groups	Count	Sum	Average	Variance		
5	Finance	25	1,640,595	65,624	360,433,294		
6	Marketing	25	1,510,570	60,423	262,228,559		
7							
8							
9	ANOVA						
10	Source of Variation	SS	df	MS	F	P-value	F crit
11	Between Groups	338,130,013	1	338,130,013	1.09	0.3026	4.04
12	Within Groups	14,943,884,470	48	311,330,926			
13							
14	Total	15,282,014,483	49				

EXCEL Data Analysis: Analysis of Variance for Example 13.5

	A	B	C	D	E	F	G
34	ANOVA						
35	Source of Variation	SS	df	MS	F	P-value	F crit
36	Rows	21,415,991,654	24	892,332,986	40.39	4.17E-14	1.98
37	Columns	320,617,035	1	320,617,035	14.51	0.0009	4.26
38	Error	530,174,605	24	22,090,609			
39							
40	Total	22,266,783,295	49				

In Example 13.4, we partition the total sum of squares [SS(Total) = 15,282,014,483] into two sources of variation: SST = 338,130,013 and SSE = 14,943,884,470. In Example 13.5, the total sum of squares is SS(Total) = 22,266,783,295, SST (sum of squares for majors) = 320,617,035, SSB (sum of squares for GPA) = 21,415,991,654, and SSE = 530,174,605. As you can see, the sums of squares for treatments are approximately equal (338,130,013 and 320,617,035). However, the two calculations differ in the sums of squares for error. SSE in Example 13.5 is much smaller than SSE in Example 13.4 because the randomized block experiment allows us to measure and remove the effect of the variation between MBA students with the same majors. The sum of squares for blocks (sum of squares for GPA groups) is 21,415,991,654, a statistic that measures how much variation exists between the salary offers within majors. As a result of removing this variation, SSE is small. Thus, we conclude in Example 13.5 that the salary offers differ between majors whereas there was not enough evidence in Example 13.4 to draw the same conclusion.

Notice that in both examples the t-statistic squared equals the F-statistic in Example 13.4, $t = 1.04$, which when squared equals 1.09, which is the F-statistic (rounded). In Example 13.5, $t = 3.81$, which when squared equals 14.51, the F-statistic for the test of the treatment means. Moreover, the p-values are also the same.

We now complete this section by listing the factors that we need to recognize to use this experiment of the analysis of variance.

> **Factors That Identify the Randomized Block of the Analysis of Variance**
>
> 1. **Problem objective:** Compare two or more populations
> 2. **Data type:** Interval
> 3. **Experimental design:** Blocked samples

EXERCISES

Developing an Understanding of Statistical Concepts

14.83 The following statistics were generated from a randomized block experiment with $k = 3$ and $b = 7$:

$$SST = 100 \quad SSB = 50 \quad SSE = 25$$

a. Test to determine whether the treatment means differ. (Use $\alpha = .05$.)
b. Test to determine whether the block means differ. (Use $\alpha = .05$.)

14.84 A randomized block experiment produced the following statistics:

$$k = 5 \quad b = 12 \quad SST = 1,500 \quad SSB = 1,000 \quad SS(Total) = 3,500$$

a. Test to determine whether the treatment means differ. (Use $\alpha = .01$.)
b. Test to determine whether the block means differ. (Use $\alpha = .01$.)

14.85 Suppose the following statistics were calculated from data gathered from a randomized block experiment with $k = 4$ and $b = 10$:

$$SS(Total) = 1,210 \quad SST = 275 \quad SSB = 625$$

a. Can we conclude from these statistics that the treatment means differ? (Use $\alpha = .01$.)
b. Can we conclude from these statistics that the block means differ? (Use $\alpha = .01$.)

14.86 A randomized block experiment produced the following statistics.

$$k = 3 \quad b = 8 \quad SST = 1,500 \quad SS(Total) = 3,500$$

a. Test at the 5% significance level to determine whether the treatment means differ given that $SSB = 500$.
b. Repeat Part a with $SSB = 1,000$.
c. Repeat Part a with $SSB = 1,500$.
d. Describe what happens to the test statistic as SSB increases.

14.87 Xr14-87 a. Assuming that the data shown here were generated from a randomized block experiment calculate SS(Total), SST, SSB, and SSE.
b. Assuming that the data below were generated from a one-way (independent samples) experiment calculate SS(Total), SST, and SSE.
c. Why does SS(Total) remain the same for both experimental designs?
d. Why does SST remain the same for both experimental designs?
e. Why does SSB + SSE in Part a equal SSE in Part b?

	Treatment	
1	**2**	**3**
7	12	8
10	8	9
12	16	13
9	13	6
12	10	11

14.88 a. Calculate SS(Total), SST, SSB, and SSE, assuming that the accompanying data were generated from a randomized block experiment.
b. Calculate SS(Total), SST, and SSE, assuming that the data below were generated from a one-way (independent samples) experiment.
c. Explain why SS(Total) remains the same for both experimental designs.
d. Explain why SST remains the same for both experimental designs.
e. Explain why SSB + SSE in Part a equals SSE in Part b.

	Treatment		
1	**2**	**3**	**4**
6	5	4	4
8	5	5	6
7	6	5	6

Applications

14.89 Xr14-89 As an experiment to understand measurement error, a statistics professor asks four students to measure the height of the professor, a male student, and a female student. The differences (in centimeters) between the correct dimension and the ones produced by the students are listed here. Can we infer that there are differences in the errors between the subjects being measured? (Use $\alpha = .05$.)

	Errors in Measuring Heights of		
Student	Professor	Male Student	Female Student
1	1.4	1.5	1.3
2	3.1	2.6	2.4
3	2.8	2.1	1.5
4	3.4	3.6	2.9

14.90 Xr14-90 How well do diets work? In a preliminary study, 20 people who were more than 50 pounds overweight were recruited to compare four diets. The people were matched by age. The oldest four became block 1, the next oldest four became block 2, and so on. The number of pounds that each person lost is listed in the following table. Can we infer at the 1% significance level that there are differences between the four diets?

		Diet		
Block	1	2	3	4
1	5	2	6	8
2	4	7	8	10
3	6	12	9	2
4	7	11	16	7
5	9	8	15	14

The following exercises require the use of a computer and software. The answers may be calculated manually. See Appendix A for the sample statistics. **Use a 5% significance level, unless specified otherwise.**

14.91 Xr14-91 In recent years, lack of confidence in the Postal Service has led many companies to send all of their correspondence by private courier. A large company is in the process of selecting one of three possible couriers to act as its sole delivery method. To help in making the decision, an experiment was performed whereby letters were sent using each of the three couriers at 12 different times of the day to a delivery point across town. The number of minutes required for delivery was recorded.
   a. Can we conclude that there are differences in delivery times between the three couriers?
   b. Did the statistics practitioner choose the correct design? Explain.

14.92 Xr14-92 Refer to Exercise 14.14. Despite failing to show that differences in the three types of fertilizer exist, the scientist continued to believe that there were differences, and that the differences were masked by the variation between the plots of land. Accordingly, he conducted another experiment. In the second experiment he found 20 three-acre plots of land scattered across the county. He divided each into three plots and applied the three types of fertilizer on each of the one-acre plots. The crop yields were recorded.
   a. Can the scientist infer that there are differences between the three types of fertilizer?
   b. What do these test results reveal about the variation between the plots?

14.93 Xr14-93 A recruiter for a computer company would like to determine whether there are differences in sales ability between business, arts, and science graduates. She takes a random sample of 20 business graduates who have been working for the company for the past 2 years. Each is then matched with an arts graduate and a science graduate with similar educational and working experience. The commission earned by each (in $1,000s) in the last year was recorded.
   a. Is there sufficient evidence to allow the recruiter to conclude that there are differences in sales ability between the holders of the three types of degrees?

   b. Conduct a test to determine whether an independent samples design would have been a better choice.
   c. What are the required conditions for the test in Part a?
   d. Are the required conditions satisfied?

14.94 Xr14-94 Exercise 14.10 described an experiment that involved comparing the completion times associated with four different income tax forms. Suppose the experiment is redone in the following way. Thirty people are asked to fill out all four forms. The completion times (in minutes) are recorded.
   a. Is there sufficient evidence at the 1% significance level to infer that differences in the completion times exist between the four forms?
   b. Comment on the suitability of this experimental design in this problem.

14.95 Xr14-95 The advertising revenues commanded by a radio station depend on the number of listeners it has. The manager of a station that plays mostly hard rock music wants to learn more about its listeners—mostly teenagers and young adults. In particular, he wants to know whether the amount of time they spend listening to radio music varies by the day of the week. If the manager discovers that the mean time per day is about the same, he will schedule the most popular music evenly throughout the week. Otherwise, the top hits will be played mostly on the days that attract the greatest audience. An opinion survey company is hired, and it randomly selects 200 teenagers and asks them to record the amount of time spent listening to music on the radio for each day of the previous week. What can the manager conclude from these data?

14.96 Xr14-96 Do medical specialists differ in the amount of time they devote to patient care? To answer this question a statistics practitioner organized a study. The numbers of hours of patient care per week were recorded for five specialists. The experimental design was randomized blocks. The physicians were blocked by age.
   a. Can we infer that there are differences in the amount of patient care between medical specialties?
   b. Can we infer that blocking by age was appropriate?

Source: Adapted from the *Statistical Abstract of the United States,* 2000, Table 190.

14.97 Xr14-97 Refer to Exercise 14.9. Another study was conducted in the following way. Students from each of the high schools who were admitted to the business program were matched according to their high school averages. The average grades in the first year were recorded. Can the university admissions officer conclude that there are differences in grading standards between the four high schools?

GENERAL SOCIAL SURVEY EXERCISES

Excel users should note that rows containing empty cells must be removed.

14.98 <u>GSS2014*</u> Is there sufficient evidence to conclude that there are differences in the years of education

between American adults and their fathers and mothers (EDUC, PAEDUC, MAEDUC)?

14.99 <u>GSS2012*</u> Repeat Exercise 14.98 for the 2012 General Social Survey.

14-5 / TWO-FACTOR ANALYSIS OF VARIANCE

In Section 14-1, we addressed problems where the data were generated from single-factor experiments. In Example 14.1, the treatments were the four age categories. Thus, there were four levels of a single factor. In this section, we address the problem where the experiment features two factors. The general term for such data-gathering procedures is **factorial experiment**. In factorial experiments, we can examine the effect on the response variable of two or more factors, although in this book we address the problem of only two factors. We can use the analysis of variance to determine whether the levels of each factor are different from one another.

We will present the technique for fixed effects only. That means we will address problems where all the levels of the factors are included in the experiment. As was the case with the randomized block design, calculating the test statistic in this type of experiment is quite time consuming. As a result, we will use Excel to produce our statistics.

EXAMPLE 14.4*

DATA
Xm14-04

Comparing the Lifetime Number of Jobs by Educational Level

One measure of the health of a nation's economy is how quickly it creates jobs. One aspect of this issue is the number of jobs individuals hold. As part of a study on job tenure, a survey was conducted in which Americans aged between 37 and 45 were asked how many jobs they have held in their lifetimes. Also recorded were gender and educational attainment. The categories are

Less than high school (E1)

High school (E2)

Some college/university but no degree (E3)

At least one university degree (E4)

The data are shown for each of the eight categories of gender and education. Can we infer that differences exist between genders and educational levels?

Male E1	Male E2	Male E3	Male E4	Female E1	Female E2	Female E3	Female E4
10	12	15	8	7	7	5	7
9	11	8	9	13	12	13	9
12	9	7	5	14	6	12	3
16	14	7	11	6	15	3	7
14	12	7	13	11	10	13	9

*Adapted from the *Statistical Abstract of the United States, 2006*, Table 598.

Male E1	Male E2	Male E3	Male E4	Female E1	Female E2	Female E3	Female E4
17	16	9	8	14	13	11	6
13	10	14	7	13	9	15	10
9	10	15	11	11	15	5	15
11	5	11	10	14	12	9	4
15	11	13	8	12	13	8	11

SOLUTION:

IDENTIFY

We begin by treating this example as a one-way analysis of variance. Notice that there are eight treatments. However, the treatments are defined by two different factors. One factor is gender, which has two levels. The second factor is educational attainment, which has four levels.

We can proceed to solve this problem in the same way we did in Section 14-1: We test the following hypotheses.

H_0: $\mu_1 = \mu_2 = \mu_3 = \mu_4 = \mu_5 = \mu_6 = \mu_7 = \mu_8$
H_1:   At least two means differ

COMPUTE

EXCEL Data Analysis

	A	B	C	D	E	F	G
1	Anova: Single Factor						
15	ANOVA						
16	Source of Variation	SS	df	MS	F	P-value	F crit
17	Between Groups	153.35	7	21.91	2.17	0.0467	2.14
18	Within Groups	726.2	72	10.09			
19							
20	Total	879.55	79				

INTERPRET

The value of the test statistic is $F = 2.17$ with a p-value of .0467. We conclude that there are differences in the number of jobs between the eight treatments.

This statistical result raises more questions—namely, can we conclude that the differences in the mean number of jobs are caused by differences between males and females? Or are they caused by differences between educational levels? Or, perhaps, are there combinations, called **interactions**, of gender and education that result in especially high or low numbers? To show how we test for each type of difference, we need to develop some terminology.

A **complete factorial experiment** is an experiment in which the data for all possible combinations of the levels of the factors are gathered. That means that in Example 14.4

we measured the number of jobs for all eight combinations. This experiment is called a complete 2 × 4 factorial experiment.

In general, we will refer to one of the factors as factor A (arbitrarily chosen). The number of levels of this factor will be denoted by a. The other factor is called factor B, and its number of levels is denoted by b. This terminology becomes clearer when we present the data from Example 14.4 in another format. Table 14.6 depicts the layout for a *two-way classification*, which is another name for the complete factorial

TABLE **14.6** Two-Way Classification for Example 14.4

	MALE	FEMALE
Less than high school	10	7
	9	13
	12	14
	16	6
	14	11
	17	14
	13	13
	9	11
	11	14
	15	12
High school	12	7
	11	12
	9	6
	14	15
	12	10
	16	13
	10	9
	10	15
	5	12
	11	13
Less than bachelor's degree	15	5
	8	13
	7	12
	7	3
	7	13
	9	11
	14	15
	15	5
	11	9
	13	8
At least one bachelor's degree	8	7
	9	9
	5	3
	11	7
	13	9
	8	6
	7	10
	11	15
	10	4
	8	11

experiment. The number of observations for each combination is called a **replicate**. The number of replicates is denoted by r. In this book, we address only problems in which the number of replicates is the same for each treatment. Such a design is called **balanced**.

Thus, we use a complete factorial experiment where the number of treatments is ab with r replicates per treatment. In Example 14.4, $a = 2$, $b = 4$, and $r = 10$. As a result, we have 10 observations for each of the eight treatments.

If you examine the ANOVA table, you can see that the total variation is SS(Total) = 879.55, the sum of squares for treatments is SST = 153.35, and the sum of squares for error is SSE = 726.20. The variation caused by the treatments is measured by SST. To determine whether the differences result from factor A, factor B, or some interaction between the two factors, we need to partition SST into three sources. These are SS(A), SS(B), and SS(AB).

For those whose mathematical confidence is high, we have provided an explanation of the notation as well as the definitions of the sums of squares. Learning how the sums of squares are calculated is useful but hardly essential to your ability to conduct the tests. Uninterested readers should jump to the box on page 562 where we describe the individual F-tests.

14-4a How the Sums of Squares for Factors A and B and Interaction are Computed

To help you understand the formulas, we will use the following notation:

$$x_{ijk} = k\text{th observation in the } ij\text{th treatment}$$

$$\bar{x}[AB]_{ij} = \text{Mean of the response variable in the } ij\text{th treatment (mean of the treatment when the factor A level is } i \text{ and the factor B level is } j)$$

$$\bar{x}[A]_i = \text{Mean of the observations when the factor A level is } i$$

$$\bar{x}[B]_j = \text{Mean of the observations when the factor B level is } j$$

$$\bar{\bar{x}} = \text{Mean of all the observations}$$

$$a = \text{Number of factor A levels}$$

$$b = \text{Number of factor B levels}$$

$$r = \text{Number of replicates}$$

In this notation, $\bar{x}[AB]_{11}$ is the mean of the responses for factor A level 1 and factor B level 1. The mean of the responses for factor A level 1 is $\bar{x}[A]_1$. The mean of the responses for factor B level 1 is $\bar{x}[B]_1$.

Table 14.7 describes the notation for the two-factor analysis of variance.

TABLE **14.7** Notation for Two-Factor Analysis of Variance

Factor B	Factor A				
	1	2	...	a	
1	x_{111} x_{112} ⋮ x_{11r} $\bar{x}[AB]_{11}$	x_{211} x_{212} ⋮ x_{21r} $\bar{x}[AB]_{21}$		x_{a11} x_{a12} ⋮ x_{a1r} $\bar{x}[AB]_{a1}$	$\bar{x}[B]_1$
2	x_{121} x_{122} ⋮ x_{12r} $\bar{x}[AB]_{12}$	x_{221} x_{222} ⋮ x_{22r} $\bar{x}[AB]_{22}$		x_{a21} x_{a22} ⋮ x_{a2r} $\bar{x}[AB]_{a2}$	$\bar{x}[B]_2$
⋮					
b	x_{1b1} x_{1b2} ⋮ x_{1br} $\bar{x}[AB]_{1b}$	x_{2b1} x_{2b2} ⋮ x_{2br} $\bar{x}[AB]_{2b}$		x_{ab1} x_{ab2} ⋮ x_{abr} $\bar{x}[AB]_{ab}$	$\bar{x}[B]_b$
	$\bar{x}[A]_1$	$\bar{x}[A]_2$		$\bar{x}[A]_a$	$\bar{\bar{x}}$

The sums of squares are defined as follows.

Sums of Squares in the Two-Factor Analysis of Variance

$$SS(\text{Total}) = \sum_{i=1}^{a} \sum_{j=1}^{b} \sum_{k=1}^{r} (x_{ijk} - \bar{\bar{x}})^2$$

$$SS(A) = rb \sum_{i=1}^{a} (\bar{x}[A]_i - \bar{\bar{x}})^2$$

$$SS(B) = ra \sum_{i=1}^{b} (\bar{x}[B]_j - \bar{\bar{x}})^2$$

$$SS(AB) = r \sum_{i=1}^{a} \sum_{j=1}^{b} (\bar{x}[AB]_{ij} - \bar{x}[A]_i - \bar{x}[B]_j + \bar{\bar{x}})^2$$

$$SSE = \sum_{i=1}^{a} \sum_{j=1}^{b} \sum_{k=1}^{r} (x_{ijk} - \bar{x}[AB]_{ij})^2$$

To compute SS(A), we calculate the sum of the squared differences between the factor A level means, which are denoted $\bar{x}[A]_i$, and the grand mean, $\bar{\bar{x}}$. The sum of squares for factor B, SS(B), is defined similarly. The interaction sum of squares, SS(AB), is calculated by taking each treatment mean (a treatment consists of a combination of a level of factor A and a level of factor B), subtracting the factor A level mean, subtracting the factor B level mean, adding the grand mean, squaring this quantity, and adding.

The sum of squares for error, SSE, is calculated by subtracting the treatment means from the observations, squaring, and adding.

To test for each possibility, we conduct several F-tests similar to the one performed in Section 14-1. Figure 14.4 illustrates the partitioning of the total sum of squares that leads to the F-tests. We've included in this figure the partitioning used in the one-way study. When the one-way analysis of variance allows us to infer that differences between the treatment means exist, we continue our analysis by partitioning the treatment sum of squares into three sources of variation. The first is sum of squares for factor A, which we label SS(A), which measures the variation between the levels of factor A. Its degrees of freedom are $a - 1$. The second is the sum of squares for factor B, whose degrees of freedom are $b - 1$. SS(B) is the variation between the levels of factor B. The interaction sum of squares is labeled SS(AB), which is a measure of the amount of variation between the combinations of factors A and B; its degrees of freedom are $(a - 1) \times (b - 1)$. The sum of squares for error is SSE, and its degrees of freedom are $n - ab$. (Recall that n is the total sample size, which in this experiment is $n = abr$.) Notice that SSE and its number of degrees of freedom are identical in both partitions. As in the previous experiment, SSE is the variation within the treatments.

FIGURE 14.4 **Partitioning SS(Total) in Single-Factor and Two-Factor Analysis of Variance**

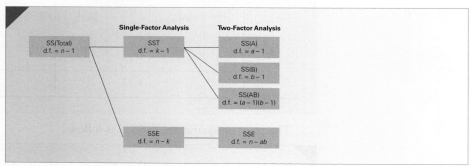

F-Tests Conducted in Two-Factor Analysis of Variance

Test for Differences between the Levels of Factor A

H_0: The means of the a levels of factor A are equal

H_1: At least two means differ

Test statistic: $F = \dfrac{\text{MS(A)}}{\text{MSE}}$

Test for Differences between the Levels of Factor B

H_0: The means of the b levels of factor B are equal

H_1: At least two means differ

Test statistic: $F = \dfrac{\text{MS(B)}}{\text{MSE}}$

Test for Interaction between Factors A and B

H_0: Factors A and B do not interact to affect the mean responses

H_1: Factors A and B do interact to affect the mean responses

Test statistic: $F = \dfrac{\text{MS(AB)}}{\text{MSE}}$

Required Conditions

1. The distribution of the response is normally distributed.
2. The variance for each treatment is identical.
3. The samples are independent.

As in the two previous experimental designs of the analysis of variance, we summarize the results in an ANOVA table. Table 14.8 depicts the general form of the table for the complete factorial experiment.

TABLE **14.8** ANOVA Table for the Two-Factor Experiment

SOURCE OF VARIATION	DEGREES OF FREEDOM	SUMS OF SQUARES	MEAN SQUARES	F-STATISTIC
Factor A	$a - 1$	SS(A)	$MS(A) = SS(A)/(a - 1)$	$F = MS(A)/MSE$
Factor B	$b - 1$	SS(B)	$MS(B) = SS(B)/(b - 1)$	$F = MS(B)/MSE$
Interaction	$(a - 1)(b - 1)$	SS(AB)	$MS(AB) = SS(AB)/[(a - 1)(b - 1)]$	$F = MS(AB)/MSE$
Error	$n - ab$	SSE	$MSE = SSE/(n - ab)$	
Total	$n - 1$	SS(Total)		

We'll illustrate the techniques using the data in Example 14.4.

EXCEL Data Analysis

	A	B	C	D	E	F	G
1	ANOVA						
2	Source of Variation	SS	df	MS	F	P-value	F crit
3	Sample	135.85	3	45.28	4.49	0.0060	2.7318
4	Columns	11.25	1	11.25	1.12	0.2944	3.9739
5	Interaction	6.25	3	2.08	0.21	0.8915	2.7318
6	Within	726.2	72	10.09			
7							
8	Total	879.55	79				

In the ANOVA table, **Sample** refers to factor B (educational level) and **Columns** refers to factor A (gender). Thus, MS(B) = 45.28, MS(A) = 11.25, MS(AB) = 2.08, and MSE = 10.09. The F-statistics are 4.49 (educational level), 1.12 (gender), and .21 (interaction).

INSTRUCTIONS

1. Type or import the data using the same format as Xm14-04 (tab Stacked A). (*Note:* You must label the rows and columns as we did.)
2. Click **Data, Data Analysis,** and **Anova: Two-Factor with Replication.**
3. Specify the **Input Range** (A1:C41). Type the number of replications in the **Rows per sample** box (10).
4. Specify a value for α (.05).

XLSTAT

	A	B	C	D	E	F
36	Type I Sum of Squares analysis (Jobs):					
37						
38	Source	DF	Sum of squares	Mean squares	F	Pr > F
39	Gender	1	11.25	11.25	1.12	0.2944
40	Education	3	135.85	45.28	4.49	0.0060
41	Gender*Education	3	6.25	2.08	0.21	0.8915

INSTRUCTIONS

1. Type or import the data in stacked format (Open Xm14-04) and click the **Stacked B** tab.
2. Click **XLSTAT, Modeling data**, and **ANOVA**.
3. In the **Quantitative** box type the input range (A1:A81). In the **X Explanatory variables** and **Qualitative** box type the input range (B1:C81).
4. Click **Options** and check **Interactions** and specify 2.
5. Click **Outputs** and select **Analysis of variance** and **Type I/II/III SS**. Click **OK**.
6. Under **Factors and Interactions** specify **All**. Click **OK**.

14-5b Test for Differences in Number of Jobs between Men and Women

H_0: The means of the two levels of factor A are equal

H_1: At least two means differ

Test statistic: $F = \dfrac{MS(A)}{MSE}$

Value of the test statistic: From the computer output, we have

$MS(A) = 11.25, MSE = 10.09$, and $F = 11.25/10.09 = 1.12$ (p-value = .2944)

There is no evidence at the 5% significance level to infer that differences in the number of jobs exist between men and women.

14-5c Test for Differences in Number of Jobs between Education Levels

H_0: The means of the four levels of factor B are equal

H_1: At least two means differ

Test statistic: $F = \dfrac{MS(B)}{MSE}$

Value of the test statistic: From the computer output, we find

$MS(B) = 45.28$ and $MSE = 10.09$. Thus, $F = 45.28/10.09 = 4.49$ (p-value = .0060).

There is sufficient evidence at the 5% significance level to infer that differences in the number of jobs exist between educational levels.

14-5d Test for Interaction between Factors A and B

H_0: Factors A and B do not interact to affect the mean number of jobs

H_1: Factors A and B do interact to affect the mean number of jobs

Test statistic: $F = \dfrac{\text{MS(AB)}}{\text{MSE}}$

Value of the test statistic: From the printouts,

MS(AB) = 2.08, MSE = 10.09, and $F = 2.08/10.09 = .21$ (p-value = .8915).

There is not enough evidence to conclude that there is an interaction between gender and education.

INTERPRET

Figure 14.5 is a graph of the mean responses for each of the eight treatments. As you can see, there are small (not significant) differences between males and females. There are significant differences between men and women with different educational backgrounds. Finally, there is no interaction.

FIGURE **14.5** **Mean Responses for Example 14.4**

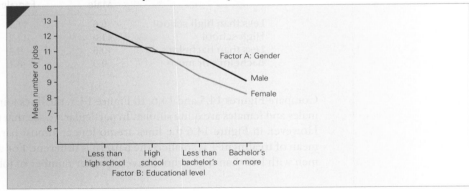

14-5e What Is Interaction?

EXAMPLE 14.5

PART 2
Xm14-05

Comparing Lifetime Number of Jobs by Education Level

To more fully understand interaction we have changed the sample associated with men who have not finished high school (Treatment 1). We subtracted 6 from the original numbers so that the data in treatment 1 is

4, 3, 6, 10, 8, 11, 7, 3, 5, 9

(The mean is 6.6.)

The new data are stored in Xm14-05 tab: Stacked A (Excel format) and Xm14-05 tab: Stacked B (XLSTAT format).

SOLUTION:

EXCEL Data Analysis

	A	B	C	D	E	F	G
34	ANOVA						
35	Source of Variation	SS	df	MS	F	P-value	F crit
36	Sample	75.85	3	25.28	2.51	0.0657	2.73
37	Columns	11.25	1	11.25	1.12	0.2944	3.97
38	Interaction	120.25	3	40.08	3.97	0.0112	2.73
39	Within	726.20	72	10.09			
40							
41	Total	933.55	79				

INTERPRET

In this example there is not enough evidence (at the 5% significance level) to infer that there are differences between men and women and between the educational levels. However, there is sufficient evidence to conclude that there is interaction between gender and education.

	Male	Female
Less than high school	6.6	11.5
High school	11.0	11.2
Less than bachelor's	10.6	9.4
Bachelor's or more	9.0	8.1

Compare Figures 14.5 and 14.6. In Figure 14.5, the lines joining the response means for males and females are quite similar. In particular we see that the lines are almost parallel. However, in Figure 14.6 the lines are no longer almost parallel. It is apparent that the mean of treatment 1 is smaller; the pattern is different. For whatever reason, in this case men with less than high school have a smaller number of jobs.

FIGURE **14.6** **Mean Responses for Example 14.4a**

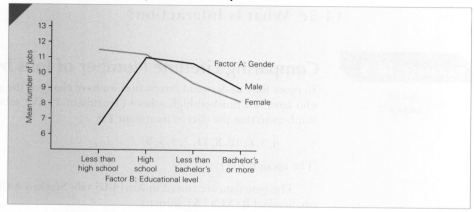

14-5f Conducting the Analysis of Variance for the Complete Factorial Experiment

In addressing the problem outlined in Example 14.4, we began by conducting a one-way analysis of variance to determine whether differences existed between the eight treatment means. This was done primarily for pedagogical reasons to enable you to see that when the treatment means differ, we need to analyze the reasons for the differences. However, in practice, we generally do not conduct this test in the complete factorial experiment (although it should be noted that some statistics practitioners prefer this "two-stage" strategy). We recommend that you proceed directly to the two-factor analysis of variance.

In the two versions of Example 14.4, we conducted the tests of each factor and then the test for interaction.

However, if there is evidence of interaction, the tests of the factors are irrelevant. There may or may not be differences between the levels of factor A and the levels of factor B. Accordingly, we change the order of conducting the F-tests.

Order of Testing in the Two-Factor Analysis of Variance

Test for interaction first. If there is enough evidence to infer that there is interaction, do not conduct the other tests.

If there is not enough evidence to conclude that there is interaction, proceed to conduct the F-tests for factors A and B.

14-5g Developing an Understanding of Statistical Concepts

You may have noticed that there are similarities between the two-factor experiment and the randomized block experiment. In fact, when the number of replicates is one, the calculations are identical. This raises the question, What is the difference between a factor in a multifactor study and a block in a randomized block experiment? In general, the difference between the two experimental designs is that in the randomized block experiment, blocking is performed specifically to reduce variation, whereas in the two-factor model the effect of the factors on the response variable is of interest to the statistics practitioner. The criteria that define the blocks are always characteristics of the experimental units. Consequently, factors that are characteristics of the experimental units will be treated not as factors in a multifactor study, but as blocks in a randomized block experiment.

Let's review how we recognize the need to use the procedure described in this section.

Factors That Identify the Independent Samples Two-Factor Analysis of Variance
1. **Problem objective**: Compare two or more populations (populations are defined as the combinations of the levels of two factors)
2. **Data type**: Interval
3. **Experimental design**: Independent samples

EXERCISES

14.100 A two-factor analysis of variance experiment was performed with $a = 3$, $b = 4$, and $r = 20$. The following sums of squares were computed:

SS(Total) = 42,450 SS(A) = 1,560
SS(B) = 2,880 SS(AB) = 7,605

Conduct whatever test you deem necessary at the 1% significance level to determine whether there are differences between the levels of factor A, the levels of factor B, or interaction between factors A and B.

14.101 A statistics practitioner conducted a two-factor analysis of variance experiment with $a = 4$, $b = 3$, and $r = 8$. The sums of squares are listed here:

SS(Total) = 9420 SS(A) = 203 SS(B) = 859
SS(AB) = 513

a. Test at the 5% significance level to determine whether factors A and B interact.
b. Test at the 5% significance level to determine whether differences exist between the levels of factor A.
c. Test at the 5% significance level to determine whether differences exist between the levels of factor B.

14.102 <u>Xr14-102</u> The following data were generated from a 2×2 factorial experiment with 3 replicates:

	Factor B	
Factor A	**1**	**2**
1	6	12
	9	10
	7	11
2	9	15
	10	14
	5	10

a. Test at the 5% significance level to determine whether factors A and B interact.
b. Test at the 5% significance level to determine whether differences exist between the levels of factor A.
c. Test at the 5% significance level to determine whether differences exist between the levels of factor B.

14.103 <u>Xr14-103</u> The data shown here were taken from a 2×3 factorial experiment with 4 replicates:

	Factor B	
Factor A	**1**	**2**
1	23	20
	18	17
	17	16
	20	19
2	27	29
	23	23
	20	27
	28	25
3	23	27
	21	19
	24	20
	16	22

a. Test at the 5% significance level to determine whether factors A and B interact.
b. Test at the 5% significance level to determine whether differences exist between the levels of factor A.
c. Test at the 5% significance level to determine whether differences exist between the levels of factor B.

14.104 <u>Xr14-104</u> Refer to Example 14.4. We've revised the data by adding 2 to each of the numbers of the men. What do these data tell you?

14.105 <u>Xr14-105</u> Refer to Example 14.4. We've altered the data by subtracting 4 from the numbers of treatment 8. What do these data tell you?

Applications

The following exercises require the use of a computer and software.

14.106 <u>Xr14-106</u> Refer to Exercise 14.10. Suppose that the experiment is redone in the following way. Thirty taxpayers fill out each of the four forms. However, 10 taxpayers in each group are in the lowest income bracket, 10 are in the next income bracket, and the remaining 10 are in the highest bracket. The amount of time needed to complete the returns is recorded.

Column 1: Group number
Column 2: Times to complete form 1 (first 10 rows = low income, next 10 rows = next income bracket, and last 10 rows = highest bracket)
Column 3: Times to complete form 2 (same format as column 2)
Column 4: Times to complete form 3 (same format as column 2)
Column 5: Times to complete form 4 (same format as column 2)

a. How many treatments are there in this experiment?
b. How many factors are there? What are they?
c. What are the levels of each factor?
d. Is there evidence at the 5% significance level of interaction between the two factors?
e. Can we conclude at the 5% significance level that differences exist between the four forms?
f. Can we conclude at the 5% significance level that taxpayers in different brackets require different amounts of time to complete their tax forms?

14.107 Xr14-107 Detergent manufacturers frequently make claims about the effectiveness of their products. A consumer-protection service decided to test the five best selling brands of detergent, where each manufacturer claims that its product produces the "whitest whites" in all water temperatures. The experiment was conducted in the following way. One hundred fifty white sheets were equally soiled. Thirty sheets were washed in each brand—l0 with cold water, 10 with warm water, and 10 with hot water. After washing, the "whiteness" scores for each sheet were measured with laser equipment.

> Column 1: Water temperature code
> Column 2: Scores for detergent 1 (first 10 rows = cold water, middle 10 rows = warm, and last 10 rows = hot)
> Column 2: Scores for detergent 2 (same format as column 2)
> Column 3: Scores for detergent 3 (same format as column 2)
> Column 4: Scores for detergent 4 (same format as column 2)
> Column 5: Scores for detergent 5 (same format as column 2)

a. What are the factors in this experiment?
b. What is the response variable?
c. Identify the levels of each factor.
d. Perform a statistic analysis using a 5% significance level to determine whether there is sufficient statistical evidence to infer that there are differences in whiteness scores between the five detergents, differences in whiteness scores between the three water temperatures, or interaction between detergents and temperatures.

14.108 Xr14-108 Headaches are one of the most common, but least understood, ailments. Most people get headaches several times per month; over-the-counter medication is usually sufficient to eliminate their pain. However, for a significant proportion of people, headaches are debilitating and make their lives almost unbearable. Many such people have investigated a wide spectrum of possible treatments, including narcotic drugs, hypnosis, bio-feedback, and acupuncture, with little or no success. In the last few years, a promising new treatment has been developed. Simply described, the treatment involves a series of injections of a local anesthetic to the occipital nerve (located in the back of the neck). The current treatment procedure is to schedule the injections once a week for 4 weeks. However, it has been suggested that another procedure may be better—one that features one injection every other day for a total of four injections. Additionally, some physicians recommend other combinations of drugs that may increase the effectiveness of the injections. To analyze the problem, an experiment was organized. It was decided to test for a difference between the two schedules of injection and to determine whether there are differences between four drug mixtures. Because of the possibility of an interaction between the schedule and the drug, a complete factorial experiment was chosen. Five headache patients were randomly selected for each combination of schedule and drug. Forty patients were treated and each was asked to report the frequency, duration, and severity of his or her headache prior to treatment and for the 30 days following the last injection. An index ranging from 0 to 100 was constructed for each patient, where 0 indicates no headache pain and 100 specifies the worst headache pain. The improvement in the headache index for each patient was recorded and reproduced in the accompanying table. (A negative value indicates a worsening condition.) (The author is grateful to Dr. Lorne Greenspan for his help in writing this example.)

a. What are the factors in this experiment?
b. What is the response variable?
c. Identify the levels of each factor.
d. Analyze the data and conduct whichever tests you deem necessary at the 5% significance level to determine whether there is sufficient statistical evidence to infer that there are differences in the improvement in the headache index between the two schedules, differences in the improvement in the headache index between the four drug mixtures, or interaction between schedules and drug mixtures.

Improvement in Headache Index

Schedule	Drug Mixture			
	1	2	3	4
One Injection	17	24	14	10
Every Week	6	15	9	−1
(Four Weeks)	10	10	12	0
	12	16	0	3
	14	14	6	−1
One Injection	18	−2	20	−2
Every Two Days	9	0	16	7
(Four Days)	17	17	12	10
	21	2	17	6
	15	6	18	7

14.109 Xr14-109 Most college instructors prefer to have their students participate actively in class. Ideally, students will ask their professor questions and answer their professor's questions, making the class-room experience more interesting and useful. Many professors seek ways to encourage their students to participate in class. A statistics professor at a community college in upper New York state believes that there are a number of external factors that affect student participation. He believes that the time of day and the configuration of seats are two such factors. Consequently, he organized the following experiment. Six classes of about 60 students each were scheduled for one semester. Two classes were scheduled at 9:00 A.M., two at 1:00 P.M., and two at 4:00 P.M. At each of the three times, one of the classes was assigned to a room where the seats were arranged in rows of 10 seats. The other class was a U-shaped, tiered room, where students not only face the instructor, but face their fellow students as well. In each of the six classrooms, over five days, student participation was measured by counting the number of times students asked and answered questions. These data are displayed in the accompanying table.

a. How many factors are there in this experiment? What are they?
b. What is the response variable?
c. Identify the levels of each factor.
d. What conclusions can the professor draw from these data?

Class Configuration	Time 9:00 A.M.	1:00 P.M.	4:00 P.M.
Rows	10	9	7
	7	12	12
	9	12	9
	6	14	20
	8	8	7
U-Shape	15	4	7
	18	4	4
	11	7	9
	13	4	8
	13	6	7

14-6 (OPTIONAL) APPLICATIONS IN OPERATIONS MANAGEMENT: FINDING AND REDUCING VARIATION

In the introduction to Example 12.3, we pointed out that variation in the size, weight, or volume of a product's components causes the product to fail or not function properly. Unfortunately, it is impossible to eliminate all variation. Designers of products and the processes that make the products understand this phenomenon. Consequently, when they specify the length, weight, or some other measurable characteristic of the product, they allow for some variation, which is called the *tolerance*. For example, the diameters of the piston rings of a car are supposed to be .826 millimeter (mm) with a tolerance of .006 mm; that is, the product will function provided that the diameter is between .826 − .006 = .820 and .826 + .006 = .832 mm. These quantities are called the *lower* and *upper specification limits* (LSL and USL), respectively.

Suppose that the diameter of the piston rings is actually a random variable that is normally distributed with a mean of .826 and a standard deviation of .003 mm. We can compute the probability that a piston ring's diameter is between the specification limits. Thus,

$$P(.820 < X < .832) = P\left(\frac{.820 - .826}{.003} < \frac{X - \mu}{\sigma} < \frac{.832 - .826}{.003}\right)$$
$$= P(-2.0 < Z < 2.0)$$
$$= .9772 - .0228$$
$$= .9544$$

The probability that the diameter does not meet specifications is $1 - .9544 = .0456$. This probability is a measure of the process capability.

If we can decrease the standard deviation, a greater proportion of piston rings will have diameters that meet specification. Suppose that the operations manager has decreased the diameter's standard deviation to .002. The proportion of piston rings that do not meet specifications is .0026. When the probabilities are quite low, we express the probabilities as the number of defective units per million or per billion. Thus, if the standard deviation is .002, the number of defective piston rings is expected to be 2,600 per million. The goal of many firms is to reduce the standard deviation so that the lower specification and upper specification limits are at least 6 standard deviations away from the mean. If the standard deviation is .001, the proportion of nonconforming piston rings is $1 - P(-6 < Z < 6)$, which is 2 per billion. (Incidentally, this figure is often erroneously quoted as 3.4 per million.) The goal is called *six sigma*. Figure 14.7 depicts the proportion of conforming and nonconforming piston rings for $\sigma = .003, .002$, and .001.

Another way to measure how well the process works is the process capability index, denoted by C_p, *which is defined as*

$$C_p = \frac{USL - LSL}{6\sigma}$$

Thus, in the illustration USL = .832 and LSL = .820. If the standard deviation is .002 then

$$C_p = \frac{USL - LSL}{6\sigma} = \frac{.832 - .820}{6(.002)} = 1.0$$

The larger the process capability index, the more capable is the process in meeting specifications. A value of 1.0 describes a production process where the specification limits are equal to 3 standard deviations above and below the mean. A process capability index of 2.0 means that the upper and lower limits are 6 standard deviations above and below the mean. This is the goal for many firms.

FIGURE **14.7** **Proportion of Conforming and Nonconforming Piston Rings**

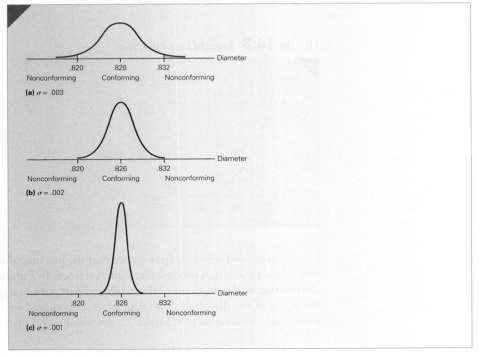

In practice, the standard deviation must be estimated from the data. We will address this issue again in Chapter 21.

14-6a Taguchi Loss Function

Historically, operations managers applied the "goalpost" philosophy, a name derived from the game of football. If the ball is kicked *anywhere* between the goalposts, the kick is equally as successful as one that is in the center of the goalposts. Under this philosophy, a piston ring that has a diameter of .821 works as well as one that is exactly .826. In other words, the company sustains a loss only when the product falls outside the goalposts. Products that lie between the goalposts suffer no financial loss. For many firms, this philosophy has now been replaced by the Taguchi loss function (named for Genichi Taguchi, a Japanese statistician whose ideas and techniques permeate any discussion of statistical applications in quality management).

Products whose length or weight fall within the tolerances of their specifications do not all function in exactly the same way. There is a difference between a product that barely falls between the goalposts and one that is in the exact center. The Taguchi loss function recognizes that any deviation from the target value results in a financial loss. In addition, the farther the product's variable is from the target value, the greater the loss. The piston ring described previously is specified to have a diameter of exactly .826 mm, an amount specified by the manufacturer to work at the optimum level. Any deviation will cause that part and perhaps other parts to wear out prematurely. Although customers will not know the reason for the problem, they will know that the unit had to be replaced. The greater the deviation, the more quickly the part will wear and need replacing. If the part is under warranty, the company will incur a loss in replacing it. If the warranty has expired, customers will have to pay to replace the unit, causing some degree of displeasure that may result in them buying another company's product in the future. In either case, the company loses money. Figure 14.8 depicts the loss function. As you can see, any deviation from the target value results in some loss, with large deviations resulting in larger losses.

FIGURE **14.8** Taguchi Loss Function

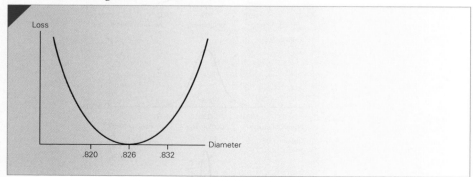

Management scientists have shown that the loss function can be expressed as a function of the production process mean and variance. In Figure 14.9 we describe a normal distribution of the diameter of the machined part with a target value of .826 mm. When the mean of the distribution is .826, any loss is caused by the variance. The statistical techniques introduced in Chapter 21 are usually employed to center the distribution on the target value. However, reducing the variance is considerably more difficult. To reduce variation, it is necessary to first find the sources of variation. We do so by conducting experiments. The principles are quite straightforward, drawing on the concepts developed in the previous section.

An important function of operations management is production design in which decisions are made about how a product is manufactured. The objective is to produce the highest quality product at a reasonable cost. This objective is achieved by choosing the machines, materials, methods, and "manpower" (personnel), the so-called 4 Ms. By altering some or all of these elements, the operations manager can alter the size, weight, or volume and, ultimately, the quality of the product.

FIGURE **14.9** **Taguchi Loss Function and the Distribution of Piston Rings**

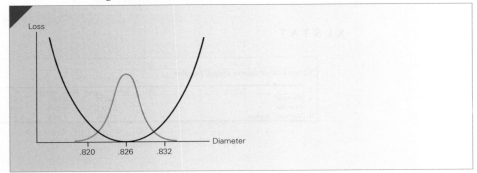

EXAMPLE 14.6

DATA
Xm14-06

Causes of Variation

A critical component in an aircraft engine is a steel rod that must be 41.387 cm long. The operations manager has noted that there has been some variation in the lengths. In some cases, the steel rods had to be discarded or reworked because they were either too short or too long. The operations manager believes that some of the variation is caused by the way the production process has been designed. Specifically, he believes that the rods vary from machine to machine and from operator to operator. To help unravel the truth, he organizes an experiment. Each of the three operators produces five rods on each of the four machines. The lengths are measured and recorded. Determine whether the machines or the operators (or both) are indeed sources of variation.

S O L U T I O N :

IDENTIFY

The response variable is the length of the rods. The two factors are the operators and the machines. There are three levels of operators and four levels of machines. The model we employ is the two-factor model with interaction. The computer output is shown here.

COMPUTE

EXCEL Data Analysis

	A	B	C	D	E	F	G
28	ANOVA						
29	Source of Variation	SS	df	MS	F	P-value	F crit
30	Sample	0.01513	2	0.00757	6.98	0.0022	3.19
31	Columns	0.00336	3	0.00112	1.04	0.3856	2.80
32	Interaction	0.00465	6	0.00077	0.71	0.6394	2.29
33	Within	0.05199	48	0.00108			
34							
35	Total	0.07514	59				

XLSTAT

	A	B	C	D	E	F
1	Type I Sum of Squares analysis (Lengths):					
2						
3	Source	DF	Sum of squares	Mean squares	F	Pr > F
4	Machine	3	0.0034	0.0011	1.04	0.3856
5	Operator	2	0.0151	0.0076	6.98	0.0022
6	Machine*Operator	6	0.0046	0.0008	0.71	0.6394

INTERPRET

The test for interaction yields $F = .71$ and a p-value of .6394. There is not enough evidence to infer that the two factors interact. The F-statistic for the operator factor (Sample) is 6.98 (p-value $= .0022$). The F-statistic for the machine factor (Columns) is 1.04 (p-value $= .3856$). We conclude that there are differences only between the levels of the operators. Thus, the only source of variation here is the different operators. The operations manager can now focus on reducing or eliminating this variation. For example, the manager may use only one operator in the future or investigate why the operators differ.

The causes of variation example that opened this chapter illustrate this strategy. Because we have limited our discussion to the two-factor model, the example features this experimental design. It should be understood, however, that more complicated models are needed to fully investigate sources of variation.

14-6b   Design of Experiments and Taguchi Methods

In the example just discussed, the experiment used only two factors. In practice, there are frequently many more factors. The problem is that the total number of treatments or combinations can be quite high, making any experimentation both time consuming and expensive. For example, if there are 10 factors each with 2 levels, the number of treatments is $2^{10} = 1,024$. If we measure each treatment with 10 replicates, the number of observations, 10,240, makes this experiment prohibitive. Fortunately, it is possible to reduce this number considerably. Through the use of *orthogonal arrays*, we can conduct *fractional factorial experiments* that can produce useful results at a small fraction of the cost. The experimental designs and statistical analyses are beyond the level of this book. Interested readers can find a variety of books at different levels of mathematical and statistical sophistication to learn more about this application.

EXERCISES

Applications

The following exercises require the use of a computer and software. **Use a 5% significance level.**

14.110 Xr14-110 The headrests on a car's front seats are designed to protect the driver and front-seat passenger from whiplash when the car is hit from behind. The frame of the headrest is made from metal rods. A machine is used to bend the rod into a U-shape exactly 440 millimeters wide. The width is critical; too wide or too narrow and it won't fit into the holes drilled into the car seat frame. The company has experimented with several different metal alloys in the hope of finding a material that will result in more headrest frames that fit. Another possible source of variation is the machines used. To learn more about the process the operations manager conducts an experiment. Both of the machines are used to produce 10 headrests from each of the five metal alloys now being used. Each frame is measured and the data (in millimeters) are recorded using the format shown here. Analyze the data to determine whether the alloys, machines, or both are sources of variation.

> Column 1: Machine 1, rows 1 to 10 alloy A, rows 11 to 20, alloy B
> Column 2: Machine 2, rows 1 to 10 alloy A, rows 11 to 20, alloy B

14.111 Xr14-111 A paint manufacturer is attempting to improve the process that fills the 1-gallon containers. The foreperson has suggested that the nozzle can be made from several different alloys. Furthermore, the way that the process "knows" when to stop the flow of paint can be accomplished in two ways: by setting a predetermined amount or by measuring the amount of paint already in the can. To determine what factors lead to variation, an experiment is conducted. For each of the four alloys that could be used to make the nozzles and the two measuring devices, five cans are filled. The amount of paint in each container is precisely measured. The data in liters were recorded in the following way:

> Column 1: Device 1, rows 1 to 5 alloy A, rows 6 to 10 alloy B, etc.
> Column 2: Device 2, rows 1 to 5 alloy A, rows 6 to 10 alloy B, etc.

Can we infer that the alloys, the measuring devices, or both are sources of variation?

14.112 Xr14-112 The marketing department of a firm that manufactures office furniture has ascertained that there is a growing market for a specialized desk that houses the various parts of a computer system. The operations manager is summoned to put together a plan that will produce high-quality desks at low cost. The characteristics of the desk have been dictated by the marketing department, which has specified the material that the desk will be made from and the machines used to produce the parts. However, there are three methods that can be utilized. Moreover, because of the complexity of the operation, the manager realizes that it is possible that different skill levels of the workers can yield different results. Accordingly, he organized an experiment. Workers from each of three skill levels were chosen. These groups were further divided into two subgroups. Each subgroup assembled the desks using methods A and B. The amount of time taken to assemble each of eight desks was recorded as follows. Columns 1 and 2 contain the times for methods A and B; rows 1 to 8, 9 to 16, and 17 to 24 store the times for the three skill levels. What can we infer from these data?

CHAPTER SUMMARY

The analysis of variance allows us to test for differences between populations when the data are interval. The analyses of the results of three different experimental designs were presented in this chapter. The one-way analysis of variance defines the populations on the basis of one factor. The second experimental design also defines the treatments on the basis of one factor. However, the randomized block design uses data gathered by observing the results of a matched or blocked experiment (two-way analysis of variance). The third design is the two-factor experiment wherein the treatments are defined as the combinations of the levels of two factors. All the analyses of variance are based on partitioning the total sum of squares into sources of variation from which the mean squares and F-statistics are computed.

In addition, we introduced three multiple comparison methods that allow us to determine which means differ in the one-way analysis of variance.

Finally, we described an important application in operations management that employs the analysis of variance.

IMPORTANT TERMS:

SYMBOLS:

Symbol	Pronounced	Represents
$\bar{\bar{x}}$	x double bar	Overall or grand mean
q		Studentized range
ω	Omega	Critical value of Tukey's multiple comparison method
$q_\alpha(k, \nu)$	q sub alpha k ν	Critical value of the Studentized range
n_g		Number of observations in each of k samples
$\bar{x}[T]_j$	x bar T sub j	Mean of the jth treatment
$\bar{x}[B]_i$	x bar B sub i	Mean of the ith block
$\bar{x}[AB]_{ij}$	x bar A B sub ij	Mean of the ijth treatment
$\bar{x}[A]_i$	x bar A sub i	Mean of the observations when the factor A level is i
$\bar{x}[B]_j$	x bar B sub j	Mean of the observations when the factor B level is j

FORMULAS:

One-way analysis of variance

$$SST = \sum_{j=1}^{k} n_j(\bar{x}_j - \bar{\bar{x}})^2$$

$$SSE = \sum_{j=1}^{k} \sum_{i=1}^{k} (x_{ij} - \bar{x}_j)^2$$

$$MST = \frac{SST}{k-1}$$

$$MST = \frac{SSE}{n-k}$$

$$F = \frac{MST}{MSE}$$

Least significant difference comparison method

$$LSD = t_{\alpha/2}\sqrt{MSE\left(\frac{1}{n_i} + \frac{1}{n_j}\right)}$$

Tukey's multiple comparison method

$$\omega = q_\alpha(k, \nu)\sqrt{\frac{MSE}{n_g}}$$

Two-way analysis of variance (randomized block design of experiment)

$$SS(Total) = \sum_{j=1}^{k} \sum_{i=1}^{b} (x_{ij} - \bar{\bar{x}})^2$$

$$SST = \sum_{j=1}^{k} b(\bar{x}[T]_i - \bar{\bar{x}})^2$$

$$SSB = \sum_{j=1}^{k} k(\bar{x}[B]_i - \bar{\bar{x}})^2$$

$$SSE = \sum_{j=1}^{k} \sum_{i=1}^{b} (x_{ij} - \bar{x}[T]_j - \bar{x}[B]_i + \bar{\bar{x}})^2$$

$$MST = \frac{SST}{k-1}$$

$$MSB = \frac{SSB}{b-1}$$

$$MSE = \frac{SSE}{n-k-b+1}$$

$$F = \frac{MST}{MSE}$$

$$F = \frac{MSB}{MSE}$$

Two-factor analysis of variance

$$SS(Total) = \sum_{i=1}^{a} \sum_{j=1}^{b} \sum_{k=1}^{r} (x_{ijk} - \bar{\bar{x}})^2$$

$$SS(A) = rb \sum_{j=1}^{a} (\bar{x}[A]_i - \bar{\bar{x}})^2$$

$$SS(B) = ra \sum_{j=1}^{b} (\bar{x}[B]_j - \bar{\bar{x}})^2$$

$$SS(AB) = r \sum_{i=1}^{a} \sum_{j=1}^{b} (\bar{x}[AB]_{ij} - \bar{x}[A]_i - \bar{x}[B]_j + \bar{\bar{x}})^2$$

$$SSE = \sum_{i=1}^{a} \sum_{j=1}^{b} \sum_{k=1}^{r} (x_{ijk} - \bar{x}[AB]_{ij})^2$$

$$MS(A) = \frac{SS(A)}{a-1}$$

$$MS(B) = \frac{SS(B)}{b-1}$$

$$MS(AB) = \frac{SS(AB)}{(a-1)(b-1)}$$

$$F = \frac{MS(A)}{MSE}$$

$$F = \frac{MS(B)}{MSE}$$

$$F = \frac{MS(AB)}{MSE}$$

COMPUTER OUTPUT AND INSTRUCTIONS:

Technique	Excel
One-way ANOVA	525
Multiple comparisons (LSD, Bonferroni adjustment, and Tukey)	542
Two-way (randomized block) ANOVA	551
Two-factor ANOVA	563

CHAPTER EXERCISES

The following exercises require the use of a computer and software.
Use a 5% significance level.

14.113 Xr14-113 Each year billions of dollars are lost because of worker injuries on the job. Costs can be decreased if injured workers can be rehabilitated quickly. As part of an analysis of the amount of time taken for workers to return to work, a sample of male blue-collar workers aged 35 to 45 who suffered a common wrist fracture was taken. The researchers believed that the mental and physical condition of the individual affects recovery time. Each man was given a questionnaire to complete, which measured whether he tended to be optimistic or pessimistic. Their physical condition was also evaluated and categorized as very physically fit, average, or in poor condition. The number of days until the wrist returned to full function was measured for each individual. These data were recorded in the following way:

> Column 1: Time to recover for optimists ((columns 1–10) = very fit, rows 11–20 = in average condition,   rows 21–30 = poor condition)
> Column 2: Time to recover for pessimists (same format as column 1)

a. What are the factors in this experiment? What are the levels of each factor?
b. Can we conclude that pessimists and optimists differ in their recovery times?
c. Can we conclude that physical condition affects recovery times?

14.114 Xr14-114 To help high school students pick a major, a company called PayScale surveys graduates of a variety of programs. In one such survey, graduates of the following degree programs were asked what

their annual salaries were after working at least 10 years in the field.

> Elementary Education
> Human Development
> Social Work
> Special Education

Can we infer that there are differences in salary between the four college degrees?

14.115 Xr14-115 The possible imposition of a residential property tax has been a sensitive political issue in a large city that consists of five boroughs. Currently, property tax is based on an assessment system that dates back to 1950. This system has produced numerous inequities whereby newer homes tend to be assessed at higher values than older homes. A new system based on the market value of the house has been proposed. Opponents of the plan argue that residents of some boroughs would have to pay considerably more on the average, while residents of other boroughs would pay less. As part of a study examining this issue, several homes in each borough were assessed under both plans. The percentage increase (a decrease is represented by a negative increase) in each case was recorded.
a. Can we conclude that there are differences in the effect the new assessment system would have on the five boroughs?
b. If differences exist, which boroughs differ? Use Tukey's multiple comparison method.
c. What are the required conditions for your conclusions to be valid?
d. Are the required conditions satisfied?

14.116 Xr14-116 The editor of the student newspaper was in the process of making some major changes in the newspaper's layout. He was also contemplating changing the typeface of the print used. To help himself make a decision, he set up an experiment in which 20 individuals were asked to read four newspaper pages, with each page printed in a different typeface. If the reading speed differed, then the typeface that was read fastest would be used. However, if there was not enough evidence to allow the editor to conclude that such differences existed, the current typeface would be continued. The times (in seconds) to completely read one page were recorded. What should the editor do?

14.117 Xr14-117 In marketing children's products, it is extremely important to produce television commercials that hold the attention of the children who view them. A psychologist hired by a marketing research firm wants to determine whether differences in attention span exist between children watching advertisements for different types of products. One hundred fifty children under 10 years of age were recruited for an experiment. One-third watched a 60-second commercial for a new computer game, one-third watched a commercial for a breakfast cereal, and one-third watched a commercial for children's clothes. Their attention spans (in seconds) were measured and recorded. Do these data provide enough evidence to conclude that there are differences in attention span between the three products advertised?

14.118 Xr14-118 On reconsidering the experiment in Exercise 14.117, the psychologist decides that the age of the child may influence the attention span. Consequently, the experiment is redone in the following way. Three 10-year-olds, three 9-year-olds, three 8-year-olds, three 7-year-olds, three 6-year-olds, three 5-year-olds, and three 4-year-olds are randomly assigned to watch one of the commercials, and their attention spans are measured. Do the results indicate that there are differences in the abilities of the products advertised to hold children's attention?

14.119 Xr14-119 It is important for salespeople to be knowledgeable about how people shop for certain products. Suppose that a new car salesman believes that the age and gender of a car shopper affect the way he or she makes an offer on a car. He records the initial offers made by a group of men and women shoppers on a $25,000 Ford Taurus. In addition to the gender of the shopper, the salesman also notes the age category. The amount of money below the asking price that each person offered initially for the car was recorded using the following format: Column 1 contains the data for the under 30 group;

the first 25 rows store the results for female shoppers and the last 25 rows are the male shoppers. Columns 2 and 3 store the data for the 30–45 age category and over 45 category, respectively. What can we conclude from these data?

14.120 Xr14-120 Many of you reading this page probably learned how to read using the whole-language method. This strategy maintains that the natural and effective way is to be exposed to whole words in context. Students learn how to read by recognizing words they have seen before. In the past generation this has been the dominant teaching strategy throughout North America. It replaced phonics, wherein children were taught to sound out the letters to form words. The whole language method was instituted with little or no research and has been severely criticized in the past. A recent study may have resolved the question of which method should be employed. An educational psychologist at the University of Houston described the experiment at the annual meeting of the American Association for the Advancement of Science. The subjects were 375 low-achieving, poor, first-grade students in Houston schools. The students were divided into three groups. One was educated according to the whole-language philosophy, a second group was taught using a pure phonics strategy, and the third was taught employing a mixed or embedded phonics technique. At the end of the term students were asked to read words on a list of 50 words. The number of words each child could read was recorded.
a. Can we infer that differences exist between the effects of the three teaching strategies?
b. If differences exist, identify which method appears to be best.

14.121 Xr14-121 Are babies who are exposed to music before their birth smarter than those who are not? And, if so, what kind of music is best? Researchers at the University of Wisconsin conducted an experiment with rats. The researchers selected a random sample of pregnant rats and divided the sample into three groups. Mozart works were played to one group, a second group was exposed to white noise (a steady hum with no musical elements), and the third group listened to Philip Glass music (very simple compositions). The researchers then trained the young rats to run a maze in search of food. The amount of time for the rats to complete the maze was measured for all three groups.
a. Can we infer from these data that there are differences between the three groups?
b. If there are differences, determine which group is best.

14.122 Xr14-122   Increasing tuition has resulted in some students being saddled with large debts on graduation. To examine this issue, a random sample of recent graduates was asked to report whether they had student loans, and if so, how much was the debt at graduation. Each person who reported that they owed money was also asked whether their degree was a B.A., B.Sc., B.B.A., or other. Can we conclude that debt levels differ between the four types of degree?

14.123 Xr14-123   Studies indicate that single male investors tend to take the most risk, whereas married female investors tend to be conservative. This raises the question, which does best? The risk-adjusted returns for single and married men, and for single and married women were recorded. Can we infer that differences exist between the four groups of investors?

14.124 Xr14-124   Virtually all restaurants attempt to have three "seatings" on weekend nights. Three seatings means that each table gets three different sets of customers. Obviously, any group that lingers over dessert and coffee may result in the loss of one seating and profit for the restaurant. In an effort to determine which types of groups tend to linger, a random sample of 150 groups was drawn. For each group, the number of members and the length of time that the group stayed were recorded in the following way:

> Column A: Length of time for 2 people
> Column B: Length of time for 3 people
> Column C: Length of time for 4 people
> Column D: Length of time for more than 4 people

Do these data allow us to infer that the length of time in the restaurant depends on the size of the party?

14.125 Xr14-125   When the stock market has a large 1-day decline, does it bounce back the next day or does the bad news endure? To answer this question, an economist examined a random sample of daily changes to the Toronto Stock Index (TSE). He recorded the percent change. He classified declines as:

> Down by less than 0.5%
> Down by 0.5% to 1.5%
> Down by 1.5% to 2.5%
> Down by more than 2.5%

For each of these days, he recorded the percent loss the following day. Do these data allow us to infer that there are differences in changes to the TSE depending on the loss the previous day? (This exercise is based on a study undertaken by Tim Whitehead, an economist for Left Bank Economics, a consulting firm near Paris, Ontario.)

14.126 Xr14-126   Stock market investors are always seeking the "Holy Grail," a sign that tells them the market has bottomed out or achieved its highest level. There are several indicators. One is the buy signal developed by Gerald Appel, who believed that a bottom has been reached when the difference between the weekly close of the New York Stock Exchange (NYSE) index and the 10-week moving average (see Chapter 20) is −4.0 points or more. Another bottom indicator is based on identifying a certain pattern in the line chart of the stock market index. As an experiment, a financial analyst randomly selected 100 weeks. For each week he determined whether there was an Appel buy, a chart buy, or no indication. For each type of week he recorded the percentage change over the next 4 weeks. Can we infer that the two buy indicators are not useful?

14.127 Xr14-127   Millions of North Americans spend up to several hours a day commuting to and from work. Other than the wasted time, are there other negative effects associated with fighting traffic? A study by Statistics Canada may shed light on the issue. A random sample of adults was surveyed. Among other questions each was asked how much time he or she slept and how much time was spent commuting. The categories for commuting time are 1 to 30 minutes, 31 to 60 minutes, and over 60 minutes. Is there sufficient evidence to conclude that the amount of sleep differs between commuting categories?

14.128 Xr14-128   A random sample of 500 teenagers were grouped in the following way: ages 13–14, 15–17, and 18–19. Each teenager was asked to record the number of Facebook friends each had. Is there sufficient evidence to infer that there are differences in the number of Facebook friends between the three teenage groups?

14.129 Xr14-129   How have 25- to 34-year-olds with university degrees fared financially since 1984? To answer this question, the Pew Research Center conducted surveys in 1984, 1996, and 2009 recording monthly earnings for graduates with three different types of degrees. The incomes were converted into 2012 dollars.
a. Is there sufficient evidence to infer that incomes differed for 25- to 34-year-olds with professional or doctorate degrees between the three periods?
b. What are the required conditions?
c. Are they satisfied? Explain.

14.130 <u>Xr14-130</u> Refer to Exercise 14.129. A similar study was conducted for Bachelor's degrees.
    a. Can we infer from the data that incomes differed for 25- to 34-year-olds with Bachelor's degrees between the three periods?
    b. Are the required conditions satisfied? Explain.

14.131 <u>Xr14-131</u> Refer to Exercise 14.129. A similar study determined the monthly household income of households headed by 25- to 34-year-olds with only a high school diploma. The incomes were converted to 2012 dollars.
    a. Is there sufficient evidence to infer that household incomes differed for 25- to 34-year-olds with high school diplomas between the three periods?
    b. Are the required conditions satisfied? Explain.

14.132 <u>Xr14-132</u> Does the day a house is listed for sale affect how long it takes for the sale to be completed or its selling price? A study conducted by economists attempted to answer the question. A random sample of houses that sold in a major city was studied. The number of days between the listing and the sale was recorded as well as the day of the week the listing started.
    a. Is there enough evidence to conclude that differences in the number of days until the sale is made exist between the seven days?
    b. If there are differences which days differ?

14.133 <u>Xr14-133</u> Another useful measure of Americans' beliefs about the state of the economy is the age at which they believe they will retire. If nonretired people believe that they will need to work longer to be able to afford their lifestyle after retirement it likely means that their confidence in the economy is not high. A Gallup survey conducted every 5 years starting in 1996 asked nonretired U.S. adults to predict at what age they would retire.
    a. Can we infer that the predicted age of retirement has fluctuated over the years?
    b. If differences exist which years differ?

14.134 <u>Xr14-134</u> Each year Michigan State University's Collegiate Employment Research Institute tracks starting salaries of graduates. The Institute recorded the starting salaries of the following engineers: chemical, civil, computer, electrical, and mechanical.
    a. Is there sufficient evidence to infer that differences exist between the starting salaries?
    b. If differences exist use Tukey's method to determine which means differ.

14.135 <u>Xr14-135</u> The U.S. Bureau of Labor Statistics conducts regular surveys to determine how Americans are spending their money. The annual expenditures for vehicle insurance of a random sample of American households in 2012, 2013, and 2014 were recorded. Is there sufficient evidence to infer that the expenditures differed in the three tear period?

14.136 <u>Xr14-136</u> Refer to Exercise 14.135. Do Americans spend more on health care as they age? To answer the question, economists turned to the Bureau of Labor Statistics to measure how much Americans in the following age groups spend annually on health care.

(1) 55–64   (2) 65–74   (3) 75 and older

Random samples of Americans 55 and older were taken and for respondent the age category and the amount spent on health care last year were recorded.
    a. Is there enough evidence to infer that differences exist between the three age groups?
    b. If differences exist which pairs differ? Use Bonferroni adjustment to answer the question.

14.137 <u>Xr14-137</u> St Catharine's-Niagara, Kitchener-Cambridge-Waterloo. Brantford, Guelph, London, and Windsor are relatively small cities in Southwest Ontario. Because of their size the expectation is that the time it takes to get from home to work would not be large. To examine the issue a statistics practitioner took random samples of workers who commute in each city and determined their commute times. (Source: Adapted from Statistics Canada: Commuting to Work)
    a. Is there sufficient evidence to conclude that the times differ between the six cities?
    b. If differences exist use Tukey's method to determine which means differ.

14.138 <u>Xr14-138</u> Automobile insurance companies use statistics to determine their premiums. The premiums are proportional to the risks and costs of accidents. Suppose that an economist conducted a study that looked at miles driven in the previous year, ages of the drivers, and their gender. The age categories are 16–19, 20–34, 35–54, 55–64, and 65+. Because of the design of the experiment there were 20 observations for each age category–gender combination.
    a. Is there enough evidence to conclude that male and female drivers differ in the number of miles they drive?
    b. Can we infer that there are differences between the age categories in the number of miles they drive?

14.139 <u>Xr14-139</u> The National Center for Charitable Statistics estimates that individual giving in the United States in 2014 was $258.51 billion. A study to determine who gave and how much they gave was undertaken. A random sample of individuals who gave to charities was drawn. For each respondent, the study recorded the total adjusted gross income (AGI) category and the charitable giving as a percentage of AGI. The AGI categories are listed next. In this study, only individuals whose AGI was between $45,000 and $100,000 were included.

$45,000 to $49,999

$50,000 to $54,999

$55,000 to $59,999

$60,000 to $74,999

$75,000 to $100,000

a. Is there sufficient evidence to conclude that there are differences between the five AGI categories?
b. If differences exist use Tukey's method to determine which groups differ.

14.140 Xr14-140 Refer to Exercise 14.139. The AGI categories for another study were

$100,000 to $199,999

$200,000 to $249,999

$250,000 to $499,999

$500,000 to $1,000,000

The proportion of charitable giving to AGI was recorded.
a. Is there sufficient evidence to conclude that there are differences between the four AGI categories?
b. If differences exist use Tukey's method to determine which groups differ.

Overeating Experiments (See page 451.)

14.141 Xr14-141   Ice Cream Experiment

This experiment consisted of graduates students given either a medium-sized 17-ounce bowls or large-sized 34-ounce bowls. Each student was invited to take as much of four different flavors of ice cream as he or she wanted. The size of the scoop also varied. One held two ounces and the other held three ounces. The students were asked to fill out a survey; while doing so, the amount of ice cream was measured and recorded. Is there sufficient evidence to conclude that either the bowl size or the scoop size or some interaction affected the amount of ice cream?

Source: Adapted from Brian Wansink, Koert van Ittersum, and James E. Painter, "Ice Cream Illusions: Bowl Size, Spoon Size, and Serving Size," *American Journal of Preventive Medicine* (September 2006).

14.142 Xr14-142   Hershey's Kisses Experiment

Deskbound secretaries were employed in this experiment. Clear-lidded candy dished filled with 30 Hershey's Kisses were placed in three different locations. The first location was the secretary's desk, the second was the top-left drawer in the secretary's desk, and the third was on the top of a file cabinet 6 feet from the secretary's desk. After 1 week, the number of Kisses consumed was counted. Do the data allow us to infer that the number of Kisses differed by location?

Source: Adapted from James E. Painter, Brian Wansink, and Julie B. Hieggelke, "How Visibility and Convenience Influence Candy Consumption," *Appetite* 38:3 (June 2002), 237–38.

14.143 Xr14-143   Brownie Experiment

A random sample of 175 people who had lunch at a company cafeteria were offered a brownie. Some were handed the brownie on a fine piece of china, others were given the brownie on a paper plate, and others were given the brownie on a paper napkin. Each person was asked how much they would be willing to pay. Is there sufficient evidence to conclude that the prices differed according to the way the brownies were offered?

The following exercises use data files associated with three exercises seen previously in this book.

14.144 Xr12-132*   In Exercise 12.132 marketing managers for the JC Penney department store chain segmented the market for women's apparel on the basis of personal and family values. The segments are Conservative, Traditional, and Contemporary. Recall that the classification was done on the basis of questionnaires. Suppose that in addition to identifying the segment the questionnaire also asked each woman to report family income (in $1,000s). Do these data allow us to infer that family incomes differ between the three market segments?

14.145 Xr13-21*   Exercise 13.21 addressed the problem of determining whether the distances young (under 25) males and females drive annually differ. Included in the data is also the number of accidents that each person was involved in the past 2 years. Responses are 0, 1, or 2 or more. Do the data allow us to infer that the distances driven differ between the drivers who have had 0, 1, or 2 or more accidents?

14.146 Xr13-165*   The objective in Exercise 13.165 was to determine whether various market segments were more likely to use the QuikLube service. Included with the data is also the age (in months) of the car. Do the data allow us to conclude that there are differences in the age between the four market segments?

CASE 14.1 Baseball Umpires: If the Strike Zone Varies, Do the Scores?*

Baseball fans who watch games on television can usually see something called the pitch tracker. It allows viewers to see whether the umpire made the correct call. According to rule 2.00 of the Major League Baseball rule book, a strike zone is defined as "that area over home plate the upper limit of which is a horizontal line at the midpoint between the top of the shoulders and the top of the uniform pants, and the lower level is a line at the hollow beneath the kneecap"

and is determined by "the batter's stance as the batter is prepared to swing at a pitched ball."

For many fans, it appears that some umpires have bigger strike zones than others. That is, they call pitches strikes when the pitch was actually not in the strike zone. Umpires with large strike zones are likely to see less runs scored since the batter is at a disadvantage. We'll call this the Unequal Strike Zone Theory, which states that some umpires routinely

enlarge the strike zone resulting in lower scores. Fortunately, this theory is testable. For every game in the 2015 season, the home plate umpire, the visiting team scores, the home team scores, and the total number of runs were recorded. Test the Unequal Strike Zone Theory. Conduct an analysis that determines whether there is sufficient evidence to infer that the total number of runs per game differs between the 91 home plate umpires?

*The author wishes to thank Mr. Stacey Albom for collecting all the data in this case.

CASE 14.2 Comparing Three Methods of Treating Childhood Ear Infections*

Acute otitis media, an infection of the middle ear, is a common childhood illness. There are various ways to treat the problem. To help determine the best way, researchers conducted an experiment. One hundred and eighty children between 10 months and 2 years with recurrent acute otitis media were divided into three equal groups. Group 1 was treated by surgically removing the adenoids (adenoidectomy), the second was treated with the drug Sulfafurazole, and the third with a placebo.

Each child was tracked for 2 years, during which time all symptoms and episodes of acute otitis media were recorded. The data were recorded in the following way:

Column 1: ID number
Column 2: Group number
Column 3: Number of episodes of the illness
Column 4: Number of visits to a physician because of any infection
Column 5: Number of prescriptions
Column 6: Number of days with symptoms of respiratory infection

Photographee.eu/
Shutterstock.com

a. Are there differences between the three groups with respect to the number of episodes, number of physician visits, number of prescriptions, and number of days with symptoms of respiratory infection?

b. Assume that you are working for the company that makes the drug Sulfafurazole. Write a report to the company's executives discussing your results.

*This case is adapted from the *British Medical Journal*, February 2004.

APPENDIX 14 / Review of Chapters 12 to 14

The number of techniques introduced in Chapters 12 to 14 is up to 20. As we did in Appendix 13, we provide a table of the techniques, a flowchart to help you identify the correct technique, and 25 exercises to give you practice in how to choose the appropriate method. The table and the flowchart have been amended to include the three analysis of variance techniques introduced in this chapter and the three multiple comparison methods.

TABLE **A14.1** Summary of Statistical Techniques in Chapters 12 to 14

t-test of μ

Estimator of μ (including estimator of $N\mu$)

χ^2 test of σ^2

Estimator of σ^2

z-test of p

Estimator of p (including estimator of Np)

Equal-variances t-test of $\mu_1 - \mu_2$

Equal-variances estimator of $\mu_1 - \mu_2$

Unequal-variances t-test of $\mu_1 - \mu_2$

Unequal-variances estimator of $\mu_1 - \mu_2$

t-test of μ_D

Estimator of μ_D

F-test of σ_1^2/σ_2^2

Estimator of σ_1^2/σ_2^2

z-test of $p_1 - p_2$ (Case 1)

z-test of $p_1 - p_2$ (Case 2)

Estimator of $p_1 - p_2$

One-way analysis of variance (including multiple comparisons)

Two-way (randomized blocks) analysis of variance

Two-factor analysis of variance

FIGURE **A14.1** **Summary of Statistical Techniques in Chapters 12 to 14**

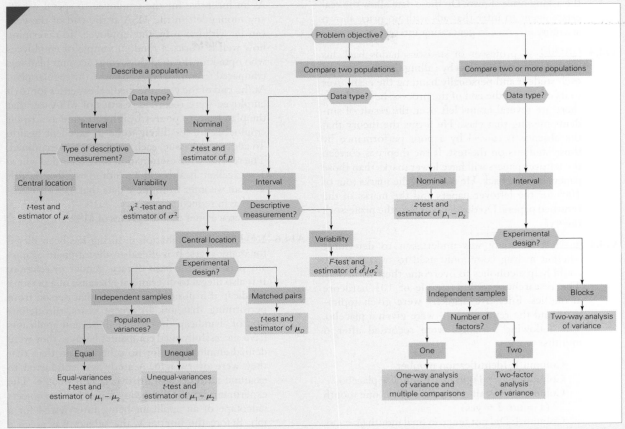

EXERCISES

Note that as we did in Appendix 13, we do not specify a significance level in exercises requiring a test of hypothesis. We leave this decision to you. After analyzing the issues raised in the exercise, use your own judgment to determine whether the p-value is small enough to reject the null hypothesis.

A14.1 <u>XrA14-01</u> Sales of a product may depend on its placement in a store. Candy manufacturers frequently offer discounts to retailers who display their products more prominently than competing brands. To examine this phenomenon more carefully, a candy manufacturer (with the assistance of a national chain of restaurants) planned the following experiment. In 20 restaurants, the manufacturer's brand was displayed behind the cashier's counter with all the other brands (this was called position 1). In another 20 restaurants, the brand was placed separately but close to the other brands (position 2).

In a third group of 20 restaurants, the candy was placed in a special display next to the cash register (position 3). The number of packages sold during 1 week at each restaurant was recorded. Is there sufficient evidence to infer that sales of candy differ according to placement?

A14.2 <u>XrA14-02</u> Advertising is critical in the residential real estate industry. Agents are always seeking ways to increase sales through improved advertising methods. A particular agent believes that he can increase the number of inquiries (and thus the probability of making a sale) by describing the house for sale without indicating its asking price. To support his belief, he conducted an experiment in which 100 houses for sale were advertised in two ways—with and without the asking price. The number of inquiries for each house was recorded as well as whether the customer saw the ad with or without the asking price shown. Do these data allow the real estate agent to infer that ads with no price shown are more effective in generating interest in a house?

A14.3 XrA14-03 A professor of statistics hands back his graded midterms in class by calling out the name of each student and personally handing the exam over to its owner. At the end of the process, he notes that there are several exams left over, the result of students missing that class. He forms the theory that the absence is caused by a poor performance by those students on the test. If the theory is correct, the leftover papers will have lower marks than those papers handed back. He recorded the marks (out of 100) for the leftover papers and the marks of the returned papers. Do the data support the professor's theory?

A14.4 XrA14-04 A study was undertaken to determine whether a drug commonly used to treat epilepsy could help alcoholics to overcome their addiction. The researchers took a sample of 103 hardcore alcoholics. Fifty-five drinkers were given topiramate and the remaining 48 were given a placebo. The following variables were recorded after 6 months:

> Column 1: Identification number
> Column 2: 1 = Topiramate and 2 = placebo
> Column 3: Abstain from alcohol for one month (1 = no, 2 = yes)
> Column 4: Did not binge in final month (1 = no, 2 = yes)

Do these data provide sufficient evidence to infer that topiramate is effective in

a. causing abstinence for the first month?
b. causing alcoholics to refrain from binge drinking in the final month?

A14.5 XrA14-05 Health-care costs in the United States and Canada are concerns for citizens and politicians. The question is, How can we devise a system wherein people's medical bills are covered but individuals attempt to reduce costs? An American company has come up with a possible solution. Golden Rule is an insurance company in Indiana with 1,300 employees. The company offered its employees a choice of programs. One choice was a medical savings account (MSA) plan. Here's how it works. To ensure that a major illness or accident does not financially destroy an employee, Golden Rule offers catastrophic insurance—a policy that covers all expenses above $2,000 per year. At the beginning of the year, the company deposits $1,000 (for a single employee) and $2,000 (for an employee with a family) into the MSA. For minor expenses, the employee pays from his or her MSA. As an incentive for the employee to spend wisely, any money left in the MSA at the end of the year can be withdrawn by the employee. To determine how well it works, a random sample of employees who opted for the medical savings account plan was compared to employees who chose the regular plan. At the end of the year, the medical expenses for each employee were recorded. Critics of MSA say that the plan leads to poorer health care, and as a result employees are less likely to be in excellent health. To address this issue, each employee was examined. The results of the examination were recorded where 1 = excellent health and 2 = not in excellent health

a. Can we infer from these data that MSA is effective in reducing costs?
b. Can we infer that the critics of MSA are correct?

A14.6 XrA14-06 Discrimination in hiring has been illegal for many years. It is illegal to discriminate against any person on the basis of race, gender, or religion. It is also illegal to discriminate because of a person's handicap if it in no way prevents that person from performing that job. In recent years, the definition of "handicap" has widened. Several applicants have successfully sued companies because they were denied employment for no other reason than that they were overweight. A study was conducted to examine attitudes toward overweight people. The experiment involved showing a number of subjects videotape of an applicant being interviewed for a job. Before the interview, the subject was given a description of the job. Following the interview, the subject was asked to score the applicant in terms of how well the applicant was suited for the job. The score was out of 100, where higher scores described greater suitability. (The scores are interval data.) The same procedure was repeated for each subject. However, the gender and weight (average and overweight) of the applicant varied. The results were recorded using the following format:

> Column 1: Score for average weight males
> Column 2: Score for overweight males
> Column 3: Score for average weight females
> Column 4: Score for overweight females

a. Can we infer that the scores of the four groups of applicants differ?
b. Are the differences detected in part (a) because of weight, gender, or some interaction?

A14.7 XrA14-07 Most automobile repair shops now charge according to a schedule that is claimed to be based on average times. This means that instead of determining the actual time to make a repair and multiplying this value by their hourly rate, repair shops determine the cost from a schedule that is calculated from average times. A critic of this policy is examining how closely this schedule adheres to the actual time to complete a job. He randomly selects five jobs. According to the schedule, these jobs should take 45 minutes, 60 minutes, 80 minutes, 100 minutes, and 125 minutes, respectively. The critic then takes a random sample of repair shops and records the actual times for each of 20 cars for each job. For each job, can we infer that the time specified by the schedule is greater than the actual time?

A14.8 XrA14-08 Automobile insurance appraisers examine cars that have been involved in accidental collisions and estimate the cost of repairs. An insurance executive claims that there are significant differences in the estimates from different appraisers. To support his claim, he takes a random sample of 25 cars that have recently been damaged in accidents. Three appraisers then estimated the repair costs of each car. The estimates were recorded for each appraiser. From the data, can we conclude that the executive's claim is true?

A14.9 XrA14-09 The widespread use of salt on roads in Canada and the northern United States during the winter and acid precipitation throughout the year combine to cause rust on cars. Car manufacturers and other companies offer rustproofing services to help purchasers preserve the value of their cars. A consumer protection agency decides to determine whether there are any differences between the rust protection provided by automobile manufacturers and that provided by two competing types of rustproofing services. As an experiment, 60 identical new cars are selected. Of these, 20 are rustproofed by the manufacturer. Another 20 are rustproofed using a method that applies a liquid to critical areas of the car. The liquid hardens, forming a (supposedly) lifetime bond with the metal. The last 20 are treated with oil and are retreated every 12 months. The cars are then driven under similar conditions in a Minnesota city. The number of months until the first rust appears was recorded. Is there sufficient evidence to conclude that at least one rustproofing method is different from the others?

A14.10 XrA14-10 One of the ways in which advertisers measure the value of television commercials is by telephone surveys conducted shortly after commercials are aired. Respondents who watched a certain television station at a given time period, during which the commercial appeared, are asked whether they can recall the name of the product in the commercial. Suppose an advertiser wants to compare the recall proportions of two commercials. The first commercial is relatively inexpensive. A second commercial shown a week later is quite expensive to produce. The advertiser decides that the second commercial is viable only if its recall proportion is more than 15% higher than the recall proportion of the first commercial. Two surveys of 500 television viewers each were conducted after each commercial was aired. Each person was asked whether he or she remembered the product name. The results are stored in columns 1 (commercial 1) and 2 (commcial 2) (2 = remembered the product name, 1 = did not remember the product name). Can we infer that the second commercial is viable?

A14.11 XrA14-11 In the door-to-door selling of vacuum cleaners, various factors influence sales. The Birk Vacuum Cleaner Company considers its sales pitch and overall package to be extremely important. As a result, it often thinks of new ways to sell its product. Because the company's management develops so many new sales pitches each year, there is a two-stage testing process. In stage 1, a new plan is tested with a relatively small sample. If there is sufficient evidence that the plan increases sales, a second, considerably larger, test is undertaken. In a stage 1 test to determine whether the inclusion of a "free" 10 -year service contract increases sales, 100 sales representatives were selected at random from the company's list of several thousand. The monthly sales of these representatives were recorded for 1 month before the use of the new sales pitch and for 1 month after its introduction. Should the company proceed to stage 2?

A14.12 XrA14-12 The cost of workplace injuries is high for the individual worker, for the company, and for society. It is in everyone's interest to rehabilitate the injured worker as quickly as possible. A statistician working for an insurance company has investigated the problem. He believes that physical condition is a major determinant in how quickly a worker returns to his or her job after sustaining an injury. To help determine whether he is on the right track, he organized an experiment. He took a random sample of male and female workers who were injured during the preceding year. He recorded their gender, their physical condition, and the number of working days until they returned to their job. These data were recorded in the following way. Columns 1 and 2 store the number of working days until return to work for men and women, respectively. In each column, the first 25 observations relate to those who are physically fit, the next 25 rows relate to individuals who are moderately fit, and the last 25 observations are for those who are in poor physical shape. Can we infer that the six groups differ? If differences exist, determine whether the differences result from gender, physical fitness, or some combination of gender and physical fitness.

A14.13 XrA14-13 Does driving an ABS-equipped car change the behavior of drivers? To help answer this question, the following experiment was undertaken. A random sample of 200 drivers who currently operate cars without ABS were selected. Each person was given an identical car to drive for 1 year. Half the sample were given cars that had ABS, and the other half were given cars with standard-equipment brakes. Computers on the cars recorded the average speed (in miles per hour) during the year. Can we infer that operating an ABS-equipped car changes the behavior of the driver?

A14.14 XrA14-14 We expect the demand for a product depends on its price: The higher the price, the lower the demand. However, this may not be entirely true. In an experiment conducted by professors at Northwestern University and MIT, a mail-order dress was available at the prices $34, $39, and $44. The number of dresses sold weekly over a 20-week period was recorded. The prices were randomized over 60 weeks. Conduct a test to determine whether demand differed and, if so, which price elicited the highest sales.

A14.15 XrA14-15 Researchers at the University of Washington conducted an experiment to determine whether the herbal remedy Echinacea is effective in treating children's colds and other respiratory infection (*National Post*, December 3, 2003). A sample of 524 children were recruited. Half the sample treated their colds with Echinacea, and the other half was given a placebo. For each infection, the duration of the colds (in days) was measured and recorded. Can we conclude that Echinacea is effective?

A14.16 XrA14-16 The marketing manager of a large ski resort wants to advertise that his ski resort has the shortest lift lines of any resort in the area. To avoid the possibility of a false advertising liability suit, he collects data on the times skiers wait in line at his resort and at each of two competing resorts on each of 14 days.
  a. Can he conclude that there are differences in waiting times between the three resorts?
  b. What are the required conditions for these techniques?
  c. How would you check to determine that the required conditions are satisfied?

A14.17 XrA14-17 A popularly held belief about university professors is that they don't work very hard and that the higher their rank, the less work they do. A statistics student decided to determine whether the belief is true. She took a random sample of 20 university instructors in the faculties of business, engineering, arts, and sciences. In each sample of

20, 5 were instructors, 5 were assistant professors, 5 were associate professors, and 5 were full professors. Each professor was surveyed and asked to report confidentially the number of weekly hours of work. These data were recorded in the following way:

> Column 1: hours of work for business professors (first 5 rows = instructors, next 5 rows = assistant professors, next 5 rows = associate professors, and last 5 rows = full professors)
> Column 2: hours of work for engineering professors (same format as column 1)
> Column 3: hours of work for arts professors (same format as column 1)
> Column 4: hours of work for science professors (same format as column 1)

  a. If we conduct the test under the single-factor analysis of variance, how many levels are there? What are they?
  b. Test to determine whether differences exist using a single-factor analysis of variance.
  c. If we conduct tests using the two-factor analysis of variance, what are the factors? What are their levels?
  d. Is there evidence of interaction?
  e. Are there differences between the four ranks of instructor?
  f. Are there differences between the four faculties?

A14.18 XrA14-18 Billions of dollars are spent annually by Americans for the care and feeding of pets. A survey conducted by the American Veterinary Medical Association drew a random sample of 1,328 American households and asked whether they owned a pet and, if so, the type of animal. In addition, each was asked to report the veterinary expenditures for the previous 12 months. Column 1 contains the expenditures for dogs, and column 2 stores the expenditures for cats. The results are that 474 households reported that they owned at least one dog and 419 owned at least one cat. The latest census indicates that there are 112 million households in the United States.

Source: Statistical Abstract of the United States, 2006, Table 1232.

  a. Estimate with 95% confidence the total number of households owning at least one dog.
  b. Repeat part (a) for cats.
  c. Assume that there are 40 million households with at least one dog and estimate with 95% confidence the total amount spent on veterinary expenditures for dogs.
  d. Assume that there are 35 million households with at least one cat and estimate with 95% confidence the total amount spent on veterinary expenditures for cats.

GENERAL SOCIAL SURVEY EXERCISES

Conduct all tests at the 5% significance level. Use a 95% confidence level for estimates.

In 2012, there were 221,963,000 Americans aged 21 years or more.

A14.19 GSS2012*   What other differences are there among liberals, moderates, and conservatives (POLVIEWS3: 1 = Liberal, 2 = Moderate, 3 = Conservative)? For example, is there sufficient statistical evidence to conclude that there are differences in income (RINCOME)?

A14.20 GSS2012*   In many countries, each succeeding generation does better financially than their predecessors. The survey asked respondents the following question. "Compared to your parents at your age is your standard of living (PARSOL) 1 = Much better, 2 = Somewhat better, 3 = About the same, 4 = Somewhat worse, 5 = Much worse". Is there enough evidence to conclude that the majority of people believe that they are doing better than their parents?

A14.21 GSS2012*   Americans are postponing marriage and starting families. Does this mean that families are having fewer children? Estimate with 95% confidence the average number of children per family (CHILDS).

A14.22 GSS2012*   Does work status (WRKSTAT: 1. Working fulltime, 2. Working part time, 3. Temporarily not working, 4. Unemployed, laid off, 5. Retired, 6. School, 7. Keeping house, 8. Other) affect their responses to the question, "Should government reduce income differences between rich and poor?" The responses are EQWLTH:1 = Government should reduce differences; 2, 3, 4, 5, 6, 7 = No government action. Conduct a test to answer the question.

A14.23 GSS2012*   The image of the public sector worker is one who doesn't work very hard (WRKGOVT: 1 = government, 2 = private). Is this image valid? Conduct a test to determine whether there is enough evidence to infer that public sector workers and private sector workers differ in the number of hours of work per week (HRS1)?

A14.24 GSS2012*   Estimate with 95% confidence the number of American adults who are neither white nor black (RACE: 1 = White, 2 = Black, 3 = Other).

A14.25 GSS2012*   In the past, government jobs had only one major advantage over private sector jobs, job security. Private sector jobs usually paid better. But now most government jobs are secure and pay better than similar work in the private sector. Estimate the number of Americans who work for the government (federal, state, county, or municipal) (WRKGOVT: 1 = Government).

A14.26 GSS2012*   Is it true that as we grow older we become more conservative? If so, there would be differences in age (AGE) between the three political groups (PARTYID3: 1 = Democrat, 2 = Independent, 3 = Republican). Do the data allow us to conclude that there are differences?

A14.27 GSS2012*   The survey asked respondents about the federal tax they pay. Estimate the number of American adults who believe that their tax is too low (TAX: 1 = Too high, 2 = About right, 3 = Too low).

A14.28 GSS2012*   Surveys around the world often try to measure the happiness of the residents of each country. Americans are typically near the middle. The General Social Survey asked respondents "Taken altogether, how would you say things are these days would you say you were (HAPPY) 1 = Very happy, 2 = Pretty happy, 3 = Not too happy" Is there sufficient evidence to infer that more than three quarters of the population is very or pretty happy?

A14.29 GSS2012*   Is it still true that men earn more than women (SEX: 1 = male, 2 = female)? Conduct a test to determine whether there is enough statistical evidence to conclude that men earn more than women (RINCOME).

A14.30 GSS2012*   Is there enough evidence to conclude that Republicans are more likely than Democrats (PARTYID3: 1 = Democrat, 3 = Republican) to answer the following question correctly. A doctor tells a couple that there is one chance in four that their child will have an inherited disease. Does this mean that each of the couple's children will have the same risk of suffering the illness (ODDS2: 1 = Yes, 2 = No, 8 = Don't know, 9 = No answer)? The correct answer is Yes.

A14.31 GSS2012*   How does the level of educational attainment affect attitudes about the role of government? Is there sufficient evidence to conclude that there are differences between the five categories of educational attainment (DEGREE: 0 = Left high school, 1 = High school, 2 = Junior college, 3 = Bachelor's degree, 4 = Graduate) in their responses to the following question: "Should government reduce income differences between rich and poor?" The responses were EQWLTH: 1 = Government should reduce differences; 2, 3, 4, 5, 6, 7 = No government action.

Survey of Consumer Finances

Conduct all tests at the 5% significance level. Use a 95% confidence level for estimates.

According to the U.S. Census there were 220,958,853 adults in the United States in 2010.

A14.32 <u>SCF2010:\ALL*</u> One measure of financial success is net worth (NETWORTH), which is the difference between assets and liabilities. If net worth is affected by education then there should be statistical evidence to infer that net worth differs between households whose heads are in one of these categories: EDCL 1 = No high school diploma, 2 = High school diploma, 3 = Some college, 4 = College degree. Is there enough statistical evidence to support the conclusion that education affects net worth?

A14.33 <u>SCF2010:\UC*</u> It is possible to have a high net worth of more than $1,345,975 without earning a high income. However, we would expect upper class households to earn high income in a variety of ways. Estimate the mean income of upper class households (INCOME).

A14.34 <u>SCF2010:\MC*</u> The middle class in the 2010 Survey of Consumer Finances had a net worth of between $61,215 and $270,603. In 2010, the average amount spent on food away from home was $2505 (Source: Bureau of Labor Statistics). Is there enough evidence to infer that the average middle-class household spent less than that amount in 2010 (FOODAWAY)?

A14.35 <u>SCF2010:\MC*</u> If a household has been turned down for credit in the past 5 years it is because their debts were too high and/or their income too low. Estimate the difference in incomes (INCOME) between those who have been turned down for credit and those who have not (TURNDOWN: 0 = No, 1 = Yes).

A14.36 <u>SCF2010:\All*</u> Are Americans becoming more educated? One way to measure is to count the number of household heads who have college degrees. Estimate the number of people who have a college degree (EDCL: 4 = college degree).

A14.37 <u>SCF2010:\All*</u> The labor force participation rate is a better indicator of the economy than the unemployment rate. The latter excludes people who may want a job but have been discouraged by their lack of success and stopped looking for work. Estimate the number of Americans who are not working (LF: 0).

A14.38 <u>SCF2010:\UC</u> The upper class in the 2010 survey had a household net worth between $1,345,975 and $7,402,095. Where do members of the upper class invest their money? Estimate the mean value of financial assets held by the household (FIN).

A14.39 <u>SCF2010:\All*</u> Because credit card companies charge very high interest for carrying debts most households attempt to pay off their credit card balances quickly. Estimate the number of people who carry a balance on credit cards (NOCCBAL: 1).

A14.40 <u>SCF2010:\MC*</u> Because of different incomes there may be substantial differences in net worth (NETWORTH) between male and female (HHSEX: 1 = male, 2 = female) heads of middle-class households. Conduct a test to determine whether male heads of middle-class households have higher net worth than female heads of middle-class households.

A14.41 <u>SCF2010:\All*</u> Are male heads (HHSEX: 1 = Male, 2 = Female) of households more likely to own his home than female heads of households (HOUSECL: 1 = Own)? Conduct a test to answer the question.

A14.42 <u>SCF2010:\All*</u> The survey asked respondents to classify their occupation. Can we infer that male heads (HHSEX: 1 = Male, 2 = Female) of households are more likely than their female counterparts to work as a manager or professional (OCCAT2: 1 = Managerial/professional)?

age fotostock/SuperStock

CHI-SQUARED TESTS

CHAPTER OUTLINE

General Social Surveys

Has Support for Capital Punishment for Murderers Changed since 2006?

Bob Daemmrich/PhotoEdit

DATA
GSS2006*
GSS2008*
GSS2010*
GSS2012*
GSS2014*

The issue of capital punishment for murderers in the United States has been argued for many years. A few states have abolished it, and others have kept their laws on the books but rarely use them. Where does the public stand on the issue, and has public support been constant or has it changed from year to year? One of the questions asked in the General Social Survey was

See Solution On page 607.

Do you favor capital punishment for murder (CAPPUN)? The responses are

1 = Favor, 2 = Oppose

Conduct a test to determine whether public support varies from year to year.

INTRODUCTION

We have seen a variety of statistical techniques that are used when the data are nominal. In Chapter 2, we introduced bar and pie charts, both graphical techniques to describe a set of nominal data. Later in Chapter 2, we showed how to describe the relationship between two sets of nominal data by producing a frequency table and a bar chart. However, these techniques simply describe the data, which may represent a sample or a population. In this chapter, we deal with similar problems, but the goal is to use statistical techniques to make inferences about populations from sample data.

This chapter develops two statistical techniques that involve nominal data. The first is a *goodness-of-fit test* applied to data produced by a *multinomial experiment*, a generalization of a binomial experiment. The second uses data arranged in a table (called a *contingency table*) to determine whether two classifications of a population of nominal data are statistically independent; this test can also be interpreted as a comparison of two or more populations. The sampling distribution of the test statistics in both tests is the chi-squared distribution introduced in Chapter 8.

15-1 / CHI-SQUARED GOODNESS-OF-FIT TEST

This section presents another test designed to describe a population of nominal data. The first such test was introduced in Section 12-3, where we discussed the statistical procedure employed to test hypotheses about a population proportion. In that case, the nominal variable could assume one of only two possible values: success or failure. Our tests dealt with hypotheses about the proportion of successes in the entire population. Recall that the experiment that produces the data is called a *binomial experiment*. In this section, we introduce the **multinomial experiment**, which is an extension of the binomial experiment, wherein there are two or more possible outcomes per trial.

> **Multinomial Experiment**
>
> A multinomial experiment is one that possesses the following properties.
>
> 1. The experiment consists of a fixed number n of trials.
> 2. The outcome of each trial can be classified into one of k categories, called *cells*.
> 3. The probability p_i that the outcome will fall into cell i remains constant for each trial. Moreover, $p_1 + p_2 + \cdots + p_k = 1$
> 4. Each trial of the experiment is independent of the other trials.

When $k = 2$, the multinomial experiment is identical to the binomial experiment. Just as we count the number of successes (recall that we label the number of successes x) and failures in a binomial experiment, we count the number of outcomes falling into each of the k cells in a multinomial experiment. In this way, we obtain a set of observed frequencies $f_1, f_2, \ldots, f_k$ where f_i is the observed frequency of outcomes falling into cell i, for $i = 1, 2, \ldots, k$. Because the experiment consists of n trials and an outcome must fall into some cell,

$$f_1 + f_2 + \cdots + f_k = n$$

Just as we used the number of successes x (by calculating the sample proportion $\hat{p}$, which is equal to x/n) to draw inferences about p, so we use the observed frequencies to draw inferences about the cell probabilities. We'll proceed in what by now has become a standard procedure. We will set up the hypotheses and develop the test statistic and its sampling distribution. We'll demonstrate the process with the following example.

EXAMPLE 15.1 Testing Market Shares

Company A has recently conducted aggressive advertising campaigns to maintain and possibly increase its share of the market (currently 45%) for fabric softener. Its main competitor, company B, has 40% of the market, and a number of other competitors account for the remaining 15%. To determine whether the market shares changed after the advertising campaign, the marketing manager for company A solicited the preferences of a random sample of 200 customers of fabric softener. Of the 200 customers, 102 indicated a preference for company A's product, 82 preferred company B's fabric softener, and the remaining 16 preferred the products of one of the competitors. Can the analyst infer at the 5% significance level that customer preferences have changed from their levels before the advertising campaigns were launched?

SOLUTION:

The population in question is composed of the brand preferences of the fabric softener customers. The data are nominal because each respondent will choose one of three possible answers: product A, product B, or other. If there were only two categories, or if we were interested only in the proportion of one company's customers (which we would label as successes and label the others as failures), we would identify the technique as the z-test of p. However, in this problem we're interested in the proportions of all three categories. We recognize this experiment as a multinomial experiment, and we identify the technique as the **chi-squared goodness-of-fit test**.

Because we want to know whether the market shares have changed, we specify those precampaign market shares in the null hypothesis.

$$H_0: \ p_1 = .45, \ p_2 = .40, \ p_3 = .15$$

The alternative hypothesis attempts to answer our question, Have the proportions changed? Thus,

$$H_1: \ \text{At least one } p_i \text{ is not equal to its specified value}$$

15-1a Test Statistic

If the null hypothesis is true, we would expect the number of customers selecting brand A, brand B, and other to be 200 times the proportions specified under the null hypothesis; that is,

$$e_1 = 200(.45) = 90$$

$$e_2 = 200(.40) = 80$$

$$e_3 = 200(.15) = 30$$

In general, the **expected frequency** for each cell is given by

$$e_i = np_i$$

This expression is derived from the formula for the expected value of a binomial random variable, introduced in Section 7-4.

Figure 15.1 is a bar chart (created by Excel) showing the comparison of actual and expected frequencies.

FIGURE **15.1**   **Bar Chart for Example 15.1**

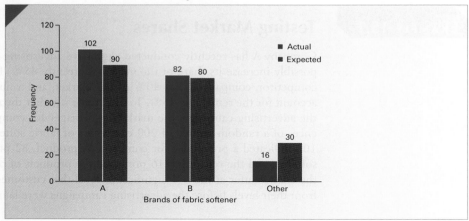

If the expected frequencies e_i and the **observed frequencies** f_i are quite different, we would conclude that the null hypothesis is false, and we would reject it. However, if the expected and observed frequencies are similar, we would not reject the null hypothesis. The test statistic defined in the box measures the similarity of the expected and observed frequencies.

Chi-Squared Goodness-of-Fit Test Statistic

$$\chi^2 = \sum_{i=1}^{k} \frac{(f_i - e_i)^2}{e_i}$$

The sampling distribution of the test statistic is approximately chi-squared distributed with $v = k - 1$ degrees of freedom, provided that the sample size is large. We will discuss this required condition later. (The chi-squared distribution was introduced in Section 8-4.)

The following table demonstrates the calculation of the test statistic. Thus, the value $\chi^2 = 8.18$. As usual, we judge the size of this test statistic by specifying the rejection region or by determining the p-value.

Company	Observed Frequency f_i	Expected Frequency e_i	$(f_i - e_i)$	$\dfrac{(f_i - e_i)^2}{e_i}$
A	102	90	12	1.60
B	82	80	2	0.05
Other	16	30	−14	6.53
Total	200	200		$\chi^2 = 8.18$

When the null hypothesis is true, the observed and expected frequencies should be similar, in which case the test statistic will be small. Thus, a small test statistic supports the null hypothesis. If the null hypothesis is untrue, some of the observed and expected

April	16.9%	October	4.9%
May	21.2%	November	4.9%
June	17.4%	December	2.8%
July	8.0%		
August	5.7%		
September	5.9%		

The monthly number of tornadoes for 2015 was recorded. Is there enough statistical evidence at the 5% significance level to infer that the percentages have changed?

APPLICATIONS in MARKETING

Market Segmentation

George Dolgikh/Shutterstock.com

Market segmentation was introduced in Section 12-4, where a statistical technique was used to estimate the size of a segment. In Chapters 13 and 14, statistical procedures were applied to determine whether market segments differ in their purchases of products and services. Exercise 15.20 requires you to apply the chi-squared goodness-of-fit test to determine whether the relative sizes of segments have changed.

15.20 Xr12-131* Refer to Exercise 12.131 where the statistics practitioner estimated the size of market segments based on education among California adults. Suppose that census figures from 10 years ago showed the education levels and the proportions of California adults, as follows:

LEVEL	PROPORTION
1. Did not complete high school	.23
2. Completed high school only	.40
3. Some college or university	.15
4. College or university graduate	.22

Determine whether there has been a change in these proportions.

GENERAL SOCIAL SURVEY EXERCISES

The following figures are from the United States Census in 2014:

Racial mix

White	77.3%
Black	13.2%
Other	9.5%

Marital status

Never married (including partnered, not married)	31.7%
Married (including separated, but not divorced)	52.5%
Widowed	5.7%
Divorced	10.0%

Education

Less than high school	12.3%
High school	29.6%
Some college including junior college	19.4%
College graduate including bachelor's and graduate degrees	38.6%

15.21 GSS2014* Test to determine whether there is sufficient evidence that the General Social Survey in 2014 overrepresented at least one race (RACE).

15.22 GSS2014* Can we infer that the General Social Survey in 2014 overrepresented at least one category of marital status (MARITAL)?

15.23 GSS2014* Can we infer that the General Social Survey in 2014 overrepresented at least one education category (DEGREE)?

SURVEY OF CONSUMER FINANCES EXERCISES

The following figures are from the United States Census in 2013:

Racial mix

White non-Hispanic	61.6%
Black	13.2%
Hispanic	17.6%
Other	7.5%

Education

Less than high school	12.6%
High school	29.6%
Some college including junior college	19.6%
College graduate including bachelor's and graduate degrees	38.3%

15.24 SCF2013:\ALL* Test to determine whether there is sufficient evidence that the Survey of Consumer Finances in 2013 overrepresented at least one race (RACE).

15.25 SCF2013:\ALL* Can we infer that the Survey of Consumer Finances in 2013 overrepresented at least one education category (EDCL)?

15-2 / CHI-SQUARED TEST OF A CONTINGENCY TABLE

In Chapter 2, we developed the **cross-classification table** as a first step in graphing the relationship between two nominal variables (see page 34). Our goal was to determine whether the two variables were related. In this section we extend the technique to statistical inference. We introduce another chi-squared test, this one designed to satisfy two different problem objectives. The **chi-squared test of a contingency table** is used to determine whether there is enough evidence to infer that two nominal variables are related and to infer that differences exist between two or more populations of nominal variables. Completing both objectives entails classifying items according to two different criteria. To see how this is done, consider the following example.

EXAMPLE 15.2

DATA
Xm15-02

Relationship between Undergraduate Degree and MBA Major

The MBA program was experiencing problems scheduling its courses. The demand for the program's optional courses and majors was quite variable from one year to the next. In one year, students seem to want marketing courses; in other years, accounting or finance are the rage. In desperation, the dean of the business school turned to a statistics professor for assistance. The statistics professor believed that the problem may be the variability in the academic background of the students and that the undergraduate degree affects the choice of major. As a start, he took a random sample of last year's MBA students and recorded the undergraduate degree and the major selected in the graduate program. The undergraduate degrees were BA, BEng, BBA, and several others. There are three possible majors for the MBA students: accounting, finance, and marketing. The results were summarized in a cross-classification table, which is shown here. Can the statistician conclude that the undergraduate degree affects the choice of major?

Undergraduate Degree	MBA Major			Total
	Accounting	**Finance**	**Marketing**	
BA	31	13	16	60
BEng	8	16	7	31
BBA	12	10	17	39
Other	10	5	7	22
Total	61	44	47	152

SOLUTION:

One way to solve the problem is to consider that there are two variables: undergraduate degree and MBA major. Both are nominal. The values of the undergraduate degree are BA, BEng, BBA, and other. The values of MBA major are accounting, finance, and marketing. The problem objective is to analyze the relationship between the two variables. Specifically, we want to know whether one variable is related to the other.

Another way of addressing the problem is to determine whether differences exist between BA's, BEng's, BBA's, and others. In other words, we treat the holders of each undergraduate degree as a separate population. Each population has three possible values represented by the MBA major. The problem objective is to compare four populations. (We can also answer the question by treating the MBA majors as populations and the undergraduate degrees as the values of the random variable.)

As you will shortly discover, both objectives lead to the same test. Consequently, we address both objectives at the same time.

The null hypothesis will specify that there is no relationship between the two variables. We state this in the following way:

H_0:   The two variables are independent

The alternative hypothesis specifies one variable affects the other, expressed as

H_1:   The two variables are dependent

15-2a Graphical Technique

Figure 15.3 depicts the graphical technique introduced in Chapter 2 to show the relationship (if any) between the two nominal variables.

The bar chart displays the data from the sample. It does appear that there is a relationship between the two nominal variables in the sample. However, to draw inferences about the population of MBA students we need to apply an inferential technique.

FIGURE **15.3**   Bar Chart for Example 15.2

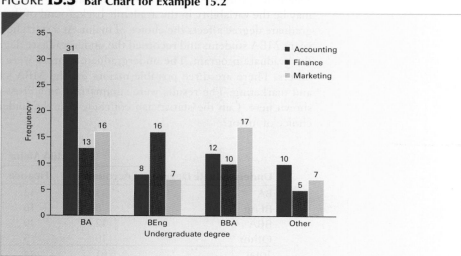

15-2b Test Statistic

The test statistic is the same as the one used to test proportions in the goodness-of-fit test; that is, the test statistic is

$$\chi^2 = \sum_{i=1}^{k} \frac{(f_i - e_i)^2}{e_i}$$

where k is the number of cells in the cross-classification table. If you examine the null hypothesis described in the goodness-of-fit test and the one described above, you will discover a major difference. In the goodness-of-fit test, the null hypothesis lists values for the probabilities p_i. The null hypothesis for the chi-squared test of a contingency table only states that the two variables are independent. However, we need the probabilities to compute the expected values e_i, which in turn are needed to calculate the value of the test statistic. (The entries in the table are the observed values f_i.) The question immediately arises, From where do we get the probabilities? The answer is that they must come from the data after we assume that the null hypothesis is true.

In Chapter 6 we introduced independent events and showed that if two events A and B are independent, the joint probability $P(A \text{ and } B)$ is equal to the product of $P(A)$ and $P(B)$. That is,

$$P(A \text{ and } B) = P(A) \times P(B)$$

The events in this example are the values each of the two nominal variables can assume. Unfortunately, we do not have the probabilities of A and B. However, these probabilities can be estimated from the data. Using relative frequencies, we calculate the estimated probabilities for the MBA major.

$$P(\text{Accounting}) = \frac{61}{152} = .401$$

$$P(\text{Finance}) = \frac{44}{152} = .289$$

$$P(\text{Marketing}) = \frac{47}{152} = .309$$

We calculate the estimated probabilities for the undergraduate degree.

$$P(BA) = \frac{60}{152} = .395$$

$$P(BEng) = \frac{31}{152} = .204$$

$$P(BBA) = \frac{39}{152} = .257$$

$$P(Other) = \frac{22}{152} = .145$$

Assuming that the null hypothesis is true, we can compute the estimated joint probabilities. To produce the expected values, we multiply the estimated joint probabilities by the sample size, $n = 152$. The results are listed in a **contingency table**, the word *contingency* derived by calculating the expected values contingent on the assumption that the null hypothesis is true (the two variables are independent).

Undergraduate Degree	MBA Major			Total
	Accounting	**Finance**	**Marketing**	
BA	$152 \times \frac{60}{152} \times \frac{61}{152} = 24.08$	$152 \times \frac{60}{152} \times \frac{44}{152} = 17.37$	$152 \times \frac{60}{152} \times \frac{47}{152} = 18.55$	60
BEng	$152 \times \frac{31}{152} \times \frac{61}{152} = 12.44$	$152 \times \frac{31}{152} \times \frac{44}{152} = 8.97$	$152 \times \frac{31}{152} \times \frac{47}{152} = 9.59$	31
BBA	$152 \times \frac{39}{152} \times \frac{61}{152} = 15.65$	$152 \times \frac{39}{152} \times \frac{44}{152} = 11.29$	$152 \times \frac{39}{152} \times \frac{47}{152} = 12.06$	39
Other	$152 \times \frac{22}{152} \times \frac{61}{152} = 8.83$	$152 \times \frac{22}{152} \times \frac{44}{152} = 6.37$	$152 \times \frac{22}{152} \times \frac{47}{152} = 6.80$	22
Total	61	44	47	152

As you can see, the expected value for each cell is computed by multiplying the row total by the column total and dividing by the sample size. For example, the BA and Accounting cell expected value is

$$152 \times \frac{60}{152} \times \frac{61}{152} = \frac{60 \times 61}{152} = 24.08$$

All the other expected values would be determined similarly.

> ### Expected Frequencies for a Contingency Table
> The expected frequency of the cell in row i and column j is
> $$e_{ij} = \frac{\text{row } i \text{ total} \times \text{column } j \text{ total}}{\text{sample size}}$$

The expected cell frequencies are shown in parentheses in the following table. As in the case of the goodness-of-fit test, the expected cell frequencies should satisfy the rule of five.

Undergraduate Degree	MBA Major		
	Accounting	**Finance**	**Marketing**
BA	31 (24.08)	13 (17.37)	16 (18.55)
BEng	8 (12.44)	16 (8.97)	7 (9.59)
BBA	12 (15.65)	10 (11.29)	17 (12.06)
Other	10 (8.83)	5 (6.37)	7 (6.80)

We can now calculate the value of the test statistic:

$$\chi^2 = \sum_{i=1}^{k} \frac{(f_i - e_i)^2}{e_i} = \frac{(31 - 24.08)^2}{24.08} + \frac{(13 - 17.37)^2}{17.37} + \frac{(16 - 18.55)^2}{18.55}$$
$$+ \frac{(8 - 12.44)^2}{12.44} + \frac{(16 - 8.97)^2}{8.97} + \frac{(7 - 9.59)^2}{9.59} + \frac{(12 - 15.65)^2}{15.65}$$
$$+ \frac{(10 - 11.29)^2}{11.29} + \frac{(17 - 12.06)^2}{12.06} + \frac{(10 - 8.83)^2}{8.83}$$
$$+ \frac{(5 - 6.37)^2}{6.37} + \frac{(7 - 6.80)^2}{6.80}$$
$$= 14.70$$

Notice that we continue to use a single subscript in the formula of the test statistic when we should use two subscripts, one for the rows and one for the columns. We believe that it is clear, that for each cell we must calculate the squared difference between the observed and expected frequencies divided by the expected frequency. We don't believe that the satisfaction of using the mathematically correct notation overcomes the unnecessary complication.

15-2c Rejection Region and p-Value

To determine the rejection region we must know the number of degrees of freedom associated with the chi-squared statistic. The number of degrees of freedom for a contingency table with r rows and c columns is $\nu = (r - 1)(c - 1)$. For this example, the number of degrees of freedom is $v = (r - 1)(c - 1) = (4 - 1)(3 - 1) = 6$.

If we employ a 5% significance level, the rejection region is

$$\chi^2 > \chi^2_{\alpha,\nu} = \chi^2_{.05,6} = 12.6$$

Because $\chi^2 = 14.70$, we reject the null hypothesis and conclude that there is evidence of a relationship between undergraduate degree and MBA major.

The p-value of the test statistic is

$$P(\chi^2 > 14.70)$$

Unfortunately, we cannot determine the p-value manually.

Do It Yourself Excel

	A	B	C	D	E	F
1	Degree	MBA Major >	1	2	3	
2	1		31	13	16	60
3	2		8	16	7	31
4	3		12	10	17	39
5	4		10	5	7	22
6			61	44	47	152
7						
8			24.08	17.37	18.55	
9			12.44	8.97	9.59	
10			15.65	11.29	12.06	
11			8.83	6.37	6.80	
12						
13			1.99	1.10	0.35	
14			1.59	5.50	0.70	
15			0.85	0.15	2.02	
16			0.16	0.29	0.01	
17						14.70
18						0.0227

INSTRUCTIONS

For this statistical technique, you will have to create the spreadsheet yourself. We call it **Do It Yourself Excel**. We demonstrate how to create a spreadsheet to solve any exercise by providing instructions for Example 15.2.

1. Use the PivotTable to create the cross-classification table.

2. Calculate the row and column totals and the total of all the cells. For example, to determine the total of column 1 type the following in cell C6.

   = SUM(C2:C5)

3. Calculate the expected values. For example to calculate the expected value for the first cell type.

   = C$6*$F2/F6

Drag down the column and then across the rows to compute all the expected values.

4. Compute the chi-squared statistic. Start in C13 and type.

   = ((C2–C8) ^ 2)/C8

   Drag down the column and then across the rows.

5. Calculate the chi-squared statistic.

   = SUM(C13:E16)

6. Compute the *p*-value using the CHIDIST function in which we specify the value of the chi-squared statistic (14.70) and the degrees of freedom (6).

   = CHIDIST(F17,6)

File Xm15-02 contains the raw data using the following codes:

Column1 (Undergraduate Degree)	Column 2 (MBA Major)
1 = BA	1 = Accounting
2 = BEng	2 = Finance
3 = BBA	3 = Marketing
4 = Other	

XLSTAT

	A	B	C	D	E	F
1	Results for the variables Degree and MBA Major:					
2						
3	Contingency table (Degree / MBA Major):					
4		1	2	3		
5	1	31	13	16		
6	2	8	16	7		
7	3	12	10	17		
8	4	10	5	7		
9						
10	Test of independence between the rows and the columns (Degree / MBA Major):					
11	Chi-square (Observed value)	14.70				
12	Chi-square (Critical value)	12.59				
13	DF	6				
14	p-value	0.0227				
15	alpha	0.05				

INTERPRET

There is strong evidence to infer that the undergraduate degree and MBA major are related. This suggests that the dean can predict the number of optional courses by counting the number of MBA students with each type of undergraduate degree. We can see that BA's favor accounting courses, BEng's prefer finance, BBA's are partial to marketing, and others show no particular preference.

If the null hypothesis is true, undergraduate degree and MBA major are independent of one another. This means that whether an MBA student earned a BA, BEng, BBA, or other degree does not affect his or her choice of major program in the MBA. Consequently, there is no difference in major choice among the graduates of the undergraduate programs. If the alternative hypothesis is true, undergraduate degree does affect the choice of MBA major. Thus, there are differences between the four undergraduate degree categories.

15-2d Rule of Five

In the previous section, we pointed out that the expected values should be at least 5 to ensure that the chi-squared distribution provides an adequate approximation of the sampling distribution. In a contingency table where one or more cells have expected values of less than 5, we need to combine rows or columns to satisfy the rule of five. This subject is discussed in the online appendix Rule of Five.

15-2e Data Formats

In Example 15.2, the data were stored in two columns, one column containing the values of one nominal variable and the second column storing the values of the second nominal variable. The data can be stored in another way. In Example 15.2, we could have recorded the data in three columns, one column for each MBA major. The columns would contain the codes representing the undergraduate degree. Alternatively, we could have stored the data in four columns, one column for each undergraduate degree. The columns would contain the codes for the MBA majors. In either case, we have to count the number of each value and construct the cross-tabulation table using the counts. We will illustrate this approach with the solution to the chapter-opening example.

General Social Survey

Has Support for Capital Punishment for Murderers Remained Constant Since 2006? Solution

IDENTIFY

The problem objective is to compare public opinion in four different years. The variable is nominal because its values are Favor and Oppose, represented by 1 and 2, respectively. The appropriate technique is the chi-squared test of a contingency table. The hypotheses are:

H_0 : The two variables are independent.
H_1 : The two variables are dependent.

In this application, the two variables are year (2006, 2008, 2010, 2012, and 2014) and the answer to the question posed by the General Social Survey (Favor and Oppose).

Unlike Example 15.2, the data are not stored in two columns. To produce the statistical result, we will need to count the number of Americans in favor and the number opposed in each of the four years. The contingency table, expected values, chi-squared statistic, and p-value were calculated as shown below.

Do It Yourself Excel

COMPUTE

G	H	I	J	K	L	M
	CAPPUN 2006	CAPPUN 2008	CAPPUN 2010	CAPPUN 2012	CAPUN 2014	
Favor	1885	1263	1297	1183	1530	7158
Oppose	930	639	624	641	849	3683
	2815	1902	1921	1824	2379	10841
	1859	1256	1268	1204	1571	
	956	646	653	620	808	
	0.373	0.041	0.646	0.378	1.059	
	0.725	0.079	1.255	0.735	2.058	
					7.35	
					0.1185	

INTERPRET

The p-value is .1185. There is not enough evidence to infer that the two variables are independent. Thus, there is not enough evidence to conclude that support for capital punishment for murder varies from year to year.

Here is a summary of the factors that tell us when to apply the chi-squared test of a contingency table. Note that there are two problem objectives satisfied by this statistical procedure.

Factors That Identify the Chi-Squared Test of a Contingency Table

1. **Problem objectives**: Analyze the relationship between two variables and compare two or more populations.
2. **Data type**: Nominal

EXERCISES

Developing an Understanding of Statistical Concepts

15.26 Conduct a test to determine whether the two classifications L and M are independent, using the data in the accompanying cross-classification table. (Use $\alpha = .05$.)

	M_1	M_2
L_1	28	68
L_2	56	36

15.27 Repeat Exercise 15.26 using the following table:

	M_1	M_2
L_1	14	34
L_2	28	18

15.28 Repeat Exercise 15.26 using the following table:

	M_1	M_2
L_1	7	17
L_2	14	9

15.29 Review the results of Exercises 15.26–15.28. What is the effect of decreasing the sample size?

15.30 Conduct a test to determine whether the two classifications R and C are independent, using the data in the accompanying cross-classification table. (Use $\alpha = .10$.)

	C_1	C_1	C_3
R_1	40	32	48
R_2	30	48	52

Applications

Use a 5% significance level unless specified otherwise.

15.31 The trustee of a company's pension plan has solicited the opinions of a sample of the company's employees about a proposed revision of the plan. A breakdown of the responses is shown in the accompanying table. Is there enough evidence to infer that the responses differ between the three groups of employees?

Responses	Blue-Collar Workers	White-Collar Workers	Managers
For	67	32	11
Against	63	18	9

15.32 The operations manager of a company that manufactures shirts wants to determine whether there are differences in the quality of workmanship among the three daily shifts. She randomly selects 600 recently made shirts and carefully inspects them. Each shirt is classified as either perfect or flawed, and the shift that produced it is also recorded. The accompanying table summarizes the number of shirts that fell into each cell. Do these data provide sufficient evidence to infer that there are differences in quality between the three shifts?

Shirt Condition	Shift 1	Shift 2	Shift 3
Perfect	240	191	139
Flawed	10	9	11

15.33 One of the issues that came up in a recent national election (and is likely to arise in many future elections) is how to deal with a sluggish economy. Specifically, should governments cut spending, raise taxes, inflate the economy (by printing more money) or do none of the above and let the deficit rise? And as with most other issues, politicians need to know which parts of the electorate support these options. Suppose that a random sample of 1,000 people was asked which option they support and their political affiliations. The possible responses to the question about political affiliation were Democrat, Republican, and Independent (which included a variety of political persuasions). The responses are summarized in the accompanying table. Do these results allow us to conclude at the 1% significance level that political affiliation affects support for the economic options?

Economic Options	Political Affiliation		
	Democrat	Republican	Independent
Cut spending	101	282	61
Raise taxes	38	67	25
Inflate the economy	131	88	31
Let deficit increase	61	90	25

15.34 Econetics Research Corporation, a well-known Montreal-based consulting firm, wants to test how it can influence the proportion of questionnaires returned from surveys. In the belief that the inclusion of an inducement to respond may be important, the firm sends out 1,000 questionnaires: Two hundred promise to send respondents a summary of the survey results, 300 indicate that 20 respondents (selected by lottery) will be awarded gifts, and 500 are accompanied by no inducements. Of these, 80 questionnaires promising a summary, 100 questionnaires offering gifts, and 120 questionnaires offering no inducements are returned. What can you conclude from these results?

Exercises 15.35–15.50 require the use of a computer and software. The answers may be calculated manually. See Appendix A for the sample statistics. **Use a 5% significance level unless specified otherwise.**

15.35 Xm02-04 (Example 2.4 revisited) A major North American city has four competing newspapers: the *Globe and Mail* (G&M), *Post*, *Sun*, and *Star*. To help design advertising campaigns, the advertising managers of the newspapers need to know which segments of the newspaper market are reading their papers. A survey was conducted to analyze the relationship between newspapers read and occupation. A sample of newspaper readers was asked to report which newspaper they read: *Globe and Mail* (1) *Post* (2), *Star* (3), *Sun* (4), and to indicate whether they were blue-collar workers (1), white-collar workers (2), or professionals (3). Can we infer that occupation and newspaper are related?

15.36 Xr15-36 To determine the actual side effects, pharmaceutical companies often conduct studies that compare the side effects of their drug versus the side effects of a placebo. One such study examined the side effects of a new cold remedy. A random sample of 250 people was given the cold remedy and

another 250 were given a placebo that looked like the cold remedy. These responses were recorded as

1 = Headache, 2 = Drowsiness, 3 = Stomach upset, 4 = No side effect

Do these data provide enough evidence to infer that the reported side effects differ between the cold remedy and the placebo?

15.37 Xr02-45 (Exercise 2.45 revisited) Is there brand loyalty among car owners in their purchases of gasoline? To help answer the question, a random sample of car owners was asked to record the brand of gasoline in their last two purchases: 1 = Exxon, 2 = Amoco, 3 = Texaco, 4 = Other. Can we conclude that there is brand loyalty in gasoline purchases?

15.38 Xr15-38 During the past decade, many cigarette smokers have attempted to quit. Unfortunately, nicotine is highly addictive. Smokers use a large number of different methods to help them quit. These include nicotine patches, hypnosis, and various forms of therapy. A researcher for the Addiction Research Council wanted to determine why some people quit while others attempted to quit but failed. He surveyed 1,000 people who planned to quit smoking. He determined their educational level and whether they continued to smoke 1 year later. Educational level was recorded in the following way:

  1 = Did not finish high school
  2 = High school graduate
  3 = University or college graduate
  4 = Completed a postgraduate degree

A continuing smoker was recorded as 1; a quitter was recorded as 2. Can we infer that the amount of education is a factor in determining whether a smoker will quit?

15.39 Xr15-39 Because television audiences of newscasts tend to be older (and because older people suffer from a variety of medical ailments), pharmaceutical companies' advertising often appears on national news on the three networks (ABC, CBS, and NBC). To determine how effective the ads are a survey was undertaken. Adults over 50 were asked about their primary sources of news. The responses are

1. ABC News   2. CBS News 3. NBC News
4. Newspapers 5. Radio   6. None of the above

Each person was also asked whether they suffer from heartburn, and if so, what remedy they take. The answers were recorded as follows:

  1. Do not suffer from heartburn
  2. Suffer from heartburn but take no remedy
  3. Suffer from heartburn and take an over-the-counter remedy (e.g., Tums, Gavoscol)

4. Suffer from heartburn and take a prescription pill (e.g., Nexium)

Is there a relationship between an adult's source of news and his or her heartburn condition?

15.40 Xr02-44 (Exercise 2.44 revisited) The associate dean of a business school was looking for ways to improve the quality of the applicants to its MBA program. In particular, she wanted to know whether the undergraduate degree of applicants differed among her school and the three nearby universities with MBA programs. She sampled 100 applicants of her program and an equal number from each of the other universities. She recorded their undergraduate degrees (1 = BA, 2 = BEng, 3 = BBA, 4 = other) as well as universities (codes 1, 2, 3, and 4). Do these data provide sufficient evidence to infer that undergraduate degree and the university each person applied are related?

15.41 Xr15-41 The relationship between drug companies and medical researchers is under scrutiny because of possible conflict of interest. The issue that started the controversy was a 1995 case control study that suggested that the use of calcium-channel blockers to treat hypertension led to an increase risk of heart disease. This led to an intense debate both in technical journals and in the press. Researchers writing in the *New England Journal of Medicine* ("Conflict of Interest in the Debate over Calcium Channel Antagonists," January 8, 1998, p. 101) looked at the 70 reports that appeared during 1996–1997, classifying them as favorable, neutral, or critical toward the drugs. The researchers then contacted the authors of the reports and questioned them about financial ties to drug companies. The results were recorded in the following way:

Column 1: Results of the scientific study; 1 = favorable, 2 = neutral, 3 = critical

Column 2: 1 = financial ties to drug companies, 2 = no ties to drug companies

Do these data allow us to infer that the research findings for calcium-channel blockers are affected by whether the research is funded by drug companies?

15.42 Xr15-42 After a thorough analysis of the market, a publisher of business and economics statistics books has divided the market into three general approaches to teach applied statistics. These are (1) use of a computer and statistical software with no manual calculations, (2) traditional teaching of concepts and solution of problems by hand, and (3) mathematical approach with emphasis on derivations and proofs. The publisher wanted to know whether this market could be segmented on the basis of the educational background of the

instructor. As a result, the statistics editor organized a survey that asked 195 professors of business and economics statistics to report their approach to teaching and which one of the following categories represents their highest degree:

1. Business (MBA or Ph.D. in business)
2. Economics
3. Mathematics or engineering
4. Other

a. Can the editor infer that there are differences in type of degree among the three teaching approaches? If so, how can the editor use this information?
b. Suppose that you work in the marketing department of a textbook publisher. Prepare a report for the editor that describes this analysis.

15.43 Xr15-43 Every year, there are more than 300,000 robberies in the United States. A researcher took a random sample of robberies in 2000, 2005, and 2010, and recorded the weapon used (1 = Firearm, 2 = Knife or other cutting instrument, 3 = Other, 4 = No weapon). Is there sufficient evidence to infer that the frequency of the use of weapons in robberies differed over the three years?

Source: Adapted from *Statistical Abstract of the United States*, 2012, Table 321.

15.44 Xr15-44 Refer to Exercise 12.139. The engineering team took samples of bridges in 2004, 2006, 2008, and 2010 and recorded whether each bridge was structurally deficient, functionally obsolete, or structurally sound. These three categories were recorded as 1, 2, and 3, respectively. Do these data allow us to conclude that the deteriorating condition of American bridges has changed over the years?

Source: Adapted from *Statistical Abstract of the United States*, 2012, Table 1090.

15.45 Xr15-45 Household types are categorized in the following way: 1. Married couple with children, 2. Married couple without children, 3. Single parent, 4. One person, 5. Other. Random samples of families in the United States, Canada, and the United Kingdom were drawn and the household types recorded. Is the sufficient evidence to infer that there are differences in household types between the three countries?

Source: Adapted from *Statistical Abstract of the United States*, 2012, Table 1338.

15.46 Xr15-46 Refer to Exercise 15.45. Random samples from Denmark, Ireland, the Netherlands, and Sweden were drawn. Is the sufficient evidence to infer that there are differences in household types between the four countries?

Source: Adapted from *Statistical Abstract of the United States*, 2012, Table 1338.

15.47 Xr15-47 A statistics practitioner took random samples from Canada, Australia, New Zealand, and the United Kingdom, and classified each person as either obese (2) or not (1). Can we conclude from these data that there are differences in obesity rates between the four Commonwealth nations?

Source: Adapted from *Statistical Abstract of the United States* 2012, Table 1342.

15.48 Xr15-48 To measure the extent of cigarette smoking around the world, random samples of adults in Denmark, Finland, Norway, and Sweden were drawn. Each was asked whether he or she smoked (2 = Yes, 1 = No). Can we conclude that there are differences in smoking between the four Scandinavian countries?

Source: Adapted from *Statistical Abstract of the United States* 2012, Table 1343.

15.49 Xr15-49 Refer to Exercise 15.48. The survey was performed in Canada, Australia, New Zealand, and the United Kingdom. Is there enough evidence to infer that there are differences in adult cigarette smoking between the four Commonwealth countries?

Source: Adapted from *Statistical Abstract of the United States* 2012, Table 1343.

15.50 Xr15-50 In 2013, the Supreme Court of the United States ruled on a California law that banned same-sex marriage. An important element of that decision was public opinion. In March, Public Policy Polling conducted a survey of Florida voters and asked each to identify themselves as either: 1. Democrat, 2. Republican, or 3. Independent, and to choose one of the following:

1. Gay couples should be allowed to marry legally.
2. Gay couples should be allowed to form civil unions but not marry.
3. There should be no legal recognition of a gay couple's relationship.

The results were recorded. Is there sufficient evidence to infer that the three political persuasions differ?

15.51 Xr15-51 A Gallup survey asked a random sample of federal government and private sector workers to judge their well-being. The responses are 1 = thriving, 2 = struggling, 3 = suffering. Is there enough evidence to conclude that government and private sector workers differ in their well-being?

15.52 Xr15-52 A critical issue for service companies is how many customers cancel. Some wireless carriers lose an average of 3% of their subscribers each month. Should companies spend more effort getting new customers or trying to win back old customers who left? Researchers have argued that it is easier and cheaper to lure back customers. One telecom firm tested four win-back offers. Their offers and their costs are listed next.

1. Discount offer: $20 off for 6 months. Cost $120
2. Upgrade offer: a $35 movie channel for 3 months. Cost $105
3. Bundled offer: $20 off for 6 months, plus a $35 movie channel free for 3 months. Cost $225
4. Tailored offer: Customers who left over price get the discount; customers who left over service get the upgrade. Cost $120/$105

A random sample of customers who left was drawn and one-quarter received one type of offer. The responses were recorded where 1 = took the offer and 2 = did not take the offer. Can we infer at the 5% significance level that there are differences in success rates between the four win-back offers?

Source: Adapted from Winning Back Lost Customers, *Harvard Business Review*, March 2016.

GENERAL SOCIAL SURVEY EXERCISES

Use a 5% significance level.

15.53 GSS2014* An important element in the business of politics is to know who supports you and who doesn't. Is there sufficient evidence to infer that men and women (SEX: 1 = Male, 2 = Female) differ in their support of the political groups (PARTYID3: 1 = Democrat, 2 = Independent, 3 = Republican)?

15.54 GSS2014* Do foreign-born Americans differ from Americans born in the United States (BORN:

1 = Born in the United States, 2 = Born elsewhere) in their support of political groups (PARTYID3: 1 = Democrat, 2 = Independent, 3 = Republican)?

15.55 GSS2014* Is it a myth that men are more conservative and women more liberal? Conduct a test to determine whether men and women (SEX: 1 = Male, 2 = Female) differ in their political views (POLVIEWS3: 1 = Liberal, 2 = Moderate, 3 = Conservative).

15.56 GSS2014*   Do Americans who work for themselves (WRKSLF: 1 = Self-employed, 2 = Someone else) support the same political groups (PARTYID3: 1 = Democrat, 2 = Independent, 3 = Republican) as Americans who work for someone else? Conduct a statistical test to answer the question.

15.57 GSS2014*   Are government workers more or less conservative than people who work in the private sector? Is there sufficient evidence to conclude that government workers (WRKGOVT: 1 = Government, 2 = Someone else) differ from private-sector workers in terms of their political views (POLVIEWS3: 1 = Liberal, 2 = Moderate, 3 = Conservative)?

15.58 GSS2006* GSS2008* GSS2010* GSS2012* GSS2014*   The issue of gun control in the United States is one that is often debated particularly during elections. The question arises, What does the public think about the issue and does support vary from year to year? Test to determine whether there is enough evidence to conclude that support for gun laws (GUNLAW: 1 = Favor, 2 = Oppose) varied from year to year.

15.59 GSS2014*   In the last two decades, an increasing proportion of women have entered the workforce.

Determine whether there is enough evidence to conclude that men and women (SEX) differ in their work status (WRKSTAT).

15.60 GSS2014*   Is there sufficient evidence to infer that support for capital punishment (CAPPUN: 1 = Favor, 2 = Oppose) is related to political affiliation (PARTYID3: 1 = Democrat, 2 = Republican, 3 = Independent)?

15.61 GSS2014*   Immigration has become a hot-button issue in American politics. One question that arises is: Are immigrants' educational attainments different from those born in the United States? Conduct a test to answer the question (BORN: 1 = U.S., 2 = outside U.S.; DEGREE: Highest degree completed of respondent, 0 = Left high school, 1 = High school, 2 = Junior college, 3 = Bachelor's degree, 4 = Graduate degree).

15.62 GSS2014*   Is there sufficient evidence to infer that there are differences in marital status between people born in the United States and those born outside the United States (BORN: 1 = U.S., 2 = outside U.S.; MARITAL: Marital status: 1. Married, 2. Widowed, 3. Divorced, 4. Separated, 5. Never married)?

SURVEY OF CONSUMER FINANCES EXERCISES

Conduct all tests at the 5% significance level.

The following exercises are based on the middle-class respondents of the 2013 survey. Exercises 15.63–15.66 address differences in educational attainment (EDCL Education category of head of household: 1 = No high school diploma, 2 = High school diploma, 3 = Some college, 4 = College degree) with respect to several demographic and financial variables. For each variable, test to determine whether there are differences between the levels of education.

15.63 SCF2013:\MC*   MARRIED: 1 = Married, 2 = Not married.

15.64 SCF2013:\MC*   Turned down for credit in the previous 5 years (TURNDOWN: 0 = No, 1 = Yes)

15.65 SCF2013:\MC*   Household has declared bankruptcy in the previous 5 years (BNKRUPTLAST5: 0 = No, 1 = Yes).

15.66 SCF2013:\MC*   Household has debt (HDEBT: Household has any debt: 0 = No, 1 = Yes).

Exercises 15.67–15.71 examine the issue of race among middle-class households (RACE: 1 = White, non-Hispanic, 2 = Black/African American, 3 = Hispanic,

5 = Other). For each variable, test to determine whether there is sufficient evidence to conclude that differences exist between the four races.

15.67 SCF2013:\MC*   House ownership (HOUSECL: 1 = Owns, 2 = Does not own).

15.68 SCF2013:\MC*   Household has been turned down for credit in the previous 5 years (TURNDOWN: 0 = No, 1 = Yes).

15.69 SCF2013:\MC*   Household has declared bankruptcy in the previous 5 years (BNKRUPTLAST5: 0 = No, 1 = Yes).

15.70 SCF2013:\MC*   Household has incurred debt (HDEBT: Household has any debt: 0 = No, 1 = Yes).

15.71 SCF2013:\MC*   Household has at least one late payment in the previous year (LATE: 0 = No, 1 = Yes).

Exercise 15.72–15.78 examine whether there are differences between the middle-class men and women with respect to several financial-related variables (HHSEX: 1 = Male, 2 = Female). For each variable, test to determine whether there is enough evidence to conclude that men and women differ.

15.72 <u>SCF2013:\MC*</u>   Education category of head of household EDCL: 1 = No high school diploma, 2 = High school diploma, 3 = Some college, 4 = College degree).

15.73 <u>SCF2013:\MC*</u>   Industry classification for head of household (INDCAT: 1 = Mining + construction + manufacturing, 2 = Transportation + communications + utilities and sanitary services + wholesale trade + finance, insurance and real estate, 4 = Agriculture + retail trade + services + public transportation).

15.74 <u>SCF2013:\MC*</u>   Household overall expenses over last 12 months (EXPENSHILO: 1 = Unusually high, 2 = Unusually low, 3 = Normal).

15.75 <u>SCF2013:\MC*</u>   Household has been turned down for credit in the previous 5 years (TURNDOWN: 0 = No, 1 = Yes).

15.76 <u>SCF2013:\MC*</u>   Household has declared bankruptcy in the previous 5 years (BNKRUPTLAST5: 0 = No, 1 = Yes).

15.77 <u>SCF2013:\MC*</u>   Household has incurred debt (HDEBT: Household has any debt: 0 = No, 1 = Yes)

15.78 <u>SCF2013:\MC*</u>   Household has at least one late payment in the previous year (LATE: 0 = No, 1 = Yes).

15-3 / SUMMARY OF TESTS ON NOMINAL DATA

At this point in the textbook, we've described four tests that are used when the data are nominal:

z-test of p (Section 12-3)

z-test of $p_1 - p_2$ (Section 13-5)

Chi-squared goodness-of-fit test (Section 15-1)

Chi-squared test of a contingency table (Section 15-2)

In the process of presenting these techniques, it was necessary to concentrate on one technique at a time and focus on the kinds of problems each addresses. However, this approach tends to conflict somewhat with our promised goal of emphasizing the "when" of statistical inference. In this section, we summarize the statistical tests on nominal data to ensure that you are capable of selecting the correct method.

There are two critical factors in identifying the technique used when the data are nominal. The first, of course, is the problem objective. The second is the number of categories that the nominal variable can assume. Table 15.1 provides a guide to help select the correct technique.

TABLE **15.1**   **Statistical Techniques for Nominal Data**

PROBLEM OBJECTIVE	NUMBER OF CATEGORIES	STATISTICAL TECHNIQUE
Describe a population	2	z-test of p or the chi-squared goodness-of-fit test
Describe a population	More than 2	Chi-squared goodness-of-fit test
Compare two populations	2	z-test of $p_1 - p_2$ or chi-squared test of a contingency table
Compare two populations	More than 2	Chi-squared test of a contingency table
Compare two or more populations	2 or more	Chi-squared test of a contingency table
Analyze the relationship between two variables	2 or more	Chi-squared test of a contingency table

Notice that when we describe a population of nominal data with exactly two categories, we can use either of two techniques. We can employ the z-test of p or the chi-squared goodness-of-fit test. These two tests are equivalent because if there are only two categories, the multinomial experiment is actually a binomial experiment (one of the categorical outcomes is labeled *success*, and the other is labeled *failure*). Mathematical statisticians have established that if we square the value of z, the test statistic for the test of p, we produce the χ^2-statistic; that is, $z^2 = \chi^2$. Thus, if we want to conduct a two-tail test of a population proportion, we can employ either technique. However, the chi-squared goodness-of-fit test can test only to determine whether the hypothesized values of p_1 (which we can label p) and p_2 (which we call $1 - p$) are not equal to their specified values. Consequently, to perform a one-tail test of a population proportion, we must use the z-test of p. (This issue was discussed in Chapter 14 when we pointed out that we can use either the t-test of $\mu_1 - \mu_2$ or the analysis of variance to conduct a test to determine whether two population means differ.)

When we test for differences between two populations of nominal data with two categories, we can also use either of two techniques: the z-test of $p_1 - p_2$ (Case 1) or the chi-squared test of a contingency table. Once again, we can use either technique to perform a two-tail test about $p_1 - p_2$. (Squaring the value of the z-statistic yields the value of the χ^2-statistic.) However, one-tail tests must be conducted by the z-test of $p_1 - p_2$. The rest of the table is quite straightforward. Notice that when we want to compare two populations when there are more than two categories, we use the chi-squared test of a contingency table.

Figure 15.4 offers another summary of the tests that deal with nominal data introduced in this book. There are two groups of tests: those that test hypotheses about single populations and those that test either for differences or for independence. In the first set, we have the z-test of p, which can be replaced by the chi-squared test of a multinomial experiment. The latter test is employed when there are more than two categories.

To test for differences between two proportions, we apply the z-test of $p_1 - p_2$. Instead we can use the chi-squared test of a contingency table, which can be applied to a variety of other problems.

15-3a Developing an Understanding of Statistical Concepts

Table 15.1 and Figure 15.4 summarize how we deal with nominal data. We determine the frequency of each category and use these frequencies to compute test statistics. We can then compute proportions to calculate z-statistics or use the frequencies to calculate χ^2-statistics. Because squaring a standard normal random variable produces a chi-squared variable, we can employ either statistic to test for differences. As a consequence, when you encounter nominal data in the problems described in this book (and other

FIGURE **15.4** Tests on Nominal Data

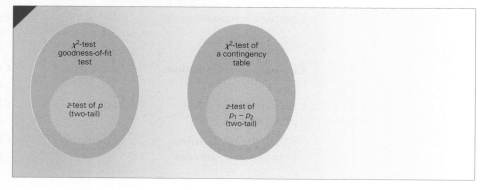

introductory applied statistics books), the most logical starting point in selecting the appropriate technique will be either a z-statistic or a χ^2-statistic. However, you should know that there are other statistical procedures that can be applied to nominal data, techniques that are not included in this book.

15-4 (OPTIONAL) CHI-SQUARED TEST FOR NORMALITY

We can use the goodness-of-fit test presented in Section 15-1 in another way. We can test to determine whether data were drawn from any distribution. The most common application of this procedure is a test of normality.

In the examples and exercises shown in Section 15-1, the probabilities specified in the null hypothesis were derived from the question. In Example 15.1, the probabilities p_1, p_2, and p_3 were the market shares before the advertising campaign. To test for normality (or any other distribution), the probabilities must first be calculated using the hypothesized distribution. To illustrate, consider Example 12.1, where we tested the mean amount of discarded newspaper using the Student t distribution. The required condition for this procedure is that the data must be normally distributed. To determine whether the 148 observations in our sample were indeed taken from a normal distribution, we must calculate the theoretical probabilities assuming a normal distribution. To do so, we must first calculate the sample mean and standard deviation: $\bar{x} = 2.18$ and $s = .981$. Next, we find the probabilities of an arbitrary number of intervals. For example, we can find the probabilities of the following intervals:

Interval 1: $X \leq .709$

Interval 2: $.709 < X \leq 1.69$

Interval 3: $1.69 < X \leq 2.67$

Interval 4: $2.67 < X \leq 3.65$

Interval 5: $X > 3.65$

We will discuss the reasons for our choices of intervals later.

The probabilities are computed using the normal distribution and the values of $\bar{x}$ and s as estimators of μ and σ. We calculated the sample mean and standard deviation as $\bar{x} = 2.18$ and $s = .981$. Thus,

$$P(X \leq .709) = P\left(\frac{X - \mu}{\sigma} \leq \frac{.709 - 2.18}{.981}\right) = P(Z \leq -1.5) = .0668$$

$$P(.709 < X \leq 1.69) = P\left(\frac{.709 - 2.18}{.981} < \frac{X - \mu}{\sigma} \leq \frac{1.69 - 2.18}{.981}\right)$$

$$= P(-1.5 < Z \leq -.5) = .2417$$

$$P(1.69 < X \leq 2.67) = P\left(\frac{1.69 - 2.18}{.981} < \frac{X - \mu}{\sigma} \leq \frac{2.67 - 2.18}{.981}\right)$$

$$= P(-.5 < Z \leq .5) = .3829$$

$$P(2.67 < X \leq 3.65) = P\left(\frac{2.67 - 2.18}{.981} < \frac{X - \mu}{\sigma} \leq \frac{3.65 - 2.18}{.981}\right)$$

$$= P(.5 < Z \leq 1.5) = .2417$$

$$P(X > 3.65) = P\left(\frac{X - \mu}{\sigma} > \frac{3.65 - 2.18}{.981}\right) = P(Z > 1.5) = .0668$$

To test for normality is to test the following hypotheses:

$$H_0: \quad p_1 = .0668, p_2 = .2417, p_3 = .3829, p_4 = .2417, p_5 = .0668$$

H_1: At least two proportions differ from their specified values

We complete the test as we did in Section 15-1, except that the number of degrees of freedom associated with the chi-squared statistic is the number of intervals minus 1 minus the number of parameters estimated, which in this illustration is two. (We estimated the population mean μ and the population standard deviation σ.) Thus, in this case, the number of degrees of freedom is $k - 1 - 2 = 5 - 1 - 2 = 2$.

The expected values are

$$e_1 = np_1 = 148(.0668) = 9.89$$
$$e_2 = np_2 = 148(.2417) = 35.78$$
$$e_3 = np_3 = 148(.3829) = 56.67$$
$$e_4 = np_4 = 148(.2417) = 35.78$$
$$e_5 = np_5 = 148(.0668) = 9.89$$

The observed values are determined manually by counting the number of values in each interval. Thus,

$$f_1 = 10$$
$$f_2 = 36$$
$$f_3 = 54$$
$$f_4 = 39$$
$$f_5 = 9$$

The chi-squared statistic is

$$\chi^2 = \sum_{i=1}^{k} \frac{(f_i - e_i)^2}{e_i} = \frac{(10 - 9.89)^2}{9.89} + \frac{(36 - 35.78)^2}{35.78} + \frac{(54 - 56.67)^2}{56.67}$$
$$+ \frac{(39 - 35.78)^2}{35.78} + \frac{(9 - 9.89)^2}{9.89}$$
$$= .50$$

The rejection region is

$$\chi^2 > \chi^2_{\alpha, k-3} = \chi^2_{.05,2} = 5.99$$

There is not enough evidence to conclude that these data are not normally distributed.

15-4a Class Intervals

In practice you can use any intervals you like. We chose the intervals we did to facilitate the calculation of the normal probabilities. The number of intervals was chosen to comply with the rule of five, which requires that all expected values be at least equal to 5. Because the number of degrees of freedom is $k - 3$, the minimum number of intervals is $k = 4$.

15-4b Interpreting the Results of a Chi-Squared Test for Normality

In the example above, we found that there was little evidence to conclude that the weight of discarded newspaper is not normally distributed. However, had we found evidence of non-normality, this would not necessarily invalidate the t-test we conducted in Example 12.1. As we pointed out in Chapter 12, the t-test of a mean is a robust procedure, which means that only if the variable is extremely nonnormal and the sample size is small can we conclude that the technique is suspect. The problem here is that if the sample size is large and the variable is only slightly nonnormal, the chi-squared test for normality will, in many cases, conclude that the variable is not normally distributed. However, if the variable is even quite nonnormal and the sample size is large, the t-test will still be valid. Although there are situations in which we need to know whether a variable is nonnormal, we continue to advocate that the way to decide if the normality requirement for almost all statistical techniques applied to interval data is satisfied is to draw histograms and look for shapes that are far from bell shaped (e.g., highly skewed or bimodal). We will use this approach in Chapter 19 when we introduce nonparametric techniques that are used when interval data are nonnormal.

EXERCISES

15.79 Suppose that a random sample of 100 observations was drawn from a population. After calculating the mean and standard deviation, each observation was standardized and the number of observations in each of the following intervals was counted. Can we infer at the 5% significance level that the data were not drawn from a normal population?

Interval	Frequency
$Z \leq 1.5$	10
$-1.5 < Z \leq -0.5$	18
$-0.5 < Z \leq 0.5$	48
$0.5 < Z \leq 1.5$	16
$Z > 1.5$	8

15.80 A random sample of 50 observations yielded the following frequencies for the standardized intervals:

Interval	Frequency
$Z \leq -1$	6
$-1 < Z \leq 0$	27
$0 < Z \leq 1$	14
$Z > 1$	3

Can we infer that the data are not normal? (Use $\alpha = .10$.)

The following exercises require the use of a computer and software.

15.81 Xr12-31   Refer to Exercise 12.31. Test at the 10% significance level to determine whether the amount of time spent working at part-time jobs is normally distributed. If there is evidence of nonnormality, is the t-test invalid?

15.82 Xr12-37   The t-test in Exercise 12.37 requires that the costs of prescriptions is normally distributed. Conduct a test with $\alpha = .05$ to determine whether the required condition is unsatisfied. If there is enough evidence to conclude that the requirement is not satisfied, does this indicate that the t-test is invalid?

15.83 Xr13-25   Exercise 13.25 required you to conduct a t-test of the difference between two means. Each samples productivity data are required to be normally distributed. Is that required condition violated? Test with $\alpha = .05$.

15.84 Xr13-26   Exercise 13.26 asked you to conduct a t-test of the difference between two means (reaction times). Test to determine whether there is enough evidence to infer that the reaction times are not normally distributed. A 5% significance level is judged to be suitable.

15.85 Xr13-115   In Exercise 13.115, you performed a test of the mean matched pairs difference. Test with a 10% significance level to determine whether the normality requirement is violated.

CHAPTER SUMMARY

This chapter introduced three statistical techniques. The first is the chi-squared goodness-of-fit test, which is applied when the problem objective is to describe a single population of nominal data with two or more categories. The second is the chi-squared test of a contingency table. This test has two objectives: to analyze the relationship between two nominal variables and to compare two or more populations of nominal data. The last procedure is designed to test for normality.

IMPORTANT TERMS:

Multinomial experiment   592
Chi-squared goodness-of-fit test   593
Expected frequency   593
Observed frequencies   594

Cross-classification table   600
Chi-squared test of a contingency table   600
Contingency table   603

SYMBOLS:

Symbol	Pronounced	Represents
f_i	f sub i	Frequency of the ith category
e_i	e sub i	Expected value of the ith category
χ^2	Chi squared	Test statistic

FORMULA:

Test statistic for all procedures

$$\chi^2 = \sum_{i=1}^{k} \frac{(f_i - e_i)^2}{e_i}$$

COMPUTER OUTPUT AND INSTRUCTIONS:

Technique	Excel
Chi-squared goodness-of-fit test	596
Chi-squared test of a contingency table	605

CHAPTER EXERCISES

Use a 5% significance level, unless specified otherwise.

15.86 An organization dedicated to ensuring fairness in television game shows is investigating *Wheel of Fortune*. In this show, three contestants are required to solve puzzles by selecting letters. Each contestant gets to select the first letter and continues selecting until he or she chooses a letter that is not in the hidden word, phrase, or name. The order of contestants is random. However, contestant 1 gets to start game 1, contestant 2 starts game 2, and so on. The contestant who wins the most money is declared the winner and he or she is given an opportunity to win a grand prize. Usually, more than three games are played per show, and as a result it appears that contestant 1 has an advantage: Contestant 1 will start two games, whereas contestant 3 will usually start only one game. To see whether this is the case, a random sample of 30 shows was taken and the starting position of the winning contestant for each show was recorded. These are shown in the following table:

Starting position	1	2	3
Number of wins	14	10	6

Do the tabulated results allow us to conclude that the game is unfair?

15.87 It has been estimated that employee absenteeism costs North American companies more than $100 billion per year. As a first step in addressing the rising cost of absenteeism, the personnel department of a large corporation recorded the weekdays during which individuals in a sample of 362 absentees were away over the past several months. Do these data suggest that absenteeism is higher on some days of the week than on others?

Day of the Week	Monday	Tuesday	Wednesday	Thursday	Friday
Number absent	87	62	71	68	74

15.88 Suppose that the personnel department in Exercise 15.87 continued its investigation by categorizing absentees according to the shift on which they worked, as shown in the accompanying table. Is there sufficient evidence at the 10% significance level of a relationship between the days on which employees are absent and the shift on which the employees work?

Shift	Monday	Tuesday	Wednesday	Thursday	Friday
Day	52	28	37	31	33
Evening	35	34	34	37	41

15.89 A management behavior analyst has been studying the relationship between male/female supervisory structures in the workplace and the level of employees' job satisfaction. The results of a recent survey are shown in the accompanying table. Is there sufficient evidence to infer that the level of job satisfaction depends on the boss/employee gender relationship?

	BOSS/EMPLOYEE			
Level of Satisfaction	Female/ Male	Female/ Female	Male/ Male	Male/ Female
Satisfied	21	25	54	71
Neutral	39	49	50	38
Dissatisfied	31	48	10	11

The following exercises require the use of a computer and software. The answers may be calculated manually. See Appendix A for the sample statistics. Use a 5% significance level, unless specified otherwise.

15.90 Xr15-90 Stress is a serious medical problem that costs businesses and government billions of dollars annually. As a result, it is important to determine the causes and possible cures. It would be helpful to know whether the causes are universal or do they vary from country to country. In a survey, American and Canadian adults were asked to report their primary source of stress in their lives. The responses are:

1 = Job, 2 = Finances, 3 = Health
4 = Family life, 5 = Other

The data were recorded using these codes plus 1 = American and 2 = Canadian. Do these data provide sufficient evidence to conclude that Americans and Canadians differ in their sources of stress?

15.91 Xr15-91 More than 3,000 Americans quit smoking each day. Because nicotine is one of the most addictive drugs, quitting smoking is a difficult and frustrating task. It usually takes several tries before success is achieved. There are various methods, including cold turkey, nicotine patch, hypnosis, and group therapy sessions. In an experiment to determine how these methods differ, a random sample of smokers who have decided to quit is selected. Each smoker has chosen one of the methods listed above. After one year, the respondents report whether they have quit (1 = Yes, 2 = No) and which method they used (1 = Cold turkey, 2 = Nicotine patch, 3 = Hypnosis, 4 = Group therapy sessions). Is there sufficient evidence to conclude that the four methods differ in their success?

15.92 Xr15-92 A newspaper publisher trying to pinpoint his market's characteristics wondered whether the way people read a newspaper is related to the reader's educational level. A survey asked adult readers which section of the paper they read first and asked to report their highest educational level. These data were recorded (column 1 = First section read where 1 = Front page, 2 = Sports, 3 = Editorial, and 4 = Other) and column 2 = Educational level where 1 = Did not complete high school, 2 = High school graduate, 3 = University or college graduate, and 4 = Postgraduate degree). What do these data tell the publisher about how educational level affects the way adults read the newspaper?

15.93 Xr15-93 Every week, the Florida Lottery draws six numbers between 1 and 49. Lottery ticket buyers are naturally interested in whether certain numbers are drawn more frequently than others. To assist players, the *Sun-Sentinel* publishes the number of times each of the 49 numbers has been drawn in the past 52 weeks. The numbers and the frequency with which each occurred were recorded.

a. If the numbers are drawn from a uniform distribution, what is the expected frequency for each number?

b. Can we infer that the data were not generated from a uniform distribution?

15.94 Xr15-94* Clinical depression is a serious disorder that affects millions of people. Depression often leads to alcohol as a means of easing the pain. A Gallup survey attempted to study the relationship between depression and alcohol. A random sample of adults was drawn and after a series of question each respondent was identified as a 1 = Nondrinker, 2 = moderate drinker, 3 = heavy drinker. Additionally, each respondent was asked whether they had ever been diagnosed as clinically depressed at some time in their lives (1 = Yes, 2 = No). Is there enough evidence to conclude that alcohol and depression are related?

15.95 Refer to Exercise 15.94. Each respondent was also asked whether they are currently depressed (1 = Yes, 2 = No). Is there sufficient evidence to infer that alcohol and current depression are related?

15.96 Xr15-96 Gallup asked in a recent survey conducted around the world, "In this country, are you satisfied or dissatisfied with your freedom to choose what you do with your life?" The responses are 1 = Satisfied, 2 = Dissatisfied. The results for 1 = Australia, 2 = Canada, 3 = New Zealand, and the 4 = United States were recorded. Can we infer that there are differences between the four countries in their satisfaction with the freedom in their countries?

15.97 Xr15-97 In a series of annual surveys of residents of the United States between 2009 and 2013 Gallup asked, "Is corruption widespread throughout the government in this country or not"? The responses (1 = Yes and 2 = No) were recorded. Is there sufficient evidence to conclude that residents' perceived corruption in the government fluctuated over the 5 year period?

In Section 15-4, we showed how to test for normality. However, we can use the same process to test for any other distribution.

15.98 Xr15-98 A scientist believes that the gender of a child is a binomial random variable with probability = .5 for a boy and .5 for a girl. To help test her belief, she randomly samples 100 families with five children. She records the number of boys. Can the scientist infer that the number of boys in families

with five children is not a binomial random variable with $p = .5$? (*Hint*: Find the probability of $X = 0, 1, 2, 3, 4$, and 5 from a binomial distribution with $n = 5$ and $p = .5$.)

15.99 Xr15-99 Given the high cost of medical care, research that points the way to avoid illness is welcome. Previously performed research tells us that stress affects the immune system. Two scientists at Carnegie Mellon Hospital in Pittsburgh asked 114 healthy adults about their social circles; they were asked to list every group they had contact with at least once every 2 weeks—family, coworkers, neighbors, friends, religious groups, and community groups. Participants also reported negative life events over the past year, events such as death of a friend or relative, divorce, or job-related problems. The participants were divided into four groups:

Group 1: Highly social and highly stressed
Group 2: Not highly social and highly stressed
Group 3: Highly social and not highly stressed
Group 4: Not highly social and not highly stressed

Each individual was classified in this way. In addition, whether each person contracted a cold over the next 12 weeks was recorded (1 = Cold, 2 = No cold). Can we infer that there are differences between the four groups in terms of contracting a cold?

The following exercises employ data files associated with examples and exercises seen earlier in this book.

15.100 Xr12-105* Exercise 12.105 described the problem of a looming shortage of professors, possibly made worse by professors desiring to retire before the age of 65. A survey asked a random sample of professors whether he or she intended to retire before 65. The responses are 1 = No and 2 = Yes. In addition, the survey asked to which faculty did the professor belong (1 = Arts, 2 = Science, 3 = Business, 4 = Engineering, 5 = Other). Do these provide sufficient evidence to infer that whether a professor wishes to retire is related to the faculty?

15.101 Xr12-110* Refer to Exercise 12.110. Determine whether there is enough evidence to infer that there are differences in the choice of Christmas tree between the three age categories.

15.102 Xr12-111* Exercise 12.111 described a study to determine whether viewers (older than 50) of the network news had contacted their physician to ask about one of the prescription drugs advertised during the newscast. The responses (1 = No, 2 = Yes) were recorded. Also recorded were which of the three networks they normally watch (1 = ABC, 2 = CBS, 3 = NBC). Can we conclude that there are differences in responses between the three network news shows?

15.103 Xr13-164* Exercise 13.164 described a survey of adults wherein, on the basis of several probing questions, each was classified as either a member of the health conscious group (code = 1) or not (code = 2) and whether he or she buys Special X (1 = No, 2 = Yes). Additionally, his or her educational attainment (1 = Did not finish high school, 2 = Finished high school, 3 = Finished college or university, 4 = Postgraduate degree) was recorded.

a. Do the data allow the surveyor to conclude that there differences in educational attainment between those who do and those who do not belong to the health-conscious group?

b. Can we infer that there is a relationship between the four educational groups and whether or not a person buys Special X?

15.104 Xm12-05* Example 12.5 described exit polls wherein people are asked whether they voted for the Democrat or Republican candidate for president. The surveyors also record gender (1 = Female, 2 = Male), educational attainment (1 = Did not finish high school, 2 = Completed high school, 3 = Completed college or university, 4 = Postgraduate degree), and income level (1 = Under $25,000, 2 = $25,000 to $49,999, 3 = $50,000 to $75,000, 4 = over $75,000).

a. Is there sufficient evidence to infer that voting and gender are related?

b. Do the data allow the conclusion that voting and educational level are related?

c. Can we infer that voting and income are related?

15.105 Xr02-65* Exercise 2.65 described a survey of the business school graduates undertaken by a university placement office. The respondents reported (among other questions) gender (1 = Female, 2 = Male) and area of employment (1= Accounting, 2 = Finance, 3 = General management, 4 = Marketing/sales, 5 = Other). Can we infer from the data that female and male graduates differ in their areas of employment?

15.106 Xr02-46 Exercise 2.46 asked the question: Are you more likely to smoke if your parents smoke? To shed light on the issue, a sample of 20- to 40-year-old people was asked whether they smoked and whether their parents smoked. The results are stored the following way: Smoke: 1 = Do not smoke, 2 = Smoke and Parent: 1 = Neither parent smoked, 2 = Father smoked, 3 = Mother smoked, 4 = Both parents smoked. Test to determine whether there is enough evidence to infer that parents' smoking and their children smoking are related.

15.107 Xr02-33* Exercises 2.33 and 2.49 described a survey that took a random sample of 285 graduating students and asked each to report which of the following is their favorite light beer: 1 =Bud Light, 2 = Busch Light, 3 = Coors Light, 4 = Michelob Light, 5 = Miller Lite, 6 = Natural Light, and 7 = other brands. Also recorded was the gender (1 = Male and 2 = Female). Do these data allow us to conclude that males and females differ in their preference for light beer?

15.108 Xr02-64 Exercise 2.64 described the survey the Red Lobster Restaurant chain conducts to monitor the performance of individual restaurants. One of the questions asks customers to rate the overall quality of their last visit. The listed responses are Poor (1), Fair (2), Good (3), Very good (4), and Excellent (5). The survey also asks respondents whether their children accompanied them (1= Yes and 2 = No) to the restaurant. Is there sufficient evidence to infer that ratings and whether children accompanied the customer are related?

APPLICATIONS in MARKETING

Pressmaster/Shutterstock.com

Market Segmentation

In Section 12-4 and in Chapters 13 and 14, we described how marketing managers use statistical analyses to estimate the size of market segments and to determine whether there are differences between segments.

The following exercises require the application of the chi-squared test of a contingency table to determine whether market segments differ with respect to some nominal variable.

15.109 Xr12-132*   Exercise 12.132 described the market segments defined by JC Penney. Another question included in the questionnaire that classified the women surveyed was asked whether each worked outside the home. The responses were:

1. No
2. Part-time job
3. Full-time job

These data plus the classifications (1 = Conservative, 2 = Traditional, 3 = Contemporary) were recorded. Can we infer from these data that there are differences in employment status between the three market segments?

15.110 Xr12-132*   Refer to Exercise 12.132. The women in the survey were also asked to define value by identifying what they considered to be the most important attribute of value. The responses are:

1. Price
2. Quality
3. Fashion

The responses and the classifications of segments (1 = Conservative, 2 = Traditional, 3 = Contemporary) were recorded. Do these data allow us to infer that there are differences in the definition of value between the three market segments?

15.111 Xm12-06*   Refer to Example 12.6. In segmenting the breakfast cereal market, a food manufacturer uses health and diet consciousness as the segmentation variable. Four segments are developed:

1. Concerned about eating healthy foods
2. Concerned primarily about weight
3. Concerned about health because of illness
4. Unconcerned

A survey was undertaken and each person was asked how often they ate a healthy breakfast (defined as cereal and/or fruit). The responses are:

1. Never
2. Seldom
3. Often
4. Always

The responses and the market segments of each respondent were recorded. Can we infer that there are differences in frequency of healthy breakfasts between the market segments?

APPENDIX 15 / REVIEW OF CHAPTERS 12 TO 15

Here are the updated list of statistical techniques (Table A15.1) and the flowchart (Figure A15.1) for Chapters 12 to 15. Counting the two techniques of chi-squared tests introduced here (we do not include the chi-squared test for normality), we have covered 22 statistical methods.

TABLE **A15.1**   **Summary of Statistical Techniques in Chapter 12 to 15**

t-test of μ

Estimator of μ (including estimator of $N\mu$)

χ^2-test of σ^2

Estimator of σ^2

z-test of p

Estimator of p (including estimator of Np)

Equal-variances t-test of $\mu_1 - \mu_2$

Equal-variances estimator of $\mu_1 - \mu_2$

Unequal-variances t-test of $\mu_1 - \mu_2$

Unequal-variances estimator of $\mu_1 - \mu_2$

t-test of μ_D

Estimator of μ_D

F-test of σ_1^2/σ_2^2

Estimator of σ_1^2/σ_2^2

z-test of $p_1 - p_2$ (Case 1)

z-test of $p_1 - p_2$ (Case 2)

Estimator of $p_1 - p_2$

One-way analysis of variance (including multiple comparisons)

Two-way (randomized blocks) analysis of variance

Two-factor analysis of variance

χ^2-goodness-of-fit test

χ^2-test of a contingency table

FIGURE **A15.1** **Summary of Statistical Techniques in Chapters 12 to 15**

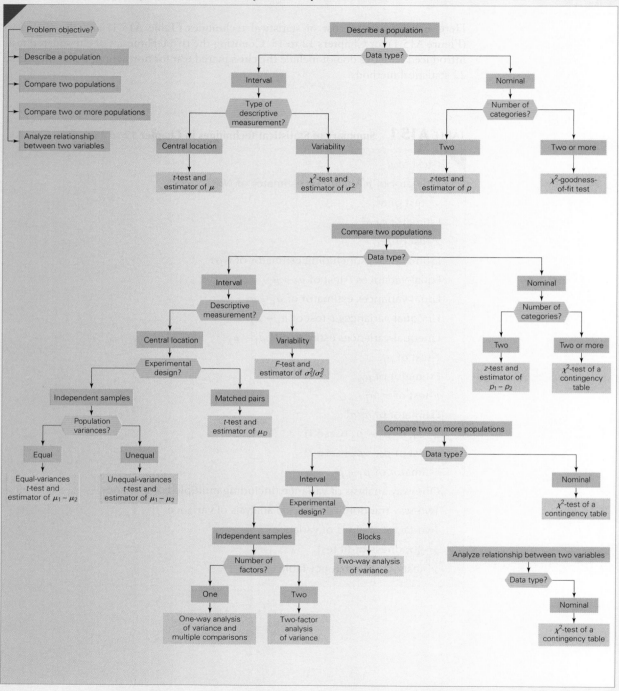

EXERCISES

We remind you that we do not specify significance levels in the exercise that follow. Choose your own.

A15.1 <u>XrA15-01</u> An analysis of the applicants of all MBA programs in North America reveals that the proportions of each type of undergraduate degree are as follows:

Undergraduate Degree	Proportion (%)
BA (1)	50
BBA (2)	20
BSc (3)	15
BEng (4)	10
Other (5)	5

The director of Wilfrid Laurier University's (WLU's) MBA program recorded the undergraduate degree of the applicants for this year using the codes in parentheses. Do these data indicate that applicants to WLU's MBA program are different in terms of their undergraduate degrees from the population of MBA applicants?

A15.3 <u>XrA15-02</u> The experiment to determine the effect of taking a preparatory course to improve SAT scores in Exercise A13.16 was criticized by other statisticians. They argued that the first test would provide a valuable learning experience that would produce a higher test score from the second exam even without the preparatory course. Consequently, another experiment was performed. Forty students wrote the SAT without taking any preparatory course. At the next scheduled exam (3 months later), these same students took the exam again (again with no preparatory course). The scores for both exams were recorded in columns 1 (first test scores) and 2 (second test scores). Can we infer that repeating the SAT produces higher exam scores even without the preparatory course?

A15.4 <u>XrA15-03</u> How does dieting affect the brain? This question was addressed by researchers in Australia. The experiment used 40 middle-age women in Adelaide, Australia; half were on a diet and half were not (*National Post*, December 1, 2003). The mental arithmetic part of the experiment required the participants to add two three-digit numbers. The amount of time taken to solve the 48 problems was recorded. The participants were given another test that required them to repeat a string of five letters they had been told 10 seconds earlier. They were asked to repeat the test with five words told to them

10 seconds earlier. The data were recorded in the following way:

> Column 1: Identification number
> Column 2: 1 = dieting, 2 = not dieting
> Column 3: Time to solve 48 problems (seconds)
> Column 4: Repeat string of 5 letters (1 = no, 2 = yes)
> Column 5: Repeat string of 5 words (1 = no, 2 = yes)

Is there sufficient evidence to infer that dieting adversely affects the brain?

A15.5 <u>XrA15-04</u> A small but important part of a university library's budget is the amount collected in fines on overdue books. Last year, a library collected $75,652.75 in fine payments; however, the head librarian suspects that some employees are not bothering to collect the fines on overdue books. In an effort to learn more about the situation, she asked a sample of 400 students (out of a total student population of 50,000) how many books they had returned late to the library in the previous 12 months. They were also asked how many days overdue the books had been. The results indicated that the total number of days overdue ranged from 0 to 55 days. The number of days overdue was recorded.

a. Estimate with 95% confidence the average number of days overdue for all 50,000 students at the university.

b. If the fine is 25 cents per day, estimate the amount that should be collected annually. Should the librarian conclude that not all the fines were collected?

A15.6 <u>XrA15-05</u> An apple juice manufacturer has developed a new product—a liquid concentrate that produces 1 liter of apple juice when mixed with water. The product has several attractive features. First, it is more convenient than bottled apple juice, which is the way apple juice is currently sold. Second, because the apple juice that is sold in cans is actually made from concentrate, the quality of the new product is at least as high as that of bottled apple juice. Third, the cost of the new product is slightly lower than that of bottled apple juice. The marketing manager has to decide how to market the new product. She can create advertising that emphasizes convenience, quality, or price. To facilitate a decision, she conducts an experiment in three different small cities. In one city, she launches the product with advertising stressing the convenience of the liquid concentrate (e.g., easy to carry from store to home and takes up less room in the freezer). In the second city, the advertisements emphasize the quality of the product ("average" shoppers are depicted discussing how good the apple juice tastes). Advertising that highlights the relatively low cost of the liquid concentrate is used in the third city. The number of packages sold weekly is recorded for the 20 weeks following the beginning of the campaign. The marketing manager wants to know whether differences in sales exist between the three advertising strategies. (We will assume that except for the type of advertising, the three cities are identical.)

A15.7   XrA15-06   Mutual funds are a popular way of investing in the stock market. A financial analyst wanted to determine the effect income had on ownership of mutual funds and whether the relationship had changed from four years earlier. She took a random sample of adults 25 years of age and older and asked each person whether he or she owned mutual funds (No = 1 and Yes = 2) and to report the annual household income. The categories are

1. Less than $25,000
2. $25,000 to $34,999
3. $35,000 to $49,999
4. $50,000 to $74,999
5. $75,000 to $100,000
6. More than $100,000

Can we infer from the data that household income and ownership of mutual funds are related?

Source: Adapted from the *Statistical Abstract of the United States, 2006*, Table 1200.

A15.7   XrA15-07   Refer to Exercise A15.5. Suppose that in addition to varying the marketing strategy, the manufacturer also decided to advertise in one of the two media that are available: television and newspapers. As a consequence, the experiment was repeated in the following way. Six different small cities were selected. In city 1, the marketing emphasized convenience, and all the advertising was conducted on television. In city 2, marketing also emphasized convenience, but all the advertising was conducted in the daily newspaper. Quality was emphasized in cities 3 and 4. City 3 learned about the product from television commercials, and city 4 saw newspaper advertising. Price was the marketing emphasis in cities 5 and 6. City 5 saw television commercials, and city 6 saw newspaper advertisements. In each city, the weekly sales for each of 10 weeks were recorded. What conclusions can be drawn from these data?

A15.8   XrA15-08   After a recent study, researchers reported on the effects of folic acid on the occurrence of spina bifida—a birth defect in which there is incomplete formation of the spine. A sample of 2,000 women who gave birth to children with spina bifida and who were planning another pregnancy was recruited. Before attempting to get pregnant again, half the sample was given regular doses of folic acid, and the other half was given a placebo. After 18 months, researchers recorded the result for each woman: 1 = birth to normal baby, 2 = birth to baby with spina bifida, 3 = not pregnant or no baby yet delivered. Can we infer that folic acid reduces the incidence of spina bifida in newborn babies?

A15.9   XrA15-09   Slow play of golfers is a serious problem for golf clubs. Slow play results in fewer rounds of golf and less profits for public course owners. To examine this problem, a random sample of British and American golf courses was selected. The amount of time taken (in minutes) was recorded for a random sample of British and American golfers. Can we conclude that British golfers play golf in less time than do American golfers?

Source: Golf Magazine, July 2001.

A15.10   XrA15-10   The United States and Canada (among others) are countries in which a significant proportion of citizens are immigrants. Many arrive in North America with few assets but quickly adapt to a changed economic environment. The question often arises, How quickly do immigrants increase their standard of living? A study initiated by Statistics Canada surveyed three different types of families:

1. Immigrants who arrived before 1976
2. Immigrants who came to Canada after 1986
3. Canadian-born families

The survey measured family wealth, which includes houses, cars, income, and savings and recorded the results (in $1,000s). Can we infer that differences exist between the three groups? If so, what are those differences?

A15.11   XrA15-11   During the decade of the 1980s, professional baseball thrived in North America. However, in the 1990s attendance dropped, and the number of television viewers also decreased. To examine the popularity of baseball relative to other sports, surveys were performed. In 1985 and again in 1992, a Harris Poll asked a random sample of 500 people to name their favorite sport. The results, which were published in the *Wall Street Journal* (July 6, 1993), were recorded in the following way: favorite sport (1 = professional football, 2 = baseball, 3 = professional basketball, 4 = college basketball, 5 = college football, 6 = golf, 7 = auto racing, 8 = tennis, and 9 = other); year (1 = 1985, 2 = 1992). Do these results indicate that North Americans changed their favorite sport between 1985 and 1992?

A15.12 XrA15-12   In an attempt to learn more about traffic congestion in a large North American city, the number of cars passing through intersections was determined (*National Post*, October 18, 2006). The number of cars was counted in 5-minute samples throughout several days. The counts for one busy intersection were recorded. Estimate with 95% confidence the mean number of cars in 5 minutes. Use the result to estimate the counts for a 24-hour day.

A15.13 XrA15-13   Organizations that sponsor various leisure activities need to know the number of people who wish to participate. Bureaucrats need to know the number because many organizations apply for government grants to pay the costs. The U.S. National Endowment for the Arts conducts surveys of American adults to acquire this type of information. One part of the survey asked a random sample of adults whether they participated in exercise programs. The responses (1 = yes and 2 = no) were recorded. A recent census reveals that there are 205.9 million adults in the United States. Estimate with 95% confidence the number of American adults who participate in exercise programs.

Source: Adapted from the *Statistical Abstract of the United States, 2006*, Table 1227.

A15.14 XrA15-14   Low back pain is a common medical problem that sometimes results in disability and absence from work. Any method of treatment that decreases absence would be welcome by individuals and insurance companies. A randomized control study (published in *Annals of Internal Medicine*, January 2004) was undertaken to determine whether an alternate form of treatment is effective. The study examined 134 workers who were absent from work because of low back pain. Half the sample was assigned to graded activity, a physical exercise program designed to stimulate rapid return to work. The other half was assigned to the usual care, which involves mostly rest. For each worker, the number of days absent from work because of low back pain in the following 6 months was recorded. Do these data provide sufficient evidence to infer that the graded activity is effective?

A15.15 XrA15-15   Clinical depression is a serious and sometimes debilitating disease. It is often treated by antidepressants such as Prozac and Zoloft. Recent studies may indicate another possible remedy. Researchers took a random sample of people who are clinically depressed and divided them into three groups. The first group was treated with antidepressants and light therapy, the second was treated with a placebo and light therapy, and the third group treated with a placebo. Whether the patient showed improvement (code = 1) or not (code = 2) and the group number were recorded. Can we infer that there are differences between the three groups?

A15.16   How well do airlines keep to their schedules? To help answer this question, an economist conducted a survey of 780 takeoffs in the United States and determined that 77.4% of them departed on time (defined as a departure that is within 15 minutes of its scheduled time). There were 7,140,596 flight departures in the United States in 2005. Estimate with 95% confidence the total number of on-time departures.

GENERAL SOCIAL SURVEY EXERCISES

Conduct all tests at the 5% significance level. Use a 95% confidence level for estimates.

In 2012, there were 221,963,000 Americans aged 21 years or more of whom 115,219,000 were female and 106,744,000 were male.

A15.17 GSS2012*   It seems obvious that political persuasion affects beliefs about what the government can and cannot do. However, do the data support this belief? Is there enough statistical evidence to infer that differences exist between the three political groups (PARTYID3: 1 = Democrat, 2 = Independent, 3 = Republican) with respect to the following question, "Should government reduce income differences between rich and poor (EQWLTH: 1 = Government should reduce differences; 2, 3, 4, 5, 6, 7 = No government action)?

A15.18 GSS2012*   Respondents were asked the following question. "Does Earth go around the Sun or does the Sun go around Earth (EARTHSUN: 1 = Earth around Sun, 2 = Sun around Earth, 8 = Don't know, 9 = No answer)? The correct answer: Earth around Sun. Is there sufficient evidence to infer that Republicans get the correct answer more frequently than do Democrats?

A15.19 GSS2012*   Are Americans optimistic that their children will do better financially than themselves? The survey asked respondents, "When your children are at your age will their standard of living be…. Can we infer that the majority of Americans believe that their children will do better than themselves (KIDSSOL: 1 = Much better, 2 = Somewhat better, 3 = About the same, 4 = Somewhat worse, 5 = Much worse)?

A15.20 GSS2012* Are married couples postponing bearing children? One way to measure this is to determine how old people are when their first child is born. Estimate with 95% confidence the average age of Americans when their first child is born (AGEKDBRN).

A15.21 GSS2012* Estimate the number of women who have never married (SEX: 2 = Female) and MARITAL: 5 = Never married).

A15.22 GSS2012* It is often argued that the reason that men earn more than women is that men work harder and longer. Examine the issue by determining whether there is sufficient evidence to conclude that men work longer hours (HRS1) than women (SEX: 1 = Male, 2 = Female).

A15.23 GSS2012* The survey asked respondents, "Taking all things together, how would you describe your marriage? Is there enough evidence to conclude that more than half of all marriages are very happy (HAPMAR: 1 = Very happy)?

A15.24 GSS2012* The survey asked respondents the following question. "Should government improve standard of living of poor people?" The responses were HELPPOOR: 1 = Government act; 2, 3, 4, 5 = People should help themselves. Is there sufficient evidence to conclude that the five categories of educational attainment differ in their responses to the question (DEGREE: 0 = Left high school, 1 = High school, 2 = Junior college, 3 = Bachelor's degree, 4 = Graduate)?

A15.25 GSS2012* Did the aftereffects of the recession that began in 2008 end in 2012? One way to judge is to determine how secure the jobs of workers were. Estimate the number of people who believed that it is very likely that they will lose their job or be laid off (JOBLOSE: 1 = Very likely).

A15.26 GSS2012* Does the race of an individual affect whether he or she is likely to be self-employed? Can we conclude that differences in whether an individual works for himself or herself (WRKSLF: 1 = Self-employed, 2 = Someone

else) exists between the races (RACE: 1 = White, 2 = Black, 3 = Other)?

A15.27 GSS2012* Do jobs in the public sector require more education (EDUC) than the ones in the private sector (WRKGOVT: 1 = Government, 2 = Private)? Conduct a test to answer the question.

A15.28 GSS2012* How much education (EDUC) do Democrats, Independents, and Republicans have (PARTYID3: 1 = Democrat, 2 = Independent, 3 = Republican)? Are they about the same or do they differ? Conduct a test to answer the question.

A15.29 GSS2012* Do teenage and adult children living with their parents contribute to household income by holding down full- or part-time jobs? And is it more likely that they do so for affluent than for less-affluent families? To answer the question, test to determine whether the data allow us to conclude that there are differences in the number of family members earning money (EARNRS) between the four classes (CLASS: 1 = Lower class, 2 = Working class, 3 = Middle class, 4 = Upper class).

A15.30 GSS2012* Estimate the number of men (SEX: 1 = Male) who work for themselves (WRKSLF: 1 = Self-employed).

A15.31 GSS2012* Capital punishment for murderers exists in most U.S. states. However, a few states ban this form of punishment. Politicians often need to know which members of the public support and which oppose. Can we conclude from the data that there is a difference between Democrats, Republicans, and Independents (PARTYID3: 1 = Democrat, 2 = Independent, 3 = Republican) in terms of support for capital punishment (CAPPUN)?

A15.32 GSS2012* In Chapter 2, we used a graphical technique and data from the American National Election Survey to attempt to determine whether men and women differ in their political affiliation. Use a suitable statistical inference technique to determine whether there is sufficient evidence to infer that men and women (SEX: 1 = Male, 2 = Female) differ in their political affiliations (PARTYID3: 1 = Democrat, 2 = Independent, 3 = Republican).

SURVEY OF COMNSUMER FINANCES

Conduct all tests at the 5% significance level. Use a 95% confidence level for estimates.

According to the U.S. Census, there were 220,958,853 adults in the United States in 2010.

A15.33 CF2010:\MC* Does home ownership (HOUSECL: 1 = Own, 2 = Not) affect how much is spent on food away from home (FOODAWAY)? Perform a statistical analysis to determine whether there is enough evidence to infer that middle-class home owners spend less on food away than do middle-class households who rent.

A15.34 SCF2010:\UC The upper class in the 2010 survey had household net worth between $1,345,975 and $7,402,095. In 2010, the interest paid by money market deposit and money market mutual funds paid very low interest. Estimate the mean invested in these accounts by households in the upper class (MMA).

A15.35 SCF2010:\MC* Who goes deeper into debt (DEBT) among heads of middle-class households, men or women (HHSEX: 1 = Male, 2 = Female)? Conduct a test to determine whether there is enough evidence to conclude that male heads of households go deeper into debt.

A15.36 SCF2010:\UC* One way to judge how well upper-class households are doing this year as opposed to other years is to determine what their normal income is. Estimate the normal income for upper-class households (NORMINC).

A15.37 SCF2010:\ALL* Do more educated heads of households have less debt? Conduct a test to determine whether there are differences in household debt (DEBT) between the four categories of education (EDCL 1 = No high school diploma, 2 = High school diploma, 3 = Some college, 4 = College degree.).

A15.38 SCF2010:\ALL* The nuclear family is defined as a pair of adults and their children. Is this going out of style? Estimate the proportion of nuclear family households (FAMSTRUCT: 4 = Married or living with partner + children).

A15.39 SCF2010:\ALL* One survey question asked in which industry was the head of the household employed in. One of the categories was mining, construction, or manufacturing, all of which may be in decline. Estimate the number of people employed in one of these industries (INDCAT: 1).

A15.40 SCF2010:\ALL* Between student loans, credit card balances, vehicle loans, and mortgages almost all household have some debt. Estimate the number of Americans with no household debt (HDEBT: 0).

A15.41 SCF2010:\ALL* Do banks and financial institutions turn down female heads (HHSEX: 1 = Male, 2 = Female) of households more frequently than male heads of households' application for credit (TURNDOWN: 1 = Turned down)? Use an appropriate statistical method to determine whether there is enough evidence to answer the question affirmatively.

A15.42 SCF2010:\ALL* One of the questions asked respondents whether their household had been late with any debt payment in the previous year (LATE: 0 = No, 1 = Yes). Is there enough evidence to conclude that male heads of households are less likely than female heads (HHSEX: 1 = Male, 2 = Female) to be late with a debt payment?

A15.43 SCF2010:\ALL* Does one's occupation affect whether the household has been turned down for credit in the previous 5 years (TURNDOWN: 1 = Yes, 2 = No)? Is there enough evidence to conclude that there are differences between the three working categories (OCCAT2: 1 = Managerial/professional, 2= Technical/sales/services, 3 = Other)?

CASE A15.1 — Which Diets Work?

Every year, millions of people start new diets. There is a bewildering array of diets to choose from. The question for many people is, Which ones work? Researchers at Tufts University in Boston made an attempt to point dieters in the right direction. Four diets were used:

1. Atkins low-carbohydrate diet
2. Zone high-protein, moderate-carbohydrate diet
3. Weight Watchers diet
4. Dr. Ornish's low-fat diet

The study recruited 160 overweight people and randomly assigned 40 to each diet. The average weight before dieting was 220 pounds, and all needed to lose between 30 and 80 pounds. All volunteers agreed to follow their diets for 2 months. No exercise or regular meetings were required. The following variables were recorded for each dieter using the format shown here:

Column 1: Identification number
Column 2: Diet
Column 3: Percent weight loss
Column 4: Percent low-density lipoprotein (LDL)—"bad" cholesterol—decrease
Column 5: Percent high-density lipoprotein (HDL)—"good" cholesterol—increase
Column 6: Quit after 2 months? 1 = yes, 2 = no
Column 7: Quit after 1 year? 1 = yes, 2 = no

Is there enough evidence to conclude that there are differences between the diets with respect to

a. percent weight loss?
b. percent LDL decrease?
c. percent HDL increase?
d. proportion quitting within 2 months?
e. proportion quitting after 1 year?

Chapters 16 to 23

Access these chapters from
your ebook.

APPENDIX A

DATA FILE SAMPLE STATISTICS

Chapter 10

10.34 $\bar{x} = 252.38$
10.35 $\bar{x} = 1810.16$
10.36 $\bar{x} = 12.10$
10.37 $\bar{x} = 10.21$
10.38 $\bar{x} = .510$
10.39 $\bar{x} = 26.81$
10.40 $\bar{x} = 19.28$
10.41 $\bar{x} = 15.00$
10.42 $\bar{x} = 585,063$
10.43 $\bar{x} = 109.6, n = 200$
10.44 $\bar{x} = 227.48, n = 300$
10.45 $\bar{x} = 314,245, n = 150$
10.46 $\bar{x} = 27.19$

Chapter 11

11.43 $\bar{x} = 5065$
11.44 $\bar{x} = 29,120$
11.45 $\bar{x} = 569$
11.46 $\bar{x} = 19.13$
11.47 $\bar{x} = -1.20$
11.48 $\bar{x} = 55.8$
11.49 $\bar{x} = 5.04$
11.50 $\bar{x} = 19.39$
11.51 $\bar{x} = 105.7$
11.52 $\bar{x} = 4.84$
11.53 $\bar{x} = 5.64$
11.54 $\bar{x} = 29.92$
11.55 $\bar{x} = 231.56$
11.56 $\bar{x} = 10.44, n = 174$
11.57 $\bar{x} = 29.51, n = 277$
11.58 $\bar{x} = 126,837, n = 410$
11.59 $\bar{x} = 7625, n = 163$

Chapter 12

12.31 $\bar{x} = 7.15, s = 1.65, n = 200$
12.32 $\bar{x} = 4.66, s = 2.37, n = 250$
12.33 $\bar{x} = 17.00, s = 4.31, n = 162$
12.34 $\bar{x} = 15,137, s = 5,263, n = 306$
12.35 $\bar{x} = 59.04, s = 20.62, n = 122$
12.36 $\bar{x} = 2.67, s = 2.50, n = 188$
12.37 $\bar{x} = 44.14, s = 7.88, n = 475$
12.38 $\bar{x} = 591.87, s = 125.06, n = 205$
12.39 $\bar{x} = 13.94, s = 2.16, n = 212$
12.40 $\bar{x} = 15.27, s = 5.72, n = 116$
12.41 $\bar{x} = 4.34, s = 4.22, n = 950$
12.42 $\bar{x} = 89.27, s = 17.30, n = 85$
12.43 $\bar{x} = 15.02, s = 8.31, n = 83$
12.44 $\bar{x} = 96,100, s = 34,468, n = 473$
12.45 $\bar{x} = 1.507, s = .640, n = 473$
12.46 $\bar{x} = 27,852, s = 9252, n = 347$
12.47 $\bar{x} = 354.55, s = 90.32, n = 681$
12.48 $\bar{x} = 25,228, s = 5544, n = 184$
12.49 $\bar{x} = 366,203, s = 122,277, n = 452$
12.50 $\bar{x} = 46,699, s = 9032, n = 608$
12.51 $\bar{x} = 7.31, s = 5.58, n = 178$

12.52 $\bar{x} = 1157.77, s = 396.51, n = 325$
12.53 $\bar{x} = 530.69, s = 97.17, n = 485$
12.77 $s^2 = 270.58, n = 25$
12.78 $s^2 = 22.56, n = 245$
12.79 $s^2 = 4.72, n = 90$
12.80 $s^2 = 174.47, n = 100$
12.81 $s^2 = 19.68, n = 25$
12.103 $n(1) = 51, n(2) = 291,$
$n(3) = 70, n(4) = 301,$
$n(5) = 261$
12.104 $n(1) = 28, n(2) = 174,$
$n(3) = 135, n(4) = 67,$
$n(5) = 51, n(6) = 107$
12.105 $n(1) = 466, n(2) = 55$
12.107 $n(1) = 140,$
$n(2) = 59. n(3) = 39,$
$n(4) = 106, n(5) = 47$
12.108 $n(1) = 153, n(2) = 24$
12.109 $n(1) = 92, n(2) = 28$
12.110 $n(1) = 603, n(2) = 905$
12.111 $n(1) = 92, n(2) = 334$
12.112 $n(1) = 57, n(2) = 35,$
$n(3) = 4, n(4) = 4$
12.114 $n(1) = 60, n(2) = 275,$
$n(3) = 20, n(4) = 180,$
$n(5) = 75, n(6) = 4390$
12.115 $n(1) = 786, n(2) = 254$
12.116 $n(1) = 518, n(2) = 132$
12.130 $n(1) = 81, n(2) = 47,$
$n(3) = 167, n(4) = 146,$
$n(5) = 34$
12.131 $n(1) = 63, n(2) = 125,$
$n(3) = 45, n(4) = 87$
12.132 $n(1) = 418, n(2) = 536,$
$n(3) = 882$
12.133 $n(1) = 290, n(2) = 35$
12.134 $n(1) = 72, n(2) = 77,$
$n(3) = 37, n(4) = 50,$
$n(5) = 176$
12.135 $n(1) = 289, n(2) = 51$

Chapter 13

13.17 Taste: $\bar{x}_1 = 36.93, s_1 = 4.23,$
$n_1 = 15;$
Competitor: $\bar{x}_2 = 31.36,$
$s_2 = 3.35, n_2 = 25$
13.18 Oat bran: $\bar{x}_1 = 10.01, s_1 = 4.43,$
$n_1 = 120;$
Other: $\bar{x}_2 = 9.12, s_2 = 4.45,$
$n_2 = 120$
13.19 18-to-34: $\bar{x}_1 = 58.99, s_1 = 30.77,$
$n_1 = 250;$ 35-to-50:
$\bar{x}_2 = 52.96, s_2 = 43.32,$
$n_2 = 250$

13.20 2 yrs ago: $\bar{x}_1 = 59.81, s_1 = 7.02,$
$n_1 = 125;$ This year:
$\bar{x}_2 = 57.40, s_2 = 6.99,$
$n_2 = 159$
13.21 Male: $\bar{x}_1 = 10.23, s_1 = 2.87,$
$n_1 = 100;$
Female: $\bar{x}_2 = 9.66, s_2 = 2.90,$
$n_2 = 100$
13.22 A: $\bar{x}_1 = 115.50, s_1 = 21.69,$
$n_1 = 30;$
B: $\bar{x}_2 = 110.20, s_2 = 21.93,$
$n_2 = 30$
13.23 Men: $\bar{x}_1 = 5.56, s_1 = 5.36,$
$n_1 = 306;$
Women: $\bar{x}_2 = 5.49, s_2 = 5.58,$
$n_2 = 290$
13.24 A: $\bar{x}_1 = 70.42, s_1 = 20.54,$
$n_1 = 24;$
B: $\bar{x}_2 = 56.44, s_2 = 9.03,$
$n_2 = 16$
13.25 Successful: $\bar{x}_1 = 5.02, s_1 = 1.39,$
$n_1 = 200;$
Unsuccessful: $\bar{x}_2 = 7.80,$
$s_2 = 3.09, n_2 = 200$
13.26 Phone: $\bar{x}_1 = .646, s_1 = .045,$
$n_1 = 125;$
Not: $\bar{x}_2 = .601,$
$s_2 = .053, n_2 = 145$
13.27 Chitchat: $\bar{x}_1 = .654, s_1 = .048,$
$n_1 = 95;$
Political: $\bar{x}_2 = .662,$
$s_2 = .045, n_2 = 90$
13.28 Planner: $\bar{x}_1 = 6.18, s_1 = 1.59,$
$n_1 = 64;$
Broker: $\bar{x}_2 = 5.94,$
$s_2 = 1.61, n_2 = 81$
13.29 Textbook: $\bar{x}_1 = 63.71, s_1 = 5.90,$
$n_1 = 173;$
No book: $\bar{x}_2 = 66.80,$
$s_2 = 6.85, n_2 = 202$
13.30 Wendy's: $\bar{x}_1 = 149.85, s_1 = 21.82,$
$n_1 = 213;$
McDonald's: $\bar{x}_2 = 154.43,$
$s_2 = 23.64, n_2 = 202$
13.31 Men: $\bar{x}_1 = 488, s_1 = 19.6,$
$n_1 = 124;$
Women: $\bar{x}_2 = 498,$
$s_2 = 21.9, n_2 = 187$
13.32 Applied: $\bar{x}_1 = 130.93, s_1 = 31.99,$
$n_1 = 100;$
Contacted: $\bar{x}_2 = 126.14,$
$s_2 = 26.00, n_2 = 100$
13.33 New: $\bar{x}_1 = 73.60, s_1 = 15.60,$
$n_1 = 20;$
Existing: $\bar{x}_2 = 69.20,$
$s_2 = 15.06, n_2 = 20$

13.34 Fixed: $\bar{x}_1 = 60{,}245$, $s_1 = 10{,}506$, $n_1 = 90$; Commission: $\bar{x}_2 = 63{,}563$, $s_2 = 10{,}755$, $n_2 = 90$

13.35 Accident: $\bar{x}_1 = 633.97$, $s_1 = 49.45$, $n_1 = 93$; No accident: $\bar{x}_2 = 661.86$, $s_2 = 52.69$, $n_2 = 338$

13.36 Cork: $\bar{x}_1 = 14.20$, $s_1 = 2.84$, $n_1 = 130$; Metal: $\bar{x}_2 = 11.27$, $s_2 = 4.42$, $n_2 = 130$

13.37 Before: $\bar{x}_1 = 497$, $s_1 = 73.8$, $n_1 = 355$; After: $\bar{x}_2 = 511$, $s_2 = 69.1$, $n_2 = 288$

13.38 Big bucket: $\bar{x}_1 = 93.82$, $s_1 = 15.89$, $n_1 = 48$; Medium bucket: $\bar{x}_2 = 61.25$, $s_2 = 9.96$, $n_2 = 48$

13.39 a. CA wine: $\bar{x}_1 = 97.71$, $s_1 = 5.10$, $n_1 = 24$; SD wine: $\bar{x}_2 = 94.58$, $s_2 = 7.36$, $n_2 = 24$ **b.** CA wine: $\bar{x}_1 = 64.00$, $s_1 = 9.44$, $n_1 = 24$; SD wine: $\bar{x}_2 = 57.33$, $s_2 = 9.14$, $n_2 = 24$

13.40 Clean plates: $\bar{x}_1 = 10.04$, $s_1 = 2.32$, $n_1 = 28$; Dirty plate: $\bar{x}_2 = 8.64$, $s_2 = 1.85$, $n_2 = 28$

13.41 One pound: $\bar{x}_1 = 136.80$, $s_1 = 24.16$, $n_1 = 20$; Half pound: $\bar{x}_2 = 72.80$, $s_2 = 9.87$, $n_2 = 20$

13.42 Apple: $\bar{x}_1 = 4.69$, $s_1 = 2.93$, $n_1 = 756$; No apple: $\bar{x}_2 = 4.86$, $s_2 = 3.05$, $n_2 = 7643$

13.43 This year: $\bar{x}_1 = 34.97$, $s_1 = 9.85$, $n_1 = 521$; 5 years ago: $\bar{x}_2 = 31.63$, $s_2 = 6.77$, $n_2 = 483$

13.44 Electrical: $\bar{x}_1 = 57{,}030$, $s_1 = 4991$, $n_1 = 129$; Mechanical: $\bar{x}_2 = 56{,}055$, $s_2 = 4421$, $n_2 = 97$

13.45 No chocolate: $\bar{x}_1 = 166.80$, $s_1 = 22.86$, $n_1 = 30$; Chocolate: $\bar{x}_2 = 116.70$, $s_2 = 14.79$, $n_2 = 30$

13.46 U.S.: $\bar{x}_1 = 7.31$, $s_1 = 5.58$, $n_1 = 178$; U.K.: $\bar{x}_2 = 6.97$, $s_2 = 6.82$, $n_2 = 177$

13.47 White: $\bar{x}_1 = 20.15$, $s_1 = 3.83$, $n_1 = 134$; Black: $\bar{x}_2 = 14.82$, $s_2 = 3.75$, $n_2 = 30$

13.48 Exercise: $\bar{x}_1 = 74.85$, $s_1 = 10.67$, $n_1 = 86$; No exercise: $\bar{x}_2 = 67.81$, $s_2 = 10.57$, $n_2 = 98$

13.49 Low income: $\bar{x}_1 = 1452.56$, $s_1 = 361.37$, $n_1 = 438$; High income: $\bar{x}_2 = 1246.61$, $s_2 = 367.80$, $n_2 = 571$

13.50 Low income: $\bar{x}_1 = 1157.77$, $s_1 = 396.51$, $n_1 = 325$; Middle income: $\bar{x}_2 = 1091.71$, $s_2 = 241.51$, $n_2 = 441$

13.51 Men: $\bar{x}_1 = 448.28$, $s_1 = 98.99$, $n_1 = 552$; Women: $\bar{x}_2 = 443.03$, $s_2 = 99.18$, $n_2 = 577$

13.52 Private sector: $\bar{x}_1 = 6.44$, $s_1 = 3.89$, $n_1 = 524$; Government: $\bar{x}_2 = 10.53$, $s_2 = 4.09$, $n_2 = 409$

13.53 This year: $\bar{x}_1 = 10.53$, $s_1 = 4.09$, $n_1 = 409$; 5 years ago: $\bar{x}_2 = 10.32$, $s_2 = 4.24$, $n_2 = 397$

13.93 $D = X[\text{This year}] - X[\text{5 years ago}]$: $\bar{x}_D = 12.4$, $s_D = 99.1$, $n_D = 150$

13.94 $D = X[\text{Waiter}] - X[\text{Waitress}]$: $\bar{x}_D = -1.16$, $s_D = 2.22$, $n_D = 50$

13.95 $D = X[\text{This year}] - X[\text{Last year}]$: $\bar{x}_D = 19.75$, $s_D = 30.63$, $n_D = 40$

13.96 $D = X[\text{Insulated}] - X[\text{Uninsulated}]$: $\bar{x}_D = -57.40$, $s_D = 13.14$, $n_D = 15$

13.97 $D = X[\text{Men}] - X[\text{Women}]$: $\bar{x}_D = -42.94$, $s_D = 317.16$, $n_D = 45$

13.98 $D = X[\text{Last year}] - X[\text{Previous year}]$: $\bar{x}_D = -183.35$, $s_D = 1568.94$, $n_D = 170$

13.99 $D = X[\text{This year}] - X[\text{Last year}]$: $\bar{x}_D = .0422$, $s_D = .1634$, $n_D = 38$

13.100 $D = X[\text{Company 1}] - X[\text{Company 2}]$: $\bar{x}_D = 520.85$, $s_D = 1854.92$, $n_D = 55$

13.101 $D = X[\text{New}] - X[\text{Existing}]$: $\bar{x}_D = 4.55$, $s_D = 7.22$, $n_D = 20$

13.103 $D = X[\text{Finance}] - X[\text{Marketing}]$: $\bar{x}_D = 4{,}587$, $s_D = 22{,}851$, $n_D = 25$

13.105 a. $D = X[\text{After}] - X[\text{Before}]$: $\bar{x}_D = -.10$, $s_D = 1.95$, $n_D = 42$ **b.** $D = X[\text{After}] - X[\text{Before}]$: $\bar{x}_D = 1.24$, $s_D = 2.83$, $n_D = 98$

13.117 Week 1: $s_1^2 = 19.38$, $n_1 = 100$; Week 2: $s_2^2 = 12.70$, $n_2 = 100$

13.118 A: $s_1^2 = 41{,}309$, $n_1 = 100$; B: $s_2^2 = 19{,}850$, $n_2 = 100$

13.119 Portfolio 1: $s_1^2 = .0261$, $n_1 = 52$; Portfolio 2: $s_2^2 = .0875$, $n_2 = 52$

13.120 Teller 1: $s_1^2 = 3.35$, $n_1 = 100$; Teller 2: $s_2^2 = 10.95$, $n_2 = 100$

13.147 Cadillac: $n_1(1) = 33$, $n_1(2) = 317$; Lincoln: $n_2(1) = 33$, $n_2(2) = 261$

13.148 Smokers: $n_1(1) = 28$, $n_1(2) = 10$; Nonsmokers: $n_2(1) = 150$, $n_2(2) = 12$

13.149 This year: $n_1(1) = 306$, $n_1(2) = 171$; 10 years ago: $n_2(1) = 304$, $n_2(2) = 158$

13.150 Canada: $n_1(1) = 230$, $n_1(2) = 215$; U.S.: $n_2(1) = 165$, $n_2(2) = 275$

13.151 A: $n_1(1) = 189$, $n_1(2) = 11$; B: $n_2(1) = 178$, $n_2(2) = 22$

13.152 High school: $n_1(1) = 17$, $n_1(2) = 63$; Postsecondary: $n_2(1) = 29$, $n_2(2) = 167$

13.153 2008: $n_1(1) = 81$, $n_1(2) = 44$; 2011: $n_2(1) = 63$, $n_2(2) = 41$

13.154 2012: $n_1(1) = 578$, $n_1(2) = 371$, $n_1(3) = 208$, $n_1(4) = 281$; 2013: $n_2(1) = 495$, $n_2(2) = 480$, $n_2(3) = 195$, $n_2(4) = 300$

13.155 Men: $n_1(1) = 501$, $n_1(2) = 155$; Women: $n_2(1) = 486$, $n_2(2) = 183$

13.156 No religion: $n_1(1) = 272$, $n_1(2) = 2928$; Religion: $n_2(1) = 240$, $n_2(2) = 2960$

13.157 Main stream: $n_1(1) = 199$, $n_1(2) = 2501$; Wallonian: $n_2(1) = 41$, $n_2(2) = 459$

13.158 Female: Total $= 1553$, $n_1(6) = 199$; Male: Total $= 1401$, $n_2(6) = 85$

13.159 Umpire A: $n_1(1) = 849$, $n_1(2) = 119$; Umpire B: $n_2(1) = 718$, $n_2(2) = 168$

13.160 Umpire A: $n_1(1) = 44$, $n_1(2) = 278$; Umpire B: $n_2(1) = 46$, $n_2(2) = 272$

13.161 a. $n_3(1) = 176$, $n_3(2) = 243$, $n_4(1) = 195$, $n_4(2) = 347$ **b.** $n_1(1) = 191$, $n_1(2) = 74$, $n_2(1) = 230$, $n_2(2) = 196$

13.162 $n_1(1) = 214$, $n_1(2) = 191$, $n_2(3) = 81$; $n_2(1) = 689$, $n_2(2) = 832$, $n_2(3) = 466$

13.163 This year: $n_1(1) = 773$, $n_1(2) = 205$; 5 years ago: $n_2(1) = 851$, $n_2(2) = 125$

13.164 Health conscious: $n_1(1) = 199$, $n_1(2) = 32$; Not health conscious: $n_2(1) = 563$, $n_2(2) = 56$

13.165 Segment 1: $n_1(1) = 68$, $n_1(2) = 95$; Segment 2: $n_2(1) = 20$, $n_2(2) = 34$; Segment 3: $n_3(1) = 10$, $n_3(2) = 13$; Segment 4: $n_4(1) = 29$, $n_4(2) = 79$

13.166 Source 1: $n_1(1) = 344$, $n_1(2) = 38$; Source 2: $n_2(1) = 275$, $n_2(2) = 41$

Chapter 14

14.9

Sample	$\bar{x}_i$	s_i^2	n_i
1	68.83	52.28	20
2	65.08	37.38	26
3	62.01	63.46	16
4	64.64	56.88	19

14.10

Sample	$\bar{x}_i$	s_i^2	n_i
1	90.17	991.5	30
2	95.77	900.9	30
3	106.8	928.7	30
4	111.2	1023	30

14.11

Sample	$\bar{x}_i$	s_i^2	n_i
1	196.8	914.1	41
2	207.8	861.1	73
3	223.4	1195	86
4	232.7	1080	79

14.12

Sample	$\bar{x}_i$	s_i^2	n_i
1	164.6	1164	25
2	185.6	1719	25
3	154.8	1113	25
4	182.6	1657	25
5	178.9	841.8	25

14.13

Sample	$\bar{x}_i$	s_i^2	n_i
1	22.21	121.6	39
2	18.46	90.39	114
3	15.49	85.25	81
4	9.31	65.40	67

14.14

Sample	$\bar{x}_i$	s_i^2	n_i
1	551.5	2742	20
2	576.8	2641	20
3	559.5	3129	20

14.15

Sample	$\bar{x}_i$	s_i^2	n_i
1	5.81	6.22	100
2	5.30	4.05	100
3	5.33	3.90	100

14.16

Sample	$\bar{x}_i$	s_i^2	n_i
1	74.10	250.0	30
2	75.67	184.2	30
3	78.50	233.4	30
4	81.30	242.9	30

14.17

Size

Sample	$\bar{x}_i$	s_i^2	n_i
1	24.97	48.23	50
2	21.65	54.54	50
3	17.84	33.85	50

Nicotine

Sample	$\bar{x}_i$	s_i^2	n_i
1	15.52	3.72	50
2	13.39	3.59	50
3	10.08	3.83	50

14.18 a.

Sample	$\bar{x}_i$	s_i^2	n_i
1	31.30	28.34	63
2	34.42	23.20	81
3	37.38	31.16	40
4	39.93	72.03	111

b.

Sample	$\bar{x}_i$	s_i^2	n_i
1	37.22	39.82	63
2	38.91	40.85	81
3	41.48	61.38	40
4	41.75	46.59	111

c.

Sample	$\bar{x}_i$	s_i^2	n_i
1	11.75	3.93	63
2	12.41	3.39	81
3	11.73	4.26	40
4	11.89	4.30	111

14.19

Sample	$\bar{x}_i$	s_i^2	n_i
1	153.6	654.3	20
2	151.5	924.0	20
3	133.3	626.8	20

14.20

Sample	$\bar{x}_i$	s_i^2	n_i
1	18.54	178.0	61
2	19.34	171.4	83
3	20.29	297.5	91

14.21

Sample	$\bar{x}_i$	s_i^2	n_i
1	26.6	97.3	315
2	31.4	159.6	404
3	24.6	113.9	352

14.22

Reading

Sample	$\bar{x}_i$	s_i^2	n_i
1	500.3	611.8	624
2	524.4	686.3	409
3	493.8	608.3	498

Mathematics

Sample	$\bar{x}_i$	s_i^2	n_i
1	486.6	619.5	624
2	527.5	654.0	409
3	492.0	648.3	498

Science

Sample	$\bar{x}_i$	s_i^2	n_i
1	502.0	659.3	624
2	528.9	882.2	409
3	513.9	716.0	498

14.63

Sample	$\bar{x}_i$	s_i^2	n_i
1	61.60	80.49	10
2	57.30	70.46	10
3	61.80	22.18	10
4	51.80	75.29	10

14.65

Sample	$\bar{x}_i$	s_i^2	n_i
1	53.17	194.6	30
2	49.37	152.6	30
3	44.33	129.9	30

14.91 $k = 3, b = 12$, SST = 204.2, SSB = 1150.2, SSE = 495.1

14.92 $k = 3, b = 20$, SST = 7131, SSB = 177,465, SSE = 1098

14.93 $k = 3, b = 20$, SST = 10.26, SSB = 3020.30, SSE = 226.71

14.94 $k = 4, b = 30$, SST = 4206, SSB = 126,843, SSE = 5764

14.95 $k = 7, b = 200$, SST = 28,674, SSB = 209,835, SSE = 479,125

14.96 $k = 5, b = 36$, SST = 1406.4, SSB = 7309.7, SSE = 4593.9

14.97 $k = 4, b = 21$, SST = 563.82, SSB = 1,327.33, SSE = 748.70

Chapter 15

15.7 $n(1) = 28, n(2) = 17,$ $n(3) = 19, n(4) = 17, n(5) = 19$

15.8 $n(1) = 41, n(2) = 107,$ $n(3) = 66, n(4) = 19$

15.9 $n(1) = 114, n(2) = 92,$ $n(3) = 84, n(4) = 101,$ $n(5) = 107, n(6) = 102$

15.10 $n(1) = 11, n(2) = 32,$ $n(3) = 62, n(4) = 29, n(5) = 16$

15.11 $n(1) = 8, n(2) = 4,$ $n(3) = 3, n(4) = 8, n(5) = 2$

15.12 $n(1) = 159, n(2) = 28,$ $n(3) = 47, n(4) = 16$

15.13 $n(1) = 36, n(2) = 58,$ $n(3) = 74, n(4) = 29$

15.14 $n(1) = 408, n(2) = 571,$ $n(3) = 221$

15.15 $n(1) = 9, n(2) = 123,$ $n(3) = 149, n(4) = 39$

15.16 $n(1) = 36, n(2) = 26,$ $n(3) = 24, n(4) = 14, n(5) = 15$

15.17 $n(1) = 248, n(2) = 108,$ $n(3) = 47, n(4) = 109$

15.20 $n(1) = 63, n(2) = 125,$ $n(3) = 45, n(4) = 87$

15.35

Occupation	Newspaper			
	G&M	Post	Star	Sun
Blue collar	27	18	38	37
White collar	29	43	21	15
Professional	33	51	22	20

15.36

Side Effect	Cold Remedy	Placebo
1	19	17
2	23	18
3	14	16
4	194	199

15.37

Second-last	Last			
	1	2	3	4
1	39	36	51	23
2	36	32	46	20
3	54	46	65	29
4	24	20	28	10

15.38

Education	Continuing	Quitter
1	34	23
2	251	212
3	159	248
4	16	57

15.39

Source	Heartburn condition			
	1	2	3	4
ABC	60	23	13	25
CBS	65	19	14	28
NBC	73	26	9	24
Newspaper	67	11	10	7
Radio	57	16	9	14
None	47	21	10	10

15.40

University	BA	BEng	BBA	Other
	Degree			
1	44	11	34	11
2	52	14	27	7
3	31	27	18	24
4	40	12	42	6

15.41

Results	Yes	No
	Financial Ties	
Favorable	29	1
Neutral	10	7
Critical	9	14

15.42

Approach	1	2	3	4
	Degree			
1	51	8	5	11
2	24	14	12	8
3	26	9	19	8

15.43

Weapon	2000	2005	2010
	Year		
1	161	175	131
2	36	37	24
3	53	39	27
4	159	166	126

15.44

Condition	2004	2006	2008	2010
	Year			
1	78	74	71	69
2	80	80	80	77
3	436	443	450	458

15.45

Household Type	United States	Canada	United Kingdom
	Country		
1	65	94	63
2	85	78	105
3	27	31	21
4	83	80	90
5	40	17	21

15.46

Household Type	Denmark	Ireland	The Netherlands	Sweden
	Country			
1	180	318	234	158
2	222	170	246	220
3	50	99	55	37
4	393	190	304	409
5	5	73	11	26

15.47

Obese?	Canada	Australia	New Zealand	United Kingdom.
	Country			
1	152	151	147	151
2	48	49	53	49

15.48

Smoker?	Denmark	Finland	Norway	Sweden
	Country			
1	420	398	395	430
2	80	102	105	70

15.49

Smoker?	Canada	Australia	New Zealand	United Kingdom
	Country			
1	165	167	164	156
2	35	33	36	44

15.50

Marriage	Democrat	Republican	Independent
	Party		
1	48	21	43
2	24	53	37
3	23	25	21

15.51

Well-Being	Government	Private Sector
1	63	69
2	50	85
3	24	49

15.51

Offer	Plan1	Plan2	Plan3	Plan4
1	521	436	567	538
2	637	627	639	658

Chapter 16

16.6 Lengths: $\bar{x} = 38.00$, $s_x^2 = 193.90$, Test: $\bar{y} = 13.80$, $s_y^2 = 47.96$; $n = 60$, $s_{xy} = 51.86$

16.7 Floors: $\bar{x} = 13.68$ $s_x^2 = 59.32$, Price: $\bar{y} = 210.42$, $s_y^2 = 496.41$; $n = 50$, $s_{xy} = 86.93$

16.8 Education: $\bar{x} = 13.17$, $s_x^2 = 11.12$, Income: $\bar{y} = 78.13$, $s_y^2 = 437.90$; $n = 150$, $s_{xy} = 46.02$

16.9 Age: $\bar{x} = 37.28$, $s_x^2 = 55.11$, Employment: $\bar{y} = 26.28$, $s_y^2 = 4.00$; $n = 80$, $s_{xy} = -6.44$

16.10 Cigarettes: $\bar{x} = 37.64$, $s_x^2 = 108.3$, Days: $\bar{y} = 14.43$, $s_y^2 = 19.80$; $n = 231$, $s_{xy} = 20.55$

16.11 Distance: $\bar{x} = 4.88$, $s_x^2 = 4.27$, Percent: $\bar{y} = 49.22$, $s_y^2 = 243.94$; $n = 85$, $s_{xy} = 22.83$

16.12 Size: $\bar{x} = 53.93$, $s_x^2 = 688.18$, Price: $\bar{y} = 6,465$, $s_y^2 = 11,918,489$; $n = 40$, $s_{xy} = 30,945$

16.13 Hours: $\bar{x} = 1199$, $s_x^2 = 59,153$, Price: $\bar{y} = 27.73$, $s_y^2 = 3.62$; $n = 60$, $s_{xy} = -81.78$

16.14 Occupants: $\bar{x} = 4.75$, $s_x^2 = 4.84$, Electricity: $\bar{y} = 762.6$, $s_y^2 = 56,725$; $n = 200$, $s_{xy} = 310.0$

16.15 Income: $\bar{x} = 59.42$, $s_x^2 = 115.24$, Food: $\bar{y} = 270.3$, $s_y^2 = 1,797.25$; $n = 150$, $s_{xy} = 225.66$

16.16 Vacancy: $\bar{x} = 11.33$, $s_x^2 = 35.47$, Rent: $\bar{y} = 17.20$, $s_y^2 = 11.24$; $n = 30$, $s_{xy} = -10.78$

16.17 Height: $\bar{x} = 68.95$, $s_x^2 = 9.966$, Income: $\bar{y} = 59.59$, $s_y^2 = 71.95$; $n = 250$, $s_{xy} = 6.020$

16.18 Test: $\bar{x} = 79.47$, $s_x^2 = 16.07$, Nondefective: $\bar{y} = 93.89$, $s_y^2 = 1.28$; $n = 45$, $s_{xy} = .83$

16.45 Education: $\bar{x} = 13.99$, $s_x^2 = 5.29$, Time: $\bar{y} = 88.15$, $s_y^2 = 417.16$; $n = 200$, $s_{xy} = 29.42$

16.46 Grade: $\bar{x} = 28.19$, $s_x^2 = 317.83$, Price: $\bar{y} = 475.27$, $s_y^2 = 903,615$; $n = 62$, $s_{xy} = 11,902$

16.47 Age: $\bar{x} = 75.94$, $s_x^2 = 37.28$, Days: $\bar{y} = 2.95$, $s_y^2 = 1.62$; $n = 320$, $s_{xy} = 5.95$

16.48 Age: $\bar{x} = 50.11$, $s_x^2 = 69.17$, Definite: $\bar{y} = 5.55$, $s_y^2 = 4.92$; $n = 270$, $s_{xy} = 10.17$

16.49 Temperature: $\bar{x} = 75.82$, $s_x^2 = 71.62$, Distance: $\bar{y} = 214.8$, $s_y^2 = 6.25$; $n = 77$, $s_{xy} = 11.90$

16.131 Ads: $\bar{x} = 4.12$, $s_x^2 = 3.47$, Customers: $\bar{y} = 384.81$, $s_y^2 = 18,552$; $n = 26$, $s_{xy} = 74.02$

16.132 Age: $\bar{x} = 113.35$, $s_x^2 = 378.77$, Repairs: $\bar{y} = 395.21$, $s_y^2 = 4,094.79$; $n = 20$, $s_{xy} = 936.82$

16.133 Fertilizer: $\bar{x} = 300$, $s_x^2 = 20,690$, Yield: $\bar{y} = 318.60$, $s_y^2 = 5,230$; $n = 30$, $s_{xy} = 2538$

16.135 Television: $\bar{x} = 30.43$, $s_x^2 = 99.11$, Debt: $\bar{y} = 126,604$, $s_y^2 = 2,152,602,614$; $n = 430$, $s_{xy} = 255,877$

16.136 Test: $\bar{x} = 71.92$, $s_x^2 = 90.97$, Nondefective: $\bar{y} = 94.44$, $s_y^2 = 11.84$; $n = 50$, $s_{xy} = 13.08$

Chapter 17

17.1 $R^2 = .2425$, $R^2(adjusted) = .2019$, $s_\varepsilon = 40.24$, $F = 5.97$, p-value = .0013

	Coefficients	Standard error	t statistic	p-value
Intercept	51.39	23.52	2.19	.0331
Lot size	.700	.559	1.25	.2156
Trees	.679	.229	2.96	.0045
Distance	−.378	.195	−1.94	.0577

17.2 $R^2 = .7629$, $R^2(adjusted) = .7453$, $s_\varepsilon = 3.75$, $F = 43.43$, p-value = 0

	Coefficients	Standard error	t statistic	p-value
Intercept	13.01	3.53	3.69	.0010
Assignment	.194	.200	.97	.3417
Midterm	1.11	.122	9.12	0

17.3 $R^2 = .8935$, $R^2(adjusted) = .8711$, $s_\varepsilon = 40.13$, $F = 39.86$, p-value = 0

	Coefficients	Standard error	t statistic	p-value
Intercept	−111.83	134.34	−.83	.4155
Permits	4.76	.395	12.06	0
Mortgage	16.99	15.16	1.12	.2764
Apartment vacancy	−10.53	6.39	−1.65	.1161
Office vacancy	1.31	2.79	.47	.6446

17.4 $R^2 = .3511$, $R^2(adjusted) = .3352$,
$s_\varepsilon = 6.99$, $F = 22.01$, p–value $= 0$

	Coeffi-cients	Stan-dard error	t sta-tistic	p-value
Inter-cept	−1.97	9.55	−.21	.8369
Minor HR	.666	.087	7.64	0
Age	.136	.524	.26	.7961
Years Pro	1.18	.671	1.75	.0819

Chapter 18

18.3 $R^2 = .4068$, $R^2(adjusted) = .3528$,
$s_\varepsilon = 41.15$, $F = 7.54$, p–value $= .0032$

	Coeffi-cients	Stan-dard error	t sta-tistic	p-value
Inter-cept	−108.99	97.24	−1.12	..2744
Space	33.09	8.59	3.85	.0009
Space²	−.666	.177	−3.75	.0011

18.4 First-order model
$R^2 = .8553$, $R^2(adjusted) = .8473$,
$s_\varepsilon = 13.29$, $F = 106.44$, p–value $= 0$

	Coeffi-cients	Stan-dard error	t sta-tistic	p-value
Inter-cept	453.6	15.18	29.87	0
Price	−68.91	6.68	−10.32	0

Second-order model
$R^2 = .9726$, $R^2(adjusted) = .9693$,
$s_\varepsilon = 5.96$, $F = 301.15$, p–value $= 0$

	Coeffi-cients	Stan-dard error	t sta-tistic	p-value
Inter-cept	766.9	37.40	20.50	0
Price	−359.1	34.19	−10.50	0
Price²	64.55	7.58	8.52	0

18.5 First-order model
$R^2 = .8504$, $R^2(adjusted) = .8317$,
$s_\varepsilon = 1.79$, $F = 45.48$, p–value $= .0001$

	Coeffi-cients	Stan-dard error	t sta-tistic	p-value
Inter-cept	41.4	1.22	33.90	0
Day	−1.33	.197	−6.74	.0001

Second-order model
$R^2 = .8852$, $R^2(adjusted) = .8524$,
$s_\varepsilon = 1.67$, $F = 26.98$, p–value $= .0005$

	Coeffi-cients	Stan-dard error	t sta-tistic	p-value
Inter-cept	43.73	1.97	22.21	0
Day	−2.49	.822	−3.03	.0191
Day²	.106	.073	1.46	.1889

18.16 $R^2 = .8051$, $R^2(adjusted) = .7947$,
$s_\varepsilon = 2.32$, $F = 77.66$, p–value $= 0$

	Coeffi-cients	Stan-dard error	t sta-tistic	p-value
Intercept	23.57	5.98	3.94	.0002
Mother	.306	.054	5.65	0
Father	.303	.048	6.37	0
Gmothers	.032	.058	.55	.5853
Gfathers	.078	.057	1.36	.1777
Smoker	−3.72	.669	−5.56	0

18.17 $R^2 = .7002$, $R^2(adjusted) = .6659$,
$s_\varepsilon = 810.8$, $F = 20.43$, p–value $= 0$

	Coeffi-cients	Stan-dard error	t sta-tistic	p-value
Inter-cept	3490	469.2	7.44	0
Yes-tAtt	.369	.078	4.73	0
I_1	1623	492.6	3.30	.0023
I_2	733.5	394.4	1.86	.0713
I_3	−766.5	484.7	−1.58	.1232

Chapter 19

19.8 $T_1 = 6{,}807$, $n_1 = 82$,
$T_2 = 5{,}596$, $n_2 = 75$

19.9 $T_1 = 797$, $n_1 = 30$,
$T_2 = 1{,}033$, $n_2 = 30$

19.10 $T_1 = 14{,}873.5$, $n_1 = 125$,
$T_2 = 16{,}501.5$, $n_2 = 125$

19.11 $T_1 = 10{,}691$, $n_1 = 100$,
$T_2 = 9{,}409$, $n_2 = 100$

19.12 $T_1 = 2{,}810$, $n_1 = 50$,
$T_2 = 2{,}240$, $n_2 = 50$

19.13 $T_1 = 383.5$, $n_1 = 15$,
$T_2 = 436.5$, $n_2 = 25$

19.14 $T_1 = 439.5$, $n_1 = 20$,
$T_2 = 380.5$, $n_2 = 20$

19.15 $T_1 = 13{,}078$, $n_1 = 125$,
$T_2 = 18{,}297$, $n_2 = 125$

19.16 $T_1 = 32{,}225.5$, $n_1 = 182$,
$T_2 = 27{,}459.5$, $n_2 = 163$

19.48 $T^+ = 378.5$, $T^- = 2{,}249.5$, $n = 72$

19.49 $T^+ = 62$, $T^- = 758$, $n = 40$

19.50 $n(positive) = 60$,
$n(negative) = 38$

19.51 $T^+ = 40.5$, $T^- = 235.5$, $n = 23$

19.52 $T^+ = 111$, $T^- = 240$, $n = 26$

19.53 $n(positive) = 30$, $n(negative) = 8$

19.54 $n(positive) = 5$, $n(negative) = 15$

19.55 $T^+ = 190$, $T^- = 135$, $n = 25$

19.56 $n(positive) = 32$,
$n(negative) = 21$

19.57 $T^+ = 48$, $T^- = 732$, $n = 39$

19.70 $T_1 = 767.5$, $n_1 = 25$, $T_2 = 917$
$n_2 = 25$, $T_3 = 1165.5$, $n_3 = 25$

19.71 $T_1 = 17{,}116.5$, $n_1 = 80$,
$T_2 = 16{,}816.5$, $n_2 = 90$, $T_3 = 17{,}277$,
$n_3 = 77$, $T_4 = 29{,}391$, $n_4 = 154$

19.73 $T_1 = 46$, $T_2 = 72$, $T_3 = 62$

19.74 $T_1 = 28.5$, $T_2 = 22.5$, $T_3 = 21$

19.76 $T_1 = 2195$, $n_1 = 33$,
$T_2 = 1650.5$, $n_2 = 34$, $T_3 = 2830$,
$n_3 = 34$, $T_4 = 2102.5$, $n_4 = 31$

19.77 $T_1 = 59.5$, $T_2 = 63.5$,
$T_3 = 64$, $T_4 = 63$

19.78 $T_1 = 33$, $T_2 = 39.5$, $T_3 = 47.5$

19.79 $T_1 = 13{,}805.5$,
$n_1 = 100$, $T_2 = 14{,}909.5$,
$n_2 = 100$, $T_3 = 16{,}390$, $n_3 = 100$

19.80 $T_1 = 4180$, $n_1 = 50$,
$T_2 = 5262$, $n_2 = 50$, $T_3 = 5653$,
$n_3 = 50$, $T_4 = 5005$, $n_4 = 50$

19.81 $T_1 = 1565$, $n_1 = 30$, $T_2 = 1358.5$,
$n_2 = 30$, $T_3 = 1171.5$, $n_3 = 30$

19.82 $T_1 = 21{,}246$, $n_1 = 100$,
$T_2 = 19{,}784$, $n_2 = 100$, $T_3 = 20{,}976$,
$n_3 = 100$, $T_4 = 18{,}194$, $n_4 = 100$

19.83 $T_1 = 28{,}304$, $n_1 = 123$,
$T_2 = 21{,}285$, $n_2 = 109$, $T_3 = 21{,}796$,
$n_3 = 102$, $T_4 = 20{,}421$, $n_4 = 94$

19.84 $T_1 = 638.5$, $n_1 = 18$,
$T_2 = 1233.5$, $n_2 = 14$, $T_3 = 1814.5$,
$n_3 = 26$, $T_4 = 3159.5$, $n_4 = 42$,
$T_5 = 2065$, $n_5 = 33$

TABLES

TABLE 1 Binomial Probabilities

Tabulated values are $P(X \le k) = \sum_{x=0}^{k} p(x_i)$. (Values are rounded to four decimal places.)

n = 5

k								p							
	0.01	0.05	0.10	0.20	0.25	0.30	0.40	0.50	0.60	0.70	0.75	0.80	0.90	0.95	0.99
0	0.9510	0.7738	0.5905	0.3277	0.2373	0.1681	0.0778	0.0313	0.0102	0.0024	0.0010	0.0003	0.0000	0.0000	0.0000
1	0.9990	0.9774	0.9185	0.7373	0.6328	0.5282	0.3370	0.1875	0.0870	0.0308	0.0156	0.0067	0.0005	0.0000	0.0000
2	1.0000	0.9988	0.9914	0.9421	0.8965	0.8369	0.6826	0.5000	0.3174	0.1631	0.1035	0.0579	0.0086	0.0012	0.0000
3	1.0000	1.0000	0.9995	0.9933	0.9844	0.9692	0.9130	0.8125	0.6630	0.4718	0.3672	0.2627	0.0815	0.0226	0.0010
4	1.0000	1.0000	1.0000	0.9997	0.9990	0.9976	0.9898	0.9688	0.9222	0.8319	0.7627	0.6723	0.4095	0.2262	0.0490

n = 6

k								p							
	0.01	0.05	0.10	0.20	0.25	0.30	0.40	0.50	0.60	0.70	0.75	0.80	0.90	0.95	0.99
0	0.9415	0.7351	0.5314	0.2621	0.1780	0.1176	0.0467	0.0156	0.0041	0.0007	0.0002	0.0001	0.0000	0.0000	0.0000
1	0.9985	0.9672	0.8857	0.6554	0.5339	0.4202	0.2333	0.1094	0.0410	0.0109	0.0046	0.0016	0.0001	0.0000	0.0000
2	1.0000	0.9978	0.9842	0.9011	0.8306	0.7443	0.5443	0.3438	0.1792	0.0705	0.0376	0.0170	0.0013	0.0001	0.0000
3	1.0000	0.9999	0.9987	0.9830	0.9624	0.9295	0.8208	0.6563	0.4557	0.2557	0.1694	0.0989	0.0159	0.0022	0.0000
4	1.0000	1.0000	0.9999	0.9984	0.9954	0.9891	0.9590	0.8906	0.7667	0.5798	0.4661	0.3446	0.1143	0.0328	0.0015
5	1.0000	1.0000	1.0000	0.9999	0.9998	0.9993	0.9959	0.9844	0.9533	0.8824	0.8220	0.7379	0.4686	0.2649	0.0585

n = 7

k								p							
	0.01	0.05	0.10	0.20	0.25	0.30	0.40	0.50	0.60	0.70	0.75	0.80	0.90	0.95	0.99
0	0.9321	0.6983	0.4783	0.2097	0.1335	0.0824	0.0280	0.0078	0.0016	0.0002	0.0001	0.0000	0.0000	0.0000	0.0000
1	0.9980	0.9556	0.8503	0.5767	0.4449	0.3294	0.1586	0.0625	0.0188	0.0038	0.0013	0.0004	0.0000	0.0000	0.0000
2	1.0000	0.9962	0.9743	0.8520	0.7564	0.6471	0.4199	0.2266	0.0963	0.0288	0.0129	0.0047	0.0002	0.0000	0.0000
3	1.0000	0.9998	0.9973	0.9667	0.9294	0.8740	0.7102	0.5000	0.2898	0.1260	0.0706	0.0333	0.0027	0.0002	0.0000
4	1.0000	1.0000	0.9998	0.9953	0.9871	0.9712	0.9037	0.7734	0.5801	0.3529	0.2436	0.1480	0.0257	0.0038	0.0000
5	1.0000	1.0000	1.0000	0.9996	0.9987	0.9962	0.9812	0.9375	0.8414	0.6706	0.5551	0.4233	0.1497	0.0444	0.0020
6	1.0000	1.0000	1.0000	1.0000	0.9999	0.9998	0.9984	0.9922	0.9720	0.9176	0.8665	0.7903	0.5217	0.3017	0.0679

(Continued)

TABLE **1** (*Continued*)

n = 8

k	0.01	0.05	0.10	0.20	0.25	0.30	0.40	0.50	0.60	0.70	0.75	0.80	0.90	0.95	0.99
0	0.9227	0.6634	0.4305	0.1678	0.1001	0.0576	0.0168	0.0039	0.0007	0.0001	0.0000	0.0000	0.0000	0.0000	0.0000
1	0.9973	0.9428	0.8131	0.5033	0.3671	0.2553	0.1064	0.0352	0.0085	0.0013	0.0004	0.0001	0.0000	0.0000	0.0000
2	0.9999	0.9942	0.9619	0.7969	0.6785	0.5518	0.3154	0.1445	0.0498	0.0113	0.0042	0.0012	0.0000	0.0000	0.0000
3	1.0000	0.9996	0.9950	0.9437	0.8862	0.8059	0.5941	0.3633	0.1737	0.0580	0.0273	0.0104	0.0004	0.0000	0.0000
4	1.0000	1.0000	0.9996	0.9896	0.9727	0.9420	0.8263	0.6367	0.4059	0.1941	0.1138	0.0563	0.0050	0.0004	0.0000
5	1.0000	1.0000	1.0000	0.9988	0.9958	0.9887	0.9502	0.8555	0.6846	0.4482	0.3215	0.2031	0.0381	0.0058	0.0001
6	1.0000	1.0000	1.0000	0.9999	0.9996	0.9987	0.9915	0.9648	0.8936	0.7447	0.6329	0.4967	0.1869	0.0572	0.0027
7	1.0000	1.0000	1.0000	1.0000	1.0000	0.9999	0.9993	0.9961	0.9832	0.9424	0.8999	0.8322	0.5695	0.3366	0.0773

n = 9

k	0.01	0.05	0.10	0.20	0.25	0.30	0.40	0.50	0.60	0.70	0.75	0.80	0.90	0.95	0.99
0	0.9135	0.6302	0.3874	0.1342	0.0751	0.0404	0.0101	0.0020	0.0003	0.0000	0.0000	0.0000	0.0000	0.0000	0.0000
1	0.9966	0.9288	0.7748	0.4362	0.3003	0.1960	0.0705	0.0195	0.0038	0.0004	0.0001	0.0000	0.0000	0.0000	0.0000
2	0.9999	0.9916	0.9470	0.7382	0.6007	0.4628	0.2318	0.0898	0.0250	0.0043	0.0013	0.0003	0.0000	0.0000	0.0000
3	1.0000	0.9994	0.9917	0.9144	0.8343	0.7297	0.4826	0.2539	0.0994	0.0253	0.0100	0.0031	0.0001	0.0000	0.0000
4	1.0000	1.0000	0.9991	0.9804	0.9511	0.9012	0.7334	0.5000	0.2666	0.0988	0.0489	0.0196	0.0009	0.0000	0.0000
5	1.0000	1.0000	0.9999	0.9969	0.9900	0.9747	0.9006	0.7461	0.5174	0.2703	0.1657	0.0856	0.0083	0.0006	0.0000
6	1.0000	1.0000	1.0000	0.9997	0.9987	0.9957	0.9750	0.9102	0.7682	0.5372	0.3993	0.2618	0.0530	0.0084	0.0001
7	1.0000	1.0000	1.0000	1.0000	0.9999	0.9996	0.9962	0.9805	0.9295	0.8040	0.6997	0.5638	0.2252	0.0712	0.0034
8	1.0000	1.0000	1.0000	1.0000	1.0000	1.0000	0.9997	0.9980	0.9899	0.9596	0.9249	0.8658	0.6126	0.3698	0.0865

TABLE **1** (*Continued*)

n = 10

k	\multicolumn{15}{c}{p}
	0.01	**0.05**	**0.10**	**0.20**	**0.25**	**0.30**	**0.40**	**0.50**	**0.60**	**0.70**	**0.75**	**0.80**	**0.90**	**0.95**	**0.99**
0	0.9044	0.5987	0.3487	0.1074	0.0563	0.0282	0.0060	0.0010	0.0001	0.0000	0.0000	0.0000	0.0000	0.0000	0.0000
1	0.9957	0.9139	0.7361	0.3758	0.2440	0.1493	0.0464	0.0107	0.0017	0.0001	0.0000	0.0000	0.0000	0.0000	0.0000
2	0.9999	0.9885	0.9298	0.6778	0.5256	0.3828	0.1673	0.0547	0.0123	0.0016	0.0004	0.0001	0.0000	0.0000	0.0000
3	1.0000	0.9990	0.9872	0.8791	0.7759	0.6496	0.3823	0.1719	0.0548	0.0106	0.0035	0.0009	0.0000	0.0000	0.0000
4	1.0000	0.9999	0.9984	0.9672	0.9219	0.8497	0.6331	0.3770	0.1662	0.0473	0.0197	0.0064	0.0001	0.0000	0.0000
5	1.0000	1.0000	0.9999	0.9936	0.9803	0.9527	0.8338	0.6230	0.3669	0.1503	0.0781	0.0328	0.0016	0.0001	0.0000
6	1.0000	1.0000	1.0000	0.9991	0.9965	0.9894	0.9452	0.8281	0.6177	0.3504	0.2241	0.1209	0.0128	0.0010	0.0000
7	1.0000	1.0000	1.0000	0.9999	0.9996	0.9984	0.9877	0.9453	0.8327	0.6172	0.4744	0.3222	0.0702	0.0115	0.0001
8	1.0000	1.0000	1.0000	1.0000	1.0000	0.9999	0.9983	0.9893	0.9536	0.8507	0.7560	0.6242	0.2639	0.0861	0.0043
9	1.0000	1.0000	1.0000	1.0000	1.0000	1.0000	0.9999	0.9990	0.9940	0.9718	0.9437	0.8926	0.6513	0.4013	0.0956

n = 15

k	\multicolumn{15}{c}{p}
	0.01	**0.05**	**0.10**	**0.20**	**0.25**	**0.30**	**0.40**	**0.50**	**0.60**	**0.70**	**0.75**	**0.80**	**0.90**	**0.95**	**0.99**
0	0.8601	0.4633	0.2059	0.0352	0.0134	0.0047	0.0005	0.0000	0.0000	0.0000	0.0000	0.0000	0.0000	0.0000	0.0000
1	0.9904	0.8290	0.5490	0.1671	0.0802	0.0353	0.0052	0.0005	0.0000	0.0000	0.0000	0.0000	0.0000	0.0000	0.0000
2	0.9996	0.9638	0.8159	0.3980	0.2361	0.1268	0.0271	0.0037	0.0003	0.0000	0.0000	0.0000	0.0000	0.0000	0.0000
3	1.0000	0.9945	0.9444	0.6482	0.4613	0.2969	0.0905	0.0176	0.0019	0.0001	0.0000	0.0000	0.0000	0.0000	0.0000
4	1.0000	0.9994	0.9873	0.8358	0.6865	0.5155	0.2173	0.0592	0.0093	0.0007	0.0001	0.0000	0.0000	0.0000	0.0000
5	1.0000	0.9999	0.9978	0.9389	0.8516	0.7216	0.4032	0.1509	0.0338	0.0037	0.0008	0.0001	0.0000	0.0000	0.0000
6	1.0000	1.0000	0.9997	0.9819	0.9434	0.8689	0.6098	0.3036	0.0950	0.0152	0.0042	0.0008	0.0000	0.0000	0.0000
7	1.0000	1.0000	1.0000	0.9958	0.9827	0.9500	0.7869	0.5000	0.2131	0.0500	0.0173	0.0042	0.0000	0.0000	0.0000
8	1.0000	1.0000	1.0000	0.9992	0.9958	0.9848	0.9050	0.6964	0.3902	0.1311	0.0566	0.0181	0.0003	0.0000	0.0000
9	1.0000	1.0000	1.0000	0.9999	0.9992	0.9963	0.9662	0.8491	0.5968	0.2784	0.1484	0.0611	0.0022	0.0001	0.0000
10	1.0000	1.0000	1.0000	1.0000	0.9999	0.9993	0.9907	0.9408	0.7827	0.4845	0.3135	0.1642	0.0127	0.0006	0.0000
11	1.0000	1.0000	1.0000	1.0000	1.0000	0.9999	0.9981	0.9824	0.9095	0.7031	0.5387	0.3518	0.0556	0.0055	0.0000
12	1.0000	1.0000	1.0000	1.0000	1.0000	1.0000	0.9997	0.9963	0.9729	0.8732	0.7639	0.6020	0.1841	0.0362	0.0004
13	1.0000	1.0000	1.0000	1.0000	1.0000	1.0000	1.0000	0.9995	0.9948	0.9647	0.9198	0.8329	0.4510	0.1710	0.0096
14	1.0000	1.0000	1.0000	1.0000	1.0000	1.0000	1.0000	1.0000	0.9995	0.9953	0.9866	0.9648	0.7941	0.5367	0.1399

(*Continued*)

TABLE **1** (*Continued*)

n = 20

k	\multicolumn{15}{c}{p}
	0.01	**0.05**	**0.10**	**0.20**	**0.25**	**0.30**	**0.40**	**0.50**	**0.60**	**0.70**	**0.75**	**0.80**	**0.90**	**0.95**	**0.99**
0	0.8179	0.3585	0.1216	0.0115	0.0032	0.0008	0.0000	0.0000	0.0000	0.0000	0.0000	0.0000	0.0000	0.0000	0.0000
1	0.9831	0.7358	0.3917	0.0692	0.0243	0.0076	0.0005	0.0000	0.0000	0.0000	0.0000	0.0000	0.0000	0.0000	0.0000
2	0.9990	0.9245	0.6769	0.2061	0.0913	0.0355	0.0036	0.0002	0.0000	0.0000	0.0000	0.0000	0.0000	0.0000	0.0000
3	1.0000	0.9841	0.8670	0.4114	0.2252	0.1071	0.0160	0.0013	0.0000	0.0000	0.0000	0.0000	0.0000	0.0000	0.0000
4	1.0000	0.9974	0.9568	0.6296	0.4148	0.2375	0.0510	0.0059	0.0003	0.0000	0.0000	0.0000	0.0000	0.0000	0.0000
5	1.0000	0.9997	0.9887	0.8042	0.6172	0.4164	0.1256	0.0207	0.0016	0.0000	0.0000	0.0000	0.0000	0.0000	0.0000
6	1.0000	1.0000	0.9976	0.9133	0.7858	0.6080	0.2500	0.0577	0.0065	0.0003	0.0000	0.0000	0.0000	0.0000	0.0000
7	1.0000	1.0000	0.9996	0.9679	0.8982	0.7723	0.4159	0.1316	0.0210	0.0013	0.0002	0.0000	0.0000	0.0000	0.0000
8	1.0000	1.0000	0.9999	0.9900	0.9591	0.8867	0.5956	0.2517	0.0565	0.0051	0.0009	0.0001	0.0000	0.0000	0.0000
9	1.0000	1.0000	1.0000	0.9974	0.9861	0.9520	0.7553	0.4119	0.1275	0.0171	0.0039	0.0006	0.0000	0.0000	0.0000
10	1.0000	1.0000	1.0000	0.9994	0.9961	0.9829	0.8725	0.5881	0.2447	0.0480	0.0139	0.0026	0.0000	0.0000	0.0000
11	1.0000	1.0000	1.0000	0.9999	0.9991	0.9949	0.9435	0.7483	0.4044	0.1133	0.0409	0.0100	0.0001	0.0000	0.0000
12	1.0000	1.0000	1.0000	1.0000	0.9998	0.9987	0.9790	0.8684	0.5841	0.2277	0.1018	0.0321	0.0004	0.0000	0.0000
13	1.0000	1.0000	1.0000	1.0000	1.0000	0.9997	0.9935	0.9423	0.7500	0.3920	0.2142	0.0867	0.0024	0.0000	0.0000
14	1.0000	1.0000	1.0000	1.0000	1.0000	1.0000	0.9984	0.9793	0.8744	0.5836	0.3828	0.1958	0.0113	0.0003	0.0000
15	1.0000	1.0000	1.0000	1.0000	1.0000	1.0000	0.9997	0.9941	0.9490	0.7625	0.5852	0.3704	0.0432	0.0026	0.0000
16	1.0000	1.0000	1.0000	1.0000	1.0000	1.0000	1.0000	0.9987	0.9840	0.8929	0.7748	0.5886	0.1330	0.0159	0.0000
17	1.0000	1.0000	1.0000	1.0000	1.0000	1.0000	1.0000	0.9998	0.9964	0.9645	0.9087	0.7939	0.3231	0.0755	0.0010
18	1.0000	1.0000	1.0000	1.0000	1.0000	1.0000	1.0000	1.0000	0.9995	0.9924	0.9757	0.9308	0.6083	0.2642	0.0169
19	1.0000	1.0000	1.0000	1.0000	1.0000	1.0000	1.0000	1.0000	1.0000	0.9992	0.9968	0.9885	0.8784	0.6415	0.1821

TABLE **1** (*Continued*)

n = 25

k	0.01	0.05	0.10	0.20	0.25	0.30	0.40	0.50	0.60	0.70	0.75	0.80	0.90	0.95	0.99
0	0.7778	0.2774	0.0718	0.0038	0.0008	0.0001	0.0000	0.0000	0.0000	0.0000	0.0000	0.0000	0.0000	0.0000	0.0000
1	0.9742	0.6424	0.2712	0.0274	0.0070	0.0016	0.0001	0.0000	0.0000	0.0000	0.0000	0.0000	0.0000	0.0000	0.0000
2	0.9980	0.8729	0.5371	0.0982	0.0321	0.0090	0.0004	0.0000	0.0000	0.0000	0.0000	0.0000	0.0000	0.0000	0.0000
3	0.9999	0.9659	0.7636	0.2340	0.0962	0.0332	0.0024	0.0001	0.0000	0.0000	0.0000	0.0000	0.0000	0.0000	0.0000
4	1.0000	0.9928	0.9020	0.4207	0.2137	0.0905	0.0095	0.0005	0.0000	0.0000	0.0000	0.0000	0.0000	0.0000	0.0000
5	1.0000	0.9988	0.9666	0.6167	0.3783	0.1935	0.0294	0.0020	0.0001	0.0000	0.0000	0.0000	0.0000	0.0000	0.0000
6	1.0000	0.9998	0.9905	0.7800	0.5611	0.3407	0.0736	0.0073	0.0003	0.0000	0.0000	0.0000	0.0000	0.0000	0.0000
7	1.0000	1.0000	0.9977	0.8909	0.7265	0.5118	0.1536	0.0216	0.0012	0.0000	0.0000	0.0000	0.0000	0.0000	0.0000
8	1.0000	1.0000	0.9995	0.9532	0.8506	0.6769	0.2735	0.0539	0.0043	0.0001	0.0000	0.0000	0.0000	0.0000	0.0000
9	1.0000	1.0000	0.9999	0.9827	0.9287	0.8106	0.4246	0.1148	0.0132	0.0005	0.0000	0.0000	0.0000	0.0000	0.0000
10	1.0000	1.0000	1.0000	0.9944	0.9703	0.9022	0.5858	0.2122	0.0344	0.0018	0.0002	0.0000	0.0000	0.0000	0.0000
11	1.0000	1.0000	1.0000	0.9985	0.9893	0.9558	0.7323	0.3450	0.0778	0.0060	0.0009	0.0001	0.0000	0.0000	0.0000
12	1.0000	1.0000	1.0000	0.9996	0.9966	0.9825	0.8462	0.5000	0.1538	0.0175	0.0034	0.0004	0.0000	0.0000	0.0000
13	1.0000	1.0000	1.0000	0.9999	0.9991	0.9940	0.9222	0.6550	0.2677	0.0442	0.0107	0.0015	0.0000	0.0000	0.0000
14	1.0000	1.0000	1.0000	1.0000	0.9998	0.9982	0.9656	0.7878	0.4142	0.0978	0.0297	0.0056	0.0000	0.0000	0.0000
15	1.0000	1.0000	1.0000	1.0000	1.0000	0.9995	0.9868	0.8852	0.5754	0.1894	0.0713	0.0173	0.0001	0.0000	0.0000
16	1.0000	1.0000	1.0000	1.0000	1.0000	0.9999	0.9957	0.9461	0.7265	0.3231	0.1494	0.0468	0.0005	0.0000	0.0000
17	1.0000	1.0000	1.0000	1.0000	1.0000	1.0000	0.9988	0.9784	0.8464	0.4882	0.2735	0.1091	0.0023	0.0000	0.0000
18	1.0000	1.0000	1.0000	1.0000	1.0000	1.0000	0.9997	0.9927	0.9264	0.6593	0.4389	0.2200	0.0095	0.0002	0.0000
19	1.0000	1.0000	1.0000	1.0000	1.0000	1.0000	0.9999	0.9980	0.9706	0.8065	0.6217	0.3833	0.0334	0.0012	0.0000
20	1.0000	1.0000	1.0000	1.0000	1.0000	1.0000	1.0000	0.9995	0.9905	0.9095	0.7863	0.5793	0.0980	0.0072	0.0000
21	1.0000	1.0000	1.0000	1.0000	1.0000	1.0000	1.0000	0.9999	0.9976	0.9668	0.9038	0.7660	0.2364	0.0341	0.0001
22	1.0000	1.0000	1.0000	1.0000	1.0000	1.0000	1.0000	1.0000	0.9996	0.9910	0.9679	0.9018	0.4629	0.1271	0.0020
23	1.0000	1.0000	1.0000	1.0000	1.0000	1.0000	1.0000	1.0000	0.9999	0.9984	0.9930	0.9726	0.7288	0.3576	0.0258
24	1.0000	1.0000	1.0000	1.0000	1.0000	1.0000	1.0000	1.0000	1.0000	0.9999	0.9992	0.9962	0.9282	0.7226	0.2222

TABLE 2 Poisson Probabilities

Tabulated values are $P(X \le k) = \sum_{x=0}^{k} p(xi)$. (Values are rounded to four decimal places.)

k	0.10	0.20	0.30	0.40	0.50	1.0	1.5	2.0	2.5	3.0	3.5	4.0	4.5	5.0	5.5	6.0
0	0.9048	0.8187	0.7408	0.6703	0.6065	0.3679	0.2231	0.1353	0.0821	0.0498	0.0302	0.0183	0.0111	0.0067	0.0041	0.0025
1	0.9953	0.9825	0.9631	0.9384	0.9098	0.7358	0.5578	0.4060	0.2873	0.1991	0.1359	0.0916	0.0611	0.0404	0.0266	0.0174
2	0.9998	0.9989	0.9964	0.9921	0.9856	0.9197	0.8088	0.6767	0.5438	0.4232	0.3208	0.2381	0.1736	0.1247	0.0884	0.0620
3	1.0000	0.9999	0.9997	0.9992	0.9982	0.9810	0.9344	0.8571	0.7576	0.6472	0.5366	0.4335	0.3423	0.2650	0.2017	0.1512
4		1.0000	1.0000	0.9999	0.9998	0.9963	0.9814	0.9473	0.8912	0.8153	0.7254	0.6288	0.5321	0.4405	0.3575	0.2851
5				1.0000	1.0000	0.9994	0.9955	0.9834	0.9580	0.9161	0.8576	0.7851	0.7029	0.6160	0.5289	0.4457
6						0.9999	0.9991	0.9955	0.9858	0.9665	0.9347	0.8893	0.8311	0.7622	0.6860	0.6063
7						1.0000	0.9998	0.9989	0.9958	0.9881	0.9733	0.9489	0.9134	0.8666	0.8095	0.7440
8							1.0000	0.9998	0.9989	0.9962	0.9901	0.9786	0.9597	0.9319	0.8944	0.8472
9								1.0000	0.9997	0.9989	0.9967	0.9919	0.9829	0.9682	0.9462	0.9161
10									0.9999	0.9997	0.9990	0.9972	0.9933	0.9863	0.9747	0.9574
11									1.0000	0.9999	0.9997	0.9991	0.9976	0.9945	0.9890	0.9799
12										1.0000	0.9999	0.9997	0.9992	0.9980	0.9955	0.9912
13											1.0000	0.9999	0.9997	0.9993	0.9983	0.9964
14												1.0000	0.9999	0.9998	0.9994	0.9986
15													1.0000	0.9999	0.9998	0.9995
16														1.0000	0.9999	0.9998
17															1.0000	0.9999
18																1.0000
19																
20																

TABLE **2** (*Continued*)

k	6.50	7.00	7.50	8.00	8.50	9.00	9.50	10	11	12	13	14	15
							μ						
0	0.0015	0.0009	0.0006	0.0003	0.0002	0.0001	0.0001	0.0000	0.0000	0.0000	0.0000	0.0000	0.0000
1	0.0113	0.0073	0.0047	0.0030	0.0019	0.0012	0.0008	0.0005	0.0002	0.0001	0.0000	0.0000	0.0000
2	0.0430	0.0296	0.0203	0.0138	0.0093	0.0062	0.0042	0.0028	0.0012	0.0005	0.0002	0.0001	0.0000
3	0.1118	0.0818	0.0591	0.0424	0.0301	0.0212	0.0149	0.0103	0.0049	0.0023	0.0011	0.0005	0.0002
4	0.2237	0.1730	0.1321	0.0996	0.0744	0.0550	0.0403	0.0293	0.0151	0.0076	0.0037	0.0018	0.0009
5	0.3690	0.3007	0.2414	0.1912	0.1496	0.1157	0.0885	0.0671	0.0375	0.0203	0.0107	0.0055	0.0028
6	0.5265	0.4497	0.3782	0.3134	0.2562	0.2068	0.1649	0.1301	0.0786	0.0458	0.0259	0.0142	0.0076
7	0.6728	0.5987	0.5246	0.4530	0.3856	0.3239	0.2687	0.2202	0.1432	0.0895	0.0540	0.0316	0.0180
8	0.7916	0.7291	0.6620	0.5925	0.5231	0.4557	0.3918	0.3328	0.2320	0.1550	0.0998	0.0621	0.0374
9	0.8774	0.8305	0.7764	0.7166	0.6530	0.5874	0.5218	0.4579	0.3405	0.2424	0.1658	0.1094	0.0699
10	0.9332	0.9015	0.8622	0.8159	0.7634	0.7060	0.6453	0.5830	0.4599	0.3472	0.2517	0.1757	0.1185
11	0.9661	0.9467	0.9208	0.8881	0.8487	0.8030	0.7520	0.6968	0.5793	0.4616	0.3532	0.2600	0.1848
12	0.9840	0.9730	0.9573	0.9362	0.9091	0.8758	0.8364	0.7916	0.6887	0.5760	0.4631	0.3585	0.2676
13	0.9929	0.9872	0.9784	0.9658	0.9486	0.9261	0.8981	0.8645	0.7813	0.6815	0.5730	0.4644	0.3632
14	0.9970	0.9943	0.9897	0.9827	0.9726	0.9585	0.9400	0.9165	0.8540	0.7720	0.6751	0.5704	0.4657
15	0.9988	0.9976	0.9954	0.9918	0.9862	0.9780	0.9665	0.9513	0.9074	0.8444	0.7636	0.6694	0.5681
16	0.9996	0.9990	0.9980	0.9963	0.9934	0.9889	0.9823	0.9730	0.9441	0.8987	0.8355	0.7559	0.6641
17	0.9998	0.9996	0.9992	0.9984	0.9970	0.9947	0.9911	0.9857	0.9678	0.9370	0.8905	0.8272	0.7489
18	0.9999	0.9999	0.9997	0.9993	0.9987	0.9976	0.9957	0.9928	0.9823	0.9626	0.9302	0.8826	0.8195
19	1.0000	1.0000	0.9999	0.9997	0.9995	0.9989	0.9980	0.9965	0.9907	0.9787	0.9573	0.9235	0.8752
20			1.0000	0.9999	0.9998	0.9996	0.9991	0.9984	0.9953	0.9884	0.9750	0.9521	0.9170
21				1.0000	0.9999	0.9998	0.9996	0.9993	0.9977	0.9939	0.9859	0.9712	0.9469
22					1.0000	0.9999	0.9999	0.9997	0.9990	0.9970	0.9924	0.9833	0.9673
23						1.0000	0.9999	0.9999	0.9995	0.9985	0.9960	0.9907	0.9805
24							1.0000	1.0000	0.9998	0.9993	0.9980	0.9950	0.9888
25									0.9999	0.9997	0.9990	0.9974	0.9938
26									1.0000	0.9999	0.9995	0.9987	0.9967
27										0.9999	0.9998	0.9994	0.9983
28										1.0000	0.9999	0.9997	0.9991
29											1.0000	0.9999	0.9996
30												0.9999	0.9998
31												1.0000	0.9999
32													1.0000

TABLE **3**   Cumulative Standardized Normal Probabilities

$P(-\infty < Z < z)$

Z	0.00	0.01	0.02	0.03	0.04	0.05	0.06	0.07	0.08	0.09
−3.0	0.0013	0.0013	0.0013	0.0012	0.0012	0.0011	0.0011	0.0011	0.0010	0.0010
−2.9	0.0019	0.0018	0.0018	0.0017	0.0016	0.0016	0.0015	0.0015	0.0014	0.0014
−2.8	0.0026	0.0025	0.0024	0.0023	0.0023	0.0022	0.0021	0.0021	0.0020	0.0019
−2.7	0.0035	0.0034	0.0033	0.0032	0.0031	0.0030	0.0029	0.0028	0.0027	0.0026
−2.6	0.0047	0.0045	0.0044	0.0043	0.0041	0.0040	0.0039	0.0038	0.0037	0.0036
−2.5	0.0062	0.0060	0.0059	0.0057	0.0055	0.0054	0.0052	0.0051	0.0049	0.0048
−2.4	0.0082	0.0080	0.0078	0.0075	0.0073	0.0071	0.0069	0.0068	0.0066	0.0064
−2.3	0.0107	0.0104	0.0102	0.0099	0.0096	0.0094	0.0091	0.0089	0.0087	0.0084
−2.2	0.0139	0.0136	0.0132	0.0129	0.0125	0.0122	0.0119	0.0116	0.0113	0.0110
−2.1	0.0179	0.0174	0.0170	0.0166	0.0162	0.0158	0.0154	0.0150	0.0146	0.0143
−2.0	0.0228	0.0222	0.0217	0.0212	0.0207	0.0202	0.0197	0.0192	0.0188	0.0183
−1.9	0.0287	0.0281	0.0274	0.0268	0.0262	0.0256	0.0250	0.0244	0.0239	0.0233
−1.8	0.0359	0.0351	0.0344	0.0336	0.0329	0.0322	0.0314	0.0307	0.0301	0.0294
−1.7	0.0446	0.0436	0.0427	0.0418	0.0409	0.0401	0.0392	0.0384	0.0375	0.0367
−1.6	0.0548	0.0537	0.0526	0.0516	0.0505	0.0495	0.0485	0.0475	0.0465	0.0455
−1.5	0.0668	0.0655	0.0643	0.0630	0.0618	0.0606	0.0594	0.0582	0.0571	0.0559
−1.4	0.0808	0.0793	0.0778	0.0764	0.0749	0.0735	0.0721	0.0708	0.0694	0.0681
−1.3	0.0968	0.0951	0.0934	0.0918	0.0901	0.0885	0.0869	0.0853	0.0838	0.0823
−1.2	0.1151	0.1131	0.1112	0.1093	0.1075	0.1056	0.1038	0.1020	0.1003	0.0985
−1.1	0.1357	0.1335	0.1314	0.1292	0.1271	0.1251	0.1230	0.1210	0.1190	0.1170
−1.0	0.1587	0.1562	0.1539	0.1515	0.1492	0.1469	0.1446	0.1423	0.1401	0.1379
−0.9	0.1841	0.1814	0.1788	0.1762	0.1736	0.1711	0.1685	0.1660	0.1635	0.1611
−0.8	0.2119	0.2090	0.2061	0.2033	0.2005	0.1977	0.1949	0.1922	0.1894	0.1867
−0.7	0.2420	0.2389	0.2358	0.2327	0.2296	0.2266	0.2236	0.2206	0.2177	0.2148
−0.6	0.2743	0.2709	0.2676	0.2643	0.2611	0.2578	0.2546	0.2514	0.2483	0.2451
−0.5	0.3085	0.3050	0.3015	0.2981	0.2946	0.2912	0.2877	0.2843	0.2810	0.2776
−0.4	0.3446	0.3409	0.3372	0.3336	0.3300	0.3264	0.3228	0.3192	0.3156	0.3121
−0.3	0.3821	0.3783	0.3745	0.3707	0.3669	0.3632	0.3594	0.3557	0.3520	0.3483
−0.2	0.4207	0.4168	0.4129	0.4090	0.4052	0.4013	0.3974	0.3936	0.3897	0.3859
−0.1	0.4602	0.4562	0.4522	0.4483	0.4443	0.4404	0.4364	0.4325	0.4286	0.4247
−0.0	0.5000	0.4960	0.4920	0.4880	0.4840	0.4801	0.4761	0.4721	0.4681	0.4641

TABLE **3** (*Continued*)

$P(-\infty < Z < z)$

Z	0.00	0.01	0.02	0.03	0.04	0.05	0.06	0.07	0.08	0.09
0.0	0.5000	0.5040	0.5080	0.5120	0.5160	0.5199	0.5239	0.5279	0.5319	0.5359
0.1	0.5398	0.5438	0.5478	0.5517	0.5557	0.5596	0.5636	0.5675	0.5714	0.5753
0.2	0.5793	0.5832	0.5871	0.5910	0.5948	0.5987	0.6026	0.6064	0.6103	0.6141
0.3	0.6179	0.6217	0.6255	0.6293	0.6331	0.6368	0.6406	0.6443	0.6480	0.6517
0.4	0.6554	0.6591	0.6628	0.6664	0.6700	0.6736	0.6772	0.6808	0.6844	0.6879
0.5	0.6915	0.6950	0.6985	0.7019	0.7054	0.7088	0.7123	0.7157	0.7190	0.7224
0.6	0.7257	0.7291	0.7324	0.7357	0.7389	0.7422	0.7454	0.7486	0.7517	0.7549
0.7	0.7580	0.7611	0.7642	0.7673	0.7704	0.7734	0.7764	0.7794	0.7823	0.7852
0.8	0.7881	0.7910	0.7939	0.7967	0.7995	0.8023	0.8051	0.8078	0.8106	0.8133
0.9	0.8159	0.8186	0.8212	0.8238	0.8264	0.8289	0.8315	0.8340	0.8365	0.8389
1.0	0.8413	0.8438	0.8461	0.8485	0.8508	0.8531	0.8554	0.8577	0.8599	0.8621
1.1	0.8643	0.8665	0.8686	0.8708	0.8729	0.8749	0.8770	0.8790	0.8810	0.8830
1.2	0.8849	0.8869	0.8888	0.8907	0.8925	0.8944	0.8962	0.8980	0.8997	0.9015
1.3	0.9032	0.9049	0.9066	0.9082	0.9099	0.9115	0.9131	0.9147	0.9162	0.9177
1.4	0.9192	0.9207	0.9222	0.9236	0.9251	0.9265	0.9279	0.9292	0.9306	0.9319
1.5	0.9332	0.9345	0.9357	0.9370	0.9382	0.9394	0.9406	0.9418	0.9429	0.9441
1.6	0.9452	0.9463	0.9474	0.9484	0.9495	0.9505	0.9515	0.9525	0.9535	0.9545
1.7	0.9554	0.9564	0.9573	0.9582	0.9591	0.9599	0.9608	0.9616	0.9625	0.9633
1.8	0.9641	0.9649	0.9656	0.9664	0.9671	0.9678	0.9686	0.9693	0.9699	0.9706
1.9	0.9713	0.9719	0.9726	0.9732	0.9738	0.9744	0.9750	0.9756	0.9761	0.9767
2.0	0.9772	0.9778	0.9783	0.9788	0.9793	0.9798	0.9803	0.9808	0.9812	0.9817
2.1	0.9821	0.9826	0.9830	0.9834	0.9838	0.9842	0.9846	0.9850	0.9854	0.9857
2.2	0.9861	0.9864	0.9868	0.9871	0.9875	0.9878	0.9881	0.9884	0.9887	0.9890
2.3	0.9893	0.9896	0.9898	0.9901	0.9904	0.9906	0.9909	0.9911	0.9913	0.9916
2.4	0.9918	0.9920	0.9922	0.9925	0.9927	0.9929	0.9931	0.9932	0.9934	0.9936
2.5	0.9938	0.9940	0.9941	0.9943	0.9945	0.9946	0.9948	0.9949	0.9951	0.9952
2.6	0.9953	0.9955	0.9956	0.9957	0.9959	0.9960	0.9961	0.9962	0.9963	0.9964
2.7	0.9965	0.9966	0.9967	0.9968	0.9969	0.9970	0.9971	0.9972	0.9973	0.9974
2.8	0.9974	0.9975	0.9976	0.9977	0.9977	0.9978	0.9979	0.9979	0.9980	0.9981
2.9	0.9981	0.9982	0.9982	0.9983	0.9984	0.9984	0.9985	0.9985	0.9986	0.9986
3.0	0.9987	0.9987	0.9987	0.9988	0.9988	0.9989	0.9989	0.9989	0.9990	0.9990

TABLE **4**
Critical Values of the Student *t* Distribution

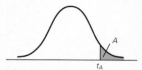

Degrees of Freedom	$t_{.100}$	$t_{.050}$	$t_{.025}$	$t_{.010}$	$t_{.005}$
1	3.078	6.314	12.706	31.821	63.657
2	1.886	2.920	4.303	6.965	9.925
3	1.638	2.353	3.182	4.541	5.841
4	1.533	2.132	2.776	3.747	4.604
5	1.476	2.015	2.571	3.365	4.032
6	1.440	1.943	2.447	3.143	3.707
7	1.415	1.895	2.365	2.998	3.499
8	1.397	1.860	2.306	2.896	3.355
9	1.383	1.833	2.262	2.821	3.250
10	1.372	1.812	2.228	2.764	3.169
11	1.363	1.796	2.201	2.718	3.106
12	1.356	1.782	2.179	2.681	3.055
13	1.350	1.771	2.160	2.650	3.012
14	1.345	1.761	2.145	2.624	2.977
15	1.341	1.753	2.131	2.602	2.947
16	1.337	1.746	2.120	2.583	2.921
17	1.333	1.740	2.110	2.567	2.898
18	1.330	1.734	2.101	2.552	2.878
19	1.328	1.729	2.093	2.539	2.861
20	1.325	1.725	2.086	2.528	2.845
21	1.323	1.721	2.080	2.518	2.831
22	1.321	1.717	2.074	2.508	2.819
23	1.319	1.714	2.069	2.500	2.807
24	1.318	1.711	2.064	2.492	2.797
25	1.316	1.708	2.060	2.485	2.787
26	1.315	1.706	2.056	2.479	2.779
27	1.314	1.703	2.052	2.473	2.771
28	1.313	1.701	2.048	2.467	2.763
29	1.311	1.699	2.045	2.462	2.756
30	1.310	1.697	2.042	2.457	2.750
35	1.306	1.690	2.030	2.438	2.724
40	1.303	1.684	2.021	2.423	2.704
45	1.301	1.679	2.014	2.412	2.690
50	1.299	1.676	2.009	2.403	2.678
55	1.297	1.673	2.004	2.396	2.668
60	1.296	1.671	2.000	2.390	2.660
65	1.295	1.669	1.997	2.385	2.654
70	1.294	1.667	1.994	2.381	2.648
75	1.293	1.665	1.992	2.377	2.643
80	1.292	1.664	1.990	2.374	2.639
85	1.292	1.663	1.988	2.371	2.635
90	1.291	1.662	1.987	2.368	2.632
95	1.291	1.661	1.985	2.366	2.629
100	1.290	1.660	1.984	2.364	2.626
110	1.289	1.659	1.982	2.361	2.621
120	1.289	1.658	1.980	2.358	2.617
130	1.288	1.657	1.978	2.355	2.614
140	1.288	1.656	1.977	2.353	2.611
150	1.287	1.655	1.976	2.351	2.609
160	1.287	1.654	1.975	2.350	2.607
170	1.287	1.654	1.974	2.348	2.605
180	1.286	1.653	1.973	2.347	2.603
190	1.286	1.653	1.973	2.346	2.602
200	1.286	1.653	1.972	2.345	2.601
∞	1.282	1.645	1.960	2.326	2.576

TABLE 5 Critical Values of the χ^2 Distribution

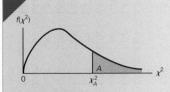

Degrees of Freedom	$\chi^2_{.995}$	$\chi^2_{.990}$	$\chi^2_{.975}$	$\chi^2_{.950}$	$\chi^2_{.900}$	$\chi^2_{.100}$	$\chi^2_{.050}$	$\chi^2_{.025}$	$\chi^2_{.010}$	$\chi^2_{.005}$
1	0.000039	0.000157	0.000982	0.00393	0.0158	2.71	3.84	5.02	6.63	7.88
2	0.0100	0.0201	0.0506	0.103	0.211	4.61	5.99	7.38	9.21	10.6
3	0.072	0.115	0.216	0.352	0.584	6.25	7.81	9.35	11.3	12.8
4	0.207	0.297	0.484	0.711	1.06	7.78	9.49	11.1	13.3	14.9
5	0.412	0.554	0.831	1.15	1.61	9.24	11.1	12.8	15.1	16.7
6	0.676	0.872	1.24	1.64	2.20	10.6	12.6	14.4	16.8	18.5
7	0.989	1.24	1.69	2.17	2.83	12.0	14.1	16.0	18.5	20.3
8	1.34	1.65	2.18	2.73	3.49	13.4	15.5	17.5	20.1	22.0
9	1.73	2.09	2.70	3.33	4.17	14.7	16.9	19.0	21.7	23.6
10	2.16	2.56	3.25	3.94	4.87	16.0	18.3	20.5	23.2	25.2
11	2.60	3.05	3.82	4.57	5.58	17.3	19.7	21.9	24.7	26.8
12	3.07	3.57	4.40	5.23	6.30	18.5	21.0	23.3	26.2	28.3
13	3.57	4.11	5.01	5.89	7.04	19.8	22.4	24.7	27.7	29.8
14	4.07	4.66	5.63	6.57	7.79	21.1	23.7	26.1	29.1	31.3
15	4.60	5.23	6.26	7.26	8.55	22.3	25.0	27.5	30.6	32.8
16	5.14	5.81	6.91	7.96	9.31	23.5	26.3	28.8	32.0	34.3
17	5.70	6.41	7.56	8.67	10.1	24.8	27.6	30.2	33.4	35.7
18	6.26	7.01	8.23	9.39	10.9	26.0	28.9	31.5	34.8	37.2
19	6.84	7.63	8.91	10.1	11.7	27.2	30.1	32.9	36.2	38.6
20	7.43	8.26	9.59	10.9	12.4	28.4	31.4	34.2	37.6	40.0
21	8.03	8.90	10.3	11.6	13.2	29.6	32.7	35.5	38.9	41.4
22	8.64	9.54	11.0	12.3	14.0	30.8	33.9	36.8	40.3	42.8
23	9.26	10.2	11.7	13.1	14.8	32.0	35.2	38.1	41.6	44.2
24	9.89	10.9	12.4	13.8	15.7	33.2	36.4	39.4	43.0	45.6
25	10.5	11.5	13.1	14.6	16.5	34.4	37.7	40.6	44.3	46.9
26	11.2	12.2	13.8	15.4	17.3	35.6	38.9	41.9	45.6	48.3
27	11.8	12.9	14.6	16.2	18.1	36.7	40.1	43.2	47.0	49.6
28	12.5	13.6	15.3	16.9	18.9	37.9	41.3	44.5	48.3	51.0
29	13.1	14.3	16.0	17.7	19.8	39.1	42.6	45.7	49.6	52.3
30	13.8	15.0	16.8	18.5	20.6	40.3	43.8	47.0	50.9	53.7
40	20.7	22.2	24.4	26.5	29.1	51.8	55.8	59.3	63.7	66.8
50	28.0	29.7	32.4	34.8	37.7	63.2	67.5	71.4	76.2	79.5
60	35.5	37.5	40.5	43.2	46.5	74.4	79.1	83.3	88.4	92.0
70	43.3	45.4	48.8	51.7	55.3	85.5	90.5	95.0	100	104
80	51.2	53.5	57.2	60.4	64.3	96.6	102	107	112	116
90	59.2	61.8	65.6	69.1	73.3	108	113	118	124	128
100	67.3	70.1	74.2	77.9	82.4	118	124	130	136	140

TABLE **6(a)** Critical Values of the *F*-Distribution: *A* = .05

NUMERATOR DEGREES OF FREEDOM

ν_2 \ ν_1	1	2	3	4	5	6	7	8	9	10	11	12	13	14	15	16	17	18	19	20
1	161	199	216	225	230	234	237	239	241	242	243	244	245	245	246	246	247	247	248	248
2	18.5	19.0	19.2	19.2	19.3	19.3	19.4	19.4	19.4	19.4	19.4	19.4	19.4	19.4	19.4	19.4	19.4	19.4	19.4	19.4
3	10.1	9.55	9.28	9.12	9.01	8.94	8.89	8.85	8.81	8.79	8.76	8.74	8.73	8.71	8.70	8.69	8.68	8.67	8.67	8.66
4	7.71	6.94	6.59	6.39	6.26	6.16	6.09	6.04	6.00	5.96	5.94	5.91	5.89	5.87	5.86	5.84	5.83	5.82	5.81	5.80
5	6.61	5.79	5.41	5.19	5.05	4.95	4.88	4.82	4.77	4.74	4.70	4.68	4.66	4.64	4.62	4.60	4.59	4.58	4.57	4.56
6	5.99	5.14	4.76	4.53	4.39	4.28	4.21	4.15	4.10	4.06	4.03	4.00	3.98	3.96	3.94	3.92	3.91	3.90	3.88	3.87
7	5.59	4.74	4.35	4.12	3.97	3.87	3.79	3.73	3.68	3.64	3.60	3.57	3.55	3.53	3.51	3.49	3.48	3.47	3.46	3.44
8	5.32	4.46	4.07	3.84	3.69	3.58	3.50	3.44	3.39	3.35	3.31	3.28	3.26	3.24	3.22	3.20	3.19	3.17	3.16	3.15
9	5.12	4.26	3.86	3.63	3.48	3.37	3.29	3.23	3.18	3.14	3.10	3.07	3.05	3.03	3.01	2.99	2.97	2.96	2.95	2.94
10	4.96	4.10	3.71	3.48	3.33	3.22	3.14	3.07	3.02	2.98	2.94	2.91	2.89	2.86	2.85	2.83	2.81	2.80	2.79	2.77
11	4.84	3.98	3.59	3.36	3.20	3.09	3.01	2.95	2.90	2.85	2.82	2.79	2.76	2.74	2.72	2.70	2.69	2.67	2.66	2.65
12	4.75	3.89	3.49	3.26	3.11	3.00	2.91	2.85	2.80	2.75	2.72	2.69	2.66	2.64	2.62	2.60	2.58	2.57	2.56	2.54
13	4.67	3.81	3.41	3.18	3.03	2.92	2.83	2.77	2.71	2.67	2.63	2.60	2.58	2.55	2.53	2.51	2.50	2.48	2.47	2.46
14	4.60	3.74	3.34	3.11	2.96	2.85	2.76	2.70	2.65	2.60	2.57	2.53	2.51	2.48	2.46	2.44	2.43	2.41	2.40	2.39
15	4.54	3.68	3.29	3.06	2.90	2.79	2.71	2.64	2.59	2.54	2.51	2.48	2.45	2.42	2.40	2.38	2.37	2.35	2.34	2.33
16	4.49	3.63	3.24	3.01	2.85	2.74	2.66	2.59	2.54	2.49	2.46	2.42	2.40	2.37	2.35	2.33	2.32	2.30	2.29	2.28
17	4.45	3.59	3.20	2.96	2.81	2.70	2.61	2.55	2.49	2.45	2.41	2.38	2.35	2.33	2.31	2.29	2.27	2.26	2.24	2.23
18	4.41	3.55	3.16	2.93	2.77	2.66	2.58	2.51	2.46	2.41	2.37	2.34	2.31	2.29	2.27	2.25	2.23	2.22	2.20	2.19
19	4.38	3.52	3.13	2.90	2.74	2.63	2.54	2.48	2.42	2.38	2.34	2.31	2.28	2.26	2.23	2.21	2.20	2.18	2.17	2.16
20	4.35	3.49	3.10	2.87	2.71	2.60	2.51	2.45	2.39	2.35	2.31	2.28	2.25	2.22	2.20	2.18	2.17	2.15	2.14	2.12
22	4.30	3.44	3.05	2.82	2.66	2.55	2.46	2.40	2.34	2.30	2.26	2.23	2.20	2.17	2.15	2.13	2.11	2.10	2.08	2.07
24	4.26	3.40	3.01	2.78	2.62	2.51	2.42	2.36	2.30	2.25	2.22	2.18	2.15	2.13	2.11	2.09	2.07	2.05	2.04	2.03
26	4.23	3.37	2.98	2.74	2.59	2.47	2.39	2.32	2.27	2.22	2.18	2.15	2.12	2.09	2.07	2.05	2.03	2.02	2.00	1.99
28	4.20	3.34	2.95	2.71	2.56	2.45	2.36	2.29	2.24	2.19	2.15	2.12	2.09	2.06	2.04	2.02	2.00	1.99	1.97	1.96
30	4.17	3.32	2.92	2.69	2.53	2.42	2.33	2.27	2.21	2.16	2.13	2.09	2.06	2.04	2.01	1.99	1.98	1.96	1.95	1.93
35	4.12	3.27	2.87	2.64	2.49	2.37	2.29	2.22	2.16	2.11	2.07	2.04	2.01	1.99	1.96	1.94	1.92	1.91	1.89	1.88
40	4.08	3.23	2.84	2.61	2.45	2.34	2.25	2.18	2.12	2.08	2.04	2.00	1.97	1.95	1.92	1.90	1.89	1.87	1.85	1.84
45	4.06	3.20	2.81	2.58	2.42	2.31	2.22	2.15	2.10	2.05	2.01	1.97	1.94	1.92	1.89	1.87	1.86	1.84	1.82	1.81
50	4.03	3.18	2.79	2.56	2.40	2.29	2.20	2.13	2.07	2.03	1.99	1.95	1.92	1.89	1.87	1.85	1.83	1.81	1.80	1.78
60	4.00	3.15	2.76	2.53	2.37	2.25	2.17	2.10	2.04	1.99	1.95	1.92	1.89	1.86	1.84	1.82	1.80	1.78	1.76	1.75
70	3.98	3.13	2.74	2.50	2.35	2.23	2.14	2.07	2.02	1.97	1.93	1.89	1.86	1.84	1.81	1.79	1.77	1.75	1.74	1.72
80	3.96	3.11	2.72	2.49	2.33	2.21	2.13	2.06	2.00	1.95	1.91	1.88	1.84	1.82	1.79	1.77	1.75	1.73	1.72	1.70
90	3.95	3.10	2.71	2.47	2.32	2.20	2.11	2.04	1.99	1.94	1.90	1.86	1.83	1.80	1.78	1.76	1.74	1.72	1.70	1.69
100	3.94	3.09	2.70	2.46	2.31	2.19	2.10	2.03	1.97	1.93	1.89	1.85	1.82	1.79	1.77	1.75	1.73	1.71	1.69	1.68
120	3.92	3.07	2.68	2.45	2.29	2.18	2.09	2.02	1.96	1.91	1.87	1.83	1.80	1.78	1.75	1.73	1.71	1.69	1.67	1.66
140	3.91	3.06	2.67	2.44	2.28	2.16	2.08	2.01	1.95	1.90	1.86	1.82	1.79	1.76	1.74	1.72	1.70	1.68	1.66	1.65
160	3.90	3.05	2.66	2.43	2.27	2.16	2.07	2.00	1.94	1.89	1.85	1.81	1.78	1.75	1.73	1.71	1.69	1.67	1.65	1.64
180	3.89	3.05	2.65	2.42	2.26	2.15	2.06	1.99	1.93	1.88	1.84	1.81	1.77	1.75	1.72	1.70	1.68	1.66	1.64	1.63
200	3.89	3.04	2.65	2.42	2.26	2.14	2.06	1.98	1.93	1.88	1.84	1.80	1.77	1.74	1.72	1.69	1.67	1.66	1.64	1.62
∞	3.84	3.00	2.61	2.37	2.21	2.10	2.01	1.94	1.88	1.83	1.79	1.75	1.72	1.69	1.67	1.64	1.62	1.60	1.59	1.57

DENOMINATOR DEGREES OF FREEDOM

NUMERATOR DEGREES OF FREEDOM

ν_2 \ ν_1	22	24	26	28	30	35	40	45	50	60	70	80	90	100	120	140	160	180	200	∞
1	249	249	249	250	250	251	251	251	252	252	252	253	253	253	253	253	254	254	254	254
2	19.5	19.5	19.5	19.5	19.5	19.5	19.5	19.5	19.5	19.5	19.5	19.5	19.5	19.5	19.5	19.5	19.5	19.5	19.5	19.5
3	8.65	8.64	8.63	8.62	8.62	8.60	8.59	8.59	8.58	8.57	8.57	8.56	8.56	8.55	8.55	8.55	8.54	8.54	8.54	8.53
4	5.79	5.77	5.76	5.75	5.75	5.73	5.72	5.71	5.70	5.69	5.68	5.67	5.67	5.66	5.66	5.65	5.65	5.65	5.65	5.63
5	4.54	4.53	4.52	4.50	4.50	4.48	4.46	4.45	4.44	4.43	4.42	4.41	4.41	4.41	4.40	4.39	4.39	4.39	4.39	4.37
6	3.86	3.84	3.83	3.82	3.81	3.79	3.77	3.76	3.75	3.74	3.73	3.72	3.72	3.71	3.70	3.70	3.70	3.69	3.69	3.67
7	3.43	3.41	3.40	3.39	3.38	3.36	3.34	3.33	3.32	3.30	3.29	3.29	3.28	3.27	3.27	3.26	3.26	3.25	3.25	3.23
8	3.13	3.12	3.10	3.09	3.08	3.06	3.04	3.03	3.02	3.01	2.99	2.99	2.98	2.97	2.97	2.96	2.96	2.95	2.95	2.93
9	2.92	2.90	2.89	2.87	2.86	2.84	2.83	2.81	2.80	2.79	2.78	2.77	2.76	2.76	2.75	2.74	2.74	2.73	2.73	2.71
10	2.75	2.74	2.72	2.71	2.70	2.68	2.66	2.65	2.64	2.62	2.61	2.60	2.59	2.59	2.58	2.57	2.57	2.57	2.56	2.54
11	2.63	2.61	2.59	2.58	2.57	2.55	2.53	2.52	2.51	2.49	2.48	2.47	2.46	2.46	2.45	2.44	2.44	2.43	2.43	2.41
12	2.52	2.51	2.49	2.48	2.47	2.44	2.43	2.41	2.40	2.38	2.37	2.36	2.36	2.35	2.34	2.33	2.33	2.33	2.32	2.30
13	2.44	2.42	2.41	2.39	2.38	2.36	2.34	2.33	2.31	2.30	2.28	2.27	2.27	2.26	2.25	2.25	2.24	2.24	2.23	2.21
14	2.37	2.35	2.33	2.32	2.31	2.28	2.27	2.25	2.24	2.22	2.21	2.20	2.19	2.19	2.18	2.17	2.17	2.16	2.16	2.13
15	2.31	2.29	2.27	2.26	2.25	2.22	2.20	2.19	2.18	2.16	2.15	2.14	2.13	2.12	2.11	2.11	2.10	2.10	2.10	2.07
16	2.25	2.24	2.22	2.21	2.19	2.17	2.15	2.14	2.12	2.11	2.09	2.08	2.07	2.07	2.06	2.05	2.05	2.04	2.04	2.01
17	2.21	2.19	2.17	2.16	2.15	2.12	2.10	2.09	2.08	2.06	2.05	2.03	2.03	2.02	2.01	2.00	2.00	1.99	1.99	1.96
18	2.17	2.15	2.13	2.12	2.11	2.08	2.06	2.05	2.04	2.02	2.00	1.99	1.98	1.98	1.97	1.96	1.96	1.95	1.95	1.92
19	2.13	2.11	2.10	2.08	2.07	2.05	2.03	2.01	2.00	1.98	1.97	1.96	1.95	1.94	1.93	1.92	1.92	1.91	1.91	1.88
20	2.10	2.08	2.07	2.05	2.04	2.01	1.99	1.98	1.97	1.95	1.93	1.92	1.91	1.91	1.90	1.89	1.88	1.88	1.88	1.84
22	2.05	2.03	2.01	2.00	1.98	1.96	1.94	1.92	1.91	1.89	1.88	1.86	1.86	1.85	1.84	1.83	1.82	1.82	1.82	1.78
24	2.00	1.98	1.97	1.95	1.94	1.91	1.89	1.88	1.86	1.84	1.83	1.82	1.81	1.80	1.79	1.78	1.78	1.77	1.77	1.73
26	1.97	1.95	1.93	1.91	1.90	1.87	1.85	1.84	1.82	1.80	1.79	1.78	1.77	1.76	1.75	1.74	1.73	1.73	1.73	1.69
28	1.93	1.91	1.90	1.88	1.87	1.84	1.82	1.80	1.79	1.77	1.75	1.74	1.73	1.73	1.71	1.71	1.70	1.69	1.69	1.65
30	1.91	1.89	1.87	1.85	1.84	1.81	1.79	1.77	1.76	1.74	1.72	1.71	1.70	1.70	1.68	1.68	1.67	1.66	1.66	1.62
35	1.85	1.83	1.82	1.80	1.79	1.76	1.74	1.72	1.70	1.68	1.66	1.65	1.64	1.63	1.62	1.61	1.61	1.60	1.60	1.56
40	1.81	1.79	1.77	1.76	1.74	1.72	1.69	1.67	1.66	1.64	1.62	1.61	1.60	1.59	1.58	1.57	1.56	1.56	1.55	1.51
45	1.78	1.76	1.74	1.73	1.71	1.68	1.66	1.64	1.63	1.60	1.59	1.57	1.56	1.55	1.54	1.53	1.52	1.52	1.51	1.47
50	1.76	1.74	1.72	1.70	1.69	1.66	1.63	1.61	1.60	1.58	1.56	1.54	1.53	1.52	1.51	1.50	1.49	1.49	1.48	1.44
60	1.72	1.70	1.68	1.66	1.65	1.62	1.59	1.57	1.56	1.53	1.52	1.50	1.49	1.48	1.47	1.46	1.45	1.44	1.44	1.39
70	1.70	1.67	1.65	1.64	1.62	1.59	1.57	1.55	1.53	1.50	1.49	1.47	1.46	1.45	1.44	1.42	1.42	1.41	1.40	1.35
80	1.68	1.65	1.63	1.62	1.60	1.57	1.54	1.52	1.51	1.48	1.46	1.45	1.44	1.43	1.41	1.40	1.39	1.38	1.38	1.33
90	1.66	1.64	1.62	1.60	1.59	1.55	1.53	1.51	1.49	1.46	1.44	1.43	1.42	1.41	1.39	1.38	1.36	1.36	1.36	1.30
100	1.65	1.63	1.61	1.59	1.57	1.54	1.52	1.49	1.48	1.45	1.43	1.41	1.40	1.39	1.38	1.36	1.35	1.35	1.34	1.28
120	1.63	1.61	1.59	1.57	1.55	1.52	1.50	1.47	1.46	1.43	1.41	1.39	1.38	1.37	1.35	1.34	1.33	1.32	1.32	1.26
140	1.62	1.60	1.57	1.56	1.54	1.51	1.48	1.46	1.44	1.41	1.39	1.38	1.36	1.35	1.33	1.32	1.31	1.30	1.30	1.23
160	1.61	1.59	1.57	1.55	1.53	1.50	1.47	1.45	1.43	1.40	1.38	1.36	1.35	1.34	1.32	1.31	1.30	1.29	1.28	1.22
180	1.60	1.58	1.56	1.54	1.52	1.49	1.46	1.44	1.42	1.39	1.37	1.35	1.34	1.33	1.31	1.30	1.29	1.28	1.27	1.20
200	1.60	1.57	1.55	1.53	1.52	1.48	1.46	1.43	1.41	1.39	1.36	1.35	1.33	1.32	1.30	1.29	1.28	1.27	1.26	1.19
∞	1.54	1.52	1.50	1.48	1.46	1.42	1.40	1.37	1.35	1.32	1.29	1.28	1.26	1.25	1.22	1.21	1.19	1.18	1.17	1.00

DENOMINATOR DEGREES OF FREEDOM

TABLE **6(b)** Values of the *F*-Distribution: *A* = .025

ν_2 \ ν_1	1	2	3	4	5	6	7	8	9	10	11	12	13	14	15	16	17	18	19	20
1	648	799	864	900	922	937	948	957	963	969	973	977	980	983	985	987	989	990	992	993
2	38.5	39.0	39.2	39.2	39.3	39.3	39.4	39.4	39.4	39.4	39.4	39.4	39.4	39.4	39.4	39.4	39.4	39.4	39.4	39.4
3	17.4	16.0	15.4	15.1	14.9	14.7	14.6	14.5	14.5	14.4	14.4	14.3	14.3	14.3	14.3	14.2	14.2	14.2	14.2	14.2
4	12.2	10.6	10.0	9.60	9.36	9.20	9.07	8.98	8.90	8.84	8.79	8.75	8.71	8.68	8.66	8.63	8.61	8.59	8.58	8.56
5	10.0	8.43	7.76	7.39	7.15	6.98	6.85	6.76	6.68	6.62	6.57	6.52	6.49	6.46	6.43	6.40	6.38	6.36	6.34	6.33
6	8.81	7.26	6.60	6.23	5.99	5.82	5.70	5.60	5.52	5.46	5.41	5.37	5.33	5.30	5.27	5.24	5.22	5.20	5.18	5.17
7	8.07	6.54	5.89	5.52	5.29	5.12	4.99	4.90	4.82	4.76	4.71	4.67	4.63	4.60	4.57	4.54	4.52	4.50	4.48	4.47
8	7.57	6.06	5.42	5.05	4.82	4.65	4.53	4.43	4.36	4.30	4.24	4.20	4.16	4.13	4.10	4.08	4.05	4.03	4.02	4.00
9	7.21	5.71	5.08	4.72	4.48	4.32	4.20	4.10	4.03	3.96	3.91	3.87	3.83	3.80	3.77	3.74	3.72	3.70	3.68	3.67
10	6.94	5.46	4.83	4.47	4.24	4.07	3.95	3.85	3.78	3.72	3.66	3.62	3.58	3.55	3.52	3.50	3.47	3.45	3.44	3.42
11	6.72	5.26	4.63	4.28	4.04	3.88	3.76	3.66	3.59	3.53	3.47	3.43	3.39	3.36	3.33	3.30	3.28	3.26	3.24	3.23
12	6.55	5.10	4.47	4.12	3.89	3.73	3.61	3.51	3.44	3.37	3.32	3.28	3.24	3.21	3.18	3.15	3.13	3.11	3.09	3.07
13	6.41	4.97	4.35	4.00	3.77	3.60	3.48	3.39	3.31	3.25	3.20	3.15	3.12	3.08	3.05	3.03	3.00	2.98	2.96	2.95
14	6.30	4.86	4.24	3.89	3.66	3.50	3.38	3.29	3.21	3.15	3.09	3.05	3.01	2.98	2.95	2.92	2.90	2.88	2.86	2.84
15	6.20	4.77	4.15	3.80	3.58	3.41	3.29	3.20	3.12	3.06	3.01	2.96	2.92	2.89	2.86	2.84	2.81	2.79	2.77	2.76
16	6.12	4.69	4.08	3.73	3.50	3.34	3.22	3.12	3.05	2.99	2.93	2.89	2.85	2.82	2.79	2.76	2.74	2.72	2.70	2.68
17	6.04	4.62	4.01	3.66	3.44	3.28	3.16	3.06	2.98	2.92	2.87	2.82	2.79	2.75	2.72	2.70	2.67	2.65	2.63	2.62
18	5.98	4.56	3.95	3.61	3.38	3.22	3.10	3.01	2.93	2.87	2.81	2.77	2.73	2.70	2.67	2.64	2.62	2.60	2.58	2.56
19	5.92	4.51	3.90	3.56	3.33	3.17	3.05	2.96	2.88	2.82	2.76	2.72	2.68	2.65	2.62	2.59	2.57	2.55	2.53	2.51
20	5.87	4.46	3.86	3.51	3.29	3.13	3.01	2.91	2.84	2.77	2.72	2.68	2.64	2.60	2.57	2.55	2.52	2.50	2.48	2.46
22	5.79	4.38	3.78	3.44	3.22	3.05	2.93	2.84	2.76	2.70	2.65	2.60	2.56	2.53	2.50	2.47	2.45	2.43	2.41	2.39
24	5.72	4.32	3.72	3.38	3.15	2.99	2.87	2.78	2.70	2.64	2.59	2.54	2.50	2.47	2.44	2.41	2.39	2.36	2.35	2.33
26	5.66	4.27	3.67	3.33	3.10	2.94	2.82	2.73	2.65	2.59	2.54	2.49	2.45	2.42	2.39	2.36	2.34	2.31	2.29	2.28
28	5.61	4.22	3.63	3.29	3.06	2.90	2.78	2.69	2.61	2.55	2.49	2.45	2.41	2.37	2.34	2.32	2.29	2.27	2.25	2.23
30	5.57	4.18	3.59	3.25	3.03	2.87	2.75	2.65	2.57	2.51	2.46	2.41	2.37	2.34	2.31	2.28	2.26	2.23	2.21	2.20
35	5.48	4.11	3.52	3.18	2.96	2.80	2.68	2.58	2.50	2.44	2.39	2.34	2.30	2.27	2.23	2.21	2.18	2.16	2.14	2.12
40	5.42	4.05	3.46	3.13	2.90	2.74	2.62	2.53	2.45	2.39	2.33	2.29	2.25	2.21	2.18	2.15	2.13	2.11	2.09	2.07
45	5.38	4.01	3.42	3.09	2.86	2.70	2.58	2.49	2.41	2.35	2.29	2.25	2.21	2.17	2.14	2.11	2.09	2.07	2.04	2.03
50	5.34	3.97	3.39	3.05	2.83	2.67	2.55	2.46	2.38	2.32	2.26	2.22	2.18	2.14	2.11	2.08	2.06	2.03	2.01	1.99
60	5.29	3.93	3.34	3.01	2.79	2.63	2.51	2.41	2.33	2.27	2.22	2.17	2.13	2.09	2.06	2.03	2.01	1.98	1.96	1.94
70	5.25	3.89	3.31	2.97	2.75	2.59	2.47	2.38	2.30	2.24	2.18	2.14	2.10	2.06	2.03	2.00	1.97	1.95	1.93	1.91
80	5.22	3.86	3.28	2.95	2.73	2.57	2.45	2.35	2.28	2.21	2.16	2.11	2.07	2.03	2.00	1.97	1.95	1.92	1.90	1.88
90	5.20	3.84	3.26	2.93	2.71	2.55	2.43	2.34	2.26	2.19	2.14	2.09	2.05	2.02	1.98	1.95	1.93	1.91	1.88	1.86
100	5.18	3.83	3.25	2.92	2.70	2.54	2.42	2.32	2.24	2.18	2.12	2.08	2.04	2.00	1.97	1.94	1.91	1.89	1.87	1.85
120	5.15	3.80	3.23	2.89	2.67	2.52	2.39	2.30	2.22	2.16	2.10	2.05	2.01	1.98	1.94	1.92	1.89	1.87	1.84	1.82
140	5.13	3.79	3.21	2.88	2.66	2.50	2.38	2.28	2.21	2.14	2.09	2.04	2.00	1.96	1.93	1.90	1.87	1.85	1.83	1.81
160	5.12	3.78	3.20	2.87	2.65	2.49	2.37	2.27	2.19	2.13	2.07	2.03	1.99	1.95	1.92	1.89	1.86	1.84	1.82	1.80
180	5.11	3.77	3.19	2.86	2.64	2.48	2.36	2.26	2.19	2.12	2.07	2.02	1.98	1.94	1.91	1.88	1.85	1.83	1.81	1.79
200	5.10	3.76	3.18	2.85	2.63	2.47	2.35	2.26	2.18	2.11	2.06	2.01	1.97	1.93	1.90	1.87	1.84	1.82	1.80	1.78
∞	5.03	3.69	3.12	2.79	2.57	2.41	2.29	2.19	2.11	2.05	1.99	1.95	1.90	1.87	1.83	1.80	1.78	1.75	1.73	1.71

NUMERATOR DEGREES OF FREEDOM

DENOMINATOR DEGREES OF FREEDOM

NUMERATOR DEGREES OF FREEDOM

ν_2 \ ν_1	22	24	26	28	30	35	40	45	50	60	70	80	90	100	120	140	160	180	200	∞
1	995	997	999	1000	1001	1004	1006	1007	1008	1010	1011	1012	1013	1013	1014	1015	1015	1015	1016	1018
2	39.5	39.5	39.5	39.5	39.5	39.5	39.5	39.5	39.5	39.5	39.5	39.5	39.5	39.5	39.5	39.5	39.5	39.5	39.5	39.5
3	14.1	14.1	14.1	14.1	14.1	14.1	14.0	14.0	14.0	14.0	14.0	14.0	14.0	14.0	13.9	13.9	13.9	13.9	13.9	13.9
4	8.53	8.51	8.49	8.48	8.46	8.43	8.41	8.39	8.38	8.36	8.35	8.33	8.33	8.32	8.31	8.30	8.30	8.29	8.29	8.26
5	6.30	6.28	6.26	6.24	6.23	6.20	6.18	6.16	6.14	6.12	6.11	6.10	6.09	6.08	6.07	6.06	6.06	6.05	6.05	6.02
6	5.14	5.12	5.10	5.08	5.07	5.04	5.01	4.99	4.98	4.96	4.94	4.93	4.92	4.92	4.90	4.90	4.89	4.89	4.88	4.85
7	4.44	4.41	4.39	4.38	4.36	4.33	4.31	4.29	4.28	4.25	4.24	4.23	4.22	4.21	4.20	4.19	4.18	4.18	4.18	4.14
8	3.97	3.95	3.93	3.91	3.89	3.86	3.84	3.82	3.81	3.78	3.77	3.76	3.75	3.74	3.73	3.72	3.71	3.71	3.70	3.67
9	3.64	3.61	3.59	3.58	3.56	3.53	3.51	3.49	3.47	3.45	3.43	3.42	3.41	3.40	3.39	3.38	3.37	3.37	3.37	3.33
10	3.39	3.37	3.34	3.33	3.31	3.28	3.26	3.24	3.22	3.20	3.18	3.17	3.16	3.15	3.14	3.13	3.13	3.12	3.12	3.08
11	3.20	3.17	3.15	3.13	3.12	3.09	3.06	3.04	3.03	3.00	2.99	2.97	2.96	2.96	2.94	2.94	2.93	2.92	2.92	2.88
12	3.04	3.02	3.00	2.98	2.96	2.93	2.91	2.89	2.87	2.85	2.83	2.82	2.81	2.80	2.79	2.78	2.77	2.77	2.76	2.73
13	2.92	2.89	2.87	2.85	2.84	2.80	2.78	2.76	2.74	2.72	2.70	2.69	2.68	2.67	2.66	2.65	2.64	2.64	2.63	2.60
14	2.81	2.79	2.77	2.75	2.73	2.70	2.67	2.65	2.64	2.61	2.60	2.58	2.57	2.56	2.55	2.54	2.54	2.53	2.53	2.49
15	2.73	2.70	2.68	2.66	2.64	2.61	2.59	2.56	2.55	2.52	2.51	2.49	2.48	2.47	2.46	2.45	2.44	2.44	2.44	2.40
16	2.65	2.63	2.60	2.58	2.57	2.53	2.51	2.49	2.47	2.45	2.43	2.42	2.40	2.40	2.38	2.37	2.37	2.36	2.36	2.32
17	2.59	2.56	2.54	2.52	2.50	2.47	2.44	2.42	2.41	2.38	2.36	2.35	2.34	2.33	2.32	2.31	2.30	2.29	2.29	2.25
18	2.53	2.50	2.48	2.46	2.44	2.41	2.38	2.36	2.35	2.32	2.30	2.29	2.28	2.27	2.26	2.25	2.24	2.23	2.23	2.19
19	2.48	2.45	2.43	2.41	2.39	2.36	2.33	2.31	2.30	2.27	2.25	2.24	2.23	2.22	2.20	2.19	2.19	2.18	2.18	2.13
20	2.43	2.41	2.39	2.37	2.35	2.31	2.29	2.27	2.25	2.22	2.20	2.19	2.18	2.17	2.16	2.15	2.14	2.13	2.13	2.09
22	2.36	2.33	2.31	2.29	2.27	2.24	2.21	2.19	2.17	2.14	2.13	2.11	2.10	2.09	2.08	2.07	2.06	2.05	2.05	2.00
24	2.30	2.27	2.25	2.23	2.21	2.17	2.15	2.12	2.11	2.08	2.06	2.05	2.03	2.02	2.01	2.00	1.99	1.99	1.98	1.94
26	2.24	2.22	2.19	2.17	2.16	2.12	2.09	2.07	2.05	2.03	2.01	1.99	1.98	1.97	1.95	1.94	1.94	1.93	1.92	1.88
28	2.20	2.17	2.15	2.13	2.11	2.08	2.05	2.03	2.01	1.98	1.96	1.94	1.93	1.92	1.91	1.90	1.89	1.88	1.88	1.83
30	2.16	2.14	2.11	2.09	2.07	2.04	2.01	1.99	1.97	1.94	1.92	1.90	1.89	1.88	1.87	1.86	1.85	1.84	1.84	1.79
35	2.09	2.06	2.04	2.02	2.00	1.96	1.93	1.91	1.89	1.86	1.84	1.82	1.81	1.80	1.79	1.77	1.77	1.76	1.75	1.70
40	2.03	2.01	1.98	1.96	1.94	1.90	1.88	1.85	1.83	1.80	1.78	1.76	1.75	1.74	1.72	1.71	1.70	1.70	1.69	1.64
45	1.99	1.96	1.94	1.92	1.90	1.86	1.83	1.81	1.79	1.76	1.74	1.72	1.70	1.69	1.68	1.66	1.66	1.65	1.64	1.59
50	1.96	1.93	1.91	1.89	1.87	1.83	1.80	1.77	1.75	1.72	1.70	1.68	1.67	1.66	1.64	1.63	1.62	1.61	1.60	1.55
60	1.91	1.88	1.86	1.83	1.82	1.78	1.74	1.72	1.70	1.67	1.64	1.63	1.61	1.60	1.58	1.57	1.56	1.55	1.54	1.48
70	1.88	1.85	1.82	1.80	1.78	1.74	1.71	1.68	1.66	1.63	1.60	1.59	1.57	1.56	1.54	1.53	1.53	1.51	1.50	1.44
80	1.85	1.82	1.79	1.77	1.75	1.71	1.68	1.65	1.63	1.60	1.57	1.55	1.54	1.53	1.51	1.49	1.48	1.47	1.47	1.40
90	1.83	1.80	1.77	1.75	1.73	1.69	1.66	1.63	1.61	1.58	1.55	1.53	1.52	1.50	1.48	1.47	1.46	1.45	1.44	1.37
100	1.81	1.78	1.76	1.74	1.71	1.67	1.64	1.61	1.59	1.56	1.53	1.51	1.50	1.48	1.46	1.45	1.44	1.43	1.42	1.35
120	1.79	1.76	1.73	1.71	1.69	1.65	1.61	1.59	1.56	1.53	1.50	1.48	1.47	1.45	1.43	1.42	1.41	1.40	1.39	1.31
140	1.77	1.74	1.72	1.69	1.67	1.63	1.60	1.57	1.55	1.51	1.48	1.46	1.45	1.43	1.41	1.39	1.38	1.37	1.36	1.28
160	1.76	1.73	1.70	1.68	1.66	1.62	1.58	1.55	1.53	1.50	1.47	1.45	1.43	1.42	1.39	1.38	1.36	1.35	1.35	1.26
180	1.75	1.72	1.69	1.67	1.65	1.61	1.57	1.54	1.52	1.48	1.46	1.43	1.42	1.40	1.38	1.36	1.35	1.34	1.33	1.25
200	1.74	1.71	1.68	1.66	1.64	1.60	1.56	1.53	1.51	1.47	1.45	1.42	1.41	1.39	1.37	1.35	1.34	1.33	1.32	1.23
∞	1.67	1.64	1.61	1.59	1.57	1.52	1.49	1.46	1.43	1.39	1.36	1.33	1.31	1.30	1.27	1.25	1.23	1.22	1.21	1.00

DENOMINATOR DEGREES OF FREEDOM

TABLE 6(C) Values of the F-Distribution: A = .01

ν_2 \ ν_1	1	2	3	4	5	6	7	8	9	10	11	12	13	14	15	16	17	18	19	20
1	4052	4999	5403	5625	5764	5859	5928	5981	6022	6056	6083	6106	6126	6143	6157	6170	6181	6192	6201	6209
2	98.5	99.0	99.2	99.2	99.3	99.3	99.4	99.4	99.4	99.4	99.4	99.4	99.4	99.4	99.4	99.4	99.4	99.4	99.4	99.4
3	34.1	30.8	29.5	28.7	28.2	27.9	27.7	27.5	27.3	27.2	27.1	27.1	27.0	26.9	26.9	26.8	26.8	26.8	26.7	26.7
4	21.2	18.0	16.7	16.0	15.5	15.2	15.0	14.8	14.7	14.5	14.5	14.4	14.3	14.2	14.2	14.2	14.1	14.1	14.0	14.0
5	16.3	13.3	12.1	11.4	11.0	10.7	10.5	10.3	10.2	10.1	9.96	9.89	9.82	9.77	9.72	9.68	9.64	9.61	9.58	9.55
6	13.7	10.9	9.78	9.15	8.75	8.47	8.26	8.10	7.98	7.87	7.79	7.72	7.66	7.60	7.56	7.52	7.48	7.45	7.42	7.40
7	12.2	9.55	8.45	7.85	7.46	7.19	6.99	6.84	6.72	6.62	6.54	6.47	6.41	6.36	6.31	6.28	6.24	6.21	6.18	6.16
8	11.3	8.65	7.59	7.01	6.63	6.37	6.18	6.03	5.91	5.81	5.73	5.67	5.61	5.56	5.52	5.48	5.44	5.41	5.38	5.36
9	10.6	8.02	6.99	6.42	6.06	5.80	5.61	5.47	5.35	5.26	5.18	5.11	5.05	5.01	4.96	4.92	4.89	4.86	4.83	4.81
10	10.0	7.56	6.55	5.99	5.64	5.39	5.20	5.06	4.94	4.85	4.77	4.71	4.65	4.60	4.56	4.52	4.49	4.46	4.43	4.41
11	9.65	7.21	6.22	5.67	5.32	5.07	4.89	4.74	4.63	4.54	4.46	4.40	4.34	4.29	4.25	4.21	4.18	4.15	4.12	4.10
12	9.33	6.93	5.95	5.41	5.06	4.82	4.64	4.50	4.39	4.30	4.22	4.16	4.10	4.05	4.01	3.97	3.94	3.91	3.88	3.86
13	9.07	6.70	5.74	5.21	4.86	4.62	4.44	4.30	4.19	4.10	4.02	3.96	3.91	3.86	3.82	3.78	3.75	3.72	3.69	3.66
14	8.86	6.51	5.56	5.04	4.69	4.46	4.28	4.14	4.03	3.94	3.86	3.80	3.75	3.70	3.66	3.62	3.59	3.56	3.53	3.51
15	8.68	6.36	5.42	4.89	4.56	4.32	4.14	4.00	3.89	3.80	3.73	3.67	3.61	3.56	3.52	3.49	3.45	3.42	3.40	3.37
16	8.53	6.23	5.29	4.77	4.44	4.20	4.03	3.89	3.78	3.69	3.62	3.55	3.50	3.45	3.41	3.37	3.34	3.31	3.28	3.26
17	8.40	6.11	5.18	4.67	4.34	4.10	3.93	3.79	3.68	3.59	3.52	3.46	3.40	3.35	3.31	3.27	3.24	3.21	3.19	3.16
18	8.29	6.01	5.09	4.58	4.25	4.01	3.84	3.71	3.60	3.51	3.43	3.37	3.32	3.27	3.23	3.19	3.16	3.13	3.10	3.08
19	8.18	5.93	5.01	4.50	4.17	3.94	3.77	3.63	3.52	3.43	3.36	3.30	3.24	3.19	3.15	3.12	3.08	3.05	3.03	3.00
20	8.10	5.85	4.94	4.43	4.10	3.87	3.70	3.56	3.46	3.37	3.29	3.23	3.18	3.13	3.09	3.05	3.02	2.99	2.96	2.94
22	7.95	5.72	4.82	4.31	3.99	3.76	3.59	3.45	3.35	3.26	3.18	3.12	3.07	3.02	2.98	2.94	2.91	2.88	2.85	2.83
24	7.82	5.61	4.72	4.22	3.90	3.67	3.50	3.36	3.26	3.17	3.09	3.03	2.98	2.93	2.89	2.85	2.82	2.79	2.76	2.74
26	7.72	5.53	4.64	4.14	3.82	3.59	3.42	3.29	3.18	3.09	3.02	2.96	2.90	2.86	2.81	2.78	2.75	2.72	2.69	2.66
28	7.64	5.45	4.57	4.07	3.75	3.53	3.36	3.23	3.12	3.03	2.96	2.90	2.84	2.79	2.75	2.72	2.68	2.65	2.63	2.60
30	7.56	5.39	4.51	4.02	3.70	3.47	3.30	3.17	3.07	2.98	2.91	2.84	2.79	2.74	2.70	2.66	2.63	2.60	2.57	2.55
35	7.42	5.27	4.40	3.91	3.59	3.37	3.20	3.07	2.96	2.88	2.80	2.74	2.69	2.64	2.60	2.56	2.53	2.50	2.47	2.44
40	7.31	5.18	4.31	3.83	3.51	3.29	3.12	2.99	2.89	2.80	2.73	2.66	2.61	2.56	2.52	2.48	2.45	2.42	2.39	2.37
45	7.23	5.11	4.25	3.77	3.45	3.23	3.07	2.94	2.83	2.74	2.67	2.61	2.55	2.51	2.46	2.43	2.39	2.36	2.34	2.31
50	7.17	5.06	4.20	3.72	3.41	3.19	3.02	2.89	2.78	2.70	2.63	2.56	2.51	2.46	2.42	2.38	2.35	2.32	2.29	2.27
60	7.08	4.98	4.13	3.65	3.34	3.12	2.95	2.82	2.72	2.63	2.56	2.50	2.44	2.39	2.35	2.31	2.28	2.25	2.22	2.20
70	7.01	4.92	4.07	3.60	3.29	3.07	2.91	2.78	2.67	2.59	2.51	2.45	2.40	2.35	2.31	2.27	2.23	2.20	2.18	2.15
80	6.96	4.88	4.04	3.56	3.26	3.04	2.87	2.74	2.64	2.55	2.48	2.42	2.36	2.31	2.27	2.23	2.20	2.17	2.14	2.12
90	6.93	4.85	4.01	3.53	3.23	3.01	2.84	2.72	2.61	2.52	2.45	2.39	2.33	2.29	2.24	2.21	2.17	2.14	2.11	2.09
100	6.90	4.82	3.98	3.51	3.21	2.99	2.82	2.69	2.59	2.50	2.43	2.37	2.31	2.27	2.22	2.19	2.15	2.12	2.09	2.07
120	6.85	4.79	3.95	3.48	3.17	2.96	2.79	2.66	2.56	2.47	2.40	2.34	2.28	2.23	2.19	2.15	2.12	2.09	2.06	2.03
140	6.82	4.76	3.92	3.46	3.15	2.93	2.77	2.64	2.54	2.45	2.38	2.31	2.26	2.21	2.17	2.13	2.10	2.07	2.04	2.01
160	6.80	4.74	3.91	3.44	3.13	2.92	2.75	2.62	2.52	2.43	2.36	2.30	2.24	2.20	2.15	2.11	2.08	2.05	2.02	1.99
180	6.78	4.73	3.89	3.43	3.12	2.90	2.74	2.61	2.51	2.42	2.35	2.28	2.23	2.18	2.14	2.10	2.07	2.04	2.01	1.98
200	6.76	4.71	3.88	3.41	3.11	2.89	2.73	2.60	2.50	2.41	2.34	2.27	2.22	2.17	2.13	2.09	2.06	2.03	2.00	1.97
∞	6.64	4.61	3.78	3.32	3.02	2.80	2.64	2.51	2.41	2.32	2.25	2.19	2.13	2.08	2.04	2.00	1.97	1.94	1.91	1.88

NUMERATOR DEGREES OF FREEDOM

DENOMINATOR DEGREES OF FREEDOM

NUMERATOR DEGREES OF FREEDOM

ν_2 \ ν_1	22	24	26	28	30	35	40	45	50	60	70	80	90	100	120	140	160	180	200	∞
1	6223	6235	6245	6253	6261	6276	6287	6296	6303	6313	6321	6326	6331	6334	6339	6343	6346	6348	6350	6366
2	99.5	99.5	99.5	99.5	99.5	99.5	99.5	99.5	99.5	99.5	99.5	99.5	99.5	99.5	99.5	99.5	99.5	99.5	99.5	99.5
3	26.6	26.6	26.6	26.5	26.5	26.5	26.4	26.4	26.4	26.3	26.3	26.3	26.3	26.2	26.2	26.2	26.2	26.2	26.2	26.1
4	14.0	13.9	13.9	13.9	13.8	13.8	13.7	13.7	13.7	13.7	13.6	13.6	13.6	13.6	13.6	13.5	13.5	13.5	13.5	13.5
5	9.51	9.47	9.43	9.40	9.38	9.33	9.29	9.26	9.24	9.20	9.18	9.16	9.14	9.13	9.11	9.10	9.09	9.08	9.08	9.02
6	7.35	7.31	7.28	7.25	7.23	7.18	7.14	7.11	7.09	7.06	7.03	7.01	7.00	6.99	6.97	6.96	6.95	6.94	6.93	6.88
7	6.11	6.07	6.04	6.02	5.99	5.94	5.91	5.88	5.86	5.82	5.80	5.78	5.77	5.75	5.74	5.72	5.72	5.71	5.70	5.65
8	5.32	5.28	5.25	5.22	5.20	5.15	5.12	5.09	5.07	5.03	5.01	4.99	4.97	4.96	4.95	4.93	4.92	4.92	4.91	4.86
9	4.77	4.73	4.70	4.67	4.65	4.60	4.57	4.54	4.52	4.48	4.46	4.44	4.43	4.41	4.40	4.39	4.38	4.37	4.36	4.31
10	4.36	4.33	4.30	4.27	4.25	4.20	4.17	4.14	4.12	4.08	4.06	4.04	4.03	4.01	4.00	3.98	3.97	3.97	3.96	3.91
11	4.06	4.02	3.99	3.96	3.94	3.89	3.86	3.83	3.81	3.78	3.75	3.73	3.72	3.71	3.69	3.68	3.67	3.66	3.66	3.60
12	3.82	3.78	3.75	3.72	3.70	3.65	3.62	3.59	3.57	3.54	3.51	3.49	3.48	3.47	3.45	3.44	3.43	3.42	3.41	3.36
13	3.62	3.59	3.56	3.53	3.51	3.46	3.43	3.40	3.38	3.34	3.32	3.30	3.28	3.27	3.25	3.24	3.23	3.23	3.22	3.17
14	3.46	3.43	3.40	3.37	3.35	3.30	3.27	3.24	3.22	3.18	3.16	3.14	3.12	3.11	3.09	3.08	3.07	3.06	3.06	3.01
15	3.33	3.29	3.26	3.24	3.21	3.17	3.13	3.10	3.08	3.05	3.02	3.00	2.99	2.98	2.96	2.95	2.94	2.93	2.92	2.87
16	3.22	3.18	3.15	3.12	3.10	3.05	3.02	2.99	2.97	2.93	2.91	2.89	2.87	2.86	2.84	2.83	2.82	2.81	2.81	2.75
17	3.12	3.08	3.05	3.03	3.00	2.96	2.92	2.89	2.87	2.83	2.81	2.79	2.78	2.76	2.75	2.73	2.72	2.72	2.71	2.65
18	3.03	3.00	2.97	2.94	2.92	2.87	2.84	2.81	2.78	2.75	2.72	2.70	2.69	2.68	2.66	2.65	2.64	2.63	2.62	2.57
19	2.96	2.92	2.89	2.87	2.84	2.80	2.76	2.73	2.71	2.67	2.65	2.63	2.61	2.60	2.58	2.57	2.56	2.55	2.55	2.49
20	2.90	2.86	2.83	2.80	2.78	2.73	2.69	2.67	2.64	2.61	2.58	2.56	2.55	2.54	2.52	2.50	2.49	2.49	2.48	2.42
22	2.78	2.75	2.72	2.69	2.67	2.62	2.58	2.55	2.53	2.50	2.47	2.45	2.43	2.42	2.40	2.39	2.38	2.37	2.36	2.31
24	2.70	2.66	2.63	2.60	2.58	2.53	2.49	2.46	2.44	2.40	2.38	2.36	2.34	2.33	2.31	2.30	2.29	2.28	2.27	2.21
26	2.62	2.58	2.55	2.53	2.50	2.45	2.42	2.39	2.36	2.33	2.30	2.28	2.26	2.25	2.23	2.22	2.21	2.20	2.19	2.13
28	2.56	2.52	2.49	2.46	2.44	2.39	2.35	2.32	2.30	2.26	2.24	2.22	2.20	2.19	2.17	2.15	2.14	2.13	2.13	2.07
30	2.51	2.47	2.44	2.41	2.39	2.34	2.30	2.27	2.25	2.21	2.18	2.16	2.14	2.13	2.11	2.10	2.09	2.08	2.07	2.01
35	2.40	2.36	2.33	2.30	2.28	2.23	2.19	2.16	2.14	2.10	2.07	2.05	2.03	2.02	2.00	1.98	1.97	1.96	1.96	1.89
40	2.33	2.29	2.26	2.23	2.20	2.15	2.11	2.08	2.06	2.02	1.99	1.97	1.95	1.94	1.92	1.90	1.89	1.88	1.87	1.81
45	2.27	2.23	2.20	2.17	2.14	2.09	2.05	2.02	2.00	1.96	1.93	1.91	1.89	1.88	1.85	1.84	1.83	1.82	1.81	1.74
50	2.22	2.18	2.15	2.12	2.10	2.05	2.01	1.97	1.95	1.91	1.88	1.86	1.84	1.82	1.80	1.79	1.77	1.76	1.76	1.68
60	2.15	2.12	2.08	2.05	2.03	1.98	1.94	1.90	1.88	1.84	1.81	1.78	1.76	1.75	1.73	1.71	1.70	1.69	1.68	1.60
70	2.11	2.07	2.03	2.01	1.98	1.93	1.89	1.85	1.83	1.78	1.75	1.73	1.71	1.70	1.67	1.65	1.64	1.63	1.62	1.54
80	2.07	2.03	2.00	1.97	1.94	1.89	1.85	1.82	1.79	1.75	1.71	1.69	1.67	1.65	1.63	1.61	1.60	1.59	1.58	1.50
90	2.04	2.00	1.97	1.94	1.92	1.86	1.82	1.79	1.76	1.72	1.68	1.66	1.64	1.62	1.60	1.58	1.57	1.55	1.55	1.46
100	2.02	1.98	1.95	1.92	1.89	1.84	1.80	1.76	1.74	1.69	1.66	1.63	1.61	1.60	1.57	1.55	1.54	1.53	1.52	1.43
120	1.99	1.95	1.92	1.89	1.86	1.81	1.76	1.73	1.70	1.66	1.62	1.60	1.58	1.56	1.53	1.51	1.50	1.49	1.48	1.38
140	1.97	1.93	1.89	1.86	1.84	1.78	1.74	1.70	1.67	1.63	1.60	1.57	1.55	1.53	1.50	1.48	1.47	1.46	1.45	1.35
160	1.95	1.91	1.88	1.85	1.82	1.76	1.72	1.68	1.66	1.61	1.58	1.55	1.53	1.51	1.48	1.46	1.45	1.43	1.42	1.32
180	1.94	1.90	1.86	1.83	1.81	1.75	1.71	1.67	1.64	1.60	1.56	1.53	1.51	1.49	1.47	1.45	1.43	1.42	1.41	1.30
200	1.93	1.89	1.85	1.82	1.79	1.74	1.69	1.66	1.63	1.58	1.55	1.52	1.50	1.48	1.45	1.43	1.42	1.40	1.39	1.28
∞	1.83	1.79	1.76	1.73	1.70	1.64	1.59	1.56	1.53	1.48	1.44	1.41	1.38	1.36	1.33	1.30	1.28	1.26	1.25	1.00

DENOMINATOR DEGREES OF FREEDOM

TABLE **6(d)** Values of the *F*-Distribution: $A = .005$

ν_2 \ ν_1	1	2	3	4	5	6	7	8	9	10	11	12	13	14	15	16	17	18	19	20
1	16211	19999	21615	22500	23056	23437	23715	23925	24091	24224	24334	24426	24505	24572	24630	24681	24727	24767	24803	24836
2	199	199	199	199	199	199	199	199	199	199	199	199	199	199	199	199	199	199	199	199
3	55.6	49.8	47.5	46.2	45.4	44.8	44.4	44.1	43.9	43.7	43.5	43.4	43.3	43.2	43.1	43.0	42.9	42.9	42.8	42.8
4	31.3	26.3	24.3	23.2	22.5	22.0	21.6	21.4	21.1	21.0	20.8	20.7	20.6	20.5	20.4	20.4	20.3	20.3	20.2	20.2
5	22.8	18.3	16.5	15.6	14.9	14.5	14.2	14.0	13.8	13.6	13.5	13.4	13.3	13.2	13.1	13.1	13.0	13.0	12.9	12.9
6	18.6	14.5	12.9	12.0	11.5	11.1	10.8	10.6	10.4	10.3	10.1	10.0	9.95	9.88	9.81	9.76	9.71	9.66	9.62	9.59
7	16.2	12.4	10.9	10.1	9.52	9.16	8.89	8.68	8.51	8.38	8.27	8.18	8.10	8.03	7.97	7.91	7.87	7.83	7.79	7.75
8	14.7	11.0	9.60	8.81	8.30	7.95	7.69	7.50	7.34	7.21	7.10	7.01	6.94	6.87	6.81	6.76	6.72	6.68	6.64	6.61
9	13.6	10.1	8.72	7.96	7.47	7.13	6.88	6.69	6.54	6.42	6.31	6.23	6.15	6.09	6.03	5.98	5.94	5.90	5.86	5.83
10	12.8	9.43	8.08	7.34	6.87	6.54	6.30	6.12	5.97	5.85	5.75	5.66	5.59	5.53	5.47	5.42	5.38	5.34	5.31	5.27
11	12.2	8.91	7.60	6.88	6.42	6.10	5.86	5.68	5.54	5.42	5.32	5.24	5.16	5.10	5.05	5.00	4.96	4.92	4.89	4.86
12	11.8	8.51	7.23	6.52	6.07	5.76	5.52	5.35	5.20	5.09	4.99	4.91	4.84	4.77	4.72	4.67	4.63	4.59	4.56	4.53
13	11.4	8.19	6.93	6.23	5.79	5.48	5.25	5.08	4.94	4.82	4.72	4.64	4.57	4.51	4.46	4.41	4.37	4.33	4.30	4.27
14	11.1	7.92	6.68	6.00	5.56	5.26	5.03	4.86	4.72	4.60	4.51	4.43	4.36	4.30	4.25	4.20	4.16	4.12	4.09	4.06
15	10.8	7.70	6.48	5.80	5.37	5.07	4.85	4.67	4.54	4.42	4.33	4.25	4.18	4.12	4.07	4.02	3.98	3.95	3.91	3.88
16	10.6	7.51	6.30	5.64	5.21	4.91	4.69	4.52	4.38	4.27	4.18	4.10	4.03	3.97	3.92	3.87	3.83	3.80	3.76	3.73
17	10.4	7.35	6.16	5.50	5.07	4.78	4.56	4.39	4.25	4.14	4.05	3.97	3.90	3.84	3.79	3.75	3.71	3.67	3.64	3.61
18	10.2	7.21	6.03	5.37	4.96	4.66	4.44	4.28	4.14	4.03	3.94	3.86	3.79	3.73	3.68	3.64	3.60	3.56	3.53	3.50
19	10.1	7.09	5.92	5.27	4.85	4.56	4.34	4.18	4.04	3.93	3.84	3.76	3.70	3.64	3.59	3.54	3.50	3.46	3.43	3.40
20	9.94	6.99	5.82	5.17	4.76	4.47	4.26	4.09	3.96	3.85	3.76	3.68	3.61	3.55	3.50	3.46	3.42	3.38	3.35	3.32
22	9.73	6.81	5.65	5.02	4.61	4.32	4.11	3.94	3.81	3.70	3.61	3.54	3.47	3.41	3.36	3.31	3.27	3.24	3.21	3.18
24	9.55	6.66	5.52	4.89	4.49	4.20	3.99	3.83	3.69	3.59	3.50	3.42	3.35	3.30	3.25	3.20	3.16	3.12	3.09	3.06
26	9.41	6.54	5.41	4.79	4.38	4.10	3.89	3.73	3.60	3.49	3.40	3.33	3.26	3.20	3.15	3.11	3.07	3.03	3.00	2.97
28	9.28	6.44	5.32	4.70	4.30	4.02	3.81	3.65	3.52	3.41	3.32	3.25	3.18	3.12	3.07	3.03	2.99	2.95	2.92	2.89
30	9.18	6.35	5.24	4.62	4.23	3.95	3.74	3.58	3.45	3.34	3.25	3.18	3.11	3.06	3.01	2.96	2.92	2.89	2.85	2.82
35	8.98	6.19	5.09	4.48	4.09	3.81	3.61	3.45	3.32	3.21	3.12	3.05	2.98	2.93	2.88	2.83	2.79	2.76	2.72	2.69
40	8.83	6.07	4.98	4.37	3.99	3.71	3.51	3.35	3.22	3.12	3.03	2.95	2.89	2.83	2.78	2.74	2.70	2.66	2.63	2.60
45	8.71	5.97	4.89	4.29	3.91	3.64	3.43	3.28	3.15	3.04	2.96	2.88	2.82	2.76	2.71	2.66	2.62	2.59	2.56	2.53
50	8.63	5.90	4.83	4.23	3.85	3.58	3.38	3.22	3.09	2.99	2.90	2.82	2.76	2.70	2.65	2.61	2.57	2.53	2.50	2.47
60	8.49	5.79	4.73	4.14	3.76	3.49	3.29	3.13	3.01	2.90	2.82	2.74	2.68	2.62	2.57	2.53	2.49	2.45	2.42	2.39
70	8.40	5.72	4.66	4.08	3.70	3.43	3.23	3.08	2.95	2.85	2.76	2.68	2.62	2.56	2.51	2.47	2.43	2.39	2.36	2.33
80	8.33	5.67	4.61	4.03	3.65	3.39	3.19	3.03	2.91	2.80	2.72	2.64	2.58	2.52	2.47	2.43	2.39	2.35	2.32	2.29
90	8.28	5.62	4.57	3.99	3.62	3.35	3.15	3.00	2.87	2.77	2.68	2.61	2.54	2.49	2.44	2.39	2.35	2.32	2.28	2.25
100	8.24	5.59	4.54	3.96	3.59	3.33	3.13	2.97	2.85	2.74	2.66	2.58	2.52	2.46	2.41	2.37	2.33	2.29	2.26	2.23
120	8.18	5.54	4.50	3.92	3.55	3.28	3.09	2.93	2.81	2.71	2.62	2.54	2.48	2.42	2.37	2.33	2.29	2.25	2.22	2.19
140	8.14	5.50	4.47	3.89	3.52	3.26	3.06	2.91	2.78	2.68	2.59	2.52	2.45	2.40	2.35	2.30	2.26	2.22	2.19	2.16
160	8.10	5.48	4.44	3.87	3.50	3.24	3.04	2.88	2.76	2.66	2.57	2.50	2.43	2.38	2.33	2.28	2.24	2.20	2.17	2.14
180	8.08	5.46	4.42	3.85	3.48	3.22	3.02	2.87	2.74	2.64	2.56	2.48	2.42	2.36	2.31	2.26	2.22	2.19	2.15	2.12
200	8.06	5.44	4.41	3.84	3.47	3.21	3.01	2.86	2.73	2.63	2.54	2.47	2.40	2.35	2.30	2.25	2.21	2.18	2.14	2.11
∞	7.88	5.30	4.28	3.72	3.35	3.09	2.90	2.75	2.62	2.52	2.43	2.36	2.30	2.24	2.19	2.14	2.10	2.07	2.03	2.00

NUMERATOR DEGREES OF FREEDOM

DENOMINATOR DEGREES OF FREEDOM

NUMERATOR DEGREES OF FREEDOM

ν_2 \ ν_1	22	24	26	28	30	35	40	45	50	60	70	80	90	100	120	140	160	180	200	∞
1	24892	24940	24980	25014	25044	25103	25148	25183	25211	25253	25283	25306	25323	25337	25359	25374	25385	25394	25401	25464
2	199	199	199	199	199	199	199	199	199	199	199	199	199	199	199	199	199	199	199	199
3	42.7	42.6	42.6	42.5	42.5	42.4	42.3	42.3	42.2	42.1	42.1	42.1	42.0	42.0	42.0	42.0	41.9	41.9	41.9	41.8
4	20.1	20.0	20.0	19.9	19.9	19.8	19.8	19.7	19.7	19.6	19.6	19.5	19.5	19.5	19.5	19.4	19.4	19.4	19.4	19.3
5	12.8	12.8	12.7	12.7	12.7	12.6	12.5	12.5	12.5	12.4	12.4	12.3	12.3	12.3	12.3	12.3	12.2	12.2	12.2	12.1
6	9.53	9.47	9.43	9.39	9.36	9.29	9.24	9.20	9.17	9.12	9.09	9.06	9.04	9.03	9.00	8.98	8.97	8.96	8.95	8.88
7	7.69	7.64	7.60	7.57	7.53	7.47	7.42	7.38	7.35	7.31	7.28	7.25	7.23	7.22	7.19	7.18	7.16	7.15	7.15	7.08
8	6.55	6.50	6.46	6.43	6.40	6.33	6.29	6.25	6.22	6.18	6.15	6.12	6.10	6.09	6.06	6.05	6.04	6.03	6.02	5.95
9	5.78	5.73	5.69	5.65	5.62	5.56	5.52	5.48	5.45	5.41	5.38	5.36	5.34	5.32	5.30	5.28	5.27	5.26	5.26	5.19
10	5.22	5.17	5.13	5.10	5.07	5.01	4.97	4.93	4.90	4.86	4.83	4.80	4.79	4.77	4.75	4.73	4.72	4.71	4.71	4.64
11	4.80	4.76	4.72	4.68	4.65	4.60	4.55	4.52	4.49	4.45	4.41	4.39	4.37	4.36	4.34	4.32	4.31	4.30	4.29	4.23
12	4.48	4.43	4.39	4.36	4.33	4.27	4.23	4.19	4.17	4.12	4.09	4.07	4.05	4.04	4.01	4.00	3.99	3.98	3.97	3.91
13	4.22	4.17	4.13	4.10	4.07	4.01	3.97	3.94	3.91	3.87	3.84	3.81	3.79	3.78	3.76	3.74	3.73	3.72	3.71	3.65
14	4.01	3.96	3.92	3.89	3.86	3.80	3.76	3.73	3.70	3.66	3.62	3.60	3.58	3.57	3.55	3.53	3.52	3.51	3.50	3.44
15	3.83	3.79	3.75	3.72	3.69	3.63	3.58	3.55	3.52	3.48	3.45	3.43	3.41	3.39	3.37	3.36	3.34	3.34	3.33	3.26
16	3.68	3.64	3.60	3.57	3.54	3.48	3.44	3.40	3.37	3.33	3.30	3.28	3.26	3.25	3.22	3.21	3.20	3.19	3.18	3.11
17	3.56	3.51	3.47	3.44	3.41	3.35	3.31	3.28	3.25	3.21	3.18	3.15	3.13	3.12	3.10	3.08	3.07	3.06	3.05	2.99
18	3.45	3.40	3.36	3.33	3.30	3.25	3.20	3.17	3.14	3.10	3.07	3.04	3.02	3.01	2.99	2.97	2.96	2.95	2.94	2.87
19	3.35	3.31	3.27	3.24	3.21	3.15	3.11	3.07	3.04	3.00	2.97	2.95	2.93	2.91	2.89	2.87	2.86	2.85	2.85	2.78
20	3.27	3.22	3.18	3.15	3.12	3.07	3.02	2.99	2.96	2.92	2.88	2.86	2.84	2.83	2.81	2.79	2.78	2.77	2.76	2.69
22	3.12	3.08	3.04	3.01	2.98	2.92	2.88	2.84	2.82	2.77	2.74	2.72	2.70	2.69	2.66	2.65	2.63	2.62	2.62	2.55
24	3.01	2.97	2.93	2.90	2.87	2.81	2.77	2.73	2.70	2.66	2.63	2.60	2.58	2.57	2.55	2.53	2.52	2.51	2.50	2.43
26	2.92	2.87	2.84	2.80	2.77	2.72	2.67	2.64	2.61	2.56	2.53	2.51	2.49	2.47	2.45	2.43	2.42	2.41	2.40	2.33
28	2.84	2.79	2.76	2.72	2.69	2.64	2.59	2.56	2.53	2.48	2.45	2.43	2.41	2.39	2.37	2.35	2.34	2.33	2.32	2.25
30	2.77	2.73	2.69	2.66	2.63	2.57	2.52	2.49	2.46	2.42	2.38	2.36	2.34	2.32	2.30	2.28	2.27	2.26	2.25	2.18
35	2.64	2.60	2.56	2.53	2.50	2.44	2.39	2.36	2.33	2.28	2.25	2.22	2.20	2.19	2.16	2.15	2.13	2.12	2.11	2.04
40	2.55	2.50	2.46	2.43	2.40	2.34	2.30	2.26	2.23	2.18	2.15	2.12	2.10	2.09	2.06	2.05	2.03	2.02	2.01	1.93
45	2.47	2.43	2.39	2.36	2.33	2.27	2.22	2.19	2.16	2.11	2.08	2.05	2.03	2.01	1.99	1.97	1.95	1.94	1.93	1.85
50	2.42	2.37	2.33	2.30	2.27	2.21	2.16	2.13	2.10	2.05	2.02	1.99	1.97	1.95	1.93	1.91	1.89	1.88	1.87	1.79
60	2.33	2.29	2.25	2.22	2.19	2.13	2.08	2.04	2.01	1.96	1.93	1.90	1.88	1.86	1.83	1.81	1.80	1.79	1.78	1.69
70	2.28	2.23	2.19	2.16	2.13	2.07	2.02	1.98	1.95	1.90	1.86	1.84	1.81	1.80	1.77	1.75	1.73	1.72	1.71	1.62
80	2.23	2.19	2.15	2.11	2.08	2.02	1.97	1.94	1.90	1.85	1.82	1.79	1.77	1.75	1.72	1.70	1.68	1.67	1.66	1.57
90	2.20	2.15	2.12	2.08	2.05	1.99	1.94	1.90	1.87	1.82	1.78	1.75	1.73	1.71	1.68	1.66	1.64	1.63	1.62	1.52
100	2.17	2.13	2.09	2.05	2.02	1.96	1.91	1.87	1.84	1.79	1.75	1.72	1.70	1.68	1.65	1.63	1.61	1.60	1.59	1.49
120	2.13	2.09	2.05	2.01	1.98	1.92	1.87	1.83	1.80	1.75	1.72	1.68	1.66	1.64	1.61	1.58	1.57	1.55	1.54	1.43
140	2.11	2.06	2.02	1.99	1.96	1.89	1.84	1.80	1.77	1.72	1.68	1.65	1.62	1.60	1.57	1.55	1.53	1.52	1.51	1.39
160	2.09	2.04	2.00	1.97	1.93	1.87	1.82	1.78	1.75	1.69	1.65	1.62	1.60	1.58	1.55	1.53	1.51	1.49	1.48	1.36
180	2.07	2.02	1.98	1.95	1.92	1.85	1.80	1.76	1.73	1.68	1.64	1.61	1.58	1.56	1.53	1.50	1.49	1.47	1.46	1.34
200	2.06	2.01	1.97	1.94	1.91	1.84	1.79	1.75	1.71	1.66	1.62	1.59	1.56	1.54	1.51	1.49	1.47	1.45	1.44	1.32
∞	1.95	1.90	1.86	1.82	1.79	1.72	1.67	1.63	1.59	1.54	1.49	1.46	1.43	1.40	1.37	1.34	1.31	1.30	1.28	1.00

DENOMINATOR DEGREES OF FREEDOM

TABLE **7(a)** Critical Values of the Studentized Range, $\alpha = .05$

ν										k									
	2	3	4	5	6	7	8	9	10	11	12	13	14	15	16	17	18	19	20
1	18.0	27.0	32.8	37.1	40.4	43.1	45.4	47.4	49.1	50.6	52.0	53.2	54.3	55.4	56.3	57.2	58.0	58.8	59.6
2	6.08	8.33	9.80	10.9	11.7	12.4	13.0	13.5	14.0	14.4	14.7	15.1	15.4	15.7	15.9	16.1	16.4	16.6	16.8
3	4.50	5.91	6.82	7.50	8.04	8.48	8.85	9.18	9.46	9.72	9.95	10.2	10.3	10.5	10.7	10.8	11.0	11.1	11.2
4	3.93	5.04	5.76	6.29	6.71	7.05	7.35	7.60	7.83	8.03	8.21	8.37	8.52	8.66	8.79	8.91	9.03	9.13	9.23
5	3.64	4.60	5.22	5.67	6.03	6.33	6.58	6.80	6.99	7.17	7.32	7.47	7.60	7.72	7.83	7.93	8.03	8.12	8.21
6	3.46	4.34	4.90	5.30	5.63	5.90	6.12	6.32	6.49	6.65	6.79	6.92	7.03	7.14	7.24	7.34	7.43	7.51	7.59
7	3.34	4.16	4.68	5.06	5.36	5.61	5.82	6.00	6.16	6.30	6.43	6.55	6.66	6.76	6.85	6.94	7.02	7.10	7.17
8	3.26	4.04	4.53	4.89	5.17	5.40	5.60	5.77	5.92	6.05	6.18	6.29	6.39	6.48	6.57	6.65	6.73	6.80	6.87
9	3.20	3.95	4.41	4.76	5.02	5.24	5.43	5.59	5.74	5.87	5.98	6.09	6.19	6.28	6.36	6.44	6.51	6.58	6.64
10	3.15	3.88	4.33	4.65	4.91	5.12	5.30	5.46	5.60	5.72	5.83	5.93	6.03	6.11	6.19	6.27	6.34	6.40	6.47
11	3.11	3.82	4.26	4.57	4.82	5.03	5.20	5.35	5.49	5.61	5.71	5.81	5.90	5.98	6.06	6.13	6.20	6.27	6.33
12	3.08	3.77	4.20	4.51	4.75	4.95	5.12	5.27	5.39	5.51	5.61	5.71	5.80	5.88	5.95	6.02	6.09	6.15	6.21
13	3.06	3.73	4.15	4.45	4.69	4.88	5.05	5.19	5.32	5.43	5.53	5.63	5.71	5.79	5.86	5.93	5.99	6.05	6.11
14	3.03	3.70	4.11	4.41	4.64	4.83	4.99	5.13	5.25	5.36	5.46	5.55	5.64	5.71	5.79	5.85	5.91	5.97	6.03
15	3.01	3.67	4.08	4.37	4.59	4.78	4.94	5.08	5.20	5.31	5.40	5.49	5.57	5.65	5.72	5.78	5.85	5.90	5.96
16	3.00	3.65	4.05	4.33	4.56	4.74	4.90	5.03	5.15	5.26	5.35	5.44	5.52	5.59	5.66	5.73	5.79	5.84	5.90
17	2.98	3.63	4.02	4.30	4.52	4.70	4.86	4.99	5.11	5.21	5.31	5.39	5.47	5.54	5.61	5.67	5.73	5.79	5.84
18	2.97	3.61	4.00	4.28	4.49	4.67	4.82	4.96	5.07	5.17	5.27	5.35	5.43	5.50	5.57	5.63	5.69	5.74	5.79
19	2.96	3.59	3.98	4.25	4.47	4.65	4.79	4.92	5.04	5.14	5.23	5.31	5.39	5.46	5.53	5.59	5.65	5.70	5.75
20	2.95	3.58	3.96	4.23	4.45	4.62	4.77	4.90	5.01	5.11	5.20	5.28	5.36	5.43	5.49	5.55	5.61	5.66	5.71
24	2.92	3.53	3.90	4.17	4.37	4.54	4.68	4.81	4.92	5.01	5.10	5.18	5.25	5.32	5.38	5.44	5.49	5.55	5.59
30	2.89	3.49	3.85	4.10	4.30	4.46	4.60	4.72	4.82	4.92	5.00	5.08	5.15	5.21	5.27	5.33	5.38	5.43	5.47
40	2.86	3.44	3.79	4.04	4.23	4.39	4.52	4.63	4.73	4.82	4.90	4.98	5.04	5.11	5.16	5.22	5.27	5.31	5.36
60	2.83	3.40	3.74	3.98	4.16	4.31	4.44	4.55	4.65	4.73	4.81	4.88	4.94	5.00	5.06	5.11	5.15	5.20	5.24
120	2.80	3.36	3.68	3.92	4.10	4.24	4.36	4.47	4.56	4.64	4.71	4.78	4.84	4.90	4.95	5.00	5.04	5.09	5.13
∞	2.77	3.31	3.63	3.86	4.03	4.17	4.29	4.39	4.47	4.55	4.62	4.68	4.74	4.80	4.85	4.89	4.93	4.97	5.01

TABLE **7(b)** Critical Values of the Studentized Range, $\alpha = .01$

ν	\multicolumn{19}{c}{k}
	2	3	4	5	6	7	8	9	10	11	12	13	14	15	16	17	18	19	20
1	90.0	135	164	186	202	216	227	237	246	253	260	266	272	277	282	286	290	294	298
2	14.0	19.0	22.3	24.7	26.6	28.2	29.5	30.7	31.7	32.6	33.4	34.1	34.8	35.4	36.0	36.5	37.0	37.5	37.9
3	8.26	10.6	12.2	13.3	14.2	15.0	15.6	16.2	16.7	17.1	17.5	17.9	18.2	18.5	18.8	19.1	19.3	19.5	19.8
4	6.51	8.12	9.17	9.96	10.6	11.1	11.5	11.9	12.3	12.6	12.8	13.1	13.3	13.5	13.7	13.9	14.1	14.2	14.4
5	5.70	6.97	7.80	8.42	8.91	9.32	9.67	9.97	10.2	10.5	10.7	10.9	11.1	11.2	11.4	11.6	11.7	11.8	11.9
6	5.24	6.33	7.03	7.56	7.97	8.32	8.61	8.87	9.10	9.30	9.49	9.65	9.81	9.95	10.1	10.2	10.3	10.4	10.5
7	4.95	5.92	6.54	7.01	7.37	7.68	7.94	8.17	8.37	8.55	8.71	8.86	9.00	9.12	9.24	9.35	9.46	9.55	9.65
8	4.74	5.63	6.20	6.63	6.96	7.24	7.47	7.68	7.87	8.03	8.18	8.31	8.44	8.55	8.66	8.76	8.85	8.94	9.03
9	4.60	5.43	5.96	6.35	6.66	6.91	7.13	7.32	7.49	7.65	7.78	7.91	8.03	8.13	8.23	8.32	8.41	8.49	8.57
10	4.48	5.27	5.77	6.14	6.43	6.67	6.87	7.05	7.21	7.36	7.48	7.60	7.71	7.81	7.91	7.99	8.07	8.15	8.22
11	4.39	5.14	5.62	5.97	6.25	6.48	6.67	6.84	6.99	7.13	7.25	7.36	7.46	7.56	7.65	7.73	7.81	7.88	7.95
12	4.32	5.04	5.50	5.84	6.10	6.32	6.51	6.67	6.81	6.94	7.06	7.17	7.26	7.36	7.44	7.52	7.59	7.66	7.73
13	4.26	4.96	5.40	5.73	5.98	6.19	6.37	6.53	6.67	6.79	6.90	7.01	7.10	7.19	7.27	7.34	7.42	7.48	7.55
14	4.21	4.89	5.32	5.63	5.88	6.08	6.26	6.41	6.54	6.66	6.77	6.87	6.96	7.05	7.12	7.20	7.27	7.33	7.39
15	4.17	4.83	5.25	5.56	5.80	5.99	6.16	6.31	6.44	6.55	6.66	6.76	6.84	6.93	7.00	7.07	7.14	7.20	7.26
16	4.13	4.78	5.19	5.49	5.72	5.92	6.08	6.22	6.35	6.46	6.56	6.66	6.74	6.82	6.90	6.97	7.03	7.09	7.15
17	4.10	4.74	5.14	5.43	5.66	5.85	6.01	6.15	6.27	6.38	6.48	6.57	6.66	6.73	6.80	6.87	6.94	7.00	7.05
18	4.07	4.70	5.09	5.38	5.60	5.79	5.94	6.08	6.20	6.31	6.41	6.50	6.58	6.65	6.72	6.79	6.85	6.91	6.96
19	4.05	4.67	5.05	5.33	5.55	5.73	5.89	6.02	6.14	6.25	6.34	6.43	6.51	6.58	6.65	6.72	6.78	6.84	6.89
20	4.02	4.64	5.02	5.29	5.51	5.69	5.84	5.97	6.09	6.19	6.29	6.37	6.45	6.52	6.59	6.65	6.71	6.76	6.82
24	3.96	4.54	4.91	5.17	5.37	5.54	5.69	5.81	5.92	6.02	6.11	6.19	6.26	6.33	6.39	6.45	6.51	6.56	6.61
30	3.89	4.45	4.80	5.05	5.24	5.40	5.54	5.65	5.76	5.85	5.93	6.01	6.08	6.14	6.20	6.26	6.31	6.36	6.41
40	3.82	4.37	4.70	4.93	5.11	5.27	5.39	5.50	5.60	5.69	5.77	5.84	5.90	5.96	6.02	6.07	6.12	6.17	6.21
60	3.76	4.28	4.60	4.82	4.99	5.13	5.25	5.36	5.45	5.53	5.60	5.67	5.73	5.79	5.84	5.89	5.93	5.98	6.02
120	3.70	4.20	4.50	4.71	4.87	5.01	5.12	5.21	5.30	5.38	5.44	5.51	5.56	5.61	5.66	5.71	5.75	5.79	5.83
∞	3.64	4.12	4.40	4.60	4.76	4.88	4.99	5.08	5.16	5.23	5.29	5.35	5.40	5.45	5.49	5.54	5.57	5.61	5.65

Source: From E. S. Pearson and H. O. Hartley, *Biometrika Tables for Statisticians*, 1: 176–77. Reproduced by permission of the Biometrika Trustees.

TABLE 8(a) Critical Values for the Durbin-Watson Statistic, $\alpha = .05$

n	d_L	d_U	d_L	d_U	d_L	d_U	d_L	d_U	d_L	d_U
	$k = 1$		**$k = 2$**		**$k = 3$**		**$k = 4$**		**$k = 5$**	
15	1.08	1.36	.95	1.54	.82	1.75	.69	1.97	.56	2.21
16	1.10	1.37	.98	1.54	.86	1.73	.74	1.93	.62	2.15
17	1.13	1.38	1.02	1.54	.90	1.71	.78	1.90	.67	2.10
18	1.16	1.39	1.05	1.53	.93	1.69	.82	1.87	.71	2.06
19	1.18	1.40	1.08	1.53	.97	1.68	.86	1.85	.75	2.02
20	1.20	1.41	1.10	1.54	1.00	1.68	.90	1.83	.79	1.99
21	1.22	1.42	1.13	1.54	1.03	1.67	.93	1.81	.83	1.96
22	1.24	1.43	1.15	1.54	1.05	1.66	.96	1.80	.86	1.94
23	1.26	1.44	1.17	1.54	1.08	1.66	.99	1.79	.90	1.92
24	1.27	1.45	1.19	1.55	1.10	1.66	1.01	1.78	.93	1.90
25	1.29	1.45	1.21	1.55	1.12	1.66	1.04	1.77	.95	1.89
26	1.30	1.46	1.22	1.55	1.14	1.65	1.06	1.76	.98	1.88
27	1.32	1.47	1.24	1.56	1.16	1.65	1.08	1.76	1.01	1.86
28	1.33	1.48	1.26	1.56	1.18	1.65	1.10	1.75	1.03	1.85
29	1.34	1.48	1.27	1.56	1.20	1.65	1.12	1.74	1.05	1.84
30	1.35	1.49	1.28	1.57	1.21	1.65	1.14	1.74	1.07	1.83
31	1.36	1.50	1.30	1.57	1.23	1.65	1.16	1.74	1.09	1.83
32	1.37	1.50	1.31	1.57	1.24	1.65	1.18	1.73	1.11	1.82
33	1.38	1.51	1.32	1.58	1.26	1.65	1.19	1.73	1.13	1.81
34	1.39	1.51	1.33	1.58	1.27	1.65	1.21	1.73	1.15	1.81
35	1.40	1.52	1.34	1.58	1.28	1.65	1.22	1.73	1.16	1.80
36	1.41	1.52	1.35	1.59	1.29	1.65	1.24	1.73	1.18	1.80
37	1.42	1.53	1.36	1.59	1.31	1.66	1.25	1.72	1.19	1.80
38	1.43	1.54	1.37	1.59	1.32	1.66	1.26	1.72	1.21	1.79
39	1.43	1.54	1.38	1.60	1.33	1.66	1.27	1.72	1.22	1.79
40	1.44	1.54	1.39	1.60	1.34	1.66	1.29	1.72	1.23	1.79
45	1.48	1.57	1.43	1.62	1.38	1.67	1.34	1.72	1.29	1.78
50	1.50	1.59	1.46	1.63	1.42	1.67	1.38	1.72	1.34	1.77
55	1.53	1.60	1.49	1.64	1.45	1.68	1.41	1.72	1.38	1.77
60	1.55	1.62	1.51	1.65	1.48	1.69	1.44	1.73	1.41	1.77
65	1.57	1.63	1.54	1.66	1.50	1.70	1.47	1.73	1.44	1.77
70	1.58	1.64	1.55	1.67	1.52	1.70	1.49	1.74	1.46	1.77
75	1.60	1.65	1.57	1.68	1.54	1.71	1.51	1.74	1.49	1.77
80	1.61	1.66	1.59	1.69	1.56	1.72	1.53	1.74	1.51	1.77
85	1.62	1.67	1.60	1.70	1.57	1.72	1.55	1.75	1.52	1.77
90	1.63	1.68	1.61	1.70	1.59	1.73	1.57	1.75	1.54	1.78
95	1.64	1.69	1.62	1.71	1.60	1.73	1.58	1.75	1.56	1.78
100	1.65	1.69	1.63	1.72	1.61	1.74	1.59	1.76	1.57	1.78

Source: From J. Durbin and G. S. Watson, "Testing for Serial Correlation in Least Squares Regression, II," *Biometrika* 30 (1951): 159–78. Reproduced by permission of the Biometrika Trustees.

TABLE **8(b)** Critical Values for the Durbin-Watson Statistic, $\alpha = .01$

	k = 1		k = 2		k = 3		k = 4		k = 5	
n	d_L	d_U	d_L	d_U	d_L	d_U	d_L	d_U	d_L	d_U
15	.81	1.07	.70	1.25	.59	1.46	.49	1.70	.39	1.96
16	.84	1.09	.74	1.25	.63	1.44	.53	1.66	.44	1.90
17	.87	1.10	.77	1.25	.67	1.43	.57	1.63	.48	1.85
18	.90	1.12	.80	1.26	.71	1.42	.61	1.60	.52	1.80
19	.93	1.13	.83	1.26	.74	1.41	.65	1.58	.56	1.77
20	.95	1.15	.86	1.27	.77	1.41	.68	1.57	.60	1.74
21	.97	1.16	.89	1.27	.80	1.41	.72	1.55	.63	1.71
22	1.00	1.17	.91	1.28	.83	1.40	.75	1.54	.66	1.69
23	1.02	1.19	.94	1.29	.86	1.40	.77	1.53	.70	1.67
24	1.04	1.20	.96	1.30	.88	1.41	.80	1.53	.72	1.66
25	1.05	1.21	.98	1.30	.90	1.41	.83	1.52	.75	1.65
26	1.07	1.22	1.00	1.31	.93	1.41	.85	1.52	.78	1.64
27	1.09	1.23	1.02	1.32	.95	1.41	.88	1.51	.81	1.63
28	1.10	1.24	1.04	1.32	.97	1.41	.90	1.51	.83	1.62
29	1.12	1.25	1.05	1.33	.99	1.42	.92	1.51	.85	1.61
30	1.13	1.26	1.07	1.34	1.01	1.42	.94	1.51	.88	1.61
31	1.15	1.27	1.08	1.34	1.02	1.42	.96	1.51	.90	1.60
32	1.16	1.28	1.10	1.35	1.04	1.43	.98	1.51	.92	1.60
33	1.17	1.29	1.11	1.36	1.05	1.43	1.00	1.51	.94	1.59
34	1.18	1.30	1.13	1.36	1.07	1.43	1.01	1.51	.95	1.59
35	1.19	1.31	1.14	1.37	1.08	1.44	1.03	1.51	.97	1.59
36	1.21	1.32	1.15	1.38	1.10	1.44	1.04	1.51	.99	1.59
37	1.22	1.32	1.16	1.38	1.11	1.45	1.06	1.51	1.00	1.59
38	1.23	1.33	1.18	1.39	1.12	1.45	1.07	1.52	1.02	1.58
39	1.24	1.34	1.19	1.39	1.14	1.45	1.09	1.52	1.03	1.58
40	1.25	1.34	1.20	1.40	1.15	1.46	1.10	1.52	1.05	1.58
45	1.29	1.38	1.24	1.42	1.20	1.48	1.16	1.53	1.11	1.58
50	1.32	1.40	1.28	1.45	1.24	1.49	1.20	1.54	1.16	1.59
55	1.36	1.43	1.32	1.47	1.28	1.51	1.25	1.55	1.21	1.59
60	1.38	1.45	1.35	1.48	1.32	1.52	1.28	1.56	1.25	1.60
65	1.41	1.47	1.38	1.50	1.35	1.53	1.31	1.57	1.28	1.61
70	1.43	1.49	1.40	1.52	1.37	1.55	1.34	1.58	1.31	1.61
75	1.45	1.50	1.42	1.53	1.39	1.56	1.37	1.59	1.34	1.62
80	1.47	1.52	1.44	1.54	1.42	1.57	1.39	1.60	1.36	1.62
85	1.48	1.53	1.46	1.55	1.43	1.58	1.41	1.60	1.39	1.63
90	1.50	1.54	1.47	1.56	1.45	1.59	1.43	1.61	1.41	1.64
95	1.51	1.55	1.49	1.57	1.47	1.60	1.45	1.62	1.42	1.64
100	1.52	1.56	1.50	1.58	1.48	1.60	1.46	1.63	1.44	1.65

TABLE 9 Critical Values for the Wilcoxon Rank Sum Test

(a) $\alpha = .025$ one-tail; $\alpha = .05$ two-tail

n_1 / n_2	3 T_L	3 T_U	4 T_L	4 T_U	5 T_L	5 T_U	6 T_L	6 T_U	7 T_L	7 T_U	8 T_L	8 T_U	9 T_L	9 T_U	10 T_L	10 T_U
4	6	18	11	25	17	33	23	43	31	53	40	64	50	76	61	89
5	6	11	12	28	18	37	25	47	33	58	42	70	52	83	64	96
6	7	23	12	32	19	41	26	52	35	63	44	76	55	89	66	104
7	7	26	13	35	20	45	28	56	37	68	47	81	58	95	70	110
8	8	28	14	38	21	49	29	61	39	63	49	87	60	102	73	117
9	8	31	15	41	22	53	31	65	41	78	51	93	63	108	76	124
10	9	33	16	44	24	56	32	70	43	83	54	98	66	114	79	131

(b) $\alpha = .05$ one-tail; $\alpha = 10$ two-tail

n_1 / n_2	3 T_L	3 T_U	4 T_L	4 T_U	5 T_L	5 T_U	6 T_L	6 T_U	7 T_L	7 T_U	8 T_L	8 T_U	9 T_L	9 T_U	10 T_L	10 T_U
3	6	15	11	21	16	29	23	37	31	46	39	57	49	68	60	80
4	7	17	12	24	18	32	25	41	33	51	42	62	52	74	63	87
5	7	20	13	27	19	37	26	46	35	56	45	67	55	80	66	94
6	8	22	14	30	20	40	28	50	37	61	47	73	57	87	69	101
7	9	24	15	33	22	43	30	54	39	66	49	79	60	93	73	107
8	9	27	16	36	24	46	32	58	41	71	52	84	63	99	76	114
9	10	29	17	39	25	50	33	63	43	76	54	90	66	105	79	121
10	11	31	18	42	26	54	35	67	46	80	57	95	69	111	83	127

Source: From F. Wilcoxon and R. A. Wilcox, "Some Rapid Approximate Statistical Procedures" (1964), p. 28. Reproduced with the permission of American Cyanamid Company.

TABLE **10**
Critical Values for the Wilcoxon Signed Rank Sum Test

n	(a) $\alpha = .025$ one-tail; $\alpha = .05$ two-tail		(b) $\alpha = .05$ one-tail; $\alpha = .10$ two-tail	
	T_L	T_U	T_L	T_U
6	1	20	2	19
7	2	26	4	24
8	4	32	6	30
9	6	39	8	37
10	8	47	11	44
11	11	55	14	52
12	14	64	17	61
13	17	74	21	70
14	21	84	26	79
15	25	95	30	90
16	30	106	36	100
17	35	118	41	112
18	40	131	47	124
19	46	144	54	136
20	52	158	60	150
21	59	172	68	163
22	66	187	75	178
23	73	203	83	193
24	81	219	92	208
25	90	235	101	224
26	98	253	110	241
27	107	271	120	258
28	117	289	130	276
29	127	308	141	294
30	137	328	152	313

Source: From F. Wilcoxon and R. A. Wilcox, "Some Rapid Approximate Statistical Procedures" (1964), p.28. Reproduced with the permission of American Cyanamid Company.

TABLE 11 Critical Values for the Spearman Rank Correlation Coefficient

The α values correspond to a one-tail test of $H_0 : \rho_s = 0$.
The value should be doubled for two-tail tests.

n	$\alpha = .05$	$\alpha = .025$	$\alpha = .01$
5	.900	—	—
6	.829	.886	.943
7	.714	.786	.893
8	.643	.738	.833
9	.600	.683	.783
10	.564	.648	.745
11	.523	.623	.736
12	.497	.591	.703
13	.475	.566	.673
14	.457	.545	.646
15	.441	.525	.623
16	.425	.507	.601
17	.412	.490	.582
18	.399	.476	.564
19	.388	.462	.549
20	.377	.450	.534
21	.368	.438	.521
22	.359	.428	.508
23	.351	.418	.496
24	.343	.409	.485
25	.336	.400	.475
26	.329	.392	.465
27	.323	.385	.456
28	.317	.377	.448
29	.311	.370	.440
30	.305	.364	.432

Source: From E. G. Olds, "Distribution of Sums of Squares of Rank Differences for Small Samples," *Annals of Mathematical Statistics* 9 (1938). Reproduced with the permission of the Institute of Mathematical Statistics.

TABLE 12   Control Chart Constants

SAMPLE SIZE n	A_2	d_2	d_3	D_3	D_4
2	1.880	1.128	.853	.000	3.267
3	1.023	1.693	.888	.000	2.575
4	.729	2.059	.880	.000	2.282
5	.577	2.326	.864	.000	2.115
6	.483	2.534	.848	.000	2.004
7	.419	2.704	.833	.076	1.924
8	.373	2.847	.820	.136	1.864
9	.337	2.970	.808	.184	1.816
10	.308	3.078	.797	.223	1.777
11	.285	3.173	.787	.256	1.744
12	.266	3.258	.778	.284	1.716
13	.249	3.336	.770	.308	1.692
14	.235	3.407	.762	.329	1.671
15	.223	3.472	.755	.348	1.652
16	.212	3.532	.749	.364	1.636
17	.203	3.588	.743	.379	1.621
18	.194	3.640	.738	.392	1.608
19	.187	3.689	.733	.404	1.596
20	.180	3.735	.729	.414	1.586
21	.173	3.778	.724	.425	1.575
22	.167	3.819	.720	.434	1.566
23	.162	3.858	.716	.443	1.557
24	.157	3.895	.712	.452	1.548
25	.153	3.931	.709	.459	1.541

Source: From E. S. Pearson, "The Percentage Limits for the Distribution of Range in Samples from a Normal Population," *Biometrika* 24 (1932): 416. Reproduced by permission of the Biometrika Trustees.

APPENDIX C

ANSWERS TO SELECTED EVEN-NUMBERED EXERCISES

All answers have been double-checked for accuracy. However, we cannot be absolutely certain that there are no errors. Students should not automatically assume that answers that don't match ours are wrong. When and if we discover mistakes we will post corrected answers on our Web page (www.kellerstatistics.com). If you find any errors, please e-mail the author (gkeller@wlu.ca). We will be happy to acknowledge you with the discovery.

Chapter 1

1.2 Descriptive statistics summarizes a set of data. Inferential statistics makes inferences about populations from samples.

1.4 a. The complete production run
  b. 1000 chips
  c. Proportion defective
  d. Proportion of sample chips that are defective (7.5%)
  e. Parameter
  f. Statistic
  g. Because the sample proportion is less than 10%, we can conclude that the claim is true.

1.6 a. Flip the coin 100 times and count the number of heads and tails
  b. Outcomes of flips
  c. Outcomes of the 100 flips
  d. Proportion of heads
  e. Proportion of heads in the 100 flips

1.8 a. Fuel mileage of all the taxis in the fleet.
  b. Mean mileage.
  c. The 50 observations.
  d. Mean of the 50 observations.
  e. The statistic would be used to estimate the parameter from which the owner can calculate total costs.
  We computed the sample mean to be 19.8 mpg.

Chapter 2

2.2 a. Interval **b.** Interval
  c. Nominal **d.** Ordinal
2.4 a. Nominal **b.** Interval
  c. Nominal **d.** Interval
  e. Ordinal
2.6 a. Interval **b.** Interval
  c. Nominal **d.** Ordinal
  e. Interval

2.8 a. Interval **b.** Ordinal
  c. Nominal **d.** Ordinal
2.10 a. Ordinal **b.** Ordinal **c.** Ordinal
2.28 The basement is the top choice followed by kitchen, bathroom, bedroom, and living/dining room.
2.32 c. Excel is the choice of about half the sample, one-quarter have opted for Minitab, and a small fraction chose SAS and SPSS.
2.36 According to the survey Republicans favor the rich and Democrats are split among the middle class, poor, and rich.
2.38 A small majority oppose the Affordable Care Act.
2.40 On economic issues the country is conservative.
2.42 Spending is increasing in all seven areas.
2.44 Universities 1 and 2 are similar and quite dissimilar from universities 3 and 4, which also differ. The two nominal variables appear to be related.
2.46 The two variables are related.
2.48 The number of prescriptions filled by all stores except independent drug stores has increased substantially.
2.50 There are differences among the five groups.
2.52 Democrats support and Republicans oppose the Affordable Care Act.
2.54 On economic issues Republicans are very conservative whereas Democrats and Moderates are mixed.
2.58 The pattern is about the same for the three households.
2.60 There are decreases in almost every state. However, there are many Americans without health insurance.
2.62 More than 40% rate the food as less than good.
2.64 Customers with children rated the restaurant more highly than did customers with no children.
2.66 The survey oversampled women slightly.
2.70 The patterns are similar.
2.72 The patterns are similar.
2.74 The "married" categories

(4 and 5) make up more than 60% of the households.
2.76 Whites make up three-quarters of the survey.
2.78 College degree holders are much more likely to own their homes.

Chapter 3

3.2 11 to 13
3.4 a. 5 (or 6)
  b. Upper limits: 5.2, 5.4, 5.6, 5.8, 6.0, 6.2.
3.8 The number of calls is bimodal.
3.10 b. The number of stores is bimodal and positively skewed.
3.12 The histogram is symmetric (approximately) and bimodal.
3.14 Most orders arrive within 12 days.
3.16 b. The histogram is somewhat bell shaped.
3.18 The histogram is unimodal, bell-shaped, and roughly symmetric. Most of the lengths lie between 18 and 23 inches.
3.20 The histogram is unimodal, symmetric, and bell-shaped. Most tomatoes weigh between 2 and 7 ounces with a small fraction weighing less than 2 ounces or more than 7 ounces.
3.22 The histogram of the number of books shipped daily is negatively skewed. It appears that there is a maximum number that the company can ship.
3.24 The histogram is bimodal. The modes represent high school completion (12 years) and university completion (16 years).
3.26 Many respondents watched less than 2 hours per day and almost all watched for less than 6 hours.
3.28 The histogram is bell shaped with the 50–60 interval being the modal class.
3.30 a. Almost all the values are in the first interval.
  b. Most of the values are greater than 200,000.
3.32 Both countries are winning an increasing number of medals.
3.34 Both types of crime have been decreasing.
3.46 d. In the period 1993–2012 crime was decreasing no matter how it was measured.

3.48 c. GDP has been steadily increasing.

3.50 d. The U.S. imports more from Japan than Japan imports from the United States.

3.52 The recent trend reveals that the Canadian dollar has been losing value relative to the U.S. dollar.

3.56 There is a weak positive linear relationship.

3.58 b. There is a positive linear relationship between calculus and statistics marks.

3.60 There is a negative linear relationship.

3.62 b. There is a moderately strong positive linear relationship.

3.64 b. There is a very weak positive linear relationship.

3.66 There is a moderately strong positive linear relationship.

3.68 There is moderately strong positive linear relationship.

3.70 There is a strong nonlinear positive relationship.

3.72 There is a positive linear relationship.

3.74 There is a weak positive linear relationship.

3.76 There is no relationship.

3.78 There is a weak positive linear relationship.

3.80 There is a negative linear relationship.

3.82 c. The accident rate generally decreases as the ages increase. The fatal accident rate decreases until the over 64 age category where there is an increase.

3.86 There is no linear relationship between the inflation rate and the return on the precious metals subindex.

3.88 There is a strong positive linear relationship.

3.90 The histogram is symmetric and bell shaped.

3.92 There is no linear relationship between the Dow Jones Industrial average and the unemployment rate.

3.94 There is a strong positive linear relationship. Poorer players take longer to complete their rounds.

3.96 There is a moderately strong negative linear relationship.

3.98 The histogram of the number of meetings is positively skewed.

3.100 The histogram is positively skewed and bimodal.

3.102 There appears to be a stronger linear relationship between marks in the mathematical statistics course and calculus than the relationship between the marks in the business statistics course and the marks in calculus.

3.104 a. The histogram is approximately bell shaped and symmetric.

b. There is no linear relationship between the amount of time needed to land a job and salary.

3.106 Per capita debt is still unmanageable.

Chapter 4

4.2 6.0, 5, 5

4.4 a. 39.33, 38, all

4.6 .19

4.8 a. .106, .10
   b. .102

4.10 a. .20, 0, .25, .33
   b. .195, .225
   c. .188

4.12 54.91, 55

4.14 a. 45.60, 45

4.16 a. .81, .84

4.18 a. 122.76, 124

4.20 13.7, 14

4.22 45,247, 32,500

4.24 853,135, 60,872

4.26 264,572, 23,690

4.28 5, 1.14

4.30 −.30, 3.89

4.32 a. 51.5   **b.** 6.5   **c.** 174.5

4.38 a. Nothing
   b. At least 75% lie between 60 and 180.
   c. At least 88.9% lie between 30 and 210.

4.40 At least 75% of the speeds lie within 12.76 mph of the mean; At least 88.9% of the speeds lie within 19.14 mph of the mean.

4.42 At least 75% of the lengths lie within .5858 of the mean; At least 88.9% of the rods will lie within .8787 cm of the mean.

4.44 a. $s = 15.01$

4.46 95.09, 7.51

4.48 749.7, 215.9

4.50 13.70, 3.07

4.52 45,247, 39,885

4.54 853,135, 5,952,380

4.56 264,572, 3,793,046

4.58 3, 5, 7

4.60 44.6, 55.2

4.62 6.6, 17.6

4.64 13, 24, 11

4.66 3, 21, 18

4.68 a. 2, 4, 8

4.70 50, 125, 260

4.72 145.51, 164.17, 174.64

4.74 a. 26, 28.5, 32

4.76 2377, 2765, 3214

4.78 12, 14, 16

4.80 28,407, 60,872, 144,063

4.82 0, 23,690, 156,100

4.84 a. −.7813   **b.** .6104.

4.86 a. 98.52   **b.** .8811   **c.** .7763
   d. $\hat{y} = 5.917 + 1.705x$

4.88 .0366

4.90 .0078

4.92 .0069

4.94 $\hat{y} = 263.4 + 71.65x$; Estimated fixed costs = $263.40, estimated variable costs = $71.65

4.100 All five commodities are negatively linearly related to the exchange rate. The relationships are moderately strong.

4.102 a. There is very little correlation between wins and away attendance.
   b. 20.90

4.104 b. 2278.1

4.106 a. $1, 467,998
   b. 3328.2
   c. 1432.3

4.108 a. A negative slope means that higher payrolls lead to fewer wins.
   b. 5796.6
   c. 855.4

4.110 a. $2,670,227
   b. 3131.3
   c. 458.6

4.112 1.1193; .4355

4.114 .8844; .4169

4.116 .8266; .3427

4.118 .9166

4.120 1.5876; .1236

4.122 .4031; .0829

4.124 1.2293

4.126 1.0815; .2846

4.128 1.7154; .1069

4.130 .8535

4.132 .4603

4.134 a. $\hat{y} = 17.933 + .6041x$
   d. .0505

4.136 a. $\hat{y} = 103.44 + .07x$

4.138 The times are positively skewed.

4.140 a. 29,913, 30,660
   b. 148,213,791, 12,174

4.142 a. .5489
   b. $\hat{y} = 49,337 − 553.7x$

4.144 Mean, median, mode: 34,656, 34,636, 35,149

4.146 .2036

4.148 .0205

4.150 .0424

4.152 .4324

Chapter 6

6.6 {Adams wins. Brown wins, Collins wins, Dalton wins}

6.8 a. {0, 1, 2, 3, 4, 5}
   b. {4, 5}
   c. .10
   d. .65
   e. 0

6.10 2/6, 3/6, 1/6

6.12 a. .40
   b. .90

6.14 a. P(single) = .15, P(married) = .50, P(divorced) = .25, P(widowed) = .10
   b. Relative frequency approach

6.20 $P(A_1) = .3, P(A_2) = .4$, $P(A_3) = .3$ $P(B_1) = .6$, $P(B_2) = .4$

6.22 a. .57
   b. .43
   c. It is not a coincidence

6.24 The events are not independent.
6.26 The events are independent.
6.28 $P(A_1) = .40, P(A_2) = .45,$
$P(A_3) = .15\ P(B_1) = .45,$
$P(B_2) = .55$
6.30 a. .85 **b.** .75 **c.** .50
6.32 a. .36 **b.** .49 **c.** .83
6.34 a. .31 **b.** .85 **c.** .387
d. .043
6.36 a. .390 **b.** .66 **c.** No
6.38 a. .11 **b.** .043 **c.** .091
d. .909
6.40 a. .33 **b.** 30
c. Yes, the events are
dependent.
6.42 a. .778 **b.** .128 **c.** .385
6.44 a. .636 **b.** .205
6.46 a. .848 **b.** .277 **c.** .077
6.48 No
6.50 a. .216 **b.** .198 **c.** .368
d. .632
6.52 a. .750 **b.** .900 **c.** .257
6.54 a. .269 **b.** .0968 **c.** .513
d. .391
6.56 a. .4000 **b.** .3111 **c.** .3797
d. .1700
6.58 a. .2048 **b.** .1400 **c.** .1800
d. .3600
6.60 .32, .48, .14, .06
6.62 .24, .56, .06, .14
6.64 a. .81 **b.** .01 **c.** .18 **d.** .99
6.66 b. .8091 **c.** .0091
d. .1818 **e.** .9909
6.68 a. .28 **b.** .30 **c.** .42
6.70 .038
6.72 .335
6.74 .698
6.76 .2520
6.78 .033
6.80 .00000001
6.82 .6125
6.84 .6408
6.86 .7376
6.88 a. .696 **b.** .304 **c.** .889
d. .111
6.90 .526
6.92 .327
6.94 .661
6.96 .593
6.98 .843
6.100 .920, .973, .1460, .9996
6.102 .4000
6.104 .2910
6.106 .4113
6.108 a. .290 **b.** .290 **c.** Yes
6.110 a. .19 **b.** .517 **c.** No
6.112 .295
6.114 .825
6.116 a. .3285 **b.** .2403
6.118 .9710
6.120 2/3
6.122 .2214
6.124 .3333

Chapter 7

7.2 b. No **c.** No **d.** Continuous
7.4 a. 0, 1, 2, . . ., 100
b. Yes **c.** Yes, 101 values
d. Discrete
7.6 $P(x) = 1/6$, for $x = 1, 2, \ldots, 6$

7.8 a. .950, .020, .680 **b.** 3.066
c. 1.085
7.10 a. .8 **b.** .8 **c.** .8 **d.** .3
7.12 .0156
7.14 a. .25 **b.** .25 **c.** .25 **d.** .25
7.18 a. 1.40, 17.04
c. 7.00, 426.00
d. 7.00, 426.00
7.20 a. .6 **b.** 1.7, .81
7.22 a. .40 **b.** .95
7.24 1.025, .168
7.26 a. .06 **b.** 0 **c.** .35 **d.** .65
7.28 a. .21 **b.** .31 **c.** .26
7.30 2.76, 1.517
7.32 3.86, 2.60
7.34 E(value of coin) = $460; take
the $500
7.36 $18
7.38 4.00, 2.40
7.40 1.85
7.42 a. .32 **b.** .68 **c.** .47
7.44 a. .04 **b.** .78 **c.** .06
7.46 .14, .58
7.48 b. 2.8, .76
7.50 0, 0
7.52 b. 2.9, .45 **c.** Yes
7.56 c. 1.07, .505 **d.** .93, .605
e. −.045, −.081
7.58 a. .412 **b.** .286 **c.** .148
7.60 a. .10 **b.** .4167 **c.** .4762
7.62 a. $P(0) = .45, P(1) = .23,$
$P(2) = .21, P(3) = .11$
b. .98, 1.100, 1.049
7.64 a. $P(0) = .38, P(1) = .30,$
$P(2) = .19, P(3) = .13$
b. 1.07, 1.085, 1.042
7.66 a. $P(0) = .14, P(1) = .23,$
$P(2) = .28, P(3) = .25,$
$P(4) = .08, P(5) = .02,$
$P(6) = 0$
b. 1.96, 1.538, 1.240
c. −.217
7.68 145, 31
7.70 168, 574
7.72 a. .211, .1081 **b.** .211, .1064
c. .211 .1052
7.74 a. .1060, .1456
7.76 a. .0074 .0667 **b.** .0056 .0675
c. .0064 .0590 **d.** (a) **e.** (b)
7.78 a. .0080 .0394
b. .0084 .0397
c. .0059 .0437
d. (c) has the smallest mean
and the largest standard
deviation.
7.80 a. .0101 .0338 **b.** .0097 .0339
c. .0110 .0360 **d.** (c) **e.** (a)
7.82 a. .0103 .0276 **b.** .0085 .0282
c. .0120 .0315 **d.** (c) **e.** (a)
7.84 .0100 .0267
7.88 a. .0119 .0350 **b.** .0135 .0326
c. .0142 .0372 **d.** (c) **e.** (b)
7.90 a. .0065 .0277 **b.** .0096 .0303
c. .0047 .0371 **d.** (b) **e.** (a)
7.94 a. .0128 .0456 **b.** .0161 .0491
c. .0117 .0437 **d.** (b) **e.** (c)
7.96 a. .0186 .0468 **b.** .0185 .0592
c. .0213 .0752 **d.** (c) **e.** (a)
7.100 a. .2668 **b.** .1029 **c.** .0014
7.102 a. .26683 **b.** .10292 **c.** .00145

7.104 a. .2457 **b.** .0819 **c.** .0015
7.106 a. .1711 **b.** .0916 **c.** .9095
d. .8106
7.108 a. .4219 **b.** .3114 **c.** .25810
7.110 a. .0646 **b.** .9666 **c.** .9282
d. 22.5
7.112 $P(0) = .0081, P(1) = .0756,$
$P(2) = .2646, P(3) = .4116,$
$P(4) = .2401$
7.114 a. 2668 **b.** .6172
7.116 .00317
7.118 a. .6761 **b.** .0326 **c.** 2.9
7.120 a. .3369 **b.** .75763
7.122 a. .2990 **b.** .91967
7.124 a. .69185 **b.** .12519
c. .44069
7.126 a. .05692 **b.** .47015
7.128 a. .1353 **b.** .1804 **c.** .0361
7.130 a. .0302 **b.** .2746 **c.** .3033
7.132 a. .1353 **b.** .0663
7.134 a. .20269 **b.** .26761
7.136 .6703
7.138 a. .3712 **b.** .4335 **c.** .1954
7.140 a. .3679 **b.** .0037
7.142 a. .4422 **b.** .1512
7.144 a. .2231 **b.** .7029 **c.** .5768
7.146 a. .2428 **b.** .9327 **c.** .5951
7.148 a. .8 **b.** .4457.
7.150 a. .0993 **b.** .8088 **c.** .8881
7.152 .0473
7.154 a. .0337 **b.** .6160 **c.** .1334
7.156 a. .2051 **b.** .0547 **c.** .3770
7.158 .0064
7.160 a. .00793 **b.** 56 **c.** 4.10
7.162 a. .1612 **b.** .0095 **c.** .0132
7.164 a. 1.46, 1.49 **b.** 2.22, 1.45
7.166 a. .1074 **b.** .6778 **c.** .6242
7.168 $P(0) = .95099, P(1) = .04803,$
$P(2) = .00097, P(3) = .00001$
7.170 .08755

Chapter 8

8.2 a. .1200 **b.** .4800 **c.** .6667
d. .1867
8.4 b. 0 **c.** .25 **d.** .005
8.6 a. .1667 **b.** .3333 **c.** 0
8.8 57 minutes
8.10 123 tons
8.12 b. .5 **c.** .25
8.14 b. .25 **c.** .33
8.16 b. .875 **c.** .50 **d.** .875
8.18 b. .60 **c.** .15 **d.** .225
8.20 .9463
8.22 .0823
8.24 .0154
8.26 .8925
8.28 .0307
8.30 .1280
8.32 .0010
8.34 0
8.36 1.51
8.38 .0122
8.40 .4435
8.42 a. .6759 **b.** .3745 **c.** .1469
8.44 .6915
8.46 1201
8.48 .3085
8.50 41,600, 47,500, 52,500, 58,400
8.52 Top 5%: 34.4675, Bottom 5%:
29.5325

8.54 .1151
8.56 a. .1170   **b.** .3559   **c.** .0162
   d. 4.05 hours
8.58 9,636 pages
8.60 .1335
8.62 a. .3336   **b.** .0314
   c. .0436   **d.** $32.88
8.64 a. .0099   **b.** $12.88
8.66 132.80 (rounded to 133)
8.68 .0409
8.70 171
8.72 873
8.74 224,800, 242,500, 257,500,
   275,200
8.76 .8159
8.78 185.05
8.82 a. .5488   **b.** .6988   **c.** .1920
   d. 0
8.84 .1353
8.86 .8647
8.88 .4857
8.90 .1889
8.92 .0768
8.94 a. 2.750   **b.** 1.282   **c.** 2.132
   d. 2.528
8.96 a. 1.6556   **b.** 2.6810
   c. 1.9600   **d.** 1.6602
8.98 a. .1744   **b.** .0231   **c.** .0251
   d. .0267
8.100 a. 17.3   **b.** 50.9   **c.** 2.71
   d. 53.5
8.102 a. 33.5705   **b.** 866.911
   c. 24.3976   **d.** 261.058
8.104 a. .4881   **b.** .9158
   c. .9988   **d.** .9077
8.106 a. 2.84   **b.** 1.93
   c. 3.60   **d.** 3.37
8.108 a. 1.5204   **b.** 1.5943
   c. 2.8397   **d.** 1.1670
8.110 a. .1050   **b.** .1576
   c. .0001   **d.** .0044

Chapter 9

9.10 a. 1/36   **b.** 1/36
9.12 The variance of $\overline{X}$ is smaller than
   the variance of X.
9.14 No, because the sample mean
   is approximately normally
   distributed.
9.16 a. .1056   **b.** .1587   **c.** .0062
9.18 a. .4435   **b.** .7333   **c.** .8185
9.20 a. .1191   **b.** .2347   **c.** .2902
9.22 a. 15.00   **b.** 21.80   **c.** 49.75
9.24 We can answer part (c) and
   possibly part (b) depending
   on how nonnormal the population is.
9.26 .0082
9.28 a. .0918   **b.** .0104
   c. .00077
9.30 a. .3085   **b.** 0
9.32 a. .0038
9.36 .1170
9.38 .9319
9.40 b. .6247
9.42 a. 0   **b.** .0409   **c.** .5
9.44 .1056
9.46 .0035
9.48 a. .1151   **b.** .0287
9.50 .0096

9.52 a. .0071
9.54 .0066
9.58 .1314
9.60 .0082
9.62 .0033
9.64 .8413
9.66 .8413
9.68 .3050
9.70 1

Chapter 10

10.14 a. 200 ± 19.60; LCL = 180.40,
   UCL = 219.60
   b. 200 ± 9.80; LCL = 190.20,
   UCL = 209.80
   c. 200 ± 3.92; LCL = 196.08,
   UCL = 203.92
   d. The interval narrows.
10.16 a. 500 ± 3.95; LCL = 496.05,
   UCL = 503.95
   b. 500 ± 3.33; LCL = 496.67,
   UCL = 503.33
   c. 500 ± 2.79; LCL = 497.21,
   UCL = 502.79
   d. The interval narrows.
10.18 a. 10 ± .82; LCL = 9.18,
   UCL = 10.82
   b. 10 ± 1.64; LCL = 8.36,
   UCL = 11.64
   c. 10 ± 2.60; LCL = 7.40,
   UCL = 12.60
   d. The interval widens.
10.20 a. 400 ± 1.29; LCL = 398.71,
   UCL = 401.29
   b. 200 ± 1.29; LCL = 198.71,
   UCL = 201.29
   c. 100 ± 1.29; LCL = 98.71,
   UCL = 101.29
   d. The width of the interval is
   unchanged.
10.22 The variance decreases as
   the sample size increases,
   which means that the difference between the estimator
   and the parameter grows
   smaller as the sample size
   grows larger.
10.24 a. 500 ± 3.50
10.26 43.75 ± 6.93; LCL = 36.82,
   UCL = 50.68
10.28 9.85 ± 2.94; LCL = 6.91,
   UCL = 12.79
10.30 16.9 ± 4.07; LCL = 12.83,
   UCL = 20.97
10.32 13.15 ± 2.74; LCL = 10.41,
   UCL = 15.89
10.34 252.38 ± 2.94; LCL = 249.44,
   UCL = 255.32
10.36 12.10 ± .24; LCL = 11.86,
   UCL = 12.34.
10.38 .510 ± .016; LCL = .494,
   UCL = .526.
10.40 19.28 ± .62; LCL = 18.66,
   UCL = 19.90.
10.42 585,063 ± 5,518; LCL = 579,545,
   UCL = 590,581.
10.44 227.48 ± 7.43; LCL = 220.05,
   UCL = 234.91
10.46 27.19 ± 1.57; LCL = 25.62,
   UCL = 28.76

10.52 a. 150 ± .5   **b.** 150 ± 2
10.54 a. 1,537   **b.** 500 ± 10
10.58 2,149
10.60 1,083
10.62 217

Chapter 11

11.2 H_0: I will complete the Ph.D.
   H_1: I will not be able to
   complete the Ph.D.
11.4 H_0: Risky investment is more
   successful.
   H_1: Risky investment is not more
   successful.
11.6 O.J. Simpson
11.8 $z = .60$; rejection region:
   $z > 1.88$; p-value = .2743; not
   enough evidence to infer that
   $\mu > 50$
11.10 $z = 0$; rejection
   region: $z < -1.96$ or
   $z > 1.96$; p-value = 1.00; not
   enough evidence to infer that
   $\mu \neq 100$
11.12 $z = -1.33$; rejection region:
   $z < -1.645$; p-value = .0918;
   not enough evidence to infer
   that $\mu < 50$
11.14 $z = 1.27$; p-value = .2040
11.16 $z = 1.50$; p-value = .0668
11.18 $z = -1.04$; p-value = .2984
11.20 a. No, because the test statistic
   will be negative.
   b. The p-value will be larger
   than .5.
11.22 a. $z = -.60$, p-value = .2743
   b. $z = -1.00$, p-value = .1587
   c. $z = -3.00$, p-value = .0013
   d. The value of the test statistic
   decreases and the p-value
   decreases.
11.24 a. $z = -1.25$, p-value = .2112
   b. $z = -.88$, p-value = .3788
   c. $z = -.56$, p-value = .5754
   d. The value of the test statistic
   increases and the p-value
   increases.
11.26 a. $z = 3.00$, p-value = .0013
   b. $z = 2.00$, p-value = .0228
   c. $z = 1.00$, p-value = .1587
   d. The value of the test statistic
   decreases and the p-value
   increases.
11.28 a. $z = 4.57$, p-value = 0
   b. $z = 1.60$, p-value = .0548
   The value of the test statistic
   decreases and the p-value
   increases.
11.30 a. $z = -.62$, p-value = .2676
   b. $z = -1.38$, p-value = .0838
   c. The value of the test statistic
   decreases and the p-value
   decreases.
11.34 a. $z = 2.30$, p-value = .0214
   b. $z = .46$, p-value = .6456
   c. The value of the test statistic
   decreases and the p-value
   increases.

11.36 $z = 2.11$, p-value = .0174, yes
11.38 $z = -1.29$, p-value = .0985, yes
11.40 $z = .95$, p-value = .1711, no
11.42 $z = 1.85$, p-value = .0322, no
11.44 $z = -2.06$, p-value = .0197, yes
11.46 a. $z = 1.65$, p-value = .0495, yes
   b. We must assume that the population standard deviation is unchanged.
11.48 $z = 2.26$, p-value = .0119, no
11.50 $z = -1.22$, p-value = .1112, no
11.52 $z = 3.33$, p-value = 0, yes
11.54 $z = -2.73$, p-value = .0032, yes
11.56 $z = 1.93$, p-value = .0268, yes
11.58 $z = 1.49$, p-value = .0681, no
11.60 .1492
11.62 .6480
11.64 a. .6103   **b.** .8554
   c. β increases.
11.68 a. .4404   **b.** .6736
   c. β increases.
11.74 .1170
11.76 .1635

Chapter 12

12.2 a. 50 ± 3.42; LCL = 46.58, UCL = 53.42
   b. 100 ± 3.42; LCL = 96.58, UCL = 103.42
   c. The interval width does not change.
12.4 a. $1,500 \pm 59.52$; LCL = 1,440.48, UCL = 1,559.52
   b. $1,500 \pm 39.68$; LCL = 1,460.32, UCL = 1,539.68
   c. $1,500 \pm 19.84$; LCL = 1,480.16, UCL = 1,519.84
   d. The interval narrows.
12.6 a. $10 \pm .20$; LCL = 9.80, UCL = 10.20
   b. $10 \pm .79$; LCL = 9.21, UCL = 10.79
   c. 10 ± 1.98; LCL = 8.02, UCL = 11.98
   d. The interval widens.
12.8 a. 63 ± 1.77; LCL = 61.23, UCL = 64.77
   b. 63 ± 2.00; LCL = 61.00, UCL = 65.00
   c. 63 ± 2.71; LCL = 60.29, UCL = 65.71
   d. The interval widens.
12.10 a. $t = -3.21$, p-value = .0015
   b. $t = -1.57$, p-value = .1177
   c. $t = -1.18$, p-value = .2400
   d. As s increases, the test statistic increases and the p-value increases.
12.12 a. $t = .67$, p-value = .5113
   b. $t = .52$, p-value = .6136
   c. $t = .30$, p-value = .7804
   d. The test statistic decreases and the p-value increases.
12.14 a. $t = 1.71$, p-value = .0448
   b. $t = 2.40$, p-value = .0091
   c. $t = 4.00$, p-value = .0001
   d. The test statistic increases and the p-value decreases.

12.16 a. 175 ± 28.60; LCL = 146.40, UCL = 203.60
   b. 175 ± 22.07; LCL = 152.93, UCL = 197.07
   c. The student t distribution is more widely dispersed than the standard normal.
12.18 a. 350 ± 11.52; LCL = 338.48, UCL = 361.52
   b. 350 ± 11.52; LCL = 338.48, UCL = 361.52
   c. The student t distribution with 999 degrees of freedom is almost identical to the standard normal distribution.
12.20 a. $t = -1.30$, p-value = .1126.
   b. $z = -1.30$, p-value = .0968.
   c. The Student t distribution is more dispersed than the standard normal.
12.22 a. $t = 1.58$, p-value = .0569
   b. $z = 1.58$, p-value = .0571
   c. The student t distribution with 999 degrees of freedom is almost identical to the standard normal distribution.
12.24 $24,051 \pm 9,628$; LCL = 14,422, UCL = 33,680
12.26 $t = -4.49$, p-value = .0002
12.28 26.67 ± 8.56; LCL = 18.11, UCL = 35.23
12.30 $t = -2.45$, p-value = .0185
12.32 $4.66 \pm .39$; LCL = 4.27, UCL = 5.05
   Total number:
   LCL = 427 million,
   UCL = 505 million
12.34 $15,137 \pm 590$; LCL = 14,547, UCL = 15,727
   Total credit card debt:
   LCL = \$727,350 million,
   UCL = \$786,350 million
12.36 $2.67 \pm .36$; LCL = 2.31, UCL = 3.03
12.38 591.87 ± 17.22; LCL = 574.65, UCL = 609.09
   Total cost of congestion:
   LCL = \$98,265 million,
   UCL = \$104,154 million
12.40 $t = .51$, p-value = .3061
12.42 $t = 2.28$, p-value = .0127
12.44 $96,100 \pm 3106$; LCL = 92,994, UCL = 99,206
   Total amount of debt:
   LCL = 650,958 million,
   UCL = 694,442 million
12.46 $27,852 \pm 977$; LCL = 26,875, UCL = 28,829
   Total: LCL = \$1,163,687,500,000,
   UCL = \$1,248,295,700,000
12.48 a. $25,228 \pm 806$; LCL = 24,422, UCL = 26,034
   b. $27,751 \pm 887$; LCL = 26,864, UCL = 28,638
12.50 a. $46,699 \pm 719$; LCL = 45,980, UCL = 47,418

   b. Total: LCL = \$5,160,611,280, UCL = 5,322,006,648
12.52 a. 1157.77 ± 36.28; LCL = 1121.49, UCL = 1194.05
12.54 LCL = 1.31, UCL = 1.39
   b. The required condition is that the variable is normally distributed.
   c. The histogram is somewhat bell shaped.
12.56 LCL = 24.09, UCL = 24.66
12.58 $61,966 \pm 2010$; LCL = 59,956, UCL = 63,976
12.60 a. LCL = 4418, UCL = 5610
   b. The required condition is that the variable is normally distributed.
   c. The histogram is positively skewed.
12.62 a. LCL = 88,564, UCL = 102,412
   b. The required condition is that the variable is normally distributed. The histogram is positively skewed.
12.64 LCL = 67,243, UCL = 78,905
12.66 $t = -9.81$, p-value = 0
12.68 $t = 7.47$, p-value = 0
12.70 a. $\chi^2 = 72.60$, p-value = .0427
   b. $\chi^2 = 35.93$, p-value = .1643
   c. Decreasing the sample size decreases the test statistic and increases the p-value of the test.
12.72 a. LCL = 7.09, UCL = 25.57
   b. LCL = 8.17, UCL = 19.66
   c. Increasing the sample size narrows the interval.
12.74 $\chi^2 = 7.57$, p-value = .4218
12.76 LCL = 7.31, UCL = 51.43
12.78 $\chi^2 = 305.81$; p-value = .0044
12.80 $\chi^2 = 86.36$; p-value = .1863
12.82 a. $.48 \pm .0692$
   b. $.48 \pm .0438$
   c. $.48 \pm .0310$
   d. The interval narrows.
12.84 a. $ = z = .61$, p-value = .2709
   b. $z = .87$, p-value = .1922
   c. $z = 1.22$, p-value = .1112
   d. The p-value decreases.
12.86 a. 752
12.88 a. $75 \pm .0260$
   b. The interval is narrower.
   c. The interval estimate is better than specified.
12.90 a. $75 \pm .03$
   b. The sample size was chosen to produce this interval.
12.92 a. $.5 \pm .0346$
   b. The interval is wider.
   c. The interval estimate is wider (worse) than specified.
12.94 $z = -1.47$, p-value = .0708
12.96 $z = .33$, p-value = .3707
12.98 $.17 \pm .0368$; LCL = .1332, UCL = .2068
12.100 $.0147 \pm .0165$;
   LCL = 0 (increased from −.0018),
   UCL = .0312

12.102 .0077 ± .0114;
LCL = 0 (increased from −.0037),
UCL = .0191
12.104 .1192 ± .0268; LCL = .0924,
UCL = .1460
12.106 LCL = 5,940, UCL = 9,900
12.108 = z = −1.58, p-value = .0571
12.110 .600 ± .025; LCL = .575,
UCL = .625
Total: LCL = 3.452 million,
UCL = 3.749 million
12.112 z = 1.40, p-value = .0808
12.114 .0360 ± .0052; LCL = .0308,
UCL = .0412
Number:
LCL = 3.89 million,
UCL = 5.21 million
12.116 .2031 ± .0309; LCL =
.1722, UCL = .2340
Number: LCL = .861 million,
UCL = 1.17 million
12.118 z = −.30, p-value = .7659
12.120 z = .15, p-value = .8777
12.122 z = .40, p-value = .6904
12.124 z = −1.11, p-value = .1329
12.126 z = .67, p-value = .2508
12.128 z = −2.01, p-value = .0223
12.130 .7305 ± .0399; LCL = .6906,
UCL = .7704;
Market segment size:
LCL = 28,715,148,
UCL = 32,033,232
12.132 a. 2919 ± .0208; LCL = .2711,
UCL = .3127
b. LCL = 33,812,406
UCL = 39,000,883
12.134 .1748 ± .0308; LCL =
.1440, UCL = .2056;
Number: LCL = 30,428.199,
UCL = 43,444,706
12.136 Proportion:
LCL = .0861, UCL = .1605.
Amount:
LCL = $8,354, UCL = $15,573
12.138 a. t = 3.04, p-value = .0015
b. LCL = $30.68,
UCL = $33.23
c. The costs are required to be
normally distributed.
12.140 χ^2 = 30.71, p-value = .0435
12.142 LCL = .3718, UCL = .4428
12.144 LCL = 9.92, UCL = 10.66
12.146 a. LCL = 69.03, UCL = 74.73
b. t = 2.74, p-value = .0043.
12.148 z = .64, p-value = .2611
12.150 LCL = 26.44, UCL = 27.55
12.152 LCL = .5818, UCL = .6822
12.154 Proportion:
LCL = .2977, UCL = .3680.
Number: LCL = 69,833,339,
UCL = 86,316,357
12.156 z = −1.33, p-value = .0912
12.158 a. t = −2.97, p-value = .0018
b. χ^2 = 101.58, p-value = .0011
12.160 Proportion:
LCL = .1245, UCL = .1822.
Total:
LCL = 49,800 UCL = 72,880

12.162 a. LCL = −5.54 UCL = 29.61
b. t = −.473, p-value = .3210
12.164 t = .908, p-value = .1823
12.166 t = .959, p-value = .1693
12.168 t = 2.44, p-value = .0083
12.170 a. LCL = .6135, UCL = .7107
b. LCL = 26,823, UCL = 37,144
c. LCL = 4.67, UCL = 5.79
d. LCL = 1.41, UCL = 1.84
12.172 Total: LCL = 43,603,024,
UCL = 51,317,781
12.174 a. t = −.32, p-value = .3762.
There is not enough evidence.
12.176 z = 3.61, p-value = .0002
12.178 t = −8.07, p-value = 0
12.180 Total: LCL = 181,510,680,
UCL = 186,755,671
12.182 Total: LCL = 15,506,576,
UCL = 17,284,400
12.184 LCL = .3904, UCL = .5029
12.186 LCL = 1,667,720,
UCL = 2,461,240
12.188 LCL = 506.583, UCL = 696,161
12.190 a. t = 9.85, p-value = 0

Chapter 13

13.2 a. Equal-variances test statistic:
t = .43, p-value = .6703
b. Equal-variances test statistic:
t = .04, p-value = .9716
c. The value of the test statistic
decreases and the p-value
increases.
d. Equal-variances test statistic:
t = 1.53, p-value = .1282
e. The value of the test statistic
increases and the p-value
decreases.
f. t = .72, p-value = .4796
g. The value of the test statistic
increases and the p-value
decreases.
13.4 a. Unequal-variances test statistic (ν = 200.4, rounded to
200): t = .62, p-value = .2689
b. Unequal-variances test
statistic (ν = 2023.1,
rounded to 223):
t = 2.46, p-value = .0074
c. The value of the test statistic
increases and the p-value
decreases.
d. Unequal-variances test statistic (ν = 25.6, rounded to 26):
t = .23, p-value = .4118
e. The value of the test statistic
decreases and the p-value
increases.
f. Unequal-variances test statistic: t = .35, p-value = .3624
g. The value of the test statistic
decreases and the p-value
increases.
13.8 t = 1.07, p-value = .3028
13.10 t = 1.86, p-value = .0465
13.12 t = −2.04, p-value = .0283
13.14 t = −1.59, p-value = .1368
13.16 t = 1.12, p-value = .2761
13.18 t = 1.55, p-value = .1204

13.20 t = 2.88, p-value = .0021
b. 2.41 ± 2.16; LCL = .25,
UCL = 4.57.
13.22 t = .94; p-value = .1753
13.24 a. t = 2.94, p-value = .0060
b. 13.98 ± 9.67; LCL = 4.31,
UCL = 23.65
c. The amount of time is required
to be normally distributed.
d. The histograms are somewhat
bell shaped.
13.26 t = 7.54, p-value = 0
13.28 t = .90, p-value = .1858
13.30 t = −2.05, p-value = .0412
13.32 t = 1.16, p-value = .2467
13.34 t = −2.09, p-value = .0189
13.36 t = 6.28, p-value = 0
13.38 t = 12.37, p-value = 0
13.40 t = 2.49, p-value = .0080
13.42 t = −1.48, p-value = .0692
13.44 t = 1.53, p-value = .0643
13.46 t = .51, p-value = .3053
13.48 t = 4.49, p-value = 0
13.50 t = 2.66, p-value = .0040
13.52 t = −15.57, p-value = 0
13.54 a. LCL = 15,826,
UCL = 23,645
b. Incomes are required to be
normally distributed.
c. The required condition is not
satisfied. However, the sample sizes are large enough to
overcome this deficiency.
13.56 a. t = 4.99, p-value = 0
b. The required condition of
normality is satisfied.
c. A nonparametric test, the
Wilcoxon rank sum test can
be used.
13.58 t = −1.73, p-value = .0420.
13.60 t = −1.46, p-value = .0730
13.62 t = −1.77, p-value = .0389
13.64 t = 4.65, p-value = 1.00. The
p-value tells us that in fact
there is enough evidence that
Liberals are more educated than
conservatives.
13.66 t = 9.25, p-value = 0
13.68 t = 3.09, p-value = .0011
13.70 a. t = 1.02, p-value = .1541
b. LCL = −6,513,
UCL = 20,433
13.72 LCL = −23,715,
UCL = −10,797
13.74 LCL = −24,385,
UCL = −3,092
13.76 t = .34, p-value = .3680
13.78 t = −.085, p-value = .4660
13.80 t = −6.03, p-value = 0
13.88 t = −3.22, p-value = .0073
13.90 t = 1.98, p-value = .0473
13.92 a. t = 1.82, p-value = .0484
b. 3.08 ± 3.74; LCL = −.66,
UCL = 6.82
c. Yes, because medical
expenses will vary by the
month of the year.
13.94 t = −3.70, p-value = .0005

13.96 a. $t = -16.92$, p-value $= 0$
  b. -57.40 ± 7.28: LCL $= -64.68$, UCL $= -50.12$
  c. Differences are required to be normally distributed.
13.98 $t = -1.52$, p-value $= .0647$. There is not enough to infer stock holdings have decreased.
13.100 $t = 2.08$, p-value $= .0210$
13.106 $t = 24.93$, p-value $= 0$
13.108 LCL $= 23,515$, UCL $= 26,929$
13.110 $t = -3.28$, p-value $= .0005$
13.112 a. $F = .50$, p-value $= .0669$
  b. $F = .50$, p-value $= .2071$
  c. The value of the test statistic is unchanged and in this exercise the conclusion changed as well.
13.114 $F = .50$, p-value $= .3179$
13.116 $F = 3.23$, p-value $= .0784$
13.118 $F = 2.08$, p-value $= .0003$
13.120 $F = .31$, p-value $= 0$
13.122 $F = 2.12$, p-value $= 0$
13.124 $F = .904$, p-value $= .2390$
13.126 $F = .652$, p-value $= .0014$
13.128 a. $z = 1.07$, p-value $= .2846$
  b. $z = 2.01$, p-value $= .0444$
  c. The p-value decreases.
13.130 $z = 1.70$, p-value $= .0446$
13.132 $z = 3.62$, p-value $= 0$
13.134 $z = -2.85$, p-value $= .0022$
13.136 $z = -4.04$, p-value $= 0$
13.138 $z = 2.00$, p-value $.0228$
13.140 $z = -1.19$, p-value $= .1170$
13.142 $z = 1.97$, p-value $= .0244$
13.144 $z = 1.79$, p-value $= .0367$
13.146 $z = -2.15$, p-value $= .0158$
13.148 a. $z = 3.35$, p-value $= 0$
  b. $.1891 \pm .1223$; LCL $= .0668$, UCL $= .3114$.
13.150 $z = 4.24$, p-value $= 0$
13.152 $z = 1.50$, p-value $= .0668$
13.154 $z = 3.64$, p-value $= .0001$
13.156 $z = 1.47$, p-value $= .0702$
13.158 $z = 6.21$, p-value $= 0$
13.160 $z = -.29$, p-value $= .7708$
13.162 $z = 3.84$, p-value $= .0001$
13.164 $z = 2.04$, p-value $= .0207$
13.166 $z = -1.25$, p-value $= .2112$
13.168 $z = 3.56$, p-value $= .0004$
13.170 $z = -2.76$, p-value $= .0029$
13.172 $z = -1.02$, p-value $= .1528$.
13.174 $z = .95$, p-value $= .3439$
13.176 $z = 7.31$, p-value $= 0$
13.178 $z = 1.64$, p-value $= .0502$
13.180 $z = -.33$, p-value $= .3693$
13.182 $z = .42$, p-value $= .6773$
13.184 $z = 6.21$, p-value $= 0$
13.186 $z = 11.34$. p-value $= 0$
13.188 $z = 53.36$, p-value $= 0$
13.190 $z = 11.82$, p-value $= 0$
13.192 $z = 14.67$, p-value $= 0$
13.194 a. $z = 2.49$, p-value $= .0065$
  b. $z = .893$, p-value $= .1859$
  c. $z = 2.61$, p-value $= .0045$.
13.196 $t = 15.82$, p-value $= 0$
13.198 $t = -6.09$, p-value $= 0$
13.200 $z = -2.30$, p-value $= .0106$
13.202 a. $t = -1.06$, p-value $= .2980$
  b. $t = -2.87$, p-value $= .0040$.

13.204 $z = 2.26$, p-value $= .0119$
13.206 $z = -4.28$, p-value $= 0$
13.208 $z = -4.53$, p-value $= 0$
13.210 a. $t = 4.14$, p-value $= .0001$
  b. LCL $= 1.84$, UCL $= 5.36$
  c. The histograms are bell shaped.
13.212 $t = -2.40$, p-value $= .0100$
13.214 $t = 6.08$, p-value $= 0$
13.216 $t = 14.07$, p-value $= 0$
13.218 $t = -2.40$, p-value $= .0092$
13.220 $t = 0.71$, p-value $= .4763$
13.222 $z = 1.57$, p-value $= .0578$
13.224 $t = 12.67$, p-value $= 0$
13.226 $t = 16.47$, p-value $= 0$
13.228 $t = 2.85$, p-value $= .0025$
13.230 $z = -3.54$, p-value $= .0002$.
13.232 $z = -2.13$, p-value $= .0171$
13.234 $z = -.45$, p-value $= .6512$
13.236 $z = -1.28$, p-value $= .1000$
13.238 $t = -1.84$, p-value $= .0326$
13.240 $z = -.74$, p-value $= .4604$.
13.242 $t = -1.55$, p-value $= .0612$
13.244 $t = .78$, p-value $= .2170$
13.246 $t = -4.97$, p-value $= 0$
13.248 $t = .006$, p-value $= .5023$
13.250 a. $t = -1.48$, p-value $= .9296$. The p-value indicates that there is some evidence that self-employed people work *less* hours than people who work for someone else.
  b. The required condition of normality is satisfied.
  c. The Wilcoxon rank sum test.
13.252 a. $t = -6.50$, p-value $= 0$
13.254 $t = -1.82$, p-value $= .0345$
13.256 $t = .69$, p-value $= .2452$
13.258 $t = -1.61$, p-value $= .0537$
13.260 $t = -2.70$, p-value $= .0038$

Chapter 14

14.2 a. $F = 2.53$
  b. $F = 1.01$
  c. The F statistic decreases.
14.4 $F = 4.82$, p-value $= .0377$
14.6 $F = 3.91$, p-value $= .0493$
14.8 $F = .81$, p-value $= .5224$
14.10 $F = 2.94$, p-value $= .0363$
14.12 $F = 3.32$, p-value $= .0129$
14.14 $F = 1.17$, p-value $= .3162$
14.16 $F = 1.33$, p-value $= .2675$
14.18 a. $F = 25.60$, p-value $= 0$
  b. $F = 7.37$, p-value $= .0001$
  c. $F = 1.82$, p-value $= .1428$
14.20 $F = .26$, p-value $= .7730$
14.22 Reading: $F = 182.43$, p-value $= 0$; Mathematics: $F = 353.45$, p-value $= 0$; Science: $F = 121.0$, p-value $= 0$
14.24 $F = 6.09$, p-value $= 0$
14.26 $F = 56.97$, p-value $= 0$
14.28 $F = 52.41$, p-value $= 0$
14.30 $F = 12.84$, p-value $= 0$
14.32 $F = .87$, p-value $= .5189$
14.34 $F = 41.85$, p-value $= 0$
14.36 $F = 41.91$, p-value $= 0$
14.38 $F = 83.86$, p-value $= 0$
14.40 $F = 2.50$, p-value $= .0406$

14.42 $F = 18.23$, p-value $= 0$
14.44 $F = 8.29$, p-value $= 0$
14.46 $F = .745$, p-value $= .5610$
14.48 $F = 39.25$, p-value $= 0$
14.50 $F = 2.52$, p-value $= .0565$
14.52 $F = 152.9$, p-value $= 0$
14.54 $F = 14.27$, p-value $= 0$
14.56 $F = 9.73$, p-value $= 0$
14.58 a. The following pairs of means differ. μ_1 and μ_2, μ_1 and μ_4, μ_1 and μ_5, μ_2 and μ_4, μ_3 and μ_4, and μ_4 and μ_5.
  b. The following pairs of means differ. μ_1 and μ_5, μ_2 and μ_4, μ_3 and μ_4, and μ_4 and μ_5
  c. The following pairs of means differ. μ_1 and μ_2, μ_1 and μ_5, μ_2 and μ_4, μ_3 and μ_4, and μ_4 and μ_5.
14.60 a. Means of BAs and BBAs differ.
  b. Means of BAs and BBAs differ.
14.62 a. The means for Forms 1 and 4 differ.
  b. No means differ.
14.64 a. The means of lacquers 2 and 3 differ.
  b. The means of lacquers 2 and 3 differ.
14.66 a. There are no differences.
  b. There are no differences.
14.68 PARTYID 3 differs from 2 and 4.
14.70 b. PARTYID 4 differs from 2 and 3.
14.72 a. $F = 14.23$, p-value $= 0$
  b. Whites differ from Blacks and Others.
14.74 a. $F = 10.63$, p-value $= 0$
  b. Independents differ from Democrats and Republicans.
14.76 b. There are no differences.
14.78 a. $F = 33.00$, p-value $= 0$
  b. All three pairs of means differ.
14.80 All three differ.
14.82 All means differ except for 1 and 2.
14.84 a. $F = 16.50$, p-value $= 0$
  b. $F = 4.00$, p-value $= .0005$.
14.86 a. $F = 7.00$, p-value $= .0078$.
  b. $F = 10.50$, p-value $= .0016$
  c. $F = 21.00$, p-value $= .0001$
  d. The test statistic increases.
14.88 c. The variation between all the data is the same for both designs.
  d. The variation between treatments is the same for both designs.
  e. Because the randomized block design divides the sum of squares for error in the one-way analysis of variance into two parts.
14.90 $F = 1.65$, p-value $= .2296$
14.92 a. $F = 123.6$, p-value $= 0$
  b. $F = 323.16$, p-value $= 0$
14.94 a. $F = 21.16$, p-value $= 0$
  b. $F = 66.02$, p-value $= 0$

14.96 a. $F = 10.72$, p-value $= 0$
   b. $F = 6.36$, p-value $= 0$
14.98 $F = 476.7$, p-value $= 0$
14.100 Interaction: $F = 9.53$; A and B interact
14.102 a. $F = .31$, p-value $= .5943$. There is not enough evidence to conclude that factors A and B interact.
   b. $F = 1.23$, p-value $= .2995$. There is not enough evidence to conclude that differences exist between the levels of factor A.
   c. $F = 13.00$, p-value $= .0069$. There is enough evidence to conclude that differences exist between the levels of factor B.
14.104 The test for interaction yields ($F = .21$, p-value $= .8915$) and the test for the differences between educational levels ($F = 4.49$, p-value $= .0060$) is the same as in Example 14.4. However, in this exercise there is evidence of a difference between men and women ($F = 15.00$, p-value $= .0002$).
14.106 d. $F = 1.04$, p-value $= .4030$. There is not enough evidence to conclude that forms and income groups interact.
   e. $F = 2.56$, p-value $= .0586$. There is not enough evidence to conclude that differences exist between the forms.
   f. $F = 4.11$, p-value $= .0190$. There is enough evidence to conclude that differences exist between the three income groups.
14.108 a. Factor A is the drug mixture and factor B is the schedule.
   b. The response variable is the improvement index.
   c. There are a $= 4$ drug mixtures and b $= 2$ schedules.
   d. Test for interaction: $F = 7.27$, p-value $= .0007$. There is sufficient evidence to conclude that the schedules and drug mixtures interact.
14.110 The p-values for interaction, machines, and alloys are .8814, .0173, and .0005, respectively. Both machines and alloys are sources of variation.
14.112 The p-values for interaction, methods, and skills are .9874, .7348, and 0, respectively. The only source of variation is skill level.
14.114 $F = 7.63$, p-value $= 0$
14.116 $F = 13.79$, p-value $= 0$
14.118 $F = 7.72$, p-value $= .0070$
14.120 a. $F = 136.58$, p-value $= 0$
   b. All three means differ.
14.122 $F = 14.47$, p-value $= 0$
14.124 $F = 13.84$, p-value $= 0$
14.126 $F = 1.62$, p-value $= .2022$

14.128 $F = 2.70$, p-value $= .0684$
14.130 $F = 21.63$, p-value $= 0$
14.132 a. $F = 9.42$, p-value $= 0$
   b. All six days differ from Thursday.
14.134 a. $F = 23.19$, p-value $= 0$
   b. All means differ except 4 and 5 and 1 and 3.
14.136 a. $F = 35.90$, p-value $= 0$
   b. Means 1 and 2 and 1 and 3 differ.
14.138 Interaction: $F = 15.63$, p-value $= 0$
14.140 $F = .451$, p-value $= .7166$
14.142 $F = 39.93$, p-value $= 0$
14.144 $F = 45.59$, p-value $= 0$
14.146 $F = 211.61$, p-value $= 0$

Chapter 15

15.2 $\chi^2 = 2.27$, p-value $= .6868$
15.4 The χ^2-statistic decreases
15.6 $\chi^2 = 9.96$, p-value $= .0189$
15.8 $\chi^2 = 6.85$, p-value $= .0769$
15.10 $\chi^2 = 14.07$, p-value $= .0071$
15.12 $\chi^2 = 33.85$, p-value $= 0$
15.14 $\chi^2 = 6.35$, p-value $= .0419$
15.16 $\chi^2 = 10.77$, p-value $= .0293$
15.18 $\chi^2 = 11.08$, p-value $= .0498$
15.20 $\chi^2 = 5.70$, p-value $= .1272$
15.22 $\chi^2 = 153.63$, p-value $= 0$
15.24 $\chi^2 = 440.96$, p-value $= 0$
15.26 $\chi^2 = 19.10$, p-value $= 0$
15.28 $\chi^2 = 4.78$, p-value $= .0289$
15.30 $\chi^2 = 4.40$, p-value $= .1110$
15.32 $\chi^2 = 2.35$, p-value $= .3087$
15.34 $\chi^2 = 19.68$, p-value $= 0$
15.36 $\chi^2 = .918$, p-value $= .8211$
15.38 $\chi^2 = 41.76$, p-value $= 0$
15.40 $\chi^2 = 43.36$, p-value $= 0$
15.42 $\chi^2 = 20.89$, p-value $= .0019$
15.44 $\chi^2 = 1.22$, p-value $= .9761$
15.46 $\chi^2 = 311.4$, p-value $= 0$
15.48 $\chi^2 = 11.82$, p-value $= .0080$
15.50 $\chi^2 = 22.49$, p-value $= .0002$
15.52 $\chi^2 = 8.52$, p-value $= .0365$
15.54 $\chi^2 = 29.70$, p-value $= 0$
15.56 $\chi^2 = 15.80$, p-value $= .0004$
15.58 $\chi^2 = 40.19$, p-value $= 0$
15.60 $\chi^2 = 146.54$, p-value $= 0$
15.62 $\chi^2 = 29.42$, p-value $= 0$
15.64 $\chi^2 = .271$, p-value $= .9653$
15.66 $\chi^2 = 50.56$, p-value $= 0$
15.68 $\chi^2 = 5.99$, p-value $= .1121$
15.70 $\chi^2 = 4.41$, p-value $= .2204$
15.72 $\chi^2 = 1.97$, p-value $= .5796$
15.74 $\chi^2 = .684$, p-value $= .7102$
15.76 $\chi^2 = 1.79$, p-value $= .1810$
15.78 $\chi^2 = 4.51$, p-value $= .0337$
15.80 $\chi^2 = 9.87$, p-value $= .0017$
15.82 $\chi^2 = 506.76$, p-value $= 0$
15.84 Phone:
   $\chi^2 = .235$, p-value $= .8891$;
   Not on phone:
   $\chi^2 = 3.18$, p-value $= .2044$
15.86 $\chi^2 = 3.20$, p-value $= .2019$
15.88 $\chi^2 = 5.42$, p-value $= .2465$
15.90 $\chi^2 = 20.38$, p-value $= .0004$
15.92 $\chi^2 = 86.62$, p-value $= 0$
15.94 $\chi^2 = 15.39$, p-value $= .0005$

15.96 $\chi^2 = 166.8$, p-value $= 0$
15.98 $\chi^2 = 4.13$, p-value $= .5310$
15.100 $\chi^2 = 9.73$, p-value $= .0452$
15.102 $\chi^2 = 4.57$, p-value $= .1016$
15.104 a. $\chi^2 = .648$, p-value $= .4207$
   b. $\chi^2 = 7.72$, p-value $= .0521$
   c. $\chi^2 = 23.11$, p-value $= 0$.
15.106 $\chi^2 = 57.45$, p-value $= 0$
15.108 $\chi^2 = 28.97$, p-value $= 0$
15.110 a. $\chi^2 = 4.51$, p-value $= .3411$

Chapter 16

16.2 $\hat{y} = 9.107 + .0582x$
16.4 $\hat{y} = -24.72 + .9675x$
16.6 $\hat{y} = 3.365 + .2675x$
16.8 $\hat{y} = 7.460 + .0899x$
16.10 $\hat{y} = 7.286 + .1898x$
16.12 $\hat{y} = 4040 + 44.97x$
16.14 $\hat{y} = 458.4 + 64.05x$
16.16 $\hat{y} = 20.64 - .3039x$
16.18 $\hat{y} = 89.81 + .0514x$
16.22 $t = 10.09$, p-value $= 0$
16.24 b. $t = 3.93$, p-value $= .0028$
   c. $.0582 \pm .0330$; LCL $= .0252$, UCL $= .0912$
   d. $.6067$
16.26 $t = 6.55$, -value $= 0$
16.28 a. 5.888
   b. $.2892$
   c. $t = 4.86$, p-value $= 0$
   d. $.2675 \pm .0919$; LCL $= .1756$, UCL $= .3594$.
16.30 $t = 2.17$, p-value $= .0305$
16.32 $t = 7.50$, p-value $= 0$
16.34 a. 3.287
   b. $t = 2.24$, p-value $= .0309$
   c. $.1167$.
16.36 $t = 10.39$, p-value $= 0$
16.38 $t = -3.39$, p-value $= .0021$
16.40 $t = 1.22$, p-value $= .2319$
16.42 $t = 4.86$, p-value $= 0$
16.44 $t = 7.49$, p-value $= 0$
16.46 a. $t = 7.64$, p-value $= 0$
   b. $.4932$
16.48 $t = 10.81$, p-value $= 0$
16.50 $t = 5.04$, p-value $= 0$
16.52 $t = -8.58$, p-value $= 0$
16.54 $t = -.239$, p-value $= .8115$
16.56 $t = 20.26$, p-value $= 0$
16.58 $t = 27.08$, p-value $= 0$
16.60 $t = 2.60$, p-value $= .0096$
16.62 $t = -10.04$, p-value $= 0$
16.64 $t = 23.41$, p-value $= 0$
16.66 a. $t = 12.40$, p-value $= 0$
   b. LCL $= 5330$, UCL $= 7334$
16.68 a. $t = 11.10$, p-value $= 0$
   b. LCL $= 11,833$, UCL $= 16,913$
   c. $.0931$.
16.70 a. $t = 6.67$, p-value $= 0$
   b. LCL $= 815.6$, UCL $= 1495$.
16.72 $t = -9.08$, p-value $= 0$
16.74 a. $t = 18.01$, p-value $= 0$
   b. LCL $= 1324$, UCL $= 1648$.
16.78 13.76 ± 2.657
16.80 a. 9.143 ± 7.057
   b. 9.143 ± 1.977
16.82 a. 11.61 ± 11.91
   b. 11.61 ± 1.757

16.84 $11.06 \pm .80$
16.86 14.88 ± 7.85
16.88 6738 ± 1079
16.90 714.6 ± 23.6
16.92 18.21 ± 6.01
16.94 $93.92 \pm .34$
16.96 Lower prediction interval = -235.426, upper prediction *interval* = 2070.219
16.98 Lower prediction interval = 2.468, upper prediction *interval* = 8.604
16.102 Lower prediction interval = -1.680, upper prediction *interval* = 8.262 LCL = 3.150, UCL = 3.432
16.104 Lower prediction *interval* = 13.64, upper prediction interval = 69.99 LCL = 40.69, UCL = 42.93
16.106 Lower prediction interval = 26,400, upper prediction interval = 205,033 LCL = 110,196, UCL = 121,237
16.108 Lower prediction interval = -1.021, upper prediction interval = 5.224 LCL = 2.019, UCL = 2.184
16.110 Lower prediction interval = 11.39, upper prediction interval = 22.13 LCL = 16.50, UCL = 17.03
16.132 a. $\hat{y} = 115.24 + 2.47x$
　c. .5659
　d. $t = 4.84$, *p*-value = .0001
　e. 411.64 ± 93.54.
16.134 a. $t = 21.78$, *p*-value = 0
　b. $t = 11.76$, *p*-value = 0
16.136 $t = 3.01$, *p*-value = .0042
16.138 $t = 1.67$, *p*-value = .0522
16.140 $t = -9.88$, *p*-value = 0
16.144 $t = 2.30$, *p*-value = .0109
16.146 $t = 15.67$, *p*-value = 0
16.148 $t = 15.51$, *p*-value = 0.

Chapter 17

17.2 a. $\hat{y} = 13.01 + .194x_1 + 1.11x_2$
　b. 3.75　**c.** .7629
　d. $F = 43.43$, *p*-value = 0; evidence that the model is valid
　f. $t = .97$, *p*-value = .3417; no
　g. $t = 9.12$, *p*-value = 0; yes
　h. 23, 39　**i.** 49, 65
17.4 c. $s_e = 6.99$, $R^2 = .3511$; model is not very good
　d. $F = 22.01$, *p*-value = 0; evidence that the model is valid.
　e. Minor league home runs: $t = 7.64$, *p*-value = 0; Age: $t = .26$, *p*-value = .7961; Years professional: $t = 1.75$, *p*-value = .0819. Only the number of minor league home runs is linearly related to the number of major league home runs.
　f. 9.86 (rounded to 10), 38.76 (rounded to 39)
　g. 14.66, 24.47

17.6 b. .2882
　c. $F = 12.96$, *p*-value = 0; evidence that the model is valid.
　d. High school GPA: $t = 6.06$, *p*-value = 0; SAT: $t = .94$, *p*-value = .3485; Activities: $t = .72$, *p*-value = .4720
　e. e.4.45, 12.00 (actual value = 12.65; 12 is the maximum)
　f. 6.90, 8.22
17.8 b. $F = 29.80$, *p*-value = 0; evidence that the model is valid.
　d. House size: $t = 3.21$, *p*-value = .0014; Number of children: $t = 7.84$ *p*-value = 0 Number of adults at home: $t = 4.48$, *p*-value = 0
17.10 b. $F = 67.97$, *p*-value = 0; evidence that the model is valid.
　d. 65.54, 77.31
　e. 68.75, 74.66
17.12 a. $\hat{y} = -28.43 + .604x_1 + .374x_2$
　b. $s_e = 7.07$ and $R^2 = .8072$; the model fits well.
　d. 35.16, 66.24
　e. 44.43, 56.96
17.14 b. $F = 24.48$, *p*-value = 0
　c. UnderGPA: t = .52, *p*-value = .6017 GMAT: t = 8.16, *p*-value = 0 Work: $t = 3.00$, *p*-value = .0036
17.16 a. $\hat{y} = 6.365 + .135$ DAYS1 + .036DAYS2 + .060DAYS3 + .107DAYS4 + .142DAYS5 + .134DAYS6
　b. $F = 11.72$, *p*-value = 0
　c. DAYS1: $t = 3.33$, *p*-value = .0009 DAYS2: $t = .81$, *p*-value = .4183 DAYS3: $t = 1.41$, *p*-value = .1582 DAYS4: $t = 3.00$, *p*-value = .0027 DAYS5: $t = 3.05$, *p*-value = .0024 DAYS6: $t = 3.71$, *p*-value = .0002
17.18 a. $\hat{y} = 9.296 + .212$ PAEDUC + .194 MAEDUC
　b. $F = 284.0$, *p*-value = 0
　c. PAEDUC: $t = 10.16$, *p*-value = 0; MAEDUC: $t = 8.49$, *p*-value = 0
17.20 a. $F = 16.41$, *p*-value = 0
　c. AGE: $t = 2.74$, *p*-value = .0062 EDUC: $t = -6.14$, *p*-value = 0 HRS1: $t = -3.92$, *p*-value = 0 CHILDS: $t = .11$, *p*-value = .9108
　d. .0618.

17.22 a. $\hat{y} = 56,326 - 883.7$ AGE + 4503 EDUC
　b. $F = 140.30$, *p*-value = 0
　c. $t = 8.69$, *p*-value = 0
　d. .1895
17.24 a. $\hat{y} = 2206 - 21.95$ AGE + 4.52EDUC + .0140INCOME
　b. $F = 62.20$, *p*-value = 0
　c. AGE: $t = -4.95$, *p*-value = 0 EDUC: $t = .17$, *p*-value = .8680 INCOME: $t = 9.50$, *p*-value = 0
17.44 The correlation between PAEDUC and MAEDUC is .6934. Multicollinearity is a problem in Exercise 17.18.
17.46 a. The correlations between AGE and CHILDS (.3314) and EDUC and CHILDS (-.1478) indicate that multicollinearity may be a problem.
17.48 $d_L = 1.16$, $d_U = 1.59$; $4 - d_L = 2.84$, $4 - d_U = 2.41$; evidence of negative first-order autocorrelation.
17.50 $d_L = 1.46$, $d_U = 1.63$. There is evidence of positive first-order autocorrelation.
17.52 $4 - d_U = 2.27$, $4 - d_L = 2.81$; no evidence of negative first-order autocorrelation.
17.54 $d = .7859$; evidence of first-order autocorrelation.
17.56 $d = 2.2003$; $d_L = 1.30$, $d_U = 1.46$, $4 - d_U = 2.70$, $4 - d_L = 2.54$; no evidence of first-order autocorrelation.
17.58 b. $t = 1.72$, *p*-value = .0974
　c. $t = 4.64$, *p*-value = .0001
　d. $s_e = 63.08$ and $R^2 = .4752$; the model fits moderately well.
　f. 69.2, 349.3
17.60 b. $R^2 = .6123$; the model fits moderately well.
　c. $F = 21.32$, *p*-value = 0; evidence that the model is valid.
　d. Vacancy rate: $t = -4.58$, *p*-value = .0001 Unemployment rate: $t = -4.73$, *p*-value = .0001
　e. The error is approximately normally distributed with a constant variance.
　f. $d = 1.28$; no evidence of first-order autocorrelation.
　g. $14.18, $23.27

Chapter 18

18.4 a. First-order model: Demand = $\beta_0 + \beta_1$ Price + ε; Second-order model: Demand = $\beta_0 + \beta_1$ Price + β_2Price^2 + ε The second order model fits better.

18.6 a. MBA GPA $= \beta_0 + \beta_1$ UnderGPA $+ \beta_2$GMAT $+ \beta_3$ Work $+ \beta_4$ UnderGPA $\times$ GMAT $+ \varepsilon$
b. $F = 18.43$, p-value $= 0$; $s_\varepsilon = .790$ and $R^2 = .4674$. The model is valid, but the fit is relatively poor.

18.8 Both models fit equally well. The standard errors of estimate and coefficients of determination are quite similar.

18.10 a. Yield $= \beta_0 + \beta_1$ Pressure $+ \beta_2$Temperature $+ \beta_3$ Pressure^2 $+ \beta_4$Temperature$^2 + \beta_5$ Pressure Temperature $+ \varepsilon$
c. $S_\varepsilon = 512$ and $R^2 = .6872$. The model's fit is good.

18.14 I_1: $t = -1.54$, p-value $= .1269$; I_2: $t = 2.93$, p-value $= .0043$; I_3: $t = .166$, p-value $= .8684$. Only I_2 is statistically significant. However, this allows us to answer the question affirmatively.

18.16 c. $t = -5.56$, p-value $= 0$
18.24 a. $\hat{y} = -91{,}255 + 639$AGE $+ 4759$EDUC $+ 995$HRS1 $+ 8429I_1$
c. $t = 3.07$, p-value $= .0011$
18.26 a. $t = -5.79$, p-value $= 0$
b. $t = 6.47$, p-value $= 0$
18.28 a. $t = -4.59$, p-value $= 0$
b. $t = 4.59$, p-value $= 0$
18.30 Whites and others: $t = -1.12$, p-value $= .2639$ Blacks and others: $t = 4.00$, p-value $= 0$
18.32 $t = -1.35$, p-value $= .1768$
18.34 $F = 344.04$, p-value $= 0$
b. $t = 1.72$, p-value $= .0440$
18.44 $F = 54.14$, p-value $= 0$
18.46 $F = 14.91$, p-value $= 0$
18.48 $s_\varepsilon = 87.98$, $R^2 = .1893$

Chapter 19

19.2 a. $z = 1.66$, p-value $= .0485$
b. $z = 0$, p-value $= .50$
19.4 $T = 118$
19.6 a. $z = 3.61$, p-value $= .0004$
b. $z = 3.61$, p-value $= .0004$
19.8 $z = 1.16$, p-value $= .1230$
19.10 $z = -1.42$, p-value $= .0778$
19.12 $z = 1.964$, p-value $= .0500$
19.14 $z = .80$, p-value $= .2119$
19.16 $z = .80$, p-value $= .4238$
19.18 $z = -.179$, p-value $= .4290$
19.20 $z = 2.90$, p-value $= .0036$
19.22 $z = -2.1?$ ~-value $= .0147$
19.24 $z = 3.7?$ lue $= .0002$
19.26 $z = .70$ lue $= .2399$
19.28 $z = -$ alue $= .3257$
19.30 $z = $ ue $= .2642$
19.32 $\models$ value $= .0011$
19.3?
1

19.44 a. $z = 1.00$, p-value $= .1587$
b. $z = 1.00$, p-value $= .1587$
c. Identical results
19.46 a. $z = -2.06$, p-value $= .0396$
b. $z = -.52$, p-value $= .6032$
c. The sign test ignores the magnitudes of the differences.
19.48 $z = -5.25$, p-value $= 0$
19.50 $z = 2.22$, p-value $= .0132$
19.52 $T = 111$
19.54 $z = -2.24$, p-value $= .0125$
19.56 $z = 1.51$, p-value $= .0655$
19.58 $z = 5.17$, p-value $= 0$
19.60 $H = 1.56$, p-value $= .4584$
19.62 $H = 6.30$, p-value $= .0429$
19.64 $H = 4.46$, p-value $= .1075$
19.66 $F_r = 7.74$, p-value $= .0517$
19.68 a. $F_r = 8.00$, p-value $= .0460$
b. $F_r = 8.00$, p-value $= .0460$
c. All codes that preserve the order produce the same results.
19.70 $H = 6.81$, p-value $= .0333$
19.72 $F_r = 9.42$, p-value $= .0242$
19.74 $F_r = 2.63$, p-value $= .2691$
19.76 $H = 14.04$, p-value $= .0029$
19.78 $F_r = 5.28$, p-value $= .0715$
19.80 $H = 6.96$, p-value $= .0733$
19.82 $H = 4.34$, p-value $= .2269$
19.84 $H = 18.73$, p-value $= .0009$
19.86 $H = 22.27$, p-value $= 0$
19.88 $H = 11.55$, p-value $= .0210$
19.90 $H = 14.39$, p-value $= .0008$
19.92 $H = 1.91$, p-value $= .3858$
19.94 $z = 1.61$, p-value $= .1074$
19.96 $r_S = .6931$
19.98 $r_S = .2250$
19.100 $z = -.20$, p-value $= .8412$
19.102 $z = .54$, p-value $= .2931$
19.104 $z = 3.87$, p-value $= .0001$
19.106 $z = 5.52$, p-value $= 0$
19.108 $z = -10.24$, p-value $= 0$.
19.110 $z = -6.59$, p-value $= 0$
19.112 $z = -.435$, p-value $= .3318$
19.114 $z = 3.04$, p-value $= .0012$
19.116 $z = -4.86$, p-value $= 0$
19.118 $z = 9.64$, p-value $= 0$
19.120 $z = -1.04$, p-value $= .1499$
19.122 $z = -3.58$, p-value $= .0002$
19.124 $H = 3.55$, p-value $= .1699$
19.126 $H = 14.87$, p-value $= .0213$
19.128 $z = 1.12$, p-value $= .1309$
19.130 $z = 1.05$, p-value $= .2960$
19.132 $z = 2.86$, p-value $.0021$
19.134 $z = -2.43$, p-value $= .0075$
19.136 $H = 42.59$, p-value $= 0$
19.138 $z = -10.06$, p-value $= 0$

Chapter 20

20.2 38.8, 35.4, 35.8, 38.8, 44.4, 46.8, 48.8, 46.2
20.4 19.00, 21.67, 24.33, 26.67, 26.67, 26.33, 24.67, 24.33, 21.00, 19.00
20.8 12.00, 16.80, 16.16, 22.43, 18.09, 16.42, 23.28, 21.46, 22.69, 15.74
20.10 38.00, 38.50, 38.85, 39.47, 40.12, 40.91, 41.82, 42.53, 42.88, 43.09; There appears to be a gradual upward trend.

20.14 33.20, 34.80, 34.00, 37.00, 36.40, 35.20, 33.00, 36.20, 34.80, 37.00, 39.40, 44.20, 44.40, 45.00, 46.00, 43.60
20.16 18.00, 19.60, 22.56, 25.94, 28.76, 25.26, 30.35, 28.61, 27.17, 30.70, 36.02, 33.21, 36.33, 35.00, 41.80, 43.08
20.18 The quadratic model would appear to be the best model.
20.20 Linear Model:
$\hat{y} = -4.96 + 2.38t (R^2 = .81)$
Quadratic model:
$\hat{y} = 3.14 - 2.48t + .54t^2$
$(R^2 = .98)$ The quadratic trend line fits better.
20.22 .675, .892, .864, 1.212, 1.357
20.24 .839, 1.058, 1.270, .833
20.26 b. $\hat{y} = 49{,}661 - 25.04$ Year
20.28 1.404, .517, .515, .621, .675, 1.145, 2.123
20.30 MAD $= 4.60$, SSE $= 125$
20.32 MAD $= 9.6$, SSE $= 552$
20.34 191.1, 331.2, 418.5, 169.2
20.36 540.5
20.38 43.08
20.40 30.71, 23.38, 22.67, 19.21
20.42 a. 17,775 **b.** 17,146.
20.44 349.20, 323.16, 318.28, 367.60
20.46 136.47, 121.44, 88.60, 164.81
20.50 .646, 1.045, 1.405, .904

Chapter 21

21.6 81
21.8 22
22.10 a. .6603 **b.** .0361
2.12 19,250
21.14 5.36
21.16 770,000
21.18 3.83
21.20 a. .3659 **b.** .0179
21.24 Zone boundaries: 170.10, 173.77, 177.44, 181.10, 184.77, 188.43, 192.10
21.26 c. The process is out of control at samples 29 and 30.
d. A level shift occurred.
21.28 The process is under control.
21.30 The process is under control.
21.32 a. The process is out of control.
b. The process is out of control at sample 19.
c. The width became too small.
21.34 The process is out of control at sample 23 (S chart).
21.36 .92
21.38 The process went out of control at sample 29.
21.40 The process is under control.
21.42 Index $= .53$. The value of the index is low because the statistics used to calculate the control limits and centerline were taken when the process was out of control.

21.44 Centerline = .0324; control limits: 0, .07. The process is out of control at sample 25.

21.46 Centerline = .0383; control limits: 0, .0959. The process is out of control at samples 25 and 30.

21.48 Centerline = .0257; control limits: .0045, .047. The process is out of control at sample 28.

21.50 Centerline = .0126; control limits: 0, .0275. The process is out of control at sample 24.

Chapter 22

22.6 a_1

22.8 a. Bake 2 cakes. b. Bake 2 cakes.

22.10 Pay flat fee.

22.12 Order 200 shirts.

22.14 a. Build a medium size plant.
b. Build a medium size plant.

22.16 Don't produce.

22.18 32.5

22.20 a. 10
b. 2

22.22 a. I_1: .50, .50, 0
b. I_2: .268, .357, .375
c. I_3: .172, .345, .483
d. I_4: .109, .435, .456

22.24 a. I_1: a_3; I_2: a_1
b. 3.191

22.26 .30

22.28 As the prior probabilities become more diverse EVSI decreases.

22.30 4.1 million

22.32 b. Switch to rock and roll
c. 194,000

22.34 Don't proceed with recycling venture.

22.36 38,104

22.38 c. Produce Battery 2
d. 50,000

22.40 315

22.42 Don't sample; Install 25 telephones.

22.44 Rave review: Release in North America; Lukewarm response: Sell to European distributor; Poor response: Sell to European distributor.

INDEX